INTERSCIENCE MONOGRAPHS AND TEXTS IN PHYSICS AND ASTRONOMY

Edited by R. E. MARSHAK

Additional volumes in preparation

INTERSCIENCE MONOGRAPHS AND TEXTS
IN PHYSICS AND ASTRONOMY

Edited by R. E. MARSHAK
University of Rochester, Rochester, New York

VOLUME IV

FAST NEUTRON PHYSICS

Edited by

J. B. MARION, *Department of Physics and Astronomy, University of Maryland, College Park, Maryland*

and

J. L. FOWLER, *Physics Division, Oak Ridge National Laboratory, Oak Ridge, Tennessee*

Part II: Experiments and Theory

INTERSCIENCE PUBLISHERS   1963
a division of **John Wiley & Sons**, New York-London

PRINTED IN THE UNITED STATES OF AMERICA
BY MACK PRINTING CO., EASTON, PA.

Contributors to Part II

R. C. ALLEN, *Los Alamos Scientific Laboratory, Los Alamos, New Mexico*

N. AUSTERN, *University of Pittsburgh, Pittsburgh, Pennsylvania*

E. BAUMGARTNER, *Physikalisches Institut der Universität, Basel, Switzerland*

L. C. BIEDENHARN, *Duke University, Durham, North Carolina*

T. W. BONNER, *Rice University, Houston, Texas*

A. G. W. CAMERON, *Institute for Space Studies, National Aeronautics and Space Administration, New York, New York*

R. E. CARTER, *Los Alamos Scientific Laboratory, Los Alamos, New Mexico*

J. M. CALVERT, *University of Manchester, Manchester, England*

W. S. EMMERICH, *Westinghouse Research Laboratories, Pittsburgh, Pennsylvania*

F. W. K. FIRK, *Atomic Energy Research Establishment, Harwell, England*

J. M. FREEMAN, *Atomic Energy Research Establishment, Harwell, England*

J. L. GAMMEL, *Los Alamos Scientific Laboratory, Los Alamos, New Mexico*

J. H. GIBBONS, *Oak Ridge National Laboratory, Oak Ridge, Tennessee*

H. GOLDSTEIN, *Columbia University, New York, New York*

J. B. GUERNSEY, *Wellesley College, Wellesley, Massachusetts*

W. HAEBERLI, *University of Wisconsin, Madison, Wisconsin*

R. L. HENKEL, *Los Alamos Scientific Laboratory, Los Alamos, New Mexico*

P. HUBER, *Physikalisches Institut der Universität, Basel, Switzerland*

A. A. JAFFE, *University of Manchester, Manchester, England*

N. H. LAZAR, *Oak Ridge National Laboratory, Oak Ridge, Tennessee*

D. A. LIND, *University of Colorado, Boulder, Colorado*

J. B. MARION, *University of Maryland, College Park, Maryland*

D. W. MILLER, *Indiana University, Bloomington, Indiana*

G. C. NEILSON, *University of Alberta, Edmonton, Canada*

HENRY W. NEWSON, *Duke University, Durham, North Carolina*

F. L. RIBE, *Los Alamos Scientific Laboratory, Los Alamos, New Mexico*

J. T. SAMPLE, *University of Alberta, Edmonton, Canada*

H. W. SCHMITT, *Oak Ridge National Laboratory, Oak Ridge, Tennessee*

H. LYNDON TAYLOR, *Texas Instruments Incorporated, Dallas, Texas*

MARTIN WALT, *Lockheed Missiles and Space Co., Research Laboratories, Palo Alto, California*

J. B. WARREN, *University of British Columbia, Vancouver, Canada*

T. A. WELTON, *Oak Ridge National Laboratory, Oak Ridge, Tennessee*

JOHN A. WHEELER, *Palmer Physical Laboratories, Princeton University, Princeton, New Jersey*

H. B. WILLARD, *Oak Ridge National Laboratory, Oak Ridge, Tennessee*

Preface

Part I of *Fast Neutron Physics*, published in 1960, is concerned with experimental techniques; Part II gives the results obtained from experiments involving fast neutrons and describes the theoretical basis for the interpretation of these results. This volume of *Fast Neutron Physics* describes the experiments which have yielded much of the neutron cross section data, and includes numerous illustrative examples of these cross sections and their theoretical interpretation. There is a rather complete system of referencing, not only to the original literature but also to the compilations in this field of neutron physics.

Neutron physics has had a profound influence on the understanding of nuclear structure. Although early in the history of nuclear physics the observation of neutron resonance at low energies emphasized the complexity of nuclear structure, in more recent years it has become apparent that the measurement of the properties of the neutron's interaction with nuclei, averaged over many resonances, leads to a simplified model of nuclei upon which the theory of the more complex behavior can be based. The arrangement of the chapters of Part II in general is such as to bring out the more easily understood features of neutron interactions with nuclei and then to proceed to more complex phenomena. For example, the first several chapters are devoted primarily to the behavior of neutrons which can be discussed in terms of an optical analogy. The direct interaction model for nuclear reactions discussed next in a sense bridges the gap between the concept of independent motion of nucleons in nuclear matter implied in the optical model and the Breit-Wigner resonance theory of nuclear reactions discussed in the following chapter.

The chapters on polarization of neutrons describe the foundation for, and include the recent information on, this rapidly developing field in nuclear physics which is offering such a powerful tool for exploring the spin-orbit interaction of a neutron with a nucleus. Inelastic neutron scattering is covered in a series of chapters, each concerned with different aspects of this rather complicated branch of neutron physics. Here again an attempt has been made to order the chapters so as to bring out the more readily explained features of inelastic scattering first. Since the techniques for performing neutron experiments in the kev energy range and the methods for handling the data differ somewhat from those used at higher energies, a chapter is devoted to this important subject.

Most of the remainder of Part II is concerned with nuclear reactions involving particles other than neutrons as either the products of nuclear reactions or as bombarding particles. Nuclear engineers and cosmologists will be particularly interested in the chapter on neutron capture cross sections, which summarizes the present state of capture measurements and the theory of the capture process. Nuclear engineers as well as nuclear physicists will find the chapters on the fission process of general interest. The concluding chapter of this book is concerned with the very fundamental interaction of a neutron with a proton. The appendices describe the system of notation used in the experimental chapters of both Part I and Part II of *Fast Neutron Physics*, and discuss several innovations in neutron detection techniques which have come into use since the appearance of Part I.

The appearance of Part II has been delayed by the late receipt of some of the manuscripts for articles which appear here. This has resulted in an unfortunate delay in the publication of a number of the chapters which were written some time ago. Some of these chapters have been extensively revised in proof; the publishers have been generous in permitting these changes. The editors apologize to those authors who submitted their manuscripts early for the additional work placed upon them as a result of the delay in publication. We sincerely regret that in a few cases the authors did not have the opportunity to revise their chapters. In spite of these difficulties and delays, we feel that Part II is timely; chapters on those fields of fast neutron physics which are changing most rapidly, such as polarization, for example, are up to date. Again we with to thank the authors for the patience they have shown during the preparation of both Part I and Part II of *Fast Neutron Physics*.

During the course of the preparation of the volume, one of the contributing authors, Professor T. W. Bonner of Rice University, passed away suddenly on December 6, 1961. Professor Bonner had been a frequent contributor to the literature of neutron physics since the early days of this field of research and his death will be a loss keenly felt by the entire physics community, but especially by those who have contributed to these volumes on *Fast Neutron Physics*, since he was both good friend and sometime co-worker with a large number of the persons who have authored these volumes.

JERRY B. MARION
JOSEPH L. FOWLER

March, 1963

Contents

Part II. EXPERIMENTS AND THEORY

xi

Neutron Total Cross Section Measurements

Dan W. Miller

Indiana University, Bloomington, Indiana

1. Experimental Techniques

A. *General Description of Procedure*

(1) **Basic Experimental Arrangement.** The total cross section of nuclei for fast neutrons is usually measured by means of a transmission experiment. This type of measurement enjoys the advantage that no absolute measurement of neutron flux is required, so that the difficulty of measuring absolute counter efficiencies is avoided. One is instead required only to make relative neutron flux measurements, which can generally be done with very good accuracy. From such a relative flux measurement, the total cross section can be calculated directly if the number of target nuclei per unit area presented to the neutron beam is known.

Transmission measurements require three basic experimental components: the neutron source, the scattering sample, and the neutron detector. These are located so that the sample completely shadows the detector from the direct beam from the source. By comparing the neutron flux at the detector with the sample inserted and with it removed, the decrease in flux in the sample due to nuclear interactions occurring there is immediately apparent. The details of the three components, particularly the source and detector, vary considerably with neutron energy. However, the basic experimental arrangement remains the same. Figure 1 shows a typical geometry employed by Barschall's group at the University of Wisconsin for transmission measurements in the 1- to 3-Mev range (Fi54).

General source, sample, and detector considerations are given in Section 1.A (3)–(5) below, while a few specific remarks concerning the sources and detectors employed in various energy regions are given in Section 1.C (1).

(2) **Determination of the Total Cross Section.** The cross section for any nuclear process is defined to be the number of processes of that type occurring per nucleus per unit time per unit incident flux. Measurements of specific cross sections therefore normally require considerable care to guarantee that absolute numbers of events of just the correct type are detected, and that the absolute

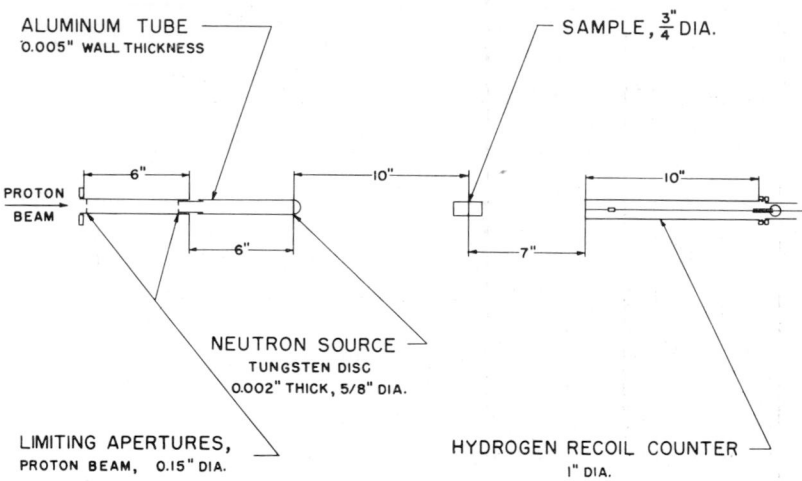

Figure 1. Typical transmission geometry for the measurement of total cross sections for fast neutrons in the 1-to 3-Mev range (Fi54).

incident flux is correctly determined. Clearly a considerable simplification occurs in measurements of the total cross section, where all processes removing particles from the beam are summed without need for distinguishing between them. Here it is only necessary to determine the flux decrease in the sample, which must then be directly related to the total number of interactions which have occurred, regardless of type. Using the definition given for cross section, the relative flux decrease in a thickness dx of the sample is then

$$dI/I = -n\sigma_T dx \tag{1}$$

where n is the number of nuclei per cm³ in the sample, I the flux in neutrons/cm² sec, and σ_T the total cross section. Integrating Eq. (1) from $x = 0$ to $x = t$, the total sample thickness, one immediately obtains the familiar form

$$I/I_0 = \exp(-nt\sigma_T) \tag{2}$$

Equation (2) exhibits the well-known exponential decrease of flux with sample thickness. This behavior is illustrated by the experimental results shown in Fig. 2 for 95-Mev neutrons (from DeJuren

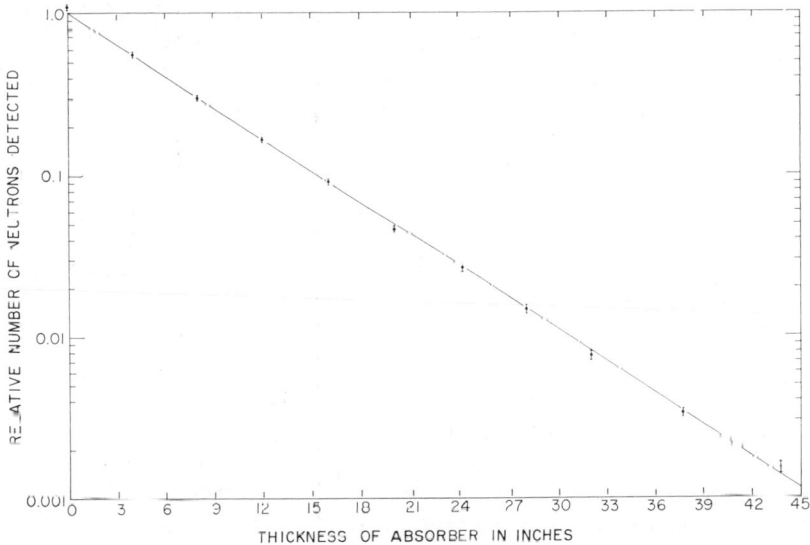

Figure 2. Experimental results showing the exponential decrease of observed neutron flux as a function of sample thickness (De50).

and Knable, De50). The experimental procedure then is simply to measure the flux at the detector with sample in (I) and with sample out (I_0), yielding the transmission $T \equiv I/I_0$. With this measurement, the cross section follows immediately by rewriting Eq. (2):

$$\sigma_T = (1/nt) \ln (1/T) \tag{3}$$

Beyond the obvious requirement that the measured transmission should be corrected for background, it should be emphasized that Eqs. (2) and (3) are valid only if two additional conditions are met.

First, it is necessary that every neutron which interacts with a sample nucleus shall not be counted by the detector; otherwise, the apparent measured flux decrease will not be the same as the actual flux decrease of the primary beam.   The most obvious difficulty here arises with neutrons which are scattered essentially forward, and therefore are detected as if they had not suffered any interaction.   This requires an *in-scattering correction* to all measured transmissions, as will be discussed in Section 1.B (2).   The second limitation imposed on Eqs. (2) and (3) is that the total cross section must not vary appreciably in the energy range represented by the spread in neutron energies present in the detected flux.   If this condition is not met, a *hardening* effect occurs which causes the total flux attenuation not to be exponential.   This will be discussed further in Section 1.B (3).

(3) **General Source Considerations.** Although important early measurements of neutron total cross sections were made (Fi47) using photoneutron sources of the type described in Chapter I.A, intensity considerations and requirements of variable energy strongly favor neutron sources induced by charged particles obtained from accelerators.   For neutrons in the 120-kev to 27-Mev energy range, the charged-particle beam normally strikes either an evaporated solid target or a gas cell which serves as the neutron source.   The details of such sources are discussed in Chapters I.C, I.D, I.E, and IV.D.   It is the purpose of this section only to remark briefly on the general requirements imposed on the source in order to perform accurate transmission measurements below 27 Mev.   As synchrocyclotron sources for the 30–100 Mev range are quite different, they will be discussed separately in Section 1.C (1).

The absolute neutron production rate per incident charged particle in an accelerator source does not enter into the total cross-section measurement in any way, for the reasons already outlined. However, if the sample-in sample-out measurements are based upon the total charge striking the target source, it is clearly necessary that the neutron production rate per incident charged particle remain constant during any particular set of transmission and background measurements.   This means that effects causing random fluctuations in the primary neutron flux, in spite of constant beam current on the target, must be carefully controlled.   For example, care should be taken to insure that the neutron-producing target be as uniform in thickness as possible and that wandering of the beam on the target

be minimized.   More subtle effects, such as beam heating of a gas
target, etc., can also cause random changes or drifts in the primary
neutron flux.   It is clearly desirable for sample-in sample-out measurements to be performed in moderately rapid sequence to minimize
the error introduced by possible difficulties of this sort.   In addition,
it is good practice to maintain a suitable neutron monitor, such as a
long counter (Ha47) (see Chapter III.A), in the vicinity of the source
to monitor such effects.   Another basic requirement for the source is
that it produce very few neutrons at the detector which are not
directly associated with the primary neutron flux from the desired
source nuclear reaction.   Thus the target assembly should be constructed with a minimum of neutron-producing material which can be
seen by the direct or scattered charged-particle beam.   For example,
gas cells are normally constructed with thin nickel beam windows
located near liquid-air traps in order to reduce buildup of carbon on the
windows.   It is also very important to minimize scattering of the
primary neutrons in the target assembly, so that it is normally
constructed as lightly as possible.   Difficulties of the two types just
discussed give rise to *extraneous neutrons from the beam direction*,
which require corrections to be discussed in Section 1.B (1).   In addition, the problem of background at the detector caused by scattering
of primary neutrons from the walls and floors of the experimental area
must be taken into account.   This effect can best be reduced by
placing the source, sample, and detector in a large room with a false
floor (see, for example, Chapter IV.F).

(4) **General Sample Considerations.**   Important considerations in accurate transmission measurements are the composition,
size, and location of the scattering samples (Ba52).   The composition
of the sample depends entirely upon the chemical and physical properties of the element under investigation.   In general, it is clear that
the pure element should be employed whenever possible.   If the
element is available in a pure, solid, chemically non-reactive form,
samples are easily prepared simply by machining to the appropriate
dimensions.   If the element reacts with the air, it is normally sealed
in a tight thin-walled can and the transmission determined by comparing with an identical empty can.   In case the element is normally
in the gaseous state, it may be contained at high pressure in a gas cell
(see, e.g. Ba51, Se55) or liquified in a suitable Dewar flask arrangement (see, e.g. Hi54).

In some cases it may be necessary or more convenient to use a compound for the sample. In this case the transmission of the compound is just the product of the transmissions of hypothetical samples made of the individual elements alone, each containing the same number of nuclei/cm^2 as are present in the compound.[1] In such an experiment it is most convenient to compare the transmission of the compound with another sample in which the element under investigation is missing, but containing the same number of nuclei/cm^2 of the rest of the elements. For example, the transmission of a BeO sample relative to a pure Be sample, each containing the same number of Be nuclei/cm^2, may be used to measure the oxygen cross section (see, e.g. Fi47, Ad49). In such a case, it is obviously wise to measure the transmission of one sample relative to the other in sequence at each neutron energy, so that effects of energy shifts due to changes in thickness of the neutron-producing target, etc. will be eliminated. It should be remarked that organic samples, such as CH_2, should in general be analyzed chemically in order to verify the atomic ratio.

Impurities in scattering samples can cause very serious errors in the results, especially when their presence is not realized and corrected for. This may happen, for example, when moisture from the air is absorbed in the sample, a process which occurs frequently in powdered substances. In some cases moisture can be removed by heating in a vacuum, as indicated by the weight loss of the sample. Other effects, such as oxidation of a sample, can also introduce appreciable errors. In general it is wise to seal substances subject to these effects in air-tight cans immediately after preparation.

The accurate determination of the total cross section from Eq. (3) requires an accurate knowledge of the number of nuclei per cm^2 (nt) in the sample. The measurement of the thickness of the sample is of little concern except for very thin samples or cross section measurements of very high accuracy, such as the neutron-proton cross section. However, because of the possibility of sample inhomogeneities, etc., the density of every sample employed should generally be carefully checked, particularly if they are made from substances like graphite, etc. Such effects are discussed in considerable detail by Hafner *et al.* (Ha53).

Requirements on the size and location of scattering samples are

---

[1] The same situation obtains for pure elements containing more than one isotope.

somewhat different for electrostatic generator measurements below 27 Mev than for synchrocyclotron measurements at higher energies, since the latter employ collimated neutron beams.   In the remainder of the present section, the general requirements on sample size and location for the lower energy measurements only will be discussed.

In general, the diameter of the scattering sample is determined by the location and size of the detector, since the sample must shadow the detector completely from the source.   It should not be any larger than necessary, however, because of the increased correction required for in-scattering into the detector, an effect which can be very important at energies above about 1 Mev.   Sample diameters typically vary from about 2 cm to 5 cm.   The sample is usually located midway between the neutron source and the detector, since this minimizes the in-scattering correction as will be shown in Section 1.B (2).   In order to reduce neutrons scattered into the detector from objects external to the sample, the sample is usually suspended by a thin wire or rod support.   The alignment of the source-sample-detector system is important, because any misalignment may allow part of the detector to "see" the source directly without being shadowed by the sample. Such an effect will result in a higher apparent transmission and a systematically low determination of the total cross section.   As an example of an alignment method (Fr50), a point source of light can be placed at the neutron source position and the shadow cast by the sample on the detector noted.   Another method (Co58a) uses a reversible telescope of the same diameter as the sample placed in the sample position; the system is then adjusted so the telescope cross hairs are centered on the source and (after reversing) on the detector. A number of other methods will be found in the literature.

The thickness of the sample (parallel to the beam) is determined by the actual cross section and the transmission desired.   This optimum transmission represents a compromise between two types of errors.   On the one hand, as the transmission decreases the statistical error in a transmission measurement also decreases.   For example, suppose the number of counts recorded with sample in is N and with sample out is N_0, and that the same counting intervals are used for both,[2] so that $N/N_0 = I/I_0$.   Then the standard statistical error in

[2] This simple case illustrates the point being made here.   Actually, for a given total interval of time available for a transmission measurement, the statistical error in the cross section can be reduced by using unequal intervals for the sample-in sample-out measurements.   "Equal intervals" here assumes the neutron production rate is constant in the source.

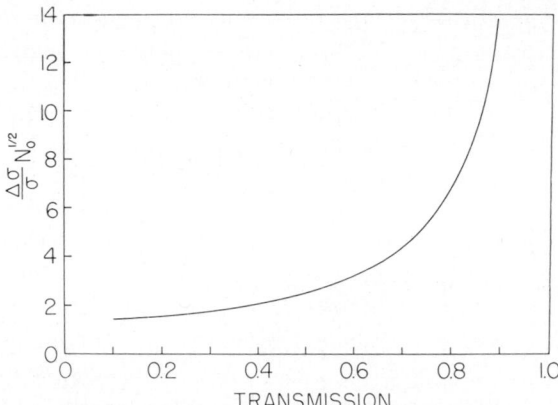

Figure 3. Graph of the variation of the relative standard statistical error in the total cross section as a function of sample transmission, assuming zero background.

the total cross section assuming zero background is given by:

$$\Delta\sigma_T/\sigma_T = (1/\ln T)[(1 + T)/N_0 T]^{1/2} \tag{4}$$

Equation (4) is plotted in Fig. 3, which clearly indicates that the statistical error is reduced by using lower transmissions and therefore thicker samples. However, the corrections due to multiple in-scattering and *hardening* effects increase as the sample thickness increases, as will be shown in Sections 1.B (2) and (3). The optimum transmission is therefore chosen as a compromise between these requirements, and is usually in the region of 50 to 70 per cent. In regions of rapidly varying transmission due to compound nucleus resonance structure, several samples of different thicknesses will usually be required to keep the transmission in the optimum region.

In some measurements, the cross section varies slowly with energy and *hardening* effects are unimportant. By choosing a very good experimental geometry, inscattering effects may also be made quite small. In cases of this type, one can arrive at an optimum sample length from a consideration of the statistical error as a function of the total time available for each measurement and the relative times allotted to the sample in, sample out, and background measurements. Such analyses have been carried out in detail (Ro48, Br58), and suggest optimum transmissions in the range of 10 to 30 per cent depending on the experimental conditions.

(5) **General Detector Considerations.** Neutron detectors are discussed in great detail in Chapters II and III; it is the purpose of this section to describe briefly the requirements imposed upon these detectors in order to obtain transmission measurements of good accuracy. Again, this section will be limited to considerations of detectors in the energy region below 27 Mev. Detectors employed in synchrocyclotron measurements will be discussed in Section 1.C (1).

The size and location of the detector are determined by several factors, such as in-scattering effects, the energy resolution required, the neutron flux available, etc. In order to keep the in-scattering correction small, it is desirable for the detector to subtend a very small solid angle at the sample. This requires either a detector of small diameter or a large source-to-detector distance. However, both of these alternatives reduce the detector counting rate, so that they are limited by the neutron production rate of the source and the counting statistics required. For high-resolution studies using neutrons produced by reactions in the light nuclei, large source-to-detector distances are also required in order to reduce the spread in energy of the neutrons incident on the detector, as described in Section 1.C (2). Depending upon the particular conditions of the experiment, typical source-to-detector distances for measurements below 27 Mev vary from 25 cm to 150 cm. Much larger source-to-detector distances are used for synchrocyclotron measurements at higher energies, as described in Section 1.C (1).

The basic requirements imposed upon the detector are that it should have a high counting efficiency for neutrons of the desired energy, but be relatively insensitive to γ rays and background neutrons of lower energies. This is not always possible; for example, at very low neutron energies it is often necessary to accept a higher background in order to have a sufficiently high counting efficiency. The use of energy-sensitive detectors is very desirable in order to bias out room-scattered background neutrons and low-energy neutrons produced in the target proper in some reactions. Brief remarks concerning typical detectors employed at various energies are given in Section 1.C (1).

B. Corrections

The observed transmission must generally be corrected for a number of effects in order to obtain the true transmission for use in

Eq. 3. Background from various sources and single and multiple in-scattering represent the principal corrections, discussed in Sections (1) and (2) to follow. The effect of nonexponential attenuation or *hardening* is discussed in Section (3).

(1) **Background Correction.** A careful check must be made in every flux measurement to determine what fraction of the neutron counts observed do not come directly from the nuclear reaction used as the neutron source. In electrostatic generator measurements below 27 Mev, these background neutrons may be subdivided into two classes: (a) room-scattered neutrons and (b) extraneous neutrons from the beam direction.

Room-scattered background is made up of source neutrons which are scattered from the floors, walls, etc. back into the neutron detector. Since these neutrons are generally considerably degraded in energy from the direct primary flux, the effect can be reduced by the use of biased energy-sensitive detectors, such as scintillation counters or recoil gas counters, or by direction-sensitive counters. To determine the room-scattered background, a shadow bar is usually inserted in place of the scattering sample. The material and dimensions of this shadow bar are chosen so that its transmission is negligible at the particular energy of the measurement. A check on this method, to see if the shadow bar itself cuts out background neutrons, is sometimes made by determining the unshadowed counting rate for different detector distances (Ba52, Po52). If this rate is due to a direct flux which decreases as an inverse square of the distance plus a constant background component, the measured counting rate as a function of distance may in favorable cases allow the background to be determined.

If the contribution to background of extraneous neutrons from the beam direction is negligible compared to the room-scattered neutrons, the corrected transmission may easily be obtained as follows. Assume that the observed counting rate at the detector with sample out is U, with the sample in is $T'U$, and with a perfect shadow bar in place is βU. Then the corrected counting rate at the detector (without background) with the sample in should be $T'U - \beta U$ and with the sample out should be $U - \beta U$. From this it follows at once that the corrected transmission T is given in terms of the uncorrected transmission T' by

$$T = (T' - \beta)/(1 - \beta) \tag{5}$$

In the above considerations, the extraneous background neutrons from the beam direction have been neglected. These neutrons arise from (a) legitimate primary neutrons produced in the target at large angles but scattered forward by parts of the target assembly, (b) neutrons produced when the beam strikes collimating slits and diaphragms, entrance foils of gas cells, etc., and (c) neutrons produced by deuteron breakup in the source itself when an incident deuteron beam is employed. Because these neutrons all come from the beam direction, corrections for them are much more difficult to evaluate than for room-scattered neutrons, for which a simple shadow-bar measurement usually suffices. Neutrons produced by process (a) may be reduced by constructing all parts of the target assembly as lightly as possible to minimize the neutron-scattering material in the source vicinity. Some estimate of the maximum magnitude of the effect can be obtained by considering the angular distributions of the neutrons produced in the source, the geometry of the target assembly, and the scattering cross sections of the materials making up the target system (Ha53). The background neutrons from (b) are particularly serious when an incident deuteron beam is employed, since such a beam will usually produce neutrons from almost any material in its path. When deuterium or tritium gas cells are used as the neutron source, the number of extraneous neutrons produced on the slits, foils, etc. may be determined by replacing the deuterium or tritium by hydrogen and measuring the neutrons remaining in the flux (see, e.g. Ha 53, Da53, Cr56). Care must be used to guarantee that all of the deuterium or tritium has been carefully flushed out before making this measurement. Even then a significant amount of exchange of deuterium or tritium (previously occluded to the walls) may occur with the hydrogen, causing the neutron production rate to increase slowly with time until the cell is reflushed (Ha53). In case (c), deuteron breakup in the source results in a typical continuum of low-energy neutrons due to a three-body breakup process, such as $D(d, np)D$. This effect, discussed in detail in Chapter I.C., prevents the $D(d, n)$ and $T(d, n)$ reactions from being monoenergetic above deuteron energies of about 4 Mev (He56, Cr56). These continuum neutrons are best eliminated by the use of time-of-flight or energy-sensitive detectors.

If one can discriminate against case (c) above, or if it is not present because of the type or energy of the reaction, the other sources of background neutrons (when a deuterium gas-target neutron source is used, for example) are summarized in Fig. 4, taken from Hafner *et al.* (Ha53). The top part of this figure represents the neutrons recorded by the detector when a deuterium filling is used. In this case the observed total counting rate with sample out (U) is due to the counting rate from the legitimate primary flux produced in the deuterium gas (ϕU), the room-scattered background counting rate with perfect shadow (βU), the extraneous background counting rate due to large-angle primary neutrons scattered forward in the target assembly (ζU), and the extraneous background counting rate due to

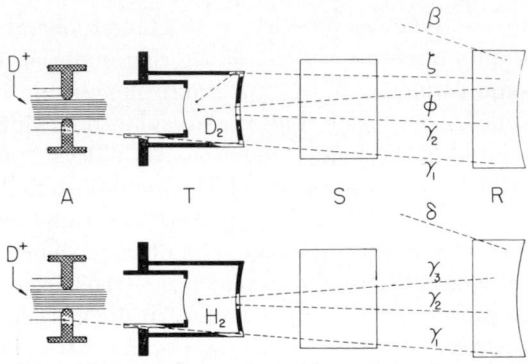

Figure 4. Origin of background neutrons (Ha53) using a deuterium gas target neutron source (top), and with the deuterium replaced by hydrogen (bottom).

neutrons produced in the collimating slits ($\gamma_1 U$) and in the target backing ($\gamma_2 U$). From these definitions it is clear that

$$\phi + \beta + \zeta + \gamma_1 + \gamma_2 = 1$$

The lower part of Fig. 4 (Ha53) shows the neutrons recorded by the detector when a hydrogen filling is used. Here γ_1 and γ_2 are the same as with the deuterium filling.[3] Let the observed total counting rate with the hydrogen target filling and the sample out be pU, the counting rate with perfect shadow be δU, and the counting rate due to the direct flux of D-D neutrons produced in traces of deuterium[4] (aris-

---

[3] Hafner *et al.* (Ha53) note that γ_2 decreases slowly with time after insertion of the hydrogen, due to diffusion of deuterium out of the target backing.

[4] The quantity γ_3 increases with time, starting at zero each time the cell is flushed and new hydrogen introduced (Ha53).

ing from exchange of hydrogen in the walls) be $\gamma_3 U$.   Then one can write

$$\delta + \gamma_1 + \gamma_2 + \gamma_3 = p$$

If one next defines the final corrected sample transmission T, the raw observed transmission T' (with deuterium target filling), and the true sample transmission T_{12} for extraneous neutrons of the type $\gamma_1 + \gamma_2$, one obtains finally an expression (Ha53) analogous to Eq. (5), but now including all but two[5] of the background effects discussed above:

$$T = T' + (\gamma_1 + \gamma_2)(T - T_{12}) - (1 - T)\beta \qquad (6)$$

In Eq. (6), $\gamma_1 + \gamma_2$ can be determined by comparing a shadow bar counting-rate measurement (δ) with an unattenuated counting-rate measurement ($\gamma_1 + \gamma_2 + \delta$) immediately after filling the target with hydrogen ($\gamma_3 = 0$).   In addition, T_{12} can be determined by measuring the transmission of the sample under the same conditions, correcting for the background δ by Eq. (5).   Equation (6) then allows the determination of the corrected transmission T from the raw observed transmission T' (with deuterium gas filling).   Details of this procedure, and of an alternate method, are discussed by Hafner et al. (Ha53).

Synchrocyclotron measurements in the 30 to 100-Mev range generally use collimators between source, scatterer, and detector, so that most of the above considerations do not apply.   However, a correction for the effect of general machine neutron background, for example due to neutrons formed by the beam hitting a dee or primary neutrons scattered in the cyclotron vacuum tank (Hi50), may be made using Eq. (5).

(2) **In-scattering Correction.**   As pointed out earlier, Eqs. (2) and (3) are strictly valid only if neutrons suffering any sort of nuclear interaction in the sample are *not* counted by the detector. However, with any sample and detector of finite size, neutrons scattered forward in the sample toward the detector will be counted as if

[5] This discussion has ignored low-energy neutrons from deuteron breakup in the target, since it has been assumed that they have been biased out with an energy-sensitive detector.   In addition, by suitable construction of the target assembly the component ζ due to large-angle primary neutrons scattered forward in the target assembly can be made negligible, and it has been ignored in Eq. (6).

no interaction had occurred. This in-scattering correction is minimized by using a small detector well-removed from the neutron source, and a sample just large enough to shadow the detector. This is referred to as a *good-geometry* transmission experiment.

Assume that the transmission of the sample after background corrections but before in-scattering corrections is defined by

$$T = T_0 + T_1 + T_2 + \ldots$$

where $T_0 = \exp(-nt\sigma_T)$ is the corrected transmission excluding all scattered neutrons, T_1 is the ratio of the flux of neutrons singly-scattered in the sample into the detector to the background-corrected flux of neutrons without the scattering sample in place, T_2 is a similar ratio for the flux of neutrons doubly-scattered in the sample into the detector, etc. It is apparent that the correction to the transmission for single scattering (T_1) will be larger than that for double scattering (T_2), etc. In the following, a brief derivation of T_1 and T_2 will be given. Previous expressions for these quantities of varying complexity and for varying conditions are to be found in the literature (see Am46, Co49, Ri51, Po52, Ha53, Se55, Co58a).

The correction to the transmission for single in-scattering is readily derived using Fig. 5. Assume initially that the detector is sufficiently energy-sensitive that it will count only elastically-scattered neutrons in the forward direction, and that the overall length of the scattering sample t is small compared to both the source-to-sample distance L_1 and the sample-to-detector distance L_2. Let n = number of scattering nuclei/cm^3, $L = L_1 + L_2$ = source-to-detector distance, Q = number of neutrons produced in the source in the direction of the sample per second per unit solid angle, D = diameter of cylindrical scattering sample of length t, A = cross sectional area of the detector as seen from the source, $\sigma_n(\psi)$ = differential elastic-scattering cross section for neutrons at the laboratory angle ψ, σ_T = true total cross section corrected for inscattering, and σ_T' = total cross section calculated neglecting inscattering.

If one assumes a good-geometry experiment, the number of neutrons scattered in the sample between x and $x + dx$ which strike the detector is given by

$$[(Q/L_1^2) \exp(-n\sigma_T x)][(n\pi D^2/4)dx][\sigma_n(0°)A/L_2^2][\exp(-n\sigma_T(t-x))]$$

In this expression, the factors in brackets represent the flux at the depth x in the sample, the number of nuclei between x and $x + dx$, the differential cross section for elastic scattering in the forward direction[6] times the solid angle of the detector subtended at the sample, and the probability that neutrons scattered at x will penetrate the rest of the sample. By integrating this expression from $x = 0$ to $x = t$ and dividing by the counter area A, one obtains the flux at the

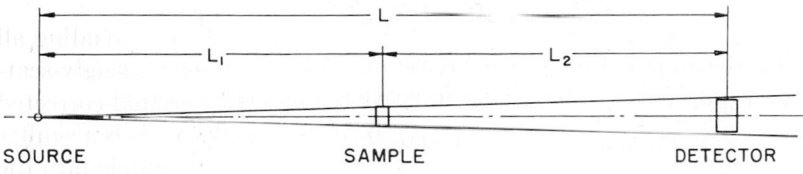

SOURCE   SAMPLE   DETECTOR

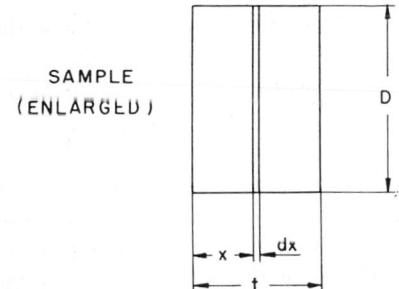

SAMPLE
(ENLARGED)

Figure 5. Geometry for calculation of in-scattering corrections (top), and enlarged view of scattering sample (bottom).

detector due to all neutrons singly-scattered in the sample into the detector (I_1):

$$I_1 = (\pi Q/4)(D/L_1 L_2)^2 \, n t \sigma_n(0°) \exp(-n t \sigma_T)$$

Since the flux with sample out is simply $I_0 = Q/L^2$, one obtains immediately

$$T_1 = I_1/I_0 = (\pi/4)(DL/L_1 L_2)^2 n t \sigma_n(0°) \exp(-n t \sigma_T) \qquad (7)$$

[6] The variation of $\sigma_n(\psi)$ over the small angles ψ through which neutrons can be singly-scattered in the sample and still be counted by the detector has been neglected, and $\sigma_n(0°)$ has been used for all scatterings.

In general, by Eq. (3),

$$\sigma_T = (1/nt) \ln (1/T),$$

$$\Delta \sigma_T = -(1/nt)(\Delta T/T)$$

For the present case, setting $\Delta T = T_1$ from Eq. (7) and $T = T_0 = \exp(-nt\sigma_T)$

$$\Delta \sigma_T = (\pi/4)(DL/L_1L_2)^2 \sigma_n(0°)$$

Thus the apparent relative decrease in the total cross section from its true value σ_T due to the singly in-scattered flux is

$$(\Delta \sigma_T/\sigma_T) = (\pi/4)(DL/L_1L_2)^2[\sigma_n(0°)/\sigma_T] \tag{8}$$

Using Eq. (8), one can obtain the true cross section σ_T from the apparent cross section σ_T' from

$$\sigma_T = \sigma_T'/[1 - (\Delta \sigma_T/\sigma_T)] \tag{9}$$

The minimum in-scattering correction is then easily found by differentiation of Eq. (8) to occur for the symmetrical geometry $L_1 = L_2 = L/2$, in which case Eq. (8) becomes

$$\Delta \sigma_T/\sigma_T = 4\pi(D/L)^2[\sigma_n(0°)/\sigma_T]. \tag{10}$$

This is the geometry most frequently used in practice. If the detector is sensitive also to inelastically-scattered neutrons in the forward direction, $\sigma_n(0°)$ must be replaced in Eqs. (8) and (10) by the differential cross section in the forward direction for elastic and inelastic scattering down to neutron energies equal to the bias setting of the detector.

In case a sample is used whose length t is *not* negligible compared to L_1 and L_2, then if $\pi D^2/4 \ll L^2$, the correction for the symmetrical case $L_1 = L_2 = L/2$ becomes (Se55)

$$(\Delta \sigma_T/\sigma_T) = 2\pi(D/L)^2[\sigma_n(0°)/\sigma_T]\{1/[1 - (t/L)^2]$$
$$+ [\tanh^{-1}(t/L)]/(t/L)\} \tag{11}$$

When $t \ll L$, this reduces at once to Eq. (10).

The practical difficulty in evaluating the corrections given in Eqs. (8), (10), and (11) is the determination of the elastic scattering differential cross section for forward scattering $\sigma_n(0°)$. If the elastic scattering angular distribution has previously been measured at the appropriate energy, then the experimental value for $\sigma_n(0°)$ can be used.   However, if this information is not available, one is faced either with measuring the angular distribution, a separate experiment in itself (see Chapter V.B), or using theoretical estimates of the quantity $\sigma_n(0°)$.   For neutron energies in the range of a few hundred kev, it is ordinarily sufficiently accurate to assume isotropic scattering.   Since in this energy region elastic scattering predominates, assuming isotropy one has simply $\sigma_n(0°) = \sigma_T/4\pi$.   For higher neutron energies, estimates of $\sigma_n(0°)$ are usually based on diffraction scattering considerations.   For small angles ψ this results in the well-known formula derived by Bethe and Placzek (Be46):

$$\sigma_n(\psi) = R^2[J_1(kR\psi)/\psi]^2 \tag{12}$$

where R is the nuclear radius, k the wave number of the incident neutrons, ψ the scattering angle, and J_1 a Bessel function of the first kind.   For $\psi = 0°$ this becomes

$$\sigma_n(0°) = k^2R^4/4 \tag{13}$$

A diffraction theory based on a continuum model developed by Feld *et al.* (Fe51) yields the result

$$\sigma_n(0°) = (kR + 1)^4/4k^2 \tag{14}$$

Forward scattering clearly becomes more pronounced with higher energies and heavier nuclei.

A recent survey of the angular distributions of elastically scattered neutrons at 14 Mev by Coon *et al.* (Co58) seems to give rather good agreement with Eq. (14) for fairly light and very heavy nuclei, assuming $R = 1.33 \, A^{1/3} \times 10^{-13}$ cm.   However, for intermediate A nuclei, Eq. (14) seems to predict values of $\sigma_n(0°)$ which are too small.   Over the whole range of A, these 14-Mev results (Co58) suggest that $\sigma_n(0°)$ may better be obtained directly from the measured total cross section using *Wick's limit* (Wi43)

$$\sigma_n(0°) = (k\sigma_T/4\pi)^2 \tag{15}$$

The evidence for this statement is presented in Fig. 6, taken from Coon *et al.* (Co58).

More detailed theories for neutron elastic-scattering angular distributions have been developed (Fe49, Fe54), which can in principle be used to determine $\sigma_n(0°)$ for the in-scattering correction once the

parameters of the theories have been established.   These are discussed
in detail in Chapter V.C.

In order to estimate the effect of neutrons doubly-scattered in
the sample into the detector, it is informative to calculate the ratio
T_2/T_1 using the above notation.   The problem for double in-scattering
is more complicated than for single in-scattering, because now neu-

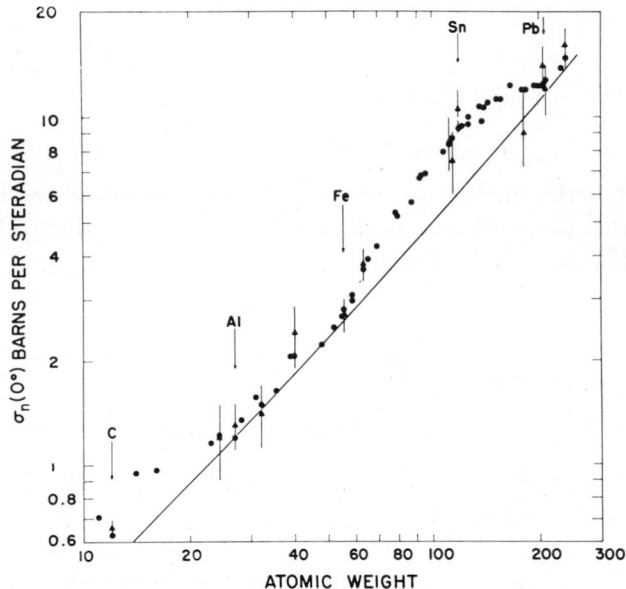

Figure 6. Values of differential cross sections for elastic scattering of 14.5-
Mev neutrons at $0°$ *versus* atomic weight (Co58).   The triangles represent the
extrapolation to $0°$ of the angular distributions measured by Coon *et al.* (Co58),
the circles are obtained from observed total cross sections using Wick's limit,
Eq. (15), and the solid line represents a plot of Eq. (14) using $R = 1.33 \, A^{1/3} \times$
10^{-13} cm.

trons scattered at large angles relative to the primary flux direction
may be rescattered forward into the detector.   As shown below, however, by suitable approximations an upper limit to the double in-
scattering correction can be obtained.   The flux of neutrons doubly-
scattered in the sample and arriving at the detector is given by an
extended expression from that for single in-scattering:

$$I_2 = 1/A \int_{\psi=0}^{\pi} \int_{x_2=0}^{t} \int_{x_1=0}^{x_2} [Q \exp (-nx_1\sigma_T)/L_1^2][(n\pi D^2/4)dx_1]$$

$$\times [\sigma_n(\psi)2\pi \sin \psi \, d\psi][\exp (-n\sigma_T(x_2 - x_1)/\cos \psi)]$$

$$\times [n \, dx_2][\sigma_n(\psi)(A/L_2^2)][\exp (-n\sigma_T(t - x_2))]$$

Here the factors in brackets represent the primary flux at a depth x_1 in the sample, the number of nuclei between x_1 and $x_1 + dx_1$, the differential cross section for elastic scattering at the angle ψ times the appropriate solid-angle increment, the probability that neutrons scattered at the angle ψ between x_1 and $x_1 + dx_1$ will arrive at x_2 before suffering a second collision, the number of nuclei/cm² in the thickness dx_2, the differential cross section for a second elastic scattering at the angle ψ (now straight forward) times the solid angle subtended by the detector, and the probability that neutrons second-scattered forward between x_2 and $x_2 + dx_2$ will penetrate the rest of the sample.   This expression can be evaluated at moderately high energies by noting that then most of the scattering is forward, and the principal contribution to the correction comes for small values of ψ. This approximation should be quite good when the detector is biased only to count elastic or nearly-elastic neutrons.   Setting $\cos \psi = 1$, and integrating only from $\psi = 0°$ to $\psi = \psi_m$ (representing the maximum angle of the forward lobe of the angular distribution), one obtains the ratio of the increase of transmission due to double in-scattering (T_2) to that due to single in-scattering (T_1) given by Eq. (7) to be

$$T_2/T_1 = \frac{\pi n t}{\sigma_n(0°)} \int_0^{\psi_m} \sigma_n^2(\psi) \sin \psi \, d\psi \qquad (16)$$

At high energies, where ψ_m is small, the upper limit for Eq. (16) can be obtained by setting $[\sigma_n (\psi)]^2 = [\sigma_n(0°)]^2$, which gives (Co58a):

$$T_2/T_1 \leq (\pi/2)n t \sigma_n(0°)\psi_m^2 \qquad (17)$$

A reasonable value of ψ_m is $1/kR$ (Fe51).

When more than two scatterings occur, the multiple in-scattering correction is best obtained using Monte Carlo methods (See Chapter IV.I), although series approximations are available (Mc47, Br58) which are very useful at high neutron energies. The total correction for in-scattering (single and multiple), as calculated by the above procedures, may be checked experimentally by determining the transmissions of samples of various lengths and diameters. A comparison of the cross section determined from the slope of the transmission *versus* sample-length curve, and that determined by extrapolating the cross section *versus* diameter curve to zero diameter, then serves as a check on the validity of the calculated in-scattering corrections (Ha53).

(3) **"Hardening" Effects.** An important condition for the validity of the expressions for the transmission and cross section [Eqs. (2) and (3)] is that the total cross section must not vary appreciably over the energy range represented by the spread in neutron energies present in the incident flux. If this condition is not met in an experiment, then the decrease of the primary beam flux in the sample will not be exponential. This is because the exit flux from the sample is filtered in such a way that neutrons of certain energies are removed more strongly than others. For example, if the total cross section is a monotonically decreasing function over the neutron spectrum employed, as is often the case, the exit neutron flux will be *hardened* because its *average* energy has increased. If a strong narrow resonance in the total cross section appears within the spectrum, neutrons of that particular energy will be largely removed from the exit flux.

It is clear that an accurate measurement of a total cross section can best be made by employing a neutron energy spread less than any energy interval in which the cross section varies appreciably. This will often require special techniques for obtaining high resolution, as discussed in Section 1.C (2). In many cases, however, it will not be feasible to employ sufficiently high resolution to fulfill this condition, for example in nuclei where sharp resonances are spaced very closely together. In this event, one is forced to make a measurement of the cross section "averaged" over the energy region determined by the neutron spectrum employed. If the fraction of incident neutrons with energies between E and $E + dE$ is $f(E)dE$, where $\int f(E)dE = 1$, the general result for the transmission expected for a sample of thickness t is given by (Th55, Da55a)

$$T = \int f(E) \exp\left[-nt\sigma_T(E)\right]dE \qquad (18)$$

If σ_T is constant, Eq. (18) reduces at once to Eq. (2). On the other hand, if σ_T is a function of energy, for very thin samples fulfilling the requirement

$$nl\sigma_T \ll 1 \tag{19}$$

Eq. (18) becomes

$$T \cong \exp\left(-nl\bar{\sigma}_T\right) \tag{20}$$

where

$$\bar{\sigma}_T = \int f(E)\sigma_T(E)dE \tag{21}$$

Normally one calculates the "average" cross section from Eq. (20). However, if condition (19) is not satisfied and if σ_T varies rapidly over the neutron spectrum, the "average" cross section calculated from Eq. (20) will be less than the "average" cross section defined by Eq. (21) (Da55a). If samples are employed which are thin enough to satisfy condition (19), in order to insure a correct measurement of the average cross section, a large number of sample-in sample-out counts must be taken to insure adequate counting statistics, as shown by Eq. (4) and Fig. 3.

Although the method for obtaining the correct average cross section has just been outlined, it might be mentioned that nonexponential effects in moderate to heavy nuclei have been directly related by Thomas (Th55) to the average resonance neutron width to spacing ratio, a quantity which is of considerable importance for comparison with various nuclear models (see Chapter V.C).

C. Particular Techniques

(1) **Techniques Employed with Accelerator Sources in Various Neutron Energy Ranges.** The purpose of this section is to enumerate very briefly the more common techniques employed in various neutron energy regions for the measurement of total cross sections using accelerator sources. These techniques are individually discussed in detail in other chapters, so only very brief remarks relative to their use for transmission measurements need be made here. A method for total cross section measurements employing a fast reactor source will be discussed separately in Section (3) below.

(a) 120 kev to 600 kev. In this energy range the $\mathrm{Li}^7(p, n)\mathrm{Be}^7$ reaction is normally employed as a neutron source, with the transmission apparatus set up in the forward direction relative to the beam. Above neutron energies of about 600 kev, a low-energy group of neutrons appears due to an excited state at 430 kev in Be^7. If one wishes to use this source above 600 kev, therefore, an energy-sensitive counter should be used to bias against the low-energy group, or corrections for the contribution of the low-energy group should be applied. Detectors employed in the 120 to 600-kev region are usually BF_3 counters or gas recoil counters. Enriched BF_3 counters have often been used in the past (see, e.g. Se47a, Ro49, Pe50, Bo54) because of their relatively high counting efficiency; however, they normally operate with moderately high background, which must be carefully measured. Gas recoil counters (see, e.g. Ba40, Ro49, Bo51, Jo54), although less efficient, have the advantage of energy discrimination. By accepting only pulses greater than a certain bias, corresponding to recoils principally forward from the incident neutron flux, the room-scattered background can be made negligible (less than one per cent) and γ rays can generally be excluded as well.

(b) 0.6 Mev to 4 Mev. In this energy region the $T(p, n)He^3$ reaction is generally used as a neutron source. Counters employed are usually hydrogen or helium gas recoil counters or scintillation counters, both incorporating energy sensitivity. Although simple organic scintillators are efficient and easy to prepare (Fa51), their sensitivity to γ rays has brought about the development of other designs, such as the Hornyak button (Ho52), which are less sensitive to γ radiation. The Bonner sphere counter (Mc54, Ta55) and various modifications (Be56, Ha57) incorporate both γ-ray insensitivity and neutron-energy discrimination, both highly desirable for low-background transmission measurements. The shadow cones used for background measurements at energies up to a few Mev are usually made of paraffin or lucite of appropriate size and length.

(c) 4 Mev to 9 Mev. The standard reaction in this energy region is the exoergic $D(d, n)He^3$ reaction. It is characterized by the usual background difficulties found with deuteron-induced neutron sources, particularly the extraneous production of neutrons from the beam direction, as discussed in Section 1.B (1). Other useful reactions in this energy range are the $Be^9(\alpha, n)C^{12}$, $C^{13}(\alpha, n)O^{16}$, and $N^{14}(d, n)O^{15}$ reactions (Be56, Bo56) (see Chapter I.C.). Although the (α, n) reactions are not beset with the background problem inherent in (d, n) reactions,[6a] their low yield makes the $C^{13}(\alpha, n)$ and $Be^9(\alpha, n)$

[6a] It should be noted, however, that carbon deposits can accumulate rapidly during α-particle bombardment, and then the $C^{13}(\alpha, n)O^{16}$ reaction can become a troublesome source of background neutrons (Wi60).

reactions practical only in the neutron energy ranges of 4.4 to 5.6 Mev and 7.0 to 8.6 Mev, respectively (Be56). Because of this fact, and because a low-energy continuum of neutrons caused by deuteron breakup is observed in the $D(d, n)$He³ reaction above 4-Mev bombarding energy (Cr 56), there is no satisfactory source of strictly monoenergetic neutrons known in the energy range from 8.6 to 12 Mev. Detectors employed for transmission measurements in the 4 to 9-Mev range are usually various types of organic scintillators already mentioned.

(d) 12 *Mev to 27 Mev.*   The highly exoergic T(d, n)He⁴ reaction, or its alternate D(t, n)He⁴, are used to produce neutrons in this energy region, the highest available to electrostatic-generator techniques at the present time.   The T(d, n)He⁴ reaction is often used with Cockroft-Walton accelerators to produce a high yield of 14-Mev neutrons in the forward direction.   By going to a backward angle relative to the beam direction, neutron energies as low as 12 Mev can be obtained from this reaction.   In addition to the usual difficulty with extraneous neutrons from the beam direction, above deuteron energies of 4-Mev low-energy neutrons are again observed (He56).   These are presumably caused by deuteron breakup in the target, and require an energy-sensitive detector to prevent the inclusion of the low-energy neutrons in the detector counting rate.   Again, various types of organic scintillators are usually used for this purpose.   Measurements of room-scattered background in this energy region normally employ shadow bars of iron, tantalum, copper, etc. (see, e.g. Co52, Po52).

It might be mentioned that the *associated particle method,* often used in neutron flux measurements (See Chapter IV.B), is sometimes used in transmission measurements to reduce the neutron background (see, e.g. Kh57).   In the T(d, n)He⁴ reaction, for example, by requiring coincidences between the usual neutron detector and an associated α-particle detector, miscellaneous background neutrons striking the neutron detector will not be recorded.

(e) 30 *Mev to 100 Mev.*   In this energy range, synchrocyclotron accelerators are normally employed.   The circulating beam in such an accelerator is allowed to strike an internal target, which then yields a high-energy neutron beam through appropriate collimating apertures in the shielding.   In some cases a deuteron beam is employed (Co49, Hi50, De50) with the production of neutrons by the *stripping* mechanism (Se47) in the target, typically beryllium.   Other-

wise a proton beam is employed (Ta51, Mo52, Ta53, Hi54, Cu55) to
produce neutrons presumably by the *charge-exchange* mechanism,
at least at higher energies.   In order to obtain measurements at different energies, internal targets placed at different radii can be used,
or the magnetic field can be decreased when a target at a particular
radius is employed, or different target materials can be introduced
(Ta53).   Such changes will alter the effective energy of the neutron
beam, but a wide spectrum of energies will still be included in general.
Such a spectrum can be narrowed somewhat by deliberately "hardening" the beam by passing it through polyethylene rods which preferentially scatter out the low-energy neutron component (Hi54).
In addition, it is desirable to make the neutron detector as energy-

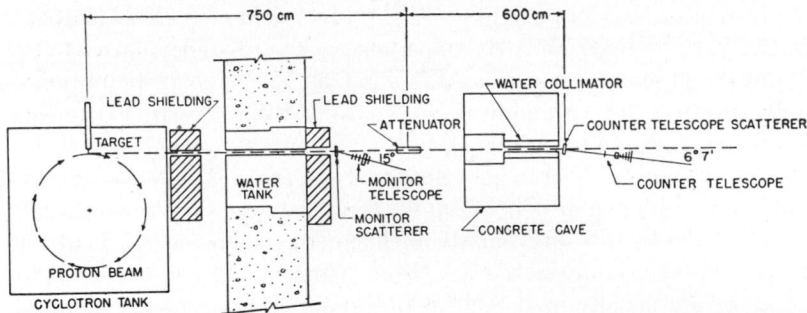

Figure 7. Typical experimental geometry for the measurement of total cross
sections in the 30-to 100-Mev range, using a synchrocyclotron (Cu55).

selective as possible, so that rather narrow bands of the entire neutron
spectrum can be employed for the measurements.   This also allows
measurements as a function of neutron energy, by choosing the bands
at different energies throughout the neutron spectrum.

The general experimental geometry used for synchrocyclotron
transmission measurements is illustrated by Fig. 7, which shows the
experimental arrangement used at Harvard (Cu55).   It must be
emphasized that this geometry differs from that used in electrostatic-
generator measurements because a collimated neutron beam is used,
so that many of the considerations of Sections 1.A and 1.B do not
apply.   The source-to-detector distances are chosen to be quite large,
usually in the range from 10 to 20 meters.   This is partly due to
collimation and background considerations, and partly to minimize

in-scattering effects, since elastic scattering at these energies is strongly forward (Br50) as expected from diffraction considerations. It is important that the effective source, sample, and detector arrangement be well-aligned. This may be done with a cathetometer, or by using γ rays produced in the target to record the shadow of the collimators and a small object centered at the sample position upon an X-ray film placed at the detector position (De50, Hi50, Ta53). The samples (or *attenuators*) employed are larger in diameter than the collimating apertures, and of a thickness usually equal to about two mean free paths for the incident neutrons.

The detector serves a particularly important role in synchro-cyclotron measurements, since it determines the neutron energy spread involved in each measurement. In the earlier work (Co49, Hi50), the 20-minute activities induced in carbon disks by the C^{12} $(n, 2n)C^{11}$ reaction (threshold 20 Mev) were measured in standard G-M counter arrangements. Bismuth fission ionization chambers, with an effective threshold of 50 Mev, were also employed (De50). In these cases a wide band of energies was accepted, determined by the characteristics of the neutron spectrum and the threshold and response of the detector. More recently, various types of recoil proton coincidence telescope arrangements have been employed (Ta51, Mo52, Ta53, Cu55). These normally use a polyethylene radiator disk placed in the collimated neutron flux, from which recoil protons are detected in a counter telescope placed at a small angle to (and shielded from) the direct beam, as shown in Fig. 7. From the energy and angle of the recoil proton, the incident neutron energy can be determined. These coincidence counter telescopes originally employed gas counters which accepted energy bands of 10–20 Mev, with the *effective energy* of each band being established to about 2 Mev out of 100 Mev (Ta51, Ta53). More recent developments using scintillation counter telescopes have reduced the total energy band widths accepted, and allow the determination of the *effective energy* of a particular band to about 0.5 Mev out of 100 Mev (Cu55). In addition to the detector, a monitor telescope is usually employed in these experiments to monitor the total flux during the transmission measurements, as shown in Fig. 7.

Corrections to the data in these measurements are usually rather small. The background (or *leakage flux*), measured by inserting an "infinite" attenuator at the sample position, is seldom over a few

per cent.   Because of the good geometry of the experiments, inscattering corrections are usually less than the statistical error, typically
amounting to about 1 per cent for the heaviest elements.   In-scattering corrections are made using the method described in Section
1.B (2), where the forward scattering cross section is estimated (see,
e.g. Co49) from diffraction theories as already described or from experimental results (Br50).

(2) **High-Resolution Techniques for Resonance Studies.**
Chapter V.E discusses the important subject of fast neutron resonance processes.   In order that the true shape of a resonance in the
total cross section be obtained, it is necessary that the experimental
energy resolution be narrower than the width of the resonance under
study, as already discussed in Section 1.B (3).   This condition often
requires that very high-resolution techniques be employed in transmission measurements.   These techniques will be described briefly
below.   Further details of various aspects of this question will be
found in Chapters I.B, I.C, I.D, I.E., and IV.A.

The energy spread of the detected neutrons in a transmission experiment is determined primarily by three factors (Ba49): (a) the
energy spread of the charged particles producing neutrons in the
target, (b) the thickness of the target, and (c) the angle subtended
by the detector at the target.   In addition, there is always an inherent Doppler spread due to the thermal motion of the atoms in the
target and sample.   Although the Doppler contribution is small, it
is not as small as one might off-hand expect, and amounts to several
hundred ev (Ba52).   These effects are discussed in more detail in
Chapter I.B.

For transmission experiments employing electrostatic accelerators,
factor (a) can be made arbitrarily small by the use of precision electrostatic or magnetic beam analyzers (see, e.g. Wa47), except for the
limitation of beam intensity.   In addition, by the use of very thin
evaporated targets, factor (b) can also be made very small, but again
at the expense of the neutron yield from the source.   Factor (c)
enters into the total energy spread because the variation in the
energy of the source neutrons with emission angle results in a spread
in energy of the neutrons striking the face of the neutron detector.
The maximum spread due to this effect can be calculated from
the reaction kinematics using the known geometry.   However,
the variation of the efficiency of the detector over its surface makes it

difficult to determine the exact shape of this contribution to the total spread. Of course factor (c) can be reduced by using a smaller detector or a larger source-to-detector distance, but either alternative will decrease the detector counting rate. As discussed in Chapter I.D, a neutron source using a reaction in a heavy target nucleus (Ha49) will essentially remove the effects of factor (c), but these sources have not yet been widely used.

It is apparent that all of the methods for reducing the neutron energy spread due to the factors (a), (b), and (c) also reduce the detector counting rate, at least for sources in the light nuclei. Therefore the length of time available for the experiment, the statistical error which can be tolerated, and the energy region to be covered ultimately determine the best resolution which can be employed. These considerations, plus the inherent Doppler spread, set a practical lower limit of about 1 kev on the energy resolution employed in transmission experiments performed on a point-by-point basis in energy (Pe50, Ba52). However, the time necessary for the accumulation of data with these high-resolution methods can be reduced by about two orders of magnitude using a technique developed by Cranberg et al. (Cr57, Cr57a). In this method, a 50 kv alternating potential is applied to the insulated beam target at a frequency of 10 cycles per second. Pulses from the detected neutrons are used to gate a 100-channel analyzer, which records each count in a channel (effective width 0.5 kev) appropriate to the target voltage (or neutron energy) at that time. The reduction in running time occurs because a thick hydrogenous scintillator is used, which is much more efficient than the usual thin proton-recoil detector. To eliminate γ rays and low-energy neutrons which are also detected in the thick scintillator, the accelerator beam is pulsed and the correct time-of-flight required on all neutron pulses accepted (Cr57a).

In high-resolution work, it is generally desirable to know the overall experimental resolution due to the factors (a), (b), and (c) previously discussed. This is particularly important when a resonance is only partly resolved, in which case its true width and height may be estimated by unfolding the experimental resolution function from the observed peak shape. The contribution to the total resolution function of the charged-particle beam spread [factor (a)] may be determined from the beam analyzer slit settings, or by observing narrow (p, γ) resonances (Wi58). As previously mentioned, the source-detector geometry and the source-reaction kinematics determine the maximum contribution to the total energy spread of the angular resolution [factor (c)], though the exact shape of the angular resolution function is somewhat more difficult to determine. The target-thickness contribution to the total energy spread [factor (b)] must be determined strictly by experimental means. If the $Li^7(p, n)$ reaction is employed as the neutron source, as is frequently the case in high-resolution work, the target thickness may be obtained (Ta48, Ba49) from the geometric peak in the observed yield of the reaction just above threshold (see Chapter I.E). However, this method is unreliable for targets thinner than about 5 kev (Pe50, Wi58). For target thicknesses in the region of a few kev, a measurement of the neutron yield from the thin target at a suitable energy relative to the yield from a thicker target measured by the rise method will give the relative target thicknesses (Pe50), provided oxygen buildup on the targets is negligible. Once the target thickness is found for one energy, it may be calculated for any other energy from the variation in stopping power of the target with the energy of the incident charged-particle beam. It should be mentioned at this point that considerable care must be used with thin lithium targets to prevent loss of lithium or deposition of oil on the target. This is normally done by using a rotating beam or rotating target to prevent excessive local beam heating of the target, and by directing a blast of heated air on the target backing to reduce oil deposition.

If the separate contributions of the three factors (a), (b), and (c) are known, the overall energy spread is normally obtained by assuming that the separate contributions add in an rms fashion. Though this method usually is based on the assumption that each function is Gaussian in shape, it is not very sensitive to changes in the shapes of the resolution functions (Pe50). If the overall resolution is in the range of a few kev, it may be determined experimentally (see, e.g. Ha53a, Wi58) using the 585-kev resonance in S^{32}, which has a natural width of about 1.5 kev (Pe50, Cr57a). If the parameters describing a narrow resonance are known, a comparison of the observed height and width with the expected theoretical height also allows one to extract the overall experimental resolution (Pe50).

(3) **Reactor Techniques.** Essentially all of the previous discussion of the present chapter has been devoted to techniques employed for the measurement of total cross sections using accelerator-

induced neutron sources. One important set of measurements which should be mentioned has been made by Nereson and Darden (Ne53, Ne54) using the Los Alamos Fast Reactor as a neutron source. By using a neutron spectrometer which determined the energy of each neutron detected, the total cross section was determined as a function of neutron energy even though the source produced a continuous spectrum of neutrons.

The neutron beam from the reactor was collimated by a $3/4$-inch steel collimator and then passed immediately through a one-inch diameter scattering sample chosen to give about 50 per cent transmission. A (hydrogen or deuterium) polyethylene radiator was placed 18 inches from the sample at the entrance to a parallel-plate ionization chamber operated with a Frisch grid. An acceptable pulse from the ionization chamber had to be in coincidence with a pulse from a small proportional counter between the radiator and main ionization chamber, and in anticoincidence with an end electrode following the main ionization chamber electrode. Ionization chamber pulses were then displayed on a multichannel analyzer to determine the number of neutrons counted as a function of their energy. Further details of this spectrometer are given in Chapter II.C.

By comparing sample-in sample-out counts in each channel, the total cross section was obtained as a function of neutron energy. The average energy spread in the measurements was 10 per cent and the overall accuracy of the results was quoted to be ±10 per cent or better. These very useful measurements then yielded the average cross section as a function of neutron energy from 3 to 12 Mev, thereby helping to fill in the gap in electrostatic-generator measurements in this energy range mentioned in Section 1.C. Some of the results of these measurements will be described in Section 2 below.

D. Accuracy of Total Cross Section Measurements

As previously pointed out, total cross section measurements can be made with very good accuracy since no absolute flux determination is required. Because of the fundamental importance of the neutron-proton cross section, it has been measured with greater care than any other total cross section. The smallest error yet achieved is quoted to be less than a half per cent (Ha53, Fi54).

As an illustration of the relative magnitudes of the various errors entering into these measurements, Table I shows the errors quoted by

Fields, Becker, and Adair (Fi54) in measurements of the neutron-proton cross section at 1.0 Mev and 2.5 Mev. Hafner, Hornyak, Falk, Snow, and Coor (Ha53) give a similar but more detailed breakdown of errors in their measurement at 4.75 Mev.

Table I. Sources of Error in $n - p$ Total Cross Section Measurement (in parts per thousand) (Fi54)

	Measurement	
Source of error	2.5 Mev	1.0 Mev
Statistical standard error	1.9	2.3
Energy	1.9	1.5
Background	1.2	1.6
In-scattering	1.3	1.6
Nuclei/cm²	1.5	1.6
Total (rms)	3.5	4.0

2. Typical Results: Total Cross Sections from 120 kev to 100 Mev

It would be out of place for this chapter to attempt any sort of a comprehensive survey of total cross sections. A complete compilation by D. J. Hughes and R. B. Schwartz (Hu58) is available, and the reader is referred to this volume for detailed results and references. Instead, typical results of the techniques described in Section 1 above will be shown for various energy regions and for nuclei of various atomic weights. In addition, brief remarks describing the general behavior of the results and their dependence upon various natural and experimental quantities will be included.

A. *Total Cross Sections as a Function of Energy*

(1) **120 kev to 3 Mev.** Measurements of the total cross sections of light nuclei in the energy range from 120 kev to 3 Mev have usually been performed with good resolution in order to study the resonance structure exhibited by these nuclei. By careful determination of the shape, width, and cross section variation of a resonance, one can usually establish the excitation energy, spin, parity, and reduced width of the corresponding excited state in the compound nucleus of the reaction. This type of analysis, which probably represents one of the most important contributions of neutron total cross section

measurements to the understanding of nuclear structure, is discussed
in detail in Chapter V.E of this volume.   To prevent duplication, the
reader is referred to that chapter for results of measurements made on
light nuclei using the techniques described in the present chapter.
The principal emphasis in the following will be on the heavier nuclei,
although a few results for light nuclei will be shown for comparison
purposes.

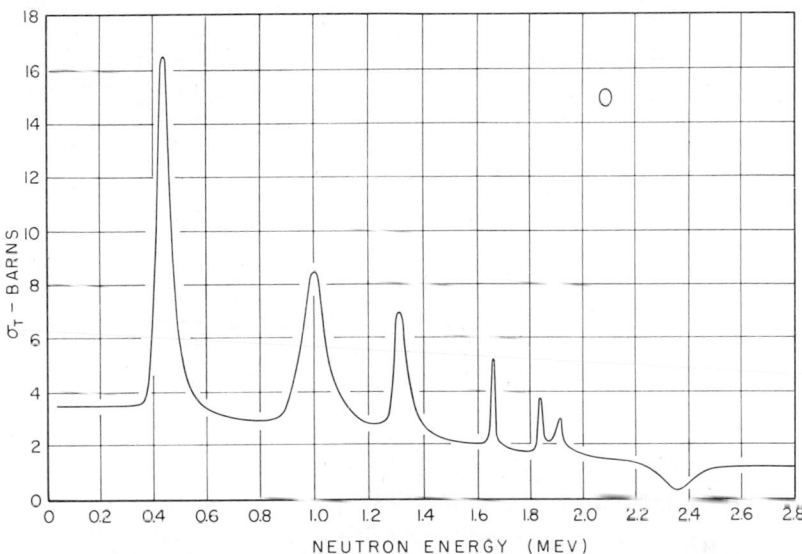

Figure 8. Total cross section of oxygen below 2.8 Mev, obtained using the Li⁷
(p, n) and T(p, n) reactions as neutron sources (Bo50, Fr50, Bo51).

    Figure 8 shows the total cross section of oxygen ($Z = 8$) below
2.8 Mev taken from Bockelman, Miller, Adair, and Barschall (Bo51)
and including previous results (Bo50, Fr50).   Although 7-kev resolution was employed, the resonances at 1.66 Mev and 1.84 Mev are not
resolved.   In fact, the observed widths of these resonances are just
about equal to the experimental energy spread, indicating that the
true peaks should be higher and narrower than observed.   Such
sharp resonances can cause obvious nonexponential attenuation
[Section 1.B (3)], and would require application of higher resolution
techniques [Section 1.C (2)] in order to attempt to extract the true

height and width of the peaks.   Examples of results obtained with
these very high resolution techniques are given in Chapter V.E.

Figure 9 shows the total cross section of magnesium ($Z = 12$) in
the range from 0.6 to 1.8 Mev taken from early results of Freier,
Fulk, Lampi, and Williams (Fr 50).   The solid curve represents data
taken with a 30-kev lithium target as the neutron source.   By reducing the source target thickness to 12 kev, the dashed curve was

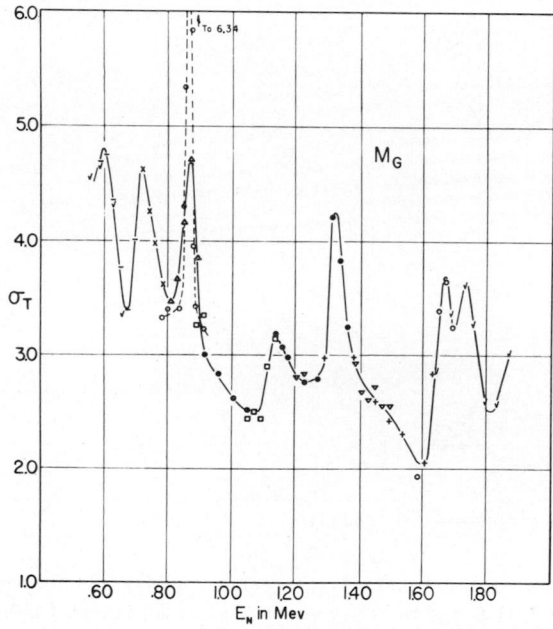

Figure 9.   Total cross section of magnesium from 0.6 to 1.8 Mev, obtained using
the Li⁷ (p, n) reaction as a neutron source (Fr50).

obtained, but the observed peak width was still about equal to the
experimental energy spread.   This figure illustrates how markedly
the height and width of a partially-resolved peak change as the energy
spread is reduced, further illustrating the discussion of Sections
1.B (3) and 1.C (2).

The complexity observed below 0.8 Mev in the resonance structure of phosphorous ($Z = 15$) by Hansen, Kiehn, and Goodman
(Ha53a) is illustrated in Fig. 10.   The energy resolution was about 2

kev and the spacing between points 2 kev.   Even with this high resolution, many of the resonances are undoubtedly not resolved. As one continues to heavier nuclei, the resonances continue to become narrower and closer together.   For this reason it clearly becomes impractical to measure individual resonances in great detail over any appreciable range.   The level density at low energies is determined by the complexity of the compound nucleus and the binding energy of the last neutron in this nucleus.   This binding energy is determined in turn by various detailed effects of the nucleus, such as whether the compound nucleus has even or odd numbers of protons and neutrons,

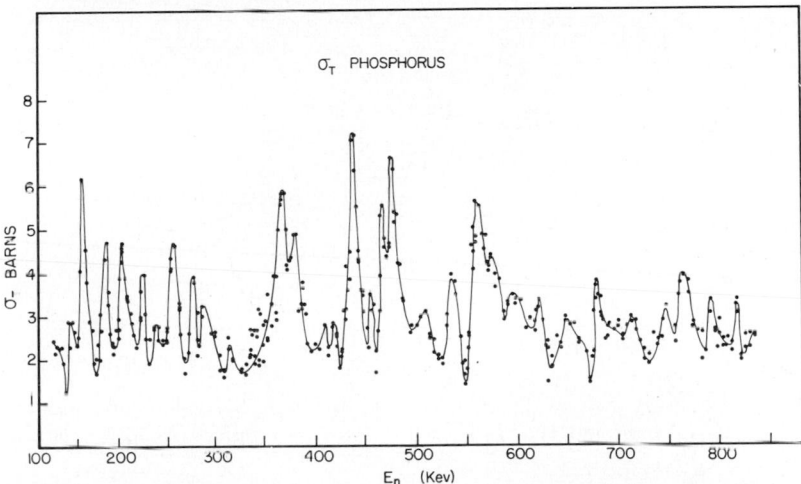

Figure 10. Total cross section of phosphorous below 0.8 Mev, obtained using the Li⁷ (p, n) reaction with about 2 kev resolution (Ha53a).

whether the target nucleus has a *closed shell* in neutrons, etc.   With convenient energy resolutions in the 20–30 kev range, resonance structure above 100 kev largely disappears for nuclei above about $Z = 30$, and one measures only the cross section averaged over resonances.   If the binding energy of the added neutron happens to be exceptionally small, then the compound nucleus will not be so highly excited, and resonance structure may yet be observed.   Several examples of this will be shown below.

Figure 11 shows the total cross section of strontium $(Z = 38)$ below 3 Mev as obtained by Miller, Adair, Bockelman, and Darden

(Mi52).   The principal isotope of strontium, Sr^{88} (83 per cent abundant) is an even Z even N nucleus containing a closed-shell of 50 neutrons.   The binding energy of a neutron added to this nucleus is about 1.5 Mev less than nearby non-closed shell nuclei of smaller Z (Ha51).   As a result, fluctuations in the cross section due to resonance structure are observed using 20-kev resolution up to about 1.4 Mev, although no attempt was made to study them in detail above 0.7 Mev.   Above 1.4 Mev, the fluctuations disappear when 20-kev resolution is employed, and the cross section averaged over resonances is obtained.

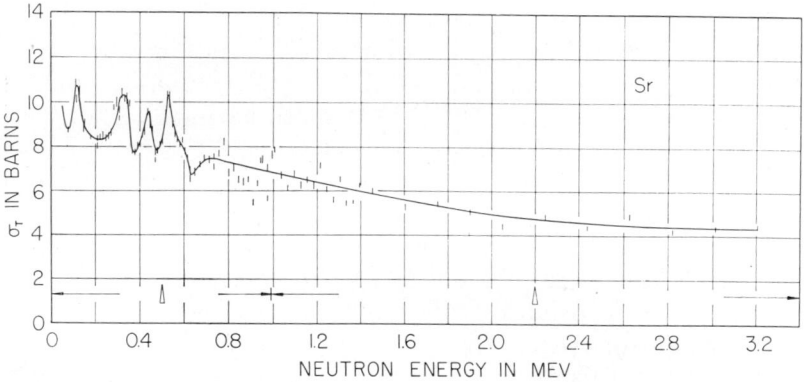

Figure 11. Total cross section of strontium below 3.2 Mev obtained using the $Li^7(p, n)$ and $T(p, n)$ reactions for neutron sources (Mi52).

The total cross sections of two elements in which the principal isotope has a closed shell of 82 neutrons are shown in Figs. 12 and 13 (Mi52).   Lanthanum ($Z = 57$) is sufficiently heavy that resonance structure at low energies cannot be resolved with 20-kev resolution. Cerium ($Z = 58$) does exhibit resonances below 100 kev in Fig. 13 (as obtained by the back-angle $Li^7(p, n)$ techniques described in Chapter V.L), but they cannot be resolved at higher energies.   The fact that resonance structure can be observed at all in this energy range again shows the effect of the reduced neutron binding energy resulting from the closed shell.   Another interesting feature of Figs. 12 and 13 is that the *average* cross sections of the neighboring elements La and Ce are essentially identical, both exhibiting a broad maximum around 1.4 Mev.   On the other hand, the average cross section of Sr in Fig. 11

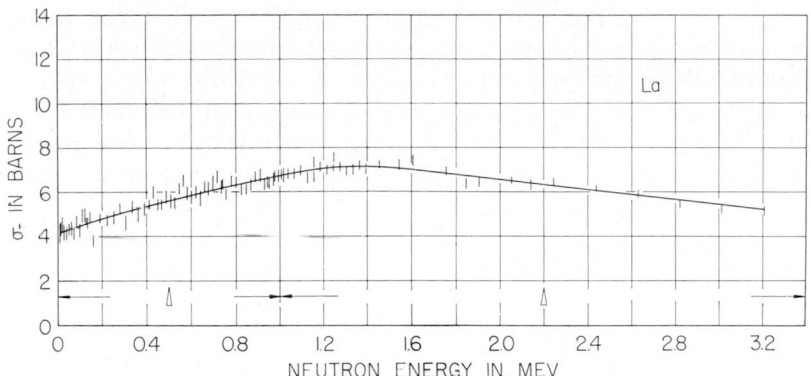

Figure 12. Total cross section of lanthanum below 3.2 Mev (Mi52).

is quite different.   The systematic trends of the average total cross section as a function of mass number will be discussed in Section 2.B (1).   It should be mentioned again that these average cross sections should be measured with thin samples, as discussed in Section 1.B (3).

(2) **3 Mev to 22 Mev.**   In this energy range a variety of neutron sources are required, as described briefly in Section 1.C(1). Figure 14 illustrates a measurement of the total cross section of deuterium by Seagrave and Henkel (Se55) over the energy range from 0.2 to 22 Mev.   This measurement was performed in a uniform manner to an accuracy of 2 per cent, using neutrons from the $T(p, n)He^3$,

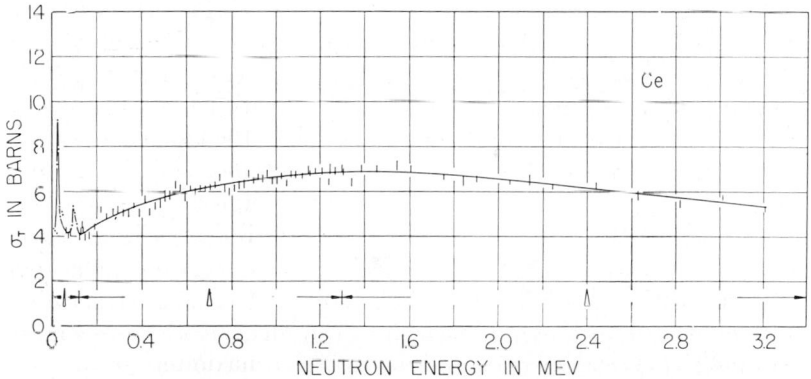

Figure 13. Total cross section of cerium below 3.2 Mev (Mi52).

$D(d, n)He^3$, and $T(d, n)He^4$ reactions respectively. The gap in the measurements in the energy range from 8 to 14 Mev has previously been mentioned in Section 1.C (1).

Becker and Barschall (Be56) have measured the total cross sections of several light elements using the $C^{12}(\alpha, n)O^{16}$ and $Be^9(\alpha,$

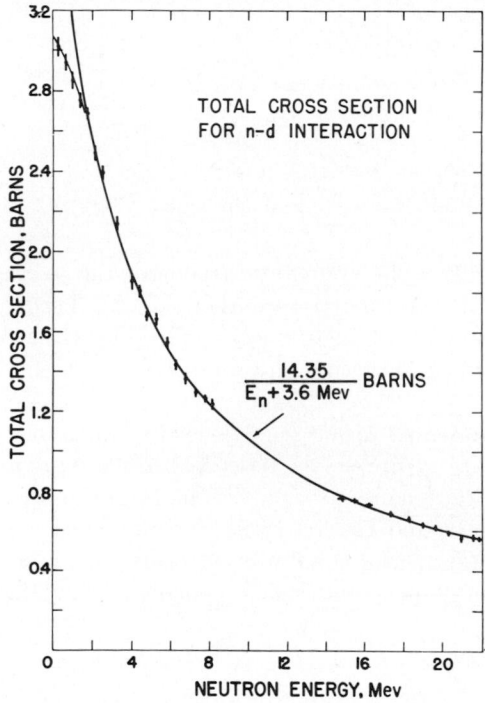

Figure 14. Total cross section of deuterium from 0.2 to 22 Mev, obtained in one experimental geometry using the reactions $T(p, n)$, $D(d, n)$, and $T(d, n)$ as neutron sources (Se55). The solid line represents an empirical fit to the data from 1.5 to 22 Mev.

$n)C^{12}$ reactions as neutron sources. A typical result is displayed in Fig. 15, which shows the total cross section of oxygen in the energy ranges from 4.4–5.6 and 7.7–8.6 Mev (Be56). Resonance structure is quite noticeable in this light element, even at these higher energies, as would be expected by comparison with Fig. 8.

Typical results of the fast reactor measurements of Nereson and

Darden (Ne53, Ne54) in the energy range from 3–13 Mev, described in Section 1.C (3), are shown in Fig. 16. As previously mentioned, these measurements were designed to determine the average total cross section, since an energy spread of 10 per cent was employed. Again it will be noted that nearby elements exhibit almost identical average cross sections, as will be discussed in Section 2.B (1).

A comparison of Figs. 12 and 16 points out the effect of the in-scattering correction, discussed in Section 1.B (2), upon the calculated

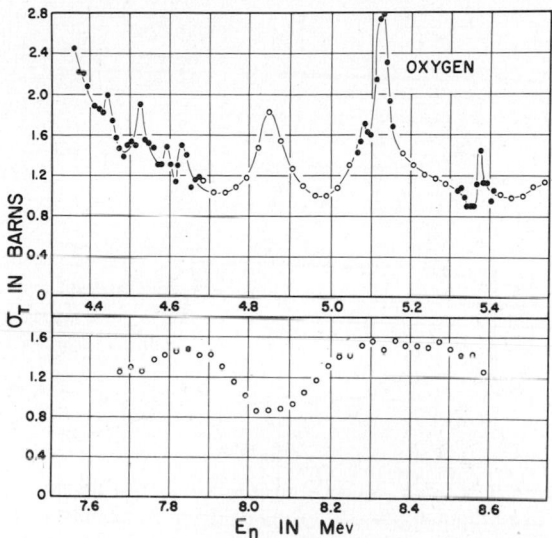

Figure 15. Total cross section of oxygen obtained using the C^{13} (α, n) and $Be^9(\alpha, n)$ reactions as neutron sources (Be56). The solid and open circles represent data taken with energy spreads of about 15 kev and 30 kev respectively.

total cross section. In the measurements from 0 to 3 Mev on lanthanum (Mi52), details of the angular distributions of neutrons scattered from heavy nuclei were not yet well known experimentally. Therefore, the in-scattering correction was made under the assumption that the scattering was isotropic. Using the theoretical expressions for forward scattering in Section 1.B (2), it was stated in the earlier results (Mi52) that the cross sections presented might be expected to be as much as 10 per cent low in the heavy elements. The subsequent

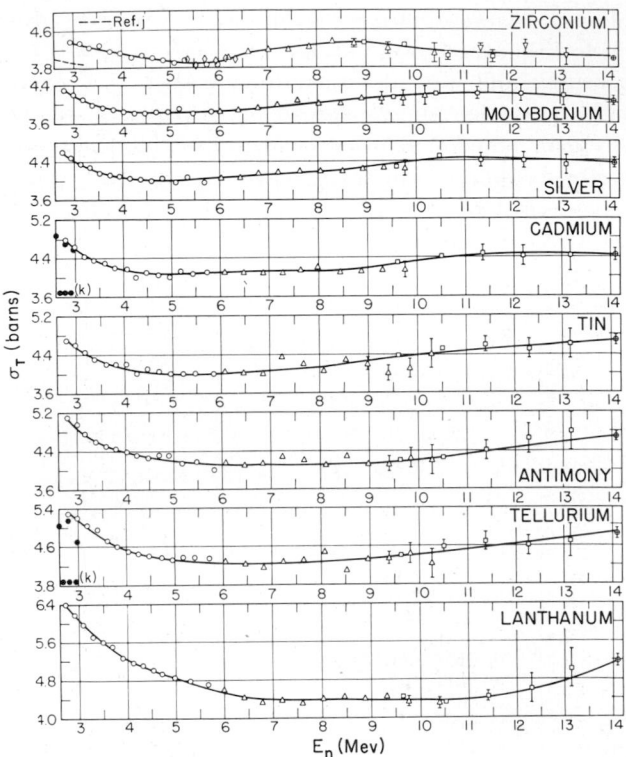

Figure 16. Average total cross sections of various elements between zirconium
$(Z = 40)$ and lanthanum $(Z = 50)$ using neutrons from a fast reactor (Ne54).

measurements of Nereson and Darden (Ne54) on lanthanum from 3
to 13 Mev were performed under much better geometry conditions,
for which the in-scattering correction was believed to be less than 1.5
per cent at 12 Mev.   Comparing the cross section of lanthanum at
3 Mev in Figs. 12 and 16, it is indeed found that the earlier results are
low by about 10 per cent.

(3) **120 kev to 100 Mev.** Synchrocyclotron measurements
have been made on a number of elements in the 30 to 100-Mev range,
using the techniques described in Section 1.C (1).   When taken together with electrostatic-generator measurements at lower energies,
it is possible to show the total cross section over the complete range of
energies discussed in the present chapter, provided logarithmic scales

are employed.   Three typical cross sections taken from the compilation by Hughes and Schwartz (Hu58) are included as examples.

The very fundamental total cross section of hydrogen for fast
neutrons in the energy range from 1 to 100 Mev is shown in Fig. 17.
The individual points represent careful measurements by various
workers (Po52, Ha53, Fi54, St54, Cu55, Co49, De50, Hi50, Hi54,
Ta53, Da55, Sh45).   These references are particularly valuable

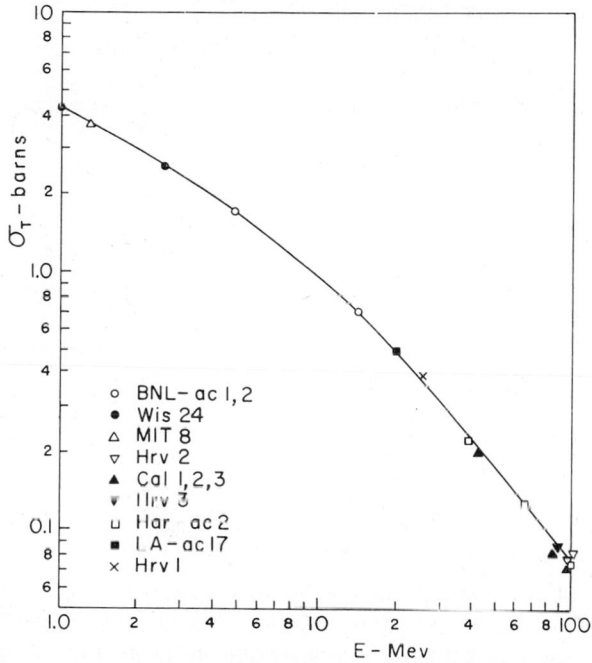

Figure 17. Total cross section of hydrogen in the energy range from 1 to 100
Mev (Hu55).

because of the detailed and careful considerations given to the corrections required in total cross section measurements.

A measurement of a typical intermediate nucleus over the complete energy range from 0.1 to 100 Mev is illustrated in Fig. 18 by the
total cross section of copper ($Z = 29$), taken from Hu55.   The energy
resolution of 100 kev employed at low energies (Ad50) was insufficient to show any resonance structure, and the results represent the

average cross section over the whole energy range. Again broad
maxima and minima are observed in the average cross section extending apparently into the 50- to 100-Mev range. For a list of the references to the original data compiled in Fig. 18, the reader is referred to
Hu58.

The total cross section of the heavy element lead ($Z = 82$) over
most of the energy region from 0.1 to 100 Mev is shown in Fig. 19, as
compiled in Hu58. It will be noted that the total cross section exhibits three narrow resonances in the energy range from 300 to 800
kev, as observed by Peterson, Barschall, and Bockelman (Pe50a) using

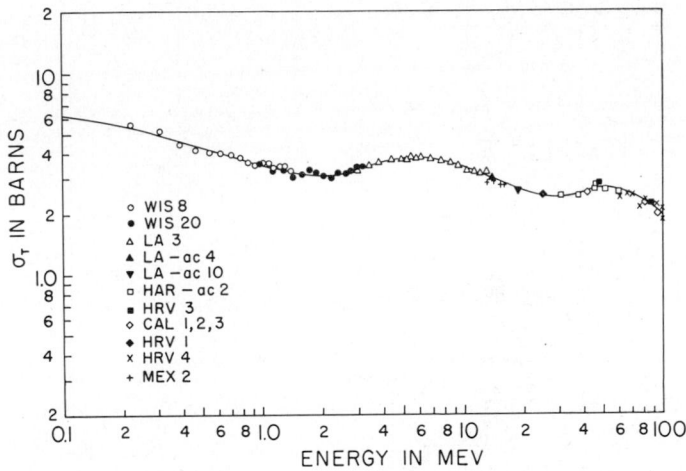

Figure 18. Total cross section of copper from 0.1 to 100 Mev (Hu55).

an energy spread of 3 kev. This would normally be very surprising
for such a heavy element, but it results from the fact that the principal
isotope of normal lead (Pb^{208}, 52 per cent abundant) is a doubly
closed-shell nucleus with the unusually low binding energy for an
added neutron of 3.9 Mev (Ha51).[7] A pronounced maximum in
the average cross section of lead is observed around 4 Mev in Fig. 19,
and an additional maximum may occur at higher energies. For the

[7] It might be mentioned that radiogenic lead (mostly Pb^{206}) also exhibits
resonances when studied with high resolution (Pe50a), but the spacing between
resonances is much smaller, as might be expected from the higher neutron binding
energy of 6.8 Mev (Ha51) in the compound nucleus Pb^{207}.

original references in Fig. 19, the reader is referred to the compilation (Hu58).

B. *Total Cross Sections as a Function of Mass Number*

(1) **Three-Dimensional Presentations:** σ_T vs. E_n vs. A. It has been found quite generally that the average total cross sections of neighboring elements throughout the periodic table are quite similar, with certain characteristic maxima and minima which shift gradually from element to element (Mi52, Ba52a). This similarity of neighboring elements has been illustrated in Figs. 12 and 13, and

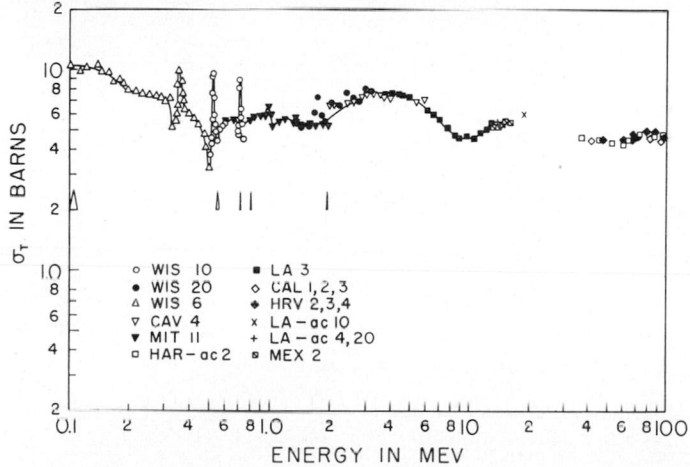

Figure 19. Total cross section of lead over most of the energy range from 0.1 to 100 Mev (Hu58).

in Fig. 16. As a result of the continual shifting of properties from element to element, the average cross sections of elements of considerably different mass bear little resemblance to each other. The characteristic broad maxima and minima are observed to be independent of specific nuclear details, such as the nuclear spin, the binding energy of the added neutron, the closed-shell property, the number of isotopes present, etc., but seem to depend only upon the nuclear mass or size (Mi52). This behavior of the average total cross section represents a second important contribution of neutron total cross section measurements to an understanding of nuclear structure. The results have been interpreted theoretically by the *cloudy crystal ball model* of Feshbach, Porter, and Weisskopf (Fe54), in which the interaction between the incident neutron and the nucleus is represented by a complex potential well of fixed depth and of radius dependent upon the mass number. This model is discussed in detail in Chapter V.C.

The systematic trends exhibited by the individual average total cross section measurements are best illustrated in three-dimensional plots (Ba52a) of the observed average total cross section divided by πR^2, where R is the nuclear radius, as a function of neutron energy

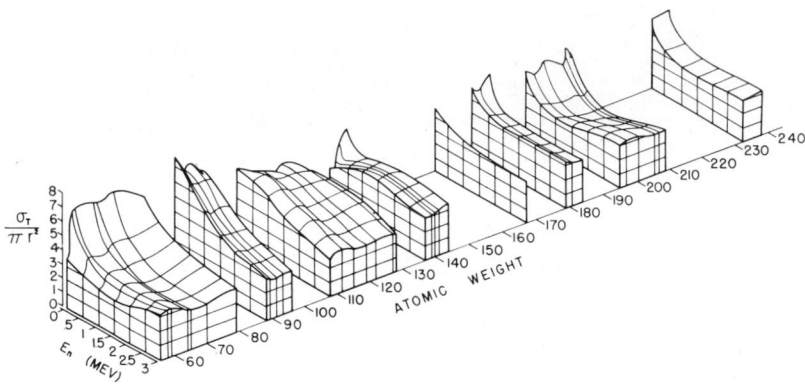

Figure 20. Three-dimensional representation of average total cross sections from 0 to 3 Mev as a function of atomic weight (Ba52a, Ok54).

and mass number A. For example, Fig. 20 shows such a plot covering the energy range from 0.1 to 3 Mev. Most of the data in this figure represent results from authors (Mi52, Wa53, Ok54) in Barschall's group at Wisconsin, summarized by the three-dimensional diagram shown (Ba52a, Ok54). The surface represents the observed cross sections averaged over resonance structure. The theoretical fit to these data for suitable choices of the parameters of the cloudy crystal ball model (Fe54, We56) is remarkably good, as will be discussed in Chapter V.C.

A similar behavior is found at higher energies, as shown in Fig. 21 for the 3 to 14-Mev energy range, taken from results of Nereson and Darden (Ne54). Figures 20 and 21 will be seen to join together smoothly,[8] giving a fairly complete picture of average cross section behavior from 0 to 14 Mev over most of the range of mass numbers.

(2) **Nuclear Radii Derived from Total Cross Section Measurements.** One of the standard methods for obtaining the nuclear radius is by the measurement of the total cross section for fast neutrons. However, the radius derived in this way depends to some extent upon the nuclear model employed. For example, at energies above the resonance region, Feshbach and Weisskopf (Fe49a) developed a schematic theory of nuclear cross sections which predicts

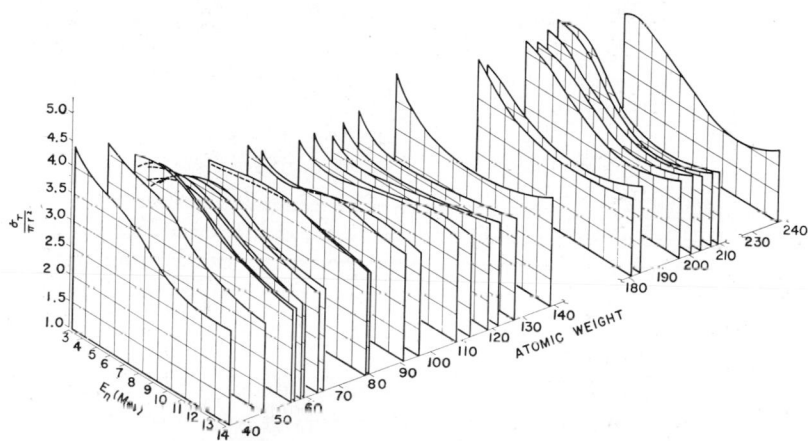

Figure 21. Three-dimensional representation of average total cross sections from 3 to 14 Mev as a function of atomic weight (Ne54).

that the total cross section should be given by

$$\sigma_T = 2\pi(R + \lambda)^2 \tag{22}$$

where R is the nuclear radius and λ the de Broglie wavelength of the incident neutron divided by 2π. This equation assumes high energy and large R, but neglects nuclear transparency. Equation (22) has been used for comparison with experimental results obtained in the energy range from 14–25 Mev (Fe49a, Co52, Da53). Figure 22 shows the results obtained by Coon, Graves, and Barschall (Co52) in a series of measurements of total cross sections of various elements

[8] Note the depressed zero and expanded ordinate scale of Fig. 21.

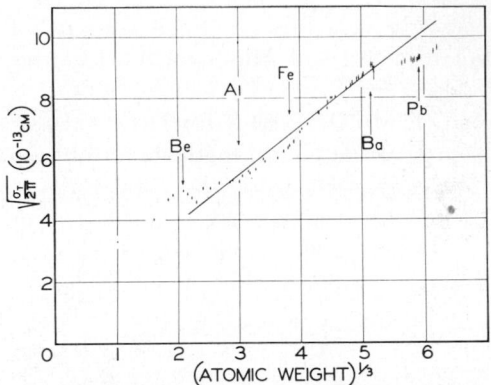

Figure 22. Graph of the square root of the total cross section at 14 Mev as a function of the cube root of the atomic weight (Co52). The straight line represents Eq. (22) plotted for $R = 1.5\,A^{1/3} \times 10^{-13}$ cm.

at 14 Mev. The points represent the square root of the total cross section plotted as a function of the cube root of the atomic weight and the straight line the prediction of Eq. (22) assuming $R = 1.5$ $A^{1/3} \times 10^{-13}$ cm. A similar plot of the results of Day and Henkel (Da53) at 20 Mev is shown in Fig. 23. The best fit of the experimental results to Eq. (22) is shown by the straight line, plotted for $R = 1.4\,A^{1/3} \times 10^{-13}$ cm.

The cloudy crystal ball model of Feshbach *et al.* (Fe54) mentioned in Section 2.A also relates the observed total cross sections to

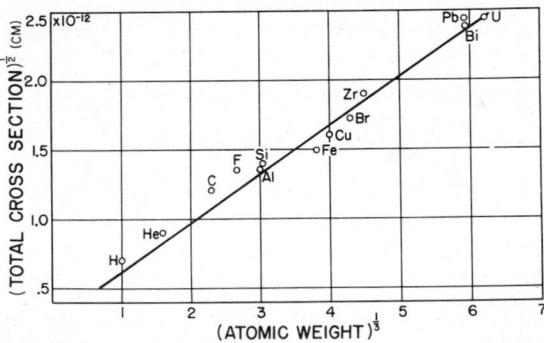

Figure 23. Graph of the square root of the total cross section at 20 Mev as a function of the cube root of the atomic weight (Da53). The straight line represents Eq. (22) plotted for $R = 1.4\,A^{1/3} \times 10^{-13}$ cm.

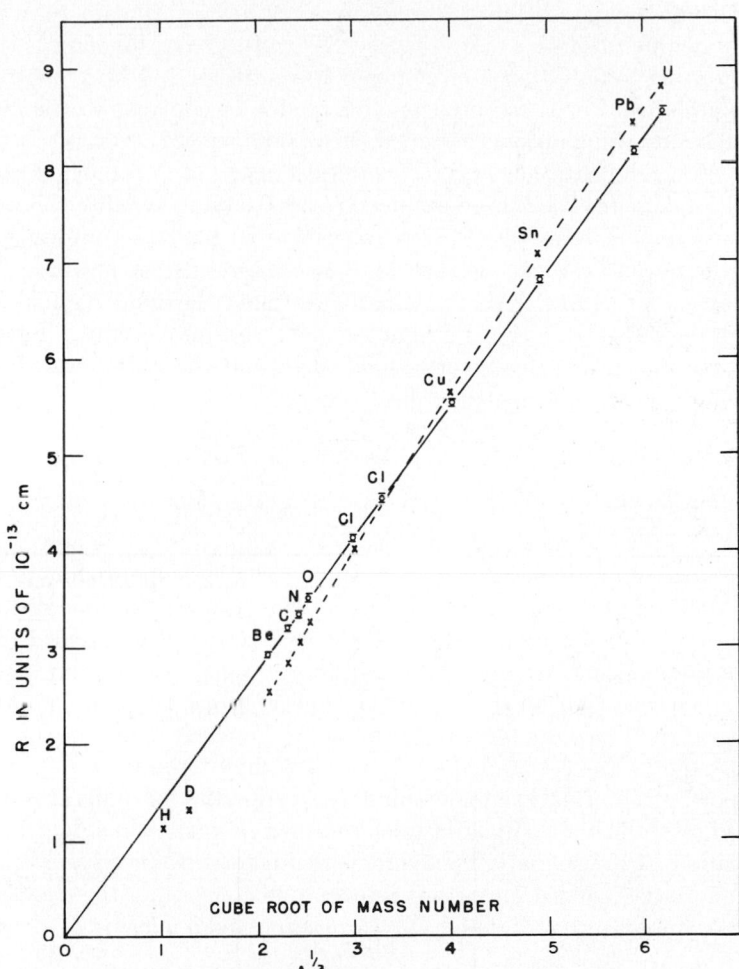

Figure 24. Graph of the nuclear radius calculated from the observed total cross section at 95 Mev (De50) using the optical model of Fernbach *et al.* (Fe49) with a particular choice of parameters (solid line), and the opaque nucleus model (dashed line).

the nuclear radius, which is a parameter of the theory to be determined by comparison with the experimental results. The best fit of this theory to the data below 3 Mev represented in Fig. 20 calls for a nuclear radius of $R = (1.26 \ A^{1/3} + 0.7) \times 10^{-13}$ cm (We56). It is interesting to note that a large mean free path for 1–3 Mev neutrons in nuclear matter is required by this model, in contrast to the completely absorbing nucleus assumed (Fe49a) in Eq. (22).

At high neutron energies, the optical model of Fernbach, Serber, and Taylor (Fe49) has been applied (De50, Cu55) to synchrocyclotron measurements in the 60–110 Mev range in order to extract information on the nuclear radius. Figure 24 shows the results of DeJuren and Knable (De50) at 95 Mev. This figure plots the *radius* calculated from the optical model of Fernbach *et al.* (Fe49) for a certain choice of the parameters in the theory (solid line), and the radius calculated assuming an opaque nucleus[9] (dashed line).

C. Conclusions

The behavior of the total cross sections of nuclei for fast neutrons as a function of atomic weight and bombarding energy is now fairly well known, particularly below 15 Mev. Further experiments in the 30–100 Mev range are probably called for to examine more carefully the maxima and minima in the total cross section which seem to appear in this range.

The existing results for total cross sections up to a few Mev have contributed to the understanding of nuclear structure in two important ways. Detailed study of individual resonances has given important information concerning the properties of individual excited states in the compound nuclei formed in various reactions. In addition, the systematic behavior of the average total cross sections of nuclei has yielded important information concerning the character of the average interaction between a neutron and a nucleus.

[9] At these energies, Eq. (22) simply becomes $\sigma_T = 2\pi R^2$.

References

(Ad49)   Adair, Barschall, Bockelman, and Sala, *Phys. Rev.* **75,** 1124 (1949).
(Ad50)   R. K. Adair, *Phys. Rev.* **77,** 748 (1950).
(Am46)   Amaldi, Bocciarelli, Cacciapuoti, and Trabacchi, *Nuovo Cim.* **3,** 203 (1946).
(Ba40)   H. H. Barschall and M. H. Kanner, *Phys. Rev.* **58,** 590 (1940).

(Ba49)   Barschall, Bockelman, Peterson, and Adair, *Phys. Rev.* **76**, 1146 (1949).
(Ba51)   Bashkin, Mooring, and Petree, *Phys. Rev.* **82**, 378 (1951).
(Ba52)   H. H. Barschall, *Revs. Modern Phys.* **24**, 120 (1952).
(Ba52a)   H. H. Barschall, *Phys. Rev.* **86**, 431 (1952).
(Be46)   H. A. Bethe and G. Placzek, *Phys. Rev.* **57**, 1075(A) (1940).
(Be56)   R. L. Becker and H. H. Barschall, *Phys. Rev.* **102**, 1384 (1956).
(Bo50)   C. K. Bockelman, *Phys. Rev.* **80**, 1011 (1950).
(Bo51)   Bockelman, Miller, Adair, and Barschall, *Phys. Rev.* **84**, 69 (1951).
(Bo54)   T. W. Bonner and C. F. Cook, *Phys. Rev.* **96**, 122 (1954).
(Bo56)   T. W. Bonner, *Proc. Intern. Conf. Peaceful Uses Atomic Energy* 4, 92 (1956).
(Br50)   Bratenahl, Fernbach, Hildebrand, Leith, and Moyer, *Phys. Rev.* **77**, 597 (1950).
(Br58)   Bratenahl, Peterson, and Stoering, *Phys. Rev.* **110**, 927 (1958).
(Co49)   Cook, McMillan, Peterson, and Sewell, *Phys. Rev.* **75**, 7 (1949).
(Co52)   Coon, Graves, and Barschall, *Phys. Rev.* **88**, 562 (1952).
(Co58)   Coon, Davis, Felthauser, and Nicodemus, *Phys. Rev.*, **111**, 250 (1958).
(Co58a)   J. P. Conner, *Phys. Rev.* **109**, 1268 (1958).
(Cr56)   Cranberg, Armstrong, and Henkel, *Phys. Rev.* **104**, 1639 (1956).
(Cr57)   Cranberg, Aiello, Beauchamp, Lang, and Levin, *Rev. Sci. Instr.* **28**, 84 (1957).
(Cr57a)   Cranberg, Beauchamp, and Levin, *Rev. Sci. Instr.* **28**, 89 (1957).
(Cu55)   V. Culler and R. W. Waniek, *Phys. Rev.* **99**, 740 (1955).
(Da53)   R. B. Day and R. L. Henkel, *Phys. Rev.* **92**, 358 (1953).
(Da55)   Day, Mills, Perry, and Scherb, *Phys. Rev.* **98**, 279(A) (1955).
(Da55a)   S. E. Darden, *Phys. Rev.* **99**, 748 (1955).
(De50)   J. DeJuren and N. Knable, *Phys. Rev.* **77**, 606 (1950).
(Fa51)   Falk, Poss, and Yuan, *Phys. Rev.* **83**, 176 (1951).
(Fo49)   Forubuuh, Sorbor, and Taylor, *Phys. Rev.* 75, 1352 (1949).
(Fe49a)   H. Feshbach and V. F. Weisskopf, *Phys. Rev.* **76**, 1550 (1949).
(Fe51)   Feld, Feshbach, Goldberger, Goldstein, and Weisskopf, *Final Report of the Fast Neutron Data Project*, NYO-636, unpublished (1951).
(Fe54)   Feshbach, Porter, and Weisskopf, *Phys. Rev.* **96**, 448 (1954).
(Fi47)   Fields, Russell, Sachs, and Wattenberg, *Phys. Rev.* **71**, 508 (1947).
(Fi54)   Fields, Becker, and Adair, *Phys. Rev.* **94**, 389 (1954).
(Fr50)   Freier, Fulk, Lampi, and Williams, *Phys. Rev.* **78**, 508 (1950).
(Ha47)   A. O. Hanson and J. L. McKibben, *Phys. Rev.* **72**, 673 (1947).
(Ha49)   Hanson, Taschek, and Williams, *Revs. Modern Phys.* **21**, 635 (1949).
(Ha51)   J. A. Harvey, *Phys. Rev.* **81**, 353 (1951).
(Ha53)   Hafner, Hornyak, Falk, Snow, and Coor, *Phys. Rev.* **89**, 204 (1953).
(Ha53a)   Hansen, Kiehn, and Goodman, *Phys. Rev.* **92**, 652 (1953).
(Ha57)   H. S. Hans and S. C. Snowdon, *Phys. Rev.* **108**, 1028 (1957).
(He56)   Henkel, Perry, and Smith, *Phys. Rev.* **99**, 1050 (1955).
(Hi50)   R. H. Hildebrand and C. E. Leith, *Phys. Rev.* **80**, 842 (1950).
(Hi52)   Hinchey, Stelson, and Preston, *Phys. Rev.* **86**, 483 (1952).
(Hi54)   Hillman, Stahl, and Ramsey, *Phys. Rev.* **96**, 115 (1954).
(Ho52)   W. F. Hornyak, *Rev. Sci. Instr.* **23**, 264 (1952).

(Hu58)   D. J. Hughes and R. B. Schwartz, ompilers, "Neutron Cross Sections,"
         Brookhaven National Lab. Report BNL-325, Second Edition (1958).
(Jo54)   Johnson, Willard, and Bair, *Phys. Rev.* **96**, 985 (1954).
(Kh57)   M. M. Khaletskii, *Doklady Akad. Nauk SSSR* **113**, 305 (1957); *Soviet
         Phys. "Doklady"* **2**, 129 (1957).
(Mc47)   E. M. McMillan and D. C. Sewell, *U. S. Atomic Energy Comm. Report*
         MDDC-1558, unpublished (1947).
(Mc54)   McCrary, Taylor, and Bonner, *Phys. Rev.* **94**, 808(A) (1954).
(Mi52)   Miller, Adair, Bockelman, and Darden, *Phys. Rev.* **88**, 83 (1952).
(Mo52)   Mott, Guernsey, and Nelson, *Phys. Rev.* **88**, 9 (1952).
(Ne53)   N. Nereson and S. Darden, *Phys. Rev.* **89**, 775 (1953).
(Ne54)   N. Nereson and S. Darden, *Phys. Rev.* **94**, 1678 (1954).
(Ok54)   Okazaki, Darden, and Walton, *Phys. Rev.* **93**, 461 (1954).
(Pe50)   Peterson, Barschall, and Bockelman, *Phys. Rev.* **79**, 593 (1950).
(Pe50a) Peterson, Adair, and Barschall, *Phys. Rev.* **79**, 935 (1950).
(Po52)   Poss, Salant, Snow, and Yuan, *Phys. Rev.* **87**, 11 (1952).
(Ri51)   R. Ricamo and W. Zunti, *Helv. Phys. Acta* **24**, 419 (1951).
(Ro48)   M. E. Rose and M. M. Shapiro, *Phys. Rev.* **74**, 1853 (1948).
(Ro49)   B. B. Rossi and H. H. Staub, *Ionization Chambers and Counters*,
         McGraw-Hill, New York, 1949.
(Se47)   R. Serber, *Phys. Rev.* **72**, 1008 (1947).
(Se47a) L. W. Seagondollar and H. H. Barschall, *Phys. Rev.* **72**, 439 (1947).
(Se55)   J. D. Seagrave and R. L. Henkel, *Phys. Rev.* **98**, 666 (1955).
(Sh45)   R. Sherr, *Phys. Rev.* **68**, 240 (1945).
(St54)   C. L. Storrs and D. H. Frisch, *Phys. Rev.* **95**, 1252 (1954).
(Ta48)   R. F. Taschek and A. Hemmendinger, *Phys. Rev.* **74**, 373 (1948).
(Ta51)   Taylor, Pickavance, Cassels, and Randle, *Phil. Mag.* **42**, 328 (1951).
(Ta53)   A. E. Taylor and E. Wood, *Phil. Mag.* **44**, 95 (1953).
(Ta55)   Taylor, Lonsjo, and Bonner, *Phys. Rev.* **100**, 174 (1955).
(Th55)   R. G. Thomas, *Phys. Rev.* **98**, 77 (1955).
(Wa47)   Warren, Powell, and Herb, *Rev. Sci. Instr.* **18**, 559 (1947).
(Wa53)   Walt, Becker, Okazaki, and Fields, *Phys. Rev.* **89**, 1271 (1953).
(We56)   V. F. Weisskopf, *Proc. Intern. Conf. Peaceful Uses Atomic Energy* **2**, 23
         (1956).
(Wi43)   G. C. Wick, *Atti accad. d'Ital.* **13**, 1203 (1943).
(Wi58)   Wills, Bair, Cohn, and Willard, *Phys. Rev.* **109**, 891(1958).
(Wi60)   Williamson, Katman, and Burton, *Phys. Rev.* **117**, 1325 (1960).

Angular Distributions of Elastically Scattered Neutrons

M. WALT

Lockheed Aircraft Corporation, Palo Alto, California

1. Introduction

It has long been recognized that experimental values of the differential cross sections for elastic scattering of fast neutrons by nuclei can provide considerable information concerning the neutron-nucleus interaction in the entrance channel. Because of the interference effects between the scattered wave and the incident wave, the differenital cross section is often a sensitive indication of the properties of the interaction. In spite of this interest in obtaining experimental information, extensive measurements of the angular distributions of scattered neutrons were first performed several years after observations of such quantities as the total neutron cross section, the activation cross section, and the cross section for (n, p) and for (n, α) reactions became routine. The main reasons for this delay were technical and centered about the difficulties of obtaining intense neutron sources, efficient neutron detectors, and low background conditions. Over a period of years these problems have been overcome, and scattering experiments are now being performed by many groups.

In discussing the scattering of fast neutrons by nuclei the neutron energy range can conveniently be divided into two intervals, the resonance region and the continuum region. The resonance region consists of the energy range below a few Mev for light elements and below a few kilovolts for most heavy elements. Within this range the scattering is characterized by the presence of isolated resonances, so that the cross sections vary rapidly with incident neutron energy. The scattering of neutrons in this region is dis-

1033

cussed in detail in Chapters V.E and V.L. In the continuum energy region, to which the material of this article is restricted, the density of the levels in the compound system is so great that many compound states are excited by the incident neutrons. Under these circumstances the experimental cross sections represent averages over many resonances and are therefore slowly varying functions of bombarding energy. For a given element there is an energy interval within which the transition from the resonance to the continuum region takes place. Within this interval the type of information obtained is dependent on the energy spread of the neutron beam employed in the experiment. For example, a measurement of the angular distribution of 1-Mev neutrons elastically scattered by iron should exhibit resonance effects if the energy spread of the incoming neutrons is less than about 100 kev; and the cross sections would be characteristic of the continuum region if obtained with a neutron beam 200 kev wide.

The success of the optical model (Fe54) in predicting the behavior of total neutron cross sections in the continuum energy region led to a series of experiments to obtain angular distributions with which to test the model. Over a period of years these experiments have been carried out both at low energies, where the detailed shape of the potential well was expected to be relatively unimportant, and at higher energies, where the effects of compound nucleus decay through the entrance channel were small. These data were then analyzed to obtain optical model parameters—a nuclear radius, a complex well depth, and in some cases a form factor defining the radial variation of the potential. The analysis of elastic scattering data to determine optical model parameters is described in Chapter V.C, and the application of electronic computer techniques to these problems is discussed in Chapter IV.I.

In addition to the demand for scattering information for the development of nuclear theory, accurate angular distributions have also been needed for reactor technology. In the design of nuclear reactors and their associated shielding, the angular distribution of the scattered neutrons is of paramount importance, since both the average distance traveled by neutrons before absorption and the number of elastic collisions required to lose a given fraction of initial energy depends upon the angular dependence of the scattering cross sections.

In the following sections the experimental techniques which have proven useful in the past few years for the determination of the angular distributions of scattered neutrons will be described. This discussion is followed by a summary of the experimental results, and illustrative examples of cross section data are presented.

2. Experimental Techniques

A. General Methods

Two general methods have been used to obtain angular distributions of elastically scattered neutrons: (a) observation of either the energy or emission angle of the recoiling nucleus and (b) direct detection of the scattered neutrons. The former method has been used extensively with light nuclei where the momentum transferred to the recoil nucleus is sufficient to allow an accurate determination of its energy. The most commonly used technique is the observation of the amplitude distribution of pulses from a proportional counter filled with a gas containing the element whose differential cross section is to be measured. Since the distribution of recoil pulses as a function of pulse amplitude is the same as the differential cross section as a function of center-of-mass angle, the angular distribution can be obtained directly from the data. The techniques for this type of experiment are given in Chapter V.E. Observation of the emission angle of the recoil nucleus by the use of cloud chambers or counter telescopes is described in Chapters II.C and II.E.

By observing the intensity of the neutron flux scattered by a small sample of the element concerned, the differential cross section can be obtained from the formula:

$$\sigma(\psi) = F_s r^2 / F_{in} N \tag{1}$$

where $\sigma(\psi)$ is the cross section for scattering into unit solid angle at angle ψ; F_s is the scattered flux (neutrons $cm^{-2}sec^{-1}$), F_{in} is the incident flux at the position of the sample, r^2 is the distance between the scattering sample and the detector, and N is the number of nuclei in the sample. Since it is necessary to know only the ratio of the scattered flux to the direct flux, it is often convenient to measure both fluxes with the same detector so that the absolute efficiency of the detector need not be known. If S is the counting rate of the detector when it is located to observe the scattered flux, I is the counting rate of the detector when placed in the position normally occupied by the scattering sample, and B is the background, usually obtained by noting the counting rate with the scattering sample removed, then Eq. (1) becomes

$$\sigma(\psi) = (S - B)r^2/IN \tag{1'}$$

Equation (1') was derived assuming that the counter sensitivity is the same for both elastically scattered neutrons and source neutrons. However, since the elastically scattered neutrons have lost energy in the laboratory system and the detector sensitivity is generally a function of energy, a correction must be made to the ratio $(S - B)/I$ for this effect. Similarly, a correction must be made if the detector efficiency changes with counting rate.

The distance from sample to detector can be measured geometrically and the average distance found by appropriate integration over the volumes of the detector and scattering sample. However, since in most cases the sensitivity of the detector is not uniform over the entire volume, the integrand should be weighted with the detector efficiency for the volume element concerned. The effective distance can also be found experimentally by measuring the counting rate with the detector at two distances from the source, one distance approximately equal to the usual sample-to-detector distance and the other distance much larger than the dimensions of the detector. The ratio of the two counting rates then gives the ratio of the squares of the effective distances, and since the larger distance is well known, the sample-to-detector length can be found.

In cases where it is not possible to observe the direct flux with the detector, the need to measure an absolute flux can be avoided by comparing the scattered flux with that produced by a sample of known cross section. Hydrogen (usually in CH_2) and carbon (La57) have been used for this purpose since their differential cross sections are fairly well known for energies up to a few Mev. Hydrogen has no sharp resonance structure which would complicate its use as a standard and carbon has only a few resonances below 3 Mev.

B. Geometries

The placement and shape of the source, scattering material, detector, and shield are usually chosen as a compromise between the desire to reduce the relative background and the desire to reduce the magnitude of the corrections which must be made to the data. The three most commonly used arrangements, the cylindrical geometry, ring geometry, and flat plate geometry are indicated in Fig. 1.

Figure 1a illustrates the *cylindrical geometry* in which a cylindrical or spherical sample is placed in the neutron flux and the counter is rotated about the scatterer to obtain the angular distribution (Wa53, Wa54, Wi55, Re56). Shielding may be in the form of wedges as shown in Fig. 1a or in the form of a collimator about the source and/or detector. One of the major virtues of this geometry is that for small samples the symmetry almost guarantees an accurate measurement of the angular variation of the scattering. Uncertainties in the estimates of source asymmetry, detector anisotropy, and errors in determining the distance from scatterer to detector affect the absolute but not the relative values of the differential cross sections. Source polarization corrections are avoided by placing the scattering material in line with the incident charged particles of the neutron source. Multiple scattering corrections are appreciable for scattering samples with dimensions greater than about 0.2 mean-free-paths, but the corrections are easier to calculate either by Monte Carlo methods or by analytic approximations than they would be for more complicated sample shapes. One serious limitation of this arrangement is that for a given sample thickness and angular resolution, less scattering material can be used than in the *ring geometry*.

In the ring geometry, as shown in Fig. 1b, a ring of the scattering material is placed with its axis on the line passing through both the source and detector, and a shadow shield of some form is used to attenuate the direct flux (Co53, Da54, Sn54, Co58). Scattering at various angles is measured by moving either scatterer or detector along the axis or by using rings with different diameters. Variations on this geometry have been used in which the ring is extended into a barrel-shaped cylinder of revolution (Am46) so that neutrons scattered from all points of the sample reach the detector after scattering through the same angle. The *poor geometry* transmission experiment (Ba47), in which the transmissions of discs of identical thickness but different diameters are compared to obtain the angular distribution, is a limiting case of the ring geometry. The principal advantage of this geometry is that, for a given angular resolution and thickness of scatterer, more material can be used and hence a greater

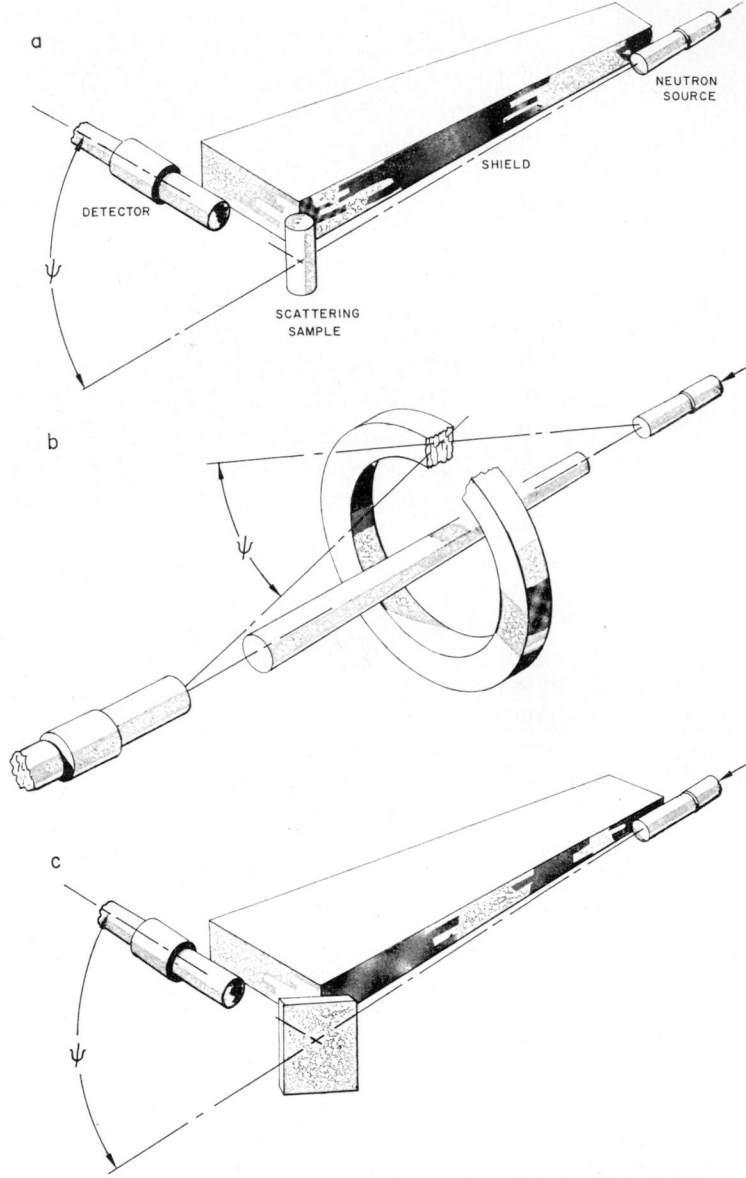

Figure 1. Typical experimental arrangements used in the measurement of differential cross sections: (a) cylindrical geometry, (b) ring geometry, and (c) flat plate geometry.

scattered intensity can be obtained than with any other arrangement. In addition, the design and construction of an efficient shield is relatively simple, although this advantage is usually more than offset by the need for contructing a number of scattering samples. One of the difficulties encountered with ring geometry is that rather large corrections must be made for both source anisotropy and detector anisotropy. Shielding problems also arise from the use of highly anisotropic sources, such as the $D(d, n)He^3$ reaction, which is strongly peaked in the forward direction. With ring geometry and such a source, the scattering material is placed out of the most intense beam while the centrally located counter must be shielded against the maximum flux. Multiple scattering corrections, although smaller than they would be if the same amount of scattering material were concentrated, are more difficult to calculate for ring geometry. Also, since distances between source, scatterer, and detector change with scattering angle, these distances must be determined separately for each angle, a difficult procedure if the distances are not large compared to the ring thickness and to the source and detector dimensions. A final possible disadvantage of this geometry is that if the source is polarized the observed angular distributions will be affected.

In order to reduce the multiple scattering correction as much as possible and still maintain adequate counting rates, the scattering material has sometimes been shaped into a thin plate and oriented so that both the incident neutrons and the neutrons scattered into the detector pass through relatively short distances of the material (La57, Je55). This *flat plate* geometry is shown in Fig. 1c. Again, shielding may be in the form of shadow shields or collimators. A comprehensive analytic discussion of the corrections required with this geometry is available (La57).

C. Neutron Sources

The source reactions which have found wide acceptance for other fast neutron experiments are also favored for angular distribution measurements. However, since one of the principal difficulties in these experiments is the low counting rate, considerable effort has been devoted to develop accelerator targets which will withstand high beam currents. Target materials which can be plated on a thin metal backing are often cooled by a blast of air or water upon the backing, and the targets are commonly rotated to spread the heat production over a larger area. Targets of gaseous materials such as deuterium present special problems since the charged particle beam must pass through a thin metal window which necessarily has poor heat conduction and low mechanical strength. High melting point metals such as molybdenum have been used to increase the foil strength under bombardment (Be56), and several methods of cooling the foil directly have been successful. In one scheme (Hi58) target gas is circulated through a heat exchanger and the cold gas is fed into the target cell in a jet directed against the entrance foil. Another cooling arrangement uses two entrance windows in series, and a cooled inert gas such as helium is circulated between the foils (No57). Further discussion of target techniques may be found in Chapter IV.D.

Neutron source reactions which have been used in conjunction with electrostatic accelerators for differential cross section measurements are the following: $Li^7(p, n)Be^7$, $T(p, n)He^3$, $D(d, n)He^3$, $Li^7(d, n)Be^8$, $N^{14}(d, n)O^{15}$, and $T(d, n)He^4$. Specific information on the use of these sources is given elsewhere (Chapters I.C and I.E). Of these reactions, the $T(p, n)He^3$, $D(d, n)He^3$, and $T(d, n)He^4$ are preferred because of their relatively high neutron yields and low γ-ray production. Although the residual nuclei in these latter reactions have no excited states which can lead to the production of additional energy groups, at high bombarding energies deuteron breakup can occur so that the neutrons produced by the D-D and D-T reactions are not monoenergetic.

The neutrons produced by the $Li^7(p, n)Be^7$ reaction with energies above 0.5 Mev and by the $N^{14}(d, n)O^{15}$ and $Li^7(d, n)Be^8$ reactions at all energies are also not monoenergetic. Therefore, if these reactions are used, some means of selecting neutrons of the desired energy is required. In most cases, the energy discrimination used to reject inelastically scattered neutrons is sufficient. In spite of this disadvantage, lithium and nitrogen targets have been used, lithium because of the convenience of target preparation and handling and nitrogen because the $N^{14}(d, n)O^{15}$ reaction is probably the simplest method of obtaining neutrons in the energy region near 9 Mev with an electrostatic accelerator of moderate size.

Additional source reactions which have been used for total cross section measurements and which may in the future be employed in differential cross section experiments are the Be^9 $(\alpha, n)C^{12}$, N^{15} $(d, n)O^{16}$, and $C^{13}(\alpha, n)O^{16}$ reactions. Although these reactions have low yields, do not yield monoenergetic neutrons, and produce many γ rays, they may be useful as sources of neutrons with energies not otherwise available.

D. Detectors

In measuring a differential cross section it is necessary to detect a low-intensity scattered flux of a given energy in the presence of a background consisting of source neutrons, room scattered neutrons, and lower energy neutrons and γ-rays from the scattering sample itself. These conditions make it important that the detector have the following properties. (a) The detector must not be sensitive to the γ rays produced by inelastic neutron scattering in the sample material. (b) The counting rate must be proportional to the neutron flux over large ranges of flux intensity; i.e., dead-time and pile-up effects should be small. (c) The detector efficiency for neutrons should have a cut-off for energies somewhat below the incident neutron energy so that ideally speaking, the detector will not respond to neutrons with less energy than the elastically scattered neutrons. (d) If possible the detector should be small in size to facilitate shielding and improve angular resolution. (e) Since in practical cases the scattered flux intensity is low, the absolute efficiency of the counter should be as high as possible.

The energy dependence of the detector efficiency, a quantity which must be known in order to estimate the detector response to inelastically scattered neutrons and to make some of the corrections discussed below, is usually determined experimentally. A direct method is to observe the counting rate of the detector as a function of incident neutron energy, while the relative magnitude of the incident neutron intensity is simultaneously measured with a monitor of known energy response. If the cross section of the source reaction is well known, the relative flux produced by bombarding with known currents at various energies can be calculated, so that it is unnecessary to calibrate the flux with an additional counter.

Scintillation detectors employing hydrogenous phosphors mounted on photomultipliers have the desirable characteristics of high efficiency, small size, and counting-rate insensitivity; and they are easily biased to reject pulses caused by neutrons with less energy than the elastically scattered neutrons. However, in their usual form scintillation counters respond to γ rays. Several methods have been used to reduce their γ-ray response; the most common and to date most successful method is to divide the phosphor into pieces small enough that a photoelectron passing through a phosphor fragment cannot lose sufficient energy to register a count. This type of detector was first proposed by Bonner and co-workers (Mc54), and it has been used in various forms by many others (Be55). Another type of scintillation detector is the Hornyak button scintillator (Ho52), which consists of ZnS particles embedded in lucite. This device has excellent discrimination against γ rays but, because of poor resolution, is difficult to bias against low energy neutrons.

Recently it has been found possible to utilize the time dependence of the scintillation to distinguish the pulses produced by recoiling protons from those caused by electrons. In some of the commonly used scintillating materials, such as stilbene and anthracine, the decay time of the light pulse depends upon the specific ionization of the particle involved. Brooks (Br59) and Owen (Ow58) have proposed circuits which make use of this effect and effectively discriminate against gamma ray pulses. There is no doubt that this extremely useful method will become common in the near future and largely eliminate one of the more serious problems in neutron detection.

Gas-filled proportional counters have been used extensively as detectors of elastically scattered neutrons. When filled with gases of low atomic weight, and with the pressure adjusted so that a photoelectron can traverse the entire counter without substantial energy loss, the γ-ray response is negligible. For neutron energies below a few Mev, hydrogen, either as molecular hydrogen or in a compound such as methane or propane, is a satisfactory counter gas. For special cases, however, helium or deuterium is preferable. For neutron energies near 1 Mev, the broad resonance in the scattering cross section of helium makes this gas attractive. The large cross section improves the counter efficiency, and since the angular distribution of 1-Mev neutrons scattered by helium is peaked in the backward direction, a large fraction of recoiling helium nuclei have close to the maximum energy. Pronounced backscattering also makes deuterium a good filling gas for detecting neutrons of several Mev energy.

In a number of experiments nuclear emulsions have been used to detect scattered neutrons in angular distribution experiments. The principal advantages of this form of detector are small size, simplicity of operation, permanent record of results for subsequent detailed analysis, good neutron energy resolution, and complete insensitivity to γ rays. The major disadvantage is that analysis of the exposed plates is tedious and exacting labor. However, as a simple and inexpensive method of obtaining not only elastic scattering cross sections but also spectra of inelastically scattered neutrons, the nuclear emulsion technique is extremely powerful.

Additional details concerning neutron detectors are given in Sections II and III of Part I.

E. Shielding

For scattering samples which are about one third of the mean free path in thickness and for geometries affording reasonable angular resolution and intensity, the scattered flux at the position of the detector is on the order of 10^{-3} the value of the flux striking the sample. It is therefore clear that the success of the experiment requires effective shielding. In general, two forms of shielding have been used, (a) shadow shielding in which a minimum solid angle subtended by the detector at the source is shielded and (b) collimation in which extensive use is made of shielding material, leaving only a narrow channel through which neutrons can pass. The choice of shield type is somewhat a matter of taste, but it is often affected by the physical conditions of the experimental area. If the neutron source is in a confined space, surrounded by concrete walls or other structural material, a *closed* geometry employing collimators is preferable. However in particularly *clean* experimental areas shadow shielding is not only more convenient but perhaps better, since the additional material of a collimator may scatter into the detector source neutrons which would otherwise escape.

For neutron energies below a few Mev, hydrogenous material is ideal for shielding because of the large total cross section of hydrogen and the large fractional energy loss suffered by a neutron in a collision with a proton. Paraffin, polyethylene, and water are commonly used and hydrogenous materials are sometimes mixed with boron or lithium compounds which absorb the low energy neutrons. However, if the counter is insensitive to γ rays and to low-energy neutrons, this added precaution is not necessary. At primary neutron energies above about 4 Mev, the decreased cross section of hydrogen makes hydrogenous shields less efficient, and heavier materials such as iron, copper, tungsten, or various types of concrete are preferred. A more complete description of shield design and shielding material is given in Chapter IV.E.

F. Special Techniques

If the spectrum of inelastically scattered neutrons is not known, the choice of detector bias and hence energy sensitivity is usually made as a compromise between the higher counting rates and higher statistical accuracy obtained with a low bias and the better energy discrimination available with high bias. For several reasons it is desirable to take data at many biases simultaneously. Comparison of the cross sections obtained with different biases indicates the highest energy at which inelastically scattered neutrons are emitted, since the cross sections obtained at all biases with thresholds above this energy should be equal. Furthermore, the comparison not only enables a choice to be made of the best bias from a statistical standpoint, but allows one to obtain a crude picture of the spectrum of inelastically scattered neutrons.

An important point is that a very highly biased channel (discriminator set at 90 to 95 per cent of maximum pulse height) gives an excellent indication of the overall quality of the experiment. The corrections for such factors as dead-time, pile-up, γ rays, and neutron energy loss are usually quite different at a very high bias than at the more standard biases; hence, errors in making such corrections will result in a different cross section being measured at the highest bias.

A simple and effective method of reducing background is to use detectors which have a preference for counting neutrons incident from the direction of the scattering sample. Directionality is easily achieved by making the dimension of the active volume of the counter small except in the desired direction. This way of reducing background has been used both with scintillation counters (Hi58) and with gas proportional counters (Be56). Another method of achieving almost complete directionality is to employ a radiator to furnish recoil protons in a particular direction (Ma46). Such a counting system has extreme directional sensitivity but suffers from low efficiency.

Considerable success has been achieved both in reducing background and in improving counting efficiency by using time-of-flight methods to select elastically scattered neutrons from the room background and from γ rays and inelastically scattered neutrons (Mu56, Cr56, Na57, Sm57). In experiments of this type the neutron source is pulsed with a period of the order of 10^{-6} sec by chopping the charged particle beam incident upon the neutron producing target. Bursts of neutrons with a duration of about 5×10^{-9} sec are thus produced. The time interval between the production of neutrons and their detection at the counter is measured, and the variation in this interval is used to separate elastically scattered neutron events from the various background processes. Since the detector need not be energy sensitive, it can be biased slightly above the detector noise level therby increasing counter efficiency. Time-of-flight apparatus may also be used to make accurate measurements of inelastic scattering cross sections. Because of its considerable advantages, time-of-flight technique is becoming increasingly popular. Its only major disadvantage is an appreciable increase in the complexity of the electronic circuits required.

A technique which is applicable to some of the source reactions, in particular the $T(d, n)He^4$ reaction, is the associated-particle gating technique (Cr55). The tritium target assembly contains an α-particle detector placed at such an angle that when a neutron is produced in the direction of the scattering sample, the product He^4 nucleus passes into the α-particle counter. Detection of the α-particle gates the neutron detector which is normally cutoff to avoid counting room background. The major disadvantage of this arrangement is that the neutron source strength is limited by the resolving time of the α-particle counter.

Another method of background reduction is possible if the scattering material is a gas suitable for use in a proportional counter (Co59). The gas scattering sample is contained inside the proportional counter, so that a count is observed each time a scattering takes place. This event serves to gate the detector used to observe the scattered neutrons. Since this method is only applicable for a few light elements, it has not been used extensively.

3. Corrections to Experimental Data

The cross sections which are obtained by the direct use of Eq. (1′) require several additional corrections for the non-ideal nature of the detectors and geometry. The more important of these corrections adjust for (a) the energy loss accompanying elastic collisions in the sample, (b) the angular asymmetry of the detector, (c) possible source polarization, (d) attenuation of the incident beam in the scatterer, and (e) multiple scattering of neutrons in the sample.

Since the detector sensitivity is often a strong function of neutron energy, even the small decrease in neutron energy accompanying elastic scattering may result in a much lower detector efficiency for scattered neutrons than for source neutrons. Correction for this effect can be made by using the counter energy sensitivity determined as described above and the scattered neutron energy computed from conservation of energy and momentum relations. Anisotropy of the detector is corrected for by a similar efficiency factor, the angular asymmetry being determined by rotating the detector about its geometrical center and measuring the counting rate as a function of the direction from which neutrons approach. This measurement should be made at several neutron energies covering the range of the elastically scattered neutrons since the directional properties of a counter are usually energy dependent.

Attenuation of the incident neutron beam can be corrected for by replacing the incident beam strength I in Eq. (1′) by the calculated quantity

$$\frac{I}{V} \int_V \exp(-nt\sigma_T)dv \tag{2}$$

where t is the distance into the scattering sample the incident neutrons must pass to reach volume element dv, n is the nuclear density (nuclei cm^{-3}) in the sample, and σ_T is the total cross section. The integration is taken over the volume V of the scattering sample.

Experiments have shown that neutrons produced by some of the common source reactions are partially polarized and that the scattering of these neutrons by most elements is not axially symmetric because of the spin-orbit forces present in the neutron-nucleus interaction (Ad54, Ok55, Re56). Therefore, with certain geometries the observed differential cross sections will not be those corresponding to the scattering of unpolarized neutrons.

This difficulty can be avoided experimentally by using only those source neutrons which are emitted in line with the incident charged particles of the source reaction, since these neutrons are not polarized. However, in the ring geometry, off-axis neutrons must be used and polarization effects will be present. From available data on the left-right asymmetry in the scattering of polarized neutrons, the errors introduced in the measured differential cross sections are expected to be less than 10 per cent for energies below 1 Mev. However, theoretical calculations indicate that the polarizations and hence the asymmetries may be much greater at higher energies, so that the effects may be much more serious. If the polarizations of the source and scatterer are known, the cross sections for unpolarized neutrons can be obtained from the experimental results with polarized neutrons by the expression:

$$\sigma_{un} \ (\psi) \ = \ \sigma_{pol} \ (\psi)/(1 \ + \ \mathbf{P}(\psi) \cdot \mathbf{P}_{inc}) \tag{3}$$

where $\sigma_{un}(\psi)$ and $\sigma_{pol}(\psi)$ are the differential cross sections for unpolarized neutrons and for incident neutrons with polarization P_{inc}, respectively. The angle ψ is the usual scattering angle. $\mathbf{P}(\psi)$ is the polarization produced by the scattering of unpolarized neutrons at angle ψ. However, the experimental data on the polarization of fast neutrons are not extensive, so that analytic corrections of this type are usually not possible.

Although only a small percentage of the neutrons scattered by thin samples have more than one collision in the sample, the corrections to the differential cross sections for these multiply scattered neutrons may be quite large at the minima in the differential cross section curves. (A correction of 50 per cent is quite common for neutron energies above 4 Mev.) Adjustment of the experimental results to correct for the effects of multiple collisions has long been a central problem in angular distribution determinations. No convenient analytic method of unquestioned rigor has been available for general cases, and even when simplifying assumptions are employed, most of the proposed schemes are tedious to apply. Since the magnitude of the correction at any angle depends upon the differential cross sections at all angles, corrections are made by iteration. A trial differential cross section curve is assumed, and the correction is applied. If the corrected curve does not agree with the experimental values, the trial curve is varied slightly and the calculation repeated until agreement is reached.

Because of the uncertainities in making an analytic correction for multiple scattering, most experimenters have attempted to keep this correction as small as possible by suitable choices of sample sizes and shapes. Attempts have also been made to evaluate the correction by measuring cross sections for a number of successively smaller samples and extrapolating to find the result expected for infinitely small samples. The basic difficulty in a purely experimental approach is that as the sample size is reduced, the scattered intensity usually decreases more rapidly than does the multiple scattering correction. For example in the cylindrical geometry, if one reduces the sample radius r, the multiple scattering correction decreases as r while the intensity falls off a r^2. A somewhat more practical approach to the extrapolation method is to reduce the density of the scattering material by drilling a number of uniformly spaced holes in the sample. Both the scattered intensity and the multiple collision correction decrease approximately as the density, giving a more favorable signal-to-background condition.

Analytic prescriptions for treating multiple scattering have been developed for various geometries. A method suitable for machine computation has been derived for the flat plate geometry (La57). In this treatment exact expressions are obtained for the singly and doubly scattered flux leaving the plate at all angles. It is then assumed that the distribution of neutrons scattered more than twice is the same as the second collision distribution and that the total flux emerging after successive collisions decreases geometrically with collision number, i.e., if F_n is the total flux emerging after n collisons, F_n/F_{n-1} is constant. Since for the thin plates used in most experiments few neutrons have more than two collisions, these assumptions do not greatly influence the results. The accuracy of the correction has been investigated by comparing cross sections obtained with various sample thicknesses. Within the experimental error of about 3 per cent the corrected cross sections were found to be independent of sample size.

A simple hand-computer method for calculating multiple scattering in cylindrical geometry has proven adequate for cases where the angular distributions can be conveniently represented by a series of

Legendre polynomials (Wa53). For neutron energies of about 7 Mev the number of Legendre polynomials necessary to represent the distribution is so large that the method becomes laborious. Three major assumptions are made: (a) the angular distribution of neutrons emerging after n collisions is the same as the distribution of neutrons after n collisons in an infinite medium of the scattering material; (b) the number of neutrons emerging after a certain number of collisions decreases geometrically with collision number, and (c) the end effects introduced by the non-spherical sample are unimportant in determining the scattered flux at the various counter positions. The validity of these assumptions is strongly dependent upon the geometry used. For scattering samples in the shape of small spheres all three assumptions are quite good; for long cylinders and rings assumption (c) becomes questionable; and for flat plates the first assumption is untenable.

Let $\Sigma_n(\psi)$ be the angular distribution of neutrons leaving the sample in unit solid angle about angle ψ after n collisions. These quantities are normalized so that

$$\int_0^\pi \Sigma_n(\psi) \sin \psi \, d\psi = 2\pi \qquad (4)$$

The experimentally observed angular distribution $\Sigma_{ex}(\psi)$ will be composed of contributions from all collision numbers so that

$$\Sigma_{ex}(\psi) = a_1\Sigma_1(\psi) + a_2\Sigma_2(\psi) + a_3\Sigma_3(\psi) + \ldots \qquad (5)$$

Since in practical cases less than 1 per cent of the neutrons have more than three collisions in the sample, only three terms will be considered here. The problem is to determine the true differential cross section from $\Sigma_{ex}(\psi)$ obtained by experiment. $\Sigma_1(\psi)$ is very nearly equal to the true differential cross section multiplied by a normalization constant. Therefore, if one is able to calculate a_1, a_2, a_3, and $\Sigma_{n\neq1}(\psi)$ using an assumed value of $\Sigma_1(\psi)$ and known quantities, one can compute $\Sigma_{ex}(\psi)$ using Eq. (5) and compare this computed value with the experimentally measured distribution. When $\Sigma_1(\psi)$ has been adjusted so that the computed $\Sigma_{ex}(\psi)$ coincides with the experimental curve, $\Sigma_1(\psi)$ will be an excellent approximation to the differential cross section, except for a normalization factor.

$\Sigma_n(\psi)$ is assumed to give the angular distribution of neutrons after n collisions in an infinite medium where the singly scattered distribution is given by $\Sigma_1(\psi)$. Formulas for the second collision distribution in terms of the first collision parameters have been published by several authors (B152). Using these formulas and assumption (b) above, one can then calculate the necessary $\Sigma_{n \neq 1}(\psi)$.

To obtain the a_n let M be the fraction of the neutrons which have had more than one collision in the sample. M is equal to $(S - S_1)/S$ where S is the total number of scattered neutrons emerging from the sample and S_1 is the number of first collision neutrons escaping (assuming no absorption or multiplication on scattering). If assumption (c) above is correct, these quantities are given by

$$S = I_0 n \sigma_T \int_V \exp(-n t_1 \, \sigma_T) dv$$

$$S_1 = I_0 n \sigma_T \int_V \exp[-n \sigma_T (t_1 + t_2)] dv$$

where t_1 is the distance the incident neutron passes into the sample to reach volume element dv and t_2 is the distance through the sample the scattered neutron passes to reach the counter. I_0 is the incident neutron flux. For cylindrical or spherical samples up to about a third of a mean-free-path in thickness, M is not a strong function of angle and an average value may be taken.

If ϵ is the ratio of the elastic scattering cross section to the total cross section, the a_n are given by

$$a_1 = (1 - M)/D$$

$$a_2 = \epsilon M (1 - M)/D \tag{6}$$

$$a_3 = \epsilon^2 M^2/D$$

where

$$D = (1 - M) + \epsilon M (1 - M) + \epsilon^2 M^2 \tag{7}$$

The value of ϵ can be determined from the angular distribution experiment. If the uncorrected, experimental ratio of the elastic to the total cross section be denoted by e, that is

$$e = \frac{2\pi}{\sigma_T} \int_0^\pi \sigma_{ex}(\psi) \sin \psi \, d\psi \tag{8}$$

then

$$e = \epsilon(1 - M) + \epsilon^2 M (1 - M) + \epsilon^3 M^2 \tag{9}$$

The only method of general applicability for calculating multiple scattering is the Monte Carlo method, which is discussed in a separate section on computer techniques (see Chapter IV.I). Basically, the method tracks individual neutrons through the scattering material, choosing events in a stochastic manner so that the probabilities of various processes are compatible with the cross sections for these events.   Statistically reliable results are obtained by tracking a large number of neutrons.   The great number of arithmetic operations necessary to obtain statistically reliable data requires the use of a digital computer so that the cost of the computation almost precludes its use on a routine basis.   However, as the speed of computers increases and the cost per operation is reduced, the method is becoming more popular.   The method is of particular value in testing the validity of approximations used in the various analytic methods.

4. Results of Measurements

Since the cross sections described here are averaged over resonances, it is to be expected that only gross characteristics of the nucleus will effect the quantities observed.   In particular, such quantities as the energies of individual excited states and the quantum parameters of individual resonances should not have a strong effect upon the angular distributions.   The physical quantities which will be important are such factors as the nuclear size, the average value of the level width-to-spacing ratio, and the wavelength of the incoming neutron.   For these reasons the differential cross sections of a particular element are expected to vary smoothly as a function of neutron energy.   Also, elements with approximately the same atomic weight and hence the same nuclear radius are expected to exhibit very similar differential cross sections.

Figure 2 indicates the variation of the differential cross section of a particular element as the neutron energy is increased.   Most of these curves are for lead, although the data at 2.5, 4, and 7 Mev are for bismuth.   Experiments have shown that, in the continuum region, the scattering from lead and bismuth are almost identical. At low energies, where the centrifugal barrier inhibits interaction in high angular momentum states, the curves are relatively flat; at energies appreciably lower than those shown here, the differential cross section is isotropic.   As the energy is increased, the forward peaking becomes more pronounced.   This forward maximum results from interference between the incident unscattered wave and the diffracted wave, and is analogous to diffraction phenomena in optics. At higher energies a larger fraction of the scattering is confined in

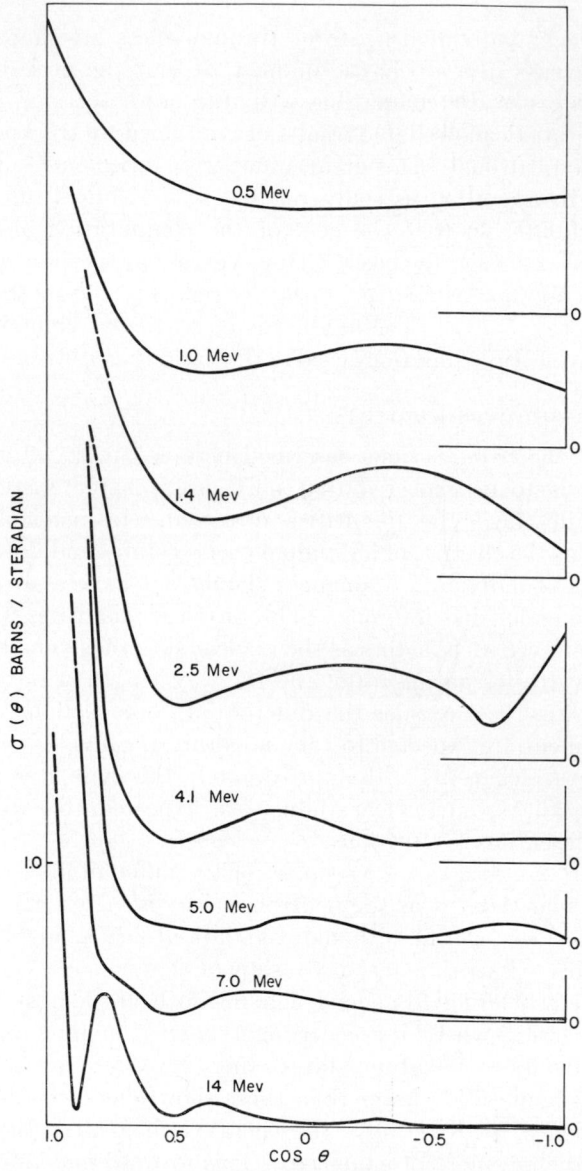

Figure 2. Differential cross section of a heavy element at several energies between 0.5 Mev and 14 Mev. The curves at 2.5, 4.1, and 7 Mev are for bismuth; cross sections at all other energies are for lead. Data are taken from Be 57, Co58, Cr55, Hi58, La57, Wa53, and Wa54.

the forward peak, and secondary maxima and minima appear at larger angles. These secondary maxima and minima move to smaller angles as the energy of the incident neutrons increases. From Fig. 2 the relative difficulties in performing experiments at high energies and large angles can be appreciated. In going from 1 Mev to 14 Mev the cross section and hence the scattered flux intensity at 150° decreases by a factor of about 30. The intensity

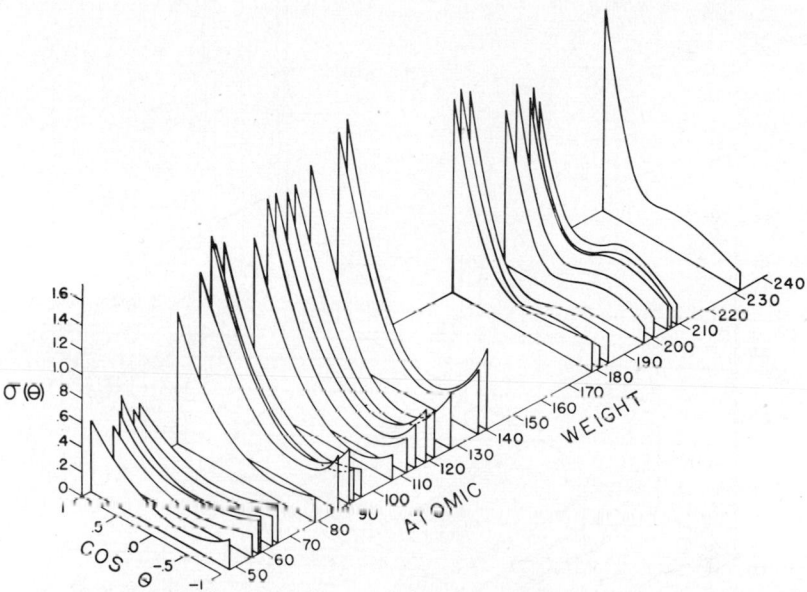

Figure 3. Differential cross sections for elastic scattering of 1-Mev neutrons by a number of elements (Wa53).

problem is further enhanced by the added difficulty of shielding against high energy neutrons.

The effect of changes in atomic weight upon the differential cross sections is illustrated in Fig. 3. In this figure the differential cross section is plotted as a function of both atomic weight and cosine of the scattering angle. All these measurements were made at 1 Mev. The variation with increasing atomic weight is similar to that which occurs with increasing energy; the forward maximum becomes more prominent and the secondary maxima and minima move to

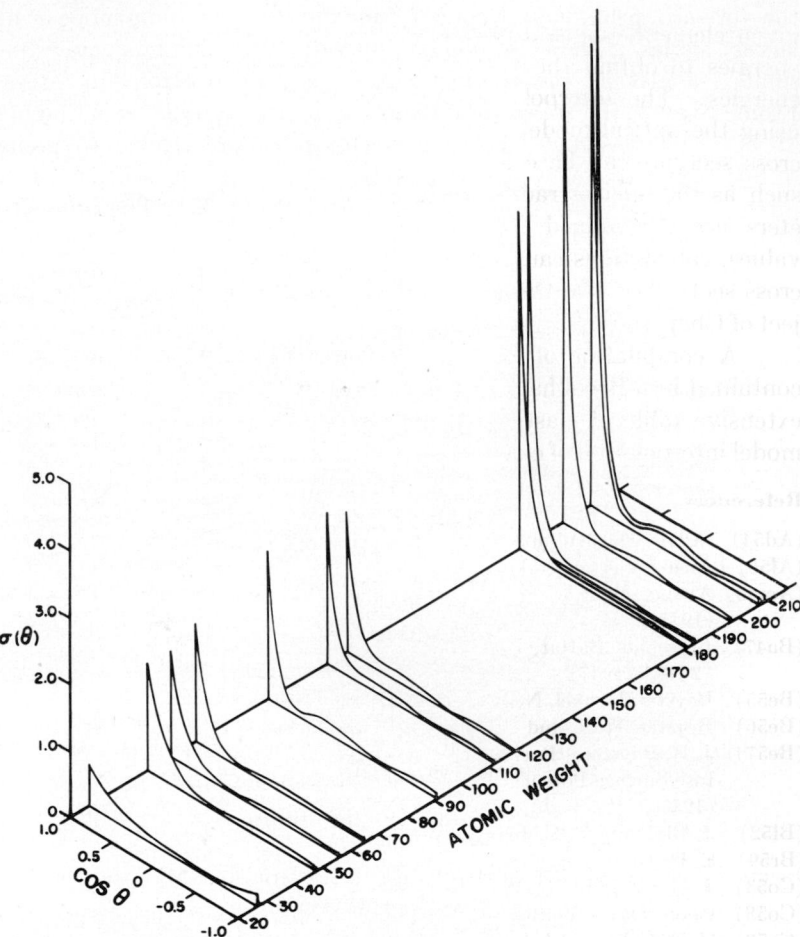

Figure 4. Differential cross sections for elastic scattering of 4.1-Mev neutrons by 12 elements (Wa54).

smaller angles. Figure 4 shows a similar plot for a bombarding energy of 4.1 Mev. Again the regular behavior can be seen, and the increased forward scattering over that of Fig. 3 is apparent.

The regular behavior of the differential cross sections suggests the possibility of obtaining the angular distribution of an element which has not been measured by interpolating between the cross sections of neighboring elements which have been measured. Similarly, for a given element, one can interpolate between curves at two different energies to obtain the values of the cross sections at intermediate energies. The interpolation and extrapolation can best be made using the optical model of the nucleus (Fe54), so that the required cross sections can be calculated in terms of adjustable parameters such as the nuclear radius, well depth, etc. Values for the parameters are determined by fitting the existing data. Using these values, calculations can be made to obtain the desired, unmeasured cross sections. The theory of optical model calculation is the subject of Chapter V.C.

A compilation of angular distribution data as of June 1956 is contained in a Brookhaven National Laboratory report (Hu56). An extensive table of elastic scattering cross sections based on optical model interpolation of existing data is also available (Be57).

References

(Ad54) Adair, Darden, and Fields, *Phys. Rev.* **96**, 503 (1954).
(Al56) Allen, Walton, Perkins, Olsen, and Taschek, *Phys. Rev.* **104**, 731 (1956).
(Am46) Amaldi, Bocciarelli, Cacciapuoti, and Trabacchi, *Nuovo Cim.* **3**, 203 (1946).
(Ba47) Barschall, Battat, Bright, Graves, Jorgenson, and Manley, *Phys. Rev.* **72**, 881 (1947).
(Be55) Beyster, Henkel, Nobles, and Ki ster, *Phys. Rev.* **98**, 1216 (1955).
(Be56) Beyster, Walt, and Salmi, *Phys. Rev.* **104**, 1319 (1956).
(Be57) J. R. Beyster, "Predictions of Fast Neutron Scattering Data with a Diffuse Surface Potential Well," *Los Alamos Scientific Lab. Report* LA-2099 (1957).
(Bl52) J. Blok and C. C. Jonker, *Physica* **18**, 809 (1952).
(Br59) F. D. Brooks, *Nuclear Instruments and Methods* **4**, 151 (1959).
(Co53) J. H. Coon and R. W. Davis, *Phys. Rev.* **94**, 785 (1953).
(Co58) Coon, Davis, Felthauser, and Nicodemus, *Phys. Rev.*, **111**, 250 (1958).
(Co59) H. O. Cohn and J. L. Fowler, *Phys. Rev.* **114**, 194 (1959).
(Cr56) L. Cranberg and J. S. Levin, *Phys. Rev.* **103**, 343 (1956).
(Cr55) W. G. Cross and R. G. Jarvis, *Phys. Rev.* **99**, 621(A) (1955).
(Da54) Darden, Haeberli, and Walton, *Phys. Rev.* **96**, 836 (1954).
(Fc54) Feshbach, Porter, and Weisskopf, *Phys. Rev.* **96**, 448 (1954).
(Hi58) R. W. Hill, *Phys. Rev.* **109**, 2105 (1958).
(Ho52) W. F. Hornyak, *Rev. Sci. Instr.* **23**, 264 (1952).
(Hu56) D. J. Hughes and R. S. Carter, "Neutron Cross Sections, Angular Distributions," *Brookhaven National Lab. Report* BNL-400(1956).
(Je55) Jennings, Weddell, Alexeff, and Hellens, *Phys. Rev.* **98**, 582 (1955).
(La57) Langsdorf, Lane, and Monahan, *Phys. Rev.* **107**, 1077 (1957).
(Ma46) Manley, Agnew, Barschall, Bright, Coon, Graves, Jorgensen, and Waldman, *Phys. Rev.* **70**, 602 (1946).

(Mc54) McCrary, Taylor, and Bonner, *Phys. Rev.* **94**, 808 (1954).

(Mu56) Muehlhause, Bloom, Wegner, and Glasoe, *Phys. Rev.* **103**, 720 (1956).

(No57) R. A. Nobles, private communication (1957).

(Na57) N. P. Nakada, private communication (1957).

(Ok55) A. Okazaki, *Phys. Rev.* **99**, 55 (1955).

(Ow58) R. B. Owen, "The Variation of Phosphor Decay Time with Specific Ionization and Its Applications," *Atomic Energy Research Establ. (Gt. Britain) Report* EL/R 2712 (1958).

(Re56) A. E. Remund, *Helv. Phys. Acta* **29**, 545 (1956).

(Sm57) R. V. Smith, private communication (1957).

(Sn54) S. C. Snowden and W. D. Whitehead, *Phys. Rev.* **94**, 1267 (1954).

(Wa53) M. Walt and H. H. Barschall, *Phys. Rev.* **93**, 1062 (1953).

(Wa54) M. Walt and J. R. Beyster, *Phys. Rev.* **98**, 677 (1954).

(Wi55) Willard, Bair, and Kington, *Phys. Rev.* **94**, 786 (1955).

Optical Model Theory of Neutron Scattering and Reactions

W. S. EMMERICH

Westinghouse Research Laboratories, Pittsburgh, Pennsylvania

1. Introduction

The optical model (also called the *complex potential model*) seeks to describe the interaction of particles with an atomic nucleus by means of a potential consisting of real and imaginary parts. It is assumed that each individual nucleus is a separate center of interaction, and that incident particles are acted upon by the average field of all the nucleons. The characteristic number describing the nucleus is, therefore, the mass number A.

The name optical model is derived from the formal analogy of a plane wave of light incident on a partially absorbing glass sphere. The wavelength and amplitude are decreased inside the sphere, and the unabsorbed portion is scattered in all directions outside. Diffraction as well as refraction is important in the nuclear case, and a partial-wave analysis is necessary for calculation (Sc49). Obviously, such a model cannot account for all the detailed events that occur in the interaction, and it will become apparent in subsequent sections what precautions must be taken in the interpretation of the optical model to prevent erroneous conclusions.

The optical model has proved to be applicable to a variety of incident particles, particularly neutrons and protons, and the information obtained from studies involving these particles is, in general, supplementary and mutually consistent. Comprehensive descriptions of the optical model are available elsewhere in the literature (Mo57, Fe58). The present discussion will be limited to the model as developed from and applicable to neutron interactions.

2. Historical

Attempts to describe neutron interactions with a potential model are by no means new. The first efforts to account for the scattering of neutrons by nuclei hypothesized simple types of potential wells, which predict a few widely spaced maxima in the cross sections wherever standing waves occur in the system (Be35). The crude experimental data then available showed many maxima due to individual resonances (Am35), but they did not indicate the expected systematic peaks. Also it was not clear at the time how to account for the various nuclear reactions induced by the incident neutrons.

A method for introducing at least one type of reaction, namely absorption, into a potential well problem was given by Ostrofsky, Breit, and Johnson (Os36), who showed that the potential becomes complex in that case. The effect can be illustrated by a simple example. Assume $l = 0$ neutrons in a complex potential well $(-V_c - iW_c)$. The radial part of the wave function is

$$\psi(r) = A(r) \exp(ikr) \tag{1}$$

where $k^2 = 2M(E - V_c - iW_c)/\hbar^2$. The complex expression k can be separated into a real and an imaginary part, $k = k_1 + ik_2$. The wave function is

$$\psi(r) = A(r) \exp[i(k_1 + ik_2)r]$$
$$= A(r) \exp(-k_2 r) \exp(ik_1 r) \tag{2}$$

The amplitude $A(r) \exp(-k_2 r)$ decreases exponentially as a function of the radial coordinate r with an absorption coefficient k_2 which entered the problem originally through W_c. The imaginary potential was discussed in further detail by Bethe (Be40), who also hinted at the use of a real potential to describe very high energy interactions.

Models with either real or imaginary potentials remained essentially dormant for almost a decade until experimental total cross sections at 90 Mev were observed to vary systematically about the geometric value of $2\pi R^2$ which had been expected at such high energies (Co49). The phenomenon was interpreted in terms of the nucleus being partially transparent to neutrons, and it was possible to reproduce the variations in the cross sections satisfactorily with the optical model (Fe49). Independently, evidence in favor of potentials was obtained from slow neutron scattering data, although in that case no imaginary part was added (Fo50).

These preliminary successes did not, however, trigger a critical review of the potential picture for neutrons in general. Rather, the impetus was supplied three years later by a systematic analysis of neutron total cross section measurements between zero and 3 Mev with results as stated by H. H. Barschall (Ba52): "It was found that, disregarding the effect of individual resonances, neighboring elements show very similar variations of cross section with energy, while there are marked differences in the shape of the cross section curves between elements of appreciably different atomic number." The marked differences referred to in the above quotation are now known as *gross structure*.

The search for a theoretical explanation was taken up quickly, and the gross structure turned out to have maxima and minima where the optical model would predict them to occur (Fe53). A thorough investigation of all the existing average neutron data with energies up to 3 Mev was then undertaken by Feshbach, Porter and Weisskopf, who used a complex square well and showed that such a model can account not only for the total cross sections but also for the average behavior of various other neutron cross sections (Fe54). Furthermore, they were able to put the model on a sound physical footing by relating the imaginary part of the potential to compound nucleus formation, thus extending the concept of *absorption* to include all nuclear reactions, inelastic scattering, and even part of the elastic scattering.

Additional results followed shortly. The energy range was extended as experimental data became available (Em55). The potential shapes were improved by rounding off the edges (Ne56, Cu56), by concentrating the imaginary potential near the surface (Bj56, Em56), by adding spin-orbit coupling (Cu56), and by taking into account deviations from the spherical shape (Ma57, Ch58). Much effort is also being expanded on investigations regarding the validity of the optical model on a theoretical basis, its relationship to resonance theory (Chapter V.E), the shell model (Ro56, Gr56), nuclear density (Br56), and in general, theories of nuclear structure.

3. Potential Wells

In developing an optical model, one is confronted with the question of what shape the potential should take. A number of criteria, some based on theoretical ideas, others influenced by past experience or limited by computational methods, restrict the choice to certain classes. Following convention, the strength of the potential can be set equal to zero at spatial infinity. When the nuclear surface is approached and penetrated by a neutron, the attractive forces predominate and lead to a reduction in potential, i.e., the

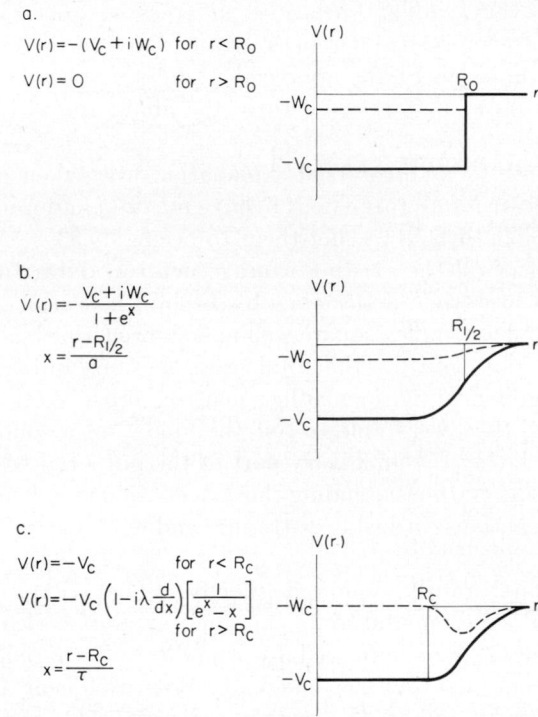

Figure 1. Common shapes for optical model potentials: a, the square well; b, the Saxon well; c, a diffuse potential with surface absorption. The solid line indicates the shape of the real part of the potential, and the dashed line indicates the imaginary part.

potential is negative. Since many nuclei are almost spheres, a spherically symmetric geometry is indicated at first. Similar considerations hold for the imaginary part of the potential. It should be deep in a region of strong interaction, probably near the surface.

From a computational point of view, there are only a few potential shapes which admit an analytic solution for the wave equa-

tion in spherical geometry. One of the simplest, and one tried at
first, is the square well potential:

$$V(r) = (-V_c - iW_c), \text{ for } r < R_0$$

$$V(r) = 0, \qquad\qquad \text{for } r > R_0 \qquad (3)$$

where V_c and W_c are constants, and R_0 is the nuclear radius as illustrated in Fig. 1a.

Computation of cross sections at fairly low energies with this
potential is sufficiently simple so that individual cases can be
computed with a desk calculator. This potential gives surprisingly
good results, considering that the sharp edge is a physically improb-
able condition. There are, however, some consistent defects. The
most severe one seems to be that the transmission through the surface
is not as large as suspected from the experiments.

This particular shortcoming of the square well can be overcome
without resorting to more elaborate calculations by introducing a
separate parameter which simulates a more transparent nuclear
surface. D. C. Peaslee has shown that the transmission indicated by
experiments is approximately twice that obtained in the square-well
calculations (Pe57). This method may also be utilized as a criterion
in the comparison of various types of potential wells among each
other.

Other approximate methods have been suggested to alleviate
the difficulties of the square well. These include trapezoidal (Ja55),
exponential (Ne56), and step wells (Cu56). If the development of
the optical model had come a few years earlier, these methods would
have been utilized more fully than they actually were. The recent
rapid development of electronic computers has made it practical,
however, to perform calculations with potentials of almost any arbitrary shape. Such a program is outlined in detail by Amster and
Culpepper (Am57) and in Chapter IV.I. It employs a square-well
core from the origin outward as far as the potential can be taken constant. This reduces the surface region over which numerical integration must be carried out and saves computing time.

The best shape of the potential in the surface region remains as
yet undetermined in detail. This is due to a number of reasons, the
principal one being that the pertinent neutron cross sections are not
particularly sensitive to the exact form of the surface. The real

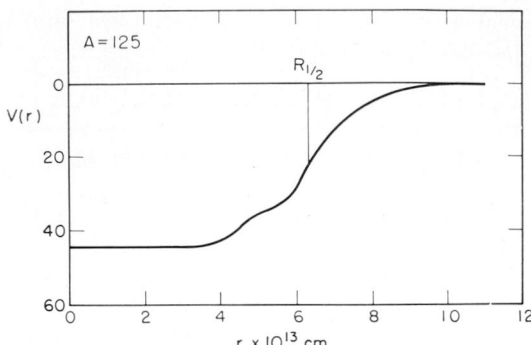

Figure 2. Example of a potential shape assuming saturating two-body interactions between nucleons.

part of the potential most often used with the particular program
discussed above has been $V = V_c/(\exp x - x)$ for $r > R_c$, where $x = (r - R_c)/\tau$, as illustrated in Fig. 1c. A similar form has been used
by McManus (Mc56). A very popular potential shape is the po-
tential $V = V_c/(1 + \exp x)$, where $x = (r - R_{1/2})/a$, now often
referred to as the *Saxon potential* (Ec30, Wo54), also shown in Fig. 1.
This potential can be calculated by the program in Chapter IV.I. In
addition, computer programs have been written especially for this
potential with excellent results (Be56a).

In the square well, the imaginary part of the potential is taken
proportional to the real part, a practice which was taken over by
several authors working with diffuse edges (Be56a, Mc56). On
physical grounds, it may be argued that the removal of neutrons
from the entrance channel depends on the forces encountered, hence on
the derivative of the potential with respect to r. More sophisticated
ideas, based on the breakdown of the Pauli exclusion principle in
the nuclear surface, lead to similar conclusions, namely, that the
imaginary part of the potential should be strongest in the surface
region. Early attempts to concentrate the imaginary potential
into a surface delta-function, or even into finite *blocks* near the
surface of a square well, failed to give the correct angular distributions of elastic scattering, although good agreement could be obtained for the total cross sections. Only after the real part of the
potential had been given a properly diffused edge did the attempts to
concentrate the imaginary part near the surface bear results. Some

common shapes for the imaginary part of the potential are also shown in Fig. 1.

In principle, it is possible to insert more complicated potential shapes into the program. For instance, the potential shape shown in Fig. 2 has been derived from a calculation assuming saturating two-body interactions between nucleons (Mo57) and may be a reasonable shape to consider in future calculations with the optical model.

So far, the discussion on potentials has assumed that a single shape and depth of potential can account for the interaction of every neutron with a given nucleus at a fixed energy. However, neutron polarization observed in scattering experiments and the success of the shell model with spin-orbit coupling suggest that the potential should depend also on the angular momentum carried in by the neutron. Similar evidence for a velocity dependent potential has been obtained recently from the neutron cross sections themselves.

At present it is not clear how the potentials should be altered. Bjorklund and Fernbach (Bj58) modify the real part of the potential by adding

$$V_o(\hbar/\mu c)^2 \ (1/r) \ d\rho(r)/dr \ (\sigma \cdot l) \tag{4}$$

where μ is the mass of the π meson, and $\rho(r)$ is the form factor of the potential, in this case $1/(1 + \exp x)$, as in the Saxon potential. The results obtained are, in general, gratifying at high energies, but there is some reason to believe that further changes, perhaps affecting the imaginary part of the potential, must be made to reach agreement with experimental data at low energies.

Another modification of the optical model is needed to account properly for the experimental data of certain nuclei with spherical deformations. So far, all exact optical model programs for fast neutrons have been limited to a spherically symmetric potential. The principal deterrant for introducing deformations is the considerably more difficult calculation required. At effectively zero energy, however, the computation is manageable for a spheroidal complex potential, and the results are supported by experimental evidence (Ma57, Ch58). If one tries to match the data from a deformed nucleus with a spherical potential, an unusually large diffuseness of the potential surface or an unusually large imaginary potential is the result. Fortunately, the deformations are not very severe for most nuclei of interest so that calculations with spherical symmetry are generally valid, or perturbation theory may be employed (Sc59).

4. Radius of the Potential

Some of the parameters in the optical model serve to specify the spatial extent of the potentials. In spherical symmetry, only one parameter is needed, namely a radius. For the square well, R_0 is uniquely defined, as can be seen in Fig. 1. If the potential surface is diffuse, however, the radius may be chosen in a variety of different ways. The $V_c/(1 + \exp x)$ potential of Fig. 1, for example, makes use of the radius $R_{1/2}$, which is located where the potential depth is $V_c/2$. A simply defined radius in example (c) of Fig. 1 is R_c, which is smaller than both R_0 and $R_{1/2}$ of the previous examples.

One may define a *mean* radius

$$\bar{R} = \int_0^\infty (V(r)/V_c)dr \tag{5}$$

which includes R_0, $R_{1/2}$, and for potential (c) in Fig. 1 is:

$$\bar{R} = R_3 + 1.35909\tau \tag{6}$$

Other radius definitions have been proposed (Fe58), but will not be considered further.

It is generally thought that the radius for the optical-model potential is related to the radius of the nucleus, and certain evidence supports this point of view (see Section 11). On the other hand, the radius of the potential, as used in the model, is selected to give good agreement between the calculated cross sections and the experimental data. It can be considered as being merely a parameter which need not *a priori* represent a physically realistic quantity.

The numerical values of $\bar{R}$ for a given set of data depend on the form factor and depth of the real part of the potential. This is illustrated in Fig. 3 for a special case. If the neutron energy is very low and the absorption is small, gross structure peaks occur at $\bar{R} \approx (\pi/K) (n + 1/2)$ for the square well, where $n = 0, 1, 2 \ldots$. For potentials (b) and (c) in Fig. 1, the corresponding peaks occur at different values of $\bar{R}$, depending on K, and therefore on V_c.

The results of Fig. 3 can be used as an indication of equivalence between radii of different potential shapes, although the relationship may not always be exact for conditions other than those cited

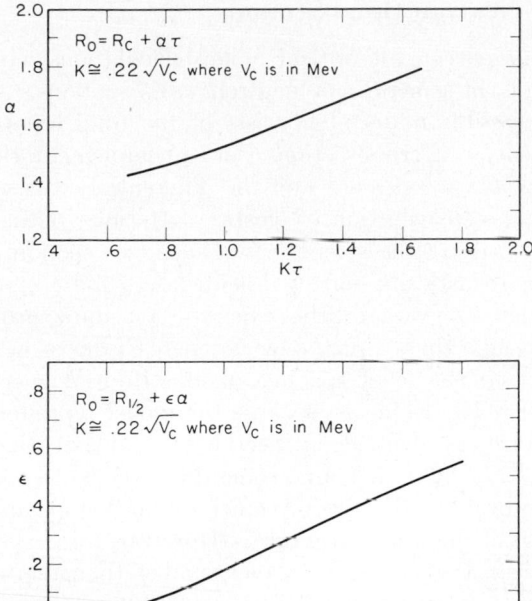

Figure 3.   Correction terms for the equivalent square well radii of the potential shapes shown in Fig. 1.

in the above example.   As illutration, R_0 and $\bar{R}$ for potential (c) in Fig. 1 can be compared using Fig. 3.   A radius function for the square well which works satisfactorily is given in Section 7 by

$$R_0 = 1.26A^{1/3} + 0.7$$

(in units of 10^{-13} cm)

Taking $\tau = 0.84$ for potential (c) and $V_c = 42$ Mev gives $R_0 = R_c + 1.34$ whereas R for the same value of τ is $R_c + 1.14$ from Eq. (6). In this case, $R_0 = \bar{R} + 0.2$, and the corresponding radius function would be

$$\bar{R} = 1.26A^{1/3} - 0.5$$

which is very close to the value [Eq. (24)] determined by comparison of potential (c) cross sections with experiments.

5. Average Neutron Cross Sections

The comparison of optical model calculations with empirical data proceeds in general via neutron cross sections. The experimentally accessible material consists of the total cross section σ_T, the elastic scattering cross section σ_n or its complement, the nonelastic cross section $\sigma_X = \sigma_T - \sigma_n$, and the differential cross section $\sigma_n(\theta)$, i.e., the angular distribution of elastic scattering. Other quantities to be considered are the strength functions (see Section 10), and the polarization of elastically scattered neutrons.

In order to evaluate the experimental data properly, it is necessary to take the average over an energy interval which is large with respect to the level spacing of the Breit-Wigner resonances (see Chapter V.E). This is because the model reproduces only the gross structure as defined in Section 1 and not the individual resonances. For light elements, some difficulty is encountered with this scheme because the Breit-Wigner resonance spacings may approach those of the gross structure. However, for elements heavier than, say, iron, the spacing is rather smaller than the usual energy resolution in experiments performed with fast neutrons, so that the required average is taken by the experimental apparatus in that case. At high energies the widths of the resonances may exceed the spacings and provide sufficient overlap to eliminate any further need for averaging. In practice, therefore, a specific need for averaging is hardly encountered.

It is then possible to employ standard expressions (Bi52) for cross sections in terms of the phase shifts determined by a complex potential which does not vary greatly as a function of neutron energy or nuclear mass. The cross sections are separated into their partial cross sections σ_l where l refers to the different angular momenta,

$$\sigma = \sum_{l=0}^{\infty} \sigma_l \qquad (7)$$

For each l, the potential prescribes a phase shift ϕ_l which is related to the complex reflection factor η_l by

$$\eta_l = \exp(2i\phi_l) \qquad (8)$$

In terms of η_l the partial cross sections take on the following form:

for scattering, $\qquad \sigma_{\mathrm{se}_l} = \pi^2 \lambdabar (2l+1) \, |1 - \eta_l|^2 \qquad (9)$

for absorption, $\quad \sigma_{c_l} = \pi \lambda^2 \, (2l + 1) \, (1 - |\eta_l|^2) \quad$ (10)

and, $\quad\quad \sigma_{t_l} = \pi \lambda^2 \, (2l + 1) \, (|1 - \eta_l|^2 + 1 - |\eta_l|^2) \quad$ (11)

for the corresponding component of the total cross section, where $\lambda^2 = k^{-1}$ is the wavelength of the incident neutrons divided by 2π.

The foregoing expressions for the cross sections originate solely from the nuclear model under discussion, and are not necessarily the same as the experimental data at hand. One must examine their meaning in more detail, keeping in mind that various nuclear reactions as well as inelastic scattering must be fitted into the scheme if Eq. (11) is to represent the observed total cross section.

The optical model can distinguish only the two cross sections given by Eqs. (9) and (10), where σ_{se} refers to neutrons remaining in the beam and σ_c refers to neutrons taken out of the beam. In the case of Eq. (9), the energy is conserved, and the exit channel coincides with the entrance channel. The scattering is elastic; it is referred to as *shape elastic scattering*. This clarifies the notation σ_{se}. In the case of Eq. (10), absorption does not necessarily refer to neutron capture. It implies that neutrons are removed from the entrance channel and are eliminated from the problem as far as the optical model is concerned. Since such usage of the term *absorption* transcends its usual meaning, it is preferable to call Eq. (10) the cross section for formation of a *compound system*, which explains the notation σ_c. Any additional information regarding the ultimate fate of such neutrons must be supplied by separate hypotheses.

6. Nuclear Reaction Scheme

One of the currently accepted schemes for the detailed description of neutron interactions is illustrated in Fig. 4. It is not necessary for an optical model analysis to deal with all the various mechanisms that are thought to contribute to the compound system. Most of them are discussed elsewhere in this volume. However, it seems appropriate to point out some characteristics of the compound nucleus, since experimental evidence indicates that most of the neutrons in the compound system belong in this category (We56).

The compound nucleus model (Bo36) supposes that an incident neutron is assimilated completely into the target nucleus. The break-up of the compound nucleus then takes place according to

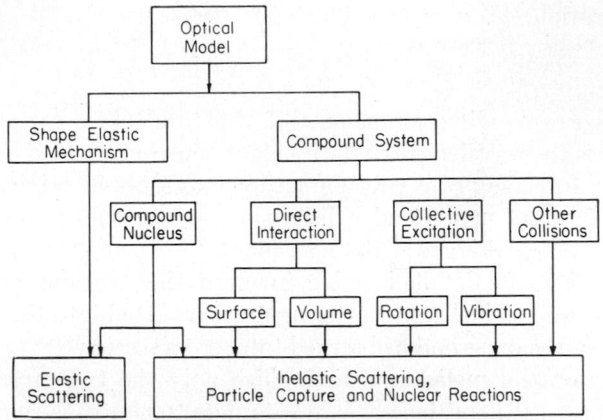

Figure 4. Nuclear reaction scheme.

statistical rules of probability (which favor the emission of neutrons), and leads to elastic and inelastic scattering as shown in Fig. 4. Neutron capture and other nuclear reactions also occur, but with much smaller cross sections. The fraction of neutrons which are scattered elastically via the compound nucleus mechanism is called *compound elastic scattering* in contrast to the previously defined *shape elastic scattering*. The experimentally observed elastic scattering cross section is the sum of these two processes, namely,

$$\sigma_n = \sigma_{se} + \sigma_{ce} \tag{12}$$

where σ_{ce} stands for *compound elastic cross section*.

When the energy of the incident neutron is less than the energy of the first excited state in the target nucleus, the compound nucleus has no choice but to decay to the ground state of the target nucleus, except for the generally small cross sections for neutron capture and other nuclear reactions. In that case,

$$\sigma_{ce} = \sigma_c$$

and

$$\sigma_t \approx \sigma_n = \sigma_{se} + \sigma_c = \sigma_{se} + \sigma_{ce} \tag{13}$$

On the other hand, when the energy of the incident neutron is so high that a large number of levels in the target nucleus can be excited, the probability is shared among all the levels according to the statistical rules, and only a vanishingly small fraction decays to the ground state. There is practically no compound elastic scattering, so that

$$\sigma_{se} \approx \sigma_n$$

$$\sigma_c \approx \sigma_x \tag{14}$$

and

$$\sigma_t = \sigma_{se} + \sigma_c \approx \sigma_n + \sigma_x \tag{15}$$

In this case, the computed cross sections σ_{se} and σ_c correspond directly to the experimental quantities σ_n and σ_x. In all other cases, at least part of the elastic scattering cross section must be accounted for by compound elastic scattering as shown in Fig. 5, which makes a direct comparison with empirical data difficult. The exact division of the compound nucleus decay into elastic and inelastic scattering can be computed only when the quantum numbers of all the relevant levels in the target nucleus are known. The presently available scheme (Ha52) assumes a statistical distribution of levels in the compound nucleus, and predicts that the cross section for a scattering event in which a target nucleus of spin i is left in a state with spin i' is given by

$$\sigma\,(i \mid i') = \pi\lambda^2/[2(2i + 1)] \sum_l T_l(E) \sum_J \epsilon_{jl}{}^J (2J + 1) \times$$
$$\sum_{l'} \epsilon_{jl'}{}^J T_{l'}(E') \div \sum_{l''E''} \epsilon_{j''l''}{}^J T_{l''}(E'') \tag{16}$$

where

$$\epsilon_{jl}{}^J = \begin{cases} 2 \text{ if both } j_1 \text{ and } j_2 \\ 1 \text{ if } j_1 \text{ or } j_2, \text{ but not both} \\ 0 \text{ if neither } j_1 \text{ nor } j_2 \end{cases} \text{ satisfy } |J - l| \le j_i \le (J + l) \tag{17}$$

and where E is the energy, l the orbital angular momentum and j the channel spin (e.g., $j_{1,2} = i \pm 1/2$) for the incident neutron; E', l', and j' are the same quantities for the final (scattered) neutron; E'', l'', and j'', are the same for any possible emergent neutron; J is the spin of a level of the compound nucleus; $T_l\,(E)$ are the transmission coefficients, also called penetrabilities. Care must be taken to conserve parity in the summations. For compound elastic scattering, the single-primed quantities are the same as the unprimed ones.

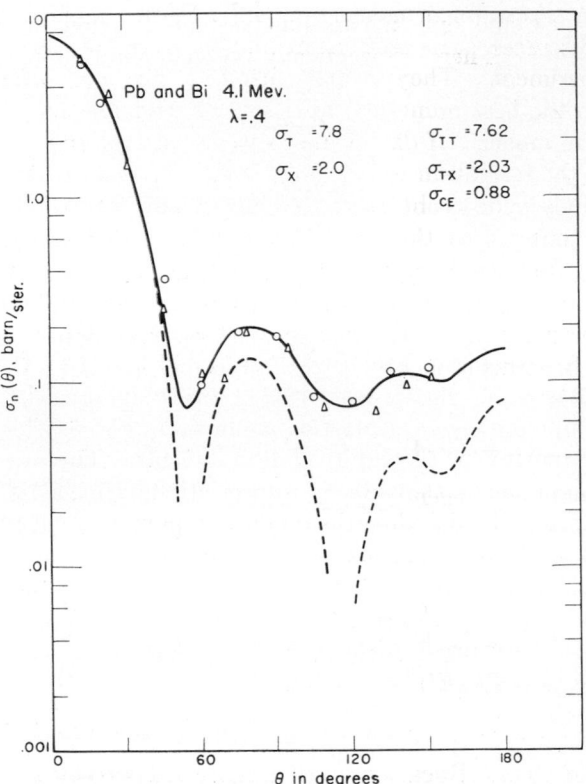

Figure 5. Angular distributions for elastic scattering of 4.1-Mev neutrons on Pb (triangles) and Bi (circles) showing the need for adding compound elastic scattering to shape elastic scattering in the optical model. The dashed line is shape scattering only, and the solid line is shape plus compound scattering where the latter is assumed to be isotropic. The computations were performed with the potential of Fig. 1c. (σ_{TT} and σ_{TX} stand for theoretical total and theoretical nonelastic cross sections.)

The transmission coefficients T_l can be calculated from the optical model by the method outlined in Chapter IV.I. A set of typical values has been computed and is given in Appendix I of this article. The transmission coefficients are useful not only for computation of compound elastic and inelastic neutron cross sections but also for their angular distributions and for that of the associated γ rays (Sa56).

The transmission coefficients differ in principle from the previously discussed cross sections in that they are not easily accessible from experiment. They do not, therefore, give any information in regard to the best numerical values to be used for the potentials in the optical model. If discrepancies with observations occur in their use with the formalism of Eq. (16), it may be just as likely that the assumptions made to obtain Eq. (16) are at fault (Dr57).

In contrast to this case, the angular distributions of elastic scattering (especially under circumstances where the contribution of compound elastic scattering is negligible) are a valuable tool in the determination of the numerical values entering the optical model. In terms of η_l, the differential cross section for shape elastic scattering is

$$\sigma_{se}(\theta) = (\lambda^2/4)|\sum_l (2l + 1) (1 - \eta_l)P_l(\cos \theta)|^2 \qquad (18)$$

where P_l are the Legendre polynomials. A differential cross section for compound elastic scattering can be obtained from the same statistical model that was used in Eq. (16), and the general expression for either compound elastic or inelastic scattering is:

$$\sigma(i \mid i',\theta) = \lambda^2/[8(2i + 1)] \sum_l T_l(E)$$
$$\times \sum_J \{\sum_{j,l',j'} T_{l'} (E') \mid \sum_L Z(lJlJ; \ jL) \ Z(l'Jl'J; \ j'L)P_L(\cos \theta)|/$$
$$\sum_{l''E''} \epsilon_{j''l''}{}^J \ T_{l''}(E'')\} \qquad (19)$$

The Z coefficients (Racah) are tabulated or may be calculated (Bi52). L is restricted to even values only and to such values that $0 \leq L \leq \min (2l, 2l', 2J)$. For compound elastic scattering, the single-primed quantities are the same as the unprimed ones. Since L occurs in even values only, the angular distributions are symmetric about $90°$ in the center-of-mass system. Furthermore, it turns out that the computed anisotropies for compound elastic scattering are much smaller than those for shape elastic scattering, and it is possible in most instances to forego the rather cumbersome computation of Eq. (19) and assume complete isotropy for the compound scattering without any noticeable effects.

7. Comparison with Experiment

Considerable efforts have been made to obtain good numerical values for the parameters in the optical model by comparison with experimental data. In general, one specifies for each part of the potential a strength V or W, and a density $\rho(r)$ which is a function of the radius R, the diffuseness a, d, or τ, and perhaps other parameters. Usually $\rho(r)$ is so arranged that the same radius and the same diffuseness can be used for each part of the potential. For example,

$$V_c\, \rho_1(r) + V_s\, \rho_2(r) + iW_c\, \rho_3(r) + iW_s\, \rho_4(r) \qquad (20)$$

where the subscript c stands for *central* and s for the noncentral part, say, *spin-orbit*. The density functions are often chosen to be either identical or closely related to each other. This prevents the specifications from becoming too complicated. For the potential shapes illustrated in Fig. 1, further simplifications have been made so that only four parameters need to be specified:

Radius of the potentials, R,

Depth of the real part of the potential, V_c,

Depth of the imaginary part of the potential, W_c or the ratio W_c/V_c denoted by ζ or λ,

Diffuseness of the potential surface a, d, or τ (not needed for the square well). If spin-orbit coupling is to be included, at least V_s must be specified in addition. If the problem is nonspherical, the densities become dependent on direction, say $\rho(r,\theta)$, *etc.*

Unfortunately, the various parameters have slightly different meanings even for the simple potential shapes shown in Fig. 1. This has led to considerable confusion in the past. The radius parameter R seems to be particularly vulnerable in this respect (see Section 4).

Because of its simplicity, the square well potential is particularly suitable for the rough determination of the numerical values of R, V_c, and ζ. Surveys have been conducted for the total cross sections and angular distributions of elastic scattering in the region from 1 to 4 Mev neutron energy. Representative numbers for the parameters are:

$$R_0 = (1.26 A^{1/3} + 0.7) \times 10^{-13} \text{ cm}$$

$$V_c = 42 \text{ Mev}$$

$$\zeta = 0.03 \text{ to } 0.10$$

These values are typical for a large number of different elements although some variation for individual isotopes is expected. The subsequent introduction of more refined potentials has not altered

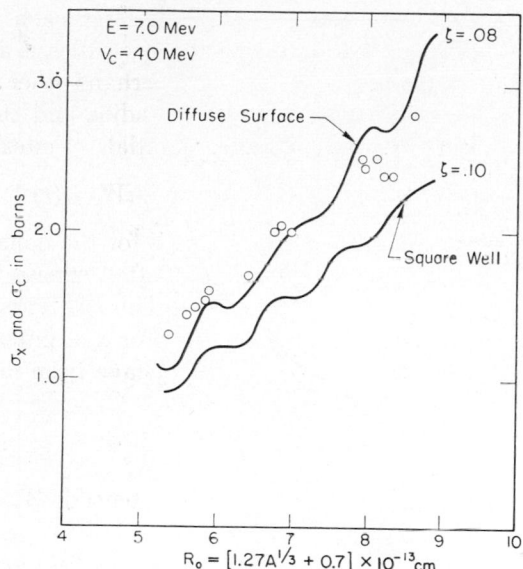

Figure 6. The cross sections for compound nucleus formation for the square well and a diffuse well.

the numerical results for these parameters materially.   The quantitative agreement with experiment, however, has been increased considerably.

In particular, the introduction of a diffuse potential surface has improved the nonelastic cross sections as shown in Fig. 6.   This is most apparent at the higher neutron energies where the compound elastic scattering can be neglected.

The simple diffuse surface model with the imaginary part of the potential proportional to the real part has been the subject of several investigations (up to 14 Mev neutron energy) by the Los Alamos group (Be56, Be56a), who adopted the Saxon shape for their model; see Fig. 1b.   The most recent set of parameters are:

$$R_{1/2} = [(1.17 \pm 0.02)A^{1/3} + (0.79 \pm 0.07)] \times 10^{-13} \text{ cm}$$
$$V_c = 39 \text{ to } 51 \text{ Mev}$$
$$\zeta = 0.03 \text{ to } 0.20$$
$$a = (0.35 \text{ to } 0.50) \times 10^{-13} \text{ cm} \tag{22}$$

For additional values of the model, see Feshbach (Fe58, p. 88).

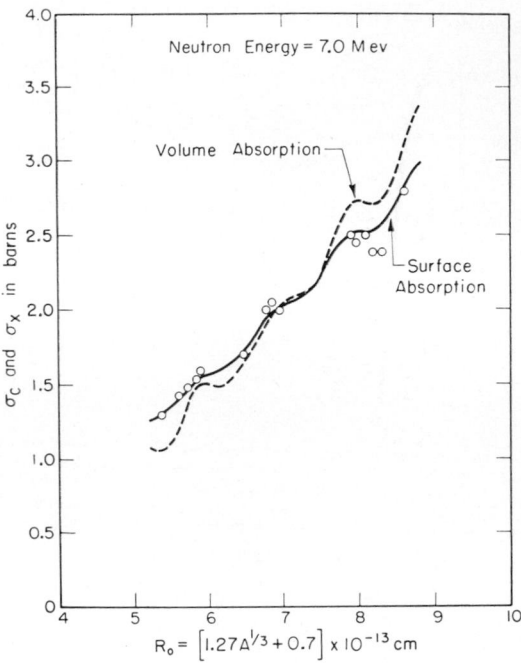

Figure 7. The cross sections for compound nucleus formation for a diffuse potential showing the effect of concentrating the imaginary part in the surface region as in Fig. 1c.

These values are not inconsistent with the square-well results, considering that $R_{1/2}$ is somewhat smaller than R_0 for the Saxon potential. A definite decrease in V_c and increase in ζ was observed at higher energies. There is also some evidence for a systematic variation of V_c, ζ, and a with nuclear mass number. Substantially identical results have been reported by other groups who also worked with a diffuse surface, but concentrated the imaginary part of the potential in the surface region (Bj58, Em57). Empirical justification for surface absorption is somewhat more subtle than that for the diffuse edge. The Westinghouse group (Am57), for instance, has made calculations with both volume and surface absorption, but otherwise identical potentials; and these show that a particular isotope can be fitted equally well with either model. However, if the nonelastic cross sections are plotted at a single neutron energy as a

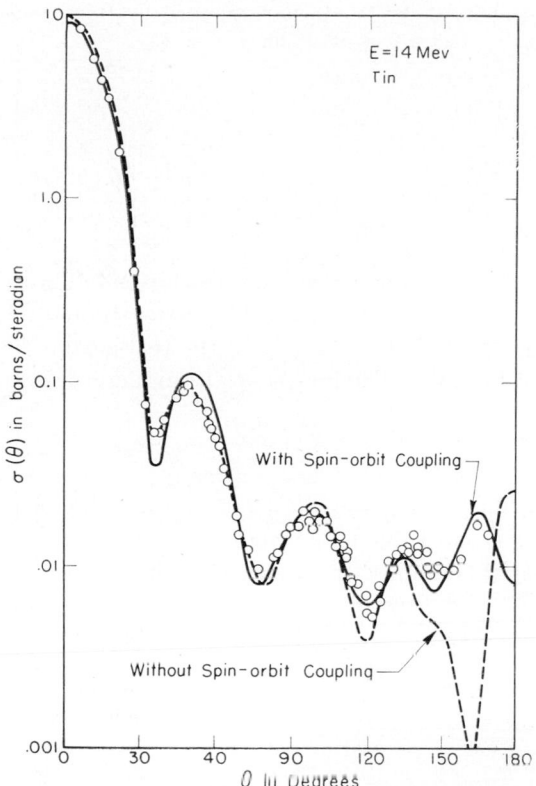

Figure 8. The angular distribution of elastic scattering of 14-Mev neutrons on tin. The dashed line is a diffuse potential with surface absorption but no spin-orbit coupling. The solid line is a similar model (not exactly the same) including spin-orbit coupling. A pronounced effect is apparent at angles > 130°.

function of the radius as shown in Fig. 7, the surface absorption matches the empirical data better than the volume absorption, without changing any of the parameters.

Some striking discrepancies remain even with the diffuse surface absorption model. For example, at 14 Mev neutron energy, a sharp dip occurs in the calculated angular distributions for elastic scattering at angles near 150°. Such minima are not observed in the experimental cross sections, which is evident from the example shown in Fig. 8. The introduction of spin-orbit coupling into the potential

Table I. Magnitude of the Parameters Adopted by Bjorklund and Fernbach (Bj58) with $R_{1/2} = 1.25\ A^{1/3} \times 10^{-13}$ cm

E (Mev)	V_c (Mev)	W_c (Mev)	V_s (Mev)	a (10^{-13} cm)	b (10^{-13} cm)
4.1	50	7	9.5	0.65	0.98
7	45.5	9.5	8.6	0.65	0.98
14	44	11	8.3	0.65	0.98

by the Livermore group (Cu56) successfully eliminates this defect, although almost any other velocity-dependent potential might have had a similar effect. They have used the real part of the Saxon well (Fig. 1b) and Eq. (4). The imaginary form factor is a gaussian given by (Bj58):

$$\rho_3(r) = \exp\ [-(r - R)^2/b^2] \tag{23}$$

The recommended parameters at 4.1, 7, and 14 Mev incident neutron energies are given in Table I. Other evidence for velocity-dependence of the potential is implied through the variation of V_c with incident neutron energy. A general decrease of V_c can be noticed for increasing neutron energies, although considerable nonuniformity exists among the various elements in this respect. Figure 9 shows the

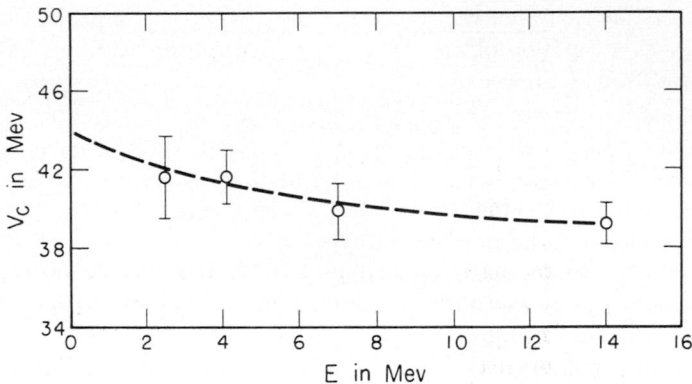

Figure 9. The average dependence of V_c on neutron energy as obtained from a comparison with six elements for which angular distributions of elastic scattering are available at the energies indicated. Whereas the absolute values of V_c may vary for different models, the downward trend indicated by the dashed line is always present.

average result for six different elements examined at the energies indicated.

The potential shapes and parameters of the Bjorklund-Fernbach model have been used in a second-order perturbation calculation by H. M. Schey (Sc59) to simulate quadrupole deformations of nuclei. The spherical potential is supplemented by a real, spin-dependent function

$$V_1 \exp \left[-(r - R_{1/2})^2/c^2 \right] P_2(\cos \gamma)$$

where V_1 and c are adjustable parameters. $P_2(\cos \gamma)$ is the second-order Legendre polynomial, and γ is the angle between the assumed nuclear symmetry axis and the radius vector to the scattered neutron. Taking as an example tantalum at 7.0 Mev neutron energy, reasonable results were obtained with $V_1 = 10$ Mev and $c = 2 \times 10^{-13}$ cm.

8. More Precise Evaluation of Parameters

The calculations depend quite strongly on $KR \propto (V_c + E)^{1/2} \times R$, but not nearly so much on V_c or R separately, which makes the determination of absolute values of these parameters somewhat difficult. Fortunately, the total cross sections give a clue on how to resolve this dilemma, as illustrated in Fig. 10.

In this example, the experiments are plotted at a given neutron energy as a function of mass number. Schematically, there exists a plateau over an appreciable range of elements where the value of the cross sections remains essentially constant. Corresponding calculations shown in Fig. 11 with the diffuse surface absorption potential indicate that the best fit would be for $V_c \approx 42$ Mev, disregarding deviations of individual data points. Similar plateaus are found in other regions of the periodic table at all energies between 2 and 20 Mev. The diffuseness parameter also affects the height of the plateaus. In contrast to V_c, however, there is no dependence on the radius. The following conclusions are reached for the diffuse surface absorption model Fig. 1c:

(a) V_c decreases from 43–45 Mev to 39–41 Mev for neutron energies ranging from 2 to 14 Mev.

(b) The variation of V_c with nuclear mass is quite small. Satisfactory results have been achieved without any change at all, but in general, V_c tends toward the upper limit for heavy elements. The

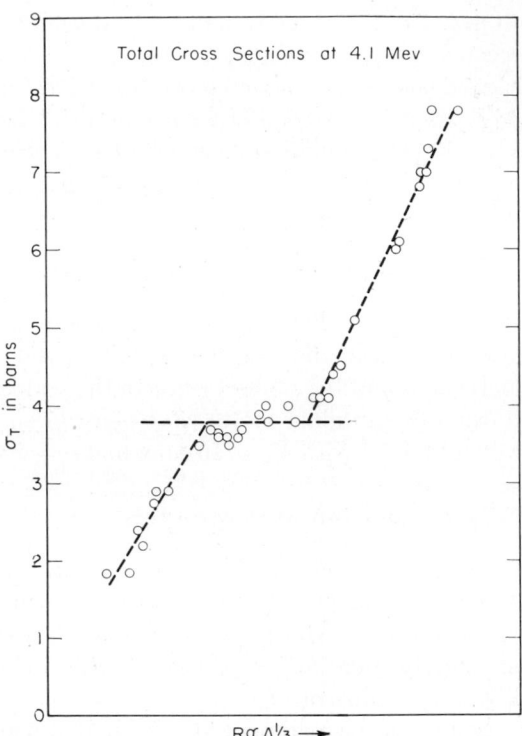

Figure 10. A schematic view of the experimental total cross sections at 4.1 Mev showing how a plateau occurs in the region of elements from Cr to Mo.

results of an investigation of six elements for which sufficient empirical data are available, averaged over the four neutron energies of 2.5, 4.1, 7.0, and 14.0 Mev, are shown in Fig. 12.

(c) The radius is independent of neutron energy but not of nuclear mass. The mean radius function can be represented with two parameters by

$$\bar{R} = (1.25A^{1/3} + 0.5) \times 10^{-13} \text{ cm} \qquad (24)$$

although a better fit might be obtained with a more complicated formula.

(d) The diffuseness parameter may vary slightly with neutron energy and with nuclear mass. Regions of the periodic table in which spherical deformations occur are benefited by larger values,

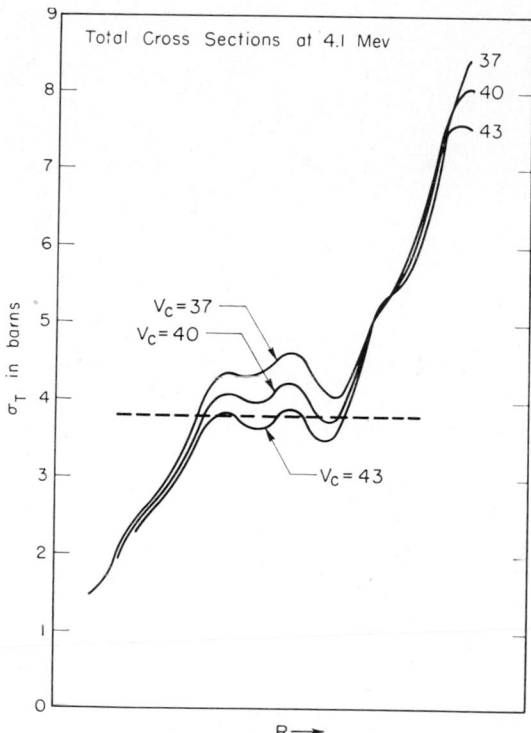

Figure 11. Total cross sections at 4.1 Mev calculated with Fig. 1c, using various values for V_c. The horizontal line indicates the position of the plateau in Fig. 10.

although this does not appear to be a good substitute for proper non-spherical calculations. A typical value is

$$\tau = 0.84 \times 10^{-13} \text{ cm} \tag{25}$$

(e) The imaginary potential increases with neutron energy but is independent of nuclear mass. Its magnitude depends strongly on the diffuseness parameter, τ. Typical values for λ (the ratio W_c/V_c) are given in Table II. A representative set of these parameters was chosen to compute the transmission coefficients and Legendre polynomial coefficients in the appendices. The total cross sections and compound system cross sections obtained from the same values of the

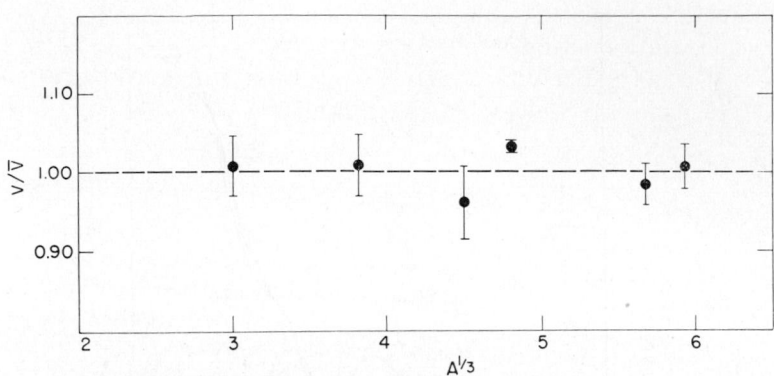

Figure 12. The average of V_c over 4 energies as a function of mass number. The data refer to the same work on which Fig. 9 is based.

Table II.   Typical Values for λ

τ	E (Mev)		
$(10^{-13}$ cm)	0	4	14
0.84	0.35	0.40	0.45
0.90	0.30	0.35	0.40

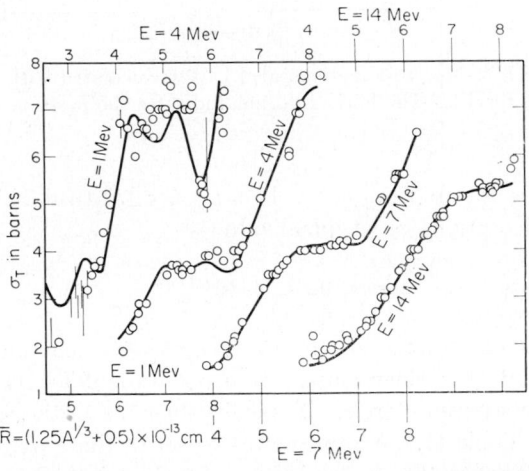

Figure 13. Total cross sections as a function of the mean radius $\overline{R}$ for neutron energies of 1, 4, 7, and 14 Mev.   (Lines are the calculations, points are experimental.)

parameters are shown in Figs. 13 and 14 as a function of $\bar{R}$ for several incident neutron energies.

It is not unlikely that further work with the optical model will lead to numerical values for the parameters which are somewhat

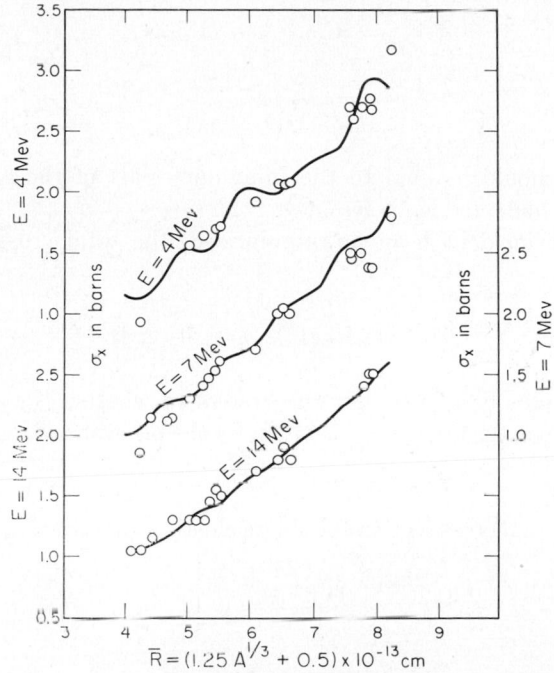

Figure 14. Cross section for compound nucleus formation (lines) and experimental nonelastic cross sections (points) as a function of the mean radius $\bar{R}$ for neutron energies of 4, 7, and 14 Mev. At 4 Mev, compound elastic cross sections obtained from an analysis of the angular distributions of elastic scattering have been added to the nonelastic cross sections.

different from those given above. Also, there seem to be some relationships among the parameters that have not yet been fully explored. As these questions become clarified, there should be an increase in accuracy of the model for neutron cross sections and a simultaneous increase in agreement with the nuclear quantities known from independent sources.

9. Computation with Spin-Orbit Coupling

The optical model program in Chapter IV.I can be used also to compute cross sections and polarizations if spin-orbit coupling is included in the potential. In that case it is necessary to proceed with two sets of calculations, namely, using

$$V^+ = V_c \rho_1(r) + l V_s \rho_2(r) \tag{26}$$

and

$$V^- = V_c \rho_1(r) - (l + 1) V_s \rho_2(r) \tag{27}$$

Attention should be paid to the imaginary part of the potential so that it is not affected inadvertently.

If the incident beam is unpolarized, the total cross section is given by

$$\sigma_t = \pi \lambda^2 \sum_{l=0}^{\infty} [2(l + 1) \, \text{Re}(1 - \eta_l^+) + 2l \, \text{Re}(1 - \eta_l^-)] \tag{28}$$

where the plus or minus sign on η refers to whether V^+ or V^- was used. The factor $\text{Re}(1 - \eta_l)$ is given by the program as

$$\text{Re}(1 - \eta_l) = 2U_l/(2l + 1) \tag{29}$$

The differential cross section for shape elastic scattering is given by

$$\sigma_{se}(\theta) = |f|^2 + |g|^2 \tag{30}$$

where

$$f = (1/2ik) \sum_{l=0}^{\infty} [(l + 1) \, (\eta_l^+ - 1) + l(\eta_l^- - 1)] P_l^0(\theta) \tag{31}$$

and

$$g = (1/2ik) \sum_{l=0}^{\infty} (\eta_l^- - \eta_l^+) P_l^1(\theta) \tag{32}$$

The expressions involving η can be computed from Eq. (29) and from

$$\text{Im}(1 - \eta_l) = 2W_l/(2l + 1) \tag{33}$$

The polarization for shape elastic scattering of an unpolarized incident beam is given by

$$P_{se} = 2[\text{Im}(fg^*)]/[|f|^2 + |g|^2] \tag{34}$$

Comparisons of calculated polarizations with experimental ones are as yet in a very preliminary stage. In general, the curves computed with the optical model fluctuate more strongly than is indicated by the experiments. There is overall qualitative agreement in many cases, but except for isolated instances, quantitative results have not yet been obtained.

10. Neutron Strength Functions

The concept of strength function has been advanced to account for optical model features among Breit-Wigner resonances. The connection between resonance theory and the optical model is demonstrated easily if the total widths Γ of the resonances are much more narrow than the spacing D between them. In that case, the single-level formula holds, and the compound nucleus cross section for a resonance (without spin) at energy E is given by

$$\sigma_{c_l} = \pi \lambda^2 (2l + 1) \; \Gamma_{n_l} \Gamma / [(E - E_s)^2 + (\Gamma/2)^2] \tag{35}$$

where Γ_n is the neutron width and E_s the incident neutron energy.

The optical model is not concerned with fluctuations in the cross sections due to individual Breit-Wigner resonances, but only with the gross structure which is obtained when the cross sections are averaged over an energy interval containing many such resonances. Computing the average of Eq. (35) with $\Gamma_n \ll D$ leads to the simple form:

$$\langle \sigma_{c_l} \rangle \simeq \pi \lambda^2 (2l + 1) \; 2\pi \langle \Gamma_{n_l} \rangle / \langle D \rangle \tag{36}$$

The averaged compound nucleus cross section [Eq. (36)] can be compared directly with the optical model formula:

$$\sigma_{c_l} = \pi \lambda^2 (2l + 1)(1 - |\eta_l|^2) \tag{10}$$

or in terms of the transmission coefficients tabulated in Appendix I to this article,

$$\sigma_{c_l} = \pi \lambda^2 (2l + 1) T_l(E) \tag{37}$$

Equating (36) and (37) gives

$$T_l(E) = 2\pi \langle \Gamma_{n_l} \rangle / \langle D \rangle, \tag{38}$$

which is discussed further in Section 12.

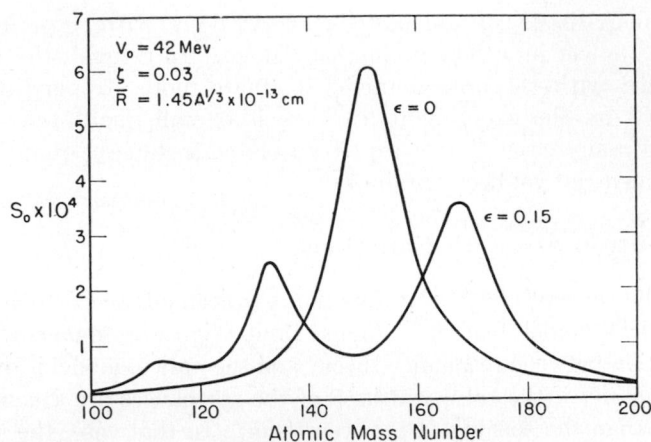

Figure 15. The neutron strength function $S_0(E)$ as a function of atomic mass number for a spheroidal square well potential of eccentricity $\epsilon = 0.15$, and for a spherical square well potential in the region of the third maximum. The eccentricity is given by

$$r = R[1 + \tfrac{2}{3} \epsilon P_2 (\cos \theta)]$$

The strength function $S_l(E)$ is defined as

$$S_l(E) = \langle \Gamma_{n_l}{}^0 \rangle / \langle D \rangle \tag{39}$$

where Γ° is the reduced width given by

$$\Gamma^\circ = \Gamma \sqrt{(E^\circ/E)} \tag{40}$$

The fixed energy E°, to which the widths are normalized, is generally taken as 1 ev. Finally,

$$S_l(E) = (1/2\pi)[\sqrt{(E^\circ/E)}] T_l(E) \tag{41}$$

A portion of S_0 is plotted in Fig. 15 as a function of atomic mass number, showing a typical sharp peak and adjacent broad valleys. Other peaks of S_0 occur in the region of carbon and of iron. If the nuclear shape under consideration is spherically symmetric and if the neutron energy is very low, only s-wave resonances can be excited by the incident neutrons, and S_0 is the only strength function to be considered. If the neutron energy is higher than a few kilovolts, however, S_1 begins to contribute appreciably. Its shape is similar to S_0, except that the peaks fall into the region of aluminum, zirconium, and the very heavy elements. *P*-wave resonances would thus be observed most readily in these regions of the periodic table.

The situation is more complicated for nuclei with spherical deformations. If the optical model potential is not a function of the radial coordinate alone, an incident partial wave gives rise to outgoing partial waves of different l (angular momentum) values. For a spheroidal potential well, a single peak in S_0 is split thereby into several peaks as shown in Fig. 15. The strength function for the spheroidal potential agrees with experimental data better than that for the spherical well in the region of A = 150 to 180 where strongly deformed nuclei are known to exist (Ma57, Ch58). Spin-orbit coupling also introduces complications through the splitting of each l value except $l = 0$ into two parts. Further details may be found in reference La58, page 315.

11. The Optical Model and Nuclear Structure

Many features of the nucleus which can be deduced from the optical model are in agreement with those derived from other approaches. For instance, the radius functions suggested by the potential contain invariably a large term proportional to $A^{1/3}$. This supports the assumption that the potential is related to the nuclear density which is believed to be fairly constant in the core of the nucleus. The diffuseness parameter, on the other hand, does not depend strongly on the mass number. This might be suspected if nuclear forces have a range which is short compared to the overall dimensions of the nucleus. The constant part of the radius function appears to be connected with several phenomena in the nuclear surface. In addition to physical causes, however, its magnitude depends also on the definition of the potential radius (see Section 4).

The decrease of V_c with increasing neutron energy is a sign of velocity dependence. Some attempts have been made to derive an expression for $V(r)$ from fundamental considerations (Ri56). Under typical conditions, Moszkowski (Mo57) gives

$$V(r) = [-112y + Ey + 24y^{5/3} - 40k^{-2}\nabla^2 y]/(1 + y) \text{ Mev} \quad (42)$$

where y is the nuclear density ratio:

$$y = \rho(r)/\rho_0 \quad (43)$$

ρ_0 is the matter density in the core of the nucleus, and k is the Fermi momentum for normal density. $V(r)$ reduces to

$$V = (-44 + E/2) \quad \text{Mev} \tag{44}$$

in the interior of the nucleus. The decrease of V is somewhat steeper than the empirical trend shown in Fig. 9. Under certain circumstances, the dependence of V on incident energy can be interpreted in terms of an effective mass M^* of the incident particle:

$$H = k^2/2M + V = k^2/2M^* + V_0 \tag{45}$$

where H is the total energy of the particle inside the potential well, $k^2/2M = E$ is the incident energy, and V_0 is a potential independent of energy. In the case of Eq. (44), $M^* = 2M/3$.

The optical-model potential is related to that used in shell-model calculations of single-particle energy levels in nuclei (Ro56, Gr56a). The shell model is equivalent in that case to the optical model with the incident particle having negative energy. For a bound particle, however, the imaginary part of the potential vanishes. Spin-orbit coupling in the shell model is of the same sign and approximately the same magnitude as that used to calculate polarizations in the optical model.

One feature of the optical model which seemed strange at first was the smallness of the imaginary part of the potential at low incident energies. This implies a mean free path in nuclear matter considerably longer than had been expected previously. For example, in a square well at low energies, the mean free path is given approximately by:

$$1/\zeta K = 1.5 \times 10^{-12} \text{ cm} \tag{46}$$

for typical values of V_c and ζ. A particle has, therefore, a good chance of traversing a nucleus without losing energy. Apparently, many of the collisions by which an incident particle might lose energy in nuclear matter would require one of the collision products to go into a state below the top of the Fermi sea. Since such states are occupied by other particles, the transition is forbidden through the action of the Pauli principle (La55, Cl55, Mo55). More detailed calculations involving the solution of the nuclear many-body problem have been initiated recently, and show that at zero incident energy less than 1 Mev imaginary potential is required if it is distributed over the volume (Be57). These estimates hold in the interior of the nucleus where the density has a maximum value, and where the Pauli principle is rigidly valid.

In the nuclear surface, on the other hand, the restrictions on particle interactions are relaxed and lead to greater absorption. In addition to collisions between single nucleons, collective excitation is possible in the nuclear surface layer, which adds further to the strength of the imaginary potential in that region. These considerations are in agreement with the experimental data as interpreted by the optical model (see Fig. 7). Many more connections between the optical model and nuclear structure could be pointed out even at the present, very elementary, stage of development in this field. Ultimately, the various approaches should lead to the same result, and the optical model, in whatever form it will finally emerge, should be explainable completely in terms of fundamental theory.

12. The Optical Model as a Source of Data for Reactor Physics[1]

The differential scattering cross sections of heavy elements present in a reactor have two separate effects on the behavior of neutrons slowing down within the medium. First, the energy lost by an elastic collision depends on the angle through which the neutron is deflected. Secondly, even if an isotope is too heavy to absorb much energy by recoil, its directional scattering properties influence the distance neutrons travel, and consequently these cross sections affect the spatial distribution of flux in heterogeneous media.

It is natural to look to the optical model for furnishing transport theory constants depending on the angular distributions of elastic scattering by heavy elements. For such practical purposes, the optical-model parameters should be based as much as possible on experimental data for a particular isotope under question in order to reduce the effect of any unusual characteristics of individual elements. For example, values of the total, elastic, and differential cross sections of an isotope should be matched whenever they have been measured, before the model is used to predict the angular distributions at other energies. Matching experimental curves of neighboring isotopes is also valuable in settling upon the model parameters, and can be used as the main criteria when little data for a

This section was contributed by Harvey J. Amster (Am 59).

particular isotope have been measured. These extrapolation procedures are useful, as is the whole concept of the optical model, because the variation of the potential with mass number and energy affects the dependence of the cross sections on these variables much less than do the optical resonance effects.

Transport theory constants depending on the angular distributions of elastic scattering often take the form of *multigroup cross sections*, which are cross sections averaged over an assumed flux spectrum throughout a finite energy interval. The flux per unit *lethargy* (the negative of the natural logarithm of the energy) generally varies much less with lethargy (or energy) than do the cross sections. When about 100 groups are used, the flux spectrum is usually assumed constant over each group, so that a multigroup cross section is taken as a simple lethargy average over the group.

When the experimental total cross section (a quantity which is almost always available) is in agreement with the corresponding optical quantity for energy intervals over which they both vary noticeably, then the optical-model angular distributions can also be interpreted as valid in principle at each energy within a group, and averaging for the group cross section is a perfectly straightforward procedure. However, when the experimental total cross section fluctuates with energy faster then the optical-model equivalent, the situation must be examined more closely. If several fluctuations of the experimental total cross section cover such a small energy interval that the optical-model values remain essentially constant within it, then the optical-model value at a particular energy can be considered as an average of the actual cross sections at neighboring energies. In this case, the group average of the optical-model differential cross sections is a good estimate of the group average of the actual differential cross sections so long as the latter has many fluctuations within the group.

The only situation left to consider is that in which the experimental total cross section fluctuates too rapidly to be in agreement with the optical-model values for all energies in a wide range (i.e., several Mev) and yet changes so slowly with energy that the optical model cross section varies in covering a few of its fluctuations. This situation, where the resonances due to individual energy levels of the compound nucleus are too widely separated to be accounted for by the optical model, is likely to occur for light elements like oxygen and carbon at low energies, and for magic number nuclei that have resonance structures like light nuclei. Typical parameters of the complex potentials are such that the cross sections calculated vary gradually and almost ideally for obtaining multigroup averages, regardless of how the experimental values behave. When all that is desired is a group constant, it is very tempting to average the optical-model values for the angular distributions over a group, regardless of the resonance structure of the isotope. However, under the conditions described at the beginning of this paragraph, such a procedure is very dangerous, even if the group covers several resonances. A group cross section is an average over the spectrum of many neutrons; an optical-model average is over the energy spread of a single neutron experiencing the *optical effect*. A target nucleus will act as an optical potential only to neutrons whose energy spread covers several levels of the compound nucleus. If covering several levels in turn requires an energy spread so wide that the optical phase shifts are not practically the same for all of the energy components, the components will interfere and prevent the net angular distribution of the scattered wave packet from being any simple average of the values that the optical model would assign to each component. Furthermore, an incident wave packet with a wide energy spread will be elongated spatially by the scattering event, and a requirement necessary for compound elastic scattering to be described by the optical model will not be fulfilled: namely, the shape-elastically scattered packet must completely depart from the compound nucleus before the compound elastic scattering starts, so that the two will not interfere (Fr55). When the energy levels of a compound nucleus are too far apart, the optical model simply is not valid, and so cannot be used for multigroup averages! It should be noted that the discussion of this paragraph invalidates the optical model even *in principle*, and is a completely separate problem from choosing the correct optical model parameters.

In transport theory (Zw54, Am58), the number of neutrons slowing down per unit time into a lethargy interval du and solid angle $d\mu$ by elastic collisions with a given moderator is often expanded into Legendre polynomials,

$$J(u,\mu) \, du \, d\mu = \sum_{L=0}^{\infty} (1/4\pi)(2L + 1) \, J_L(u) \, P_L(\mu) \, du \, d\mu \quad (47)$$

and for heavy moderators, the flux in the integrands of $J_L(u)$ are expanded in a power series about the value at u, so that

$$J_L(u) = (d^n/du^n) F_L(u) G_L{}^n(u) \qquad (48)$$

where $F_L(u)$ is a Legendre component of the flux, and $G_L{}^n(u)$ are coefficients depending on $1/\gamma$, which is the moderator mass number, and the differential cross section in the center-of-mass system, $\sigma_n(\mu_c)$.

$$G_L{}^n(E) = (2\pi/n!) \int_{-1}^{1} [-U(\mu_c)]^n P_L[\mu_0(\mu_c)]\sigma_n(E,\mu_c)d\mu_c \qquad (49)$$

The symbol μ_c is the cosine of the scattering angle in the center-of mass system; $\mu_0 = (\gamma + \mu_c)/(1 + 2\gamma\mu_c + \gamma^2)^{1/2}$ is the cosine of the scattering angle in the laboratory system, and $U = -\log_e [1-2\gamma (1 + \gamma)^{-2}(1 - \mu_c)]$ is the lethargy gain of a neutron which is scattered through the angle $\cos^{-1}\mu_c$.

When the differential scattering cross sections from the optical model can be used, one way of obtaining the $G_L{}^n$'s is to calculate the Legendre polynomial expansion coefficients of $\sigma_n(\mu_c)$ directly from the partial wave phase shifts of the optical model and to insert the expansion for $\sigma_n(\mu_c)$ into the definition of $G_L{}^n$ to get a sum of products of the expansion coefficients of $\sigma_n(\mu_c)$ and integrals of analytic functions which can be evaluated (Am58). Since it is the amplitude of a given partial wave that is proportional to a Legendre polynomial, and since it is the square of the sum of the amplitudes that makes up a differential cross section, there will be twice as many terms in the expansion of $\sigma_n(\mu_c)$ as there are partial waves contributing to the cross section.

Although it can be shown (Am58) that expansion coefficients of $\sigma_n(\mu_c)$ corresponding to Legendre polynomials of order different from L by more than n become increasingly less important to the evaluation of $G_L{}^n$, so many terms may become involved at high energies that it is beneficial for a digital computer to calculate the complete integrand of $G_L{}^n$ from the optical parameters and target mass number, and then to perform the integration numerically.

Another use of the optical model for reactor physics is in estimating the effects of fine structure resonances above a few kev where they cannot be resolved experimentally. This type of information requires obtaining the compound-nucleus-formation cross section for the various partial waves, and such quantities are very sensitive to the values of the imaginary part of the potential, to the diffuseness of its surface, and to any eccentricity of the nuclear shape. Although the complex square well gives roughly satisfactory values for the total cross sections and shape elastic angular distributions, it usually implies much too small a probability for the formation of the compound nucleus.

Until very recently, optical-model calculations for $\langle \Gamma_n{}^0 \rangle / \langle D \rangle$, the average s-wave neutron reduced width to spacing ratio, compared very poorly with experimental data at energies in which resonances could be resolved, and most estimates of the higher energy unresolved resonances were first obtained by extrapolating information from lower energies. That is, no partial waves other than s-waves were expected to contribute throughout the whole resonance region, and the average neutron reduced width $\langle \Gamma_n{}^0 \rangle = \langle E^{-1/2} \Gamma_n \rangle$, the average radiation width $\langle \Gamma_\lambda \rangle$, and average spacing between resonances $\langle D \rangle$ were assigned the same values in the unresolved region as were measured at lower energies. When it was later discovered that higher partial waves might contribute to the resonance structure in the unresolved region, the effect was investigated by simple *continuum theory* or *black nucleus* models, which provide very simple formulas but which seem to be too crude (Dr56, Gr57).

The failure of these simple theories to prove anything about the higher partial waves except whether or not they might contribute is really not surprising since the theories provide no description of the partial wave *giant resonances* (gross structure) that are quite evident in experimental total cross sections and angular distributions. Thus, while few calculations have, to date, relied on the optical model, its use now seems called for: better potential shapes are available, and the effect of higher partial waves has recently become more clear— even in obtaining matches with the resolved resonances. However, since only crude assumptions about individual unresolved resonances can be made, the technique still remains unreliable.

The *transmission coefficient* T_l is a number between zero and one, and defined in terms of σ_{c_l}, the cross section for the formation of the compound nucleus from partial wave l:

$$\sigma_{c_l} = (2l + 1)\pi\lambda^2 \, T_l \tag{50}$$

T_l is thus obtainable from the optical model. Since the optical model cross section is defined in the resonance region as an average over an energy interval containing many resonances but small enough to have nearly the same phase shifts according to the optical model, σ_{c_l} can be evaluated in the case of widely separated Breit-Wigner resonances to give

$$T_l = 2\pi\langle\Gamma_{n_l}\rangle/\langle D\rangle, \tag{51}$$

where, in the absence of other information, the average spacing $\langle D\rangle$ between levels of any given spin of the compound nucleus is usually taken to be the same as those resolved at lower energy. The validity of this last assumption is very much in doubt. Strictly speaking, the averaging technique (Gr57) should be carried out over the energies covered by one Breit-Wigner resonance, and then this quantity should be averaged over a distribution function in Γ_{n_l} and D. Although Eq. (51) was derived on the basis of a single level formula, it is hypothesized a sbeing true for overlapping levels, since interference terms will cancel in averaging over many of them.

The capture cross section for a target nucleus with no spin interaction, averaged over a few resonances, is

$$\sigma_\gamma = \sum_{l=0}^{\infty} \sigma_{c_l} \langle\Gamma_\gamma\rangle/(\langle\Gamma_\gamma\rangle + \langle\Gamma_{n_l}\rangle) \tag{52}$$

where $\langle\Gamma_\gamma\rangle$ is assumed to be the same value as measured in the resolved resonance region, and $\langle\Gamma_{n_l}\rangle$ can be obtained from Eq. (51). As before, Eq. (52) should really be averaged over a distribution function in $\langle\Gamma_{n_l}\rangle$, and in this case the averaging may have a large effect.

Equation (52) is useful for obtaining a group cross section in the sense of a straight lethargy average, as discussed in the second paragraph of this section. If, however, the concentration of a particular isotope in a mixture is so great that it strongly depresses the flux at its resonance energies, then the average capture cross section above is not of sufficient use; the Breit-Wigner parameters for individual resonances are needed. Although the optical model cannot possibly furnish such information, its prediction of $\langle\Gamma_{n_l}\rangle/\langle D\rangle$ along with a distribution function of $\langle\Gamma_{n_l}\rangle$ do enable one to get a distribution of the probable effects of a single resonance on some gross behavior like resonance escape probability, and when many individual resonances are present, the distribution of their possible net effects should have a reasonably narrow spread.

Acknowledgment

The author is indebted to the Westinghouse Atomic Power Division for furnishing many of the computations included in this article. Thanks are due to Dr. Harvey J. Amster for writing Section 12 and working with the author on some of the previously unpublished material in the other sections.

Appendix I. Optical Model Transmission Coefficients

The optical model with a diffuse edge potential and surface absorption (Fig. 1c) has been used to compute $T_l(E)$, the nuclear transmission coefficients, also known as penetrabilities. They are defined through σ_{c_l}, the cross section for formation of a compound system from the partial wave l by:

$$\sigma_{c_l}(E) = \pi \lambda^2 (2l + 1) T_l(E) \qquad (A.1)$$

where λ is the wavelength divided by 2π of a neutron beam with energy E. The following tables give the T_l up to $l = 8$ as a function of the neutron energy E in Mev at a given mean radius $\bar{R}$. For an isotope of mass number A, the radius can be obtained from the relation

$$R = 1.25 \, A^{1/3} + 0.5 \quad \text{(units of } 10^{-13} \text{ cm)} \qquad (A.2)$$

which has been found satisfactory for the particular set of parameters chosen in the computation. This radius function represents an average over many elements, and the most advantageous $\bar{R}$ for an individual isotope may differ somewhat from that average. The tables cover a region of $\bar{R}$ from 4.0 to 8.2 in intervals of 0.3 (units of 10^{-13} cm). Due to the stepwise change in the model parameters V_c in Mev and λ as a function of energy, the corresponding T_l do not always follow a smooth curve. However, representative graphs can be obtained from the data given in the tables with sufficient accuracy for practical purposes. [The tables in this and the following appendix were computed on the NORC by the SUMNUM code (Am-57).]

Table III. $\bar{R} = 4.0,$ $\tau = 0.84$

E	V_c	λ	T_0	T_1	T_2	T_3	T_4	T_5	T_6	T_7	T_8
0.1	44	0.34	0.138	0.065							
0.4	44	0.34	0.252	0.415	0.003						
0.7	44	0.34	0.312	0.697	0.012	0.001					
1.0	44	0.34	0.353	0.859	0.026	0.005					
1.5	43	0.37	0.424	0.943	0.063	0.018					
2.0	43	0.37	0.457	0.988	0.108	0.047	0.001				
2.5	43	0.37	0.479	0.997	0.158	0.093	0.002				
3.0	43	0.37	0.496	0.990	0.209	0.152	0.004				
4.0	42	0.40	0.541	0.973	0.306	0.292	0.012	0.001			
5.0	42	0.40	0.552	0.949	0.382	0.414	0.031	0.002			
6.0	42	0.40	0.557	0.925	0.441	0.493	0.065	0.004			
7.0	41	0.43	0.580	0.920	0.485	0.575	0.118	0.008	0.001		
8.0	41	0.43	0.578	0.901	0.519	0.602	0.194	0.015	0.001		
9.0	41	0.43	0.575	0.884	0.545	0.615	0.294	0.026	0.003		
10.0	41	0.43	0.571	0.869	0.565	0.618	0.411	0.040	0.005		
12.0	40	0.46	0.583	0.859	0.594	0.655	0.636	0.086	0.012	0.002	
14.0	40	0.46	0.575	0.833	0.617	0.638	0.830	0.155	0.024	0.004	

Table IV. $\bar{R} = 4.3,$ $\tau = 0.84$

E	V_c	λ	T_0	T_1	T_2	T_3	T_4	T_5	T_6	T_7	T_8
0.1	44	0.34	0.148	0.097							
0.4	44	0.34	0.269	0.433	0.005						
0.7	44	0.34	0.333	0.614	0.018	0.001					
1.0	44	0.34	0.377	0.704	0.041	0.004					
1.5	43	0.37	0.428	0.829	0.097	0.017					
2.0	43	0.37	0.463	0.850	0.170	0.037	0.001				
2.5	43	0.37	0.488	0.852	0.251	0.064	0.004				
3.0	43	0.37	0.506	0.847	0.332	0.095	0.008				
4.0	42	0.40	0.537	0.872	0.455	0.183	0.027	0.001			
5.0	42	0.40	0.553	0.849	0.555	0.249	0.068	0.003			
6.0	42	0.40	0.563	0.827	0.624	0.304	0.145	0.007	0.001		
7.0	41	0.43	0.576	0.842	0.657	0.378	0.250	0.015	0.001		
8.0	41	0.43	0.581	0.822	0.690	0.411	0.393	0.028	0.003		
9.0	41	0.43	0.585	0.803	0.714	0.437	0.547	0.047	0.005		
10.0	41	0.43	0.589	0.784	0.732	0.456	0.684	0.075	0.008		
12.0	40	0.46	0.602	0.783	0.747	0.508	0.842	0.159	0.020	0.003	
14.0	40	0.46	0.610	0.749	0.764	0.520	0.898	0.285	0.042	0.006	0.001

Table V. $\bar{R} = 4.6,$ $\tau = 0.84$

E	V_c	λ	T_0	T_1	T_2	T_3	T_4	T_5	T_6	T_7	T_8
0.1	44	0.34	0.247	0.042							
0.4	44	0.34	0.421	0.200	0.009						
0.7	44	0.34	0.501	0.310	0.037	0.001					
1.0	44	0.34	0.550	0.383	0.086	0.003					
1.5	43	0.37	0.575	0.518	0.195	0.010	0.001				
2.0	43	0.37	0.608	0.561	0.339	0.023	0.003				
2.5	43	0.37	0.630	0.587	0.484	0.042	0.009				
3.0	43	0.37	0.645	0.603	0.609	0.066	0.019				
4.0	42	0.40	0.655	0.664	0.742	0.134	0.062	0.002			
5.0	42	0.40	0.668	0.664	0.833	0.200	0.152	0.006			
6.0	42	0.40	0.678	0.659	0.875	0.264	0.283	0.014	0.001		
7.0	41	0.43	0.680	0.689	0.878	0.331	0.413	0.029	0.002		
8.0	41	0.43	0.687	0.677	0.888	0.379	0.528	0.054	0.005		
9.0	41	0.43	0.694	0.665	0.890	0.419	0.601	0.092	0.008		
10.0	41	0.43	0.700	0.652	0.888	0.452	0.637	0.148	0.014	0.002	
12.0	40	0.46	0.709	0.660	0.879	0.507	0.697	0.305	0.036	0.005	0.001
14.0	40	0.46	0.720	0.633	0.868	0.543	0.680	0.520	0.074	0.011	0.002

Table VI. $\bar{R} = 4.9$ $\tau = 0.84$

E	V_c	λ	T_0	T_1	T_2	T_3	T_4	T_5	T_6	T_7	T_8
0.1	44	0.34	0.540	0.021							
0.4	44	0.34	0.771	0.113	0.024						
0.7	44	0.34	0.837	0.189	0.096	0.001					
1.0	44	0.34	0.864	0.247	0.221	0.003					
1.5	43	0.37	0.842	0.349	0.440	0.011	0.002				
2.0	43	0.37	0.852	0.398	0.678	0.026	0.007				
2.5	43	0.37	0.853	0.432	0.845	0.049	0.017				
3.0	43	0.37	0.851	0.458	0.940	0.080	0.034	0.001			
4.0	42	0.40	0.835	0.520	0.989	0.163	0.091	0.004			
5.0	42	0.40	0.831	0.536	0.996	0.256	0.164	0.011	0.001		
6.0	42	0.40	0.826	0.544	0.977	0.347	0.232	0.028	0.002		
7.0	41	0.43	0.822	0.573	0.967	0.420	0.320	0.060	0.004		
8.0	41	0.43	0.819	0.572	0.944	0.487	0.365	0.113	0.008	0.001	
9.0	41	0.43	0.816	0.569	0.921	0.541	0.397	0.195	0.015	0.002	
10.0	41	0.43	0.813	0.566	0.899	0.586	0.421	0.306	0.026	0.003	
12.0	40	0.46	0.812	0.579	0.883	0.637	0.489	0.552	0.066	0.008	0.001
14.0	40	0.46	0.804	0.572	0.845	0.684	0.502	0.773	0.136	0.019	0.003

Table VII. $\bar{R} = 5.2$ $\tau = 0.84$

E	V_c	λ	T_0	T_1	T_2	T_3	T_4	T_5	T_6	T_7	T_8
0.1	44	0.34	0.763	0.017	0.002						
0.4	44	0.34	0.957	0.099	0.061						
0.7	44	0.34	0.984	0.173	0.205	0.001					
1.0	44	0.34	0.982	0.233	0.379	0.005					
1.5	43	0.37	0.986	0.316	0.620	0.017	0.002				
2.0	43	0.37	0.967	0.371	0.757	0.043	0.005				
2.5	43	0.37	0.947	0.412	0.816	0.083	0.012	0.001			
3.0	43	0.37	0.929	0.443	0.835	0.139	0.021	0.002			
4.0	42	0.40	0.918	0.493	0.882	0.273	0.058	0.008			
5.0	42	0.40	0.893	0.521	0.858	0.425	0.101	0.026	0.001		
6.0	42	0.40	0.871	0.539	0.830	0.561	0.150	0.065	0.003		
7.0	41	0.43	0.873	0.558	0.848	0.637	0.218	0.131	0.007	0.001	
8.0	41	0.43	0.857	0.568	0.822	0.713	0.266	0.236	0.015	0.001	
9.0	41	0.43	0.840	0.576	0.797	0.766	0.310	0.366	0.028	0.003	
10.0	41	0.43	0.824	0.584	0.773	0.802	0.349	0.490	0.050	0.005	0.001
12.0	40	0.46	0.818	0.600	0.770	0.827	0.427	0.655	0.125	0.015	0.002
14.0	40	0.46	0.786	0.615	0.728	0.850	0.474	0.698	0.262	0.034	0.005

Table VIII. $\bar{R} = 5.5$ $\tau = 0.84$

E	V_c	λ	T_0	T_1	T_2	T_3	T_4	T_5	T_6	T_7	T_8
0.1	44	0.34	0.424	0.024	0.002						
0.4	44	0.34	0.631	0.140	0.042						
0.7	44	0.34	0.696	0.248	0.118	0.003					
1.0	44	0.34	0.725	0.333	0.198	0.010					
1.5	43	0.37	0.815	0.413	0.367	0.055	0.001				
2.0	43	0.37	0.813	0.481	0.448	0.088	0.004	0.001			
2.5	43	0.37	0.805	0.531	0.498	0.174	0.009	0.002			
3.0	43	0.37	0.796	0.567	0.530	0.291	0.018	0.004			
4.0	42	0.40	0.823	0.598	0.620	0.519	0.049	0.018	0.001		
5.0	42	0.40	0.799	0.631	0.627	0.736	0.096	0.055	0.002		
6.0	42	0.40	0.777	0.653	0.625	0.871	0.156	0.118	0.006		
7.0	41	0.43	0.795	0.660	0.664	0.907	0.227	0.201	0.014	0.001	
8.0	41	0.43	0.773	0.675	0.652	0.943	0.294	0.282	0.030	0.002	
9.0	41	0.43	0.752	0.688	0.639	0.955	0.359	0.341	0.057	0.005	
10.0	41	0.43	0.731	0.700	0.626	0.952	0.419	0.381	0.103	0.009	0.001
12.0	40	0.46	0.729	0.713	0.636	0.936	0.509	0.471	0.252	0.027	0.003
14.0	40	0.46	0.691	0.732	0.609	0.911	0.583	0.485	0.488	0.063	0.009

Table IX. $\bar{R} = 5.8$, $\tau = 0.84$

E	V_c	λ	T_0	T_1	T_2	T_3	T_4	T_5	T_6	T_7	T_8
0.1	44	0.34	0.216	0.049	0.001						
0.4	44	0.34	0.367	0.287	0.019	0.001					
0.7	44	0.34	0.434	0.479	0.057	0.007					
1.0	44	0.34	0.474	0.609	0.103	0.024					
1.5	43	0.37	0.575	0.669	0.207	0.084	0.002				
2.0	43	0.37	0.594	0.740	0.275	0.211	0.005	0.001			
2.5	43	0.37	0.604	0.780	0.327	0.399	0.012	0.003			
3.0	43	0.37	0.609	0.803	0.367	0.604	0.024	0.006			
4.0	42	0.40	0.658	0.801	0.456	0.850	0.069	0.023	0.001		
5.0	42	0.40	0.649	0.815	0.487	0.973	0.142	0.050	0.004		
6.0	42	0.40	0.637	0.822	0.506	0.991	0.240	0.084	0.012	0.001	
7.0	41	0.43	0.664	0.816	0.543	0.990	0.336	0.142	0.030	0.002	
8.0	41	0.43	0.648	0.821	0.547	0.965	0.440	0.185	0.065	0.004	
9.0	41	0.43	0.632	0.823	0.549	0.934	0.535	0.225	0.126	0.009	0.001
10.0	41	0.43	0.617	0.823	0.551	0.903	0.615	0.263	0.218	0.017	0.002
12.0	40	0.46	0.622	0.823	0.569	0.881	0.703	0.354	0.441	0.050	0.006
14.0	40	0.46	0.596	0.817	0.569	0.828	0.778	0.406	0.625	0.120	0.016

Table X. $\bar{R} = 6.1$, $\tau = 0.84$

E	V_c	λ	T_0	T_1	T_2	T_3	T_4	T_5	T_6	T_7	T_8
0.1	44	0.34	0.143	0.135	0.001						
0.4	44	0.34	0.258	0.630	0.014	0.003					
0.7	44	0.34	0.318	0.865	0.045	0.019					
1.0	44	0.34	0.358	0.957	0.086	0.062					
1.5	43	0.37	0.434	0.970	0.169	0.190	0.003				
2.0	43	0.37	0.463	0.983	0.239	0.385	0.009	0.001			
2.5	43	0.37	0.483	0.977	0.299	0.556	0.022	0.002			
3.0	43	0.37	0.497	0.964	0.349	0.662	0.044	0.004			
4.0	42	0.40	0.543	0.943	0.428	0.798	0.125	0.015	0.002		
5.0	42	0.40	0.549	0.920	0.477	0.803	0.262	0.035	0.010		
6.0	42	0.40	0.551	0.897	0.512	0.781	0.437	0.065	0.029	0.001	
7.0	41	0.43	0.573	0.894	0.539	0.814	0.570	0.113	0.065	0.003	
8.0	41	0.43	0.570	0.877	0.558	0.784	0.708	0.162	0.129	0.008	0.001
9.0	41	0.43	0.567	0.860	0.575	0.756	0.808	0.215	0.211	0.017	0.002
10.0	41	0.43	0.565	0.842	0.590	0.729	0.873	0.272	0.289	0.033	0.003
12.0	40	0.46	0.577	0.832	0.612	0.730	0.911	0.380	0.423	0.099	0.011
14.0	40	0.46	0.580	0.797	0.639	0.684	0.930	0.473	0.461	0.240	0.028

Table XI. $\bar{R} = 6.4,$ $\tau = 0.84$

E	V_c	λ	T_0	T_1	T_2	T_3	T_4	T_5	T_6	T_7	T_8
0.1	44	0.34	0.142	0.190	0.001						
0.4	44	0.34	0.259	0.607	0.018	0.003					
0.7	44	0.34	0.323	0.747	0.059	0.019					
1.0	44	0.34	0.368	0.798	0.117	0.049	0.001				
1.5	43	0.37	0.419	0.899	0.216	0.152	0.005				
2.0	43	0.37	0.456	0.891	0.314	0.246	0.018	0.001			
2.5	43	0.37	0.483	0.876	0.398	0.322	0.045	0.002			
3.0	43	0.37	0.504	0.858	0.466	0.377	0.096	0.004			
4.0	42	0.40	0.535	0.876	0.537	0.509	0.261	0.016	0.005		
5.0	42	0.40	0.556	0.842	0.601	0.537	0.522	0.041	0.017	0.001	
6.0	42	0.40	0.571	0.812	0.645	0.549	0.770	0.083	0.041	0.002	
7.0	41	0.43	0.584	0.827	0.657	0.603	0.882	0.144	0.081	0.007	
8.0	41	0.43	0.595	0.800	0.684	0.596	0.967	0.218	0.122	0.017	0.001
9.0	41	0.43	0.606	0.774	0.706	0.589	0.995	0.304	0.160	0.036	0.003
10.0	41	0.43	0.618	0.749	0.724	0.580	0.991	0.393	0.195	0.071	0.006
12.0	40	0.46	0.637	0.742	0.741	0.598	0.967	0.532	0.290	0.203	0.020
14.0	40	0.46	0.663	0.696	0.766	0.578	0.918	0.658	0.342	0.424	0.053

Table XII. $\bar{R} = 6.7,$ $\tau = 0.84$

E	V_c	λ	T_0	T_1	T_2	T_3	T_4	T_5	T_6	T_7	T_8
0.1	44	0.34	0.220	0.081	0.001						
0.4	44	0.34	0.386	0.297	0.033	0.002					
0.7	44	0.34	0.469	0.408	0.115	0.008					
1.0	44	0.34	0.523	0.470	0.230	0.023	0.002				
1.5	43	0.37	0.544	0.607	0.383	0.076	0.012				
2.0	43	0.37	0.586	0.629	0.538	0.132	0.043	0.001			
2.5	43	0.37	0.617	0.638	0.651	0.188	0.111	0.003			
3.0	43	0.37	0.640	0.640	0.729	0.238	0.232	0.007	0.001		
4.0	42	0.40	0.650	0.694	0.769	0.351	0.528	0.025	0.005		
5.0	42	0.40	0.676	0.677	0.817	0.405	0.809	0.068	0.013	0.002	
6.0	42	0.40	0.696	0.659	0.840	0.443	0.918	0.144	0.028	0.005	
7.0	41	0.43	0.698	0.688	0.834	0.493	0.955	0.242	0.056	0.015	0.001
8.0	41	0.43	0.715	0.666	0.845	0.509	0.936	0.371	0.086	0.037	0.002
9.0	41	0.43	0.730	0.646	0.850	0.522	0.900	0.508	0.123	0.078	0.005
10.0	41	0.43	0.743	0.627	0.851	0.533	0.860	0.636	0.165	0.143	0.011
12.0	40	0.46	0.757	0.629	0.849	0.560	0.840	0.779	0.268	0.204	0.038
14.0	40	0.46	0.774	0.598	0.839	0.576	0.775	0.882	0.364	0.410	0.106

Table XIII. $\bar{R} = 7.0$, $\tau = 0.84$

E	V_c	λ	T_0	T_1	T_2	T_3	T_4	T_5	T_6	T_7	T_8
0.1	44	0.34	0.471	0.040	0.003						
0.4	44	0.34	0.708	0.169	0.084	0.001					
0.7	44	0.34	0.790	0.251	0.284	0.006	0.001				
1.0	44	0.34	0.831	0.308	0.528	0.018	0.006				
1.5	43	0.37	0.802	0.414	0.730	0.057	0.031				
2.0	43	0.37	0.827	0.451	0.890	0.109	0.099	0.001			
2.5	43	0.37	0.840	0.475	0.959	0.167	0.216	0.005			
3.0	43	0.37	0.846	0.491	0.982	0.226	0.347	0.012	0.001		
4.0	42	0.40	0.831	0.548	0.968	0.334	0.577	0.048	0.004		
5.0	42	0.40	0.837	0.552	0.953	0.413	0.655	0.133	0.012	0.004	
6.0	42	0.40	0.839	0.552	0.930	0.475	0.663	0.286	0.028	0.012	0.001
7.0	41	0.43	0.835	0.579	0.922	0.514	0.723	0.453	0.057	0.030	0.002
8.0	41	0.43	0.837	0.573	0.902	0.550	0.700	0.653	0.097	0.061	0.004
9.0	41	0.43	0.835	0.567	0.880	0.581	0.676	0.817	0.150	0.099	0.010
10.0	41	0.43	0.830	0.564	0.857	0.608	0.653	0.922	0.217	0.136	0.022
12.0	40	0.46	0.828	0.576	0.843	0.639	0.644	0.977	0.359	0.231	0.078
14.0	40	0.46	0.808	0.578	0.798	0.681	0.624	0.977	0.509	0.283	0.217

Table XIV. $\bar{R} = 7.3$, $\tau = 0.84$

E	V_c	λ	T_0	T_1	T_2	T_3	T_4	T_5	T_6	T_7	T_8
0.1	44	0.34	0.779	0.030	0.008						
0.4	44	0.34	0.972	0.139	0.197	0.001					
0.7	44	0.34	0.996	0.218	0.493	0.008					
1.0	44	0.34	0.992	0.276	0.691	0.023	0.001				
1.5	43	0.37	0.986	0.355	0.880	0.071	0.034	0.001			
2.0	43	0.37	0.969	0.401	0.921	0.144	0.081	0.003			
2.5	43	0.37	0.949	0.436	0.916	0.232	0.138	0.011	0.001		
3.0	43	0.37	0.930	0.463	0.897	0.322	0.194	0.027	0.001		
4.0	42	0.40	0.919	0.507	0.913	0.447	0.341	0.103	0.005	0.001	
5.0	42	0.40	0.892	0.531	0.870	0.559	0.401	0.290	0.017	0.005	
6.0	42	0.40	0.866	0.550	0.830	0.640	0.436	0.572	0.042	0.012	0.001
7.0	41	0.43	0.870	0.567	0.845	0.663	0.509	0.770	0.085	0.028	0.003
8.0	41	0.43	0.848	0.579	0.811	0.707	0.517	0.926	0.153	0.046	0.009
9.0	41	0.43	0.826	0.592	0.779	0.741	0.521	0.981	0.247	0.069	0.023
10.0	41	0.43	0.802	0.606	0.749	0.767	0.524	0.976	0.361	0.097	0.049
12.0	40	0.46	0.791	0.628	0.740	0.786	0.555	0.948	0.564	0.182	0.155
14.0	40	0.46	0.742	0.661	0.686	0.813	0.554	0.873	0.753	0.266	0.307

Table XV. $\bar{R} = 7.6$, $\tau = 0.84$

E	V_c	λ	T_0	T_1	T_2	T_3	T_4	T_5	T_6	T_7	T_8
0.1	44	0.34	0.483	0.038	0.007						
0.4	44	0.34	0.687	0.181	0.124	0.002					
0.7	44	0.34	0.740	0.288	0.267	0.014	0.001				
1.0	44	0.34	0.757	0.366	0.370	0.044	0.003				
1.5	43	0.37	0.851	0.426	0.567	0.128	0.017	0.002			
2.0	43	0.37	0.836	0.487	0.611	0.266	0.042	0.008			
2.5	43	0.37	0.819	0.533	0.628	0.423	0.076	0.026	0.001		
3.0	43	0.37	0.801	0.568	0.634	0.569	0.116	0.067	0.002		
4.0	42	0.40	0.827	0.594	0.701	0.703	0.225	0.235	0.009	0.001	
5.0	42	0.40	0.792	0.632	0.680	0.815	0.300	0.528	0.030	0.004	0.001
6.0	42	0.40	0.760	0.662	0.658	0.870	0.362	0.729	0.077	0.009	0.002
7.0	41	0.43	0.780	0.667	0.690	0.866	0.428	0.833	0.156	0.022	0.007
8.0	41	0.43	0.750	0.690	0.665	0.884	0.463	0.834	0.286	0.041	0.020
9.0	41	0.43	0.720	0.712	0.642	0.890	0.494	0.802	0.453	0.070	0.044
10.0	41	0.43	0.692	0.731	0.621	0.888	0.520	0.763	0.631	0.109	0.077
12.0	40	0.46	0.685	0.750	0.623	0.880	0.562	0.757	0.846	0.220	0.168
14.0	40	0.46	0.636	0.776	0.590	0.858	0.602	0.692	0.967	0.359	0.228

Table XVI. $\bar{R} = 7.9$, $\tau = 0.84$

E	V_c	λ	T_0	T_1	T_2	T_3	T_4	T_5	T_6	T_7	T_8
0.1	44	0.34	0.240	0.074	0.003						
0.4	44	0.34	0.395	0.343	0.055	0.005					
0.7	44	0.34	0.459	0.519	0.132	0.034	0.001				
1.0	44	0.34	0.494	0.627	0.201	0.109	0.002	0.001			
1.5	43	0.37	0.605	0.651	0.339	0.289	0.013	0.004			
2.0	43	0.37	0.614	0.717	0.395	0.557	0.034	0.019			
2.5	43	0.37	0.616	0.758	0.431	0.782	0.068	0.056	0.001		
3.0	43	0.37	0.613	0.786	0.456	0.916	0.113	0.119	0.003		
4.0	42	0.40	0.662	0.781	0.530	0.971	0.222	0.303	0.017	0.001	
5.0	42	0.40	0.642	0.807	0.538	0.986	0.329	0.431	0.060	0.004	0.001
6.0	42	0.40	0.622	0.822	0.540	0.963	0.425	0.482	0.162	0.012	0.004
7.0	41	0.43	0.649	0.817	0.572	0.952	0.484	0.577	0.315	0.029	0.012
8.0	41	0.43	0.626	0.827	0.566	0.925	0.545	0.573	0.546	0.058	0.024
9.0	41	0.43	0.607	0.833	0.561	0.895	0.597	0.564	0.771	0.105	0.039
10.0	41	0.43	0.590	0.833	0.559	0.864	0.642	0.555	0.921	0.173	0.057
12.0	40	0.46	0.593	0.833	0.574	0.844	0.684	0.586	0.977	0.347	0.122
14.0	40	0.46	0.575	0.816	0.582	0.786	0.741	0.564	0.962	0.565	0.187

Table XVII. $\bar{R} = 8.2,$ $\tau = 0.84$

E	V_c	λ	T_0	T_1	T_2	T_3	T_4	T_5	T_6	T_7	T_8
0.1	44	0.34	0.150	0.195	0.002						
0.4	44	0.34	0.267	0.713	0.037	0.014					
0.7	44	0.34	0.326	0.900	0.096	0.092	0.001				
1.0	44	0.34	0.364	0.966	0.157	0.261	0.003	0.001			
1.5	43	0.37	0.447	0.946	0.259	0.558	0.016	0.005			
2.0	43	0.37	0.482	0.961	0.323	0.791	0.046	0.018	0.001		
2.5	43	0.37	0.488	0.958	0.372	0.877	0.097	0.040	0.002		
3.0	43	0.37	0.499	0.948	0.410	0.891	0.171	0.069	0.007		
4.0	42	0.40	0.545	0.927	0.473	0.928	0.323	0.175	0.037	0.002	
5.0	42	0.40	0.547	0.908	0.506	0.878	0.489	0.248	0.136	0.007	0.001
6.0	42	0.40	0.547	0.886	0.533	0.829	0.624	0.306	0.355	0.020	0.003
7.0	41	0.43	0.569	0.886	0.554	0.847	0.670	0.394	0.586	0.048	0.009
8.0	41	0.43	0.566	0.867	0.571	0.806	0.741	0.424	0.801	0.102	0.018
9.0	41	0.43	0.566	0.845	0.588	0.768	0.791	0.448	0.885	0.190	0.032
10.0	41	0.43	0.570	0.820	0.607	0.732	0.825	0.470	0.880	0.318	0.053
12.0	40	0.46	0.588	0.806	0.634	0.722	0.843	0.521	0.865	0.588	0.127
14.0	40	0.46	0.613	0.753	0.675	0.663	0.862	0.548	0.777	0.846	0.235

Appendix II.   Legendre Polynomial Coefficients of the Shape Elastic Scattering Cross Section

The differential cross sections σ_{se} (θ) are expanded in a series of Legendre polynomials P_l $(\cos \theta)$ with coefficients B_l, *viz:*

$$\sigma_{se}(\theta) = \sum_{l=0}^{\infty} \frac{2l+1}{4\pi} B_l P_l (\cos \theta). \qquad (\Lambda.3)$$

Values for b_l up to $l = 4$ are given in the following tables for the same neutron energies and mean radii as the transmission coefficients in Appendix I.   The data are not sufficient to allow the generation of the complete differential cross sections by means of Eq. (A.3), except at low energies.   In that case, however, the experiments do not usually give σ_{se} (θ) so that a direct comparison is not appropriate.

The usefulness of the tables becomes apparent when experimental data are also expanded in the manner of Eq. (A.3) as is done by Langsdorf *et al.* (La57).   At high energies, a comparison of calculated *vs.* experimental expansion coefficients may lead to further insight into the behavior of optical models.   This approach has not as

Table XVIII. $\bar{R} = 4.00,$ $\tau = 0.84$

E	V_c	λ	B_0	B_1	B_2	B_3	B_4
0.1	44	0.34	2.151	0.019	0.010		
0.4	44	0.34	2.066	0.414	0.115	0.001	
0.7	44	0.34	2.113	0.792	0.237	0.007	
1.0	44	0.34	2.116	1.006	0.327	0.017	0.003
1.5	43	0.37	1.877	1.028	0.357	0.038	0.009
2.0	43	0.37	1.705	1.014	0.410	0.067	0.021
2.5	43	0.37	1.526	0.952	0.424	0.099	0.037
3.0	43	0.37	1.360	0.877	0.434	0.129	0.055
4.0	42	0.40	0.999	0.674	0.391	0.164	0.086
5.0	42	0.40	0.815	0.559	0.364	0.176	0.108
6.0	42	0.40	0.686	0.468	0.323	0.173	0.121
7.0	41	0.43	0.575	0.386	0.278	0.171	0.138
8.0	41	0.43	0.531	0.348	0.254	0.169	0.147
9.0	41	0.43	0.510	0.327	0.240	0.173	0.157
10.0	41	0.43	0.508	0.323	0.237	0.183	0.168
12.0	40	0.46	0.569	0.386	0.285	0.232	0.208
14.0	40	0.46	0.643	0.459	0.343	0.277	0.241

Table XIX. $\bar{R} = 4.3,$ $\tau = 0.84$

E	V_c	λ	B_0	B_1	B_2	B_3	B_4
0.1	44	0.34	1.743	0.292	0.025		
0.4	44	0.34	1.943	0.938	0.204	0.001	
0.7	44	0.34	2.137	1.203	0.354	0.001	
1.0	44	0.34	2.226	1.296	0.454	0.014	0.004
1.5	43	0.37	2.210	1.321	0.541	0.048	0.012
2.0	43	0.37	2.093	1.278	0.600	0.087	0.026
2.5	43	0.37	1.947	1.220	0.634	0.129	0.042
3.0	43	0.37	1.796	1.160	0.652	0.168	0.058
4.0	42	0.40	1.431	0.987	0.611	0.219	0.090
5.0	42	0.40	1.191	0.851	0.566	0.243	0.114
6.0	42	0.40	1.000	0.726	0.508	0.254	0.136
7.0	41	0.43	0.799	0.578	0.421	0.245	0.154
8.0	41	0.43	0.705	0.502	0.380	0.251	0.171
9.0	41	0.43	0.647	0.452	0.352	0.256	0.186
10.0	41	0.43	0.616	0.424	0.334	0.258	0.196
12.0	40	0.46	0.598	0.415	0.319	0.257	0.215
14.0	40	0.46	0.630	0.448	0.336	0.268	0.233

Table XX. $\bar{R} = 4.6$, $\tau = 0.84$

E	V_c	λ	B_0	B_1	B_2	B_3	B_4
0.1	44	0.34	1.227	0.249	0.015		
0.4	44	0.34	1.320	0.652	0.135	0.002	
0.7	44	0.34	1.499	0.822	0.260	0.005	0.001
1.0	44	0.34	1.647	0.904	0.368	−0.004	0.005
1.5	43	0.37	1.918	1.082	0.539	0.036	0.016
2.0	43	0.37	1.968	1.142	0.659	0.099	0.037
2.5	43	0.37	1.975	1.205	0.756	0.179	0.065
3.0	43	0.37	1.952	1.258	0.828	0.261	0.096
4.0	42	0.40	1.774	1.261	0.863	0.372	0.146
5.0	42	0.40	1.592	1.194	0.856	0.446	0.201
6.0	42	0.40	1.412	1.093	0.817	0.487	0.245
7.0	41	0.43	1.162	0.910	0.704	0.459	0.255
8.0	41	0.43	1.031	0.809	0.641	0.446	0.265
9.0	41	0.43	0.924	0.719	0.575	0.416	0.263
10.0	41	0.43	0.836	0.642	0.512	0.380	0.256
12.0	40	0.46	0.692	0.511	0.398	0.309	0.242
14.0	40	0.46	0.658	0.476	0.361	0.290	0.247

Table XXI. $\bar{R} = 4.9$, $\tau = 0.84$

E	V_c	λ	B_0	B_1	B_2	B_3	B_4
0.1	44	0.34	1.232	0.148	0.010		
0.4	44	0.34	0.971	0.333	0.102	0.004	
0.7	44	0.34	1.006	0.410	0.228	0.006	0.005
1.0	44	0.34	1.124	0.480	0.363	0.008	0.017
1.5	43	0.37	1.500	0.768	0.586	0.091	0.048
2.0	43	0.37	1.745	1.000	0.781	0.231	0.102
2.5	43	0.37	1.941	1.224	0.929	0.379	0.159
3.0	43	0.37	2.068	1.394	1.031	0.503	0.213
4.0	42	0.40	2.090	1.545	1.118	0.636	0.278
5.0	42	0.40	1.999	1.544	1.138	0.713	0.342
6.0	42	0.40	1.850	1.469	1.108	0.733	0.382
7.0	41	0.43	1.587	1.289	0.997	0.684	0.382
8.0	41	0.43	1.423	1.163	0.917	0.649	0.389
9.0	41	0.43	1.275	1.041	0.833	0.609	0.391
10.0	41	0.43	1.148	0.930	0.755	0.571	0.391
12.0	40	0.46	0.898	0.705	0.576	0.464	0.355
14.0	40	0.46	0.810	0.620	0.502	0.416	0.339

Table XXII. $\bar{R} = 5.2,$ $\tau = 0.84$

E	V_c	λ	B_0	B_1	B_2	B_3	B_4
0.1	44	0.34	3.994	0.196	0.013		
0.4	44	0.34	2.090	0.327	0.163	0.008	0.002
0.7	44	0.34	1.513	0.359	0.355	0.046	0.016
1.0	44	0.34	1.336	0.442	0.502	0.124	0.045
1.5	43	0.37	1.418	0.713	0.683	0.277	0.106
2.0	43	0.37	1.637	0.959	0.793	0.436	0.174
2.5	43	0.37	1.830	1.155	0.876	0.556	0.233
3.0	43	0.37	1.975	1.302	0.951	0.644	0.285
4.0	42	0.40	2.178	1.569	1.135	0.777	0.377
5.0	42	0.40	2.192	1.651	1.224	0.851	0.463
6.0	42	0.40	2.134	1.670	1.276	0.898	0.536
7.0	41	0.43	1.960	1.593	1.254	0.901	0.567
8.0	41	0.43	1.823	1.508	1.219	0.903	0.603
9.0	41	0.43	1.686	1.410	1.166	0.893	0.626
10.0	41	0.43	1.557	1.308	1.100	0.868	0.630
12.0	40	0.46	1.228	1.022	0.868	0.710	0.543
14.0	40	0.46	1.057	0.863	0.724	0.600	0.480

Table XXIII. $R = 5.5,$ $\tau = 0.84$

E	V_c	λ	B_0	B_1	B_2	B_3	B_4
0.1	44	0.34	5.556	0.225	0.017		
0.4	44	0.34	3.381	0.519	0.159	0.016	0.002
0.7	44	0.34	2.387	0.576	0.279	0.059	0.012
1.0	44	0.34	1.849	0.580	0.336	0.119	0.032
1.5	43	0.37	1.458	0.635	0.444	0.266	0.088
2.0	43	0.37	1.415	0.706	0.486	0.380	0.147
2.5	43	0.37	1.481	0.797	0.551	0.474	0.209
3.0	43	0.37	1.593	0.908	0.643	0.554	0.279
4.0	42	0.40	1.961	1.309	0.969	0.747	0.444
5.0	42	0.40	2.152	1.562	1.198	0.887	0.596
6.0	42	0.40	2.260	1.748	1.373	1.014	0.723
7.0	41	0.43	2.244	1.831	1.473	1.105	0.791
8.0	41	0.43	2.183	1.826	1.497	1.149	0.838
9.0	41	0.43	2.086	1.774	1.474	1.154	0.852
10.0	41	0.43	1.970	1.691	1.420	1.131	0.846
12.0	40	0.46	1.607	1.386	1.183	0.974	0.757
14.0	40	0.46	1.390	1.185	1.018	0.864	0.703

Table XXIV. $\bar{R} = 5.8,$ $\tau = 0.84$

E	V_c	λ	B_0	B_1	B_2	B_3	B_4
0.1	44	0.34	5.230	0.171	0.014		
0.4	44	0.34	3.732	0.709	0.134	0.008	0.001
0.7	44	0.34	2.864	0.922	0.238	0.035	0.008
1.0	44	0.34	2.280	0.934	0.291	0.077	0.024
1.5	43	0.37	1.609	0.749	0.322	0.197	0.074
2.0	43	0.37	1.356	0.660	0.355	0.306	0.148
2.5	43	0.37	1.300	0.650	0.432	0.406	0.243
3.0	43	0.37	1.376	0.732	0.550	0.494	0.352
4.0	42	0.40	1.768	1.146	0.887	0.702	0.560
5.0	42	0.40	2.071	1.489	1.148	0.872	0.717
6.0	42	0.40	2.275	1.739	1.346	1.024	0.825
7.0	41	0.43	2.401	1.947	1.544	1.190	0.918
8.0	41	0.43	2.416	2.011	1.624	1.271	0.973
9.0	41	0.43	2.383	2.021	1.663	1.323	1.016
10.0	41	0.43	2.317	1.993	1.671	1.354	1.051
12.0	40	0.46	2.022	1.771	1.534	1.291	1.035
14.0	40	0.46	1.807	1.583	1.389	1.199	0.989

Table XXV. $\bar{R} = 6.1,$ $\tau = 0.84$

E	V_c	λ	B_0	B_1	B_2	B_3	B_4
0.1	44	0.34	4.771	0.328	0.044		
0.4	44	0.34	4.228	1.608	0.365	0.017	0.003
0.7	44	0.34	3.808	2.003	0.592	0.066	0.018
1.0	44	0.34	3.339	1.957	0.707	0.143	0.053
1.5	43	0.37	2.327	1.409	0.645	0.266	0.136
2.0	43	0.37	1.896	1.160	0.682	0.371	0.249
2.5	43	0.37	1.667	1.017	0.691	0.420	0.343
3.0	43	0.37	1.573	0.961	0.686	0.442	0.410
4.0	42	0.40	1.659	1.073	0.781	0.578	0.553
5.0	42	0.40	1.857	1.267	0.921	0.714	0.646
6.0	42	0.40	2.066	1.489	1.110	0.876	0.744
7.0	41	0.43	2.339	1.829	1.426	1.129	0.909
8.0	41	0.43	2.457	1.995	1.603	1.281	1.021
9.0	41	0.43	2.527	2.113	1.743	1.411	1.127
10.0	41	0.43	2.551	2.181	1.835	1.506	1.212
12.0	40	0.46	2.401	2.119	1.842	1.555	1.269
14.0	40	0.46	2.214	1.970	1.734	1.493	1.245

Table XXVI. $\bar{R} = 6.4,$ $\tau = 0.84$

E	V_c	λ	B_0	B_1	B_2	B_3	B_4
0.1	44	0.34	4.364	1.164	0.013		
0.4	44	0.34	4.775	2.663	0.718	0.032	0.005
0.7	44	0.34	4.743	2.837	1.055	0.109	0.027
1.0	44	0.34	4.430	2.706	1.225	0.202	0.067
1.5	43	0.37	3.479	2.216	1.199	0.340	0.160
2.0	43	0.37	2.836	1.836	1.129	0.393	0.231
2.5	43	0.37	2.342	1.517	0.996	0.402	0.277
3.0	43	0.37	1.990	1.267	0.858	0.405	0.311
4.0	42	0.40	1.629	1.000	0.695	0.475	0.433
5.0	42	0.40	1.662	1.036	0.749	0.597	0.517
6.0	42	0.40	1.859	1.249	0.940	0.760	0.647
7.0	41	0.43	2.195	1.649	1.287	1.029	0.858
8.0	41	0.43	2.402	1.903	1.519	1.213	1.008
9.0	41	0.43	2.555	2.102	1.710	1.375	1.138
10.0	41	0.43	2.654	2.243	1.856	1.511	1.248
12.0	40	0.46	2.683	2.367	2.039	1.720	1.427
14.0	40	0.46	2.588	2.317	2.042	1.774	1.502

Table XXVII. $\bar{R} = 6.7,$ $\tau = 0.84$

E	V_c	λ	B_0	B_1	B_2	B_3	B_4
0.1	44	0.34	3.460	0.993	0.093		
0.4	44	0.34	3.890	2.083	0.616	0.013	0.004
0.7	44	0.34	4.185	2.345	1.032	0.074	0.021
1.0	44	0.34	4.226	2.429	1.323	0.184	0.057
1.5	43	0.37	3.958	2.470	1.536	0.401	0.142
2.0	43	0.37	3.446	2.274	1.536	0.537	0.223
2.5	43	0.37	2.954	2.018	1.428	0.620	0.294
3.0	43	0.37	2.536	1.750	1.287	0.678	0.360
4.0	42	0.40	1.889	1.245	0.958	0.674	0.449
5.0	42	0.40	1.774	1.166	0.909	0.709	0.537
6.0	42	0.40	1.842	1.254	0.951	0.741	0.619
7.0	41	0.43	2.070	1.522	1.157	0.907	0.783
8.0	41	0.43	2.257	1.737	1.336	1.057	0.909
9.0	41	0.43	2.433	1.945	1.531	1.230	1.044
10.0	41	0.43	2.588	2.136	1.726	1.410	1.185
12.0	40	0.46	2.833	2.480	2.121	1.799	1.511
14.0	40	0.46	2.864	2.562	2.251	1.951	1.659

Table XXVIII. $\bar{R} = 7.0,$ $\tau = 0.84$

E	V_c	λ	B_0	B_1	B_2	B_3	B_4
0.1	44	0.34	2.594	0.624	0.065		
0.4	44	0.34	2.701	1.263	0.532	0.001	0.006
0.7	44	0.34	3.151	1.588	1.043	0.099	0.046
1.0	44	0.34	3.568	1.985	1.486	0.335	0.127
1.5	43	0.37	4.009	2.612	1.892	0.702	0.250
2.0	43	0.37	3.932	2.797	2.051	1.012	0.408
2.5	43	0.37	3.678	2.743	2.056	1.198	0.543
3.0	43	0.37	3.356	2.557	1.968	1.271	0.633
4.0	42	0.40	2.507	1.886	1.491	1.063	0.629
5.0	42	0.40	2.119	1.538	1.188	0.883	0.614
6.0	42	0.40	1.920	1.338	0.994	0.770	0.614
7.0	41	0.43	1.945	1.380	1.014	0.808	0.695
8.0	41	0.43	2.076	1.522	1.139	0.921	0.794
9.0	41	0.43	2.261	1.733	1.337	1.084	0.924
10.0	41	0.43	2.457	1.963	1.558	1.267	1.072
12.0	40	0.46	2.861	2.468	2.081	1.742	1.471
14.0	40	0.46	3.017	2.682	2.330	1.999	1.709

Table XXIX. $\bar{R} = 7.3,$ $\tau = 0.84$

E	V_c	λ	B_0	B_1	B_2	B_3	B_4
0.1	44	0.34	4.862	0.553	0.080	0.001	
0.4	44	0.34	2.907	0.861	0.736	0.091	0.026
0.7	44	0.34	2.937	1.326	1.288	0.416	0.133
1.0	44	0.34	3.381	1.919	1.616	0.806	0.282
1.5	43	0.37	4.137	2.810	2.093	1.241	0.481
2.0	43	0.37	4.381	3.158	2.305	1.525	0.669
2.5	43	0.37	4.331	3.226	2.393	1.647	0.806
3.0	43	0.37	4.110	3.127	2.376	1.662	0.891
4.0	42	0.40	3.251	2.524	1.985	1.428	0.877
5.0	42	0.40	2.656	1.005	1.602	1.221	0.858
6.0	42	0.40	2.277	1.647	1.323	1.080	0.836
7.0	41	0.43	2.058	1.461	1.135	0.941	0.778
8.0	41	0.43	2.098	1.520	1.170	0.953	0.808
9.0	41	0.43	2.208	1.656	1.272	1.015	0.871
10.0	41	0.43	2.349	1.826	1.415	1.125	0.967
12.0	40	0.46	2.781	2.353	1.938	1.601	1.365
14.0	40	0.46	3.040	2.671	2.287	1.955	1.677

Table XXX.　$\bar{R} = 7.6$,　　$\tau = 0.84$

E	V_c	λ	B_0	B_1	B_2	B_3	B_4
0.1	44	0.34	8.206	0.758	0.099	0.004	
0.4	44	0.34	4.498	1.170	0.644	0.154	0.027
0.7	44	0.34	3.422	1.302	0.889	0.446	0.115
1.0	44	0.34	3.198	1.508	1.020	0.740	0.240
1.5	43	0.37	3.718	2.244	1.562	1.234	0.508
2.0	43	0.37	4.053	2.647	1.900	1.486	0.742
2.5	43	0.37	4.230	2.938	2.204	1.652	0.954
3.0	43	0.37	4.256	3.110	2.423	1.771	1.131
4.0	42	0.40	3.842	3.006	2.455	1.832	1.273
5.0	42	0.40	3.334	2.639	2.237	1.783	1.327
6.0	42	0.40	2.903	2.277	1.934	1.597	1.236
7.0	41	0.43	2.426	1.843	1.505	1.244	1.010
8.0	41	0.43	2.269	1.700	1.333	1.087	0.922
9.0	41	0.43	2.219	1.659	1.265	1.025	0.892
10.0	41	0.43	2.262	1.718	1.304	1.056	0.922
12.0	40	0.46	2.643	2.182	1.753	1.443	1.230
14.0	40	0.46	2.968	2.564	2.151	1.808	1.540

Table XXXI.　$\bar{R} = 7.9$,　　$\tau = 0.84$

E	V_c	λ	B_0	B_1	B_2	B_3	B_4
0.1	44	0.34	8.442	0.755	0.071	0.003	
0.4	44	0.34	5.188	1.536	0.443	0.098	0.016
0.7	44	0.34	3.688	1.485	0.580	0.299	0.081
1.0	44	0.34	2.998	1.355	0.635	0.532	0.198
1.5	43	0.37	3.043	1.595	1.039	0.987	0.498
2.0	43	0.37	3.391	2.024	1.505	1.272	0.841
2.5	43	0.37	3.827	2.574	2.014	1.552	1.173
3.0	43	0.37	4.174	3.056	2.439	1.834	1.443
4.0	42	0.40	4.328	3.482	2.879	2.229	1.699
5.0	42	0.40	4.033	3.333	2.802	2.248	1.721
6.0	42	0.40	3.580	2.948	2.483	2.044	1.601
7.0	41	0.43	2.921	2.336	1.937	1.629	1.331
8.0	41	0.43	2.618	2.031	1.650	1.414	1.202
9.0	41	0.43	2.456	1.872	1.489	1.277	1.109
10.0	41	0.43	2.409	1.837	1.438	1.207	1.050
12.0	40	0.46	2.577	2.082	1.646	1.336	1.142
14.0	40	0.46	2.860	2.421	1.985	1.640	1.402

Table XXXII. $\bar{R} = 8.2$, $\tau = 0.84$

E	V_c	λ	B_0	B_1	B_2	B_3	B_4
0.1	44	0.34	8.123	1.106	0.122	0.002	
0.4	44	0.34	6.107	2.855	0.714	0.102	0.023
0.7	44	0.34	4.718	2.667	0.956	0.330	0.132
1.0	44	0.34	3.771	2.196	1.069	0.577	0.336
1.5	43	0.37	2.955	1.675	1.140	0.883	0.688
2.0	43	0.37	3.186	1.986	1.483	1.110	1.028
2.5	43	0.37	3.606	2.445	1.826	1.372	1.270
3.0	43	0.37	3.998	2.872	2.159	1.659	1.453
4.0	42	0.40	4.561	3.625	2.890	2.283	1.811
5.0	42	0.40	4.499	3.692	3.055	2.475	1.946
6.0	42	0.40	4.195	3.478	2.970	2.493	2.011
7.0	41	0.43	3.582	2.946	2.539	2.205	1.832
8.0	41	0.43	3.234	2.620	2.250	1.980	1.685
9.0	41	0.43	2.956	2.358	1.982	1.724	1.493
10.0	41	0.43	2.745	2.163	1.762	1.500	1.320
12.0	40	0.46	2.581	2.060	1.618	1.322	1.157
14.0	40	0.46	2.761	2.290	1.838	1.509	1.294

yet been pursued to any appreciable extent. At lower energies, the expansion coefficients can be used to advantage in the determination of compound elastic scattering as described by Emmerich and Sinclair (Em56a).

References

(Am35) Amaldi, D'Agustino, Fermi, Pontecorvo, Rasetti, and Segrè, *Proc. Roy. Soc.* (*London*) **149A**, 522 (1935).

(Am57) H. J. Amster and L. M. Culpepper, "Surface Modified Nuclear Optical Model: Description of the SUMNUM Code for the NORC Computer," *Westinghouse Atomic Power Division Report* WAPD-TM-87 (Bettis Plant of the A.E.C., Pittsburgh, Pennsylvania) (1957).

(Am58) H. Amster, *J. Appl. Phys.* **29**, 623 (1958).

(Am59) H. J. Amster, *Phys. Rev.* **113**, 911 (1959).

(Ba52) H. H. Barschall, *Phys. Rev.* **86**, 431 (1952).

(Be35) H. A. Bethe, *Phys. Rev.* **47**, 747 (1935).

(Be40) H. A. Bethe, *Phys. Rev.* **57**, 1125 (1940).

(Be56) J. R. Beyster, "Predictions of Fast Neutron Scattering Data With a Diffuse Potential Well," *Los Alamos Sci. Lab. Report* LA-2099 (1956).

(Be56a) Beyster, Walt, and Salmi, *Phys. Rev.* **104**, 1319 (1956).

(Be57)   H. A. Bethe, Conference on Nuclear Structure, University of Pittsburgh, unpublished (1957).

(Bi52)   L. C. Biedenharn, "Tables of Racah Coefficients," *Oak Ridge Natl. Lab. Report* ORNL-1098 (1952).

(Bj56)   Bjorklund, Fernbach, and Sherman, *Phys. Rev.* **101**, 1832 (1956).

(Bj58)   F. Bjorklund and S. Fernbach, *Phys. Rev.* **109**, 1295 (1958).

(Bl52)   Blatt and Weisskopf, *Theoretical Nuclear Physics*, Wiley, New York, 1952, Chapter 8.

(Bo36)   N. Bohr, *Nature (London)* **137**, 344 (1936).

(Br56)   K. A. Brueckner, *Phys. Rev.* **103**, 1121 (1956).

(Ch58)   Chase, Wilets, and Edmunds, *Phys. Rev.* **110**, 1080 (1958).

(Cl55)   E. Clementel and C. Villi, *Nuovo Cim.* **2**, 176 (1955).

(Co49)   Cook, McMillan, Peterson, and Sewell, *Phys. Rev.* **75**, 7 (1949).

(Cu56)   Culler, Fernbach, and Sherman, *Phys. Rev.* **101**, 1047 (1956).

(Dr56)   L. Dresner, *Nuclear Sci. and Eng.* **1**, 103 (1956).

(Dr57)   L. Dresner, *Proc. Intern. Conf. Neutron Interaction (Columbia Univ.)* (1957), p. 71.

(Ec30)   C. Eckart, *Phys. Rev.* **35**, 1303 (1930).

(Em55)   W. S. Emmerich, *Phys. Rev.* **98**, 1148 (1955).

(Em56)   W. S. Emmerich and H. J. Amster, *Physica* **22**, 1163 (1956).

(Em56a)   W. S. Emmerich and R. M. Sinclair, *Phys. Rev.* **104**, 1399 (1956).

(Em57)   W. S. Emmerich, *Westinghouse Research Report* 6-94511-6-R17 (1957).

(Fe49)   Fernbach, Serber, and Taylor, *Phys. Rev.* **75**, 1352 (1949).

(Fe53)   Feshbach, Porter, and Weisskopf, *Phys. Rev.* **90**, 166 (1953).

(Fe54)   Feshbach, Porter, and Weisskopf, *Phys. Rev.* **96**, 448 (1954).

(Fe58)   H. Feshbach, *Ann. Revs. Nuclear Sci.*, (1958).

(Fo50)   K. W. Ford and D. Bohm, *Phys. Rev.* **79**, 745 (1950).

(Fr55)   F. L. Friedman and V. F. Weisskopf, in W. Pauli, ed., *Niels Bohr and the Development of Physics*, McGraw-Hill, New York, 1955, p. 134.

(Gr56)   A. E. S. Green, *Phys. Rev.* **104**, 1617 (1956).

(Gr56a)   Green, Lee, and Berkley, *Phys. Rev.* **104**, 1625 (1956).

(Gr57)   Greebler, Hurwitz, and Storm, *Nuclear Sci. and Eng.* **2**, 334 (1957).

(Ha52)   W. Hauser and H. Feshbach, *Phys. Rev.* **87**, 366 (1952).

(Ja55)   Z. Jankovic, *Phil. Mag.* **46**, 376 (1955).

(La55)   A. M. Lane and C. F. Wandel, *Phys. Rev.* **98**, 1524 (1955).

(La57)   Langsdorf, Lane, and Monahan, *Phys. Rev.* **107**, 1077 (1957).

(La58)   A. M. Lane and R. G. Thomas, *Revs. Modern Phys.* **30**, 257 (1958).

(Ma57)   B. Margolis and E. S. Troubetskoy, *Phys. Rev.* **106**, 105 (1957).

(Mc56)   H. McManus, *Bull. Am. Phys. Soc.* **1**, 56 (1956).

(Mo55)   Morrison, Muirhead, and Murdoch, *Phil. Mag.* **46**, 795 (1955).

(Mo57)   S. A. Moszkowski, in *Handbuch der Physik*, S. Flügge, Ed., Springer-Verlag, Berlin, 1957, Vol. 39, p. 459.

(Ne56)   P. E. Nemirovski, *Proc. Intern. Conf. Peaceful Uses Atomic Energy*, Vol. II, Geneva, 1955.

(Os36)   Ostrofsky, Breit, and Johnson, *Phys. Rev.* **49**, 22 (1936).

(Pe57)   D. C. Peaslee, *Nucl. Phys.* **3**, 255 (1957).

(Ri56)   W. B. Riesenfeld and K. M. Watson, *Phys. Rev.* **102,** 4 (1956).
(Ro56)   Ross, Mark, and Lawson, *Phys. Rev.* **102,** 1613 (1956).
(Sa56)   G. R. Satchler, *Phys. Rev.* **104,** 1198 (1956).
(Sc49)   L. I. Schiff, *Quantum Mechanics*, McGraw-Hill, New York, 1949, p. 103.
(Sc59)   H. M. Schey, *Phys. Rev.* **113,** 900 (1959).
(We56)   V. F. Weisskopf, *Physica* **22,** 952 (1956).
(Wo54)   R. D. Woods and D. S. Saxon, *Phys. Rev.* **95,** 577 (1954).
(Zw54)   P. F. Zweifel and H. Hurwitz, Jr., *J. Appl. Phys.* **25,** 1241 (1954).

Direct Reaction Theories

N. AUSTERN[1]

University of Pittsburgh, Pittsburgh, Pennsylvania

1. Introduction

A. *Nature and History of the Phenomenon*

Recent discussions of nuclear reactions place a great deal of emphasis upon *direct reaction processes*. These may be defined, in a rather general fashion, as those reaction processes whose calculation only requires the consideration of a small number of all the degrees of freedom of the nuclear system, ordinarily only of those degrees of freedom which already are required simply to describe the incident and outgoing wave functions in the channel region of configuration space. The importance of such processes is based upon the physical fact, as yet not completely assessed, that under some circumstances the various degrees of freedom of a nucleus are only loosely coupled to each other. Then two channels can be equally or more strongly coupled by the *direct* matrix element of some simple interaction operator than by the complicated excitation of many intermediate degrees of freedom, the competing *compound nucleus process*. Current research still is being devoted to determining which degrees of freedom are important under which conditions, and to determining what sorts of approximations can be feasible for calculation. As this research is at a very preliminary stage the present report must be largely qualitative.

[1] This article was written at the University of Sydney, Sydney, Australia, during the tenure of a Fulbright research grant (1957–1958). It was very much assisted by the hospitality and cooperation of Prof. H. Messel and the staff of the School of Physics. A later revision of the article gives a partial coverage of research published in 1958. The article then was modified again in proof.

A separation of the wave function into a part involving many degrees of freedom and a part involving only a few degrees of freedom is equivalent to a heuristic picture Weisskopf and his collaborators have stressed (Bl52b, Fr55, Be56e). If a collision is initiated by way of a wave packet with a very brief duration in time, the motions which involve the fewest degrees of freedom lead to the earliest emission of particles into the outgoing channel. It is in this sense that they are *direct*.

Most attention currently is being devoted just to three, especially simple direct processes, each of which is a three-body rearrangement collision. (a) A bombarding particle (which need not be a nucleon) may interact with a particle in a target nucleus, both particles making transitions to new states of motion. This is inelastic scattering, or *knock-on scattering*. (b) A bombarding particle may collide with the surface of a nucleus, thereby inducing a *collective oscillation*, again a case of inelastic scattering. (c) A particle bound in one of a pair of colliding nuclei may make a transition to a bound state about the other nucleus. This is *stripping*. Antisymmetrization of the wave function tends to connect all these processes (Fr57b). More complicated direct processes than these will be ignored in the present report. (It is interesting to note, however, that the interaction of photons with nuclei, even at rather low energies, frequently is a direct process (Co55, Mo56a, Ch57a, Sa57a, La58). The theories of the giant dipole resonance, in particular, all picture the photon *absorption* as being by a direct process.)

As a matter of history (Be37, Wi56, Wi55, Be56e, Ch57a), direct reaction models first were employed at a very early stage of nuclear theory, before the compound nucleus model. Their deficiencies led Bohr to propose the compound nucleus model (Bo36), and until a few years ago it was believed that this would give an excellent description of the results of most nuclear reaction experiments. Thus in the low energy region where sharp resonances appear, this theory indicated how the simultaneous excitation of many degrees of freedom could cause the resonances to be sharp, and how large radiative transition probabilities could occur. In the higher energy region, where individual levels cannot be resolved, the semi-classical ideas of Bohr were exploited in a statistical fashion (We37, We40, Wo51, Ha52). Within the possibilities allowed by the good quantum numbers of the reacting system it could be proved from this statistical theory that the manner of decay of the compound nucleus would be independent of the manner of formation, and would depend only on the energy and upon the statistical weights and barrier penetration probabilities for the different decay alternatives. The angular distributions predicted by the statistical model would be symmetric about 90°, the interferences between levels of opposite parity averaging out, and frequently the distribution even would be isotropic. The spectrum of energies of particles of a given type would be Maxwellian, after correction for the energy variation of the barrier penetrability, a consequence of the rapid increase with energy of the level density of the product nucleus. All these predictions of the statistical model have been found to be violated in an important way in one experiment or another, and have led to a partial return of the direct reaction models.

Along with the statistical model there also was developed a rigorous approach to nuclear reaction theory, of a form adapted to the inclusion of the Bohr hypotheses, the so-called *eigenstate decomposition* (Ka38, Wi47, Ka58a) method. Here the short range of the nuclear force was exploited, the rather localized region in which the strong interactions appear being studied in terms of a complete set of states defined within a box of radius R, enclosing this region. Insofar as the simple dynamical models could be expressed in the formalism of the eigenstate decomposition their consequences could be derived in a reliable fashion. Only for circumstances giving widely separated states of the inner region, however, corresponding to well-separated sharp resonances, has the accurate method, until recently, been able to substantiate any of the simple models. And even in the case of sharp resonances, the resonance peaks are known to sit upon a smoothly varying background, which has not always been clearly understood. Sometimes (Ja51, Ja53, Fo58a) this background can be identified with the wings of other, nearby broad resonances. Most often, however, it is classed as *potential scattering* and treated on an *ad hoc* basis.

In nearly all cases authors now are explaining the difficulties of the compound nucleus model as consequences of competition from direct reaction processes. The importance of the direct processes has become increasingly clearly recognized, to the extent that the author of a recent review of heavy-particle reactions (Pe55) could wonder whether there were *any* conditions under which the statistical model would be strictly valid.

Weisskopf has suggested (We57, Fr55, Be56e) that it may be useful to consider *every* nuclear reaction as being initiated through a direct reaction sort of motion.   In place of the two-stage Bohr mechanism: (a) formation of the compound nucleus, followed by (b) decay of the compound nucleus, he suggests that all reactions should be thought to proceed in three stages: (a) independent particle motion, (b) *gradual* transition to a compound nucleus, and (c) decay of the compound nucleus.   The three-stage view of reactions actually is the basis of most direct reaction theories.   It is precisely in accord with the shell model picture of the bound states.

The shell model and the direct reaction models have had similar histories, both having been employed many years ago, then partially abandoned (for related reasons), then both restored again as serious theoretical models.   Both models are consequences of the underlying property that to good approximation nucleons within a nucleus often move as independent particles, with long mean free paths against incoherent collisions.   In first approximation the mean free paths are infinite, particles move entirely independently, and the shell model (and optical model) ensues.   In second approximation the particles make occasional collisions, and the direct reactions (and shell model level splittings) ensue.   Shell model evidence for believing in independent particle motion also is evidence for expecting the importance of direct processes.

Figure 1 shows some current estimates of the mean free path Λ, for the motion of a nucleon within nuclear matter.   Evidently Λ has a broad minimum, in the range of about 20–80 Mev, and with even its minimum value a significant fraction of the radius of a typical nucleus. An incident nucleon can travel for a long distance before it begins to be scattered out of the entrance channel.

There is a widespread belief that most of the wave function which describes a given collision must be of compound nucleus form (see Chapter V.N and Bu57a), with the direct reaction part only a small perturbation.   This belief may have to be revised.   It is based upon data such as that of Rosen and Stewart (Ro57) and Ahn and Roberts (Ah57), which seem to show that more than 80 per cent of the spectrum of inelastically scattered neutrons in various (n, n') reactions is produced through compound nucleus processes. Unfortunately theory and experiment as yet make contact only from time to time. The definition of direct reactions is rather remote from experiment,

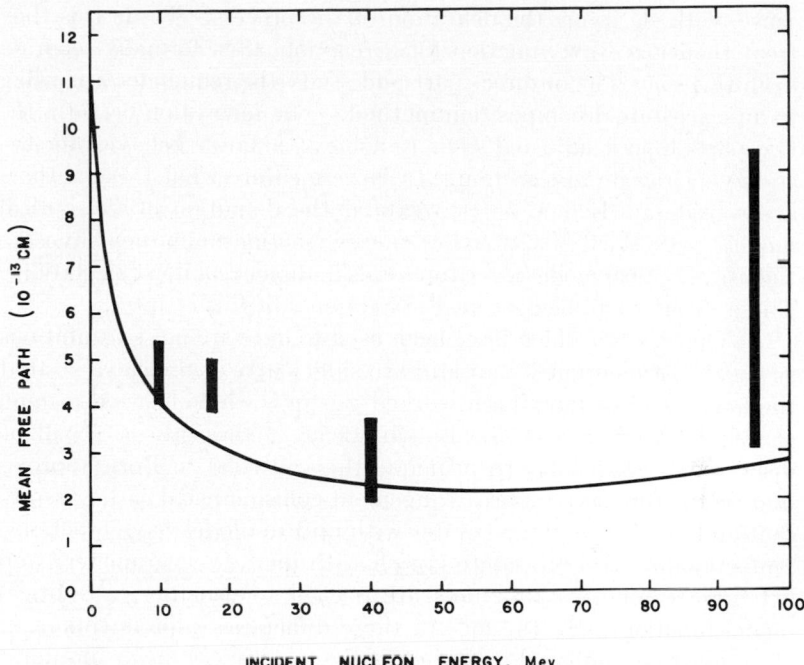

INCIDENT NUCLEON ENERGY, Mev

Figure 1. Mean free path of nucleons in nuclear matter. The curve is computed from the optical model parameters of La57 and We57, according to the method described by Lane (La57). The "experimental" points are computed in the same fashion from the optical parameters of Gl58. A standard radius $R = 1.3A^{1/3}$ is used throughout. A standard radius $R = 1.1A^{1/3}$ (advocated by Peaslee, private communication) would drop the minimum value of Λ by a factor of about $(1.3/1.1)^2$.

and the above experiments have had to be interpreted on the basis of fairly superficial criteria, which are consistent with the definition, but are not necessarily consequences of it. These criteria will be discussed in Section 1.B of this chapter. *They tend to underestimate the direct processes.* Certain authors already have suggested (Co57d, Sh57) that direct processes are important in a far larger portion of cases than those in which they have been identified.

Quite sophisticated theories of the direct processes have been proposed very recently by a number of authors (Na56, Ui56, Br57c, Bl57b, Sa58b, Fe58, Br59b). These theories are all concerned, in a sense, with clarifying the definition of the process. To do this they treat the *entire* wave function for a reaction, then formally separate from this some sort of direct part and study the remainder according to an eigenstate decomposition method. The separation between the two parts then is adjusted so as to achieve a simple behavior for the energy-averaged cross section. In large measure what these authors are considering is how best to extend the definition of the optical model (Fe49, Wa53, Ri56) to low energy reactions, and they advocate the use of optical model wave functions in direct reaction calculations. These theories will be discussed in Section 4 of this chapter.

The theories which have been used to date are not so ambitious as those just mentioned, but still are sufficiently complicated so that they very seldom have been worked out in a whole hearted fashion (La56, Ka56, Ka57a, Le57, Ba57b, Le58). These theories will be discussed in Section 3. In principle they all treat in Born approximation the three types of rearrangement collision listed earlier, representing the initial and final states with optical model wave functions. Unfortunately this procedure is rich with unknown parameters, and extensive computing programs are needed to generate the optical model functions. In the face of these difficulties experiments most often must be compared with the predictions of very much simplified theories, and it is no surprise that the status of many reactions for which direct models seem relevant should have to remain vague. It almost is a surprise that certain experiments give excellent fits to the crude theories. It is to be hoped that the more sophisticated theories eventually will be able to prescribe the values of the optical model parameters to be used in the simple models, as in the attempt by Fowler (Fo58b), so encouraging the more accurate evaluation of the consequences of those models.

B. *Identification of Direct Processes*

The identification of some observed reaction as proceeding by way of a direct mechanism is achieved in quite different ways according as sharp levels of the product nucleus can or cannot be resolved.

(1) **Sharp Levels Not Resolved.** The evidence for direct reactions here concerns the relative yields of particles of different types and energies, and the rather consistent tendency of the angular distribution to peak in the forward direction. One of the earliest

surveys of this class of data was presented by Eisberg (Ei54), and provided an eloquent plea for the direct mechanism.   Very thorough discussions are given by F. L. Ribe (Chapter V.N in the present book)
and H. A. Bethe *et al.* (Be56e).   Only a few aspects of interpretation
will be sketched here.

   The evidence from energy spectra gave the first indications of
the importance of direct processes for intermediate energy reactions
involving single nucleons.   In a typical experiment the energy distribution of inelastically scattered neutrons is observed, and the
spectrum is found to contain many more high energy neutrons than
would be consistent with the Maxwellian spectrum predicted by the
statistical theory.   In other words, the final nucleus is left in its low
excited states rather more often than one would suppose from the
fact that its density of states increases very rapidly with excitation
energy.   Apparently statistical equilibrium is not reached in the
collision process.   A direct reaction model explains these facts very
easily.   It merely notes that most of the rapidly increasing density of
states represents the appearance of patterns of motion within the
nucleus which involve many degrees of freedom.   If processes involving only a few degrees of freedom are favored, then, only occasional ones of the states envisaged by the statistical model will be
formed, and the spectrum will be very much altered.   The direct
processes will appear in it as a part which is comparatively *uniformly*
distributed in energy   Indeed, as the modes of motion of any given
type tend to be concentrated within small regions of energy, those
levels which are produced by a direct process sometimes may be
concentrated among the low-lying final states.

   The evidence regarding types of decay particles also is strikingly in favor of a role for direct processes, and by arguments which
also follow directly from the definition.   Briefly, if statistical equilibrium is reached the greatest rates of decay of a compound nucleus
should be into those channels in which the barriers are least and the
densities of states are greatest.   Competition between different
modes of decay almost suppresses those which are unfavored.   By
contrast, competition plays no role in the direct processes so the
importance of the barrier is much less.   It is easy to understand how
the emission of charged particles from a heavy nucleus might be 10^4
times more probable (Pa53, also see Chapter V.N) than the statistical
theory predicts, the excitation of the nucleus not being drained away

by neutron emission. It also is easy to see that re-emission of the incident particle is likely in a direct reaction, in agreement with the observations that $(p, 2n)$ reactions do not compete strongly with (p, pn) modes, and often are weaker (Co54, Co57g).

At the time when the high probabilities for charged particle emission first were coming to be appreciated, there was some thought that they might result from a very great effective lowering of the Coulomb barrier, through the presence of surface oscillations. Careful measurements of yield curves near threshold (Co54, and private communication) established agreement with barriers of approximately normal size (La60, Ne60).

The evidence from angular distributions is obtained in the same experiments which yield the information about energy spectra and particle types. It is observed (see Chapter V.N) that the angular distributions of product particles, particularly those of higher energy, frequently are peaked in the forward direction. (The resolution of sharp levels is not envisaged in the present discussion.) Now compound nucleus processes tend to give angular distributions which are symmetrical about 90°, the compound nucleus cross sections being precisely symmetrical about 90° both in the limit of isolated sharp resonances and in the limit of the statistical theory. Fore-aft asymmetry can appear between these two limits, where only a few levels of opposite parity may be interfering, but distributions should peak backwards as often as forwards. A consistent tendency to peak forwards cannot be ascribed merely to fluctuations about the statistical average; instead such a tendency must be interpreted as evidence for some fundamental physical mechanism which correlates the amplitudes and phases of neighboring compound nucleus levels, and which the compound nucleus formalism was not designed to discuss.

Unfortunately, although the forward peaking tendency undoubtedly indicates the importance of direct processes, *whenever it is observed*, it is not reliable as a quantitative measure of the amount of direct process. Direct processes must be more frequent than this criterion can indicate, more frequent than the 10–15 per cent of neutron inelastic scattering events which Rosen and Stewart (Ro57) and Ahn and Roberts (Ah57) assign to them, and perhaps more frequent even than the 30 per cent which March and Morton (Ma58a) assign in Ni^{60} (n, p). The difficulty with the angular distribution as a criterion is that it is not based directly on the definition of direct process. It requires as an intervening step the application of semi-classical ideas, and in a fashion which is not suitable at medium energies for reactions in the nuclear interior. (It would seem best to base quantitative measures of the amount of direct interaction upon the yield curve anomalies, which are closely related to the definition. This would become possible if the parameters of the statistical theory could be sufficiently well known so that "normal" yield curves could be predicted with some accuracy.)

Given high enough bombarding energies the semi-classical argument for forward peaking is simple enough. All the direct reaction models picture the collision of two nuclei, A and B, as the collision of A, say, with a sub-unit b_1 of B; the other sub-unit b_2 of B only being a spectator to the interaction. Any one of the three particles A, b_1, or b_2 may emerge, the other two remaining bound together. Thus the possible reactions are

$$A + B \rightarrow A + (b_1 + b_2) \rightarrow (A + b_1) + b_2$$
$$\rightarrow A + (b_1 + b_2)^*$$
$$\rightarrow (A + b_2) + b_1$$

In these reactions the spectator b_2 evidently retains its original momentum. For this reason b_2 emerges preferentially in the original direction of B in the first of the reactions, and A and b_1 emerge preferentially in the original direction of A in the latter two reactions. It is easy for the initial momenta to carry through the reaction in the latter cases because the actual collision between A and b_1 generally is isotropic. These ideas normally predict "forward scattering," it being understood that the "forward" direction is the direction of the lighter incident particle and that the "scattered" particle is the lighter one of the reaction products. Backward emission does occur if A is the lighter incident particle, however, and also if the spectator b_2 is the lighter emerging particle. This case gives the so-called *heavy particle stripping*, introduced by Owen and Madansky (Ma55, Ow57).

These semi-classical ideas also predict the breadth of the forward peak. So long as the fundamental interaction between the two interacting particles varies slowly in energy and angle, as for nucleons, the form factor of the forward peak will be given by the momentum distribution of the sub-unit within B. If the fundamental interaction itself varies rapidly, as for the nucleon-alpha elastic angular distribution, the forward peak will be determined by the product of this distribution times the momentum distribution.

Toward lower energy such semi-classical ideas become less reliable. Particles no longer follow straight line paths, and the initial and final state wave functions must be expected to be distorted appreciably by the optical potential, and by the Coulomb potential; reflection becomes important (see Section 2). Several of the partial waves which enter the calculation may be affected by optical potential resonances. All these effects, as has been observed explicitly for discrete final states, tend to make the direct angular distribution more isotropic.

Indeed, observations of transitions to sharp levels show clearly that it is fallacious to use forward peaking as a sole criterion for identifying direct processes. Transitions whose direct reaction nature cannot be doubted frequently show peaks in the backward hemisphere, of a height comparable to or greater than the ones in the forward hemisphere (Bo56, Ge56, Jo56, Ma56b, Il57, Di58, Ri58a, Co59b, No59, Kl60, On60). More data at back angles for such transitions to sharp levels could be very useful for showing the relative importance of the front and back hemispheres. A systematic study of particles emitted backwards also may give information about optical model wave functions, about exchange effects, and about cluster structures in the nuclear surface.

Morinaga and Peaslee (Mo57) have attempted a more general demonstration that forward peaking is to be expected, over an energy-averaged region, by using the quantum mechanical principle of closure. Unfortunately their calculation is defective.

(2) **Sharp Levels Resolved.** In this case the identification of a reaction process as direct must employ entirely different methods from those used if sharp levels are not resolved. For one thing, of course, yield curve arguments are not relevant. The angular distributions still do tend to peak forwards, and for the same reasons, but in a much more complicated way. Angular momentum selection rules may force the cross section to vanish near zero degrees.[2] Fortu-

_____

[2] A particularly interesting illustration of a direct reaction angular distribution which does not peak near $0°$ is given by the reaction $Ne^{20}(p, p')$, proceeding to the 1.58-Mev level of Ne^{20}. At 9.5 Mev (lab) the cross section for this reaction almost appears to be fore-aft symmetric, having a single large peak at slightly over $80°$. In fact, one of the simpler direct reaction theories gives an excellent fit to this angular distribution. (Although, c.f. Yo56).

nately, although the identification methods of Section 1.B(1) cannot be used, they are considerably less powerful than those new ones which become available. By the observation of characteristic angular distributions, angular correlations, and polarizations, it not only is possible to identify the reaction process for sharp levels but also to obtain valuable spectroscopic data for the levels involved.

Most of Sections 2 and 3 will be devoted to a detailed discussion of these questions.

The angular distributions often show striking diffraction-like oscillations, of the sort which have become so well known for deuteron stripping (Ro51, Bu51), where the position of the first maximum measures the angular momentum transfer in the reaction. The patterns for other types of direct reactions sometimes show even more strikingly defined oscillations (Wa56, Be56c, Gu56a, Bl57a, Su58) with many secondary maxima. However it is not surprising, as will become evident later, that other curves are found (Fi54, Fr54b, Sc54, Gu56b, Ra56, Co57c, Gi57, Pe57a, Pe57b, Su58) which give tantalizing suggestions of a direct process, but cannot by any means be fitted by the cruder theories.

In this situation, it is best not to forget that very complicated angular distributions, involving high order spherical harmonics, are sufficient evidence for classifying a reaction as a direct reaction of one particular type, even if a detailed theoretical fit cannot be achieved. At medium energies such rapidly varying angular distributions only can be produced by *surface reactions*, which take place in the distant tail of the nuclear density distribution. If the reactions take place at large radii it is easy for high partial waves to participate. This observation was important in the early development of deuteron stripping theory (Bu51, Bu57b).

Sherr (Sh57) has described several cases, from the above list, where the angular distribution is ambiguous, but where the angular correlation $(p, p'\gamma)$ or $(\alpha, p\gamma)$ or $(d, p\gamma)$ gives clear evidence for a simple direct process. Gamma rays emitted in these experiments should be correlated, in the simple theory, with the recoil vector

$$\mathbf{q} \equiv \mathbf{k}_i - \mathbf{k}_f$$

where $\mathbf{k}_i$ is the wave vector of the incident particle, and $\mathbf{k}_f$ that of the outgoing particle. This $\mathbf{q}$ vector is the momentum transferred to the target nucleus, so should be the polar axis of the subsequent γ-ray emission pattern. A statistical theory compound process will not select this polar axis. For example, if a compound state were formed by absorption of an s-wave particle the polar axis would be $\mathbf{k}_f$; if it were to emit an s-wave particle the polar axis would be $\mathbf{k}_i$. Many such states would contribute, washing out the correlation. Only for a direct process will there be a well-marked correlation with $\mathbf{q}$. Apparently this correlation can survive the complicating features which lead to ambiguous angular distributions. Some justification for this point of view will be given in Section 2.

Measurement of the polarization of the emitted particle also gives information about the reaction process, although of a complicated sort. Both the statistical theory and the crude direct reaction theories predict zero polarization. The observation of nonzero polarization over a broad region of energy therefore indicates (a) that a direct reaction mechanism is called for, and (b) that some care must be used in its analysis.

C. Surface Reactions

Direct reactions may take place either throughout the volume of a nucleus, or only near the surface. Those which are limited to occurring near the surface are an important special case. It is these which seem responsible for the striking diffraction-like angular distributions which often give good agreement with crude theories.

Several effects can cooperate to give a predominant role to the surface region. These effects may be classed under two headings: (a) optical model effects in the wave functions of the incident and outgoing projectiles, (b) structure effects in the wave functions of the target nucleus. The important role which collective excitations play in inelastic scattering reactions (Co57e, Co57f, Al58, Co58b, Sc58, Be59, Bl59, Co59a) particularly suggests effects of type (b). Thus the excitation of collective motions requires some sort of coupling to the surface deformations and tends to limit direct reactions of this type to the surface region (see Section 3.C). Accurate shell model wave functions which are constructed to show collective effects give a similar result (Le60). Other sorts of nuclear excitations also are more likely at the surface than in the interior. The Pauli principle does not inhibit particle excitations there (Be56d, Br58a, Go58), and the surface is rich in two, three, and four particle clusters (Ho58b, Ma58a, Wi59) which can be excited or ejected.

Reactions involving composite particles would seem most apt to be surface reactions, as in the deep interior the composite structure presumably has a small mean free path against being dissolved. (See especially Ig58 for the α-particle mean free path.) Indeed, the clearest diffraction patterns are obtained when deuterons, tritons, or α particles are incident or outgoing (Gu56a, Li56, Se56, Wa56, Hu57a, Hu57b, Co58c, Da58, Fi58, Kn58, Ma58b, Pr58, Se58a, Sh58, Su58). Such mean free path effects are optical model effects, mentioned as topic (a) in the preceding paragraph, and have been much emphasized as causes of surface reactions (see, for example, Bu57a). Refraction by the optical potential also can enhance the surface region, through an interesting total internal reflection effect (El57, Od58), which inhibits the nuclear interior.

Actually the role of optical model effects and structure effects in causing surface reactions must be treated with much more care than the above remarks suggest. Not only must the region of reaction be localized, but it must be localized in such a way that *diffraction oscillations in the angular distribution are not averaged out.* Probably this happens through an interplay (Ro60) between optical model absorption, which need not be exceedingly strong, and optical model refraction. Apparently those projectiles which approach closest to the nucleus and yet are not absorbed always have the property of lingering a long time near the nuclear surface, where the combination of the centrifugal potential and the optical potential is most slowly varying. Radial wave functions are large in that region and oscillate particularly slowly. In this way the surface is selected in a manner which sharply limits the phase of the oscillating functions.

When only single nucleons are involved the absorption apparently is so slight that the surface does not predominate at all, contrary to some early suggestions (Au53), and the diffraction patterns for such cases usually are found to be blurred. Direct reactions with single nucleons seem to take place rather freely throughout the entire nuclear volume. Even so, some recent (p,p') experiments (Hu59, Ki59, Od60) do show well-defined diffraction oscillations in the 14 Mev (p,p') excitation of levels in A, Fe, Ni, Cr, and Ti, indicating almost perfect agreement with Au53. Also Ov58 find such agreement in the reaction $Al^{27}(n,p)$ at 14 Mev, as do Hi60b for $B^{11}(p,n)$ and $Al^{27}(p,n)$ at 8 to 14 Mev.

Careful developments of the theory of surface reactions have been given (Th55, Na56, Ui57, Br59a), relating these reactions to the eigenstate decomposition method (Ka38, Wi47, Ka58a). Such questions are treated in Section 4.

D. The Semi-Classical Approach

Semi-classical methods have been used very freely for the analysis of direct processes. Partly this is because (especially at high energy) they give good descriptions of the physical events. Partly it is because the semi-classical methods permit one to take account of effects which would be burdensome by more accurate methods, so providing some insight into the consequences of those effects, and serving as a guide for future, accurate calculations. Section 2 of this article will present a detailed development of the method for the transitions between sharp levels. The present discussion will treat those situations where sharp levels are not resolved.

The use of direct reaction models and semi-classical methods is a well-established procedure for high energy reactions, going back (Se47) to the first experiments above 100 Mev. At such energies a successful description of events generally is obtained by ignoring the nuclear structure, and regarding a target nucleus as an assemblage of individual nucleons, with which a bombarding particle makes single collisions. Otherwise, the particle moves through the nucleus as through an optical potential, and WKB wave functions may be used. A compound nucleus seldom forms at all, a simplification which is not available at lower energies. These procedures were developed first at high energies, of course, on the basis of the observation that the wavelength of a 100-Mev nucleon is 0.46×10^{-13} cm, less than one-third of the average spacing between nucleons in nuclear matter, and less than one-tenth of the mean free path of a nucleon (Fig. 1). The use of single scattering encounters within a nucleus is carried so far, in many calculations, that the participating nucleons are followed from collision to collision, as a Monte Carlo cascade develops in the nuclear interior (Go48, Be52, Me55, Me58). The yields of knock-out nucleons, pickup formation of deuterons, etc., agree quite well with experiment. In these calculations each participating nucleon is followed through the knock-on cascade until it either has escaped from the nucleus or it no longer has sufficient energy to escape. At

the end of the calculation all the energy which has not already left
the nucleus with the knock-on particles is summed, and regarded as
excitation energy of a compound nucleus; this finally completes its
decay by the usual boil-off process.

Such calculations frequently are employed for the interpretation
of spallation experiments (Wa54, Me55, Sh56a, Be56b, Ja56, Ko56,
Co57b, Fo57), and appear to describe them successfully. Direct
reactions play an important role in those experiments. Direct interactions also are important in a related class of experiments: the
production of transuranic elements by α-particle bombardment,
through (α, p) and (α, n) reactions. Competition with fission would
leave almost zero probability for such reactions if a statistical equilibrium were established. Their actual probability is quite high, a
consequence of the weak coupling into the fission modes.

Elton and Gomes (El57, also Od58) made a very interesting application of semi-classical techniques for the inelastic scattering of
31-Mev protons by medium and heavy nuclei. They employed the
above-mentioned Monte Carlo approach (which it was not necessary
to follow beyond the first collision), and found that about ninety per
cent of all protons which have engaged in an inelastic collision *inside*
the nucleus subsequently are totally reflected at the nuclear surface,
and are unable to escape. This effect so suppresses the volume direct
interaction that nearly all the direct transitions in these experiments
must take place at the surface. Indeed, their estimates of the contribution from the surface seem in agreement with experiment. The
Coulomb barrier not only effectively suppresses the compound nucleus contribution, but also emphasizes the surface scattering by shifting the reaction energy to lower effective values, for which the basic
cross section is larger. The surface scattering also is emphasized over
that in the interior by virtue of the fact that the Pauli principle does
not suppress any possible scattering events. These results of Elton
and Gomes differ from those of Hayakawa *et al.* (Ha55c), who used
simplifying approximations which lost them the total internal reflection effect. It is unfortunate that the total reflection effect probably
is not effective as a simplification for neutron inelastic scattering calculations (El58).

The Monte Carlo cascade method has been used for energies as
low as 10 and 20 Mev (Br57a, Br57b, Na55) to estimate branching
ratios for the various possible final states in neutron-induced reactions.

At the very low energy end Brown and Muirhead use their direct reaction model only to compute ratios for various processes *within* the nucleus. The likelihood that a nucleon *enters* the nucleus they take from experiment. This calculation is described at length in Chapter V.N. It gives fair agreement with a large collection of (n, p) data, including that of an experiment by the same authors at 13.2 Mev (Br-57b), and provides important support for the three-stage reaction model.

Other interesting calculations are described by Winsberg (Wi-57a), indicating several cross section ratios which bear out the idea that the first step in a high energy reaction always is a nucleon-nucleon collision. A distorted wave modification of the 100-Mev (p, d) pickup theory also has recently been completed (Gr59).

E. Compound-Direct Interference

At sufficiently high bombarding energies the "levels" of the compound nucleus for a reaction become so closely spaced that any excitation curve must become a slowly varying function of the energy. At most the excitation curve for a given final state could show the slow fluctuations of the optical model shape resonances. The amplitude, whose square is the cross section, need not be so slowly varying. Certainly the direct reaction part of the amplitude is a slow function of the energy, merely on the fact that just a few degrees of freedom are excited (Bo36). But the compound nucleus contribution in the amplitude cannot be a very slow function of energy, even though the levels are broad and overlap a great deal, because then it would re-emit incident time packets just as quickly as does the direct process (Fr55), statistical equilibrium would not be established, and the compound part would be no different from the direct part. Presumably the compound part of the amplitude has a comparatively rapidly varying phase, and is to be identified, at these energies as well as at the lower ones, as that part of the amplitude which averages to zero when averaged over an energy spread about equal to that of the incident beam. Then this amplitude does not interfere with the direct amplitude when the cross section is computed, but contributes additively a part which Brown and De Dominicis have called the "compound-inelastic" cross section (Br57e). The compound-inelastic cross section is symmetrical about 90°, and may be computed by the methods of Wolfenstein, and of Hauser and Feshbach (Wo51, Ha52).

The near-by compound nucleus levels average out to give a smooth excitation curve and a cancellation of interference, only if enough of them are contained within the energy spread of the incident beam. Fluctuations in level widths, spacings, and phases must appear at intermediate energies, however, long before the energy is so low that individual levels are resolvable. These fluctuations are seen as fairly rapid changes in the cross section as a function of bombarding energy, and as a nonvanishing and rapidly varying direct-compound interference part. Only quantitative investigation can decide whether enough levels are participating in a given reaction to give a good averaging out of interference, enough levels furthermore with the right quantum numbers to produce the particular sharp final state in question. Fluctuations apparently have been found by many authors (Ei56, Co57c, Gr57a, He57, and others). For the bombardment of Mg^{24} and Si^{28} with 12-Mev protons, Conzett (Co57c), for example, estimated the average number of levels of Al^{25} and P^{29} within his beam spread to be 10 and 20, respectively. Fluctuations are quite likely with such small numbers.

For sufficiently low energy or for sufficiently light nuclei the excitation curve for a transition shows isolated sharp resonances. The direct reaction process may contribute a slowly varying background between the resonances, or it may give a slow modulation of the reduced widths of the resonances. These are just the same effects as at higher energy, except that with isolated resonances the language now is more meaningful and the details can be seen more clearly. Once again the energy-averaged amplitude can be identified with the direct process, in agreement with the procedure of Feshbach, Porter, and Weisskopf (Fe54) for the elastic scattering. The averaging now must extend over a sufficient number of the sharp resonances.

Several authors have studied the direct-compound interference in a detailed way in the neighborhood of isolated sharp resonances. In principle this is no different from the interference of resonance elastic scattering with *hard-sphere* scattering, which is described in the textbooks. Such interference has been seen, for example, by Be54, St55, Bo56, Ma56c, and Ba57a. In the references Bo56, Ma56c, and Da57, efforts are made to separate the direct and compound amplitudes. The cross section is written as

$$\sigma(E,\theta) = \left| \sigma_B^{1/2}(E,\theta)\exp[i\delta(\theta)] + (i\Gamma/2)\,\sigma_R^{1/2}(\theta)/(E - E_R + i\Gamma/2) \right|^2$$

Here $\sigma_B(E,\theta)$ is the direct reaction, or *background* cross section, as it would be if no resonance occurred, σ_R is the resonance cross section, as it would be if σ_B were absent, Γ is the resonance width, E_R its position, and $\delta(\theta)$ the phase of the direct part relative to the resonant part. The above formula is fitted to the observations by a process of trial. Choice of the quantum numbers of the partial wave which is resonant determines the angle variation of σ_R. Then the resonant part is fairly well determined from theory, within the limitations of the one-level formula, and the analysis is meaningful. Of course there is the ambiguity caused by the incoherent contributions of the different channel spins, but nothing much can be done about this. The function $\delta(\theta)$ is a bit mysterious. It is found to be a rapidly varying function and to take on values as large as $90°$. In the "crude" direct reaction theories (see Section 3) it would be constant. Perhaps this sort of phenomenological analysis eventually will be of value.

It is interesting to remark that the direct amplitude need not always be slowly varying. Surface reactions, such as stripping, involve channel wave functions which are modified by interaction with the core. If one of these has a resonant interaction with the core the direct reaction outside the core will be influenced accordingly. The direct process, itself, can show resonant enhancement.

Some of these questions will be discussed again in Section 4.

2. Semi-Classical Model

[The material in this Section was originally condensed from references Au58 and Bu58, which were written in conjunction with the present article. I am grateful to S. T. Butler and C. Pearson for the considerate help which made this possible. I am grateful to K. J. Le Couteur and D. C. Peaslee for useful conversations about some of this material. Some earlier versions of these ideas were given by Butler (Bu57a, Bu57b), and by K. M. Watson (unpublished).]

In the more accurate semi-classical methods the initial state and final state optical model wave functions for a reaction simply are replaced by their WKB equivalents, and with these the distorted wave calculations to be described in Section 3 then are carried through. Several calculations of this sort have been performed, and are listed in Section 3. WKB wave functions are reasonably accurate at high energies (of the order of 100 Mev) and give useful indications of the important quantum mechanical interference effects even at much lower energies.

A less complete semi-classical model is presented in the present section. Not only are semi-classical wave functions used, but a semi-classical condition of angular momentum conservation is imposed on the reaction mechanism. This condition imposes restrictions on the region of the nucleus which can contribute to the direct reaction. These restrictions then have heuristic value for discussing the transitions between sharp levels. Despite its shortcomings (see Section 2.C), the model gives considerable insight into results which come only with difficulty out of more reliable approaches, and it will be used throughout the present article as a basis for discussion of other calculations. In the model: (a) The oscillatory behavior of angular distributions is seen as a typical interference effect, as in ordinary physical optics. (b) For those reactions in which the angular momentum transfer l is nonzero, it is readily to be understood why the differential cross sections are often small at small angles of scattering, with a first maximum displaced from the forward direction. (c) The semi-classical method shows some of the consequences of a consistent use of the imaginary part of the optical potential. (d) A significant effect of refraction by the real part of the optical potential also is seen, in that an angular distribution may be peaked forward, even if on the simple theory there is a "forbidden region" in the forward direction (e) It also is seen to be possible for a forward peak to be accompanied by a backward peaking, reflection producing an *image* of the main forward peak in the backward direction.

Evidently the method is very much concerned with optical analogies. A partial justification of the approach is presented in Section 2.C. For some additional remarks see Bu58 and Ro60.

A. Nature of the Model

In a given direct reaction, let the wave-vectors for the incident and outgoing particles be k_i and k_f respectively, the angle between these vectors being the angle of scattering, and let the angular momentum transfer be $l\hbar$. The semi-classical picture of the reaction is depicted in Fig. 2. A particular incident ray enters the nucleus at A, where it is subjected to *refraction*, and beyond which its amplitude

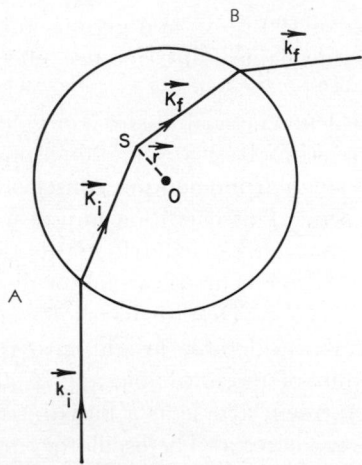

Figure 2. The path traveled by a typical ray in the semi-classical picture of a direct reaction.

suffers damping due to *absorption*. At some point S a direct "scattering" occurs in which the wave-length of the ray is changed. The outgoing ray penetrates to the nuclear surface at B, is refracted, and emerges with wave-vector k_f.

The momentum transfer to the nucleus is $\hbar\mathbf{q}$, where

$$\mathbf{q} = \mathbf{k}_i - \mathbf{k}_f \qquad (1)$$

Part of this momentum transfer occurs at the points A and B, but all of the angular momentum transfer occurs at S.

Let the wave-vectors of the incident and outgoing rays within the nucleus be $\mathbf{K}_i$ and $\mathbf{K}_f$ respectively, and let the position vector of the point S be $\mathbf{r}$. Then the orbital angular momenta of the incident and outgoing rays may be written $\hbar\mathbf{K}_i \times \mathbf{r}$ and $\hbar\mathbf{K}_f \times \mathbf{r}$ (since refraction at the nuclear surface does not change the angular momentum of a ray), and the orbital angular momentum change $\Delta\mathbf{L}$ as a result of the direct scattering is given by

$$\Delta\mathbf{L} = \hbar\,\mathbf{Q} \times \mathbf{r} \qquad (2)$$

where

$$\mathbf{Q} = \mathbf{K}_i - \mathbf{K}_f \qquad (3)$$

This $\Delta\mathbf{L}$ is the angular momentum transferred to the nucleus by the impulse $\mathbf{Q}$ at the point $\mathbf{r}$.

Since the angular momentum transfer is quantized, and taken to be restricted to the value $l\hbar$, the reaction must be pictured as taking place only at those points $\mathbf{r}$ which satisfy the equation

$$l = \left| \mathbf{Q} \times \mathbf{r} \right| \tag{4}$$

It is this condition which is to be imposed on each direct scattering event, and which for a given angle of scattering severely limits the regions of the nucleus which can contribute to the reaction.

Illustration in a Simple Case. The "crude" quantum mechanical derivations (see Section 3), which yield closed form expressions for the direct reaction cross sections, all employ undistorted plane waves for the initial and final states. In the semi-classical model this assumption implies $\mathbf{k}_i = \mathbf{K}_i$ and $\mathbf{k}_f = \mathbf{K}_f$. Then the condition (4) takes the simplified form

$$l = \left| \mathbf{q} \times \mathbf{r} \right| \tag{5}$$

in terms of the actual recoil vector $\mathbf{q}$. For a given angle of scattering, Eq. (5) restricts the possible points of reaction S to lie on the surface of a cylinder of radius (l/q), and whose axis passes through the center of the nucleus in the direction $\mathbf{q}$. We shall for convenience call this the *active cylinder*.

The present illustration will be further simplified with the *ad hoc* assumption that only those points S contribute which lie outside the nuclear surface, with $r > R$.

We wish to add coherently all the outgoing rays, and to do this must take into account the differing total path lengths of rays scattered at different points on the active surface. Because of these differences a phase-factor $\exp(i\,\mathbf{q}\cdot\mathbf{r})$ must be associated with each outgoing ray, a phase which varies as the reaction point S moves in the direction of $\mathbf{q}$, along the length of the cylinder. The total amplitude for the reaction is obtained by summing all the factors $\exp(i\,\mathbf{q}\cdot\mathbf{r})$ over the active cylinder, weighting each point S by a probability amplitude $p(r)$ that a reaction could occur at that point. Then, using the abbreviation ac for "active cylinder,"

$$T = \int_{ac(r \geq R)} d\mathbf{r}\, p(r)\exp(i\,\mathbf{q}\cdot\mathbf{r}) \tag{6}$$

After performing the angle integration this becomes

$$T = 4\pi l \int_{qr}^{\infty} r\, dr\, p(r) \cos(q^2 r^2 - l^2)^{1/2}/(q^2 r^2 - l^2)^{1/2} \tag{7}$$

where qr in the lower limit of the integral is qR or l, whichever is greater.

The factor $p(r)$ must fall off fairly rapidly with increasing $r(>R)$ because (a) it is proportional to the availability at S of a nucleon (or nucleon group) to produce the reaction, (b) it is proportional to the amplitude at S for the nucleon (or nucleon group) which remains in the final state.

As long as $qR > l$, so that the active cylinder does in fact intersect the main core of the nucleus, the amplitude may be approximated as

$$T \approx 4\pi l P \cos(q^2 R^2 - l^2)^{1/2}/(q^2 R^2 - l^2)^{1/2} \tag{8}$$

$$P \equiv \int_R^\infty r \, dr \, p(r)$$

In the event that $qR < l$ the active cylinder misses the nuclear core altogether, and merely passes through the fringes of the decreasing nuclear density distribution. Combining these results, the angular distribution is seen to be of the form[3]

$$\sigma(\theta) \propto \cos^2(q^2 R^2 - l^2)^{1/2}/(q^2 R^2 - l^2), \qquad qR > l \tag{9a}$$

$$\sigma(\theta) \to 0, \qquad \text{for } qR < l \tag{9b}$$

For a reaction in which $l > 0$ it can well happen for small angles of scattering (i.e., small values of q) that $qR < l$. For such forward angles of scattering the differential cross section will be very small, according to Eq. (9b). This is then a *forbidden region* in the angular distribution due to the fact that the active cylinder does not cut the nucleus—or, in other words, to the fact that there is no point within the nucleus at which a direct reaction can produce the required orbital angular momentum change.

As the angle of scattering increases, the cross section will rise as qR approaches l, and will reach a maximum at the point $qR = l$. Somewhat beyond this point Eq. (8) becomes a good approximation to Eq. (7), and the angular distribution will describe oscillations according to the factor

$$\cos^2(q^2 R^2 - l^2)^{1/2}$$

the amplitude of which will decrease as $(q^2 R^2 - l^2)^{-1}$. These oscilla-

---

[3] Strictly, the function $p(r)$ also depends on q, since the physical mechanism can well depend on the magnitude of the momentum transfer. Thus the quantity P in Eq. (8) can be q-dependent, and provide a smoothly varying, angle-dependent form factor to multiply Eq. (8).

tions stem solely from the factor $\cos{(q^2R^2 - l^2)^{1/2}}$ in the integrand of Eq. (7), which arises as a result of the coherent addition of the amplitudes from two circles around the opposite ends of the active cylinder.

The behavior of the direct reaction angular distribution given by Eqs. (9a) and (9b) is very like that obtained from quantum mechanical calculations. The similarity may be brought out even more closely. Under the approximations mentioned at the beginning of this discussion, the quantum mechanical result for the amplitude for a surface direct reaction takes the standard form (cf., Section 3.):

$$T_{\mathrm{fi}} = K \int_R^\infty r^2 \, dr \, y(r) j_l(qr) \tag{10}$$

Here K is a constant (we are not at present concerned with absolute magnitudes), $y(r)$ is a function dependent on the bound state wave functions, and $j_l(qr)$ is the usual spherical Bessel function (Sc49). The function $y(r)$ decreases fairly rapidly as r increases above R, so the factor $j_l(qr)$ in Eq. (10) can be replaced as a first approximation by $j_l(qR)$. Then the angular distribution becomes proportional to the factor $[j_l(qR)]^2$. Equations (9a) and (9b) may be seen to be good approximations of this Bessel function factor.

Apart from the fact that it yields angular distributions very like those of quantum mechanical calculations, the semi-classical method is of interest in showing how the familiar oscillations of these angular distributions arise. They arise as a result of interference between outgoing rays which have been produced at different points of the nucleus, the same sort of effect as produces the well-known interference fringes of physical optics. This effect is basic to a semi-classical method and does not depend on the use of the angular momentum condition.

It is interesting to extend the example just discussed, by including into it some absorption of the incident and emerging rays. Then we can see in a simple context some of the consequences of such absorption. With absorption, not all points in any shell of radius r within the nucleus will be equally accessible for a direct reaction. In particular the two circles around the active cylinder corresponding to a certain radial distance r may really contribute with quite different magnitudes. Thus it may be very much less likely for an incident ray to penetrate to a circle which is largely towards the rear "shaded" side of the nucleus than to the corresponding one on the near "light" side. In this case the interference between the outgoing rays emanating from these circles never can be complete.

The respective phase factors for the two circles have different weights, so that in adding their contributions the sum

$$\exp(-i\,\mathbf{q}\cdot\mathbf{r}) + a\,\exp(i\,\mathbf{q}\cdot\mathbf{r}), \qquad a < 1$$

$$= (1 - a)\exp(-i\,\mathbf{q}\cdot\mathbf{r}) + 2a\,\cos(\mathbf{q}\cdot\mathbf{r})$$

$$= (1 - a)\exp(-i\,\mathbf{q}\cdot\mathbf{r}) + 2a\,\cos(q^2r^2 - l^2)^{1/2} \qquad (11)$$

replaces what was a pure cosine term in the previous treatment. It is clear that a more realistic inclusion of absorption in the calculation must fill in the valleys between the peaks in the angular distribution.   However the peaks still will occur at the same places.

B. Several Qualitative Results

The semi-classical model can be applied very easily, in the examination of any particular experiment, by sketching the active cylinders for a variety of scattering angles.   Then the paths which the incident and emerging rays must take to reach these cylinders may suggest the effects which are influencing the angular distribution.

A few typical effects now will be discussed.

(1) **Absorption.**   The discussion of absorption primarily concerns volume direct reactions.   A suitable, simplified $p(r)$ to use in Eq. (6) is the step function

$$p(r) = p_0, \qquad r < R$$

$$= 0, \qquad r > R$$

Thus we are ignoring the decreasing density distribution outside the surface.

The probability that the incident ray can reach a given point S without being absorbed is given by a factor $\exp(-\Gamma_i R_i)$, where R_i is the distance the ray has had to penetrate through the nucleus in order to reach S.   The ray has been attenuated by the amount $\exp(-\Gamma_i R_i)$. Similarly the probability of the outgoing ray actually emerging is taken to be a factor $\exp(-\Gamma_f R_f)$ where R_f is the distance this ray must traverse before escaping from the nucleus.

If we neglect refraction effects and the corresponding change in wave length of a ray as it penetrates into the nuclear matter, the following expression for the amplitude T for the direct reaction replaces Eq. (6):

$$T = \int_{ac} d\mathbf{r}\, p(r)\exp(i\,\mathbf{q}\cdot\mathbf{r})\exp(-\Gamma_i R_i)\exp(-\Gamma_f R_f) \qquad (12)$$

In the event that $\Gamma_i = \Gamma_f = 0$, no absorption, this amplitude may be evaluated, and simply is

$$T = 4\pi l p_0 q^{-2} \sin(q^2 R^2 - l^2)^{1/2}, \qquad \text{if } qR > l$$

In this case the angular distribution is

$$\sigma \propto q^{-4}\sin^2(q^2 R^2 - l^2)^{1/2}, \qquad qR > l \qquad (13a)$$

$$= 0, \qquad qR < l \qquad (13b)$$

Thus once again the angular distribution exhibits the familiar oscillations, although they now are damped toward large q by the factor q^{-4}.

For specific, nonzero values of Γ_i and Γ_f the integral of Eq. (12) is best evaluated numerically. Some typical results are shown in Figs. 3 and 4, which pertain to reactions of the types (p, p'), and (α, p) respectively. In each case a variety of different values of the absorption is used, but always with the fixed ratios:

Fig. 3 (p, p') $\Gamma_i/\Gamma_f = 1$
Fig. 4 (α, p) $\Gamma_i/\Gamma_f = 4$

The expectations of the previous section are seen to be realized. As the absorption is increased the valleys between oscillations are more and more filled in. The positions of the peaks and valleys remain essentially the same irrespective of absorption, and the first maximum corresponding to $qR \approx l$ is always in evidence. Subsequent peaks can however be smoothed out entirely in cases of very strong absorption. Similar results are found in all cases studied. Evidently absorption is by itself sufficient to give the well-known smoothing out of interference oscillations. When such effects are observed experimentally they often are confused with compound nucleus contributions, which in fact may not be present at all.

Probably the greatest one of the absorptions indicated in Fig. 4 is the most reasonable, corresponding to the smallest Λ_α, inasmuch as nuclei tend to be quite black to α particles. The curves of Fig. 4 would then seem to suggest that the angular distributions for (α, p) reactions and (α, α') reactions should not show interference oscilla-

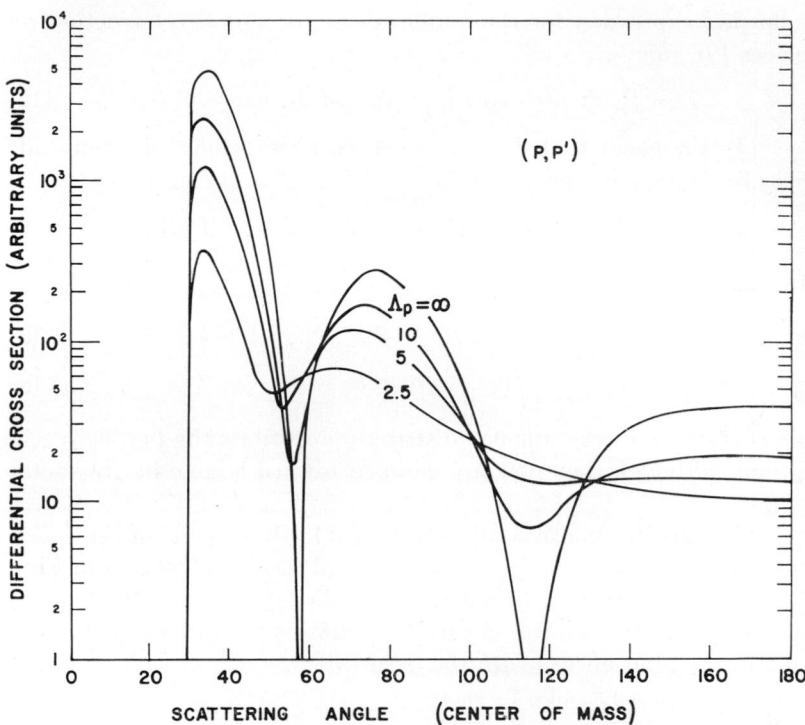

Figure 3. Angular distributions for a (p, p') reaction as computed with the semi-classical model, for a variety of absorptivities, and using the step function form of the nuclear density $p(r)$. For these curves $l = 2$, $R = 5.0 \times 10^{-13}$ cm, and the incident and outgoing energies (c.m.) are 14 Mev and 11.7 Mev respectively. Also $\Gamma_i = \Gamma_f$ is assumed, with $\Gamma = \Lambda^{-1}$, the reciprocal of the mean free path. The values of Λ, in units 10^{-13} cm, are indicated on each curve.

tions. But this is contrary to experimental fact, for it is just in these reactions that the most regularly defined oscillations are found (Gu56a, Li56, Se56, Wa56, Hu57a, Hu57b, Co58c, Kn58, Ma58b. Pr58, Ri58a, Se58a, Su58, Sh59). The dilemma is resolved by noting (Section 2.C) that the quantum mechanical justification of the semi-classical model breaks down if absorptive distortion of the wave functions becomes too great. The reaction then is not well localized about the active cylinder and it is necessary to give up the semi-classical model. Fortunately, quantum mechanical wave functions which correspond to diffraction about a black obstacle furnish an

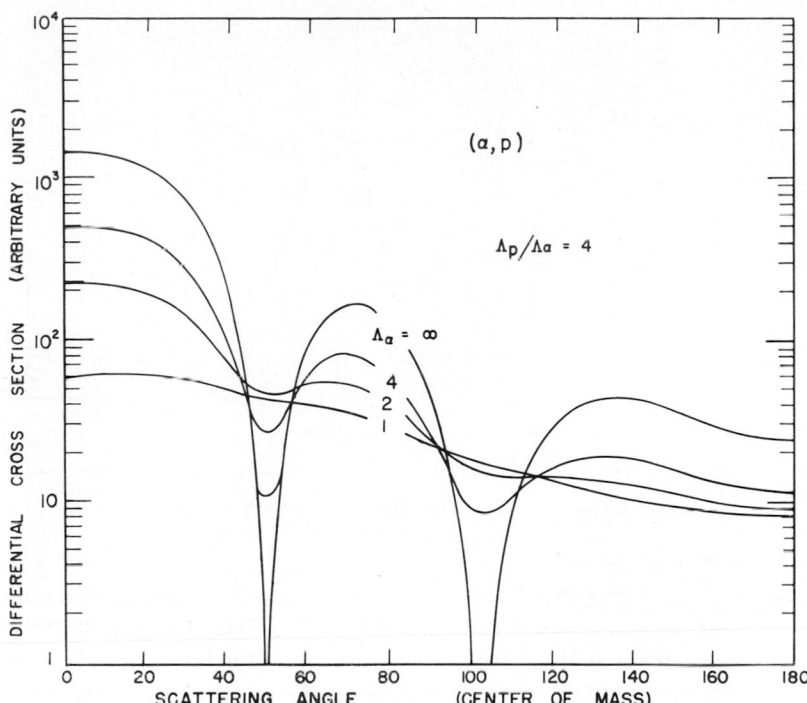

Figure 4. Angular distributions for an (α, p) reaction, computed as described in the caption of Fig 3. Parameters are l 1, R = 4.0 × 10^{-10} cm, 20.8 Mev incident, 16.8 Mev outgoing, $\Gamma_i/\Gamma_f = 4$.

alternative simple model, which is accurate (Bl59). The results of the present section pertain primarily to cases of weak absorption.

(2) **Refraction.** One of the most significant effects of refraction is that it is capable of producing a violation of a rule that often is considered quite basic for direct reactions, that the differential cross section is small at those forward angles of scattering for which $qR < l$ (the "forbidden region").

All that need happen to violate this rule is that QR [cf. Eq. (3)] be greater than l for forward scattering, even though qR be less than l. This is illustrated in Fig. 5, in which we see how refraction at the nuclear surface can produce an outgoing ray *parallel* to the incoming ray, but with a *quite different impact parameter*. Thus an appreciable angular momentum transfer can be achieved, even for

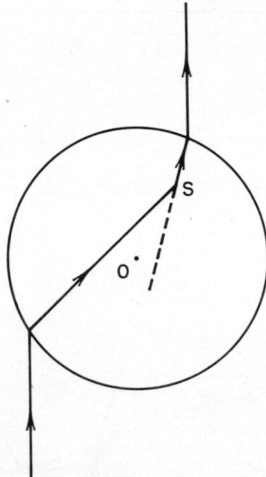

Figure 5. Refraction can be responsible for forward emergent rays with
non-zero angular momentum transfers.

zero angle of scattering.   In such cases the angular distributions may
well peak in the forward direction even if a certain region of small
angles of scatter is "forbidden" when refraction is ignored.

The above effect almost certainly occurs in the case of the reaction C^{12} $(p,\ p')C^{12*}$ $(Q\ =\ -4.4$ Mev$)$ which peaks in the forward
direction for all bombarding energies in the range 11.8–96 Mev.
This reaction has $l\ =\ 2$, and it is known from angular correlation
measurements (Sh56b, Sh57) that it proceeds as a direct reaction.
We therefore expect that for an appreciable portion of the energy
range studied the angular distribution should have a "forbidden
region" at small angles of scattering.   The results of this particular
reaction have been fitted by the detailed distorted waves calculations
of Levinson and Banerjee (Le58).   They obtained the forward peaking.

(3) **Reflection.**   Another interesting effect can occur when
either the incident or outgoing particles see the nucleus as being sufficiently transparent. The possibility exists that a large peak in the
angular distribution at or near the forward direction may be "imaged" in the backward direction.   To illustrate this point, suppose
that it is the outgoing ray which suffers little absorption, and that
the direct reaction is one which leads to a strong forward peaking.

As each outgoing ray which can contribute to this forward peak strikes the nuclear surface, it splits into two rays.   One is the transmitted ray which does contribute to the forward peak; the other is a reflected ray which then proceeds backwards and can penetrate through the back surface of the nucleus and contribute toward a backward peak.

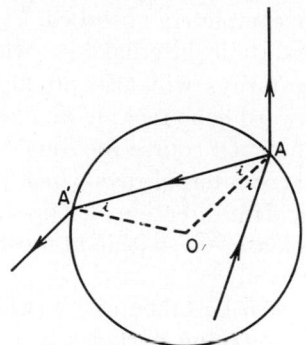

Figure 6. Reflection may cause images of forward peaks to be formed in the backwards direction.

This is depicted in Fig. 6, in which refraction and reflection at the nuclear surface is illustrated for a number of rays which would contribute to a forward peak.   Twice-reflected rays are ignored. If the nuclear surface be assumed sharp, and if the ratio of the wave-number of the outgoing particle *outside* the nucleus to that *inside* the nucleus be n, then the reflection coefficient $R(i)$ for the ray striking the surface at point A with angle of incidence i is given by the equation

$$R(i) = \{[\cos i - (n^2 - \sin^2 i)^{1/2}]/[\cos i + (n^2 - \sin^2 i)^{1/2}]\}^2 \quad (14)$$

Thus the ray reflected at A has its intensity reduced by the factor $R(i)$.

The probability $P(i)$ that the initial ray incident on the surface at A produces an outgoing backward ray at A' is equal to

$$P(i) = R(i) [1 - R(i)] \quad (15)$$

It may readily be ascertained that the angle between the two rays— the one emerging at A and the other at A'—is $(\pi - 2i)$.   If the first ray proceeds exactly forward, for example, the second ray emerges in the backward hemisphere and proceeds in a direction making an angle of $2i$ with the true backward direction.

The probability $P(i)$ is a fairly flat function of the angle i, increasing slightly as i increases from zero, until finally it abruptly drops to zero at the critical angle of incidence i_c for which $\sin i_c = n$. All rays with angles of incidence greater than this will be totally reflected, and ultimately completely absorbed.

We thus see that those internal rays which contribute to exactly forward emergent rays will also produce outgoing rays proceeding within a backward cone making an angle of at most $2i_c$ with the backward direction.   Of course the same is also true of any outgoing direction; all those internal rays which produce rays emerging at an angle θ to the incident direction also produce rays emerging in a cone around the direction $\pi - \theta$, within at most an angle $2i_c$ from this direction.

As one example, if n be taken as $1/2$ (which is roughly the appropriate value if the outgoing particles be say 10-Mev protons or neutrons), then the angle i_c is $30°$. The average value of the probability $P(i)$ in the range of $0°$ to $30°$ is about 0.13. Thus forward emerging rays are accompanied by less intense backward rays which are spread out in a cone making an angle of $<60°$ with the backward direction.

It is seen that this backward imaging effect is probably incapable of reproducing any detailed forward oscillations. On the other hand if an angular distribution has a very strong forward peak, followed by subsidiary oscillations of smaller magnitude, the tendency of the reflection effect is to produce a smeared out backward peak which resembles the main forward peak.

Such an effect could be one of the causes of the backward peaking observed by Rickey and Sherr (Ri58a) for the reaction $C^{12}(\alpha,p)N^{15}$, also for several (He^3, p) reactions (Ge56, Jo56), and also observed for some low-energy (d, p) reactions (Bo56, Ma56b, Il57, Di58). When the outgoing proton energy is low, the protons have long mean free paths in nuclear matter and the parameter n of the above discussion can be sufficiently small that the backward imaging becomes particularly precise. Accurate calculation would be required to determine to what extent *heavy particle stripping* competes with the reflection effect in producing backward peaks (see Section 3).

C. *Justification of the Model*

It is most convenient just to indicate the derivation of the semi-classical model in the limit of the "crude" quantum mechanical theories, wherein the incident and emerging particles are represented with plane waves. In these theories (see Section 3) the transition amplitude has the form

$$T_{fi} = C \int d\mathbf{r}\, F(r)\exp(i\,\mathbf{q}\cdot\mathbf{r})P_l(\cos x) \tag{16}$$

in which x is the angle between the vectors $\mathbf{r}$ and $\mathbf{q}$, and C is an angle-independent constant.

Under the same approximations which lead to Eq. (16) as the quantum mechanical result, the semi-classical result is

$$T = C' \int_{ac} d\mathbf{r}\, F(r)\exp(i\,\mathbf{q}\cdot\mathbf{r}) \tag{17}$$

The question of deriving Eq. (17) thus reduces to the question of the approximations under which Eq. (17) follows from Eq. (16). An integration must be performed, for Eq. (16) is a three-dimensional integral, while Eq. (17) is a two-dimensional integral.

The integral

$$\Theta_l(qr) = \int_0^\pi \sin x\, dx \exp(i\, qr \cos x)\, P_l(\cos x) \tag{18}$$

is the part of Eq. (16) which involves the angle x. This integral may be performed exactly, but would merely give as a result the spherical Bessel function in Eq. (10). We are interested rather in approximately evaluating this integral in such a way as to obtain the form (17).

The required evaluation of Eq. (18) is performed by the method of stationary phase. The integrand in Eq. (18) is a product of two oscillating functions, an exponential and a Legendre function. If there is some point x_l where the product has no net oscillation, a point where its phase has zero rate of change, then this point would give most of the contribution to the integral. If in addition

$$qr \sin x_l = l \tag{19}$$

then the result (17) would be achieved. In fact just such a stationary point does occur. This may be investigated with the aid of an expansion for the Legendre function

$$P_l(\cos x) = \sum_{n}^{l} A_n \cos nx \tag{20}$$

where n has either all odd values up to l, or all even values. Stationary phase occurs separately for each term of Eq. (20), at the points

$$qr \sin x_n = n \tag{21}$$

Thus a succession of active cylinders is defined, one cylinder for each value of n. If l is small the number of these cylinders is very limited. Detailed study (Bu58) then shows that the first cylinder is of greatest importance, the cylinder for which $n = l$. Thus, the principal region of stationary phase indeed is located in accordance with Eq. (19). A similar result follows even more easily if l is large. In that case one does not use Eq. (20), but rather must employ the rapidly converging asymptotic (WKB) expansion for $P_l(\cos \chi)$. From the first term of this expansion it is found that stationary phase occurs at

$$qr \sin x = l + \tfrac{1}{2} \tag{22}$$

which also is in good accord with Eq. (19).

The reliability of localization of an integrand about a region of stationary phase is determined by the rate of increase of phase as one moves away from the stationary point. If this rate is large, other regions of the integrand will oscillate rapidly, and contributions from those regions will average out; then slow modulations of the integrand (as by distorted waves effects) will not matter, and the end points of the integral will not matter. For the present case the second derivative of phase with respect to angle is given by the quantity a_l, where

$$a_l{}^2 = \tfrac{1}{2}(qr/l)^2(q^2r^2 - l^2)^{1/2} \tag{23}$$

The stationary phase method, hence the semi-classical model, would seem to be accurate if

$$a_l{}^2 \gg 1 \tag{24}$$

Evidently this condition is not fulfilled at the first peak of the angular distribution, where $qR = l$, but for surface reactions it would seem to become fairly satisfactory for the subsequent portions of the angular distribution, where qR is significantly greater than l. Thus the semi-classical model would seem to give useful information about the oscillations of the angular distribution.

Unfortunately, a_l only gives the rate of increase of oscillation *at the stationary point*, and even a large value for a_l cannot by itself guarantee rapid oscillations far from the stationary point. For the present problem, the rate of oscillation of the integrand becomes large only if l also is large. For this reason, if l is small the region of stationary phase does not dominate the integral and modulation of the integral by distorted waves effects does matter. Our extreme semi-classical model thus cannot be accurate if distorted waves effects are very strong, because under such circumstances the condition of localization of the region of reaction is not reliable, and for just the l values of greatest interest.

3. The Simple Theories

The standard formulas of the simple theories will be presented in this section. Attention will be limited to the circumstance that sharp final state levels are resolved, as the circumstance that sharp levels cannot be resolved largely only can be treated qualitatively, and already has been considered in the Introduction. Contributions from competing compound nucleus processes also will not be considered here.

A. General Formulation: Distorted Waves, Crude Theories

A collision is described by the wave function $\Phi^{(+)}(\mathbf{k}_i)$, which has the form of *outgoing* spherical waves in all channels, together with a plane wave of unit amplitude and wave vector $\mathbf{k}_i$ in the incident channel. The Schrödinger equation is

$$H \, \Phi^+ = E \, \Phi^{(+)} \tag{25}$$

It is customary to decompose H in the fashion

$$H = H_0{}^i + V_i \tag{26a}$$

$$= H_0{}^f + V_f \tag{26b}$$

where $H_0{}^i$ gives the unperturbed motions of the particles in the entrance channel, and V_i is the remaining part of H, the interaction which induces transitions; alternatively $H_0{}^f$ gives unperturbed motion in the outgoing channel (two-body breakup is assumed) and V_f induces transitions. The transition amplitude for the reaction $i \to f$ is obtained from general scattering theory as

$$T_{fi} = \langle \Phi_f{}^{(-)} (\mathbf{k}_f) | V_f | \Phi^{(+)} (\mathbf{k}_i) \rangle \tag{27}$$

with the motion in the outgoing channel being given by $\Phi_f{}^{(-)}(\mathbf{k}_f)$.

The outgoing state wave function is not an eigenstate of the entire hamiltonian, but only of the part $H_0{}^f$:

$$H_0{}^f \Phi_f{}^{(-)} (\mathbf{k}_f) = E \, \Phi_f{}^{(-)} (\mathbf{k}_f) \tag{28}$$

Since V_f is omitted in (28) any interchannel transitions contained in $\Phi_f{}^{(-)} (\mathbf{k}_f)$ are of compound nucleus nature; the sorts of transitions one would get, for example, if V_f were the nuclear interaction in the surface region, and $H_0{}^f$ were to include *all* the interactions in the interior (Th55). Accurate treatment of $\Phi_f{}^{(-)}$ on such terms belongs in the realm of "more sophisticated theories," to be discussed in Section 4. For computing the direct transition $i \to f$ only that part of $\Phi_f{}^{(-)}$ in channel f itself is important, and for that it is adequate to counterfeit the other interchannel couplings by the use of a suitable imaginary potential in solving for $\Phi_f{}^{(-)}$. With this approximation $\Phi_f{}^{(-)}(\mathbf{k}_f)$ is a product function, the product of the internal wave functions of the two separating fragments, times a function describing their elastic scattering in the channel f, to the extent that this should be required by $H_0{}^f$. Asymptotically $\Phi_f{}^{(-)} (\mathbf{k}_f)$ has the form of a plane wave of unit amplitude and wave vector $\mathbf{k}_f$, together with an *ingoing* spherical wave.

The cross section is computed in terms of T_{fi} as

$$d\sigma_{fi} = M_i M_f (2\pi\hbar^2)^{-2} (k_f/k_i) \Sigma_{\mathrm{Av}} |T_{fi}|^2 \tag{29}$$

Here M_f and M_i are the reduced masses of the fragments in the entrance and exit channels, respectively, and the symbol Σ_{Av} is used to represent a summation over final spins and an average over initial spins. The cross section for producing polarized particles is obtained by suitable modifications of the operation Σ_{Av}.

Distorted wave Born approximation now is introduced in the expression for T_{fi} by replacing $\Phi^{(+)}(\mathbf{k}_i)$ there by $\Phi_i{}^{(+)} (\mathbf{k}_i)$, the wave function for the elastic scattering in channel i. In other words, the complete wave function is written as

$$\Phi^{(+)}(\mathbf{k}_i) = \Phi_i{}^{(+)}(\mathbf{k}_i) + \{\text{outgoing waves in other channels}\} \tag{30}$$

and for purposes of computing T_{fi} the approximation

$$\{\text{outgoing waves in other channels}\} \approx 0 \qquad (31)$$

then is made.

Born approximation is not always justified. Obviously, it breaks down if the direct coupling between channels, itself, should be so strong that the transition to one channel seriously perturbs the motion in another. This effect will be discussed later.

Two important circumstances exist in which the Born approximation is well justified. (a) It may be that independent particle motion is an excellent first approximation, so that the channel i actually is very weakly coupled to other channels. This will be the case for single nucleons incident on nuclei, either at very low energies or at very high energies. (b) Alternatively (Bu57a) it may be that channel i is strongly coupled to $many$ other channels, i.e., that compound nucleus formation is extremely important for the problem as a whole, but that the compound nucleus amplitude to channel f is very much smaller than the direct amplitude. In this circumstance the direct reactions will tend to be surface reactions, and T_{fi} will receive contributions only from the region where particles are well separated.

Even in the two limits of very weak or very strong interchannel coupling it is a bit delicate to defend the actual use of Born approximation as a calculation method, as the nuclear interactions which are responsible for the direct processes certainly themselves are strong. The defense rests principally on the ground that because of the short range of the interaction V_f (some sort of close collision is involved) it makes very little difference just how the process is computed. The initial state and final state wave functions in T_{fi} always are independent particle functions of some sort. While V_f does induce some amount of close correlation between the particles which interact, they are not otherwise closely correlated to any other particles; their wave functions are determined by the overall size and shape of the nucleus. Thus V_f induces transitions between functions which are primarily made up of low momenta. (Care must be taken that this is true to sufficiently good approximation, c. f. Au53). The high momentum parts of V_f may be treated quite incorrectly, so long as the low momentum parts are inserted correctly. Born approximation will tend to do just this, its principal error for low momenta probably taking the form of an incorrect constant multiplicative coefficient;

the volume integral of V_f appearing in place of the volume integral of the reaction operator.

Indeed, short of an exact solution for the relative motions of the three "particles" which participate in a direct collision, it probably is impulse approximation which agrees most closely with the spirit of the situation. Two, comparatively light particles interact very strongly with each other, and rather more weakly with a heavy core. This method has been used to treat inelastic scattering of nucleons (Au53), and under the conditions discussed in the preceding paragraph gives the same results as Born approximation. For stripping, Tobocman argues (To57) that the wave function required by impulse approximation is *identical* to the one which appears automatically in the Born approximation. Various other authors have attempted to accomplish the same result by measuring V_f, as used in Born approximation, in terms of the *effective* two-body interaction of the shell model intermediate coupling theory.

With these conditions stated, Eq. (31) now is accepted, and we proceed with the evaluation of T_{fi}.

The product function $\Phi_i^{(+)}(\mathbf{k}_i)$ is written in explicit form as

$$\Phi_i^{(+)}(\mathbf{k}_i) = v_a(\zeta_a)v_b(\zeta_b)\psi_i^{(+)}(\mathbf{k}_i, \mathbf{r}_i) \qquad (32)$$

where v_a and v_b are the internal wave functions for the two colliding nuclei, the types and internal states of these nuclei (spin projections, etc.) being specified by the symbols a and b; thus (a, b) together are equivalent to the channel index i. The function $\psi_i^{(+)}(\mathbf{k}_i, \mathbf{r}_i)$ describes the relative motion of a and b, with $\mathbf{r}_i$ the distance between their mass centers. In corresponding fashion

$$\Phi_f^{(-)}(\mathbf{k}_f) = v_c(\zeta_c)v_d(\zeta_d)\psi_f^{(-)}(\mathbf{k}_f, \mathbf{r}_f) \qquad (33)$$

In summary, the notation describing the collision is

$$i(a + b) \rightarrow f(c + d) \qquad (34)$$

It is to be noted that the wave functions (32) and (33) have not been antisymmetrized. Direct reaction calculations treat nuclear systems so very explicitly that they easily become cumbersome, and the antisymmetrization generally is left out. Its omission does not disturb any of the calculations to be reported in the present section. At worst one may be led to give such exclusive attention to one of the three types of rearrangement collision (see Introduction) as not to notice that the Pauli principle requires the simultaneous presence of one or more of the other two (see Fr57b).

The transition amplitude is

$$T_{fi} = \langle v_c v_d \psi_f^{(-)} \, (\mathbf{k}_f, \, \mathbf{r}_f) \, \big| V_f \big| \, v_a v_b \psi_i^{(+)} \, (\mathbf{k}_i, \, \mathbf{r}_i) \rangle \qquad (35)$$

At least two of the four functions v_a, ..., v_d must be treated as composite, and broken up into the forms ("particle" + "core"), and perhaps all four of them must be treated this way, according as it is inelastic scattering or stripping which is being computed. The coordinates which specify the breaking up of the v_a, ..., v_d must appear in V_f, along with the coordinates $\mathbf{r}_f$ and $\mathbf{r}_i$, so V_f cannot be made explicit until the process will have been specialized to the point that the v_a, ..., v_d have been made explicit. The roles of the functions $\psi_f^{(-)}$ and $\psi_i^{(+)}$ however may be discussed.

The functions $\psi_f^{(-)}$ and $\psi_i^{(+)}$ are *distorted* waves for the relative motions of the separating and colliding particles. That is, the elastic scattering *within* the channels f and i is treated accurately, consistent with the approximation of ignoring V_f, and only the interchannel coupling induced by V_f actually is taken in Born approximation. To compute the functions $\psi_f^{(-)}$ and $\psi_i^{(+)}$, only a preliminary step in the evaluation of T_{fi}, it is necessary to carry through the rather massive job of solving for the motion of a and b (and c and d) in the appropriate optical potential: This optical potential must include a Coulomb term, if the particles are charged, and in addition is very likely to require a significant spin-orbit coupling term (Bj58). The imaginary parts of the optical potentials somewhat compensate for those terms omitted by the approximation (31). Surface reactions are obtained if the imaginary parts of the optical potentials should be so strong that $\psi_f^{(-)} \, (\mathbf{k}_f, \, \mathbf{r}_f)$ or $\psi_i^{(+)} \, (\mathbf{k}_i, \, \mathbf{r}_i)$ effectively vanish for r_f or r_i less than the nuclear radius. In the event that the direct reaction is a surface reaction the distorted waves simply are free waves, cut off at the nuclear surface, with the coefficients of their outgoing parts chosen to satisfy appropriate boundary conditions at the surface (Ho53a, Ho53b, Ho54, To54, Th55).

It is understandable that the actual use of distorted waves in Eq. (35) is not generally practiced, although it is generally advocated. Not only are distorted wave calculations difficult, but a separate calculation is required for each experiment that is performed.

As a first resort, therefore, it is worthwhile to approximate $\psi_f^{(-)}$ and $\psi_i^{(+)}$ yet further, and merely take them to be plane waves

$$\psi_i^{(+)} (\mathbf{k}_i, \mathbf{r}_i) \rightarrow \exp i(\mathbf{k}_i \cdot \mathbf{r}_i) \qquad (36)$$

$$\psi_f^{(-)} (\mathbf{k}_f, \mathbf{r}_f) \rightarrow \exp i(\mathbf{k}_f \cdot \mathbf{r}_f) \qquad (37)$$

where for the special case of surface reactions the functions (36) and (37) are in addition understood to equal zero for $r_i < R$, and for $r_f < R$. The approximations (36) and (37) are the basis of what are called "crude" theories in the present article.

Some of the best known results of the crude theories may be derived already, anticipating the more detailed expositions in parts 3.B, 3.C, and 3.D. Thus, Eqs. (36) and (37) are inserted in Eq. (35). Then, if we accept as a good first approximation the procedure of taking V_f in (35) to have zero range of interaction, it is possible to write $\mathbf{r}_i = \mathbf{r}_f = \mathbf{r}$ (say) and to take the integration over $\mathbf{r}$ out from the matrix element symbol. This gives

$$T_{fi} = \int_{0 \text{ or } R}^{\infty} [\exp i(\mathbf{q} \cdot \mathbf{r})] \langle v_c v_d | V_f(\mathbf{r}, ...) | v_a v_b \rangle \, d\mathbf{r} \qquad (38)$$

where $\mathbf{q} = \mathbf{k}_i - \mathbf{k}_f$, as in Eq. (1). (The dependence of V_f on $\mathbf{r}$ is indicated explicitly, as a reminder of the overall structure of the expression.) The characteristic angular distribution of the direct process already is apparent in Eq. (38). Upon integrating over the angles of $\mathbf{r}$ the spherical Bessel functions $j_l(qr)$ are obtained from the exponential in (38). The factor $\langle \cdots \rangle$ is responsible for the selection rule in the process. It also gives rise to the *form factor* of the angular distribution.

Kinematic corrections to $\mathbf{k}_i$ and $\mathbf{k}_f$ sometimes are important enough to be significant for the calculation of $\mathbf{q}$ in (38), particularly for those reactions in which $\mathbf{q}$ is very small at forward scattering angles. In principle they always should be made.

These corrections are required because $\mathbf{r}_i$ in (36), say, measures the distance between the mass centers of the colliding nuclei a and b, not the distance between the actual sub-units which interact. Suppose it is b which participates in the reaction as two particles, s and n. Suppose a interacts with n with a zero range interaction. Then the exponential $\exp i[\mathbf{k}_i \cdot \mathbf{r}_i]$ must be equal to

$$\exp i\{\mathbf{k}_i \cdot [\mathbf{r}_a - (M_s \mathbf{r}_s + M_n \mathbf{r}_n)/(M_s + M_n)]\}$$

This expression may be reduced to the form used in Eq. (38) by: taking the "core" particle to the origin for *internal* coordinates, so $\mathbf{r}_s = 0$; taking the zero range approximation, so $\mathbf{r}_a = \mathbf{r}_n = \mathbf{r}$. The reduced form then is

$$\exp\{i(\mathbf{k}_i \cdot \mathbf{r})[M_s/(M_s + M_n)]\}$$

and the value of $\mathbf{k}_i$ to be used in computing $\mathbf{q}$ is

$$\mathbf{k}_i^* = [M_s/(M_s + M_n)]\mathbf{k}_i$$

Distorted wave calculations ("simple" theories) with Eq. (35) will not be described in detail in this article. Rather, the modifications they give to the crude theories will be discussed qualitatively, from time to time, and compared with the indications from the semi-classical model.

Table I lists most of the distorted wave calculations that have been published thus far. The earlier calculations nearly all were of a very tentative sort, largely undertaken as explorations of the effects which might be found. This work is being very much extended at present, and some detailed fits to experiment are being demonstrated. It still is not clear whether there is sufficient *a priori* knowledge of the parameters of the necessary optical wells so that this work can be undertaken with confidence. A few general remarks now will be made about the papers listed in Table I, with further reference to several of them to be made later. It should be noted that only a selection of the more recent calculations is listed.

Only twelve of the papers listed (other than those on deuteron stripping) actually are attempts to achieve interpretations of definite experiments. Of these, the Chase, Wilets, and Edmonds paper (Ch58) does not use Born approximation [see Section 8.C(2)]; and the Yoshida (Yo56) paper is outmoded by the Yoshida (Yo58a) paper, which demonstrates sufficient uncertainties in parameters as to bring into question the significance of the moderate agreement with experiment found in the earlier work. Uncertainty regarding the choice of parameters also reduces the interest of the calculations by Mohr (Mo58c) and Nishimura (Ni58). Also Lamarsh and Feshbach (La56) find the direct contribution to the $C^{12}(n, n')$ total cross section, just above threshold for the 4.43-Mev level, to be an order of magnitude smaller than required. This is a serious disagreement with experiment. Kajikawa and Watari (Ka57a) suggest, however, that Lamarsh and Feshbach used an inadequate form for the function v which represents the C^{12} ground state. Significant agreement with experiment is found only for Fe^{56} (p, p') by Kajikawa, Sasakawa, and Watari (Ka56), and for C^{12} (p, p') by Levinson and Banerjee (Le58), and by Squires (Sq58). The more recent papers tend to show better

Table I. List of Distorted Wave Calculations

Reference	Reaction	Energy range, Mev	Object[a]
Ho53a, Ho53b, Ho54	————————deuteron stripping————————		
Au53	$Al^{27}(n, p)$	14	SP($-$)
Ha54	$Si^{28}(n, p)Al^{28}$	5–50	V($-$)
To55	————————deuteron stripping————————		
Ha55a, Ha55b	$Fe^{56}(p, p')$	17	
	$Fe^{56}(n, n')$	2	SR($-$)
Br55	$Z^A(n, n')$		
	$\langle 100 \leq A \leq 240 \rangle$	1	SR($-$)
Yo56	$Mg^{24}(p, p')$	10	SR(f)
	$\langle C^{12}(p, p'), Ne^{20}(p, p') \rangle$	9	SR($-$)
La56	$C^{12}(n, n')$	5–7	V(x)
Ka56	$Fe^{56}(p, p')$	17	V(f)
Sa56b	$Si^{29}(p, n)P^{29}$	6	V($-$)
Sa57c	$Si^{29}(p, n)P^{29}$	6	(SR + V)($-$)
Ka57a	$\langle C^{12}(p, p'), Mg^{24}(p, p') \rangle$	5–20	V($-$)
Ui57	$\langle$all nuclei$\rangle$		(SP + SR)($-$)
Le58	$C^{12}(p, p')$	14–185	V(f)
Yo58a	$Mg^{24}(n, n')$	1–6	SR($-$)
Ch58	$U^{238}(n, n')$	$\leqq 5$	SR(f)
Ni58	$C^{12}(p, p')$	96	SR(f)
Mo58c	$C^{12}(p, p')$	89	V(f)
Sq58	$C^{12}(p, p')$	180	V(f)
Ri58b	————————deuteron stripping————————		
Te58	————————deuteron stripping————————		
Ne58	————————deuteron stripping————————		
Eg59a, Eg59b	$B^{11}(p,p'), O^{16}(p, p')$	180	V(f)
Gr59	$C^{12}(p, d)$	95, 145	V(f)
Ri59	$C^{12}(p, 2p)$	180	V(f)
Ro60	$C^{12}(\alpha, \alpha'), Mg^{24}(\alpha, \alpha'),$ $A^{40}(\alpha, \alpha')$	18, 40	SR(f)

[a] This column gives the nature of the calculation and the conclusion reached. S indicates a surface reaction; P, with individual-particle excitation; R, with surface wave excitation; V, individual-particle excitation throughout the nuclear volume.   The symbol ($-$) indicates no attempt made to fit any particular experiment; (f), fit achieved; (x), fit attempted but not found.

agreement with experiment.   The three papers by Egardt (Eg59a, Eg59b), Greider (Gr59), and Riley (Ri59) all employ WKB approximation for the distorted wave functions, and use the Brueckner t matrix for the basic two-nucleon interaction.   Ro60 is discussed in

Section 3.C(3). Distorted waves appropriate to a black nucleus are used in that paper.

The C^{12} work is illustrative of the kind of material with which direct reaction theories have to deal and also of the sorts of difficulties to which they are subject. A vast body of data concerning the excitation of the 4.43-Mev level of this nucleus now is available, from such experiments as (α, α'), (p, p'), (n, n') and (e, e'). The (p, p') angular distribution is known over the full energy range from threshold to 185 Mev, with the $(p, p'\gamma)$ correlation also known at the lower energies, and the polarization angular distribution known at the high energy end. The cross section is extremely large.

Levinson and Banerjee interpreted this C^{12} (p, p') excitation as the result of a single particle-particle interaction in the nuclear interior, and their ambitious calculation shows fairly good agreement with both the shape and the magnitude of the angular distribution for excitation of the 4.43-Mev level, over the entire energy range 14–185 Mev. They also are able to explain the small departures of the $(p, p'\gamma)$ angular correlation from the Satchler prediction (see Section 3.E), and they demonstrate that j-j coupled C^{12} wave functions must be used for this explanation. The parameters which give all these results have the following features: The C^{12} eigenfunctions are eigenstates in a square well potential of radius $1.6A^{1/3}f$. Simplified angular momentum coupling is used, the structure of the wave function being that for two nucleons outside an inert B^{10} core. The imaginary part of the optical potential for the continuum functions is identical with that used to fit $C^{12} + p$ elastic scattering; the real part only is $2/3$ as strong. The interaction V_f has finite range, about that required by the two-nucleon scattering, but its depth is about twice as great.

Squires' calculation for 180 Mev starts with the same physical model as do Levinson and Banerjee. WKB approximation for the distorted waves is feasible at this high energy, and in place of γ-ray correlation data there exists polarization data. To fit the polarization it is necessary to use L-S coupled C^{12} wave functions. Once again, Squires finds that straight-forward use of the free space two-nucleon force (he uses reaction matrix data) gives too small an excitation cross section.

Aside from the uncertainty regarding the form of the C^{12} wave function, which may be settled by some new polarization data at 18 Mev (Br58b), the authors of both of the above calculations express concern about the interaction strength which must be used to give the required large cross section. Shell model work demonstrates, if anything, that the *effective* two-nucleon interaction is weaker in nuclear matter than in free space. Squires finds the explanation in terms of a small admixture of collective character in the C^{12} wave functions, just as also seems required for the electron inelastic scattering. By comparing with the (e, e') he is able to fit the magnitude of the (p, p') cross section. Complete p shell intermediate coupling wave functions presumably would give the same result. An alternative explanation of the enhanced interaction strength has been offered by M. Baranger (private communication). He suggests that the virtual excitation of the nucleons of the Fermi sea may mediate between a projectile and the one particular nucleon which it is to excite, and in such a way as to make it easier for the projectile to find that nucleon. In effect the range of interaction is increased. This idea may be related to the one Squires employs.

It may be that C^{12} was an unfortunate first case to treat in such detail. The total cross section for excitation of the 4.43-Mev level is of the same order of magnitude as the total cross section for elastic scattering of neutrons (for example, An58), and near 12 Mev is nearly as large as the full geometrical cross section of the nucleus, πR^2. Thus C^{12} may be a case of the type emphasized by Yoshida (Yo56, Yo58a), and discussed by Chase, Wilets, and Edmonds (Ch58), for which the direct interaction is so strong as seriously to modify the elastic scattering. These authors suggest that the elastic and inelastic scattering may have to be treated in coupled form, in a sort of Tamm-Dancoff theory. This suggestion is entirely within the definition of direct processes: the very same small number of degrees of freedom which are responsible for the direct inelastic scattering merely happen to participate significantly in the elastic scattering. Levinson and Banerjee were not unaware of this problem, and in the first pages of their article discuss a "two-channel approximation." They conclude that the influence of each channel upon the motion in the other is adequately accounted for by the use of a *phenomenological* optical potential. This may not be satisfactory, however, an error coming about, for example, if the wave function in the elastic channel were to depend not merely upon the probability for the inelastic transition, but also upon the detailed shape of the inelastic channel wave function. One can imagine the spectre that all direct transitions with single nucleons which are strong enough to be free of significant compound nucleus contamination also are so strong as seriously to modify the elastic scattering, and that they must be treated by a Yoshida-type calculation.

It is interesting that Levinson and Banerjee, in common with several of the other distorted wave calculations, find a differential cross section which has a peak at $\theta = 0°$, whereas the angular momentum transfer is $l = 2$ and the crude theories predict that $d\sigma$ should vanish in the forward direction. The semi-classical model suggests an explanation for this effect (Au58), as already remarked in Section 2. Distorted waves accomplish a shift of impact parameter in the collision; then even when the linear momentum transfer is very small it still is possible to have $l = 2$ with high probability.

Fowler (Fo58b) has presented an argument that optical wells of reduced depth are to be used for elastic scattering calculations.

B. Volume Direct Excitation

(1) **Derivation of Formulas.**—The incoming and outgoing particles are considered to be nucleons, inasmuch as direct reactions with composite particles tend to be surface reactions. It is assumed that V_f in Eq. (35) is a sum of two-body interactions of the incident nucleon with each one of the nucleons of the target nucleus, and that some one of the interacting particles, either the incident nucleon or one of the struck nucleons subsequently is emitted. This assumption specifically neglects direct processes of the stripping type, whereby the incident nucleon would interact with the core of the target nucleus and adhere to it, so shaking out a nucleon from the target.

Inelastic scattering reactions, (n, n') and (p, p') are slightly different from exchange scattering reactions, (n, p) and (p, n). The reaction (n, p) requires the incident neutron to interact *only with protons* in the target, whereas in the case (n, n') the incident neutron may interact either with neutrons or protons, and generally with both. Butler has suggested (Bu57a) that the (n, n') excitation of the target to a definite excited state usually will involve only one of these, either a neutron or a proton interaction. Most low excited states lie within the same configuration as the ground state, however, only some angular momentum recoupling being involved, so for these the general case probably is needed.

For definiteness the formulas to be given here will refer to the (n, p) case. By considering this case it also will be seen in detail how a zero-range V_f leads T_{fi} to reduce to the form (38), in which $\mathbf{k}_i$ and $\mathbf{k}_f$ appear only in the combination $\mathbf{k}_i - \mathbf{k}_f = \mathbf{q}$. This reduction is trivial for the cases (n, n') and (p, p'), evidently requiring nothing more than the use of plane waves.

Let the spin of the initial nucleus be J_i with projection M_i, and of the final nucleus be J_f with projection M_f. Let σ be the spin projection of the incident neutron, and σ' that of the outgoing proton. Then, with the use of (36) and (37), (35) takes the form

$$T_{fi} = \int \exp\left\{i(\mathbf{k}_i \cdot \mathbf{r}_n) - i(\mathbf{k}_f \cdot \mathbf{r}_p)\right\}$$
$$\times \langle \chi_{1/2}^{\sigma'}(p)v_f(\zeta_f, M_f)|V_f|\chi_{1/2}^{\sigma}(n)v_i(\zeta_i, M_i)\rangle \, d\mathbf{r}_n d\mathbf{r}_p \quad (39)$$

the internal functions for n and p being indicated as spin functions for particles of spin, $\mathbf{S} = 1/2$. [$\boldsymbol{\mathfrak{S}}$ is used for the vector spin operator, and $\mathbf{S}$ for the corresponding spin magnitude.]

The normalized eigenfunctions v_f and v_i next are expanded into series of products of a single particle state times a remaining "core" state, the "parentage" expansion.

$$v_f(\zeta_f, M_f) = \sum\nolimits_{(1)} u_s(\xi; J_s, M_s)f_s(r_n; l_n, j_{sn})Y_{l_n}^{m_n}(\theta_n, \phi_n)\chi_{1/2}^{\mu_n}$$
$$\times \langle J_s, \mathbf{S}_n; M_s, \mu_n | j_{sn}, a_{sn}\rangle \langle j_{sn}, l_n; a_{sn}, m_n | J_f, M_f\rangle \quad (40)$$

where

$$\sum\nolimits_{(1)} = \sum\nolimits_{s, M_s, l_n, m_n, \mu_n, j_{sn}, a_{sn}}$$

$$v_i(\zeta_i, M_i) = \sum\nolimits_{(2)} u_s(\xi; J_s, M_s)g_s(r_p; l_p, j_{sp})Y_{l_p}^{m_p}(\theta_p, \phi_p)\chi_{1/2}^{\mu_p}$$
$$\times \langle J_s, \mathbf{S}_p; M_s, \mu_p | j_{sp}, a_{sp}\rangle \langle j_{sp}, l_p; a_{sp}, m_p | J_i, M_i\rangle \quad (41)$$

where

$$\sum\nolimits_{(2)} = \sum\nolimits_{s, M_s, l_p, m_p, \mu_p, j_{sp}, a_{sp}}$$

Here $u_s(\xi; J_s, M_s)$ is the sth normalized eigenstate of the nucleus which is defined by f minus one neutron, or by i minus one proton, and having spin J_s, with projection M_s. The remainder of the expressions (40) and (41) gives the coefficients which appear in the expansions of v_f and v_i in terms of the complete set u_s; the coefficients themselves having been expanded in terms of spherical harmonics. The notation used for the Clebsch-Gordan coefficients is

$$\langle j_1, j_2; m_1, m_2 | J, m_1 + m_2\rangle$$

It is to be noted that the possible values of l_n and l_p associated with each s in Eq. (40) or Eq. (41) either must be all odd or all even, for u_s, v_f, and v_i each have definite parity.

While all the N neutrons and all the Z protons of a nucleus are identical, they do have distinguishing labels which are used in calculation. The expansions (40) and (41) are defined in terms of eigenstates $u_s(\xi;J_s,M_s)$ of the problem for which one *particular* labelled particle has been removed. The label has been suppressed in Eqs. (40) and (41). Naturally the same expansion goes through, whichever numbered nucleon is considered to be removed. The coefficient functions f_s and g_s which appear in the various possible expansions can differ from each other at most in their signs, in such a fashion as to reflect the antisymmetrization of v_f and v_i. For details see Bu52a, Au53, Bu57a, and Bu57b.

The interaction V_f is the sum of two-particle interactions

$$V_f = \sum_\alpha V_{np} \left(|\mathbf{r}_p - \mathbf{r}_{n\alpha}|\right) \tag{42}$$

giving the interaction of the outgoing proton with each of the neutrons in the residual nucleus. The index α is the one suppressed in Eqs. (40) and (41), as noted in the preceding paragraph. Only one value of α from Eq. (42) need be carried, for in a complete formulation of the problem the wave function would be antisymmetrized with the outgoing proton, and normalized by dividing by the total number of protons. Naturally, the value of T_{fi} must be proportional to the number of equivalent particles which participate on equal terms in the transition in question, but this enters via the magnitudes of the coefficients f_s and g_s, provided the u_s functions all are distinct.

Finally V_{np} is taken to be

$$V_{np} = V_o\delta(\mathbf{r}_n - \mathbf{r}_p) \tag{43}$$

the expressions (40), (41), and (43) are inserted into Eq. (39), and T_{fi} is computed. The exponential in Eq. (39) evidently goes over to the form of (38), $\exp i(\mathbf{q}\cdot\mathbf{r})$. The result of the calculation[4] resembles that given by Butler (Bu57a), and is:

[4] The calculation which yields Eq. (44) is elementary at all steps. The reader who wishes to verify Eq. (44) may find it helpful to refer to (5.11) of Appendix A of the text by Blatt and Weisskopf (Bl52b), which gives the expansion for the product of two spherical harmonics having the *same* argument.

$$T_{fi} = V_0 \sum_{(3)} i^l (2l_n + 1)^{1/2} (2l_p + 1)^{1/2} \, \Re(q;l;s;l_p,l_n;j_{sn},j_{sp})$$

$$\times \, \lambda(J_i,J_f,J_s;M_i,M_f;l_n,l_p;j_{sn},j_{sp};l) \quad (44)$$

where

$$\sum_{(3)} = \sum_{s,l,l_n,l_p,j_{sn},j_{sp}}$$

$$\Re(q,l;s;l_p,l_n;j_{sn},j_{sp}) \equiv \int_0^\infty r^2 dr \, j_l(qr) f_s(r;l_n,j_{sn}) g_s(r;l_p,j_{sp}) \quad (45)$$

The coefficient λ is defined in terms of a sum over Clebsch-Gordan coefficients,

$$\lambda(J_i,J_f,J_s;M_i,M_f;l_n,l_p;j_{sn},j_{sp};l)$$

$$= \langle l_n,l_p;0,0|l,0\rangle \sum_m \langle l_n,l_p;-m,m|l,0\rangle$$

$$\times \, \langle J_s,s_n;M_f-m-\sigma,\sigma|j_{sn},M_f-m\rangle \, \langle j_{sn},l_n;M_f-m,m|J_f,M_f\rangle$$

$$\times \, \langle J_s,s_p;M_i-m-\sigma',\sigma'|j_{sp},M_i-m\rangle \, \langle j_{sp},l_p;M_i-m,m|J_i,M_i\rangle \quad (46)$$

This expression for λ can be simplified with the aid of Racah methods; however, as the calculations will not be carried much further this will not be done.

The differential cross section is to be obtained from Eq. (44), as indicated in Eq. (29), by summing and averaging over final and initial spins:

$$\sigma(\mathbf{k}_i,\mathbf{k}_f) = {}^1\!/_2 \, (2J_i + 1)^{-1} \, M^2 (2\pi \, \hbar^2)^{-2} (k_f/k_i)$$

$$\times \, \sum_{(4)} |T_{fi}(\mathbf{k}_i,\mathbf{k}_f;M_i,M_f;\sigma,\sigma')|^2 \quad (47)$$

where

$$\sum_{(4)} = \sum_{M_i,M_f,\sigma,\sigma'}$$

All the selection rules for the transition are obtained as properties of the coefficient λ, and are expressed in the notation of the vector model of atomic spectroscopy as:

$$M_i + \sigma = M_f + \sigma' \quad (48a)$$

$$\mathbf{J}_f = \mathbf{J}_s + \mathbf{l}_n + \mathbf{s}_n \quad (48b)$$

$$\mathbf{J}_i = \mathbf{J}_s + \mathbf{l}_p + \mathbf{s}_p \quad (48c)$$

$$\mathbf{l}_n + \mathbf{l}_p + \mathbf{l} = 0 \quad (48d)$$

$$\mathbf{J}_i + \mathbf{J}_f + \mathbf{l} + \mathbf{s}_n + \mathbf{s}_p = 0 \quad (48e)$$

parity change (yes, no) as l is (odd, even) \quad (48f)

Several simplifications can be employed in Eq. (44). For one, the assumption that only one value of s appears in (44), and only one or two values of l, is consistent with the spirit of the assumption that the transition is direct. That the states involved have only a single parent state, that there is not much configuration mixing, is equivalent to the statement that only a few degrees of freedom are involved, and that these already are represented in the calculation. The states involved must be well-represented by the shell model. Certainly, with only one s, the sum over l automatically is restricted to all odd or all even values. When these simplifications are applicable there is a good chance that angular distributions useful for spectroscopy will appear.

Under several circumstances the overall selection rule (48e) also simplifies, and takes the form

$$J_i + J_f + 1 = 0 \qquad\qquad (48e')$$

Of course, this result is obtained if S_n and S_p are zero, as would be the case for α particles. For nucleons (48e') would not be possible if the basic interaction V_f were strongly spin-dependent. However the shell-model effective interaction apparently is weakly spin-dependent (Fr57a), so Eq. (48e') can be used for cases of inelastic scattering, (n, n') or (p, p') where exchange scattering is unlikely. Such cases would be, say, the (n, n') excitation of states in a proton shell. For (n, p) reactions the spin-orbit coupling of the bound states precludes the simplification.

In the fortunate circumstance that the possible values of l in Eq. (44) are so limited that only one appears, the angular distribution assumes its simplest form. The cross section is proportional to

$$\left| \mathfrak{R}(q,1; \dots) \right|^2 = \left| \int_0^\infty r^2 dr \, j_l(qr) f_s g_s \right|^2 \qquad (49)$$

Unfortunately it is impossible (see Ha54, Ka57a) to make any accurate *general* statements about the form of the angular distribution predicted by Eq. (49). Such statements must be reserved for the case of surface reactions. Obviously the integral does tend to decrease in magnitude as q goes to large values, i.e., for protons which emerge at large scattering angles, and just because the increasingly rapid oscillations of j_l tend to average out the integrand. This effect was mentioned in Section 2 as being of a semi-classical nature, and yielding the *form factor* of the angular distribution. In addition, oscillations are found in the angular distribution, but only if the product $f_s(r)g_s(r)$ should change so rapidly, at some radius, so as to give special emphasis to the value of j_l at that radius. Thus if $f_s g_s$ should be concentrated near the surface, as for large values of l_n and l_p, or if $f_s g_s$ should fall off very rapidly near the surface, oscillations of the form $j_l(qR)$ must result. It is easy to choose functions $f_s g_s$ which are so diffuse as to give no oscillations at all, but such complete suppression of oscillations requires a rather extreme diffuseness. Similar calculations for the elastic scattering of neutrons, using optical wells with *reasonable* diffuse edges (Bj58), show very pronounced oscillations, in good agreement with experiment (Co58a).

Distorted wave corrections to Eq. (49) in part are as indicated by the semi-classical model in Section 2. Equation (49) corresponds to the case of incoming and outgoing rays which follow straight line paths, and with no attenuation. The first consequence both of refraction and of absorption is to damp what diffraction patterns Eq. (49) otherwise would give, lowering the maxima, filling in the minima, and reducing the forward to backward ratio. All these simply are results of the suppression of interferences between distant parts of the nuclear volume.

Two more specific consequences of refraction were already discussed in Section 2, the shift of impact parameter effect, and the backwards imaging effect.

Kajikawa and Watari (Ka57a) give many illustrations of the sorts of effects distorted waves introduce. They place particular emphasis upon the possible importance of a single-particle resonance of one or more of the partial waves of the distorted functions $\psi_i{}^{(+)}$ and $\psi_f{}^{(-)}$. At resonance these partial waves would have large amplitudes in the nuclear interior and contribute disproportionately to the cross section. The angular distribution would tend to become symmetric about $90°$, a consequence of the dominating importance of just one partial wave, having one definite parity. This effect cannot be considered in the semi-classical model. It is interesting that the broad peak in the total cross section, which such a resonance would cause, may have been seen already in a recent experiment by Pieper and Heydenburg (Pi58). The reaction F^{19} $(\alpha, p)\mathrm{Ne}^{22}$*, to the 1.28-Mev level of Ne^{22}, has a broad peak at 6.2 Mev bombarding energy, looking rather like one of the predicted curves of Kajikawa and Watari.

Peaks of similar nature apparently also have been seen in other experiments (Bl 57c, Co57a, No57, Co58d, Ka58b, Mo58b).

(2) **Several Examples.** **Magnitude of Total Cross Section.** For the important transitions which involve only recoupling of orbitals within the same shell (the p shell, or the d shell), the functions f_s and g_s are likely to have the same shape, and to differ only in values of angular momentum coupling coefficients. It is interesting to evaluate the integral in Eq. (49) for several simple shapes for the function $f_s g_s$, normalizing this function to unity, and leaving for later the question of the coupling coefficients. In this way the angular distributions predicted by Eq. (49) can be seen explicitly, and some idea can be gained of the magnitude of the total cross section and of its energy variation.

Suppose $f_s g_s$ is concentrated as a thin shell at the surface of the nucleus. The normalized function is

$$f_s g_s = CR^{-2}\delta(r - R) \qquad (50)$$

where C symbolizes the unknown angular momentum coupling coefficients. The result for Eq. (49) is

$$\Re(q,l;\ldots) = Cj_l(qR) \qquad (51)$$

Then if only one value of each of the parameters in Eq. (44) should contribute, the cross section is found to be

$$\sigma = (MV_0/2\pi\hbar^2)^2 (k_p/k_i)[j_l(qR)]^2\Omega \qquad (52)$$

where Ω is a number less than unity;

$$\Omega = (2J_i + 1)^{-1} \sum_{M_i,M_f} (2l_n + 1)(2l_p + 1)C^2\lambda^2 \qquad (53)$$

representing the product of all the coupling coefficients which may enter the problem. Equation (52) essentially is the result published by Austern, Butler, and McManus (Au53). The cross section is an oscillatory function of angle, having minima which go to zero, and without any form factor to reduce the heights of the successive peaks.

The magnitude of the cross section depends upon the coefficient Ω, which may range from values close to unity, down to values of the order 10^{-2} or 10^{-3}. It also depends upon the value of V_0. A first approach to the evaluation of V_0 is to compute n-p scattering, using the same force and to the same order of approximation, and to fit V_0 to the measured cross section at zero energy. (Necessarily at zero energy, for it is the matrix elements of V_{np} between states of low momentum which are believed to be of interest, and which can be treated at all adequately with the present methods.)

The result for n-p scattering is

$$\sigma_{n-p}(0) = (MV_0/2\pi \hbar^2)^2$$

$$= 1.62 \text{ barns/sterad} \tag{54}$$

Then

$$\sigma = \sigma_{n-p}(0)(k_f/k_i) \; [j_l(qR)]^2 \Omega \tag{55}$$

This cross section evidently varies very slowly with energy, for a given value of q, and is capable of being either of the order of barns/sterad or of millibarns/sterad, depending only upon the amount of angular momentum recoupling which takes place in the transition.

The effective two-body force in shell model calculations presumably is more suitable than Eq. (54) for the determination of V_0, and gives a somewhat lower value. But the more recent shell model values do not depart *very* far from (54), and the determination of V_0 from the pairing energy (Yo58a) may be an underestimate.

Suppose $f_s g_s$ is uniform throughout the nuclear volume,

$$f_s g_s = 3R^{-3}C, \qquad \text{for } r < R$$

$$= 0 \qquad \text{for } r > R \tag{56}$$

With this distribution the value of the integral (49) in the case $l = 0$ is

$$\mathcal{R}(q,0; \ldots) = (3C/qR)j_1(qR) \tag{57}$$

It is to be noted that this expression is not much different in magnitude from that of Eq. (51), that it is about equally as oscillatory, and that it now displays a *form factor*, the denominator qR, which suppresses large values of qR. This form factor appears in the present example because the Fourier transform of (56) falls off for large momentum values; that of (50) does not. Other values of l give similar results.

Suppose $f_s g_s$ is the exponential distribution

$$f_s g_s = C\kappa r^{-2} \exp(-\kappa r) \tag{58}$$

With this distribution the value of the integral (49) in the case $l = 0$ is

$$\Re(q,0; \ldots) = C(\kappa/q) \text{ arc cot } (\kappa/q) \qquad (59)$$

This expression, again, is not much different in magnitude from that of Eq. (51) but now the oscillations have disappeared.

Suppose $f_s g_s$ has the Saxon form

$$f_s g_s \propto [1 + \exp((r - R)/a)]^{-1} \qquad (60)$$

In this case the integral (49) cannot be carried through analytically. The result is well known, however, from the many investigations of neutron elastic scattering. The function $\Re$ displays well-defined oscillations, and has a strong form factor decrease toward large values of qR.

C. Surface Reactions

The nuclear surface plays an especially important role in direct reactions, as already discussed in the Introduction and in Section 3.A. Nearly always, it may be expected that nuclei are black to projectiles composed of more than one nucleon. Accordingly, knock-on reactions and collective excitations which involve composite projectiles are expected to take place at the surface, before the projectiles have become lost to compound nucleus motion. Similar generalizations do not yet seem possible if only single nucleons are involved, but still surface reaction results sometimes are seen in experiments with single nucleons.

Surface reactions may be discussed in terms of the theories described in Sections 3.A and 3.B. Important simplifications become possible, however, which permit developing those theories both more explicitly and more accurately. Section 3.C(1) is modeled on Section 3.B. It will be considered that an incident particle, which may be either a nucleon or a cluster, strikes another such particle in the surface region; as a consequence either the struck particle is raised to an excited state, or it is ejected and the incident particle is trapped into a bound state. In section 3.C(2) a similar calculation is presented for a case of collective excitation. It will be considered that the nucleus is permanently deformed, according to the picture of Bohr and Mottelson. A new process then is possible, chiefly for the case of inelastic scattering with $l = 2$, an optical-well interaction with the rotating nucleus, exciting it to a higher state of rotation. In Section 3.C(3) some more recent techniques for inelastic scattering are presented. They are based upon the *adiabatic method* and are especially suitable for cases of collective excitation. It will be seen that the adiabatic method is closely related to the distorted waves method of Section 3.A and that as a consequence its results may be generalized to reactions other than simple inelastic scattering.

It is worthwhile to refer back briefly to Eq. 38, Section 3.A, in which the results of all the "crude" theories were anticipated. For a surface reaction the lower limit of the integral is R. Now it frequently happens that a single value of l in the spherical harmonic expansion of the exponential is of interest, and that the Bessel function $j_l(qr)$ is the slower of the two factors in the integrand, so that it may be taken outside the integral and replaced by its value at $r = R$. Then Eq. (38) yields the result

$$T_{fi}(l, R) \approx i^l j_l(qR)(4\pi)^{1/2}(2l + 1)^{1/2}$$

$$\times \int_R^\infty Y_l^0(\theta, \phi) \langle v_c v_d | V_f(\mathbf{r}, \ldots) | v_a v_b \rangle \, d\mathbf{r} \quad (61)$$

It is seen that the selection rules *alone* have determined the shape of the cross section. The exact nature of the process determines its *magnitude*, with rotational excitation considerably enhancing the magnitude in some cases of inelastic scattering, but otherwise giving (in Born approximation) just the shape shown in Eq. (61).

A similar conclusion can be reached even if plane waves are not used. Glendenning has observed (Gl59) that for surface reactions the basic equation of the distorted waves theory, Eq. (35), almost always can be factored in the manner of Eq. (61). Provided the parentage of the direct reaction is simple it always is possible to write T_{fi} as a product. One factor involves the distorted waves, and gives the angular distribution. A completely separate factor involves the internal wave functions of the target nucleus and gives the magnitude of the cross section. It is the latter factor which depends on the detailed mechanism of the reaction.

(1) Single Particle Reactions. Most of the analysis of the single-particle surface reactions may be taken over without change from Section 3.B, provided the meaning of the notation n and p is generalized a bit. Rather than introduce new notation, it merely will be understood that n refers to the cluster particle at the surface of the *final* nucleus, and p that at the surface of the *initial* nucleus. Appropriate masses and spins must be inserted where necessary.

The selection rules are obvious generalizations of those stated in Eqs. (48a, b, c, d, e, f, e′) and will not be repeated here. The other equations follow from those in Section 3.B by inserting R for the lower limit of the integration in Eq. (45), in place of zero. With this change it becomes possible to write all the equations much more explicitly, the forms of the functions f_s and g_s being determined uniquely by the energetics. Unique predictions are obtained for the angular distributions.

Thus, for $r_n > R$, and $r_p > R$ the wave functions for the radial motion, f_s and g_s, may be written as

$$f_s(r_n;l_n,j_{sn}) = (2M_n/\hbar^2 R)^{1/2} \gamma_{s,j_{sn},l_n} \{h_{l_n}^{(1)}(i\kappa_n r_n)/h_{l_n}^{(1)}(i\kappa_n R)\} \quad (62)$$

$$g_s(r_p;l_p,j_{sp}) = (2M_p/\hbar^2 R)^{1/2} \gamma_{s,j_{sp},l_p} \{h_{l_p}^{(1)}(i\kappa_p r_p)/h_{l_p}^{(1)}(i\kappa_p R)\} \quad (63)$$

Here $h_l^{(1)}(i\kappa r)$ are the spherical Hankel functions, or in a slightly more accurate approach, their Coulomb analogs. The masses M_n and M_p are the reduced masses for the relative motion of core and cluster particle, and κ_n and κ_p are the damping parameters for this relative motion, such that $\hbar^2 \kappa_n^2/2M_n$ is the energy needed to separate the cluster particle from the final nucleus, etc. Also γ_{s,j_{sn},l_n} is the reduced width (as defined by Thomas, Th55), having the dimensions of $(\text{energy})^{1/2}$, and giving the amplitude, at the nuclear surface, for the final nucleus to appear in the form of a core with properties s and a single particle with properties l_n and j_{sn}. The reduced width γ_{s,j_{sp},l_p} has the corresponding interpretation for the initial nucleus. These widths, of course, express properties of bound state wave functions, and do not ever appear in any resonance formulas. Nevertheless they have the same meaning, and sometimes it is possible to compare such a bound state reduced width with a scattering reduced width for the corresponding level of a mirror nucleus.

The radial integral for surface reactions, corresponding to Eq. (45) is

$$\mathcal{R}(q,R,l;s;l_p,l_n,j_{sn},j_{sp})$$
$$= (2M_n^{1/2} M_p^{1/2}/\hbar^2 R) \gamma_{s,j_{sn},l_n} \gamma_{s,j_{sp},l_p}$$
$$\times \int_R^\infty r^2 dr\, j_l(qr) \{h_{l_n}^{(1)}(i\kappa_n r)/h_{l_n}^{(1)}(i\kappa_n R)\} \{h_{l_p}^{(1)}(i\kappa_p r)/h_{l_p}^{(1)}(i\kappa_p R)\} \quad (64)$$

This integral cannot be evaluated analytically, unlike the corresponding integral in stripping calculations. Short of the straightforward numerical evaluation of the integral in each case of interest, two approximations commonly are employed. The cruder of these regards κ_n and κ_p as being so much larger than q that $j_l(qR)$ is the slowest varying factor in the integral; so much so that it may be taken out from the integral and replaced by its value at $r = R$. This approximation is the one used in (Au53), and already discussed in this article. It probably seldom is accurate.

An alternative approximation (Bu57a), whose accuracy very likely is as good as the basic formulation justifies, notes that for large values of κr the function $h_l^{(1)}(i\kappa r)$ assumes as its asymptotic form

$$h_l^{(1)}(i\kappa r) \approx \exp(-\kappa r)/\kappa r$$

It then makes a rough blend of the asymptotic forms of the two hankel functions in Eq. (64):

$$h_{l_n}^{(1)}(i\kappa_n r)h_{l_p}^{(1)}(i\kappa_p r) \approx \exp\left\{-(\kappa_n + \kappa_p)r\right\}/\kappa_n\kappa_p r^2$$

$$\approx [(\kappa_n + \kappa_p)/\kappa_n\kappa_p r]\, h_l^{(1)}(i(\kappa_p + \kappa_n)r) \quad (65)$$

With this approximation Eq. (64) goes over to the form well known for stripping, and may be evaluated to give

$$\mathcal{R} \approx 2\hbar^{-2}\, R(M_n M_p)^{1/2}\, \gamma_{s,j_{sn},l_n}\gamma_{s,j_{sp},l_p}$$

$$\times \mathcal{W}\,[j_l(qr),h_l^{(1)}(i(\kappa_n + \kappa_p)r)]_{r=R} \quad (66)$$

$$\div\, [q^2 + (\kappa_n + \kappa_p)^2]\, h_l^{(1)}(i(\kappa_n + \kappa_p)R)$$

where $\mathcal{W}\,[...]_{r=R}$ is the Wronskian of the two functions indicated, evaluated at $r = R$. By definition

$$\mathcal{W}\,[f(r),\, g(r)] = g(df/dr) - f(dg/dr)$$

The result (66) differs from that of the cruder approximation principally in the appearance of the form factor $[q^2 + (\kappa_n + \kappa_p)^2]^{-1}$.

The cross section is obtained by inserting (66) into (44), and (44) into (29), as before. This result will not be written explicitly. It is to be noted that the appropriate reduced masses M_i and M_f must be used in Eq. (29). In the final formula for *volume* direct excitation, Eq. (47), these masses only are indicated as nucleon masses.

The discussion of the magnitude and energy dependence of the cross section goes through here just as in Section 3.B(2). Except for the factor (k_f/k_i) the cross section depends on the energies only through the momentum transfer vector, $\mathbf{q} = \mathbf{k}_i - \mathbf{k}_f$. The total cross section for surface reactions probably lies one or two orders of magnitude below that estimated for volume direct reactions, as only the tails of the bound state wave functions can participate.

The nature of V_f enters in, in the crude theory, in producing one important modification of the angular distribution. This effect has been suppressed by taking $V_f = V_0 \delta(\mathbf{r}_n - \mathbf{r}_p)$, the zero range form. It is that the basic interaction represented by V_f gives an energy and angle dependent scattering cross section, imposing an additional form factor on the direct reaction angular distribution. With only nucleons involved this form factor is sufficiently slowly varying as to be only a small correction. In the recent very interesting experiments with α particles, however, this correction probably is not small, the $p - \alpha$ scattering cross section being sharply peaked at $0°$ and at $180°$ (Ho58a). A recent calculation in Born approximation (Yn60) suggests that an alpha particle direct reaction angular distribution as calculated with a zero range interaction should be corrected through multiplication by the p-α scattering angular distribution. This would only be correct for single particle excitations.

Techniques for introducing distorted wave corrections for surface reactions are discussed in detail by Thomas (Th55), as generalizations of the method of Horowitz and Messiah (Ho53a, Ho53b, Ho54) and of Tobocman (To54), and have been employed recently by Ui (Ui 57). Thomas suggested that the accurate method of the eigenstate decomposition be applied only for the actual saturated interior of a nucleus, and that the assumptions of the statistical theory be considered to hold for this region. The results of such a calculation then are to be corrected for the presence of the surface region by adding in, in perturbation approximation, the contributions from the surface. Then the wave functions to be used in the surface region are free functions satisfying the boundary conditions prescribed by the eigenstate decomposition. Ui discussed the total cross section by this method, interpreting the unknown coefficients at the surface in terms of transmission coefficients of the compound nucleus theory. His results do not seem to be much altered by the distortion.

The distorted wave functions required for surface reactions thus are fully described by the boundary conditions they satisfy at the surface.   Because direct reactions are properties of the energy-averaged cross section, these boundary conditions probably are best obtained by solving for the motion in the interior as in an optical potential.   For composite projectiles it probably is nearly always correct to simplify this calculation by treating the surface as black (Bl54, To55, Ig58, Bl59, Ro60).   Even these simplified boundary conditions can lead to lengthy computations.

Hard sphere boundary conditions have sometimes been used (Ho53a, Ho53b, Ho54, To55).   For the usual experiments, which concern energy-averaged cross sections, such boundary conditions certainly are wrong.   They may be correct for very low energies, between sharp resonances (see Section 1.E), but the applicability of the distorted waves theory may then be in doubt.

(2) **Rotational Excitation.**   Simplified expressions are obtained if the discussion is limited to the inelastic scattering from even-even nuclei.   Then we are interested in the inelastic transitions from the $J = 0$ ground state to the low-lying excited rotational states, $J = 2$, $J = 4$.   Calculations of the direct inelastic scattering to these states are of interest not so much for elucidating the spectroscopic properties of the levels involved, which tend to be known already by other means, as for a better understanding of the scattering processes themselves.   It is sufficiently illustrative of the general situation to consider the strong coupling case of Bohr and Mottelson, wherein the nucleus has a large, stable deformation from spherical shape.   The low-lying states of the nucleus then are viewed as states of rotation of this deformed body, rather than as states of vibration of the amount of the deformation.   Nuclei which have such stable deformations are found well away from the closed shells.

The nature of the inelastic scattering process, and of the approximations which are justifiable in calculating it, is rather different from that for single particle excitation.   It will be helpful to refer to a recent extensive numerical calculation by Chase, Wilets, and Edmonds (Ch58), treating neutron inelastic scattering.   Some related work has been done by Gribov (Gr57b).

The physical process considered involves no excitation of internal motions of the nucleus.   Instead, the impinging particle merely sees the nucleus *as an optical well* of deformed shape; by virtue of the deformation it exerts a torque on the nucleus, which can set the nucleus into rotation.   Evidently the spin of the nucleon and the $(\mathbf{L} \cdot \mathbf{S})$

part of the potential play no essential role, and may be ignored. Evidently also the physical picture is not very consistent with the use of plane waves for the initial and final states, the very potential which induces the inelastic transitions also being the one which distorts wave functions from plane wave form. (Note that "distort" and "deform" have been given distinct meanings.)

A rather different direct reaction process in which the surface plays a role is discussed by Sawicki and Szymanski (Sa57c). They consider that a projectile can excite a virtual surface wave on the nuclear core, perhaps becoming captured in the process. The surface wave then de-excites by interaction with another nucleon, perhaps ejecting it. In the example treated this process apparently only made a small contribution.

One can attempt to expand the optical potential in a series of spherical harmonics

$$V(r, \theta') = \sum_\lambda v_\lambda (r) P_\lambda(\cos \theta') \tag{67}$$

where θ' is the angle measured from the nuclear symmetry axis, and $\lambda = 0, 2, 4, \ldots$. (Odd values do not appear for λ because nuclear deformations nearly always are symmetrical.) Several authors (Br55, Ha55a, Ha55b, Mo56b, Ya56) have employed distorted wave Born approximation in computing the rotational excitation, in the sense that $v_0(r)$ in Eq. (67) is taken into account exactly, as a distorting potential, while the terms with $\lambda \geq 2$ are treated in Born approximation. Unfortunately this procedure seriously overestimates the cross section for rotational excitation.

Since only even values of λ appear in Eq. (67) the rotational excitation involves no change of parity. Also $v_4 \ll v_2$ in Eq. (67), so in Born approximation the $J = 2$ level would be excited much more strongly than the $J = 4$ level. This feature survives to some degree in the more accurate calculation.

Actually, it is interesting to consider why the expansion (67) has any terms at all with $\lambda > 2$, and also why and under what conditions they can be expected to be small. Thus the nucleus normally is thought to be approximately of quadrupole shape

$$R(\theta') = R_0[1 + \beta Y_2^0(\theta')] \tag{68}$$

with β the deformation parameter, and it might be supposed that the series (67) therefore should end with the term of quadrupole order.

But if the optical potential is a function only of the distance from the nuclear surface, its explicit form is

$$V(r, \theta') = V\{r - R_0[1 + \beta Y_2^0(\theta')]\} \tag{69}$$

The coefficients in the spherical harmonic expansion of $V(r, \theta')$ concern its angular variation *at a definite radius*, and there is no reason for them to terminate at $\lambda = 2$. What can be said is that Eqs. (68) and (69) imply that the coefficients with $\lambda > 2$ are oscillatory functions of r, having zero as their average value. This last fact determines their relative importance. They can play no role for long wavelength neutrons. (Distortion modifies this result.) They tend to be reduced very much by the diffuse nuclear surface structure.

The importance of surface diffuseness in reducing the magnitude of v_4 is shown very clearly by Chase, Wilets, and Edmonds. For a deformed square well the peak value of v_4 is about 70 per cent of v_0. For a well with realistic surface diffuseness the peak v_4 drops to about 20 per cent of v_0. Clearly v_4 is not very important, and the higher v_λ in Eq. (67) may be neglected altogether.

Quantitative understanding of the rotational excitation is best developed, according to the plan of the present article, by first examining the theory in the limit of Born approximation and using undistorted plane waves for the initial and final states. This approximation gives cross sections at all correctly only to terms of no higher than the second degree in β, and accordingly is appropriate only for small deformation. To the same order in β, all contributions from $\lambda > 2$ in Eq. (67) vanish. Only the state $J = 2$ is excited, the cross section for its excitation being $\sigma_2(\text{rot})$. That part of $\sigma_2(\text{rot})$ of lowest degree in β is proportional to β^2 and corresponds to retaining only the term in $v_2(r)$ of first degree in β. All of $v_2(r)$ is concentrated near the nuclear surface, but especially this term of first degree in β. In the case of a square (nondiffuse) optical well, this term assumes the form

$$v_2(r) \rightarrow -(5/4\pi)^{1/2} V_0(1 + i\zeta) R_0 \beta \delta(r - R_0) \tag{70}$$

where ζV_0 is the imaginary part of the optical well.

Upon inserting (70) for V_f in Eq. (38) the result obtained for T_{fi} is

$$T_{fi} = -\int [\exp i(\mathbf{q} \cdot \mathbf{R})] V_0(1 + i\zeta) R_0^3 \beta \langle v_f | Y_2^0(\theta', \phi') | v_i \rangle \, d\Omega_{\mathbf{R}} \tag{71}$$

the radial integration having been performed with the aid of the δ function in Eq. (70) and only the integrals on angles remaining to be done.

The normalized wave functions of the target nucleus, v_i and v_f are the functions

$$Y_J^M(\theta_1, \theta_2) = (4\pi/2J + 1)^{-1/2}(-1)^M D_{M,0}{}^J(\theta_i) \qquad (72)$$

where $D_{M,K}{}^J(\theta_i)$ is the (unnormalized) symmetric top wave function corresponding to a state of angular momentum J with projections M and K, respectively, along a space fixed z axis (chosen in the direction of $\mathbf{q}$) and the nuclear symmetry axis; θ_i are the Euler angles of a set of principal nuclear axes relative to the space-fixed set. For the special case of the ground state band of even-even nuclei $K = 0$, and the symmetric top functions reduce to the $Y_J^M(\theta_1,\theta_2)$, ordinary spherical harmonics for the orientation of the nuclear symmetry axis with respect to the space-fixed axis. Interband transitions are weak (Ma58c).

Only the $L = 2$ term of the exponential contributes in (71), giving

$$T_{fi} \approx (20\pi)^{1/2}\beta R_0{}^3 V_0 j_2(qR_0)$$

$$\times \int Y_2^0(\hat{\mathbf{q}}\cdot\hat{\mathbf{R}}) Y_2^{-M}(\theta_1, \theta_2) Y_2^0(\theta', \phi') Y_0^0(\theta_1, \theta_2)\sin\theta'\, d\theta'\, d\phi'\, \sin\theta_1\, d\theta_1\, d\theta_2$$

The addition theorem for the spherical harmonics (B152b, Appendix A) may be used to express the position of the neutron in terms of the nuclear symmetry axis, in place of the axis $\mathbf{q}$.

$$Y_2^0(\hat{\mathbf{q}}\cdot\hat{\mathbf{R}}) = (4\pi/5)^{1/2} \sum_m Y_2^{-m}(\theta_1, \theta_2) Y_2^m(\theta', \phi')$$

With this substitution the (θ', ϕ') integration may be done, leaving the (θ_1, θ_2) integration a triviality, so that the result is

$$T_{fi} = (4\pi)^{1/2}\beta R_0{}^3 V_0 j_2(qR_0) \qquad (73)$$

The cross section is obtained by substituting T_{fi} into Eq. (29),

$$d\sigma_2(\text{rot}) = (1/\pi)(k_f/k_i)\,(MR_0{}^2 V_0/\hbar^2)^2\beta^2 R_0{}^2 [j_2(qR_0)]^2 \qquad (74)$$

The deformation parameter frequently is expressed in terms of the intrinsic quadrupole moment Q_0, the quadrupole moment calculated with the nuclear symmetry axis as the z axis,

$$Q_0 = 3(5\pi)^{-1/2} ZR_0{}^2\beta \qquad (75)$$

The cross section becomes

$$d\sigma_2(\text{rot}) = (5/9) \ R_0{}^2 \ (k_f/k_i)(MR_0{}^2 V_0/\hbar^2)^2 \ (Q_0/ZR_0{}^2)^2 [j_2(qR_0)]^2 \quad (76)$$

The quadrupole moments of the nuclei with well-developed rotational spectra are appreciable fractions of the nuclear cross sectional area, and V_0 is about 40 Mev, so it is seen that $d\sigma(\text{rot})$ is a cross section of the order of magnitude of barns/sterad. The angular distribution in Eq. (76) tends to have a very well-defined zero at forward angles, for there is little energy loss in exciting the first rotational state, so $k_f \approx k_i$, so at forward angles $q \approx 0$. For 1-Mev neutrons on medium mass nuclei the first peak of $[j_2]^2$ comes near $90°$ scattering angle.

Born approximation with distorted wave functions (Br55, Ha55a, Ha55b, Mo56b, Ya56) gives results which differ from those just derived, both in the form of the angular distribution and in the magnitude of the total cross section. The angular distribution tends to be influenced in the fashion described in Section 2. In place of a forward zero it has a forward peak, the result of displacement of impact parameter. This peak also tends to be imaged in the backwards direction.

The total cross section tends, on the whole, to be reduced by distortion, since boundary matching requirements at the nuclear surface reduce the magnitudes of the wave functions there. Some additional reduction is accomplished by the imaginary part of the optical potential, which transfers probability from the direct process into the compound nucleus process. But superimposed on this overall reduction of rotational excitation by the distorting potential there is the periodic enhancement of the process at single-particle resonances. S and D partial waves are in resonance near $A = 170$, and enhance the cross section there, while near $A = 240$ the cross section is enhanced by a P-wave resonance. Although smaller than the cross sections predicted by Eq. (76) these distorted wave resonance cross sections are extremely large, and tend to exceed the values allowed by the conservation of probability.

It is entirely natural for the rotational excitation cross sections to be so large as to create difficulties of self-consistency, as was noted earlier, inasmuch as the same potential which distorts the wave functions and is responsible for all the elastic scattering also is the one which effects the inelastic scattering. In this circumstance dis-

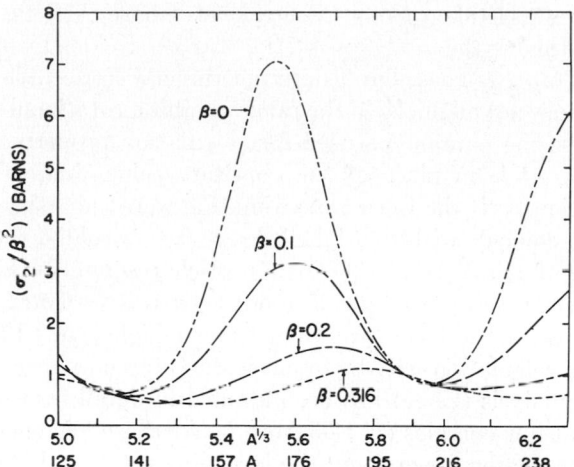

Figure 7. Ratio of cross section σ_2 (rot) for direct rotational excitation of the $J = 2$ level to the square of the deformation parameter β, *vs.* cube root of mass number A, for various values of β. A nondiffuse (square) optical well of average radius $R = 1.35A^{1/3} \times 10^{-13}$ cm was used, with well depth $V_0 = 42.2$ Mev, and ratio of imaginary to real potential, $\zeta = 0.08$. Also 1-Mev neutrons are assumed incident, and a 50-kev $J = 2$ level is assumed to be excited. If a distorted wave Born approximation based on a δ function (linear in β) approximation to the extra-spherical interaction were valid, all curves would coincide, independently of β. The lowering with increasing β shows that such an approximation grossly overestimates σ_2 (rot). (Taken from Ch58).

torted wave Born approximation only could be accurate if nuclei were close to having spherical shape. But the nuclei with important rotational spectra also all depart very far from spherical shape, such that values $\beta \approx 0.3$ in Eq. (68) are common.

This objection can be met only by abandoning the Born approximation (Yo56, Yo58a, Ch58). In place of breaking the Schrödinger equation into two parts, one part for the rotational motion which gives the nuclear levels, and one part for the motion of the neutron in the field of the nucleus, these two motions must be treated together. The calculation is made feasible (Ch58) by treating only the lowest three levels of the rotational band. With only these three levels being kept in the analysis, the Schrödinger equation simplifies to the form of three coupled differential equations for the motion of the neutron. These may be solved numerically.

Figure 7 is taken from the work of Chase, Wilets, and Edmonds, and shows the total cross section $\sigma_2(\text{rot})$, divided by β^2, for various values of β. (These curves are not directly applicable to actual nuclei because not all nuclei in the range exhibit a rotational spectrum, and because the parameters used for calculation properly should be dependent on A, in place of the constant values indicated in the figure caption.) If the Born approximation were valid the curves for all β would coincide with that labelled $\beta = 0$. Actually, the absolute magnitude of $\sigma_2(\text{rot})/\beta^2$ at the single particle resonances is seen from Fig. 7 to decrease by a factor of about 6 from $\beta = 0$ to $\beta = 0.316$. Also the resonance structure moves toward higher A. Further details of the calculation may be found in the original paper.

The analysis (Ch58) has been applied in detail for experiments with U^{238} at low energies ($E \leq 5$ Mev). At these low energies most of the cross section for exciting the low lying rotational states seems to be contributed by the compound nucleus process, and straightforward calculation with the equations of Hauser and Feshbach (Wo-51, Ha52) effectively reproduces the measured excitation curves. The direct rotational excitation is noticeable in the angular distributions, however, for these peaks near 90° to a significantly greater extent than the statistical theory predicts, and closely enough by the amount which is achieved by adding in the direct process. Toward higher energy the direct process presumably becomes more significant in the total cross section.

Elastic scattering naturally is influenced by the strong coupling to the low rotational levels. The most significant fashion in which this appears in the calculations is in the requirement that the imaginary part of the optical potential be smaller in the coupled calculation than in a calculation of the elastic scattering by itself. This is as expected, for the imaginary potential no longer need represent the direct inelastic transitions to the rotational levels (see Section 4).

(3) **The Adiabatic Method.** This method (Ch56) seems particularly well suited for the analysis of collective excitations of the nuclear surface (Dr55, Dr56, Dr58, In56, Bl59) of the sort discussed in the preceding section. T_{fi} is calculated in two steps, a division being made on the basis that the wave function of the target nucleus, initially $v_i(\zeta)$, responds slowly to the perturbation $V_f(\mathbf{r}, \zeta)$. First the elastic scattering amplitude is computed for each fixed value of

the internal variable ζ, i.e., for each of the variety of possible nuclear shapes. This gives

$$f(\theta, \phi, \zeta) = (M/2\pi\hbar^2)\int d^3r[\exp - i(\mathbf{k}_f\cdot\mathbf{r})][U(r) + V_f(\mathbf{r},\zeta)]\psi_i^{(+)}$$

where $U(r)$ is the spherically symmetric part of the optical potential experienced by the projectile, and where $\psi_i^{(+)}$ is not computed in Born approximation but is the complete scattering eigenstate of $\{U + V_f\}$. In the next step an integral over ζ is computed, and

$$T_{fi} = (2\pi\hbar^2/M)\langle v_f(\zeta)|f(\theta, \phi, \zeta)|v_i(\zeta)\rangle$$

Evidently the exact evaluation of the equations of the adiabatic method is even more difficult than a distorted waves calculation, because $\psi_i^{(+)}$ $(\mathbf{r}, \zeta)$ is difficult to compute and must be computed for each ζ. Thus far, the adiabatic method has been employed only in the limit of small deformations, however, in which case it reduces (Ro60) to the distorted waves method as already discussed.

The adiabatic method has important advantages for studying the inelastic scattering from strongly absorbing ("black") deformed nuclei, as for (α, α') reactions. For such nuclei the small angle

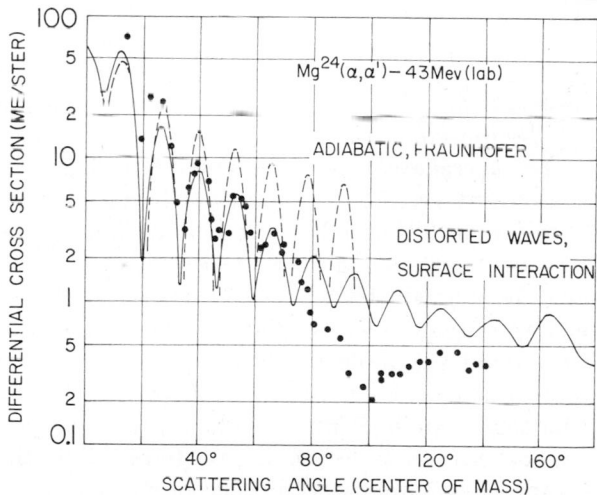

Figure 8. Experimental data of Sh59 is compared with distorted waves theory (solid line) and adiabatic theory (dotted line). Distorted waves calculation assumes surface interaction; uses accurate optical model wave functions. Adiabatic calculation uses Fraunhofer approximation to the wave functions.

scattering of fast projectiles may be treated by a Fraunhofer approximation, and closed form expressions for the cross section may be obtained (Bl59). Those expressions have been tested by more accurate distorted waves calculations (Ro60) and have been found to be surprisingly accurate (see Fig. 8). Not only does the adiabatic method yield simple formulas for inelastic scattering, but it relates the absolute cross section to the nuclear deformation, and it shows important relationships between elastic and inelastic scattering. It shows that for even parity excitation the inelastic angular distributions oscillate out of phase with the elastic angular distribution, while for odd parity the oscillations are in phase.

The adiabatic method already has been of considerable use for understanding (α, α') experiments, and to some extent for (d, d') experiments. It cannot in itself be extended to other reaction types, such as (p, α), (d, α), or (d, p), but its success is an encouraging indication that closely related calculations that can treat these reactions also are likely to be successful. Calculations using distorted waves that satisfy black nucleus boundary conditions (Ro60) already have shown some indications of success.

D. Stripping

(1) **Deuteron Stripping.** Deuteron stripping is the best known direct reaction. It will be discussed first, and the other possible stripping reactions compared with it later. The discussion will be kept brief, for several excellent reviews exist (Hu53, To56, Bu57b). Also Ki57 gives a discussion of the excitation curve for pickup. Only a few departures from the "crude" theory will be indicated here, of a sort which are not emphasized in the references cited.

Consider the reaction (d, p). Until distortion effects will be discussed, all (d, p) formulas apply equally well for (d, n). The wave functions to be used are those for surface reactions, as composite particles always are involved in the stripping process. Then the wave function of the final state nucleus, with the captured neutron bound to it, is given by Eq. (40), with f_s taking the form (62) in the surface region. The transition amplitude (35) becomes

$$T_{fi} = \langle v_f(\zeta_f, M_f) [\exp i(\mathbf{k}_p \cdot \mathbf{r}_p)] \chi_{1/2}{}^\sigma(p) | V_{np} + V_{p\xi} | u_i(\xi; J_i, M_i) \phi_D$$

$$[\exp i(\mathbf{k}_D \cdot \mathbf{r}_D)] \rangle \quad (77)$$

where ϕ_D is the normalized internal wave function of the deuteron and $\chi_{1/2}{}^\sigma(p)$ is the proton spin function. The operator V_f of Eq. (35), consisting of those nuclear interactions which are not included when setting up the final state wave functions, has in Eq. (77) taken the form of $(V_{np} + V_{p\xi})$; V_{np} is the interaction between the neutron and proton which had arrived together in the deuteron, and $V_{p\xi}$ is the proton-core interaction. In the distorted wave modification of (77), to be discussed later, only the off-diagonal matrix elements of $V_{p\xi}$ enter its diagonal elements just giving the distortion. The off-diagonal elements of $V_{p\xi}$ generally are considered to be small (Bu51). For these reasons the present discussion will emphasize only the role of V_{np}.

With V_{np} a zero range force the form of the wave function ϕ_D is

$$\phi_D = N(4\pi)^{-1/2}|\mathbf{r}_n - \mathbf{r}_p|^{-1}[\exp -\gamma|\mathbf{r}_n - \mathbf{r}_p|]\chi_1{}^m \quad (78)$$

and it is found that

$$V_{np}\phi_D = -N(4\pi)^{1/2}(\hbar^2/M)\delta(\mathbf{r}_n - \mathbf{r}_p)\chi_1{}^m \quad (79)$$

Here $\chi_1{}^m$ is the triplet spin function. The value of the factor N may be determined by normalizing the wave function (78); thus it is determined as $(2\gamma)^{1/2}$. On the other hand, effective range theory gives a sizeable correction to the value of N, and the corrected value may as well be adopted immediately:

$$N = [2\gamma/(1 - \gamma\rho_t)]^{1/2} = 2.77 \times 10^6 \text{ cm}^{1/2} \quad (80)$$

where ρ_t is the triplet effective range.

Upon substituting Eq. (78) into Eq. (77), and Eq. (77) into Eq. (29), the result obtained for the differential cross section is

$$d\sigma = 4N^2 (k_p/k_D) [A(A + 1)/(A + 2)^2][(2J_f + 1)/(2J_i + 1)]$$
$$\cdot \sum_{l_n, j_{ni}} [\int_R^\infty r^2 dr j_{ln}(qr)f_i(r;l_n,j_{in})]^2 \quad (81)$$

This is brought into the usual explicit form by substituting the surface region form of f_i, Eq. (62). Then

$$d\sigma = (8N^2M/\hbar^2)(k_p/k_D)[(A + 1)^2/(A + 2)^2]$$
$$[(2J_f + 1)/(2J_i + 1)]R^3\sum_{l_n}[\gamma_{l_n}{}^2 Q_{l_n}{}^2(q,\kappa,R)] \quad (82a)$$

where

$$Q_{l_n}(q,\kappa,R) \equiv \left\{ \mathcal{W} \left[j_{l_n}(qr), h_{l_n}^{(1)}(i\kappa r) \right]_{r=R} \right\} \left[(q^2 + \kappa^2) \, h_{l_n}^{(1)}(i\kappa R) \right]^{-1} \quad (82b)$$

with the selection rules

$$\mathbf{J}_f + \mathbf{J}_i + 1 + \mathbf{\$}_n = 0 \qquad (83a)$$

parity change (yes, no), as l is (odd, even)   (83b)

and

$$\gamma_{l_n}^2 \equiv \sum_{j_{in}} \gamma_{i,l_n,j_{in}}^2 \qquad (83c)$$

The factors that depend on reduced mass have been inserted explicitly in Eqs. (81) and (82). Equation (82) first was derived by Butler (Bu51), using a method of boundary condition matching, as described in the references cited.[5]

The form factor denominator in Eq. (82b) is given in terms of the properties of the bound state of the neutron in the final nucleus, as $(q^2 + \kappa^2)$. This probably is the most useful form. Another form which is quoted frequently is given in terms of the properties of the deuteron. They are related by energy conservation, so that

$$q^2 + \kappa^2 = 2\gamma^2 + 2 \, (\tfrac{1}{2} \, \mathbf{k}_d - \mathbf{k}_p)^2 \qquad (84)$$

The pickup and stripping cross sections are related by the expression

$$d\sigma_{\text{pickup}}/d\sigma_{\text{stripping}} = (3/2) \left[(2J_i + 1)/(2J_f + 1) \right] (k_d/k_p)^2 \quad (85)$$

which is derived from the principle of detailed balance.

Equation (82) is the one which customarily is used for fitting experiments. Ordinarily only one value of l_n is of importance in the sum,[6] and the cross sections are simple. Most stripping experiments

---

[5] The corresponding equation of Bu57b is his (3.26). The reader should note that the function $h_l^{(1)}(ikr)$ as used in that reference does not conform to the standard definition (Sc49) as used here and in the other references.

[6] Deuteron stripping on spheroidal nuclei, which gives some automatic mixing of l values, has been discussed by J. Sawicki and G. R. Satchler (Sa58a, Sa58d, Sa58e). In part their concern is to analyze in detail how the reduced widths follow from the mixture of l values which makes up an orbital of a nucleon in a deformed well. Also (Sa58e) they show how the use of the distorted waves produced by a deformed well can transfer some angular momentum into core rotation. The latter effect is a true collective modification of the reaction mechanism.

are exothermic, and such that q is very small in the forward direction. Then the cross section will tend to be zero in the forward direction, except if $l_n = 0$. In general the cross section tends to have one large peak, the first peak of $j_l(qR)$, this occurring approximately at $qR = l$. The subsequent peaks are suppressed by the form factor. The location of the first peak serves to determine the value of l, thus providing valuable spectroscopic information. Many stripping experiments have been performed, and the l values determined in this fashion. It is well known that Eq. (82) frequently provides an excellent fit to experiment, and seldom is grossly in error.

The function $Q_{l_n}{}^2$ in Eq. (82) can readily be tabulated in numerical form, obviating the task of calculating it anew for each experiment. This has been done (Lu57). The tables give $Q_{l_n}{}^2$ as a function of (qR), for a variety of values of l_n and of the parameter (κ/q). The tables include an approximate correction for a finite range for V_{NP}.

It is to be noted that Eq. (82) is the correct result in Born approximation, in the usual sense that the nuclear interior is excluded. Bhatia et al. (Bh52) made the first computation in Born approximation, and obtained a result which differed from Eq. (82) in including only the first term of the Wronskian. This was because they had made the additional approximation, in the integral in Eq. (81), of treating $j_l(qr)$ as so slowly varying that it could be replaced by its value at $r = R$, a procedure discussed in Section 3.C(1) of this article. Fortunately the Bhatia et al. approximation need not ever be used, as the integral which they evaluated approximately can be computed exactly, giving the result (82). It is strange that authors sometimes prefer the Bhatia et al. formula (Hu53) as giving a better fit to some particular experiments. In circumstances where Eq. (82) fits badly it is irrelevant that a mere mutilated version of Eq. (82) might happen to fit better. Furthermore, simple *physical* arguments suggest minor modifications of Eq. (82) which improve the fit in just the fashion desired, in the cases which are at issue (see below, and Bu57b).

It is possible to interpret Eq. (82) as the cross section for the capture (Bo59) of a virtual plane wave beam of neutrons of wave vector **q**. Indeed, Eq. (82) can be derived on the basis of this interpretation. The form factor appears in the alternative version given in Eq. (84), and plays the role of the probability for the deuteron to yield a neutron of momentum **q**. The selection rules [Eqs. (83a) and (83b)] may be understood as those for a nucleus of spin J_i to capture a neutron of orbital angular momentum l, to form a nucleus of spin J_f. In this interpretation it is easy to see that the consideration of a finite range V_{NP} and of the deuteron D-state part give no essential modification of Eq. (82).

With a finite range V_{NP} the momentum transform of the deuteron is not

$$[\gamma^2 + (\mathbf{k}_p - {}^1/_2\mathbf{k}_D)^2]^{-1}$$

but rather is

$$[\gamma^2 + (\mathbf{k}_p - {}^1/_2\mathbf{k}_D)^2]^{-1} - [\zeta^2 + (\mathbf{k}_p - {}^1/_2\mathbf{k}_D)^2]^{-1}$$

where $\zeta \approx 7\gamma$. At small angles the second term is negligible compared to the first. It is noticeable at large angles, but there the theory is not too accurate anyhow.

The deuteron D-state is of equally little importance (Da53), despite its *large* probability (Sw58a), as only the momentum transform of the deuteron, averaged over angles and spins, enters into the computation of the cross section. By using the effective range normalization factor N, Eq. (80), the D-state probability is correctly accounted for.

Corrections to the crude stripping theory have been considered by many authors, and the literature by now is vast. Most authors have emphasized the very reasonable corrections which are introduced by the use of distorted waves, taking us over from the "crude" theory to the "simple" theory, as discussed in this article. In these corrections the distortion by the nuclear Coulomb field might be expected to be more important than that by the nuclear optical potential, for by the original arguments of Butler the stripping takes advantage of the loose structure of the deuteron and occurs far outside the main body of the target nucleus, giving high order partial waves a predominating role. Then these partial waves should be only weakly affected by the short-range nuclear optical potential, even if strongly affected by the long-range Coulomb potential. Nevertheless, this argument seems to be wrong. Most experiments show good agreement with the uncorrected crude theory, Eq. (82). When the consequences of the crude theory are recalculated with increased accuracy, with the use of Coulomb wave functions, the peak in the angular distribution generally is pushed towards larger angles to such an extent as to destroy the *apparent* good agreement which was found initially (To55, Ri58b, Te58, To59). But further calculation then discloses that the addition of the short range nuclear optical well often largely restores the original form of the wholly uncorrected crude theory angular distribution. In other words, there seems to be some general tendency for the nuclear distortion to oppose the Coulomb distortion in its effect on the angular distribution, even though both cooperate to reduce the absolute value of the cross section. This tendency is especially exhibited in the recent detailed calculations by Tobocman (To59), who uses the nuclear distortions predicted by carefully chosen optical wells, so avoiding the previous *ad hoc* guessing of distortion parameters. The cancellation of errors tendency has not been proved in any general way, however, so the real accuracy of the crude theory must be regarded as in doubt.

The semi-classical model of Section 2 agrees with a number of the results of explicit calculations of distortion effects. It does show such effects to be most important at back angles, as for those angles several wavelengths of the outgoing proton wave exp $i(\mathbf{q} \cdot \mathbf{r})$ extend across the nucleus, and it becomes relatively easy to upset the interferences between distant parts of the nucleus. In this way isotropy can be introduced at back angles, even without any compound nucleus participation. The semi-classical model is of interest also for suggesting a reason for the characteristic accuracy of the theory at small angles. This is that $k_d \approx k_p$ for most deuteron stripping experiments ever performed. Not only does this (somewhat fortuitous) property give well separated peaks for different l values, but for the smaller scattering angles it causes the active cylinder of the semi-classical model to lie approximately perpendicular to the deuteron beam direction. Then the interference between outgoing protons which originate at opposite ends of the active cylinder does not rely upon their having to pass through the nucleus.

Dispersion theory demonstrates (Am59) that stripping formulas must always involve a pole, of the nature of the form factor denominator $(q^2 + \kappa^2)^{-2}$ in Eq. (82). In our Born approximation derivation this pole corresponds to the stripping of deuterons which pass far from the nucleus. Such events have high probability if both q and κ are small. Distortion effects are negligible for deuterons which are far from the nucleus, so the crude formula, Eq. (82), should be especially accurate for such experimental conditions. Just such results have been found (Wi58, Se59, Se60) and the agreement with Eq. (82)

has been spectacular. To approach the pole most closely one must perform experiments both with small Q and at low energy, as otherwise q and κ cannot both be made small. It already has been seen that the $Li^7(d, p)Li^8$ reaction is better described by Eq. (82) at low energy than at high energy. Of course these experiments avoid the distorted waves problem. Presumably, accurate distorted waves calculations which would replace Eq. (82) would fit well at all energies.

Equation (82) does seem to give very good fits for many experiments with fairly light nuclei, $A \lesssim 40$, for deuteron energies of the order of 8 to 20 Mev. However, even for nuclei in this range, Eq. (82) tends to be used more as an interpolation formula than as a completely theoretical result, and the parameters of the formula are always *fitted* to the experiments. By means of such fits different nuclei may be compared, or different levels of one nucleus may be compared. To some extent such a procedure only accepts the *idea* of stripping and is not too concerned about the details of the formula. This procedure is the basis of the spectroscopic studies of Auerbach and French (Au55), as recently reviewed by MacFarlane and French (Ma60). It permits the determination of *relative* reduced widths from experiment. The basic assumption of the spectroscopic approach is that for the various levels in any one nuclear subshell, the distorted waves corrections to the stripping cross section are slow functions of the bombarding energy, the excitation energy, and the mass number (see also Hu58). This approach remains valid even for very heavy nuclei, for which Eq. (82) cannot be applied at all.

One rather simple distortion effect relates to the value of κ in Eq. (82). In all (d, n) experiments it should be helpful to replace κ by κ^*, where

$$\kappa^{*2} = \kappa^2 + (2M/\hbar^2)(Ze^2/R) \tag{86}$$

The rate of decrease of a bound proton wave function is not to be determined by a spherical Hankel function, but by its Coulomb analog. This may be counterfeited, for the region immediately outside the core nucleus, by using in a Hankel function expression not the actual (negative) energy by which the proton is bound to the nucleus, but rather the larger (negative) value of its kinetic energy just outside the surface. This correction is particularly important if the proton binding energy should be very small, as for the $C^{12}(d, n)N^{13*}$

experiment discussed by Huby (Hu53). It increases the coefficient of the first term in the Wronskian. It should be a fairly accurate correction.

The choice of the best value of κ to be used in Eq. (82) is closely related to the choice of the best value to be used for R. Both are somewhat adjustable. An increase of κ shifts the phase of the oscillations in the angular distribution, such that the peaks move toward larger angles. An increase of R decreases the spacing between successive peaks, crowding them all toward smaller angles. As usually only the first peak is observed, the two effects almost necessarily are confused, and only for one (α, p) experiment were Likely and Brady (Li56) able to separate them.

It is not obvious *a priori* what value would be best for R. A nonzero lower limit on the radial integral in Eq. (81), in the first instance is introduced to simulate the more important distorted wave effects, these supposedly suppressing contributions from $r < R$. Actually it has been known for a long time that the inclusion of contributions from $r < R$ makes very little difference right around the first peak (Da52), and several authors have suggested that for larger angles their inclusion would improve the agreement with experiment (Gr57c, To59). Despite this, some important change in the wave functions evidently does happen at a characteristic radius R, which plays an important role in the fit to experiment. Now the *optical* phenomena which might establish such a characteristic R are of the usual two sorts: partly the interior is suppressed because nucleons are absorbed into compound nucleus modes of motion, and partly because the deuteron tends to be dissociated as it enters the nucleus. No stripping can result in the interior if the neutron and proton move independently there. Ultimately a three-body wave function may be found which is sufficiently accurate as to permit a reasonable analysis of these phenomena, perhaps along the lines of the impulse approximation wave function of Rakavy (Ra58). Meanwhile vague estimates must be made. Deuteron dissociation probably is the more important of the effects which might minimize the role of the interior, for even the outermost tail of the optical potential seems sufficient to break up a deuteron of, say, 10 Mev. This suggests that the effective R will be of the order of or somewhat greater than the half-depth radius of the optical potential, about $(1.27 A^{1/3} + 0.6) \times 10^{-13}$ cm (We57).

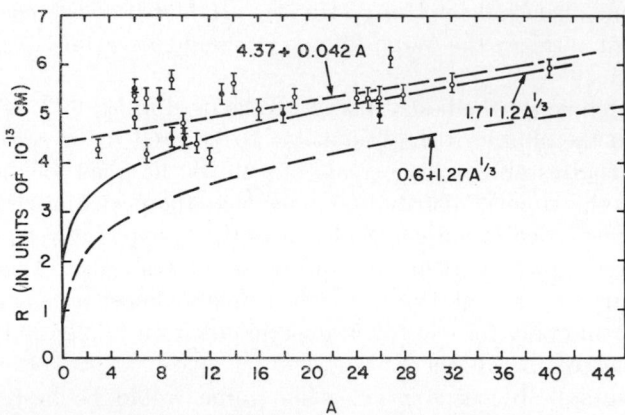

Figure 9. "Experimental" values of stripping radii, as determined to give best fits in Eq. (82). This graph largely taken from Re56. For more recent information see Ma60.

It has become the custom in experimental laboratories to seek that value for R which enables Eq. (82) to give the best possible fit to the measured curve. The Gamow-Critchfield value, cited by Huby (Hu53).

$$R = (1.7 + 1.22 \, A^{1/3}) \times 10^{-13} \text{ cm}$$

has been much used, and fits the radius values compiled by Holt and Marsham (Ho53c). Figure 9 shows a recent compilation of "experimental" values of R, as determined to give best fits with Eq. (82). These values all lie well above the optical model radius. There is a good ideal of scatter, but seldom so much as to cast in doubt the determination of l. More recent data show that the best-fit R values decrease as deuteron bombarding energy is increased (Se60, Mo60, Ha60b).

A simple modification of the radial integral in Eq. (81) gives some insight as to the meaning of the parameters R and κ in Eq. (82), and also as to the numerical value of the reduced width. For simplicity consider the case $l = 0$. Then

$$j_0(qr) = (\sin qr)/qr$$

$$h_0^{(1)}(i\kappa r) = (\exp - \kappa r)/\kappa r$$

Then if the asymptotic form (62) is used for f_i the integral becomes

$$\int_R^\infty r^2 dr j_0 f_i = (2MR/\hbar^2)^{1/2} \gamma_{ijl}(q^2 + \kappa^2)^{-1} \left\{ (\kappa/q) \sin qR + \cos qR \right\}$$
(87)

In Eq. (87) we now see explicitly that the second term of the Wronskian serves to shift the peaks of the angular distribution toward smaller angles. Normally $(\kappa/q) \gg 1$ and the second term only is a correction. However, if it were omitted fairly large values of R would be needed in order to fit the position of the first peak (cf., Bhatia *et al.*). The value of κ controls the relative importance of the two terms.

Now consider a reasonable modification of the integral. Suppose R to be the radius below which contributions to stripping are *wholly* suppressed. For radii slightly greater than R the integrand certainly must be smaller than its asymptotic value, both because f_i must lie below its asymptotic value, and because the onset of dissociation depletes the incident beam. It is easiest to modify the integrand in the required fashion by changing the expression used for f_i, taking

$$f_i \approx (2M/\hbar^2 R)^{1/2} \gamma_{ijl} \left\{ [h_l^{(1)}(i\kappa r) - A h_l^{(1)}(i\lambda r)]/h_l^{(1)}(i\kappa R) \right\} \quad (88)$$

where $\lambda > \kappa$, and $0 < A < 1$. All the other quantities in Eq. (88) have the same values as before. With this f_i it is found for $l = 0$ that

$$\int_R^\infty r^2 dr j_0 f_i = (2MR/\hbar^2)^{1/2} \gamma_{ijl}(q^2 + \kappa^2)^{-1}$$
$$\times \left\{ (\kappa/q) \sin qR \left[1 - A(\lambda/\kappa)(q^2 + \kappa^2)/(q^2 + \lambda^2) \right] \right.$$
$$\left. + \cos qR \left[1 - A(q^2 + \kappa^2)/(q^2 + \lambda^2) \right] \right\} \quad (89)$$

Upon comparing Eq. (89) with Eq. (87) it is seen that the first term has been reduced more than the second, so that our modification of the integrand has shifted the angular distribution pattern toward smaller angles, as if R had been increased in Eq. (87) or κ decreased. This effect is superimposed upon the dissociation effect, previously discussed, in causing the usual "experimental" values of R to be larger than the optical model radii.

In summary, many worthwhile corrections to the deuteron stripping theory can be made. Its most noteworthy feature remains, however, the remarkable accuracy of the most elementary version of the theory, particularly in fitting to experimental *angular* distributions. In part this must be because the crude theory is identical with impulse approximation, as noted earlier; in part because the deuteron is so large and loose that it is easy for one particle to interact while the other goes free; in part because the deuteron is very easily dissociated as it enters the nucleus, so that the process is reliably confined to the surface; and in part because nearly all experiments have been performed under conditions which are favorable for the theory, wherein q is very small at forward angles.

(2a) **Heavy Particle Stripping.** Many experiments show large peaks at backward angles, as mentioned in the Introduction. If this backward angle structure varies very rapidly with angle or if it varies slowly with bombarding energy, a direct reaction mechanism must be regarded as important. One partly expects the same mechanisms which are important at forward angles to also contribute at backward angles. Calculations with plane waves suggest otherwise, but with the use of distorted waves the refraction by the optical potential often increases the back angle cross section. The reflection effect is of this nature (Section 2). But refraction undoubtedly is not a complete explanation for the back angle effects. One must also expect new direct reaction mechanisms to become important for such effects, mechanisms which involve the detailed internal structure of the target nucleus. The *heavy particle stripping* of Madansky and Owen (Ma55, Ow57, Fu57, Ze58, Ha59, Na59, Ne59, Ow59), originally proposed for (d, p) reactions, was the first such mechanism to receive much discussion.

In the heavy particle stripping the outgoing proton is considered not to come from the deuteron at all, but from the target nucleus. The target is separated into the form $\{p + \text{core}\}$, the deuteron strikes the core and adheres to it, the proton remains a spectator, so tends to emerge preferentially in the backwards direction. This process is "stripping" in the sense that the deuteron has stripped off the *core* from the target nucleus. It is to be noted that the process is a consequence of considering a nuclear interaction which is omitted in the Butler stripping theory, and is *not* the result of antisymmetrizing that theory. On the other hand the use of antisymmetrized wave functions is desirable in calculations of this process. Protons are indistinguishable from each other, the two processes interfere coherently, and if antisymmetrized wave functions are not used it is possible to lose track of the many (four) particles which participate in the reaction.

From the Born approximation it would seem that the heavy particle process must usually be of smaller amplitude than the Butler process; such an extensive rearrangement of the nucleus is involved that the amplitude must be held down by poor overlap between the initial and final wave functions (the parentage is small). However, because of the clustering in the nuclear surface, the reduced width for adding a deuteron to a nucleus probably is much bigger than the product of reduced widths for separately adding a neutron and a proton, which appears in Born approximation. Nuclei are black to composite particles. For this reason the heavy particle process may be much more probable than at first suspected, and the back angle cross section may give useful measures of clustering in the nuclear surface.

Of course, the heavy particle process also is assisted if the target nucleus on to which a neutron (proton) is to be added has a "valence" proton (neutron) which is bound very loosely. Such a case is provided by the reaction $Be^9(d, n)B^{10}$, the results from which led Madansky and Owen to propose the heavy particle process.

The only simple quantitative theory for the heavy particle process is the appropriate analog of Eq. (82). The resulting angular distribution tends to be very slowly varying, inasmuch as a proton left as a spectator from the incident heavy nucleus can only have a small velocity. In Eq. (82) this effect appears through the small value found for the momentum transfer

$$\mathbf{q} = -(M_p/M_s + M_p)\mathbf{k}_D - (M_D/M_s + M_D)\mathbf{k}_p \qquad (90)$$

after the reduced mass effects discussed on page(1150) have been inserted. Some additional modifications also enter through the form factor of the angular distribution. This now is the momentum transform of the wave function of the proton bound in the incident heavy nucleus. This momentum transform may itself have oscillations (Ow57, Ow59) if the proton is initially in a state with non-zero angular momentum. The angular distribution thereby is made more complicated and the back-angle peak tends to be sharpened.

(2b) **Spin-Flip Stripping.** The selection rules for the Butler stripping process [Section 3.D(1)] are more restrictive than those for the general (d, p) reaction, inasmuch as the Butler process pictures the proton as not participating in the reaction. Certain reactions otherwise possible, become pictured as forbidden. A notable example is the reaction $B^{10}(d, p)B^{11}*$ to the first excited state of B^{11}. Here it is known that the neutron is added to B^{10} in a p orbit, so that it can bring to the nucleus either $1/2$ or $3/2$ units of angular momentum. Since the J values of B^{10} and $B^{11}*$ are 3 and $1/2$, respectively, it is evident that the transition cannot proceed by Butler stripping. The interest which attaches to the reaction then lies in the fact that the cross section is moderately large and that the angular distribution sometimes (Ev54) suggestively resembles the usual stripping form for $l = 1$. Evidently the proton participates in the reaction, weakening the selection rule, but in some such way that the overall process may resemble the one in which the proton does not interact.

The proton interacts with the target nucleus, the "core" of the product nucleus, through the off-diagonal parts of the $V_{p\xi}$ interaction of Eq. (77). In so doing it changes either the internal structure or the spin of the core, properties the Butler process carefully keeps fixed. Two simple models of the $V_{p\xi}$ interaction have been proposed to date, both giving satisfactory fits to the data of Ev54.

The mechanism of A. P. French (Fr57b) is not even properly called stripping. It requires the target nucleus to have a loosely bound proton, as in the heavy-particle stripping. Then the deuteron strikes the loosely bound nucleon of the target, ejects it, and remains bound to the target in its stead. In the crude theory approximation this gives a sharply defined peak in the forward direction, and at just the same angle as the ordinary stripping. The process is precisely of the nature of the knock-on inelastic scattering discussed in Sections 3.B and 3.C. It may be called *exchange stripping*, however, as antisymmetrization of the nuclear model connects it with the ordinary stripping. In place of the usual stripping selection rule

$$\mathbf{J}_f + \mathbf{J}_i + 1 + \mathbf{S}_n = 0$$

which expresses angular momentum conservation when a neutron is added to the target, the exchange stripping of French incorporates the full complication of Eq. (48e) for the knock-on process, as appropriately generalized for a deuteron as one projectile:

$$\mathbf{J}_f + \mathbf{J}_i + 1 + \mathbf{S}_n + \mathbf{S}_D = 0$$

This weakened selection rule allows the B^{10} reaction.

The exchange stripping is smaller than Butler stripping, for the usual reason that additional overlap integrals are involved, and that these are between wave functions which are at their largest in different regions of space. The nature of the overlap also blurs the angular distribution from Butler form and raises it at back angles. In the absence of the short range V_{np} interaction in the matrix element, and in the presence of only the weak range-correlation imposed by the deuteron wave function, the neutron and proton need not be close together when entering the nucleus. Averaging over the different possibilities blurs the angular distribution.

The mechanism of Bowcock (Bo58a), in contrast, does not assign any internal structure to the target nucleus or require that it have any special internal properties. Instead it requires that the outgoing proton, which comes from the deuteron, make a spin-dependent interaction at the nuclear surface. The matrix element of this interaction, assumed to be a part of $V_{p\xi}$ in Eq. (77), gives the entire amplitude for the (d, p) process. By enabling the proton to flip its spin in this way the B^{10} reaction becomes allowed, as above. A considerable blurring from the simple Bessel function angular distribution occurs in this mechanism, as in the French mechanism, and for the same reasons.

The French model and Bowcock model seem different, but for some nuclei may be alternative pictures of the same physical situation. Whether the outgoing proton originates in the target or in the deuteron is somewhat only a matter of language, of course, the Pauli principle allowing no such distinction when overlap is strong. Apparently one or the other of these mechanisms, or a combination of them both, indeed is wholly responsible for the B^{10} reaction (Ev54, He58a, Wi57b).

J. B. French has suggested (private communication) that the B^{10} reaction may be a rather special case, in showing an angular distribution of stripping form. Experiments thus far available for other reactions forbidden in stripping show no indications of any characteristic spin-flip contribution; the cross sections merely are "low" and "isotropic." He lists

(a) $Ne^{20}(d, p)Ne^{21}$(g.s.) $0^+ \rightarrow 3/2^+$, $d_{3/2}$ orbital unfavored here, but spin-flip would allow $d_{5/2}$

(b) $Na^{23}(d, n)Mg^{24}$(g.s.) $3/2^+ \rightarrow 0^+$, same as in (a)

(c) $Mg^{24}(d, p)Mg^{25}(1.61 \text{ Mev})$ $0^+ \rightarrow 7/2^+$, $g_{7/2}$ forbidden, but spin-flip would allow $d_{5/2}$

(d) $Ca^{42}(d, p)Ca^{43}(0.37 \text{ Mev})$ $0^+ \rightarrow 5/2^-$, $f_{5/2}$ forbidden, but spin-flip would allow $f_{7/2}$

(e) $Ca^{44}(d, p)Ca^{45}(0.176 \text{ Mev})$ $0^+ \rightarrow 5/2^-$, same as in (d)

Other similar cases also are available, but the experiments have not yet been performed (Ma60). The unique status of the B^{10} reaction as the only observed application of a rather general theoretical model suggests further study of the experiments. The most complete study thus far seems to be that of Zeidman and Fowler (Ze58) who measured the cross section at 10.0, 9.2, and 8.1 Mev, and who review the earlier literature. They observe that the $B^{10}(d, p)B^{11}$ (first excited state) angular distribution goes through considerable changes of form as bombarding energy changes, so that the resemblance to an $l = 1$ form at 8 Mev (Ev54) may be entirely accidental. The theoretical models (Fr57b, Ev58, Bo58a) may be overreaching themselves in attempting to describe a reaction which is of an essentially compound nucleus nature. It is extremely interesting, despite these pessimistic remarks, that at 7.6 and 9 Mev the apparent mirror transition $B^{10}(d, n)C^{11}$ (first excited state) does show a very clear $l = 1$ stripping peak. No final conclusion seems possible yet.

(2c) **Deuteron Inelastic Scattering.** Deuterons undoubtedly are strongly absorbed at the nuclear surface. Accordingly, deuteron inelastic scattering is most likely to proceed by a *diffraction inelastic scattering* process and to excite collective motions of the nucleus, as already discussed in Section 3.C(3). The deuterons that emerge from the reaction are those described by waves that "pass by" the nucleus. At present, the best available theories for this process are the adiabatic theory (Bl59) and the distorted waves theory using black nucleus wave functions (Ro60). Both these theories ignore the internal structure of the deuteron. however, and may therefore be significantly in error.

Earlier theories stress the internal structure of the deuteron but make no attempt to introduce distorted waves. The target is thought to be excited through a direct interaction with only one of the nucleons of the deuteron (Hu51, Bu57b, Sa58c, Ed60, Fa60), the other nucleon of the deuteron standing by as a spectator, as in a stripping process. Calculation of this model requires both that the incident deuteron be decomposed into momentum eigenstates, which are virtually stripped and reemitted by the nucleus, and that the outgoing deuteron then be reassembled from these momentum eigenstates. These dual requirements combine to yield a more rapidly varying form factor than appears for the simple stripping. Complications may appear if the intermediate states of this second order process are limited in any way (Ed60, Fa60).

Experiments agree with the predictions of this model to varying degrees (Ho49, Fr54a, Le55, Be56a, Be58, Ha56, Hi56b, Hi57, He58b, Su58, Vo58, Yn58), frequently showing a sharp peak at low angles, such as the theory predicts, and occasionally showing suggestions of secondary peaks. On the whole, however, the agreement between theory and experiment is sporadic, and never very good.

(3) Projectiles Other Than Deuterons. Reactions such as (H^3, d), (H^3, n), (α, He^3), (α, d), (α, n) can be visualized as proceeding by the stripping mechanism, and occasionally have been discussed in such terms. Insofar as there is any theory for the process it simply is the appropriate analog of Eq. (82), with due attention paid to the use of proper reduced masses, especially in computing $\mathbf{q}$. The numerical coefficient in front of the entire expression also must be changed, to allow for the probability that the projectile is able to yield the sub-unit which is stripped off. For most of these reactions with heavier projectiles one can be a bit skeptical regarding the applicability of the "crude" theory. It is hard to imagine the accuracy of the basic assumption that the outgoing particle only participates in the reaction as a spectator. As a matter of fact these reactions with composite particles probably are sufficiently well characterized just as *surface reactions* and treated by the methods of Section 3.C(3). Whether the detailed mechanism of the reaction is stripping or knock on has little influence on the angular distribution. Many such reactions have now been studied experimentally, and their angular distributions show the strong diffraction structure which characterizes surface reactions.

The reaction (H^3, d) has the most hope of being describable as stripping (Bu52b, We56, Bu57b). It is best understood in terms of the interpretation that the stripping formula describes the capture of a virtual plane wave beam of neutrons. Then (H^3, d) differs from (d, p) in no other way except by the *angle-independent* multiplying factor:

{Asymptotic probability for H^3 to appear as $(n + d)$

$\qquad \div$ Asymptotic probability for H^2 to appear as $(n + p)$}

The full result (Bu57b) analogous to (82), with proper account taken of the triton spin and mass, is

$$d\sigma = (4/\hbar^2)(M_t{}^*M_D{}^*/M_n{}^*)(k_D/k_t)[(2J_f + 1)/(2J_i + 1)](N_i{}^2 A_0{}^2)$$
$$\cdot R^3 \sum_{l_n} \gamma_{l_n}{}^2 Q_{l_n}{}^2 \quad (91)$$

The incident and outgoing particle reduced masses are indicated in Eq. (91). The quantity $(N_i{}^2 A_0{}^2)$ represents the asymptotic normalization factor of the projection of the H^3 wave function onto the product of a neutron $\times$ an unpolarized deuteron. It is of the nature of a reduced width.

Of the two expressions for the form factor denominator, related by Eq. (84), the one in terms of the properties of the bound state of the final nucleus is the more helpful in showing the essential identity of the (H^3, d) and (d, p) cross sections for a given nuclear transition. If the cross sections are quoted as functions of q, then, provided the simple stripping assumptions hold, one should be a numerical multiple of the other. The multiplier is entirely known *a priori*, except for the one factor $(N_i{}^2 A_0{}^2)$, which thus may be measured.

Many (d, H^3) and (d, He^3) experiments have been performed by now, showing angular distributions in good agreement with the above predictions, as in the work of Vo58 and Mo58a. Values of $N_i{}^2 A_0{}^2$ occasionally have been extracted. Thus Werner (We56) discussed the reactions $C^{13}(p, d)C^{12}$ and $C^{13}(d, H^3)C^{12}$, and obtained $N_i{}^2 A_0{}^2 \approx 1.8 \times 10^{13}$ cm^{-1}. This value was interpreted as indicating a fairly small projection (less than ten per cent) for the triton wave function on to the state (neutron $\times$ unpolarized deuteron). In like fashion Hamburger (Ha60a) also has found close proportionality between the angular distributions for the (p, d) and (d, H^3) reactions for $Li^7 \rightarrow Li^6$ and Li^{6*}, $C^{13} \rightarrow C^{12}$ and C^{12*}, $C^{14} \rightarrow C^{13}$, $F^{19} \rightarrow F^{18}$, $Mg^{25} \rightarrow Mg^{24}$, $Na^{23} \rightarrow Na^{22}$ and Na^{22*}. The corresponding $N_i{}^2 A_0{}^2$ values are 1.2, 1.2, 1.1, 0.7, 1.1, 0.13, 0.8, 0.8, and 1.1 respectively. El Nadi and Abou Hadid (Na58) also analyzed $Li^7 \rightarrow Li^6$ and $F^{19} \rightarrow F^{18}$, finding the values 1.08 and 0.27. General agreement among the results is seen, making it appear that these reactions probably give much the same spectroscopic data as do (d, p) and (d, n) reactions. It is interesting that French and Fujii (Fr57c) calculated $N_t^2 A_0^2$ from first principles, from Irving's triton wave function, finding a value only a factor or two larger than the experimental values.

Additional data indicating the stripping character of (d, H^3) and (d, He^3) reactions have been published by Vl59a, Vl59b, Ku59, and Fo60; see also Ma60.

E. Angular Correlations

Angular correlation experiments $(a, b\ \gamma)$ concern the two-step reaction $i \to f \to g$. In the first step the particle b is emitted, as discussed already. We now go further, for those reactions in which f is an excited state, and study the γ-ray transition to the ultimate final state g. The study of the γ ray can give interesting additional information about the step $i \to f$, because in that step the state f generally is formed partly polarized, and the angular momentum J_f will tend to lie along some preferred axis. The γ-ray angular distribution will have the preferred axis of J_f as its axis of symmetry, so indicating the direction of that axis, and the form of the distribution may help to determine J_f.

All angular correlations $(a, b\ \gamma)$ initiated by direct reactions are formally identical, so long as their analysis is conducted *within the crude theory* approximations, with incident and outgoing plane waves. The preferred axis always is the recoil vector $\mathbf{q} = \mathbf{k}_i - \mathbf{k}_f$, the momentum of the virtual "particle" which the nucleus "captures." Thus the matrix element for the formation of state f has the same structure as the matrix element for the formation of this state by a plane wave beam of wave vector $\mathbf{q}$. Discussions of these correlations are given, for example, by Bi52, Bi53, Bl52a, Ga52, Ho54, Sa52, Sa53, Sa55, Sa56a, Kr56, To56, Ba57b, Bu57b, and Bi60.

Deuteron stripping $(d, p\ \gamma)$ clearly illustrates the above ideas. Here the state f is formed through the capture of an actual tangible particle, a neutron, and $\mathbf{q}$ is the momentum of this neutron. The matrix element for the formation of state f is T_{fi}, of Eq. (77). Also, with randomly polarized deuterons incident and with no observation of the outgoing proton polarization, the spin of the virtual neutron beam is unpolarized. These remarks suffice to reduce the calculation of the $(d, p\ \gamma)$ correlation to that of a problem previously solved, the (n, γ) angular distribution. Biedenharn, Boyer, and Charpie (Bi52) give an explicit expression for the p-γ correlation, for the case that the $f \rightarrow g$ transition takes place by a pure multipole gamma ray of multipolarity 2^L. It is

$$w(q,\gamma) = \sum_{l_n,l'_n,j_{in},\nu} (2l_n + 1)^{1/2}(2l'_n + 1)^{1/2}\, \gamma_{i,l_n,j_{in}}\gamma_{i,l'_n,j_{in}}$$

$$\times \langle l_n l'_n,00|\nu 0\rangle \langle LL,\, 1,\, -1|\nu 0\rangle\, i^{l_n - l'_n}(-)^{j_{in} - J_f}$$

$$\times W(J_f J_f LL;\nu J_g)W(J_f J_f l_n l'_n;\nu j_{in})\, Q_{l_n}Q_{l'_n}P_\nu(\hat{\mathbf{q}}\cdot\hat{\boldsymbol{\gamma}}) \quad (92)$$

where Q_{l_n} is the expression in Eq. (82b). The W functions are the usual unnormalized Racah coefficients, and P_ν is a Legendre function of the cosine of the angle between $\mathbf{q}$ and $\boldsymbol{\gamma}$, the gamma-ray direction. The distribution is predicted to be isotropic in the plane perpendicular to $\mathbf{q}$.

Mixtures of different l_n values seldom occur in stripping reactions, so the summation over l_n and l_n' in Eq. (92) generally is restricted to only one value, this value being known beforehand from observation of the (d, p) angular distribution. The channel spin $j_{in} = |\mathbf{J}_i + \boldsymbol{\mathfrak{S}}_n|$ has only two values, $J_i \pm 1/2$, and these are incoherent with one another because $\mathbf{J}_i$ and $\boldsymbol{\mathfrak{S}}_n$ both are unpolarized. Evidently Eq. (92) really is rather simple. The usual ambiguity of the spin J_f, which is left by the stripping selection rule,

$$J_f = |\mathbf{J}_i + \mathbf{l}_n + \boldsymbol{\mathfrak{S}}_n|$$

is likely to be resolved by observing the angular correlation pattern.

One noteworthy feature of Eq. (92) is the appearance of interference between different l_n values. (This effect was overlooked by Ga52.) When only the proton angular distribution is computed this interference averages out, in just the same way that the different partial waves contribute independently to the *total* cross section for neutron capture (n, γ). Thus there is some slight possibility that l_n admixtures can be detected by $(d, p\,\gamma)$ measurements. It also is to be noted that ν runs only over even values, so that the γ rays are not correlated to the *sense* of the vector $\mathbf{q}$. Also there generally is a one parameter ambiguity in the angular correlation pattern, the parameter being

$$(\gamma_{i,l_n,J_i + 1/2})^2/(\gamma_{i,l_n,J_i - 1/2})^2$$

and depending on the dynamics of the nuclear wave function of state f.

Sometimes this parameter can be determined by the $(d, p\ \gamma)$ experiment, and distinguishes sharply between L-S and j-j coupling. It is worthwhile to perform angular correlation experiments for the sake of determining this parameter, even if no ambiguity of J_f needs to be resolved.

For other direct reactions the virtual "particle" which is captured is not as tangible as the captured neutron of the (d, p) stripping, but is equally as effective (Sa55) conceptually in reducing the problem to a case of resonant capture. Equation (39), say, illustrates the situation well enough. Once again state f is formed from state i by a plane wave beam of wave vector $\mathbf{q}$, which is the symmetry axis for the γ-ray distribution. This "incident" beam, however, need not have spin $1/2$. Its spin is a composite of the incoming and outgoing particle spins,

$$\left| \mathfrak{S}_i + \mathfrak{S}_f \right|$$

and unless one of these is zero it must include several values. Explicit formulas for particular cases which may be of interest can be achieved by referring to the articles of Biedenharn and Rose (Bi53) or Biedenharn (Bi58). The only rather general features which can be quoted for such formulas are (a) that $\mathbf{q}$ is the symmetry axis, (b) that the γ-ray distribution involves only *even* functions of the angle between $\mathbf{q}$ and γ.

Sometimes the predicted correlation pattern for the inelastic scattering is particularly simple and striking. Thus for (n, n') or (p, p') excitation of the transition $0^+ \rightarrow 2^+$ for even-even nuclei it is found (Sa55, Ba57b) that the correlation function is $\sin^2 2(\theta_\gamma - \theta_q)$, if the excitation is achieved just by recoupling the spins of definite orbitals. This function is predicted for the $0^+ \rightarrow 2^+$ excitation of C^{12} if this nucleus is $L - S$ coupled, the detailed description of the transition then being $^1S_0 \rightarrow {}^1D_2$. In j-j coupling the transition is achieved by promoting one nucleon from $p_{3/2}$ to $p_{1/2}$, a change of orbitals, and the simple result must be modified (Ba57b). A twenty-five per cent isotropic term must be added to the $\sin^2 2(\theta_\gamma - \theta_q)$ term.

Distorted waves corrections for the $(d, p\ \gamma)$ have been discussed most recently in great detail in the excellent paper of Huby, Refai, and Satchler (Hu58). These authors emphasize that despite all the adjustable parameters in a distorted waves calculation it still is significantly more restricted than general scattering theory. It retains the basic stripping assumption, that the outgoing particle makes no inelastic interactions with the nucleus. Suppose l is the orbital angular momentum of the captured neutron and μ the z-projection of l. Then all the distorted waves matrix elements turn out to be expressed in terms of the set of overlap integrals $B_{l\mu}(\mathbf{k}_d,\mathbf{k}_p)$, functions of the scattering angle. At any given scattering angle the set of all possible angular correlation and polarization experiments actually *over-determines* the $B_{l\mu}$ parameters, exhibiting the restrictions introduced by the stripping assumption. Equations of redundancy thus connect the possible correlation and polarization experiments. Checking the accuracy of these equations gives an elegant, if difficult, test of the direct reaction mechanism. A few simple limits can be considered, even without any detailed calculation of the $B_{l\mu}$, or any discussion of their variation with angle. In the plane wave limit (the "crude" theory) $\mathbf{q}$ is the most convenient z-axis and $\mu = 0$ then gives the only nonvanishing $B_{l\mu}$. Distortion, particularly for scattering angles off the main stripping peak, modifies the relative contributions to the overlap integrals from different parts of the nucleus. This can so change the pattern of values of the $B_{l\mu}$ that in extreme cases there again may be only one which is nonvanishing, but this one corresponding to an axis lying *perpendicular* to $\mathbf{q}$. In the latter case the γ-ray distribution in the $(\mathbf{k}_d, \mathbf{k}_p)$ plane would be isotropic! Such extremes are thought by Hu58 to be frequent. A few more explicit distorted waves $(d, p\ \gamma)$ calculations are given by Sa60.

Several $(d, n\ \gamma)$ experiments are described in Chapter V.Q., by Neilson, Sample, and Warren. Interesting $(d, p\ \gamma)$ experiments were reported by Allen *et al.* (Al56) for Si^{28} at 9.02 Mev, and by Cox and Williamson for Be^9, B^{10}, and Mg^{24} targets over the range 2.5–4 Mev (Co57h). In the Si^{28} experiment M1-E2 interference was possible, preventing any clear cut theoretical prediction. Considerable azimuthal anisotropy, in the plane perpendicular to $\mathbf{q}$, was found, indicating distorted wave effects, and together with near isotropy in the plane of $\mathbf{k}_d$ and $\mathbf{k}_p$. Perhaps the extreme distorted wave case of Hu58 is exhibited in this reaction. The Cox-Williamson experiments are simpler, as they were intended to test the theory, and cases which would have pure E1 γ rays were chosen. The azimuthal anisotropy was slight, the over all agreement with theory was rather good, and the correlations were seen to persist to low energy.

Recent $(d, p\, \gamma)$ experiments apply the Huby, Refai, and Satchler ideas to test in detail the applicability of the distorted waves theory. Bromley, Kuehner, and Almqvist (Br60) measured the angular correlation for two excited states in $Si^{28}(d, p\, \gamma)Si^{29}$. On the assumption that the levels are members of the same shell model multiplet and therefore, that the $B_{l\mu}$ parameters are the same for both levels, it was found that the correlation measured for one level implied that of the other. A more straightforward experiment was performed by Martin (Ma59). For the $l - 1$ transition $Mg^{24}(d, p\gamma)Mg^{25}$ he was able to measure the correlation patterns both in the reaction plane and perpendicular to the reaction plane, and at two proton angles. By means of the formulas of Hu58 it could then be seen that (a) the amount of distortion in this reaction is large, (b) a correct description of the reaction mechanism is given by the distorted waves theory.

Distorted waves analyses for other direct reactions can be carried through, just as for stripping, and equations of redundancy like those of Hu58 evidently can be derived. To test such equations would require a lengthy program of experimentation.

The semi-classical model permits some simple observations about distorted waves effects. It is seen to be possible that distortion due to absorption may modify the correlation much less strongly than it does the angular distribution patterns. The angular distributions are very sensitive to interferences between widely separated parts of the nucleus, and tend to wash out toward large angles. The γ-ray correlations depend only on there being a well-defined role for the vector $\mathbf{q}$, irrespective of the extent of the nucleus in which this role is played. These remarks are in good agreement with a number of observations already reported (Sh56b, Sh57, Ba57b, Pi58, Se58b, Sh58, Yo58b, La59), where a correlation measurement established the direct reaction nature of a transition. For deuteron stripping in particular it would seem to be of the greatest interest to perform a variety of angular correlation experiments over wide ranges of proton angles. The stripping angular distribution generally is observed experimentally to depart from the form of Eq. (82) toward large angles, becoming rather isotropic. This part of the cross section often is attributed to compound nucleus formation. There is a good chance that this idea is mistaken, that the backwards cross section is a direct reaction result. A measurement of the $(d, p\, \gamma)$ correlation as a function of proton direction could decide this question.

Some residual simplicity sometimes still can be found, even when pronounced refractive distortion has destroyed the role of **q** as a symmetry axis for the γ rays. For $C^{12}(p, p')$, $0^+ \rightarrow 2^+$, Banerjee and Levinson (Ba57b) show that the distorted waves result is

$$A + B \sin^2 2(\theta_\gamma - \theta_0)$$

largely preserving the elegance of the Satchler prediction. They find that distortion does not much affect A, so that the value of A can be used to distinguish between L-S and j-j coupling. Experiment agrees with the value $A/B \approx 0.25$, predicted for j-j coupling. The angle θ_0 is found to differ from θ_q, the direction of recoil, only for those protons which emerge rather far forwards. As $\theta_{p'} \rightarrow 0°$, it is found that $\theta_0 \rightarrow 90°$, perpendicular to the incident beam direction, whereas $\theta_q \rightarrow 0°$. This result also agrees with experiment.

F. Polarization

Zero polarization would appear in all direct reactions, were it not for distorted waves effects. Almost any sort of distortion from plane waves can be a cause of polarization, however, and it can become quite large. Distortion leads to polarization *whether or not* one includes the large (**L·S**) part of the optical potential (Bj58).

The physical mechanism which produces the polarization is easy enough to see. The nuclear transition has the form of an absorption of orbital angular momentum l, together with (channel) spin $S = |\mathfrak{S}_i + \mathfrak{S}_f|$, with $j = |1 + \mathfrak{S}|$ the total angular momentum which is absorbed. Different *directions* for **j** participate in the reaction on equal terms, of course, and do not select any favored direction for $\mathfrak{S}$, because the target nucleus is making a transition from an unpolarized initial state J_i to a final state J_f whose polarization is not measured. Different *values* of j participate in the reaction with different strengths, however, giving a significant coupling between **l** and $\mathfrak{S}$ and permitting a favored direction for $\mathfrak{S}$ to be selected if there is a favored direction for **l**. Distortion selects favored directions for **l**.

In the crude theory approximation **q** may be used as the axis of quantization and with respect to this axis the orbital motion merely is described by Y_l^0. As a result all components of l have zero as their expectation values, so **l** has no favored direction and $\mathfrak{S}$ has no favored direction. Since $\mathfrak{S}_i$ and $\mathfrak{S}_i + \mathfrak{S}_f$ both are unpolarized, we see that $\mathfrak{S}_f$ must be unpolarized, as was asserted above. Zero polari-

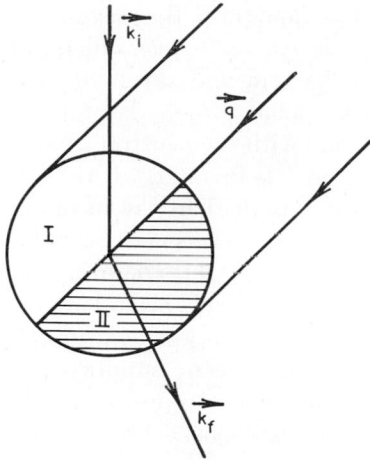

Figure 10.   Classical picture illustrating how absorptive distortion can lead to polarization in a direct reaction.   The pseudo particles captured in regions I and II have oppositely directed orbital angular momenta.   With absorption these two regions can contribute different amounts to the transition amplitude, so that spin-orbit coupling implies polarization.

zation is a rigorous result of the crude theories.   Spin dependence of the elementary interaction V_f, in Eq. (27), for example, plays no role in modifying this result.

Absorptive distortion, whereby the incident and/or outgoing beams do not penetrate throughout the entire nucleus, gives the simplest sort of polarization.   This first was discussed by Newns (Ne53), for the deuteron stripping, using a semi-classical picture (of rather good validity).   Recent accurate distorted waves calculations by Newns and Refai (Ne58) substantiate the semi-classical results in at least one reasonable case at low energy.   According to the Newns picture a given region in the nucleus is able to absorb the momentum transfer $\mathbf{q}$ only if it is illuminated by both the incoming and outgoing beams of particles.   Because these beams are subject to absorption the nucleus actually is illuminated nonuniformly by the momentum $\mathbf{q}$, so it receives a net *oriented* pulse of orbital angular momentum.   These remarks are illustrated by Fig. 10.   If the recoil momentum $\mathbf{q}$ is absorbed primarily in region I the nucleus is left with an orbital angular momentum $\mathbf{l}$ in the positive z direction (out of the page); if primarily in region II it is left with $\mathbf{l}$ pointing in the negative z direction (into the page). Any amount of spin-orbit coupling *in the bound final state* which is formed then gives a correlation between the spin and the favored direction of l, as explained, and leads to polarization. Example: Consider a (d, p) reaction with $l \neq 0$, and with the neutron captured into a $j = l + \frac{1}{2}$ orbit. Probably region I is favored, for the outgoing proton should have a longer mean free path than the incoming deuteron. Then l points up, so to get $j = l + \frac{1}{2}$ it is necessary that $\mathfrak{S}_n$ point up, therefore the protons emerge with $\mathfrak{S}_p$ also pointing up, because in the original deuteron $\mathfrak{S}_n$ and $\mathfrak{S}_p$ had been coupled to give spin one. Such a polarization effect certainly is a feature of all surface reactions. Absorption of the ingoing beam suppresses region II, while absorption of the emerging beam suppresses I; these two thus produce oppositely directed polarizations. Absorptive distortion evidently gives a polarization whose magnitude changes with angle, but whose sign remains constant. In the case discussed, where region I is favored the polarization is $(\pm)$ according as $j = l \pm \frac{1}{2}$, the direction of $[\mathbf{k}_d \times \mathbf{k}_p]$ defined as positive, according to the Basle convention.

Discussions for deuteron stripping have been given by many authors (Ne53, Ho53b, Ch54, Hi56c, To56, Bu57b, Sa57b, Hu58, Ne58, Sa58f, We58, To59). Both from the semi-classical model and from accurate distorted waves calculations it is found that if the $(\mathbf{L} \cdot \mathbf{S})$ part of the optical potential is ignored the polarization has $\frac{1}{3}$ as its upper limit. The limit arises because the (outgoing) proton spin is coupled to the (captured) neutron spin only through the deuteron spin as an intermediary. Predictions which ignore the $(\mathbf{L} \cdot \mathbf{S})$ potential and other confusing effects presumably are best near the main stripping peak, and the experiments performed so far have emphasized that region. Experiments have been reported by Hillman (Hi56a) for $C^{12}(d, p)$, by Haeberli and Rolland (Ha57) for C^{12} (d, n), by Bokhari *et al.* (Bo58b) for $C^{12}(d, p)$, by Hensel and Parkinson (He58a) for $B^{10}(d, p)$ and $C^{12}(d, p)$, and by Juveland and Jentschke (Ju58) for $C^{12}(d, p)$ and $Si^{29}(d, p)$. Polarizations as large as 58 per cent are observed, exceeding the 33.3 per cent limit. The experiments suggest that the polarization indeed is $(\pm)$ near the main peak, according as $j = l \pm \frac{1}{2}$. Huby, Refai, and Satchler (Hu58) attach considerable importance to the large observed stripping polarizations, and consider that these indicate that frequently only one of the $B_{l\mu}$ (see preceding Section) is nonvanishing. This observation implies that the distortion frequently is very large.

The $(L \cdot S)$ optical potential gives the most interesting refractive distortion. It acts directly on the spin of the outgoing particle, so its influence might be thought to be strong. For deuteron stripping this first was considered by Cheston (Ch54), whose work unfortunately had some errors (Sa57b). The paper by Newns and Refai (Ne58) corrects these errors. Their work and that of other authors (Hu58, Ne58, Sa58f, We58) suggests that the $(L \cdot S)$ potential plays a comparatively small role in the stripping polarization. Ju58 contend that a part of their data bears out this idea, as they find small polarization for a level for which the Newns effect should be absent. Nevertheless it is hard to believe that the $(L \cdot S)$ influence must be small in all cases, and while it does not make qualitative changes in the results of Ne58, it certainly is noticeable quantitatively. In view of the large polarizations observed it is much too early to conclude that the role of the $(L \cdot S)$ potential has been assessed. After all, it is this potential which is responsible for all of the very large polarizations (up to 100 per cent) observed in elastic scattering experiments. A discussion of refractive polarization in the simple inelastic scattering $Si^{29}(p, n)P^{29}$ has been given by Sawicki (Sa56).

For the elastic scattering the role of the $(L \cdot S)$ potential may be understood easily in Born approximation. As Peaslee points out (Pe55), it is possible to separate the angular distribution into two parts, for spin "up" and spin "down" particles, which add incoherently. Because of the several Mev differences in depth of the optical potentials for these two parts the minima of their angular distributions will be slightly displaced from each other. Then if the minima are quite deep it is possible to find very large polarizations in their vicinity, up to one hundred per cent. The polarization as a function of angle increases steadily as one approaches a minimum, becomes very large, then rapidly goes through zero and becomes equally large with the opposite sign; then it steadily decreases in magnitude until the next minimum is approached. Similar effects may occur in inelastic scattering. Köhler (Ko58) does find that similar results can be expected for the elastic and inelastic polarizations at high energy, and at 220 Mev an inelastic polarization as large as 90 per cent has been observed (Ha58).

Some additional polarization data has been obtained recently in the deuteron stripping. For $Be^{9}(d, p)Be^{10}$ at 7.8 Mev Green and Parkinson (Gr60) measured the angular distribution of the polarization. Near the stripping peak their data agrees with semi-classical ideas, but toward larger angles it shows some of the complications predicted by distorted waves calculations (Sa60). A simplified distorted waves model by Lubitz (Lu60) agrees with the main features of their data. For Be⁹(d, p)Be⁸ and Be⁸* at 6 Mev Hird and Strzalkowski (Hi60a) measured the asymmetry obtained if *polarized deuterons* are incident. The asymmetries measured for the two levels of Be⁸ are quite different and seem to correlate with J in the manner predicted by the absorption mechanism of Newns. Hi60a give the additional argument that an absorption which depends strongly on J probably cannot be caused by the $(\mathbf{L} \cdot \mathbf{S})$ optical potential.

4. Fundamental Theories

These approaches all follow the procedure of rearranging the eigenstate decomposition formalism so as to incorporate from the first the physical ideas of the simple direct reaction theories. Quantitative investigation then is made to see how much of the wave function can be described in such terms, and how much is left over. The discussion in this Section will follow fairly closely the work of Brown and De Dominicis (Br57c, Br57d, Br57e) and of Sano, Yoshida, and Terasawa (Sa58b).

Inelastic scattering of nucleons is sufficiently illustrative of the general method. Suppose ξ is all the co-ordinates of the target nucleus, plus the spin of the incident nucleon, and $\mathbf{r}$ is the separation between the incident nucleon and the target. The complete wave function of the system, Ψ is a function of ξ and $\mathbf{r}$. The hamiltonian for the system is

$$H = H_\xi + T + V(\mathbf{r}, \xi)$$

where H_ξ is the hamiltonian of the initial nucleus, T the kinetic energy of the incident nucleon, and $V(\mathbf{r}, \xi)$ the potential between the incident nucleon and the nucleus. The eigenstates of H_ξ are $\chi_j(\xi)$,

$$H_\xi \chi_j = E_j \chi_j \tag{93}$$

with χ_0 the ground state of the target nucleus.

We decompose H in the fashion

$$H = H(\xi, \mathbf{r}) + T + \Delta V(\mathbf{r}, \xi) \tag{94}$$

where $\mathbf{r}$ appears in $H(\xi, \mathbf{r})$ only as a parameter. For each fixed value of $\mathbf{r}$ the eigenstates of $H(\xi, \mathbf{r})$ are $\chi_j(\xi, \mathbf{r})$.

$$H(\xi, \mathbf{r})\chi_j(\xi, \mathbf{r}) = E_j\chi_j(\xi, \mathbf{r}) \tag{95}$$

and at each $\mathbf{r}$ have the same energy spectrum as the $\chi_j(\xi)$. Each $\chi_j(\xi, \mathbf{r})$ is the adiabatic continuation to small $\mathbf{r}$ of the corresponding $\chi_j(\xi)$, with $\chi_j(\xi)$ being $\chi_j(\xi, \infty)$. Thus the impinging neutron is allowed to *polarize* the target, according to the picture of Vo57, but the term $H(\xi, \mathbf{r})$ is not allowed to induce transitions between target nucleus levels. The residual interaction $\Delta V(\mathbf{r}, \xi)$ is the part of H which induces transitions.

The average of $H(\xi, \mathbf{r})$ over $\chi_j(\xi, \mathbf{r})$ with $\mathbf{r}$ being constant, gives the optical potential in state j. It is approximately independent of j (Vo57), so need merely be denoted by $\hat{V}(\mathbf{r})$. It will be evaluated later. In the same approximation which makes $\hat{V}$ independent of j the perturbing potential $\Delta V(\mathbf{r}, \xi)$ also simplifies, at least from the standpoint of the impinging neutron, to

$$\Delta V(\mathbf{r}, \xi) \approx V(\mathbf{r}, \xi) - \hat{V}(\mathbf{r}) \tag{96}$$

In a definite channel α (definite orbital angular momentum and definite channel spin) the motion of the neutron in the average potential $\hat{V}(\mathbf{r})$ is described by the functions $\psi_{\alpha j}(\mathbf{r})$. This set of functions is defined to be regular at the origin, to have energy $(E - E_j)$, and to satisfy the equation

$$(T + \hat{V})\psi_{\alpha j} = (E - E_j)\psi_{\alpha j} \tag{97}$$

Omission of the j on $\psi_{\alpha j}$ will imply $E_j = E_0 = 0$, the ground state of the target. Insertion of a superscript $+$ on $\psi_{\alpha j}$ will imply replacement of the boundary condition at the origin by the boundary condition that $\psi_{\alpha j}^+$ is entirely outgoing as $r \to \infty$.

Then Ψ is written in the form

$$\Psi = \chi_0(\xi, \mathbf{r})\psi_\alpha(\mathbf{r}) + \Delta\Psi \tag{98}$$

with the first term both incorporating the incident wave and giving the optical (shape elastic) scattering. The $\Delta\Psi$ term incorporates the departures from the optical model, the compound elastic scattering and all the inelastic scattering. It can be expressed in terms of channel wave functions, similar to the first term, only for $r > R$, for which circumstance Ψ is

$$\Psi = \chi_0(\xi)\psi_\alpha(\mathbf{r}) + S_\alpha^{ce}\chi_0(\xi)\psi_\alpha^+(\mathbf{r}) + \sum_{\alpha'j}S_{\alpha,\alpha'j}\chi_j(\xi)\psi_{\alpha'j}^+ \quad (99)$$

For $r < R$ the channel wave functions are not eigenfunctions of H, and Eq. (99) is not a suitable decomposition.

The physical discussion of the inelastic scattering now centers upon the integral equation form of the Schrodinger equation. In Dirac notation this is

$$|\Psi\rangle = |\chi_0(\xi,\mathbf{r})\psi_\alpha\rangle + (E - H)^{-1}\,\Delta V\,|\chi_0(\xi,\,\mathbf{r})\psi_\alpha\rangle \quad (100)$$

If the kernel $(E - H)^{-1}$ could be computed explicitly, the various S matrix coefficients of Eq. (99) would be obtained merely by projecting Eq. (100) on to the appropriate channel functions. Of course this cannot be done without approximations. The approximation of interest in the present discussion is the replacement of the exact kernel

$$(E - H)^{-1} = [E - H_\xi - T - V(\mathbf{r},\xi)]^{-1} \quad (101)$$

by the approximate kernel

$$(E - H)^{-1} \approx (E - \hat{H})^{-1} = [E - H(\xi,\mathbf{r}) - T]^{-1} \quad (102)$$

with $\hat{H} \equiv H - \Delta V$. With Eq. (102) the computation of the S coefficients is straightforward. The channel wave functions are eigenstates of $\hat{H}$, so Eq. (99) may be continued in to $r = 0$. The S coefficients are found to be precisely of the form of the distorted wave Born approximation (Section 3). *The validity of the distorted waves method thus is equivalent to the validity of the replacement of Eq. (101) by Eq. (102).*

Lane, Thomas, and Wigner (La55) suggested an *intermediate model* of nuclear structure, wherein the approach to independent particle motion is sufficiently good, ΔV is sufficiently small, so that the expansion coefficients of the actual nuclear eigenfunctions in terms of the independent-particle-model eigenfunctions have certain well-marked properties. These properties prove to be sufficient to support the use of Eq. (102) in place of Eq. (101), provided Eq. (102) is supplemented with a term for "compound nucleus formation."

The analysis takes the form of a separation of the eigenstate spectrum into *near* levels and *distant* levels.

To make the discussion explicit, two appropriate complete sets of states now are introduced. Both are defined to be regular in the interior and to satisfy the boundary condition at the nuclear surface that in each channel the logarithmic derivative equals that for outgoing waves. In addition, the Kapur-Peierls eigenstates satisfy

$$H\Phi^{(p)} = W_p\Phi^{(p)} \qquad (103)$$

These are eigenstates for the exact problem, so the density of eigenvalues W_p equals the density of levels of the compound nucleus. The W_p occur at essentially the locations of the scattering resonances, but because of the nature of the boundary condition assumed they are complex and are functions of the total energy.

The other functions we introduce satisfy the same boundary conditions, but involve only the single particle co-ordinate $\mathbf{r}$, and obey the equation

$$(T + \hat{V})\hat{\psi}_m = E_m\hat{\psi}_m \qquad (104)$$

The eigenvalues E_m are a discrete set, and are located approximately at the single-particle scattering resonances, thus are separated by intervals of 20–40 Mev (Br57d). The discrete set $\hat{\psi}_m$ is complete for the motion of the neutron with respect to the core. It is extended into a set which is complete for the entire problem by using the $\hat{\psi}_m$ to build the product functions

$$\chi_j(\xi,\mathbf{r})\hat{\psi}_m^j(\mathbf{r}) \qquad (105)$$

Here the superscript j on $\hat{\psi}_m^j$ implies that the boundary condition on $\hat{\psi}_m$ is defined for the energy $(E - E_j)$. The corresponding eigenvalue in Eq. (104) is E_{jm}.

The transformation coefficients between the set of Eq. (105) and the set of the $\Phi^{(p)}$ are the

$$\langle j, m|p\rangle \equiv a_{jm}^{\ p} \qquad (106)$$

and their complex conjugates. Now the useful property which these coefficients have, if independent particle motion is well-marked, is that the $a_{jm}^{\ p}$ are large only where W_p is close to $(E_j + E_{jm})$. As W_p departs from this value, for given j and m, the coefficient $a_{jm}^{\ p}$ diminishes very rapidly. Any given product wave function, in other words, is mixed only into those eigenstates $\Phi^{(p)}$ whose energy lies close to the energy of the product function.

In terms of the above complete sets the two kernels of Eqs. (101) and (102) may be written explicitly. The exact kernel is

$$(E - H)^{-1} = \sum_p |\Phi^{(p)}\rangle\langle\Phi^{(p)}|(E - W_p)^{-1} \qquad (101')$$

while the approximate kernel is

$$(E - \hat{H})^{-1} = \sum_{j,m} |\chi_j(\xi,\mathbf{r})\hat{\psi}_m{}^j\rangle \langle\chi_j(\xi,\mathbf{r})\hat{\psi}_m{}^j|(E - E_j - E_{jm})^{-1}$$

$$(102')$$

If the denominators were constant the transformation from Eq. (101') to (102') would be exact, and merely would be the transformation of the numerator from one representation to another, using the coefficients $a_{jm}{}^p$. The giant resonance property of the $a_{jm}{}^p$ achieves something close to this, leading these coefficients to link only functions which lie close together in energy. Thus for each $(E_j + E_{jm})$ *local closure* of the transformation occurs over a small range of values of W_p, and the transformation of the kernel need only assume the denominator to be locally constant. It is plausible, therefore, that the approximate kernel is a good approximation, so that the distorted waves Born approximation is a valid approach for the computation of nuclear reaction results.

We now also can understand the deficiencies of the replacement of Eq. (101) by Eq. (102). Certainly this replacement relies upon the intermediate model (La55). However it also requires that the levels W_p which are of interest are sufficiently far from E so that $(E - W_p)$ can be large compared to the width of the giant resonance. For the nearby levels the assumption of a constant energy denominator cannot be valid. It is precisely the rapid variation of the denominator which leads these very same near levels to be displayed in the scattering as isolated sharp resonances, if the resolution is sufficient. The near levels may be accounted for, however, by adding to Eq. (102) a term which varies rapidly with energy, having resonance properties. With high resolution this term gives sharp resonances in the excitation curve. With coarse resolution it appears as the compound elastic or compound inelastic part of the cross section. Naturally, the role of the near levels becomes more important if E lies on a giant resonance of the elastic scattering.

The preceding analysis makes it plausible that Eq. (102), supplemented by a compound nucleus term, should be a very useful first approximation to Eq. (101). But for accurate calculation it is desirable to use more formal methods to go from Eq. (101) to Eq. (102), thus permitting the explicit computation of the compound nucleus term, and providing a criterion for the goodness of the average potential $\hat{V}(\mathbf{r})$. This is achieved by one step of iteration of the integral equation, using the identity

$$(E - H)^{-1} = (E - \hat{H})^{-1} \{1 + \Delta V(E - H)^{-1}\} \qquad (107)$$

Then Eq. (100) goes over to the form

$$\Psi = |\chi_0 \psi_\alpha\rangle + (E - \hat{H})^{-1} \Delta V |\chi_0 \psi_\alpha\rangle$$
$$+ (E - \hat{H})^{-1} \Delta V (E - H)^{-1} \Delta V |\chi_0 \psi_\alpha\rangle \qquad (108)$$

In Eq. (108) the first term gives the shape elastic scattering, the second term gives the direct reaction inelastic scattering, as before, and the third term gives everything that is left over, principally the contributions from the nearby resonance levels. The third term cannot contain much contribution from the distant compound nucleus levels, as we already have seen, for in the approximation of the intermediate model these all are contained in the second term. It is this third term in Eq. (108) which now is treated by the eigenstate decomposition method, and for which it is believed that the statistical formulas of Wolfenstein (Wo51) and Hauser and Feshbach (Ha52) can be used.

The published discussions now are concluded (Br57c, Br57d, Br57e, Sa58b) by obtaining from Eq. (108) a definition for the potential $\hat{V}$. The criterion of Feshbach, Porter, and Weisskopf (Fe54) is used. Thus Br57c project Eq. (108) on to the ground state, to get the elastic scattering, and require of $\hat{V}$ the property that the energy average of the sum of the second and third terms equal zero, when averaged over a broad range of compound nucleus eigenstates. Thus the second and third terms of Eq. (108), together, give the compound elastic scattering, and this is required not to interfere with the shape elastic scattering (Fe54). The theory is self-consistent, and $\hat{V}$ is well-defined, only if the parameters of $\hat{V}$ vary slowly over an energy interval large compared to the interval over which we do the averaging which defines $\hat{V}$. This is a matter for investigation, and final answers have not yet been reached (Br59b). It is not altogether clear just what the definition for $\hat{V}$ implies regarding the interference *between* the second and third terms when they are projected on to some other than the ground state channel, to give the inelastic scattering. The third term has much of the nature of a compound inelastic term. It tends to average to zero, and probably to the extent that it does not, the use of the second term to give the direct interaction must be regarded as defective. Sano, Yoshida, and Terasawa (Sa58b) treat this problem, and suggest that for some cases it may be best to generalize $\hat{V}$ to matrix form, with off-diagonal components which link a few of the more closely coupled channels. Then for these closely coupled channels the interference between the direct and compound inelastic scattering can be *forced* to vanish. In fact, the method they suggest is a generalization, now based on the eigenstate decomposition theory, of the Tamm-Dancoff type method already described in Section 3.

Acknowledgments

I am very grateful for useful conversations with J. M. Blatt, K. J. LeCouteur, D. C. Peaslee, and R. Schafroth, and especially with S. T. Butler, whose advice has influenced nearly all sections of this article. I am grateful for prepublication copies of articles by F. Bjorklund and S. Fernbach, J. S. Blair, C. Bloch, B. L. Cohen, J. H. Coon, T. Fulton and G. E. Owen, A. E. Glassgold, C. A. Levinson and M. K. Banerjee, R. Marshak, G. F. Pieper and N. P. Heydenburg, M. Rickey and R. Sherr, F. L. Ribe, J. Sawicki, W. Tobocman, E. Vogt, N. S. Wall, and L. Wilets. The completed manuscript very kindly was read and criticized by J. C. Armstrong, G. E. Brown, G. E. Owen, G. R. Satchler, and W. Tobocman.

References

(Ah57)   S. H. Ahn and J. H. Roberts, *Phys. Rev.* **108**, 110 (1957).
(Al56)   Allen, Collinge, Hird, Maglic, and Orman, *Proc. Phys. Soc.* (*London*) **69A**, 705 (1956).
(Al58)   D. L. Allan, *Nuclear Phys.* **6**, 464 (1958).
(Am59)   R. D. Amado, *Phys. Rev. Letters* **2**, 399 (1959).
(An58)   Anderson, Gardner, McClure, Nakada, and Wong, *Phys. Rev.* **111**, 572 (1958).
(Au53)   Austern, Butler, and McManus, *Phys. Rev.* **92**, 350 (1953).

(Au55)   T. Auerbach and J. B. French, *Phys. Rev.* **98**, 1276 (1955).
(Au58)   N. Austern and S. T. Butler, *Phys. Rev.* **109**, 1402 (1958).
(Ba57a)   E. Baumgartner and H. W. Fulbright, *Phys. Rev.* **107**, 219 (1957).
(Ba57b)   M. Banerjee and C. A. Levinson, *Ann. Physics* **2**, 499 (1957).
(Be37)   H. A. Bethe, *Revs. Modern Phys.* **9**, 71 (1937).
(Be52)   Bernardini, Booth, and Lindenbaum, *Phys. Rev.* **88**, 1017 (1952).
(Be54)   Berthelot, Cohen, Cotton, Faraggi, Grjebine, Leveque, Naggiar, Roclawksi-Conjeaud, and Szteinsznaider, *Compt. rend.* **238**, 1312 (1954).
(Be56a)   F. A. El Bedewi, *Proc. Phys. Soc. (London)* **69A**, 221 (1956).
(Be56b)   R. E. Bell and H. M. Skarsgard, *Can. J. Phys.* **34**, 745 (1956).
(Be56c)   Benveniste, Finke, and Martinelli, *Phys. Rev.* **101**, 655 (1956).
(Be56d)   H. A. Bethe, *Phys. Rev.* **103**, 1353 (1956).
(Be56e)   H. A. Bethe *et al.*, "Proceedings of the Amsterdam Conference on Nuclear Reactions," *Physica* **22**, 941 (1956).
(Be58)   F. A. El Bedewi and S. Tadros, *Nuclear Phys.* **6**, 434 (1958).
(Be59)   Beurtey, Catillon, Chaminade, Faraggi, Papineau, and Thirion, *Nuclear Phys.* **13**, 397 (1959).
(Bh52)   Bhatia, Huang, Huby, and Newns, *Phil. Mag.* **43**, 485 (1952).
(Bi52)   Biedenharn, Boyer, and Charpie, *Phys. Rev.* **88**, 517 (1952).
(Bi53)   L. C. Biedenharn and M. E. Rose, *Revs. Modern Phys.* **25**, 729 (1953).
(Bi60)   L. C. Biedenharn, in *Nuclear Spectroscopy*, F. Ajzenberg-Selove, Ed., Academic Press, New York, 1960 Part B, p. 732.
(Bj58)   F. Bjorklund and S. Fernbach, *Phys. Rev.* **109**, 1295 (1958).
(Bl52a)   J. M. Blatt and L. C. Biedenharn, *Revs. Modern Phys.* **24**, 258 (1952).
(Bl52b)   J. M. Blatt and V. F. Weisskopf, *Theoretical Nuclear Physics*, Wiley, New York, 1952.
(Bl54)   J. S. Blair, *Phys. Rev.* **95**, 1218 (1954).
(Bl57a)   W. Blanpied and R. Sherr, *Bull. Am. Phys. Soc.* **2**, 303 (1957).
(Bl57b)   C. Bloch, *Nuclear Phys.* **4**, 503 (1957).
(Bl57c)   J. Blok and C. C. Jonker, *Nuovo cimento* **6**, 378 (1957).
(Bl59)   J. S. Blair, *Phys. Rev.* **115**, 928 (1959).
(Bo36)   N. Bohr, *Nature (London)* **137**, 344 (1936).
(Bo56)   Bonner, Eisinger, Kraus, and Marion, *Phys. Rev.* **101**, 209 (1956).
(Bo58a)   J. E. Bowcock, *Phys. Rev.* **112**, 923 (1958).
(Bo58b)   Bokhari, Cookson, Hird, and Weesakul, *Proc. Phys. Soc. (London)* **72A**, 88 (1958).
(Bo59)   C. K. Bockelman, *Nuclear Phys.* **13**, 205 (1959).
(Br55)   D. M. Brink, *Proc. Phys. Soc. (London)* **68A**, 994 (1955).
(Br57a)   G. Brown and H. Muirhead, *Phil. Mag.* **2**, 473 (1957).
(Br57b)   Brown, Morrison, Muirhead, and Morton, *Phil. Mag.* **2**, 785 (1957).
(Br57c)   G. E. Brown and C. T. De Dominicis, *Proc. Phys. Soc. (London)* **70A**, 668 (1957).
(Br57d)   G. E. Brown and C. T. De Dominicis, *Proc. Phys. Soc. (London)* **70A**, 681 (1957).
(Br57e)   G. E. Brown and C. T. De Dominicis, *Proc. Phys. Soc. (London)* **70A**, 686 (1957).

(Br58a)   K. A. Brueckner and J. L. Gammel, *Phys. Rev.* **109**, 1023 (1958).
(Br58b)   K. W. Brockman, Jr., *Phys. Rev.* **110**, 163 (1958).
(Br59a)   G. Breit, in *Handbuch der Physik*, S. Flügge, ed., Springer, Berlin, 1959 Vol. 41/1, p. 1.
(Br59b)   G. E. Brown, *Revs. Modern Phys.* **31**, 893 (1959).
(Br60)   Bromley, Kuehner, Almqvist, *Phys. Rev. Letters* **4**, 132 (1960).
(Bu51)   S. T. Butler, *Proc. Roy. Soc. (London)* **208A**, 559 (1951).
(Bu52a)   S. T. Butler, *Phys. Rev.* **87**, 1117 (1952).
(Bu52b)   S. T. Butler and E. E. Salpeter, *Phys. Rev.* **88**, 133 (1952).
(Bu57a)   S. T. Butler, *Phys. Rev.* **106**, 272 (1957).
(Bu57b)   S. T. Butler, *Nuclear Stripping Reactions*, Wiley, New York, 1957.
(Bu58)   Butler, Austern, and Pearson, *Phys. Rev.* **112**, 1227 (1958).
(Ce56)   M. Cerineo, *Nuclear Phys.* **2**, 113 (1956).
(Ch54)   W. B. Cheston, *Phys. Rev.* **96**, 1590 (1954).
(Ch56)   D. M. Chase, *Phys. Rev.* **104**, 838 (1956).
(Ch57a)   R. F. Christy, *Conf. on Nuclear Structure*, Univ. of Pittsburgh, 1957, unpublished.
(Ch57b)   W. B. Cheston and A. E. Glassgold, *Phys. Rev.* **106**, 1215 (1957).
(Ch58)   Chase, Wilets, and Edmonds, *Phys. Rev.* **110**, 1080 (1958).
(Co54)   B. L. Cohen, Newman, Charpie, and Handley, *Phys. Rev.* **94**, 620 (1954).
(Co55)   B. L. Cohen, *Phys. Rev.* **100**, 206 (1955).
(Co57a)   Colli, Facchini, and Micheletti, *Nuovo cimento* **5**, 502 (1957).
(Co57b)   Coleman, Thomas, and Seaborg, *Bull. Am. Phys. Soc.* **2**, 386 (1957).
(Co57c)   H. E. Conzett, *Phys. Rev.* **105**, 1324 (1957).
(Co57d)   B. L. Cohen, *Conf. on Nuclear Structure*, Univ, of Pittsburgh, 1957, unpublished.
(Co57e)   B. L. Cohen, *Phys. Rev.* **105**, 1549 (1957).
(Co57f)   B. L. Cohen and S. W. Mosko, *Phys. Rev.* **106**, 995 (1957).
(Co57g)   B. L. Cohen, *Phys. Rev.* **108**, 768 (1957).
(Co57h)   S. A. Cox and R. M. Williamson, *Phys. Rev.* **105**, 1799 (1957).
(Co58a)   Coon, Davis, Felthauser, and Nicodemus, *Phys. Rev.* **111**, 250 (1958).
(Co58b)   B. L. Cohen and A. G. Rubin, *Phys. Rev.* **111**, 1568 (1958).
(Co58c)   Corelli, Bleuler, and Tendam, *Bull. Am. Phys. Soc.* **3**, 200 (1958).
(Co58d)   Colli, Pignanelli, Rytz, and Zurmühle, *Nuovo cimento* **9**, 280 (1958).
(Co59a)   B. L. Cohen, *Phys. Rev.* **116**, 426 (1959).
(Co59b)   Corelli, Bleuler, and Tendam, *Phys. Rev.* **116**, 1184 (1959).
(Da52)   P. B. Daitch and J. B. French, *Phys. Rev.* **87**, 900 (1952).
(Da53)   R. H. Dalitz, *Proc. Phys. Soc. (London)* **66A**, 28 (1953).
(Da57)   J. Dabrowski and B. Tulczjew, *Acta Phys. Polonica* **16**, 231 (1957).
(Da58)   Dalton, Hinds, and Parry, *Proc. Phys. Soc. (London)* **71A**, 252 (1958).
(Di58)   C. E. Dickerman, *Phys. Rev.* **109**, 443 (1958).
(Dr55)   S. I. Drozdov, *Zhur. Eksptl. i Teoret Fiz.* **28**, 734 (1955); *J. Exptl. Theoret, Phys. (U. S. S. R.)* **1**, 591 (1955).
(Dr56)   S. I. Drozdov, *Zhur. Eksptl. i Teoret, Fiz.* **30**, 786 (1956); *J. Exptl. Theoret. Phys. (U. S. S. R.)* **3**, 759 (1956).

(Dr58) S. I. Drozdov, *Zhur. Eksptl. i Teoret. Fiz.* **34**, 1288 (1958); *J. Exptl. Theoret. Phys.* (*U. S. S. R.*) **7**, 889 (1958).

(Ed60) Edakova, Neudachin, Romanovskii, *Zhur. Eksptl. i Teoret. Fiz.* **38**, 248 (1960); *J. Exptl. Theoret. Phys.* (*U. S. S. R.*) **11**, 180 (1960).

(Eg59a) L. Egardt, *Nuclear Phys.* **11**, 349 (1959).

(Eg59b) L. Egardt, *Nuclear Phys.* **12**, 84 (1959).

(Ei54) R. M. Eisberg, *Phys. Rev.* **94**, 739 (1954).

(Ei56) R. M. Eisberg and N. M. Hintz, *Phys. Rev.* **103**, 645 (1956).

(El57) L. R. B. Elton and L. C. Gomes, *Phys. Rev.* **105**, 1027 (1957).

(El58) L. R. B. Elton, private communication (1958).

(Ev54) N. T. S. Evans and W. C. Parkinson, *Proc. Phys. Soc.* (*London*) **67A**, 684 (1954).

(Ev58) N. T. S. Evans and A. P. French, *Phys. Rev.* **109**, 1272 (1958).

(Fa60) W. M. Fairbairn, *Nuclear Phys.* **15**, 678 (1960).

(Fe49) Fernbach, Serber, and Taylor, *Phys. Rev.* **75**, 1352 (1949).

(Fe54) Feshbach, Porter, and Weisskopf, *Phys. Rev.* **96**, 448 (1954).

(Fe58) H. Feshbach, *Ann. Physics* **5**, 357 (1958).

(Fi54) G. E. Fischer, *Phys. Rev.* **96**, 704 (1954).

(Fi58) V. K. Fischer and G. E. Fischer, *Bull. Am. Phys. Soc.* **3**, 199 (1958).

(Fo57) B. M. Foreman and G. T. Seaborg, *Bull. Am. Phys. Soc.* **2**, 386 (1957).

(Fo58a) J. L. Fowler and H. O. Cohn, *Phys. Rev.* **109**, 89 (1958).

(Fo58b) T. K. Fowler, *Phys. Rev. Letters* **1**, 371 (1958).

(Fo60) Forsyth, Barros, Jaffe, Taylor, and Ramavataram, *Proc. Phys. Soc.* (*London*) **75A**, 291 (1960).

(Fr54a) Freemantle, Gibson, and Rotblat, *Phil. Mag.* **45**, 1200 (1954).

(Fr54b) Freemantle, Prowse, and Rotblat, *Phys. Rev.* **96**, 1268 (1954); Freemantle, Prowse, Hossain, and Rotblat, *Phys. Rev.* **96**, 1270 (1954).

(Fr55) F. L. Friedman and V. F. Weisskopf, in *Niels Bohr and the Development of Physics*, W. Pauli, ed., Pergamon, London, 1955.

(Fr56) J. D. French, private communication (1956).

(Fr57a) J. B. French, *Conf. on Nuclear Structure*, Univ. of Pittsburgh, 1957, unpublished.

(Fr57b) A. P. French, *Phys. Rev.* **107**, 1655 (1957).

(Fr57c) J. B. French and A. Fujii, *Phys. Rev.* **105**, 652 (1957).

(Fu57) T. Fulton and G. E. Owen, *Phys. Rev.* **108**, 789 (1957).

(Ga52) L. J. Gallaher and W. B. Cheston, *Phys. Rev.* **88**, 684 (1952).

(Ge56) Geer, Holmgren, Johnston, and Wolicki, *Bull. Am. Phys. Soc.* **1**, 211 (1956).

(Gi57) Gibson, Prowse, and Rotblat, *Proc. Roy. Soc.* (*London*) **243A**, 237 (1957).

(Gl58) A. E. Glassgold and P. J. Kellog, *Phys. Rev.* **109**, 1291 (1958).

(Gl59) N. K. Glendenning, *Phys. Rev.* **114**, 1297 (1959).

(Go48) M. L. Goldberger, *Phys. Rev.* **74**, 1269 (1948).

(Go58) L. C. Gomes, J. D. Walecka, and V. F. Weisskopf, *Ann. Physics* **3**, 241 (1958). A preliminary account may be found in *Conf. on Nuclear Structure*, Univ. of Pittsburgh, 1957, unpublished.

(Gr57a)   Greenlees, Haywood, Kuo, and Petravic, *Proc. Phys. Soc.* (*London*)
           70A, 331 (1957).
(Gr57b)   V. N. Gribov, *Zhur. Eksptl. i Teoret. Fiz.* **32**, 842; *J. Exptl. Theoret.*
           Phys. (*U. S. S. R.*) **5**, 688 (1957).
(Gr57c)   D. P. Grechkin, *Zhur. Eksptl. i Teoret. Fiz.* **32**, 1460; *J. Exptl. Theoret.*
           Phys. (*U. S. S. R.*) **5**, 1188 (1957).
(Gr59)   K. R. Greider, *Phys. Rev.* **114**, 786 (1959).
(Gr60)   J. A. Green and W. C. Parkinson, *Bull. Am. Phys. Soc.* **5**, 345 (1960).
(Gu56a)   P. C. Gugelot and M. Rickey, *Phys. Rev.* **101**, 1613 (1956).
(Gu56b)   P. C. Gugelot and P. R. Phillips, *Phys. Rev.* **101**, 1614 (1956).
(Ha52)   W. Hauser and H. Feshbach, *Phys. Rev.* **87**, 366 (1952).
(Ha54)   S. Hayakawa and T. Sasakawa, *Progr. Theoret. Phys.* **12**, 401 (1954).
(Ha55a)   S. Hayakawa and S. Yoshida, *Proc. Phys. Soc.* (*London*) **68A**, 656
           (1955).
(Ha55b)   S. Hayakawa and S. Yoshida, *Progr. Theoret. Phys.* **14**, 1 (1955).
(Ha55c)   Hayakawa, Kawai, and Kikuchi, *Progr. Theoret. Phys.* **13**, 415 (1955).
(Ha56)   J. W. Haffner, *Phys. Rev.* **103**, 1398 (1956).
(Ha57)   W. Haeberli and W. W. Rolland, *Bull. Am. Phys. Soc.* **2**, 234 (1957).
(Ha58)   E. M. Hafner, *Phys. Rev.* **111**, 297 (1958).
(Ha59)   K. Hasegawa and Y. H. Ichikawa, *Progr. Theoret. Phys.* **21**, 569
           (1959).
(Ha60a)   A. I. Hamburger, *Phys. Rev.* **118**, 1271 (1960).
(Ha60b)   E. W. Hamburger, private communication (1960).
(He57)   P. von Herrmann and G. F. Pieper, *Phys. Rev.* **105**, 1556 (1957).
(He58a)   J. C. Hensel and W. C. Parkinson, *Phys. Rev.* **110**, 128 (1958).
(He58b)   I. J. van Heerden, *Nuclear Phys.* **6**, 55 (1958).
(Hi56a)   P. Hillman, *Phys. Rev.* **104**, 176 (1956).
(Hi56b)   S. Hinds and R. Middleton, *Proc. Phys. Soc.* (*London*) **69A**, 347 (1956).
(Hi56c)   O. Hittmair, *Z. Physik* **144**, 449 (1956).
(Hi57)   Hinds, Middleton, and Parry, *Proc. Phys. Soc.* (*London*) **70A**, 900
           (1957).
(Hi60a)   B. Hird and A. Strzalkowski, *Proc. Phys. Soc.* (*London*) **75A**, 868
           (1960).
(Hi60b)   Hisatake, Ishizaki, Isoya, Nakamura, Nakano, Saheki, Saji, and
           Yuasa, *J. Phys. Soc. Japan* **15**, 741 (1960).
(Ho49)   J. R. Holt and C. T. Young, *Nature* (*London*) **164**, 1000 (1949).
(Ho53a)   J. Horowitz and A. M. L. Messiah, *J. phys. radium* **14**, 695 (1953).
(Ho53b)   J. Horowitz and A. M. L. Messiah, *J. phys. radium* **14**, 731 (1953).
(Ho53c)   J. R. Holt and T. N. Marsham, *Proc. Phys. Soc.* (*London*) **66A**, 1032
           (1953).
(Ho54)   J. Horowitz and A. M. L. Messiah, *J. phys. radium* **15**, 142 (1954).
(Ho58a)   P. E. Hodgson, *Advances in Physics* **7**, 1 (1958).
(Ho58b)   P. E. Hodgson, *Nuclear Phys.* **8**, 1 (1958).
(Hu51)   R. Huby and H. C. Newns, *Phil. Mag.* **42**, 1442 (1951).
(Hu53)   R. Huby, *Progress in Nuclear Physics* **3**, 177 (1953).
(Hu57a)   C. E. Hunting and N. S. Wall, *Phys. Rev.* **108**, 901 (1957).
(Hu57b)   C. E. Hunting and N. S. Wall, *Bull Am. Phys. Soc.* **2**, 181 (1957).
(Hu58)   R. Huby, M. Y. Refai, and G. R. Satchler, *Nuclear Phys.* **9**, 94 (1958).

(Hu59)   Hu, Kikuchi, Kobayashi, Matsuda, Nagahara, Oda, Takano, Takeka, and Yamazaki, *J. Phys. Soc. Japan* **14**, 861 (1959).
(Ig57)   G. Igo and R. M. Thaler, *Phys. Rev.* **106**, 126 (1957).
(Ig58)   G. Igo, *Phys. Rev. Letters* **1**, 72 (1958).
(Il57)   Illsley, Holmgren, Johnston, and Wolicki, *Phys. Rev.* **107**, 538 (1957).
(In56)   E. V. Inopin, *Zhur. Eksptl. i Teoret. Fiz.* **31**, 901 (1956); *J. Exptl. Theoret. Phys.* (*U. S. S. R.*) **4**, 764 (1957).
(Ja51)   H. L. Jackson and A. I. Galonsky, *Phys. Rev.* **84**, 401 (1951).
(Ja53)   H. L. Jackson and A. I. Galonsky, *Phys. Rev.* **89**, 370 (1953).
(Ja56)   J. D. Jackson, *Can. J. Phys.* **34**, 767 (1956).
(Jo56)   Johnston, Wolicki, Heer, and Holmgren, *Bull. Am. Phys. Soc.* **1**, 197 (1956).
(Ju58)   A. C. Juveland and W. Jentschke, *Phys. Rev.* **110**, 456 (1958).
(Ka38)   P. L. Kapur and R. E. Peierls, *Proc. Roy. Soc.* (*London*) **166A**, 277 (1938).
(Ka56)   Kajikawa, Sasakawa, and Watari, *Progr. Theoret. Phys.* **16**, 152 (1956).
(Ka57a)   R. Kajikawa and W. Watari, *Progr. Theoret. Phys.* **18**, 103 (1957).
(Ka57b)   Kawai *et al.*, *Progr. Theoret. Phys.* **18**, 66 (1957).
(Ka58a)   M. Kawai and M. Nagasaki, *Progr. Theoret. Phys.*, **19**, 77 (1958).
(Ka58b)   Kane, Elwyn, Ofer, and Wilkinson, *Bull. Am. Phys. Soc.* **3**, 381 (1958).
(Ki57)   K. Kikuchi, *Prog. Theoret. Phys.* **18**, 503 (1957).
(Ki59)   Kikuchi, Kobayashi, and Matsuda, *J. Phys. Soc. Japan* **14**, 121 (1959).
(Kl60)   Klein, Cindro, Swenson, and Wall, *Nuclear Phys.* **16**, 374 (1960).
(Kn58)   H. B. Knowles, *Bull. Am. Phys. Soc.* **3**, 330 (1958).
(Ko56)   R. Koch and A. Turkevitch, *Bull. Am. Phys. Soc.* **1**, 94 (1956).
(Ko58)   H. S. Köhler, *Nuclear Phys.* **9**, 49 (1958).
(Kr56)   Kraus, Schiffer, Prosser, and Biedenharn, *Phys. Rev.* **104**, 1667 (1956).
(Ku59)   A. B. Kurepin and V. G. Neudachin, *Zhur. Eksptl. i Teoret. Fiz.* **36**, 1725 (1959); *J. Exptl. Theoret. Phys.* (*U. S. S. R.*) **9**, 1229 (1959).
(La55)   Lane, Thomas, and Wigner, *Phys. Rev.* **98**, 693 (1955).
(La56)   J. T. Lamarsh and H. Feshbach, *Phys. Rev.* **104**, 1633 (1956).
(La57)   A. M. Lane, *Revs. Modern Phys.* **29**, 191 (1957).
(La58)   A. M. Lane, private communication (1958).
(La59)   Lackner, Dell, Hausman, *Phys. Rev.* **114**, 560 (1959).
(La60)   A. M. Lane and K. Parker, *Nuclear Phys.* **16**, 690 (1960).
(Le55)   Levine, Bender, and McGruer, *Phys. Rev.* **97**, 1249 (1955).
(Le57)   C. A. Levinson and M. K. Banerjee, *Ann. Phys.* **2**, 471 (1957).
(Le58)   C. A. Levinson and M. K. Banerjee, *Ann. Phys.* **3**, 67 (1958).
(Le60)   C. A. Levinson, private communication (1960).
(Li56)   J. G. Likely and F. P. Brady, *Phys. Rev.* **104**, 118 (1956).
(Lu57)   C. R. Lubitz, *Numerical Table of Butler-Born Approximation Stripping Cross Section*, Univ. of Michigan Report (1957).
(Lu60)   C. R. Lubitz, *Bull. Am. Phys. Soc.* **5**, 346 (1960).
(Ma55)   L. Madansky and G. E. Owen, *Phys. Rev.* **99**, 1608 (1955).
(Ma56a)   Maslin, Calvert, and Jaffe, *Proc. Phys. Soc.* (*London*) **69A**, 754 (1956).

(Ma56b)   J. B. Marion and G. Weber, *Phys. Rev.* **103**, 167 (1956).
(Ma56c)   J. B. Marion and G. Weber, *Phys. Rev.* **102**, 1355 (1956).
(Ma58a)   P. V. March and W. T. Morton, *Phil. Mag.* **3**, 577 (1958).
(Ma58b)   D. R. Maxson and J. H. Terrell, *Bull. Am. Phys. Soc.* **3**, 381 (1958).
(Ma58c)   H. Matsunobu and S. Yoshida, *Progr. Theoret. Phys.* **19**, 599 (1958).
(Ma59)   J. P. Martin, Ph.D. thesis, University of Pittsburgh, unpublished
          (1959).
(Ma60)   M. MacFarlane and J. B. French, *Rev. Modern Phys.* **32**, 567 (1960).
(McE58)   McEllistrem, Martin, Miller, and Sampson, *Phys. Rev.* **111**, 1636
          (1958).
(Me55)   J. W. Meadows, *Phys. Rev.* **98**, 744 (1955).
(Me58)   Metropolis, Bivins, Storm, Turkevich, Miller, and Friedlander, *Phys.
          Rev.* **110**, 185, 204 (1958).
(Mo33)   N. F. Mott and H. S. W. Massey, *Theory of Atomic Collisions*, Oxford
          Univ., Oxford, 1933.
(Mo56a)   H. Morinaga, *Phys. Rev.* **101**, 100 (1956).
(Mo56b)   H. Moshinsky, *Rev. mex. fis.* **5**, 1 (1956).
(Mo57)   H. Morinaga and D. C. Peaslee, *Nuclear Phys.* **3**, 115 (1957).
(Mo58a)   Moore, McGruer, and Hamburger, *Phys. Rev. Letters* **1**, 29 (1958).
(Mo58b)   S. Morita, *Jour. Phys. Soc. (Japan)* **13**, 126 (1958).
(Mo58c)   C. B. O. Mohr, *Proc. Phys. Soc. (London)* **71A**, 717 (1958).
(Mo60)   Morita, Kawai, Takano, Goto, Hanada, Nakajima, Takemoto, and
          Yaegashi, *J. Phys. Soc. Japan* **15**, 550 (1960).
(Na55)   R. Nakasima and K. Kikuchi, *Progr. Theoret. Phys.* **14**, 126 (1955).
(Na56)   M. Nagasaki, *Progr. Theoret. Phys.* **16**, 429 (1956).
(Na58)   M. El Nadi and L. Abou Hadid, *Nuclear Phys.* **8**, 51 (1958).
(Na59)   K. Nakamura and M. Soga, *Progr. Theoret. Phys.* **21**, 837 (1959).
(Ne53)   H. C. Newns, *Proc. Phys. Soc. (London)* **66A**, 477 (1953).
(Ne58)   H. C. Newns and M. Y. Refai, *Proc. Phys. Soc. (London)* **71A**, 627
          (1958).
(Ne59)   Neudachin, Teplov, and Shevchenko, *Zhur. Eksptl. i Teoret, Fiz.*
          36, 850 (1959); *J. Exptl. Theoret Phys. (U. S. S. R.)* **9**, 599 (1959).
(Ne60)   J. Németh, *Nuclear Phys.* **16**, 331 (1960).
(Ni58)   R. Nishimura, *Nucl. Phys.* **7**, 425 (1958).
(No57)   Nonaka, Morita, Kawai, Ishimatsu, Takeshita, Nakajima, and
          Takano, *J. Phys. Soc. Japan* **12**, 841 (1957).
(No59)   Nonaka, Yamaguchi, Mikumo, Umeda, Tabata, and Hitaka, *J.
          Phys. Soc. Japan* **14**, 1260 (1959).
(Od58)   N. Oda and K. Harada, *Nuclear Phys.* **7**, 251 (1958).
(Od60)   Oda, Takeda, Takano, Yamezaki, Hu, Kikuchi, Kobayashi, Matsuda,
          and Nagahara, *J. Phys. Soc. Japan* **15**, 760 (1960).
(On60)   K. Ono and K. Kuroda, *Phys. Rev.* **117**, 214 (1960).
(Ov58)   O. E. Overseth, Jr. and R. A. Peck, Jr., *Bull. Am. Phys. Soc.* **3**, 209
          (1958).
(Ow57)   G. E. Owen and L. Madansky, *Phys. Rev.* **105**, 1766 (1957).
(Ow59)   Owen, Madansky, and Edwards, *Phys. Rev.* **113**, 1575 (1959).

(Pa53) E. B. Paul and R. L. Clarke, *Can. J. Phys.* **31**, 267 (1953).
(Pe55) D. C. Peaslee, *Annual Rev. Nuclear Sci.* **5**, 99 (1955).
(Pe57a) R. W. Peelle, *Phys. Rev.* **105**, 1311 (1957).
(Pe57b) R. A. Peck, Jr., *Phys. Rev.* **106**, 965 (1957).
(Pi58) G. F. Peiper and N. P. Heydenburg, *Phys. Rev.* **111**, 264 (1958).
(Pr58) Priest, Corelli, Bleuler, and Tendam, *Bull. Am. Phys. Soc.* **3**, 199 (1958).
(Ra56) S. W. Rasmussen, *Phys. Rev.* **103**, 186 (1956).
(Ra58) G. Rakavy, *Nuclear Phys.* **7**, 553 (1958).
(Re56) J. B. Reynolds and K. G. Standing, *Phys. Rev.* **101**, 158 (1956).
(Ri56) W. B. Riesenfeld and K. M. Watson, *Phys. Rev.* **102**, 1157 (1956).
(Ri58a) M. Rickey and R. Sherr, to be published (1958).
(Ri58b) J. L. Richter and E. V. Ivash, *Phys. Rev.* **111**, 245 (1958).
(Ri59) K. F. Riley, *Nuclear Phys.* **13**, 407 (1959).
(Ro51) J. Rotblat, *Nature (London)*, **167**, 1027 (1951).
(Ro57) L. Rosen and L. Stewart, *Phys. Rev.* **107**, 824 (1957).
(Ro60) E. Rost and N. Austern, *Phys. Rev.* **120** 1375 (1960).
(Ru58) A. G. Rubin and B. L. Cohen, *Phys. Rev.* **111**, 1568 (1958).
(Sa52) G. R. Satchler and J. A. Speirs, *Proc. Phys. Soc. (London)* **65A**, 980 (1952).
(Sa53) G. R. Satchler, *Proc. Phys. Soc. (London)* **66A**, 1081 (1953).
(Sa55) G. R. Satchler, *Proc. Phys. Soc. (London)* **68A**, 1037 (1955).
(Sa56a) G. R. Satchler, *Phys. Rev.* **104**, 1198 (1956).
(Sa56b) J. Sawicki, *Phys. Rev.* **104**, 1441 (1956).
(Sa57a) J. Sawicki and W. Czyz, *Nuclear Phys.* **4**, 248, 695 (1957).
(Sa57b) J. Sawicki, *Phys. Rev.* **106**, 172 (1957).
(Sa57c) J. Sawicki and Z. Szymanski, *Nuovo cimento* **5**, 1777 (1957).
(Sa58a) J. Sawicki, *Nuclear Phys.* **6**, 575 (1958).
(Sa58b) Sano, Yoshida, and Terasawa, *Nuclear Phys.* **6**, 20 (1958).
(Sa58c) J. Sawicki, *Nuclear Phys.* **6**, 613 (1958).
(Sa58d) G. R. Satchler, *Ann. Phys.* **3**, 275 (1958).
(Sa58e) J. Sawicki and G. R. Satchler, *Nuclear Phys.* **7**, 289 (1958).
(Sa58f) G. R. Satchler, *Nuclear Phys.* **6**, 543 (1958).
(Sa60) G. R. Satchler and W. Tobocman, *Phys. Rev.* **118**, 1566 (1960).
(Sc49) L. I. Schiff, *Quantum Mechanics*, McGraw-Hill, New York, 1949, 1st ed., p. 77.
(Sc54) Schrank, Gugelot, and Dayton, *Phys. Rev.* **96**, 1156 (1954).
(Sc58) Schiffer, Lee, Yntema, and Zeidman, *Phys. Rev.* **110**, 1216 (1958).
(Se47) R. Serber, *Phys. Rev.* **72**, 1114 (1947).
(Se56) Seidlitz, Bleuler, and Tendam, *Bull. Am. Phys. Soc.* **1**, 29 (1956).
(Se58a) Seidlitz, Bleuler, and Tendam, *Phys. Rev.* **110**, 682 (1958).
(Se58b) F. D. Seward, *Bull. Am. Phys. Soc.* **3**, 200 (1958); also Univ. of Rochester Progr. Report (1958).
(Se59) J. P. F. Sellschop, *Phys. Rev. Letters* **3**, 346 (1959).
(Se60) J. P. F. Sellschop, *Phys. Rev.* **119**, 251 (1960).
(Sh56a) Sharp, Diamond, and Wilkinson, *Phys. Rev.* **101**, 1493 (1956).
(Sh56b) R. Sherr and W. F. Hornyak, *Bull. Am. Phys. Soc.* **1**, 197 (1956).

(Sh57)   R. Sherr, *Conf. on Nuclear Structure*, Univ. of Pittsburgh, 1957, un-published.
(Sh59)   G. B. Shook, *Phys. Rev.* **114**, 310 (1959).
(Sq58)   E. J. Squires, *Nuclear Phys.* **6**, 504 (1958).
(St55)   Stratton, Blair, Famularo, and Stuart, *Phys. Rev.* **98**, 629 (1955).
(Sw58)   J. J. de Swart and R. E. Marshak, *Phys. Rev.* **11**, 272 (1958).
(Su58)   R. G. Summers-Gill, *Phys. Rev.* **109**, 1591 (1958).
(Te58)   I. B. Teplov and B. A. Yur'ev, *Zhur. Eksptl. i Teoret. Fiz.* **34**, 334 (1958).
(Th55)   R. G. Thomas, *Phys. Rev.* **100**, 25 (1955).
(To54)   W. Tobocman, *Phys. Rev.* **94**, 1655 (1954).
(To55)   W. Tobocman and M. H. Kalos, *Phys. Rev.* **97**, 132 (1955).
(To56)   W. Tobocman, *Case Institute of Technology Technical Report* No. 29, (1956).   A preliminary version was circulated in 1955 as a U. S. Naval Research Laboratory Report.
(To57)   W. Tobocman, *Phys. Rev.* **108**, 74 (1957).
(To59)   W. Tobocman, *Phys. Rev.* **115**, 98 (1959).
(Ui56)   H. Ui, *Progr. Theoret. Phys.* **16**, 299 (1956).
(Ui57)   H. Ui, *Progr. Theoret. Phys.* **18**, 163 (1957).
(Vl59a)   N. A. Vlasov and A. A. Ogloblin, *Zhur. Eksptl. i Theoret. Fiz.* **37**, 54 (1959); *J. Exptl. Theoret. Phys.* (*U. S. S. R.*) **10**, 39 (1960).
(Vl59b)   Vlasov, Kalinin, Ogloblin, and Chuev, *Zhur. Eksptl. i Teoret. Fiz.* **37**, 1187 (1959); *J. Exptl. Theoret. Phys.* (*U. S. S. R.*) **10**, 844 (1960).
(Vo57)   E. Vogt and J. Lascoux, *Phys. Rev.* **107**, 1028 (1957).
(Vo58)   W. F. Vogelsang and J. N. McGruer, *Phys. Rev.* **109**, 1663 (1958).
(Wa53)   K. M. Watson, *Phys. Rev.* **89**, 575 (1953).
(Wa54)   G. D. Wagner and E. A. Wiig, *Phys. Rev.* **96**, 1100 (1954).
(Wa56)   H. J. Watters, *Phys. Rev.* **103**, 1763 (1956).
(We37)   V. F. Weisskopf, *Phys. Rev.* **52**, 295 (1937).
(We40)   V. F. Weisskopf and D. H. Ewing, *Phys. Rev.* **57**, 472, 935 (1940).
(We56)   A. Werner, *Nuclear Phys.* **1**, 9 (1956).
(We57)   V. F. Weisskopf, *Revs. Modern Phys.* **29**, 174 (1957).
(We58)   H. A. Weidenmüller, *Z. Phys.* **150**, 389 (1958).
(Wi47)   E. P. Wigner and L. Eisenbud, *Phys. Rev.* **72**, 29 (1947).
(Wi55)   E. P. Wigner, *Am. J. Phys.* **23**, 371 (1955).
(Wi56)   E. P. Wigner, "L. Farkas Memorial Volume," *Research Council Israel Spec. Pubn.* No. 1 (1952).
(Wi57a)   L. Winsberg, *Bull. Am. Phys. Soc.* **2**, 381 (1957).
(Wi57b)   D. H. Wilkinson, *Phys. Rev.* **105**, 666 (1957).
(Wi58)   D. H. Wilkinson, *Phil. Mag.* **3**, 1185 (1958).
(Wi59)   D. W. Wilkinson, *Phil. Mag.* **4**, 215 (1959).
(Wo51)   L. Wolfenstein, *Phys. Rev.* **82**, 690 (1951).
(Ya56)   M. Yasuno, *Progr. Theoret. Phys.* **15**, 586 (1956).
(Yn58)   J. L. Yntema and B. Zeidman, *Bull. Am. Phys. Soc.* **3**, 56 (1958).
(Yn60)   Yntema, Zeidman, and Raz, *Phys. Rev*, **117**, 801 (1960).
(Yo56)   S. Yoshida, *Proc. Phys. Soc.* (*London*) **69A**, 668 (1956).
(Yo58a)   S. Yoshida, *Progr. Theoret. Phys.*, **19**, 169 (1958).
(Yo58b)   H. Yoshiki and R. Sherr, *Bull. Am. Phys. Soc.* **3**, 200 (1958).
(Ze58)   B. Zeidman and J. M. Fowler, *Phys. Rev.* **112**, 2020 (1958).

Resonance Processes with Fast Neutrons

H. B. WILLARD

Oak Ridge Natural Laboratory, Oak Ridge, Tennessee

L. C. BIEDENHARN[1]

Duke University, Durham, North Carolina

P. HUBER and E. BAUMGARTNER

Physikalisches Institut der Universität Basel, Basel, Switzerland

1. Introduction and Summary

The present article is intended as a survey and summary of nuclear reaction theory and experiment as it applies in particular to neutron induced processes in the resonance region. The characteristic feature of the problem under consideration is that the reactions proceed through at most only a few states of a well-defined compound system; this is to be contrasted with both direct interactions (stripping, pickup, Coulomb excitation, discussed in Chapter V.D) and reactions that involve a great many (overlapping) compound states, for which statistical considerations are applied. This latter is the subject of the *gross structure* problem and the complex potential representation as discussed in Chapter V.C. Our concern here is with the region typified by the famous Breit-Wigner formula, and with the angular distributions of scattering and reactions in this region.[2]

[1] Fulbright Fellow 1958, on leave at the University of Manchester, England.

[2] This article was essentially completed in mid-1958, and was subsequently revised. In the intervening time a number of valuable surveys, reviews, and even extensions of the theory of nuclear reactions have appeared in

Footnote continued

For the theory of nuclear reactions as developed most completely by Wigner (Wi46, Wi46a, Wi47, Wi48, Te52), the central idea is the separation of physical space into two regions: the *internal region*, where the nucleons are all in strong interaction, and the *external region*, where the nucleons are physically separated into groups (channels), and the interaction between any two groups is, *by assumption*, limited to a simple potential (centrifugal and perhaps Coulomb). The usefulness of this basic postulate lies in the fact that it enables one to replace the unknown nature of the internal region by the equally unknown, but logically more elementary derivative matrix (*R* matrix), and to treat *explicitly* the external features of the reactions (e.g., the penetration and shift factors). This basic postulate does, however, have its limitations, since the assumption that the nucleons in the external region form two groups of nucleons (channels) that interact as particles means that the minimum size of the internal region is not precise, but is limited by the overlap of the wave functions in the most extended channel. *More importantly, this shows that the size of the internal region becomes infinitely large as three-body breakup becomes possible.* However, if three-body breakup is energetically forbidden, as we shall assume, the Wigner theory may be regarded as *exact* for a sufficiently large internal region.[3] The nuclear reaction theory

the literature, many of which bear directly on the subject at hand. Among these are: "Unified Theory of Nuclear Reactions" by H. Feshbach (Fe58); "The Compound Nucleus" by H. Feshbach, Chapter V.A of *Nuclear Spectroscopy* (Aj60); "The R-Matrix Theory of Nuclear Reactions" by A. M. Lane and R. G. Thomas (La58); "Resonance Reactions: Experimental" by H. E. Gove, Chapter VI of *Nuclear Reactions* (En59); "Resonance Reactions: Theoretical" by E. Vogt, Chapter V of *Nuclear Reactions* (En59).

Among the yet unpublished works we would like to mention: "A Review of Phenomenological Descriptions for Neutron Induced Reactions" by Chase, Klahr, and Temkin (Ch58); and "Lectures on the Theory of Nuclear Reactions" (in French) by C. Bloch (Bl56).

We would like, in particular, to call attention to the very excellent article by G. Breit on the "Theory of Resonance Reactions and Allied Topics" in the *Handbuch der Physik* (Br59). This remarkably thorough and comprehensive survey will prove invaluable for an authoritative discussion of the theory treated in the present work.

[3] Three-body processes are not unimportant even at moderate energies, but fortunately we may in most cases avoid the problem by regarding these either as direct interactions (e.g., deuteron breakup), and employing special techniques (usually a modified Born approximation), or regarding the process as a sequence of two-body breakups [e.g., (n,n',γ), employing the Wigner theory at each step]. [The intermediate cases are a topic of current investigation (Le57, Yo58).]

thus obtained is completely general, and any nuclear reaction can be described by a suitable specialization of the parameters of the R matrix. As such, one sees that the theory of nuclear reactions is not so much a theory as it is a framework for a description of nuclear reactions—a point whose significance has been discussed by Wigner in his Richtmyer lecture of 1955 (Wi55b). The emphasis thus shifts to the parameters of the R matrix and, more fundamentally, to the underlying reasons for its general, but not completely arbitrary, form [Eq. (21)]. It is particularly valuable then to have physical insight into the parameters of the R matrix; the Wigner sum rules are a step in this direction. The essential point here is that the internal region must be of nuclear size in order that parameters of the R matrix have any direct significance.

Sections 2.A and 2.B deal with a brief development of the Wigner theory, following for the most part the treatment given by Thomas (Th55, Th56). The concern here, as, in fact, in the Wigner theory itself, is two-fold: (a) a formal concern to obtain general features of the scattering matrix and its expansion into nuclear levels in a precise way, and (b) a practical concern to develop simple formulas for the analysis of experimental data. In these sections we lean heavily on the elementary example of the elastic scattering of spinless particles, employing this as the prototype for the general case (see end of Section 2.A).

Next the general problem of obtaining differential cross sections for scattering and reactions involving unpolarized neutrons is discussed. (Reactions involving polarized neutrons are discussed by Welton, Chapter V.F.) Our discussion follows, by and large, the treatment of Blatt and Biedenharn (Bl52a), but contains also an extension to the case of interfering levels.

The formalism thus developed is then applied to special problems such as the many-level expansion (both in terms of Wigner parameters and the spectral form), the general one-level approximation and its interpretation, and the two-level approximation.

Finally, the theoretical section is concluded with miscellaneous considerations including the dependence upon the size of the internal region, Wigner sum rules, and γ-ray processes.

The literature is rich with experimental studies of resonance processes with neutrons. It was in fact the slow neutron work of Bjerge and Westcott (Bj35), later followed by Moon and Tillman

(Mo35), which first established the resonance behavior of nuclear reactions. Many groups have observed resonances with fast neutrons, but it is the work of Barschall and his co-workers which is outstanding in this field.

There are numerous surveys of the data on fast neutron resonances. Collections of total and partial cross sections are contained in the summary by Hughes and Harvey (Hu55; revised in Hu58). Differential cross sections appear in the summary by Hughes and Carter (Hu56). The noteworthy reviews of energy levels in light nuclei by Ajzenberg and Lauritsen for $Z \leq 10$ (Aj55, Aj59), and by Endt and Braams (En57) for $11 \leq Z \leq 20$ contain the pertinent information of the level parameters for all modes of formation and decay. Rainwater (Ra57) has written a very comprehensive review of resonance processes by neutrons.

A general survey of the experimental problems and techniques involved in the measurement of fast neutron total interaction cross sections appears in Chapter V.A. by D. Miller. An earlier review of the subject by H. H. Barschall (Ba52) also summarizes the pertinent details. The brief discussion here (Section 3) is limited to those particular difficulties germane to studies of individual, or slightly overlapping, resonances. This is followed by a discussion of the interpretation of data thus obtained in terms of nuclear resonance theory. Included are several examples illustrative of the methods.

Next the general problem of measuring elastic scattering differential cross sections is covered (Section 4). Gas recoil techniques are discussed in detail. Most of the pertinent information bearing on techniques involving solid sample appears in Chapter V.B. by Walt; therefore, this treatment is limited to those special considerations associated with high resolution work. This is followed by a discussion of the data in terms of nuclear resonance theory. Again several illustrative examples are included.

2. Nuclear Resonance Theory

A. Elastic Scattering of Spinless Uncharged Particles

The Wigner theory of nuclear reactions is necessarily so complicated by the details of spin, orbital angular momentum, many channels, and Coulomb fields that the essential simplicity of the theory is apt to be obscured. To circumvent this we shall consider first the elementary case of distinguishable, spinless, uncharged particles which are elastically scattered from a potential of finite range. This is a useful procedure since, as we shall see, *every essential feature of the general case finds an exact analog in this elementary example.* Let us first sketch the argument before going into detail. This argument can be separated into two parts. The first part is concerned with the *description of the scattering*, initially in terms of the *scattering function*, S_l, and then transcribed into an alternative formulation employing the *derivative functions*, R_l. Introducing the R_l is an essential step in the Wigner theory, and it is at this point that the separation into internal and external quantities occurs. The second part investigates the properties of the derivative function itself, employing for this purpose Green's theorem to construct a formal series for R_l [Eq. (20)], in terms of energy independent real parameters—the resonance energies, E_λ, and the reduced widths, γ_λ^2 [Eq. (21b)].

The scattering problem deals with quantities defined asymptotically in the external region which for the present example is field free, i.e., only the centrifugal potential enters. The collision function, S_l (also called the *scattering function*), is defined as the amplitude of a unit-flux outgoing wave $\mathcal{O}_l$ of angular momentum l which results from an ingoing wave $\mathcal{I}_l$ of unit flux and angular momentum l. That is:

$$\psi_l = \mathcal{I}_l - S_l \mathcal{O}_l = v^{-1/2} r^{-1} Y_l(\theta, \varphi)(I_l - S_l O_l) \tag{1}$$

where

$$O_l = (ikr)h_l(kr) \sim \exp\{i[kr - (l\pi/2)]\} \tag{2a}$$

$$I_l = O_l^* \tag{2b}$$

and the wave number k and relative velocity v are given by the energetics of the reaction.

The ingoing and outgoing waves of angular momentum l are spherical Bessel functions; [see Section 2.B(1)]. $Y_l(\theta, \varphi)$ is the normalized spherical harmonic defined in Blatt and Weisskopf (Bl52) using the phase conventions as in Condon and Shortley (Co35).

The differential cross section for the scattering process is obtained from the scattering amplitude, $f(\theta)$, which, in turn, is defined as the amplitude of the outgoing wave $r^{-1} \exp(ikr)$ produced by an incident plane wave of unit intensity. Using the Rayleigh expansion for a plane wave in terms of spherical waves (to fix the amplitude of the ingoing waves) and the scattering function, S_l, one finds in the familiar way (Mo33) that

$$f(\theta) = i\pi^{1/2}\lambdabar \sum_{l=0}^{\infty} (2l + 1)^{1/2}(1 - S_l) Y_l^0(\theta) \qquad (3)$$

and the differential cross section

$$d\sigma/d\Omega = |f(\theta)|^2 \qquad (4)$$

where $\lambdabar = \lambda/2\pi = k^{-1}$ is the de Broglie wave length divided by 2π. A more convenient form of the differential cross section results from an expansion in terms of the usual Legendre polynomials, i.e.,

$$d\sigma/d\Omega = \lambdabar^2 \sum_{L=0}^{\infty} B_L P_L (\cos \theta) \qquad (5a)$$

where B_L is defined by

$$B_L \equiv \tfrac{1}{4} \sum_{ll'} (2l + 1)(2l' + 1)(ll'00|L0)^2(1 - S_l)(1 - S_{l'}^*) \qquad (5b)$$

or alternatively, using phase shifts, by

$$B_L \equiv \sum_{ll'} (2l + 1)(2l' + 1)(ll'00|L0)^2 \sin \delta_l \sin \delta_{l'} \cos (\delta_l - \delta_{l'}) \qquad (5c)$$

In going from Eq. (4) to Eq. (5) we have used:
(a) The result for the product of spherical harmonics

$$Y_l^0(\theta, \phi)Y_{l'}^0(\theta, \phi) = \sum_L (4\pi)^{-1}[(2l + 1)(2l' + 1)]^{1/2}(ll'00|L0)^2 P_L(\cos \theta)$$

with $(ll'00|L0)$ being a Wigner coefficient (see Wi31, Co35, and Bi52; tabulations by Sh53, Si54, and Ro59). These quantities are known alternatively as Clebsch-Gordan or vector addition coefficients.
(b) The well-known result (discussed below) that the scattering function may be related to a phase shift through $S_l = \exp (2i\delta_l)$.

The convenience of Eq. (5) may not be immediately evident, for it appears at first glance to be only a rather complicated re-write of Eq. (4). The advantage becomes evident when one considers the general case with spin. For angular distributions involving no polarization measurements, a result of exactly the same form as

Eq. (5) still obtains, [Eq. (68)]. On the other hand, the scattering amplitude in the general case [Eq. (64)] is necessarily very much more complicated than its spinless analog, Eq. (3).

The total elastic cross section follows directly from Eq. (5)

$$\sigma = 4\pi\lambda^2 \sum_{l=0}^{\infty} (2l + 1) \sin^2 \delta_l$$

[This uses $(ll'00|00) = \delta_{ll'}(-)^l(2l + 1)^{-1/2}$]   (6)

The next step, the transcription of these equations in terms of the derivative functions, results from the observation that since we know explicitly the basic solutions (ingoing and outgoing waves of angular momentum l) in the external region, then (for angular momentum l) we know any wave function in the external region (to within a normalization), if we know the logarithmic derivative at any one point in the external region. The derivative function, R_l, is defined as the reciprocal of the logarithmic derivative taken at the boundary, $r = a_c$, of the external region, i.e.,

$$R_l \equiv \left[\psi_l \Big/ \frac{d}{dr}(r\psi_l) \right]_{r=a_c}$$ (7)

[Note that the boundary a_c varies from channel to channel. A commonly used value is $a_c = a_0(A_a^{1/3} + A_b^{1/3})$ with $a_0 = 1.2$ to 1.5 fermis and $A_{a,b}$ are the atomic weights of the channel particles.] In particular, this allows one to write the scattering functions in terms of the derivative function

$$R_l = \{ [I_l(a_c) - S_l O_l(a_c)]/(a_c[I_l'(a_c) - S_l O_l'(a_c)]) \}$$ (8)

where the prime denotes differentiation with respect to r. The corresponding solution for S_l is then

$$S_l = e^{-2i\phi_l}[(1 - L_l^* R_l)/(1 - L_l R_l)]$$ (9)

Here we have introduced the external quantities:
(a) The logarithmic derivative, L_l

$$L_l \equiv [a_c O_l'(a_c)/O_l(a_c)] \equiv \mathfrak{s}_l + iP_l$$ (10)

(the interpretation of $\mathfrak{s}_l$ and P_l as shift and penetration factors, respectively, will be discussed at the end of this section), and
(b) The "hard sphere" phase, ϕ_l

$$e^{-2i\phi_l} \equiv I_l(a_c)/O_l(a_c)$$ (11)

To determine the general properties of the derivative function, let us consider now the internal region. Here the radial wave function $u_l(r) \equiv r\psi_l / Y_l^0(\theta)$ obeys the Schrödinger equation

$$\frac{d^2 u_l}{dr^2} - \frac{l(l+1)u_l}{r^2} + \frac{2M}{\hbar^2}(E - V)u_l = 0 \qquad (12)$$

with the unknown (but real) potential V such that $V = 0$ for $r \geq a_c$. (Here M is the reduced mass of the system.) From Eq. (12) one obtains in the usual way (Mo53) Green's relation (the index l will be dropped in the following equations)

$$[u(E_2)u'(E_1) - u(E_1)u'(E_2)]_{r=a_c}$$

$$= (2M/\hbar^2)(E_2 - E_1) \int_0^{a_c} u(E_2)u(E_1)dr \qquad (13)$$

where the integral extends over the internal region and we take

$$u(r = 0) = 0 \text{ and } u' \equiv du/dr$$

The next step is the introduction of an orthonormal set of internal wave functions, X_λ, defined by the same Schrödinger equation as in Eq. (12) with E replaced by E_λ, the characteristic energy, and having the same boundary condition at the origin, but with a general boundary condition imposed, at $r = a_c$, on the logarithmic derivative of X_λ. That is:

$$(rX_\lambda'/X_\lambda)_{a_c} = b_c \qquad (14)$$

where b_c is independent of λ, and possibly complex. It follows from Eqs. (13) and (14) that the X_λ can be taken as an orthonormal set of basic functions, i.e.,

$$\int_0^{a_c} X_\lambda X_{\lambda'} dr = \delta_{\lambda\lambda'} \qquad (15)$$

An arbitrary wave function, $u(E)$, which satisfies Eq. (12) at energy E (and vanishes at the origin) may be expanded in terms of the basic set, X_λ

$$u(E) = \sum_\lambda A_\lambda X_\lambda \qquad (16a)$$

where

$$A_\lambda = \int_0^{a_c} X_\lambda u_E dr = (\hbar^2/2Ma_c)(E_\lambda - E)^{-1} X_\lambda(a_c)[a_c u'(a_c)$$

$$- b_c u(a_c)] \qquad (16b)$$

It should be pointed out that the derivative of the series given by Eqs. (16a) and (16b) is not uniformly convergent; a detailed discussion is given by Thomas (Th56).

An alternative form of Eq. (16) uses the language of Green's function, $G(r,r')$, which is defined by

$$\left[\frac{d^2}{dr^2} - \frac{l(l+1)}{r^2} + \frac{2M}{\hbar^2}(E - V)\right] G(r,r') = -\frac{\delta(r - r')}{a_c} \quad (17a)$$

$$\left[r\frac{d}{dr} G(r,r')/G(r,r')\right]_{r=a_c} = b_c \quad (17b)$$

i.e., this Green's function obeys the same boundary conditions as the X_λ and also the Schrödinger equation, except that for $r \rightarrow r'$, G behaves as a unit source. Expressing G in terms of the basic set one has

$$G(r,r') = \frac{\hbar^2}{2Ma_c} \sum_\lambda \frac{X_\lambda(r)X_\lambda(r')}{E_\lambda - E} \quad (18)$$

In terms of this Green's function, Eq. (16) takes the form

$$u(E, r) = G(a_c, r)\left[\frac{a_c u'(a_c)}{u(a_c)} - b_c\right] u(a_c) \quad (19)$$

Introducing now the derivative function, R, one finds that

$$R(1 - b_c R)^{-1} = G(a_c, a_c) = \left(\frac{\hbar^2}{2Ma_c}\right) \sum_\lambda \frac{X_\lambda^2(a_c)}{E_\lambda - E} \quad (20)$$

This equation establishes the general form of the derivative function. In the particular case where $b_c = 0$, as originally used in reference (Wi47), one notes that R itself is just the Green's function at $r = r' = a_c$.

An important point about the development is the fact that $G(a_c, a_c)$ can be taken as *real*, provided only that b_c is real (unless otherwise stated this will be assumed in the following). In this case R is also real, but since R is independent of b_c it follows the R is *always* real. From this one concludes, using Eq. (9), that *the scattering function S may be written in the form $S = \exp(2i\delta)$, with the phase shift δ being real.*

If b_c is zero, R takes the form

$$R = \sum_\lambda [\gamma_\lambda^2/(E_\lambda - E)] \tag{21a}$$

$$\gamma_\lambda \equiv (\hbar^2/2Ma_c)^{1/2}X_\lambda(a_c) \tag{21b}$$

where γ_λ^2, an internal parameter, is called the *reduced width*, and has the dimensions of energy.

Functions of the form of Eq. (21) have been designated as R-functions by Wigner, and studied in detail (Wi51, Wi52, Wi52a). Among their properties is the fact that if A is an R-function, then $A/(1 + \alpha A)$ is also an R-function for α real. Hence an arbitrary real boundary condition b_c, according to Eq. (20), still leaves R to be an R-function.

Although the series [Eq. (21)] for an R-function is quite general, it is not a completely arbitrary function of the energy; in particular its energy derivative is always positive. The underlying reason for this, and other properties of the derivative function, is to be found in the "causality condition"—the physical requirement that the scattered wave cannot leave the internal region before the ingoing wave has reached it (Wi55b; this reference also gives a list of further references).

The value of the boundary condition, b_c, has no effect on Eq. (9), since the derivative function, and the external functions as well, are independent of b_c. A given expansion of R, however, does involve quantities that are functions of b_c, e.g., the Green's function, $G(a_c, a_c)$. Using Eq. (20), we may write Eq. (9) in the form:

$$S = e^{-2i\phi}[(1 - (L^* - b_c)G)/(1 - (L - b_c)G)] \tag{9'}$$

where $G = G(a_c, a_c)$ and is a function of b_c. This equation is valid for complex b_c.

For real b_c, G is real and is an R-function in Wigner's sense of the term. Equation (9') may then be abbreviated by introducing Thomas' barred notation $\bar{L}_c \equiv L_c - b_c$, $\bar{P}_c \equiv P_c$, $\bar{S}_c \equiv S_c - b_c$; in addition, we write, $R(b_c) \equiv G(a_c, a_c)$. Then we find

$$S = e^{-2i\phi}[(1 - \bar{L}_c^*R(b_c))/(1 - \bar{L}_cR(b_c))] \tag{9''}$$

This is of the *same* form as Eq. (9), and is a convenient (and customary) way to include the effect of real b_c. [It suffers from the fact that R now denotes two quite different things: an R-function (a Green's function) as in Eq. (9''), which varies with b_c, and the derivative function as in Eq. (9), which is independent of b_c.]

The physical content of the results obtained thus far [Eqs. (9) and (20)] is best illustrated by the single-level approximation to R; i.e., we approximate R by

$$R \cong \gamma_\lambda^2/(E_\lambda - E) \tag{22}$$

which is valid in a sufficiently small neighborhood of E_λ. Then letting $S = e^{2i\delta}$ one finds that

$$\delta \;\; = \cot^{-1}[(1 - R\bar{s}_c)/RP_c] - \phi = \beta - \phi \tag{23}$$

with

$$\beta \;\; \equiv \cot^{-1}[(E_\lambda + \Delta_\lambda - E)/{}^1\!/_2\Gamma_\lambda] \tag{23a}$$

$$\Gamma_\lambda \equiv 2P_c\gamma_\lambda^2 \tag{23b}$$

$$\Delta_\lambda \equiv -\bar{s}_c\gamma_\lambda^2 \tag{23c}$$

where we have used $\bar{s}_c$ to take into account an arbitrary (real) b_c boundary condition as discussed above.

The interpretation of the terms (23a...c) then follows:

(a) The phase β increases rapidly to π as E goes through $E_\lambda + \Delta_\lambda$, hence the designation *resonance phase shift* for β, which is of the familiar Breit-Wigner form.

(b) The width of the resonance is Γ_λ, which is a product of a reduced (energy independent) width γ_λ^2 (an internal quantity) and the external (energy dependent) quantity P_c. The interpretation of P_c as a *penetration factor* comes from the fact that (aside from a factor kr), P_c is just the ratio of the intensity of an outgoing wave at infinity to the intensity at the point r.

(c) The resonance is shifted from E_λ by an amount Δ_λ, which is the product of γ_λ^2 and the external (energy dependent) factor $\bar{s}_c$. Thus the designation of $\bar{s}_c$ as the *shift factor* becomes meaningful.

(d) Finally we see that on resonance the scattering is given essentially by ϕ. Since *hard-sphere scattering* requires that the wave function vanish at $r = a_c$, the derivative function R becomes zero, and therefore from Eq. (23) we see that $\delta = -\phi$. Thus the designation of ϕ is the *hard-sphere phase shift*.

A less extreme form of the one-level approximation occurs when we assume that the remaining levels, λ', contribute a constant background R^0 to the derivative matrix. i.e..

$$R = R^0 + \gamma_\lambda{}^2/(E_\lambda - E). \tag{24}$$

The phase shift δ' now assumes the form

$$\delta' \;\; = \beta' - \phi' \tag{25}$$

where

$$\beta' = \cot^{-1}[(E_\lambda + \Delta'_\lambda - E)/\Gamma'_\lambda/2] \tag{25a}$$

$$\Gamma'_\lambda = 2P'_c\gamma_\lambda^2 \tag{25b}$$

$$\Delta'_\lambda = -S'_c\gamma_\lambda^2 \tag{25c}$$

$$\phi' = \phi - \cot^{-1}[(1 - R^0\bar{S}_c)/R^0P_c] \tag{25d}$$

$$S'_c = [\bar{S}_c(1 - R^0\bar{S}_c) - R^0P_c^2][(1 - R^0\bar{S}_c)^2 + (R^0P_c)^2]^{-1} \tag{25e}$$

$$P'_c = P_c[(1 - R^0\bar{S}_c)^2 + (R^0P_c)^2]^{-1} \tag{25f}$$

where it should be noted that S'_c and P'_c are *not* simply shift and penetration factors (Os36, Fr53).

It will be noted that this result is similar in form to Eq. (23), but now however, the background scattering, ϕ', consists of two contributions: the hard-sphere scattering, ϕ, and the contribution from R^0—*both contributions being generally of a similar order of magnitude* (see examples in Section 4).

In the following two sections we shall generalize each of the steps taken in this spinless particle example. In order to give an over-all view of our procedure, we shall indicate it schematically, with references to the place where each step is taken, by the diagram on the next page.

B. Generalization of the Results in Section A

(1) **The Form of the Wave Functions in the External Region, Notational Conventions.** It is necessary to be quite explicit about notational conventions, and this section is concerned with this tedious chore. The basic assumption of the theory is that in the external region *any wave function, which satisfies the wave equation at energy E, may be written uniquely as a sum of two particle (channel) wave functions.* A channel is to be specified by:

(a) Two physically separated groups of nucleons (nuclei), which interact with each other as structureless particles. A given set of two nuclei will be designated as an *alternative* (α) which specifies, besides the type of nuclei, the spins (**a** and **b**) of the two nuclei, and their state of excitation (if any).

(b) The relative orbital angular momentum, l, between the two nuclei.

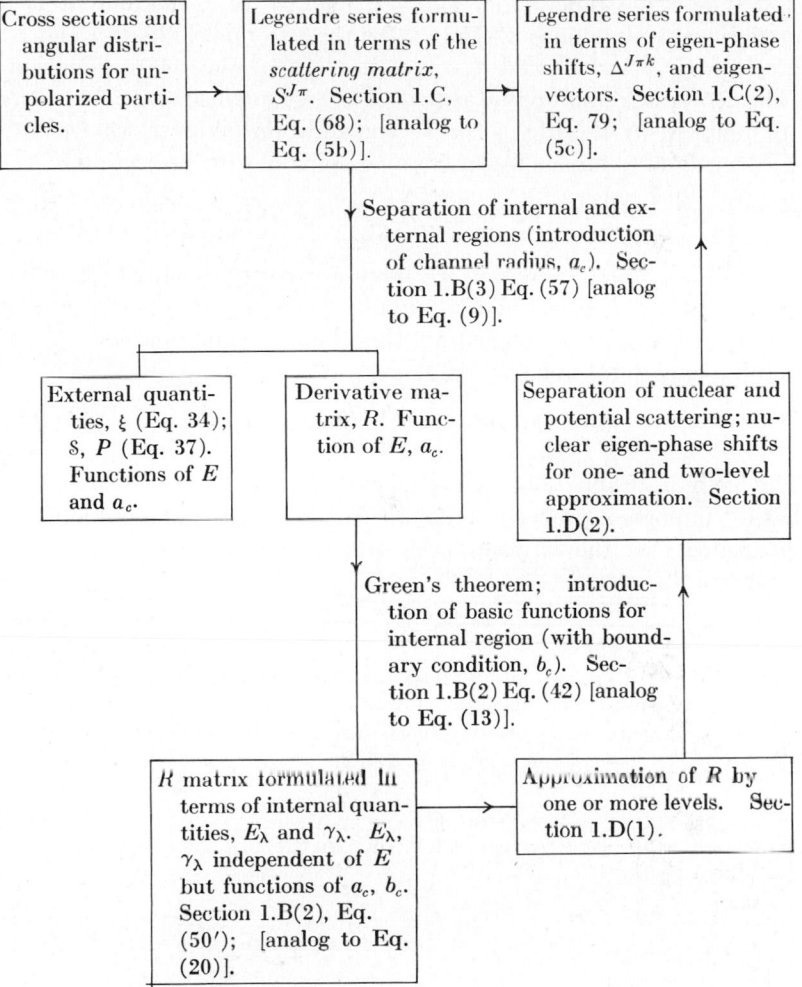

(c) The spins **a** and **b** of the interacting nuclei coupled to give a resultant *channel spin*, **s**, i.e., (**s** = **a** + **b**).

(d) The total angular momentum, **J**, (**J** = **l** + **s**), and projection M. A given channel, c, is therefore designated by the indices $\alpha slJM$, although in actuality, since J, M are sharp, the indices αsl are often sufficient to distinguish the channels.

The wave funct'on in a given channel is a product of two intrinsic wave functions ψ_a^α and ψ_b^β for the two nuclei (spins **a** and **b**; projections α and β) and a wave function of the relative motion. (The center of mass is put at rest.)   The two intrinsic wave functions are coupled, by the use of the vector addition (Wigner) coefficients (Co35), so as to have a sharp channel spin, **s,** with projection σ

$$\psi_s^\sigma = \sum_{\alpha\beta} (\mathbf{ab}\alpha\beta \mid s\sigma)\psi_a^\alpha\psi_b^\beta \qquad (26a)$$

For the relative motion we have a wave function which is the product of a radial part and an angular part: $\psi_{\text{rel}} = r^{-1}u_c\mathcal{Y}_l^m$. The angular part, $\mathcal{Y}_l^m$, is coupled to the channel spin function, ψ_s^σ, to obtain sharp total angular momentum, J, M

$$\phi_c = \phi_{\alpha slJM} \equiv r^{-1} \sum_{\alpha\lambda} (sl\sigma\lambda \mid JM)\psi_s^\sigma\mathcal{Y}_l^\lambda \qquad (26b)$$

This composite function, ϕ_c, is designated as a *surface function*, and has the important property that such functions are orthonormal when integrated over the surface of the internal region (see discussion in Footnote 4, however).   Thus

$$\int \phi_c^*\phi_{c'}dA = \delta_{cc'} \qquad (27)$$

The normalization conventions on these functions are important.   For the angular part we use the convention introduced in Bi51, i.e., $\mathcal{Y}_l^m = i^l Y_l^m(\theta,\varphi)$ [where Y_l^m is the usual spherical harmonic (Bl52)]. Thus, if $K\varphi(-x)$ is the time reversal operator (Wi32), we obtain

$$K(\mathcal{Y}_l^m) = (-)^{l-m}(\mathcal{Y}_l^{-m}) \qquad (28a)$$

Assuming that the same convention holds for the intrinsic wave functions of the alternative α, viz.,

$$K(\psi_a^\alpha) = (-)^{a-\alpha}\psi_a^{-\alpha} \qquad (28b)$$

then it follows that the surface functions, ϕ_c, also obey the relation

$$K\phi_{\alpha slJM} = (-)^{J-M}\phi_{\alpha slJ,-M} \qquad (28c)$$

which results from the properties of the Wigner coefficients.

This choice of phase convention leads to reduced widths which are real [Section 2.D(2)].

For convenience, the necessary notational conventions on radial functions are summarized here.   The radial part obeys the differential equation

$$\frac{d^2u_c}{dr^2} - \left\{ \frac{l(l+1)}{r^2} + \frac{2M}{\hbar^2}\left[\left(\frac{Z_aZ_be^2}{r}\right) - E \right] \right\} u_c = 0 \qquad (29)$$

$Z_{a,b}$ are the atomic numbers of the colliding particles.   Although we are concerned with neutrons, the exit channels may be charged.   It is customary to introduce the quantities:

$\rho \equiv kr$ (the dimensionless radial coordinate)
$\eta \equiv Z_a Z_b e^2 / \hbar v$ (the Sommerfeld parameter for the Coulomb field)
$k \equiv (2ME/\hbar^2)^{1/2}$ (the magnitude of the wave vector)

where the channel index, c, has been dropped.   Equation (29) thus takes the dimensionless form

$$u_c'' - [l(l+1)/\rho^2 + (2\eta/\rho) - 1]u_c = 0 \tag{29'}$$

where the primes now denote differentiation with respect to ρ.

For positive energy channels the solutions to Eq. (29′) are the regular (F_l) and irregular (G_l) Coulomb functions (Ab52, Hu59)

$$F_l(\eta, \rho) \sim \sin\left(\rho - \frac{\pi l}{2} - \eta \ln 2\rho + \sigma_l\right) \tag{30a}$$

$$G_l(\eta, \rho) \sim \cos\left(\rho - \frac{\pi l}{2} - \eta \ln 2\rho + \sigma_l\right) \tag{30b}$$

where

$$\sigma_l \equiv arg \ \Gamma(l + 1 + i\eta) \tag{30c}$$

These functions obey the Wronskian relation

$$F_l' G_l - G_l' F_l = 1 \tag{31}$$

For the developments which follow it is useful to introduce combinations of F_l and G_l that are asymptotically ingoing and outgoing spherical (Coulomb) waves,

$$I_l \equiv (G_l - iF_l)e^{i\psi_l} \tag{32a}$$

$$O_l \equiv (G_l + iF_l)e^{-i\psi_l} = (I_l)^* \tag{32b}$$

$$\psi_l \equiv \sigma_l - \sigma_0 \tag{32c}$$

The amplitude, A_l, and the phase, ϕ_l, are defined by

$$G_l + iF_l \equiv A_l e^{i\phi_l} \tag{33}$$

In the discussion which follows, $\phi_l(a_c)$ is also referred to as the *hard-sphere phase shift.*

ξ_l, another phase which is necessary in the development, is defined by

$$\Omega_c \equiv e^{i\xi_l} = (I_l/O_l)^{1/2} \tag{34}$$

From Eqs. (32) and (33) it follows that

$$\xi_l = \psi_l - \phi_l$$

Table I

l	P_l	S_l	ϕ_l
0	ρ	0	$-\rho$
1	$\dfrac{\rho^3}{1+\rho^2}$	$\dfrac{-1}{1+\rho^2}$	$-\rho + \dfrac{\pi}{2} - \cot^{-1}\rho$
2	$\dfrac{\rho^5}{9+3\rho^2+\rho^4}$	$\dfrac{-3(6+\rho^2)}{9+3\rho^2+\rho^4}$	$-\rho + \pi - \cot^{-1}\left(\dfrac{\rho^2-3}{3\rho}\right)$
3	$\dfrac{\rho^7}{225+45\rho^2+6\rho^4+\rho^6}$	$\dfrac{-3(225+30\rho^2+2\rho^4)}{225+45\rho^2+6\rho^4+\rho^6}$	$-\rho + \dfrac{3\pi}{2} - \cot^{-1}\dfrac{\rho(\rho^2-15)}{6\rho^2-15}$

For neutrons, the radial functions are the spherical Bessel functions (Mo53).

$$F_l = \rho j_l(\rho) \tag{35a}$$

$$G_l = -\rho n_l(\rho) \tag{35b}$$

$$I_l = -i\rho h_l^{(-)}(\rho) \tag{35c}$$

$$O_l = -i\rho h_l^{(+)}(\rho) \tag{35d}$$

One introduces next the logarithmic derivative, L_l, for the outgoing waves

$$L_l \equiv \rho \frac{d}{d\rho} (O_l)/O_l \tag{36a}$$

$$\equiv S_l(\eta\rho) + iP_l(\eta\rho) \tag{36b}$$

Here the S_l and P_l are, respectively, the real and imaginary parts of L_l, which are later to be interpreted as the (energy) *shift factor* (S_l) and *penetration factor* (P_l). Alternatively, they may be written

$$P_l = \rho(F_l^2 + G_l^2)^{-1} \tag{37a}$$

$$S_l = {}^\rho/_2 \frac{d}{d\rho} \ln (F_l^2 + G_l^2) \tag{37b}$$

These factors have certain monotonic properties, and, for the (neutron) case ($\eta = 0$) can be given a quite simple explicit form (Pr58)

$$P(0\rho) = \rho/{}_3F_o(-l, l + 1, {}^1/_2; -\rho^{-2}) \tag{38a}$$

$$S(0\rho) = {}^1/_2 l(l + 1)\rho^{-2} \frac{{}_3F_o(1 - l, l + 2, {}^3/_2; -\rho^{-2})}{{}_3F_o(-l, l + 1, {}^1/_2; -\rho^{-2})} \tag{38b}$$

where

$${}_3F_o(a, b, c; x) = \sum_n \frac{\Gamma(a + n)}{\Gamma(a)} \frac{\Gamma(b + n)}{\Gamma(b)} \frac{\Gamma(c + n)}{\Gamma(c)} x^n/\Gamma(n + 1)$$

(Note that for the case at hand the series terminates.)

It is useful in the neutron case to give the exact results for the first few units of orbital angular momentum (see Table I).

The usefulness of the Wigner theory is dependent in part upon the availability of suitable tabulations of the necessary functions, in particular the Coulomb functions, and the shift and penetration factors; a comprehensive tabulation is, however, not presently available. For charged particles there are the Coulomb function tables of Breit and collaborators (Bl51), as well as the tables and graphs given by Christy (Ch48); by Abramowitz (Ab52); by Feshbach, Shapiro, and Weisskopf (Fe53a); by Sharp, Gove, and Paul (Sh56); and by Tubis (Tu58). For large η, asymptotic approximations are useful (Ab54, Bi55). The tables of C. E. Froberg (Fr55) also apply to the region of large η.

A tabulation of the shift and penetration factors for uncharged particles has been compiled recently by Monahan, Biedenharn, and Schiffer (Mo58), and similarly some penetrabilities for charged particles have been compiled by Schiffer (Sc57).

The final preliminary step concerns the normalization of the wave functions in the external region. The basic set of functions comprises ingoing and outgoing waves with sharp JM: $I_c\phi_c$ and $O_c\phi_c$. It is useful, however, to normalize these functions by $v_c^{-1/2} = \left(\dfrac{M_c}{\hbar k_c}\right)^{1/2}$, (where M_c is the reduced mass of the two fragments of channel c) in order to eliminate such factors from the scattering matrix. This set of functions is designated by:

$$\mathcal{I}_c \equiv v_c^{-1/2} I_c\phi_c \tag{39a}$$

$$\mathcal{O}_c \equiv v_c^{-1/2} O_c\phi_c \tag{39b}$$

(2) The Matrix Generalization of the Derivative Function. The desired generalization is effected by means of a *many-channel Green's theorem*, the analog to Eq. (13) which served as the basis for deriving Eq. (20) in the spinless particle example. The essential step (an approximation to be precise[4]) is to note that on the surface of the internal region we may expand a given wave function in terms of the surface functions for the various channels, ϕ_c, which are orthonormal. But for any given channel we may manipulate[5] the kinetic energy so as to write the kinetic energy operator in the form

$$T = T_{CM} + T_{\text{rel}} + T_a + T_b \tag{40}$$

where T_{CM} is the kinetic energy of the center-of-mass system, T_{rel} the kinetic energy of the relative motion of the composite particles a and b (defined by the channel label c), and T_a, T_b are the internal kinetic energies of particles a and b. For any given channel c one

---

[4] The point here is the physical approximation that in a given channel the wave functions for the composite particles making up that channel do not overlap appreciably so that the "surface" can be taken as $r_c = $ fixed $= a_c$ and *all of space* for the remaining coordinates. Thus we get strict orthogonality for the surface functions, using this enlarged surface. [cf. Wigner (Wi47), his footnote 9.]

[5] This manipulation is the usual series of transformations typified for two particles by $[\mathbf{r}_1\mathbf{r}_2] \rightarrow [\mathbf{R} \ (m_1\mathbf{r}_1 + m_2\mathbf{r}_2)/(m_1 + m_2), \rho = \mathbf{r}_1 - \mathbf{r}_2]$ (Th56, Br40).

has an integral of the relative kinetic energy operator, T_{rel}, in the form of Green's theorem, i.e.,

$$\int dV[\psi_2^*(T_{\text{rel}}\psi_1) - (T_{\text{rel}}\psi_2)^*\psi_1]$$

$$= \left(\frac{\hbar^2}{2M_c}\right)\int dA\left(\psi_2^* \frac{d}{dr_c}\psi_1 - \frac{d\psi_2^*}{dr_c}\psi_1\right)_0^{r_c} \quad (41)$$

where M_c is the reduced mass for channel c [$M_c = M_a M_b/(M_a + M_b)$]. Upon extending the surface as mentioned in Footnote 4, we find the result

$$\sum_c \left(\frac{\hbar^2}{2M_c}\right)\left[u_{c2}\left(\frac{d}{dr_c}u_{c1}\right) - \left(\frac{d}{dr_c}u_{c2}\right)u_{c1}\right]_{r_c=a_c}$$

$$= (E_2 - E_1)\int_{\text{internal region}}\psi_2^*\psi_1\, dV \quad (42)$$

This then is *the many-channel generalization of Green's theorem* (Wi47). To the extent that only two-body breakup is energetically allowed, the result is exact in the limit of a sufficiently large internal region.

Following Wigner (Wi47), one designates the value of the channel radial function by V_c, and the derivative by D_c, with the normalization

$$(\hbar^2/2M_c a_c)^{1/2}\, u_c(a_c) = V_c \quad (43a)$$

$$\left(\frac{\hbar^2}{2M_c a_c}\right)^{1/2}\left(r_c \frac{du_c}{dr_c}\right)_{a_c} = D_c \quad (43b)$$

Just as in the spinless particle example, the next step is to define an orthonormal set of functions, X_λ, for the internal region. These functions satisfy the equation

$$HX_\lambda = E_\lambda X_\lambda \quad (44)$$

with the boundary condition

$$\int_{\text{(surface)}} dA\phi_c^*\left(r_c \frac{d}{dr_c}X_\lambda - b_c X\right)_{r_c=a_c} = 0 \quad (45)$$

The functions, X_λ, are then orthogonal and may be normalized to give

$$\int dV\, X_\lambda^* X_{\lambda'} = \delta_{\lambda\lambda'} \tag{46}$$

$$\begin{pmatrix} \text{internal} \\ \text{region} \end{pmatrix}$$

It follows that any wave function, ψ_E, in the internal region may be written as a series in the internal functions, X_λ,

$$\psi_E = \sum_{\lambda c} (E_\lambda - E)^{-1}(V_{\lambda c}D_c - D_{\lambda c}V_c)X_\lambda \tag{47}$$

where $V_{\lambda c}$, $D_{\lambda c}$ are the value and derivative of X_λ at the channel surface c and similarly V_c, D_c are the value and derivative of ψ_E.

From our phase conventions V_c and D_c are real (b_c is real by hypothesis).[6] The $V_{\lambda c}$ are customarily given the designation, $\gamma_{\lambda c}$. Since the $\gamma_{\lambda c}$ are basic parameters for the Wigner theory it is well to give the definition explicitly

$$V_{\lambda c} \equiv \gamma_{\lambda c} \equiv (\hbar^2/2M_c a_c)^{1/2} \int \phi_c^* X_\lambda dA \tag{48}$$

where the (surface) integral is evaluated at $r_c = a_c$. The reduced widths $\gamma_{\lambda c}^2$ used here have the dimensions of energy, as in references Th55 and Th56 and in Chapter VIII of Blatt and Weisskopf (Bl52) rather than energy–distance, as in references Te52 and Br59. They differ from the latter by a factor a_c. Note the factor $a_c^{-1/2}$ in the definition above.

The definition of the derivative matrix, $R_{cc'}$, is that the value V_c in any channel is a linear function of the derivative quantities D_c in all the channels, i.e., $V_c = \sum_{c'} R_{cc'}D_{c'}$. A relation between V_c and the derivative quantities D_c follows from Eq. (47) (by multi-

---

[6] To see this we note that

$$V_{\lambda c} = (\hbar^2/2M_c a_c)^{1/2} \int dA \phi_c^* X_\lambda^{JM}$$

and

$$(V_{\lambda c})^* = (\hbar^2/2M_c a_c)^{1/2} \int dA (K\phi_c)^*(K X_\lambda^{JM})$$
$$= (\hbar^2/2M_c a_c)^{1/2} \int dA \phi_{\alpha s J - M}^* X_\lambda^{-M} = V_{\lambda c}$$

using

$$K\phi_c = (-)^{J-M}\phi_{\alpha s l J, -M}$$
$$K X_\lambda^{JM} = (-)^{J-M} X_{\lambda J, -M}$$

and the fact that the integral is independent of M.

plying by ϕ_c^* and integrating over the surface of the internal region A). That is:

$$\int \phi_c^* \psi_E dA \equiv V_c = \sum_{\lambda c'} (E_\lambda - E)^{-1} \gamma_{\lambda c} \gamma_{\lambda c'} (D_c - b_c V_c) \qquad (49)$$

Upon introducing the definition of the derivative matrix, $R_{cc'}$, Eq. (49) becomes

$$\sum_{c'} R_{cc'} D_{c'} = \sum_{\lambda c'} (E_\lambda - E) \gamma_{\lambda c} \gamma_{\lambda c'} (D_{c'} - b_{c'} \sum_{c''} R_{c'c''} D_{c''}) \qquad (50)$$

Eqattion (50) is a basic result of the Wigner theory, but it is rather unwieldy in its present form. By introducing a matrix notation the formulas become much more perspicuous. We shall designate two index quantities such as $R_{cc'}$ (noting that this is a shorthand for the set of numbers $R_{asl;\ \alpha's'l'}^{J\pi}$) by a matrix $(R_{cc'}) = \mathbf{R}$. Similarly the quantities D_c, V_c, and b_c can be written as diagonal matrices $\mathbf{D}$, $\mathbf{V}$, and $\mathbf{b}$. Finally we write the reduced widths $\gamma_{\lambda c}$ as a vector, γ_λ, and the notation $\gamma_\lambda \times \gamma_\lambda$ means the matrix whose elements are $\gamma_{\lambda c} \gamma_{\lambda c'}$. Equation (50) then reads

$$\mathbf{R}(1 - \mathbf{bR})^{-1} = \sum_\lambda [\gamma_\lambda \times \gamma_\lambda / (E_\lambda - E)] \qquad (50')$$

This relation is a major result of the Wigner-Eisenbud (Wi47) *theory;* it is seen to be the complete analog to Eq. (20) for the spinless particle case.

(3) **The Scattering Matrix.** In the external region the most general wave function in channel c having total angular momentum J, M consists of a superposition of ingoing and outgoing spherical waves with the spin-angle dependence ϕ_c. That is:

$$\psi_c = (A_c \mathcal{I}_c - B_c \mathcal{O}_c) \qquad (51)$$

where the normalization of the spherical waves $\mathcal{I}$, $\mathcal{O}$ [cf. Eq. (39)] is chosen so that the coefficients A_c and B_c correspond to *amplitudes of probability flux*, rather than of probability density.

The coefficients A_c and B_c are not independent of each other, but are related by the wave equation. The relation between them defines the *scattering matrix*, $\mathbf{S}$ (alternatively called the *collision matrix*)

$$B_c = \sum_{c'} S_{cc'} A_{c'} \qquad (52)$$

The relation between the derivative matrix, $\mathbf{R}$, and the scattering matrix, $\mathbf{S}$, now follows from Eqs. (51) and (52), if we consider a wave function ψ_E in the external region, which satisfies the wave equation for energy E, and utilize the definition of $\mathbf{R}$. The most general such wave function is of the form

$$\psi_E = \sum_{cc'} (\mathcal{I}_c \delta_{cc'} - \mathcal{O}_c S_{cc'}) A_{c'} \qquad (53)$$

where the amplitudes of the ingoing waves, $A_{c'}$, are completely arbitrary.

The derivative matrix relates the *value* of ψ_E to the *derivative* of ψ_E on the surface of the internal region; noting the normalization [Eq. (43)] for these quantities we have explicitly the relation

$$(\hbar^2/2Ma_c)^{1/2} \int \phi_c^* \psi_E dA$$
$$= \sum_{c'} R_{cc'} (\hbar^2/2M_{c'}a_{c'})^{1/2} \int \phi_{c'}^* \, (r_{c'}(d/dr_{c'})\psi_E) dA \quad (54)$$

Using Eq. (53), and noting that the $A_{c'}$, are arbitrary, we find

$$\varrho^{-1/2}(\mathbf{I} - \mathbf{OS}) = \mathbf{R}\varrho^{1/2}(\mathbf{I'} - \mathbf{O'S}) \qquad (55a)$$

where we have introduced the diagonal matrices

$$\mathbf{I} = (I_c \delta_{cc'}), \; \mathbf{I'} = (\rho_c(d/d\rho_c)I_c \delta_{cc'}) \qquad (55b)$$

and, in addition, the diagonal matrix

$$\varrho = [(a_c m_c v_c/\hbar)\delta_{cc'}] \qquad (55c)$$

and similarly for $\mathbf{O}$, $\mathbf{O'}$.

This can be put into the form

$$\mathbf{S} = \mathbf{\Omega P}^{1/2}(1 - \mathbf{RL})^{-1}(1 - \mathbf{RL}^*)\mathbf{P}^{-1/2}\mathbf{\Omega} \qquad (56)$$

or

$$\mathbf{S} = \mathbf{\Omega}(1 + 2i\mathbf{P}^{1/2}(1 - \mathbf{RL})^{-1}\mathbf{RP}^{1/2})\mathbf{\Omega} \qquad (57)$$

[where we have further introduced the diagonal matrices $\mathbf{\Omega}$ and $\mathbf{L}$ whose diagonal elements are defined in Eqs. (34) and (36), and P is defined in Eq. (37a)].

Equations (56) and (57) give the desired connection between the scattering and derivative matrix; once again we note the complete formal equivalence to Eq. (9) of the spinless particle example.

It is often useful to introduce another matrix (Te52), the reactance matrix Q, which expresses the connection between the regular and irregular radial functions in the external region (rather than between the ingoing and outgoing radial functions which gives the scattering matrix). Thus

$$\psi_E = \sum_c (\bar{A}_c \phi_c F_c - \bar{B}_c \phi_c G_c) V_c^{-1/2} \tag{58a}$$

with

$$\bar{B}_c = \sum_{c'} Q_{cc'} \bar{A}_{c'} \tag{58b}$$

From this one sees that

$$S = (1 + iQ)^{-1}(1 - iQ) \tag{58c}$$

The one dimensional case shows that Q is just the matrix generalization of the tangent function.

The introduction of the Q matrix is motivated by the observation (Te52) that for an energy region where the external parameters can be treated as constants, Q is an R-function, and thus permits an expansion of the form of Eq. (21).

(4) **General Properties of the Scattering Matrix.** Since the scattering matrix is defined asymptotically, and since the derivative matrix development of the preceding sections becomes precise also asymptotically, we see that the properties of S can be rigorously established from those of R.

From Eq. (50) we see that R is both *real and symmetric*. Introducing this in Eq. (57), we conclude that: (a) S is symmetric (since all the matrices in Eq. (57) are symmetric), and (b) $S^* = S^{-1}$ (noting that $\Omega^{-1} = \Omega^*$, $P^* = P$). *These considerations establish the two general properties of the S matrix: S is symmetric, $\tilde{S} = S$, (reciprocity) and S is unitary, $S^* = S^{-1}$ (conservation of flux).*

One may write an arbitrary symmetric unitary matrix in the form (Wi46b)

$$S = (U)^{-1} \exp(2i\Delta)(U) \tag{59}$$

where Δ is a real diagonal matrix, and U is a real orthogonal matrix. For an N channel scattering matrix there are then only $\frac{1}{2}N(N+1)$ free parameters for every value of J, π; N of these parameters are the elements of the diagonal matrix, Δ, the *eigen phase shifts;* the remaining $\frac{1}{2}N(N-1)$ parameters characterize the matrix U. This parametrization enables one to write the general scattering formula in the same form as for the spinless particle case (Bl52a) (see Section 2.C).

C. *The Scattering Amplitude and the Differential Cross Sections*

The physical problem with which we are concerned deals with states of sharp *linear* momentum, the incident plane wave, and the emergent plane wave of scattered or reaction produced particles. On the other hand, the compound nucleus is described most simply in states of sharp *angular* momentum and parity. The connection between these two different descriptions is the chief object of angular correlation calculational techniques, of which many discussions are available. We shall simply sketch the steps involved (Bl52a, Lu60) which are once again analogs to those of the spinless particle example. The first step is to define the reaction amplitude, $q_{\alpha s\sigma;\alpha's'\sigma'}(\theta\phi)$, for the process $\alpha s\sigma \rightarrow \alpha's'\sigma'$, i.e., a process whereby a plane wave of particles, alternative α with channel spin s and projection σ, is observed to emerge as a plane wave along θ, ϕ of alternative α' with channel spin s' and projection σ'. The projections σ, σ' are measured in a fixed coordinate system whose axis is, say, along the incident direction. One notes that the primed variables do not necessarily differ from the unprimed variables.

A given channel for these plane waves is to be designated slightly differently than previously, i.e., the scheme $\bar{c} \equiv (\alpha s l\sigma\lambda)$ (λ is the projection of angular momentum l) replaces the previous $c \equiv (\alpha s l JM)$. The spin-angle functions in these two schemes are related by the Wigner coefficients, i.e.,

$$\phi_{\alpha s l JM} = \sum_{\sigma\lambda} (s l\sigma\lambda | JM)\psi_{\alpha s l\sigma\lambda} \tag{60a}$$

and the converse

$$\psi_{\alpha s l\sigma\lambda} = \sum_{JM} (s l\sigma\lambda | JM)\phi_{\alpha s l JM} \tag{60b}$$

Similarly the scattering matrices for these two channel designation schemes are related by the Wigner coefficients

$$S_{\alpha's'l'\sigma\lambda';\,\alpha s l\sigma\lambda} = \sum_{JM} (s'l'\sigma'\lambda' | JM)S^J_{\alpha's'l';\,\alpha s l} (s l\sigma\lambda | JM) \tag{61}$$

Now Eq. (53) gives the general form for a wave function at energy E in the external region for the scheme $c = (\alpha s l JM)$. Writing this in the $\bar{c}$ scheme we have

$$\psi_E = \sum \psi_{\alpha s l\sigma\lambda}(I_{\alpha l}\delta_{\alpha's'l';\,\alpha s l} - O_{\alpha l}S^{JM}_{\alpha's'l';\,\alpha s l})v_\alpha^{-1/2}$$
$$\cdot (s l\sigma\lambda | JM)(s'l'\sigma'\lambda' | JM)A_{\alpha's'l'\sigma'\lambda'} \tag{62}$$

where the sum is over $\alpha s l \sigma \lambda \alpha' s l' \sigma' \lambda' JM$. For brevity one also writes this as

$$\psi_E = \sum_{\bar{c}\bar{c}'} (I_{\bar{c}'}\delta_{\bar{c}\bar{c}'} - O_{\bar{c}}S_{\bar{c}\bar{c}'})A_{\bar{c}'}$$

An incident plane wave of particles $\alpha's'l'$ has for its ingoing part the coefficient

$$A_{\alpha's'l'\sigma'\lambda'} = i(\pi v_{\alpha'})^{1/2}\lambda_{\alpha'}(2l'+1)^{1/2}\delta_{\lambda'}^0 \tag{63}$$

Introducing this value for $A_{\bar{c}}$ in Eq. (62), and adding and subtracting an equal amount of outgoing waves we find

$$\psi_E \sim \psi_{\text{plane wave}}(\alpha's'\sigma') + \psi_{\text{reaction}}$$

where $\psi_{\text{reaction}} = (i\pi^{1/2}\lambda_{\alpha'}) \sum_{\substack{\alpha s l \sigma \lambda \\ JMl'}} \psi_{\alpha s l \sigma \lambda}O_{\alpha l}(\delta_{\alpha s l;\ \alpha's'l'} - S^J_{\alpha s l;\ \alpha's'l'})$

$$\cdot (v_{\alpha'}/v_\alpha)^{1/2}(s l \sigma \lambda | JM)(s'l'\sigma'0 | JM)(2l'+1)^{1/2} \tag{62'}$$

The reaction amplitude is obtained from Eq. (62') as $(v_\alpha/v_{\alpha'})^{1/2}$ times the coefficient of $\psi_{\alpha s \sigma}O_{\alpha l}$ in ψ_{reaction}—i.e., the amplitude of the spherical outgoing waves corresponding to alternative α, channel spin s, with projection σ (normalized so as to eliminate the ratio of velocities that enters in the definition of the cross section). Thus

$$q_{\alpha s \sigma;\ \alpha's'\sigma'}(\theta\phi) = i\pi^{1/2}\lambda_{\alpha'} \sum_{\substack{JM \\ l'\lambda}} (2l'+1)^{1/2}(s l \sigma \lambda | JM)Y_l^\lambda(\theta\phi)$$

$$\cdot (s'l'\sigma'0 | JM)(\delta_{\alpha s l;\ \alpha's'l'} - S^J_{\alpha s l;\ \alpha's'l'}) \tag{64}$$

The differential cross sections now follow as

$$d\sigma_{\alpha's'\sigma';\ \alpha s \sigma}/d\Omega = |q_{\alpha s \sigma;\ \alpha's\sigma'}(\theta\phi)|^2 \tag{65}$$

For unpolarized processes where σ', σ are not measured we sum over the states σ', and average over σ, so that

$$d\sigma_{\alpha's';\ \alpha s}/d\Omega = (2s+1)^{-1}\sum_{\sigma\sigma'} |q_{\alpha s \sigma;\ \alpha's\sigma'}|^2 \tag{66}$$

The observed process is, however, to be considered as $\alpha \to \alpha'$, and thus must be averaged over the possible incident channel spins and summed over the possible outgoing channel spins, i.e.,

$$d\sigma_{\alpha';\ \alpha}/d\Omega = \sum_{ss'} (2s+1)(2a+1)^{-1}(2b+1)^{-1}(d\sigma_{\alpha's';\ \alpha s}/d\Omega) \tag{67}$$

(a, b are the intrinsic spins of the two particles in alternative α). Angular momentum techniques simplify only Eq. (66), and not Eq. (67), because, as is now familiar, such techniques are geometrical in essence and the s,s' dependence is dynamical. Application of these techniques leads to a Legendre series for the differential cross section—the Blatt-Biedenharn formula (Bl51a)—which is the generalization of Eq. (5) to particles with spin

$$d\sigma_{\alpha's';\ as}/d\Omega = (2s+1)^{-1}\lambda_\alpha^2 \sum_L B_L(\alpha's';\ as)P_L(\cos\theta) \quad (68a)$$

where the coefficients B_L are defined by

$$B_L(\alpha's';\ as) \equiv \tfrac{1}{4}(-)^{s-s'} \sum \bar{Z}(l_1J_1l_2J_2;\ sL)\bar{Z}(l_1'J_1l_2'J_2;\ s'L)$$

$$\times \operatorname{Re}[(\delta_{l_1l_1'} - S_{\alpha's'l_1';\ asl_1}^{J_1\pi_1})(\delta_{l_2l_2'} - S_{\alpha's'l_2';\ asl_2}^{J_2\pi_2})] \quad (68b)$$

(Re signifies taking the real part of the expression.)
The sum in Eq. (68b) is over J_1, J_2, π_1, π_2, l_1, l_1', l_2, l_2'. The $\bar{Z}$ coefficient is defined by

$$\bar{Z} \equiv [(2l_1+1)(2l_2+1)(2J_1+1)(2J_2+1)]^{1/2}$$

$$(l_1l_200|L0)W(l_1J_1l_2J_2;\ sL) \quad (69)$$

where W here is a Racah coefficient (Si54a, Ro59).

The $\bar{Z}$ coefficients defined by Eq. (69) are as originally introduced in (Bl51a) but differ in sign from the Z coefficient used in Bl52a (the change arises from an unfortunate phase convention used in Wi47; see Hu54). The explicit relation is

$$Z(l_1J_1l_2J_2;\ sL) = exp\,(\pi i/2)(-l_1+L+l_2)\bar{Z}(l_1J_1l_2J_2;\ sL) \quad (70)$$

($-l_1+L+l_2$ is always an even integer due to parity conservation, so that $\bar{Z}$ differs at most by a sign from Z.)

At present, only the Z coefficients are tabulated (Bi53, Sh53), *so that the $\bar{Z}$ coefficients are, practically speaking, only a shorthand to avoid writing the phase* $exp[(i(\pi)/2)(-l_1+L+l_2)]$. This should be borne in mind in applying the formulas to follow.

(1) Two General Results.   (a) *Total Cross Section and Forward Scattering Amplitude* (Bl52a).   The total (transmission) cross section is obtained from Eqs. (67–68) by integrating over $d\Omega$ and summing over s,s',α'. From the integration only $L = 0$ contributes and we obtain

$$\sigma_0(\alpha) = (2a+1)^{-1}(2b+1)^{-1}\pi\lambda_\alpha^2 \sum_{s,s',\alpha',J,\pi,l,l'} (2J+1)Re\,[(1-S^{J\pi})(1-S^{J\pi})^*]$$

$$= (2a+1)^{-1}(2b+1)^{-1}\pi\lambda_\alpha^2 \sum_{slJ\pi} (2J+1)[(2-S^{J\pi}-S^{J\pi*})_{\alpha sl;\,\alpha sl} \quad (71)$$

The forward scattering amplitude for *elastic* scattering (i.e., $s' = s$ as well as $\alpha' = \alpha$) is given by Eq. (64), with $Y_l^m(00) = \delta_m^0 \left(\dfrac{2l+1}{4\pi}\right)^{1/2}$. That is:

$$q_{\alpha s\sigma;\,\alpha s\sigma'}(0) = \delta_{\sigma'\sigma}(\tfrac{1}{2}\,i\lambda_\alpha) \sum_{JMll'} (2l'+1)^{1/2}(2l+1)^{1/2}$$

$$\cdot (sl\sigma 0\,|\,JM)(sl'\sigma 0\,|\,JM)(1-S^{J\pi}) \quad (72)$$

The average value of this amplitude is

$$\langle q_{el}(0)\rangle = (2a+1)^{-1}(2b+1)^{-1} \sum_{s\sigma} q_{\alpha s\sigma;\,\alpha s\sigma}$$

$$= (2a+1)^{-1}(2b+1)^{-1} \frac{i\lambda_\alpha}{2} \sum_{Jsl} (2J+1)(1-S^{J\pi}_{\alpha sl;\,\alpha sl}) \quad (73)$$

Comparing this to Eq. (71), one obtains the familiar relation between the total cross section and the imaginary part (Im) of the forward elastic scattering

$$\sigma_0(\alpha) = 4\pi\lambda_\alpha\,\mathrm{Im}\,\langle q_{el}(0)\rangle. \quad (74)$$

(b) *The Forward Elastic Differential Scattering.* This is obtained from $q_{el}(0)$, and is

$$d\sigma_{\alpha,\alpha}(0)/d\Omega = (2a+1)^{-1}(2b+1)^{-1} \sum_{s\sigma} |q_{el}(0)|^2 \quad (75)$$

One can obtain an inequality from this by neglecting $\mathrm{Re}\,[q_{el}(0)]$:

$$\sum_{s\sigma} |q_{el}(0)|^2 \geq \sum_{s\sigma} \{\mathrm{Im}\,[q_{el}(0)]\}^2 \quad (76a)$$

and

$$\sum_{s\sigma} [\mathrm{Im}\,q_{el}(0)]^2 > (2a+1)(2b+1)[\langle\mathrm{Im}\,[q_{el}(0)]\rangle]^2 \quad (76b)$$

Thus, comparing this with Eq. (74) one finds the inequality

$$d\sigma_{\alpha,\alpha}(0)/d\Omega \geq (\sigma_0(\alpha)/4\pi\lambda_\alpha)^2 \quad (77)$$

A stronger inequality (*Wick's inequality*, Wi49a; see also Th56) results from the inclusion of $\alpha s \to \alpha's'$ as part of the elastic forward scattering.

(2) Differential Cross Sections in Terms of Eigen Phase Shifts (Bl52a).

One of the important results of the Wigner theory is to provide a general framework in which to discuss nuclear reactions; the elements of this framework, $\gamma_{\lambda c}$, E_λ, are then the proper objects for further investigation. A quite different approach to the question of a *framework to describe nuclear reactions* is provided by the general properties of the scattering matrix; this is the subject of the present section. Again the spinless particle example will serve to make the distinction between these two approaches clear. The *general properties of the scattering matrix* are expressed by the simple result that S, for each l, may be written as a phase shift, $S_l = \exp(2i\delta_l)$. The δ_l's then provide a complete framework to discuss the scattering in general [Eq. (5c)]. The object of nuclear reaction theory is then to discuss the energy dependence of a given δ in terms of the internal parameters, $\gamma_{\lambda c}$, E_λ, and the external parameters, S, P, and Ω. The general properties of the scattering matrix thus serve to define the *independent* parameters for describing the scattering (the *"parametrization problem"*), while (Wigner) nuclear reaction theory seeks to describe these scattering parameters in terms of physically defined quantities related to the separation of space into internal and external regions.

The appropriate parametrization for the general case is implicit in the results of Section 2.B(4), i.e., S may be written as

$$S^{J\pi} = (U^{J\pi})^{-1}[\exp(2i\Delta^{J\pi})]U^{J\pi} \tag{59'}$$

where $U^{J\pi}$ is a real and orthogonal matrix and $\Delta^{J\pi}$ is a real and diagonal matrix. The matrices U can be written in terms of their eigenvectors, U_k with $k = 1, \ldots, N$ (N = number of open channels). The scattering matrix may then be expressed in terms of the components of these eigenvectors (which represent the proportions of the various channels that enter a given eigenstate; in a perturbation sense they are the (real) reduced matrix elements of the interaction). Thus:

$$\mathbf{S} = \sum_{k=1}^{N} [\exp(2i\Delta_k)]\mathbf{U}_k \times \mathbf{U}_k \tag{78a}$$

or equivalently

$$S = \sum_{k=1}^{N} \exp(2i\Delta_k)\mathbf{P}_k \tag{78b}$$

where

$$(P_k)_{\alpha sl;\alpha's'l'} \equiv (U_k)_{\alpha sl}(U_k)_{\alpha's'l'}$$

This latter form for **S** has a direct interpretation, for the P_k operator simply picks out of any state the part belonging to the kth eigenstate, and this part is then multiplied by the phase $\exp(2i\Delta_k)$.

Introducing Eq. (78) into Eq. (68), we find the desired *parametrization of the cross sections*. The coefficient, B_L, now has the form

$$B_L(\alpha's'; \alpha s) = (-)^{s-s'} \sum_{J_1 J_2 \pi_1 \pi_2 k_1 k_2} T_{J_1 \pi_1 k_1;\ J_2 \pi_2 k_2} \sin \Delta_{J_1 \pi_1 k_1} \sin \Delta_{J_2 \pi_2 k_2}$$

$$\cdot \cos \left(\Delta_{J_1 \pi_1 k_1} - \Delta_{J_2 \pi_2 k_2} \right) \quad (79a)$$

where

$$T_{\ldots} = \left(\sum_{l_1 l_2} \bar{Z}(l_1 J_1 l_2 J_2;\ sL)(U_{J_1 \pi_1 k_1})_{\alpha s l_1}(U_{J_2 \pi_2 k_2})_{\alpha s l_2} \right)$$

$$\cdot \left(\sum_{l_1' l_2'} \bar{Z}(l_1' J_1 l_2' J_2;\ s'L)(U_{J_1 \pi_1 k_1})_{\alpha's'l_1'}(U_{J_2 \pi_2 k_2})_{\alpha's'l_2'} \right) \quad (79b)$$

This result is the direct analog of Eq. (5c) for spinless particles. Although it appears quite complicated, Eq. (79) is actually a simpler form than Eq. (68), since in Eq. (68) the various elements of **S** are not all independent. *The real difficulty inherent in Eq. (79) is the fact that the $U_{J\pi k}$ and $\Delta_{J\pi k}$ are not always convenient when expressed in terms of the Wigner parameters.*

The form of the differential cross section given by Eq. (79) shows that *whenever the reaction takes place via a single sharp compound state $(J\pi k)$ the angular distribution coefficient B_L factors into two independent parts, one part relating to the mode of formation (and its various channel components), the other part to the decay.* The independence of the formation and decay processes is a basic feature of Bohr's compound nucleus model for nuclear reactions; this is well known to apply to the integral cross sections for an isolated resonance. *Equation (79b) shows in what sense this "independence" also applies to the angular properties as well.*

We can apply this general formalism to determine the maximum value of the cross section resulting from a single resonance level. Using Eq. (79), and the result that

$$\bar{Z}(l_1 J_1 l_2 J_2;\ s0) = \delta_{l_1 l_2} \delta_{J_1 J_2} \cdot (-)^{s-J_1} (2J_1 + 1)^{1/2} \quad (80)$$

one finds for the total cross section, in general,

$$\sigma(\alpha's';\ \alpha s) = 4\pi\lambda^2 B_0/(2s + 1)$$

$$= [4\pi\lambda^2/(2s + 1)] \sum_{J\pi k_1 k_2} (2J + 1) \sin \Delta_{J\pi k_1} \sin \Delta_{J\pi k_2}$$

$$\cdot \cos (\Delta_{J\pi k_1} - \Delta_{J\pi k_2}) \cdot [\sum_l (U_{J\pi k_1})_{\alpha sl}(U_{J\pi k_2})_{\alpha sl}]$$

$$\cdot [\sum_{l'} (U_{J\pi k_1})_{\alpha's'l'}(U_{J\pi k_2})_{\alpha's'l'}] \tag{81}$$

The total cross section for a *single* resonance $(J\pi k)$, without regard to channel spins, is then

$$\sigma(\alpha', \alpha) = 4\pi\lambda^2[(2J + 1)/(2a + 1)(2b + 1)] \sin^2 \Delta_{J\pi k}$$

$$\cdot (\sum_{sl} [(U_{J\pi k})_{\alpha sl}]^2) \cdot (\sum_{s'l'} [(U_{J\pi k})_{\alpha's'l'}]^2) \tag{82}$$

Since $\sum_{\alpha sl} [(U_{J\pi k})_{\alpha sl}]^2 = 1$ (the eigenvectors are normalized), it follows that the *maximum value of the cross section for a single resonance is*

$$\sigma(\alpha', \alpha) \le 4\pi\lambda_\alpha^2[(2J + 1)/(2a + 1)(2b + 1)] \tag{83}$$

Note that in contrast to the statement of Feld (Fe53), this is true whether or not there exists a channel-spin degeneracy. [See also Simon and Welton (Si53).] Although it is perhaps an academic point, this maximum can be exceeded if *several* resonances of the same J, π (but different k) occur very close together.

For pure elastic scattering ($\alpha' = \alpha$; $s' = s$) the T coefficient is particularly simple

$$T_{\text{pure elastic}} = \left[\sum_{l_1 l_2} \bar{Z}(l_1 J_1 l_2 J_2;\ sL)(U_{J_1\pi_1 k_1})\ (U_{J_2\pi_2 k_2})_{\alpha sl_2}\right]^2 \tag{84}$$

The total cross section also shows some simplification. One finds

$$\sigma_0(\alpha) = 4\pi\lambda_\alpha^2(2a + 1)^{-1}(2b + 1)^{-1} \sum_{J\pi ksl} (2J + 1) \sin^2 \Delta_{J\pi k} (U_{J\pi k})_{\alpha sl}^2 \tag{85}$$

which compares with the analog Eq. (6).

D. Application of the Formalism

(1) **The Level Expansion.** The practical object of the previous dispersion theory is the development of suitable approximate

formulas for the analysis of the experimental data in terms of parameters that are reasonably direct in meaning.   The *difficult step in the Wigner theory occurs in the matrix inversion,* $(1 - RL)^{-1}R$, *that appears in Eq. (57).* The dimensionality of the matrices involved is that of the number of open channels.[7]   Unless this number is small, say, one or two channels, the inversion is not really very feasible.[8]

There is a way to avoid the inversion problem, but this method suffers from a compensating difficulty.   This is to generalize the allowable values of the boundary condition (**b**) to complex numbers, and in particular to set **b** = **L**.   Thus $\overline{\mathbf{L}} = 0$ [but $\overline{\mathbf{L}}^{*}$ is not, see Eq. (9′)], and the inversion is avoided from the outset.   This ingenious procedure is that employed very early by Kapur and Peierls

___

[7] This is true only if the size of the internal region is sufficiently large. Since, however, we desire the internal region to be of the order of nuclear size, there may be closed channels which are still appreciably large at a surface of nuclear size.   There are two procedures possible: the channel elimination scheme [see Section 2.B (5b)], or the formal scheme of retaining the closed channels which increases the number of dimensions of all the matrices (including S)—since $P = 0$ for closed channels there are no reactions for the closed channels, but there is an effect on the level shifts of the open channels.

[8] Teichmann(Te50) has discussed the feasible cases in detail.   A particularly interesting case is that of T. D. Newton (Ne52), who assumed that all of the γ_λs are multiples of a *single* vector **b**, i.e.,

$$\gamma_\lambda = a_\lambda \mathbf{b}$$

then

$$\mathbf{R} = (\mathbf{b} \times \mathbf{b}) \sum_\lambda [a_\lambda^2/(E_\lambda - E)] = (\mathbf{b} \times \mathbf{b})t^{-1}(E)$$

and

$$S = \mathbf{\Omega} \left\{1 + 2i[(\mathbf{G} \times \mathbf{G})/(t(E) - \xi)]\right\}\mathbf{\Omega}$$

with

$$\mathbf{G} \equiv P^{1/2}\,\mathbf{b} \qquad \text{and} \qquad \xi = \sum_c b_c^2 L_c$$

This results in a scattering matrix of the form of the one-level approximation [Section 2.C (2)] (but with a more complicated energy dependence).

The interest in this result is that it leads to cross sections that satisfy the Bohr assumption (decay modes independent of formation mode) *at all energies.* Thomas [(Th55) cf. pp. 227,228] shows, however, that for high energies the absorption cross section (for the scattering matrix above) vanishes, and thus does not correspond to the conventional idea of a compound nucleus.

(Ka38).[9] Unfortunately the resulting **R** matrix is now complex, but even more important, the (complex) quantities γ_λ, E_λ *are no longer independent of the energy* (E). While we have indeed succeeded in avoiding the inversion problem, the complicated behavior of the parameters of the theory more than offsets this advantage.[10]

A very useful approximation that simplifies the inversion is to separate the actual **R** matrix into two parts

$$\mathbf{R} = \mathbf{R}^0 + \mathbf{R}'$$

where **R'** is the contribution of one or two important levels, while **R**^{0} is the remainder of the **R** matrix, and approximated by a *constant* (energy independent) matrix. *The number of dimensions in the matrix inversion is now the number of levels taken for* **R'** *and not the number of channels* (Wi47, Th55).

To obtain practical formulas we shall assume here that, in addition to being energy independent, **R**^{0} is diagonal. The procedure is as follows. First we employ the identity

$$(1 - \mathbf{R}L)^{-1}\mathbf{R} = (1 - \mathbf{R}^0L)^{-1}\mathbf{R}^0 + (1 - \mathbf{R}^0L)^{-1}(1 - \mathbf{R}'L')^{-1}$$

$$\cdot \mathbf{R}'(1 - L\mathbf{R}^0)^{-1} \quad (86a)$$

where

$$\mathbf{L}' \equiv \mathbf{L}(1 - \mathbf{R}^0\mathbf{L})^{-1} \quad (86b)$$

The purpose of this identity is to separate the contributions of **R**^{0} and **R'** to the **S** matrix. Using this identity, and the fact that **R**^{0} is diagonal, the scattering matrix becomes

$$\mathbf{S} = \mathbf{\Omega}'[1 + 2i(\mathbf{P}')^{1/2}(1 - \mathbf{R}'L')^{-1}\mathbf{R}'(\mathbf{P}')^{1/2}]\mathbf{\Omega}' \quad (87)$$

[9] Recently, C. Bloch (Bl57) has given a general formulation of nuclear reaction theory that facilitates the comparison of the Wigner and Kapur-Peierls viewpoints. Bloch's formulation is quite elegant, and uses operator techniques to great advantage (see also DeW55). The results, however, are all contained (though less directly) in the Wigner (and Thomas) formulation with a general (complex) boundary condition.

[10] The Kapur-Peierls technique has, however, advantages in the derivation of the optical model from dispersion theory (see Br57a, Br59a).

where Ω', $\mathbf{L}'$, $\mathbf{P}'$ are diagonal matrices with the elements:

$$\Omega'_c = \exp(2i\xi_c') \tag{88a}$$

$$\xi'_c = \xi_c + \tan^{-1}[R_c^0 P_c/(1 - R_c^0 S_c)] \tag{88b}$$

$$L'_c = S'_c + iP'_c \tag{88c}$$

$$P'_c = P_c[(1 - R^0 S_c)^2 + (R^0 P_c)^2]^{-1} \tag{88d}$$

$$S'_c = (S_c - R^0 S_c^2 - R^0 P_c^2)[(1 - R^0 S_c)^2 + (R^0 P_c)^2]^{-1} \tag{88e}$$

again noting that P'_c and S'_c are not simply penetration and shift factors (Os36, Fr53). The scattering matrix thus has the same form in the primed quantities as the original scattering matrix in the unprimed quantities, but now the scattering produced by $\mathbf{R}^0$ has been explicitly taken into account. It should be noted in particular that the ξ'_c, unlike the ξ_c, may differ for channels with the same α, l but different s—*the background scattering, in other words, may now be channel-spin dependent.* In addition, the phase shifts ξ'_c may also become functions of the angular momentum J and the parity π, (through R^0), again unlike the original potential scattering phase shifts.

The important step now is the level expansion of the matrix $(1 - \mathbf{RL})^{-1}\mathbf{R}'$. This expansion has been given as (Wi47)

$$(1 - \mathbf{R}'\mathbf{L}')^{-1}\mathbf{R}' = \sum_{ij} \gamma_i \times \gamma_j A_{ij} \tag{89}$$

where

$$A_{ij} = [(\overline{\mathbf{E}} - \mathbf{E} - \Xi)^{-1}]_{ij} \tag{90a}$$

$$\Xi_{ij} = \sum_{cc'} \gamma_{ic} L_c (1 - \mathbf{R}^0 \overline{\mathbf{L}})_{cc'}^{-1} \gamma_{jc'} = -\Delta_{ij} + {}^1/_2 i\Gamma_{ij} \tag{90b}$$

$$(\mathbf{E})_{ij} = \delta_{ij}E_i; \quad (\mathbf{E})_{ij} = E\delta_{ij} \tag{90c}$$

Introducing this into Eq. (87), one finds that

$$\mathbf{S} = \Omega'[1 + 2i(\mathbf{P}')^{1/2}(\sum_{ij} \gamma_i \times \gamma_j A_{ij})(\mathbf{P}')^{1/2}]\Omega' \tag{91}$$

The application of these formulas to the case of one or two levels is given below.[11,12]

The matrix $\mathbf{A}$ is symmetric, although complex. It is possible to take advantage of this symmetry (Th56, Wi46a), and write $\mathbf{A}$ in the form: $\mathbf{A} = \mathbf{THT}^{-1}$, where $\mathbf{H}$ is diagonal and of the form $H_{ii} = F_i - E - iG_i/2$, and $\mathbf{T}$ is complex orthogonal ($\widetilde{\mathbf{T}}\mathbf{T} = 1$). (This requires that all eigenvalues of $\mathbf{A}$ differ.) The matrix $\sum_{ij} \boldsymbol{\gamma}_i \times \boldsymbol{\gamma}_j A_{ij}$ then may be written in the much simpler (diagonal) form $\sum_i \mathbf{O}_i \times \mathbf{O}_i H_{ii}$ where $\mathbf{O}_i = \mathbf{T}\boldsymbol{\gamma}_i$. Note, however, that the $\mathbf{O}_i$ are now complex, and moreover depend on the energy in a complicated way.

(2) **The Many-Level Expansion in Spectral Form** (Bi58). The spectral form of the scattering matrix, Eq. (59), makes full use of the general properties of the scattering matrix and is the simplest form in which the general angular distribution results may be given. This spectral form, however, suffers from the difficulty that the parameters that appear here,—the eigen phase shifts $\Delta(J\pi k)$ and the (real) components of the eigenvectors, $U^{J\pi k}$—are not directly related to the parameters of the Wigner theory—the reduced widths, $\gamma_{\lambda c}$ and the shift and penetration factors—and, in fact, the relationship has not been given explicitly. It is the purpose of the present section to discuss this question.

In order to simplify the notation we shall take the background $\mathbf{R}$ matrix, $\mathbf{R}^0$, to be zero. [The resulting formulas can readily be generalized by the pre-

---

[11] One notes in passing that if $\mathbf{R}'$ includes *all* the levels λ, then $\mathbf{R}^\circ = 0$ and we get the formal result

$$\mathbf{S} = \boldsymbol{\Omega}\Big[1 + 2i\mathbf{P}^{1/2}\Big(\sum_{ij} \boldsymbol{\gamma}_i \times \boldsymbol{\gamma}_j A_{ij}\Big)\mathbf{P}^{1/2}\Big]\boldsymbol{\Omega}$$
$$\mathbf{A} = (\overline{\mathbf{E}} - E\mathbf{1} - \boldsymbol{\Xi})^{-1}.$$

This is the end result of the Wigner theory, but it is fully as complicated as Eq. (57). One notes that $\boldsymbol{\Xi}$ is not diagonal, but if we *assume* it so, we get: $\mathbf{S} = \boldsymbol{\Omega}\{1 + 2i \sum_s [(\boldsymbol{\gamma}_s \times \boldsymbol{\gamma}_s)/(E_s - E - \Delta_s - i\Gamma_s/2)]\}$. This is the so-called many-level Breit-Wigner formula, but it is actually not a correct generalization. [See S. Flugge (Fl48), also E. P. Wigner (Wi46a) who shows that for widths of the order of the level spacing, or larger, this approximation is poor.]

[12] An interesting application of these level formulas to neutron fission has been given by C. W. Reich (Re58), who considered two channels (incident neutron channel and fission channel), plus many γ-ray channels. Statistical considerations were applied to the latter channels, to simplify the required matrix inversion.

scription given earlier in connection with Eqs. (88a...e).] The problem is then to write the general **S** matrix

$$\mathbf{S} = \mathbf{\Omega}[1 + 2i\mathbf{P}^{1/2}(1 - \mathbf{RL})^{-1}\mathbf{RP}^{1/2}]\mathbf{\Omega} \qquad (57)$$

in the spectral form: $\mathbf{S} = \widetilde{\mathbf{U}}[\exp{(2i\mathbf{\Delta})}]\mathbf{U}$, with **U** a real orthogonal matrix and **Δ** a real diagonal matrix. This problem, however, is made intrinsically quite difficult by the presence of the hard-sphere (and in the general case Coulomb) scattering phase shifts, i.e., the matrix **Ω**. The point here is that the potential scattering phase shift is diagonal in the scheme $\{\alpha sl\}$, whereas the nuclear scattering is generally not diagonal for this scheme. To attempt a solution for a system diagonal for the *complete* scattering problem necessarily must mix the two scattering components in a complicated way.

We may avoid this problem by separating explicitly the nuclear and potential scattering. The nuclear part of the **S** matrix is taken to be

$$\mathbf{N} \equiv \mathbf{\Omega}^{-1}\mathbf{S}\mathbf{\Omega}^{-1} = 1 + 2i\mathbf{P}^{1/2}(1 - \mathbf{RL})^{-1}\mathbf{RP}^{1/2} \qquad (92)$$

which has the same general properties as the **S** matrix, $\mathbf{N}^* = \mathbf{N}^{-1}$ and $\mathbf{N} = \mathbf{N}$. Thus we may parametrize **N** in the same spectral form

$$\mathbf{N} = \widetilde{\mathbf{u}}[\exp{(2i\,\boldsymbol{\delta})}]\mathbf{u} \qquad (93)$$

(We distinguish the eigen phase shifts, and eigenvectors, for the *nuclear* scattering by the use of small letters, i.e., **δ** replaces **Δ** and **u** replaces **U**.) In order to calculate the cross sections one needs $(1 - \mathbf{S})$ and using the above separation into nuclear and potential scattering the result is

$$(1 - \mathbf{S}) = 2i[\sin{\xi}\exp{(i\xi)} + \sum_{k} \mathbf{\Omega}\mathbf{u}^{(k)} \times \mathbf{\Omega}\mathbf{u}^{(k)} \sin{\delta^{(k)}}\exp{(i\delta^{(k)})}] \qquad (94)$$

where the $\mathbf{u}^{(k)}$ are the eigenvectors of the matrix **u**. The differential cross sections obtained from Eq. (94) are given in detail below Eqs. (105) to (109).

It remains now to observe that the Wigner many-level expansion [Eq. (91)] *provides the basis for carrying out the reduction implied by Eq. (93)*. It will be recalled that the level expansion allowed one to replace the $N \times N$ matrix inversion, $(1 - \mathbf{RL})^{-1}\mathbf{R}$, by a level inversion, $(\overline{\mathbf{E}} - \mathbf{E} - \boldsymbol{\Xi})^{-1}$, whose dimensionality is the number of levels. We shall now show that the n level $(n < N)$ inversion provides explicitly n of the eigenvectors $\mathbf{u}^{(k)}$; the remaining $(N - n)$ eigenvectors have zero phase shift and do not, therefore, cause any effect.

The level expansion gave for **N** the form

$$\mathbf{N} = 1 + 2i\mathbf{P}^{1/2} \sum_{ij} \boldsymbol{\gamma}_i \times \boldsymbol{\gamma}_j A_{ij}\mathbf{P}^{1/2} \qquad (95)$$

with

$$A_{ij} = [(\overline{\mathbf{E}} - \mathbf{E} - \boldsymbol{\Xi})^{-1}]_{ij} \qquad (95a)$$

and

$$\Xi_{ij} = \sum_{c} \gamma_{ic}\overline{L}_c\gamma_{jc} = \Xi_{ji} \qquad (95b)$$

From Eq. (93) this may be written as

$$\sum_{ij} (\mathbf{P}^{1/2}\boldsymbol{\gamma}_i) \times (\mathbf{P}^{1/2}\boldsymbol{\gamma}_j A_{ij}) = \mathbf{u}[\sin \boldsymbol{\delta} \exp (i\boldsymbol{\delta})]\mathbf{u} \tag{96}$$

The vectors, $\mathbf{P}^{1/2}\boldsymbol{\gamma}_i = \mathbf{v}_i$, may be expressed in terms of the eigenvectors, $\mathbf{u}^{(k)}$, (which are orthonormal, i.e., $\mathbf{u}^{(k)} \cdot \mathbf{u}^{(k')} = \sum_c u_c^{(k)} u_c^{(k')} = \delta_{kk'}$). This step assumes that the vectors $\mathbf{v}_i$ are all linearly independent. The changes introduced by the more general case are straightforward, but will not be given here. Therefore

$$\mathbf{v}_i = \mathbf{P}^{1/2}\boldsymbol{\gamma}_i = \sum_k w_{ik}\mathbf{u}^{(k)} \tag{97}$$

(but note that the w_{ik} are not square but rectangular matrices—since i runs over the n levels ($n < N$) whereas k runs over the N channels). Introducing this into Eq. (96) we find

$$\sum_{\substack{kk' \\ ij}} (\mathbf{u}^{(k)} \times \mathbf{u}^{(k')})w_{ik}A_{ij}w_{jk'} = \mathbf{u}\sin \boldsymbol{\delta} \exp (i\boldsymbol{\delta})\mathbf{u}$$

$$= \sum_k \mathbf{u}^{(k)} \times \mathbf{u}^{(k)} \sin \delta^{(k)} \exp (i\delta^{(k)}) \tag{98}$$

and thus

$$\sum_{ij} w_{ik}A_{ij}w_{jk'} = \delta_{kk'} \sin \delta^{(k)} \exp i\delta^{(k)} \tag{99}$$

A solution to these equations can be obtained by noting that $w_{ik} = 0$ (and $\delta^{(k)} = 0$) for k not in the set $1, \ldots, n$. We restrict attention only to this range of values, for which the w_{ik} are now *square* matrices. [In other words, one notes that the n vectors $\mathbf{v}_i = \mathbf{P}\boldsymbol{\gamma}_i$ are linear combinations of n particular eigenvectors $\mathbf{u}^{(1)}$, and are perpendicular to the remaining eigenvectors. In the one-level case these results are clear.] The problem to be solved is then the $n \times n$ matrix problem

$$\tilde{\mathbf{w}}\mathbf{A}\mathbf{w} = \sin \boldsymbol{\delta} \exp (i\boldsymbol{\delta}) \tag{100a}$$

where it should be noted that, in addition, we have the equation

$$\mathbf{w}\tilde{\mathbf{w}} = \boldsymbol{\Gamma}/2 \tag{100b}$$

Introducing the definition of A one finds

$$(\overline{\mathbf{E}} + \boldsymbol{\Delta} - \mathbf{E}) = \mathbf{w}(\cot \boldsymbol{\delta})\tilde{\mathbf{w}} \tag{101}$$

Since $\boldsymbol{\Gamma}$ is symmetrical, and real, it may be written in the form:

$$\boldsymbol{\Gamma} = 2\mathbf{V}\mathbf{g}^2\tilde{\mathbf{V}} \tag{102}$$

with $\mathbf{V}$ real and orthogonal, and $\mathbf{g}^2$ real, positive and diagonal.

It follows that the general solution for w is

$$w = VgW \tag{103}$$

where $\mathbf{W}$ is an arbitrary, real, orthogonal matrix. Equation (100) then becomes

$$g^{-1/2}\tilde{V}(\overline{E} + \Delta - E)Vg^{-1/2} = W(\cot \tilde{\delta})\tilde{W} \tag{104}$$

This is the desired matrix formulation for the spectral form of the scattering. All the matrices on the left-hand side are known, while the right-hand side is to be determined. Since the product on the left is clearly a real and symmetric matrix, the desired solution is straightforward; we may henceforth regard the δ^k and w as known, and thus the $\mathbf{u}^{(k)}$ for $k = 1, \ldots, n$.

It remains now to formulate explicitly the differential scattering cross section in terms of these parameters. Introducing Eq. (94) for the matrix $(1 - S)$ into Eq. (79) for $B_L(\alpha s; \alpha' s')$, one obtains
(a) Elastic scattering ($\alpha = \alpha'; s = s'$):

$$B_L(\alpha s; \alpha s) \equiv H_L(\alpha s) + I_L(\alpha s) + N_L(\alpha s; \alpha s) \tag{105}$$

where the terms on the right respectively designate potential, interference, and resonance (*nuclear*) scattering.

$$H_L(\alpha s; \alpha s) = (2s + 1) \sum_{l_1 l_2} (2l_1 + 1)(2l_2 + 1)(l_1 l_2 00 | L0)^2$$

$$\cdot \sin \xi_{\alpha s l_1} \sin \xi_{\alpha s l_2} \cdot \cos (\xi_{\alpha s l_1} - \xi_{\alpha s l_2}) \tag{106}$$

(This assumes that uncharged particles are incident. For the Coulomb case see Bl52a.)

$$I_L(\alpha s) = 2 \sum_{\substack{J \pi l_1 l_2 \\ k = 1, \ldots n}} (2l_1 + 1)(2J + 1)(l_1 l_2 00 | L0)^2$$

$$\cdot \sin \delta^{J\pi k} \sin \xi_{\alpha s l_1} \cdot \cos (\delta^{J\pi k} + 2\xi_{\alpha s l_2} - \xi_{\alpha s l_1}) \cdot (u_{\alpha s l_2}^{J\pi k})^2 \tag{107}$$

for the interference between potential and nuclear scattering, and lastly for the resonance scattering

$$N_L(\alpha s; \alpha s) = \sum \sin \delta^{J_1 \pi_1 k_1} \sin \delta^{J_2 \pi_2 k_2}$$

$$\cdot \cos [\delta^{J_1 \pi_1 k_1} - \delta^{J_2 \pi_2 k_2} + \xi_{\alpha s l_1} - \xi_{\alpha s l_2} + \xi_{\alpha s l_1'} - \xi_{\alpha s l_2'}]$$

$$\cdot \overline{Z}(l_1 J_1 l_2 J_2; sL)\overline{Z}(l_1' J_1 l_2' J_2; sL)$$

$$\cdot u_{\alpha s l_1}^{J_1 \pi_1 k_1} u_{\alpha s l_2}^{J_2 \pi_2 k_2} u_{\alpha s l_1'}^{J_1 \pi_1 k_1} u_{\alpha s l_2'}^{J_2 \pi_2 k_2} \tag{108}$$

where the sum is over $(J_1 \pi_1 k_1, J_2 \pi_2 k_2, l_1 l_1' l_1 l_2')$ and the k's run from 1 to n. Note that in the resonance scattering part, we can no longer get a simple product expression for the sums over ll' because the potential scattering phase shifts have coupled the various l's together. It is clear that any attempt to put these results in the elegant form of Eq. (79) must involve a determination of *all* the (coupled) eigenvectors and would necessarily be too complicated for any use. (It should be noted that the results in Eqs. (105 to 108) explicitly depend on the assumption that ξ_c is independent of J, which is the case if $\mathbf{R}^0 = 0$.)

(b) Reactions ($\alpha \neq \alpha'$, or $s \neq s'$, or both):

$$B_L(\alpha s; \; \alpha's') = \sum \sin \delta^{J_1 \pi_1 k_1} \sin \delta^{J_2 \pi_2 k_2}$$

$$\cdot \cos [\delta^{J_1 \pi_1 k_1} - \delta^{J_2 \pi_2 k_2} + \xi_{\alpha s l_1} - \xi_{\alpha s l_2} + \xi_{\alpha' s' l_1'} - \xi_{\alpha' s' l_2'}]$$

$$\cdot (\bar{Z}(l_1 J_1 l_2 J_2; \; sL) u_{\alpha s l_1}^{J_1 \pi_1 k_1} u_{\alpha s l_2}^{J_2 \pi_2 k_2}) \cdot (\bar{Z}(l'_1 J_1 l'_2 J_2; \; s'L) \; u_{\alpha' s' l_1'}^{J_1 \pi_1 k_1} u_{\alpha' s' l_2'}^{J_2 \pi_2 k_2}) \quad (109)$$

We note again that the potential scattering phase shifts, ξ, complicate this formula in that they prevent a product form for the sums over l. However, this formula is practical in that the sums over $J\pi k$ are restricted to just the number of levels (one or two) actually considered. The values of u, δ are, to repeat, given by the solutions to Eqs. (97) and (104).

(3) **What Is a Resonance?** The question as to what constitutes a resonance level does not have an unambiguous answer, for there are at least two different definitions in the literature, each with advantages and disadvantages. The most natural definition (I) would seem to be that a resonance energy is defined as that energy for which an eigen phase shift has the value $\pi/2 + k\pi$. This is a generalization of the familiar spinless particle elastic scattering result, where $S_l = -1$ is the definition of a resonance, with the scattering having then the maximum possible value, $4\pi\lambda^2(2l + 1)$. Although this definition seems reasonable enough, it suffers from the fact that the potential scattering phase shifts make any determination of the eigen phase shifts in terms of the Wigner parameters a difficult task, as discussed in the above section. Consequently a different definition (II) of a resonance level has been introduced: a resonance energy is defined as that energy for which the eigen phase shifts assume the value $\pi/2 + k\pi$, *with the potential scattering set equal to zero*. [These phase shifts are just those obtained in Eqs. (105) to (109) above.] The advantage of definition (II) is that the resonance energies so

defined are directly related to the poles of the R matrix.[13] The disadvantage of definition (II) is that the resonances so defined may not actually appear as maxima in the cross sections and in fact may be a minimum. *The point at issue is simply that the split into potential and resonance scattering is not physically well defined.* [A particularly striking example has been given by Wigner (Wi47) for the one-dimensional case where there is no interaction at all. A formal definition of an R matrix leads to resonance scattering which is, however, *exactly* cancelled by the potential scattering.] Nevertheless, definition (II) is in common usage; in the one-level expansion it agrees with the usual resonance energy of the Breit-Wigner dispersion shape. In order to apply definition (II) to the Wigner n-level expansion it is necessary to put the nuclear scattering into the spectral form. The results of the previous section [Eq. (93)] show that *the resonance energies are just the zeros of the determinant of* $(\mathbf{E} + \mathbf{\Delta} - \mathbf{E})$.

As discussed earlier [last paragraph of Section 2.D(1)] the level matrix $\mathbf{A}$ may be diagonalized by a complex orthogonal transformation so that the diagonal elements have the form $\left(F_i - E - \dfrac{iG_i}{2} \right)^{-1}$. It should be noted that the F_i are not in general the "resonance energies" under either definition (I) or (II).

(4) **The Generalized One-Level Approximation** (La58, Lu60a) This is the most important application of the preceding theory; because of the usefulness of this approximation we shall give the resulting formulas in detail.

Since only one resonant level (E_0, J_0, π_0) is considered, the level matrices, $\mathbf{A}$, $\mathbf{w}$, $\mathbf{\Delta}$, all become one-dimensional and the operations are now algebraic. The single-level eigen phase shift β_0 is given by

$$\beta_0 \equiv \cot^{-1} \left[(E_0 + \Delta - E)/\tfrac{1}{2}\Gamma \right] \tag{110}$$

where the level shift, Δ, is given by

$$\Delta = - \sum_c \gamma_{0c}^2 S_c'$$
$$= - \sum_c \gamma_{0c}^2 \{ (S_c - b_c) - R_c^0(S_c - b_c)^2 - R_c^0(P_c)^2 \}$$
$$\cdot \{ [1 - R_c^0(S_c - b_c)]^2 + (R_c^0 P_c)^2 \}^{-1} \tag{110a}$$

[13] At least for the one-dimensional case, where a proof has been given by Thomas (Th56) that the resonance energies are in a one-to-one correspondence with the poles of the derivative R-functions.

and, the total width, Γ, is

$$
\begin{aligned}
{}^1\!/_2\Gamma &= \sum_c \gamma_{0c}^2 P'_c \\
&= \sum_c \gamma_{0c}^2 P_c\{[1 - R_c^0(\mathcal{S}_c - b_c)]^2 + (R_c^0 P_c)^2\}^{-1} \quad (110b)
\end{aligned}
$$

Again, it should be emphasized that $\mathcal{S}'_c$ and P'_c are not simply penetration and shift factors (Os36, Fr53).

It should be noted that the sum over channels which occurs in the above definition of the level shift Δ, includes both *open and closed channels*. Since $P_c = 0$ for closed channels, the width Γ comes only from the open channels (the reduced widths, however, do not depend upon whether a channel is open or closed, e.g., they are energy independent). The penetration and shift factors, P_c and $\mathcal{S}_c$, are defined by Eqs. (37a) and (37b). References to available tabulations of these external parameters are cited in Section 2.B. Finally we recall that b_c is the boundary condition applied to channel c; a discussion of a suitable choice of this parameter is given below.

The unnormalized eigenvector is given by $(\mathbf{P}')^{1/2}\gamma_0$ where $\mathbf{P}'$ is defined in Eq. (25f) and implicitly in Eq. (110b) above. Therefore

$$
u_c^{(0)} = ({}^1\!/_2\Gamma)^{-1/2}(P'_c)^{1/2}\gamma_{0c} \quad (111a)
$$

Since the partial widths are defined by $\Gamma_c = 2P'_c\gamma_{0c}^2$, we see that the elements of the eigenvector $\mathbf{u}$ are just

$$
u_c^{(0)} = \pm(\Gamma_c/\Gamma)^{1/2} \quad (111b)
$$

The sign of the square root is a physical quantity, and in principle the relative sign is measurable through its effect on the angular distribution. Following (Bl52a) we designate this quantity by

$$
g_c \equiv \pm (\Gamma_c/\Gamma)^{1/2} = u_c^{(0)} \quad (111c)
$$

The differential cross sections which result from the one-level approximation are obtained by introducing the values for β_0 and u_0 into Eqs. (106) to (109), and using Eq. (68a) for the cross sections. It should be noted that because $\mathbf{R}^0$ has not been taken as zero, the *potential* scattering phase shifts are now ξ'_c[Eq. (88b)], and thus contain also the effects of the (diagonal) background scattering which may be spin dependent, but more importantly may be dependent on J (and π).

Equation (68a), when applied to elastic scattering, gives the differential cross section without either change of energy or channel spin s. Experimentally one does not measure this quantity, for the observed cross section includes events in which the channel spins are not distinguished. Thus the relevant cross sections are

$$\frac{d\sigma_{\alpha\alpha'}}{d\Omega} = (2a + 1)^{-1}(2b + 1)^{-1} \sum_{ss'} (2s + 1) \frac{d\sigma_{\alpha s;\,\alpha's'}}{d\Omega} \quad (112)$$

$$= \lambda_\alpha^2 (2a + 1)^{-1}(2b + 1)^{-1} \sum_{ss'L} B_L(\alpha s,\, \alpha's') P_L(\cos\theta)$$

where we have for
   (a) Elastic scattering:

$$B_L(\alpha s,\, \alpha s') = H_L(\alpha s,\, \alpha s') + I_L(\alpha s,\, \alpha s') + N_L(\alpha s,\, \alpha s') \quad (113)$$

with

$$H_L(\alpha s;\, \alpha s') = \delta_{s's} \sum_{\substack{l_1 J_1 \\ l_2 J_2}} [\bar{Z}(l_1 J_1 l_2 J_2;\, sL)]^2 \sin(\xi'_{\alpha s l_1 J_1}) \sin(\xi'_{\alpha s l_2 J_2})$$

$$\cdot \cos(\xi'_{\alpha s l_1 J_1} - \xi'_{\alpha s l_2 J_2}) \quad (114a)$$

(If the ξ'_c are independent of J, this result simplifies to Eq. (106), with $\xi \to \xi'_{\alpha s l}$.)

$$I_L(\alpha s;\, \alpha s') = 2\sin\beta_0 \delta_{ss'} \sum_{\substack{l_1 J \\ l_2 l_2'}} \bar{Z}(l_1 J l_2 J_0;\, sL)\bar{Z}(l_1 J l_2' J_0;\, sL) g_{\alpha s l_2} g_{\alpha s l_2'}$$

$$\cdot \sin\xi'_{\alpha s l_1 J} \cos(\xi'_{\alpha s l_2 J_0} + \xi'_{\alpha s l_2' J_0} - \xi'_{\alpha s l_1 J} + \beta_0) \quad (114b)$$

[This result also simplifies if the ξ'_c are independent of J; see Eq. (107).]

$$N_L = \sin^2\beta_0 \sum_{\substack{l_1 l_2 \\ l_1' l_2'}} (-)^{s'-s} \bar{Z}(l_1 J_0 l_2 J_0;\, sL)\bar{Z}(l_1' J_0 l_2' J_0;\, s'L)$$

$$\cdot g_{\alpha s l_1} g_{\alpha s l_2} g_{\alpha s' l_1'} g_{\alpha s' l_2'} \cos(\xi'_{\alpha s l_1 J_0} - \xi'_{\alpha s l_2 J_0} + \xi'_{\alpha s' l_1' J_0} - \xi'_{\alpha s' l_2' J_0})$$

$$\quad (114c)$$

   (b) Reactions:

$$B_L(\alpha s,\, \alpha's') = N_L(\alpha s,\, \alpha's') \quad (115)$$

with

$$N_L = \sin^2\beta_0 \sum_{\substack{l_1 l_2 \\ l_1' l_2'}} (-)^{s'-s} \bar{Z}(l_1 J_0 l_2 J_0;\, sL)\bar{Z}(l_1' J_0 l_2' J_0;\, s'L)$$

$$\cdot g_{\alpha s l_1} g_{\alpha s l_2} g_{\alpha' s' l_1'} g_{\alpha' s' l_2'} \cos(\xi'_{\alpha s l_1} - \xi'_{\alpha s l_2} + \xi'_{\alpha' s' l_1'} - \xi'_{\alpha' s' l_2'}) \quad (115a)$$

(The definition of the $\bar{Z}$, Eq. (69) and the discussion about tabulations given there should be noted.) It should be pointed out here that Eq. (114) *does not assume a statistical channel-spin mixture for the nonresonant scattering.* A statistical mixture is equivalent to hard-sphere scattering, but unwarranted if part of the potential scattering is due to tails of distant levels, i.e., $\boldsymbol{R}^0 \neq 0$.

The maximum complexity of the resonance contributions in (114c) and (115a) will be

$$L_{\max} \leq 2J_0, \ 2l_{\max}, \ 2l'_{\max}, \text{ whichever is least.} \tag{116}$$

Parity conservation is expressed as

$$(-)^{l_1} = (-)^{l_2} = \Pi_n \Pi_0; \ (-)^{l_1'} = (-)^{l_2'} = \Pi_0 \Pi_y \tag{117}$$

where Π_n is the parity of the entrance channel, Π_0 is the parity of the compound nucleus state, and Π_y is the parity of the exit channel. Thus $l_1 + l_2$ is always an even number which means that N_L vanishes for odd values of L.

As is typical of the subject, the notation has become so cumbersome that the formulas are apt to be either unduly discouraging, or repugnant, or both. There is in fact a genuine "barrier" to be overcome in order to apply these results! An example of a typical physical case, with emphasis on the methodology and the details, might serve to aid in surmounting this barrier.

Let us consider the elastic scattering of neutrons on B^{11} in the energy range from, say, 250 kev to about 1500 kev. In this region there are two prominent resonances in B^{12*}; a narrow $(2+)$ resonance at 430 kev and a broader $(3-)$ resonance at 1280 kev (Aj59).

(We shall assume that the resonance at 20 kev (of unknown J) (Aj59) is not important above 200 kev; experimentally the angular distribution is isotropic in this region and this assumption is probably justified physically.)

The background scattering will be taken to consist of s- and p-waves only, and, moreover, assumed to be channel-spin independent. To simplify the analysis the $\boldsymbol{R}$ matrix for each of the two resonances considered will be assumed to have but a single term, and the remainder, $\boldsymbol{R}^0$, will be neglected. The emphasis here is on the actual mechanics of the calculation, for a reasonable physical situation that illustrates the various complications that can enter.

B^{11} has $(3/2-)$ for its ground state; thus there are two channel spins, $s = 1$ and $s = 2$. For the compound system the parity is given by $(-)^{l+1}$, where l is the orbital angular momentum in the channel $c = (\alpha s l)$, α here denoting B^{11} plus a neutron. We may construct the requisite table of channels for the resonant states of the compound system to be:

	$J\pi$	$(2+)$	$(3-)$
$s = 1$			
l		$1, (3)$	$2, (4)$
$s = 2$			
l		$1, (3)$	$2, (4)$

If we allow only s-, p-, and d-waves, there is then but a single l value for each resonance; we shall make this simplifying (and physically reasonable) assumption for convenience.

With these simplifying assumptions, the potential scattering for a single channel [given in general by Eq. (114a)] takes the less complicated form given by Eq. (106). Using Eqs. (112) and (106) to obtain the *complete* potential scattering we have

$$\left(\frac{d\sigma_{\alpha\alpha}}{d\Omega}\right)_H = \frac{\lambda_\alpha^2}{(2 \cdot \frac{1}{2} + 1)(2 \cdot \frac{3}{2} + 1)} \sum_{\substack{s,'s = 1,2 \\ L = 0,1,2}} P_L(\cos\theta) \cdot \delta_{ss'} \cdot (2s + 1)$$

$$\cdot \sum_{l_1,l_2 = 0,1} (2l_1 + 1)(2l_2 + 1)(l_1 l_2 00 | L0)^2 \sin \xi_{sl_1} \sin \xi_{sl_2} \cos(\xi_{sl_1} - \xi_{sl_2})$$

$$= \frac{1}{8}\lambda_\alpha^2 \{ [3(\Delta_{00}^{(1)} + 3\Delta_{11}^{(1)}) + 5(\Delta_{00}^{(2)} + 3\Delta_{11}^{(2)})]P_0$$

$$+ [18\Delta_{01}^{(1)} + 30\Delta_{01}^{(2)}]P_1 + [18\Delta_{11}^{(1)} + 30\Delta_{11}^{(2)}]P_2 \}$$

If the potential scattering is independent of channel spin, as we have assumed, then the above expression reduces to

$$\left(\frac{d\sigma_{\alpha\alpha}}{d\Omega}\right)_H = \lambda_\alpha^2 [(\Delta_{00} + 3\Delta_{11})P_0 + (6\Delta_{01})P_1 + (6\Delta_{11})P_2]$$

In the above results we used the abbreviation

$$\Delta_{l_1 l_2}^{(s)} \equiv \sin \xi_{sl_1} \sin \xi_{sl_2} \cos(\xi_{sl_1} - \xi_{sl_2})$$

to shorten the expressions. One should note that the modification for channel-spin dependence was easily accomplished, but that making the potential scattering dependent on J would require the much more complicated Eq. (114a).

The interference between potential and resonance scattering for each channel spin is given by Eq. (114b); for the case at hand this simplifies to Eq. (107), but we shall indicate how this simplification comes about explicitly and in detail. From Eqs. (112) and (114b) one has for the *complete* interference between resonance and potential scattering the formula

$$(d\sigma_{\alpha\alpha}/d\Omega)_I = \frac{1}{8} \lambda_\alpha^2 \sum_{\substack{(J_0\pi_0) = (2+),(3+) \\ s,s' = 1,2 \\ L = 0,1,2,3}} \sum P_L(\cos\theta)(2\sin\beta_{J_0\pi_0})\delta_{ss'}$$

$$\cdot \sum_{l_1 = 0,1} \sum_J \bar{Z}(l_1 J l_2 J_0; sL)\bar{Z}(l_1' J l_2' J_0; sL)g_{\alpha s l_2}g_{\alpha s l_2'}$$

$$\cdot \sin \xi_{\alpha s l_1 J} \cos(\xi_{\alpha s l_2 J_0} + \xi_{\alpha s l_2' J_0} - \xi_{\alpha s l_1 J} + \beta_{J_0\pi_0})$$

(Note the additional sum over $J_0 \pi_0$, which is not explicitly indicated in Eq. (112).) This is in general very complicated, but we have assumed that ξ'_c is independent of J. The sum over J can therefore be carried out analytically (Bi52). That is

$$\sum_J \bar{Z}(l_1 J l_2 J_0; sL)\bar{Z}(l_1 J l'_2 J_0; sL) = \delta_{l_2, l'_2} \cdot (2l_1 + 1)(2J_0 + 1)(l_1 l_2 00|L0)^2$$

We get then the much simpler result:

$$\left(\frac{d\sigma_{\alpha\alpha}}{d\Omega}\right)_I = \frac{1}{8}\chi_\alpha^2 \left\{ [10 \sin \beta_{2+} \sin \xi'_1 \cos (\xi'_1 + \beta_{2+})]P_0 \right.$$

$$+ [10 \sin \beta_{2+} \sin \xi'_0 \cos (2\xi'_1 - \xi'_0 + \beta_{2+}) + \frac{84}{5} \sin \beta_{3-} \sin \xi'_1 \cos (-\xi'_1 + \beta_{3-})]P_1$$

$$+ [20 \sin \beta_{2+} \sin \xi'_1 \cos (\xi'_1 + \beta_{2+}) + 14 \sin \beta_{3-} \sin \xi'_0 \cos (-\xi'_0 + \beta_{3-})]P_2$$

$$+ \left. \left[\frac{126}{5} \sin \beta_{3-} \sin \xi'_1 \cos (-\xi'_1 + \beta_{3-}) \right] P_3 \right\}$$

(In obtaining this result, we have explicitly used the assumption that the ξ's are independent of s, and that only ξ'_0 and ξ'_1 are appreciable. Note further that the definition of $\beta_{J\pi}$ is given by Eq. (110) with $E_0 + \Delta \equiv E_{\text{resonance}}$; and that, since elastic scattering is the only open channel, $\sum_s g_{\alpha s l}^2 = 1$.)

The remainder of the elastic scattering is the purely nuclear contribution. Using Eqs. (112) and (114c) [and also summing coherently over the two resonances, (2+) and (3−), as is required from the basic result given in Eq. (79a, b); see also Sec. 6 following], we obtain:

$$(d\sigma_{\alpha\alpha}/d\Omega)_N = \frac{1}{8}\chi_\alpha^2 \sum_{\substack{s,s'=1,2 \\ L=0,1,2,3,4}} N_L(\alpha s, \alpha s')P_L(\cos \theta)$$

with

$$N_L(\alpha s, \alpha s') = \sum_{(J_1\pi_1)(J_2\pi_2)=(2+)(3-)} \sin \beta_{J_1\pi_1} \sin \beta_{J_2\pi_2} (-)^{s-s'}$$

$$\cdot \sum_{\substack{l_1 l_2 \\ l'_1 l'_2}} \bar{Z}(l_1 J_1 l_2 J_2; sL)\bar{Z}(l'_1 J_1 l'_2 J_2; s'L)$$

$$\cdot g_{sl_1}^{J_1\pi_1} g_{s'l'_1}^{J_1\pi_1} g_{sl_2}^{J_2\pi_2} g_{s'l'_2}^{J_2\pi_2} \cos (\beta_{J_1\pi_1} - \beta_{J_2\pi_2} + \xi'_{sl_1} - \xi'_{sl_2} + \xi'_{s'l'_1} - \xi'_{s'l'_2})$$

N_L consists of the contributions of each resonance separately, and an interference term between the two resonances. Because of our simplifying assumptions, the contribution of each resonance separately has but a single term in the sum over l_1, l'_1, l_2, l'_2. The interference between the two resonances similarly simplifies; the sum over the l's again becoming a single term.

Substituting the numerical values of the various $\bar{Z}$ coefficients, one finds for the nuclear contribution to the elastic scattering

$$\left(\frac{d\sigma_{\alpha\alpha}}{d\Omega}\right)_N = \frac{1}{8}\lambda_\alpha^2 \left\{(\sin^2 \beta_{2+})\left[5P_0 + \frac{7}{2}\left(\frac{\Gamma_1^{(2+)} - \Gamma_2^{(2+)}}{\Gamma^{(2+)}}\right)^2 P_2\right]\right.$$

$$+ (\sin^2 \beta_{3-})\left[7P_0 + \frac{3}{7}\left(\frac{4\Gamma_1^{(3-)} + \Gamma_2^{(3-)}}{\Gamma^{(3-)}}\right)^2 P_2\right.$$

$$+ \frac{11}{14}\left(\frac{2\Gamma_1^{(3-)} - 3\Gamma_2^{(3-)}}{\Gamma^{(3-)}}\right)^2 P_4\right]$$

$$+ 2 \sin \beta_{2+} \sin \beta_{3-} \cos (\beta_{2+} - \beta_{3-} + 2\xi_1)$$

$$\cdot\left[\frac{14}{5}(\sqrt{3}g_1^{(2+)} g_1^{(3-)} + \sqrt{2} g_2^{(2+)} g_2^{(3-)})^2 P_1\right.$$

$$\left.\left. + \frac{9}{5}(\sqrt{2} g_1^{(2+)} g_1^{(3-)} - \sqrt{3} g_2^{(2+)} g_2^{(3-)})^2 P_3\right]\right\}$$

(Here we have used the definition of the g's, Eq. (111c), to write $(g_{s=1}^{(2+)})^2 = \Gamma_1^{(2+)}/\Gamma^{(2+)}, \ldots$. It should be noted that the nuclear cross-term is sensitive to the relative signs of the g's unlike any of the other terms.)

The complete answer for the total elastic scattering angular distribution, $(d\sigma_{\alpha\alpha}/d\Omega)$, is the sum of the above three parts.

In actual practice the spins, parities, and the g's must be regarded as unknowns, and varied to achieve a satisfactory fit to the experimental results. This can be a very laborious task, and no doubt in complicated cases should be automated. It was the purpose of this example, however, to indicate by a detailed example the application of the results obtained in previous sections, and we shall not attempt to discuss further how well this distribution fits the experimental data.

Finally the partial cross sections integrated over the solid angle $d\Omega$ may be obtained by multiplying 4π times the coefficient of the $P_0 (\cos \theta)$ term in Eq. (112). Thus the *integral scattering* cross section becomes

$$\sigma_{\alpha\alpha} = \frac{4\pi\lambda_\alpha^2}{(2a + 1)(2b + 1)}\cdot\left[\sum_{slJ} (2J + 1) \sin^2 \xi_{\alpha slJ}'\right.$$

$$+ 2(2J_0 + 1) \sin \beta_0 \sum_{sl} \cos (\beta_0 + \xi_{\alpha slJ_0}') \cdot \sin \xi_{\alpha slJ_0}' \cdot (g_{\alpha sl})^2$$

$$\left. + (2J_0 + 1) \sin^2 \beta_0\left(\sum_{sl} g_{\alpha sl}^2\right)^2\right] \tag{118}$$

and the *integral reaction* cross section is

$$\sigma_{\alpha\alpha'} = \{4\pi\lambda_\alpha^2/[(2a+1)(2b+1)]\}(2J_0+1)\sin^2\beta_0 \sum_{\substack{ll'\\ss'}} g_{asl}^2 g_{\alpha's'l'}^2$$

$$(119)$$

If one now introduces the result [which follows from Eq. (110)] that

$$\sin^2\beta_0 = (\tfrac{1}{2}\Gamma)^2/[(\tfrac{1}{2}\Gamma)^2 + (E_0 + \Delta - E)^2] \qquad (120)$$

then the equations assume the usual Breit-Wigner dispersion form.

The application of the above formulas is greatly simplified by choosing the value of the boundary condition b_c to equal the shift factor, S_c, at the energy E_0; then $\bar{S}_c(E_0) = 0$. The level shift, Δ, is not quite zero for $E = E_0$; one finds that

$$\Delta(E_0) = \sum_c \gamma_{0c}^2 R_c^0 P_c^2 [1 + (R_c^0 P_c)^2]^{-1} \qquad (121)$$

which will be taken to be negligible since it involves the square of the penetration factor multiplied by R_c^0, presumably also small.

Teichmann and Wigner (Te52) introduced the boundary condition $b_c = \rho G'/G$ as the choice which makes the one-level approximation most nearly independent of the size of the internal region [see Section 2.D(7)]. For this choice the shift factor is

$$\bar{S} = S - b_c$$

$$= \rho\left(\frac{FF' + GG'}{F^2 + G^2}\right) - \rho G'/G$$

$$= \frac{F}{G}\left(\frac{\rho}{F^2 + G^2}\right) \qquad (122)$$

Now $G \gg F$ in general, so that the Teichmann-Wigner result is, to a good approximation, equivalent to our choice of $S(E_0) = 0$.

The width, Γ, corresponding to the choice $\bar{S}(E_0) = 0$ is given by:

$$\Gamma(E_0) = 2 \sum \gamma_{0c}^2 P_c [1 + (R_c^0 P_c)^2]^{-1} \qquad (123)$$

The difficulty in applying these formulas to an actual case comes from several sources: (a) the determination of suitable values for the internal parameters, in particular the γ_{0c} for negative energy channels, and (b) the external parameters, S and P, ξ, have not been comprehensively tabulated. Moreover the variation of the energy dependent external parameters over the width of the resonance may be important (Th51).

Except for cross sections in the vicinity of thresholds [which require separate consideration (Wi48, Br57, Pr58, Ba58)] it is satisfactory to assume that the shift function is linearly dependent on energy. That is:

$$S(E) = S(E_0) + \dot{S}(E) \cdot (E - E_0) \tag{124a}$$

$$\dot{S}(E_0) \equiv (dS/dE)_{E_0} \tag{124b}$$

$\dot{S}$ is negative for neutrons (Pr58) and for all practical purposes, this is also true for charged particles. Introducing (124) into Eq. (110a) and neglecting $\sum_c R_c^0 P_c^2 \gamma_{0c}^2$ we find

$$\Delta(E) \cong (E_0 - E) \sum_c \gamma_{0c}^2 \dot{S}_c \tag{125}$$

With this approximation, Eq. (119) for the reaction cross section $\sigma_{\alpha\alpha'}$ becomes

$$\sigma_{\alpha\alpha'} = \frac{\pi \lambda_\alpha^2 (2J_0 + 1)}{(2a + 1)(2b + 1)} \frac{\bar{\Gamma}_{\alpha l} \bar{\Gamma}_{\alpha' l'}}{(E_0 - E)^2 + (\bar{\Gamma}/2)^2} \tag{126}$$

where the barred widths are

$$\bar{\Gamma}_{\alpha l} = \sum_s \Gamma_{\alpha s l}(1 + \sum_c \gamma_{0c}^2 \dot{S}_c)^{-1}$$

$$\Gamma_{\alpha s l} = \Gamma_c \cong 2\gamma_0^2 P_c / (1 + \sum_c \gamma_{0c}^2 \dot{S}_c) \tag{127}$$

The approximation in the last step is the neglect of $(R_c^0 P_o)^3$. The barred widths also appear in a similar way for the cross sections where $\alpha', s' = \alpha, s$.

Since $\dot{S}_c < 0$, the widths obtained from fitting to the Breit-Wigner form will exceed the "correct" widths $\Gamma_c = 2\gamma_{0c}^2 P_c$. Very little can be said about the general order of magnitude of the sum, $\sum_c \gamma_{0c}^2 \dot{S}_c$, for the negative energy (closed) channels, but Thomas (Th56) has shown that the magnitude of this sum is the ratio of the probability of finding the system in a closed channel outside the internal region to the probability of the system being in the internal region.

(5) **Interpretation of the One-Level Approximation.** The significance of the one-level approximation can be seen most directly from the analysis in the first paper of Wigner (Wi46), where he showed that the one-level approximation takes the form of the compound nucleus wave function to be independent of energy. Green's theorem

then appears in the sense of an approximate means of developing the wave function to one order higher in the energy.

In order to clarify the first point, consider the overlap integral (taken over the internal region only) of two wave functions, Ψ_1 and Ψ_2, corresponding to two different energies E_1 and E_2. From the general Green's theorem, Eq. (42), we see that

$$(E_1 - E_2) \int_{\text{int}} \Psi_1^* \Psi d\tau = \sum_c (D_{1c}^* V_{2c} - V_{1c}^* D_{2c})$$

$$= \sum_{cc'} D_{1c}^* D_{2c} [R_{cc'}(E_2) - R_{cc'}(E_1)], \qquad (128)$$

where the last step uses the fact that $\mathbf{R}$ is real.

Introducing the one-level assumption, i.e.,

$$\mathbf{R} = \mathbf{R}^0 + (\gamma_\lambda \times \gamma_\lambda)/(E\gamma_\lambda - E)$$

one finds

$$\int_{\text{int}} \Psi_1^* \Psi_2 d\tau = (E_\lambda - E_1)^{-1}(E_\lambda - E_2)^{-1}(\sum_c D_{1c}\gamma_c)^*(\sum_c D_{2c}\gamma_c) \qquad (129)$$

This equation is valid in the limit that $E_1 \to E_2$, so that

$$\int_{\text{int}} |\Psi_1|^2 d\tau = (E_\lambda - E_1)^{-2}|\sum_c D_{1c}\gamma_{\lambda c}|^2 \qquad (130)$$

It follows then that the overlap of Ψ_1 and Ψ_2 in the internal region is complete, i.e.,

$$\left| \int_{\text{int}} \Psi_1^* \Psi_2 d\tau \right|^2 = (\int_{\text{int}} |\Psi_1|^2 d\tau)(\int_{\text{int}} |\Psi_2|^2 d\tau) \qquad (131)$$

from which we conclude that

$\Psi_1 = A_{12}\Psi_2$, for the internal region, where A_{12} is an arbitrary complex multiplicative factor.

This furnishes the desired interpretation of the one-level approximation; aside from an arbitrary amplitude and phase, *the internal wave function is independent of energy, and of the mode of formation.* That Green's theorem provides an approximate means of integration is clear from Eq. (128), where the right-hand side is of higher order [in $(E_1 - E_2)$] than the overlap integral. [Wigner (Wi46) also gives an interesting interpretation of the one-level formula in terms of conservation of flux.]

A slightly different view of the significance of the one-level formula has been given by Jackson (Ja51), who obtained a variational principle for the $\mathbf{R}$ matrix, and showed that the n level $\mathbf{R}$ matrix is the best approximation (in a variational sense) to the correct **R** matrix, that can be obtained from n independent wave functions in the internal region.

Yet another interpretation of the one-level formula can be given by examining the energy derivative of the phase shift in the entrance channel as determined from the one-level formula; this derivative is related to the development in time of the scattering of a wave packet (Th56, Ei48, Ei51, Wi55). [Note added in proof: the paper by F. T. Smith, "Lifetime Matrix in Collision Theory," *Phys. Rev.* **118,** 349 (1960), is a particularly nice discussion of this point.]

If the additional assumptions are made that $R^0 = 0$, and that only channel c has ingoing waves, then we can obtain an explicit form (Th56) for the integral in Eq. (130)

$$\int_{\text{int}} |\psi_E|^2 d\tau = \frac{\pi \lambda^2 (2J + 1)}{(2a + 1)(2b + 1)} \frac{\hbar \, \Gamma_{\lambda c}}{(E_\lambda + \Delta_\lambda - E)^2 + (\Gamma_\lambda/2)^2}$$

(132)

which furnishes, therefore, an explicit form for the energy variation of $|A_{12}|^2$.

(6) **The Interference between Two Resonance Levels.** There are two general situations to be considered here, depending upon whether or not the two levels have the same angular momentum and parity.

If the levels differ in either J or π or both, then—since those are good quantum numbers for the scattering matrix—one uses the single-level eigen phase shifts and eigenvectors of Eqs. (110) and (111) in Section 4 for each of the two scattering matrices, $S^{J\pi}$. The sums over $(J\pi k)$ in Eqs. (107) to (109) now run over the two levels, and the differential cross sections show coherent interference. In particular, if $\pi_1 \neq \pi_2$, Legendre functions with odd L will appear in the angular distribution.

The remaining case is that in which the two levels have the same angular momentum and parity. This is a rather interesting case (Fl48, Te52)—though perhaps of infrequent occurrence.[14] The distinguishing feature is that now *both* the differential and total cross sections show coherent interference, as can be seen from Eq. (79a, b).

[14] Such an example exists in the elastic scattering of neutrons by C^{12}. Levels at 2.95 and 3.6 Mev are both $D_{3/2}$ (Wi58, Me54).

In order to treat this case one first considers the level matrix in the two-level approximation. For simplicity, set $\mathbf{R}^0 = 0$. The level matrix, $\mathbf{A}$ [Eq. (90a)], is then

$$\mathbf{A} = [(E_1 - E + \Xi_{11})(E_2 - E + \Xi_{22}) - \Xi_{12}{}^2]^{-1}$$

$$\begin{pmatrix} E_2 - E + \Xi_{22} & \Xi_{12} \\ -\Xi_{12} & E_1 - E + \Xi_{11} \end{pmatrix} \quad (133)$$

where

$$\Xi_{ij} = \sum_c \gamma_{ic} \bar{L}_c \gamma_{jc} = \Xi_{ji}$$

$$= -\Delta_{ij} + i\Gamma_{iJ}/2 \quad (134)$$

The resonance energies, E_a and E_b, are found to be

$$E_{a,b} = \frac{1}{2}(E_1 + \Delta_{11} + E_2 + \Delta_{22})$$

$$\pm \frac{1}{2}[(E_1 + \Delta_{11} - E_2 - \Delta_{22})^2 + \Delta^2{}_{12}]^{1/2} \quad (135)$$

It will be noted that a nonzero cross-term, Δ_{12}, for the level shift prevents the resonance energies from being equal.

The eigen phase shifts and the eigenvectors are determined from Eqs. (100) to (104). Although the solution is straightforward, the results are nevertheless complicated for the general case (see B156). Much of the complication can, however, be avoided, as we shall now indicate.

Let us consider, as the simplest possible example of a two-level problem, that *both* Γ_{12} and Δ_{12} are zero. The eigen phase shifts and eigenvectors are then given by

$$\cot \delta_1 = 2(E_1 + \Delta_{11} - E)/\Gamma_{11} \qquad \mathbf{u}_1 = \mathbf{P}^{1/2}\boldsymbol{\gamma}_1/(\Gamma_1)^{1/2}$$

and similarly for the second level with $1 \leftrightarrow 2$. In other words, this particular case is equivalent to two one-level cases; the differential and integral cross sections are obtained from Eqs. (105) through (108), where the sums now range over the two eigenstates, $k = 1$ and $k = 2$. Even in this simple example the integral cross sections can show for their energy variation a wide variety of shapes, symmetric or asymmetric shapes, double or single peaks, etc., depending on the choice of the parameters.

To see this, let us take an illustration (Fl48):

$$\sigma_{cc'} = 4\pi\lambda_\alpha^2 \left(\frac{2J+1}{2s+1}\right) \frac{\gamma_{2c}^2\gamma_{2c'}^2/4}{[1 + ((E_1 - E)/\Gamma_1)^2][1 + ((E_2 - E)/\Gamma_2)^2]}$$

$$\cdot \left\{ \left[\left(\frac{E_1 - E}{\Gamma_1}\right) + x\left(\frac{E_2 - E}{\Gamma_2}\right)\right]^2 + (1 + x)^2 \right\}$$

where

$$\gamma_{1c}\gamma_{1c'}/\gamma_{2c}\gamma_{2c'} \equiv x$$

The general situation is an asymmetric double-peaked curve, but special cases can be quite different. Take, for example, the (admittedly unlikely) case, $\Gamma_{11} = \Gamma_{22}$, $x = \pm 1$. If the energy separation, $E_1 - E_2$, is approximately Γ or larger, the two peaks coalesce, but the resulting curve is very different from the usual dispersion curve. With $x = +1$ we get an anomalously flat-topped maximum; with $x = -1$ a very steep maximum falling off as E^{-4} in the wings. For the opposite extreme where $\Gamma/(E_1 - E_2)$ is small, the situation, as expected, is two well-separated dispersion curves.

Let us consider next the general case where Γ_{12} and Δ_{12} are both nonzero, and seek conditions such that eigen phase shifts and eigenvectors correspond to two one-level cases. This condition is found to be

$$\Delta_{12}/(E_1 + \Delta_{11} - E_2 - \Delta_{22}) = \Gamma_{12}/(\Gamma_{11} - \Gamma_{22}) \qquad (136)$$

which expresses the fact that the "mixing" produced by the Γ matrix and the $\mathbf{E} \mid \Delta$ matrix are equal and opposite. But as the Δ's are effectively at our disposal, through varying the arbitrary boundary conditions b_c, it appears reasonable that we can require Eq. (136) to be satisfied at some given energy.[15] To the extent that the energy variation of the external functions is negligible,[16] this choice of b_c reduces the general situation to the special case treated above. {Although now the eigenvectors are linear combinations of the $\mathbf{P}^{1/2}\boldsymbol{\gamma}^{(i)}$, [Eqs. (97) and (103), with $W = 1$], we might equally well

---

[15] The $\gamma_{\lambda c}$ and the E_λ are themselves functions of the boundary conditions b_c (Te52) and Eq. (136) is therefore very complicated to treat in any general way. There does not appear to be any essential restriction which would prevent Eq. (136) from having a solution.

[16] The energy variation can be taken into account in first order by taking both P_c and S_c to vary linearly. The energy at which Eq. (136) is chosen to hold is then given by $(E_a - E)/\Gamma_a = (E_b - E)/\Gamma_b$, so that the elements of W will still be independent of energy to this order.

treat the elements of these eigenvectors as unknown parameters, subject only to the requirement of orthonormality.}

Very few examples of the application of the Wigner two-level formula to experimental data appear in the literature, particularly for neutrons incident. Krotkov (Kr55) applies the Wigner two-level theory to the neutron cross section for Mn in the low energy region (up to 10 kev). Reich (Re58) has analyzed neutrons on uranium using the Wigner many-level theory as a basis; Vogt (Vo58) has also discussed this same problem.

(7) **Miscellaneous Considerations.** (a) *Dependence on the Size of the Internal Region.* The scattering matrix and the reaction matrix are both quantities defined in terms of the asymptotic form of the wave functions at energy E. As such the number of dimensions is fixed as the number of open channels, and, moreover, the question of a (finite) internal region never enters. On the other hand, the derivative matrix is clearly dependent on the size of the internal region, as are the external matrices Ω and $L = S + iP$.

It is desirable to take the internal region as close to the actual nuclear surface as possible (a) in order that the parameters $\gamma_{\lambda c}$ (and E_λ) have some connection with the properties of the physical nucleus (see, for example, the sum rules), and (b) because the analysis of experimental data requires some simple, yet valid, form such as Eqs. (112) to (120); this latter depends upon the replacement of the external parameters by constants approximately independent of the energy, which in turn is most valid for small a_c (Wi47, Te52).

On the other hand, if one makes the internal region small, the closed channels begin to be appreciable at the channel surface. This situation is particularly important at the threshold for a new (open) channel, for in this case the internal region just below threshold must become indefinitely large (Wi48). One can allow for this by first including the closed channels and then explicitly eliminating them. That is, let the **R** matrix be defined by (taking $b_c = 0$ for convenience)

$$V_c = \sum_{c'} R_{cc'} D_{c'} \tag{137}$$

where the sum is over both open (r = retained) and closed (e = eliminated) channels. Making the separation explicit, we have

$$V_r = \sum_{r'} R_{rr'} D_{r'} + \sum_{e'} R_{re'} D_{e'} \tag{138a}$$

$$V_e = \sum_{r'} R_{er'} D_{r'} + \sum_{e'} R_{ee'} D_{e'} \tag{138b}$$

But the closed channels obey the rule

$$V_e = L_e^{-1} D_e \qquad \text{where } L_e = \text{real} \tag{139}$$

Thus, if we define the reduced **R** matrix, $\mathfrak{R}$ (whose rows and columns refer only to the open channels) by

$$V_r \equiv \sum_{r'} \mathfrak{R}_{rr'} D_{r'} \tag{140}$$

then these equations lead to

$$\mathcal{R}_{rr} = R_{rr} + R_{re}(L_e^{-1} - R_{ee})^{-1}R_{er} \qquad (141)$$

This reduced $\mathcal{R}$-matrix is appreciably more complicated; e.g., it has branch points as well as poles.

The reduced $\mathcal{R}$-matrix is useful for discussing the behavior of the cross sections in the vicinity of thresholds (Wi48). The results of this general theory turn out not to differ in any essential way from the results obtained from the one-level approximation; for this latter case, the energy dependence of the external parameters, S_c and L_c, is essential (Pr58).

We may summarize these results for the one-level approximation by noting that:

(a) If the threshold channel is an exit channel (with orbital angular momentum l) then $\sigma_{thr} \propto P_{thr\ \text{channel}}$

$$P \propto E^{l+1/2} \quad \text{(non Coulomb)}$$

$$P \propto e^{-2\pi\eta} \quad \text{(Coulomb repulsion)}$$

(b) If the threshold channel is the entrance channel then the above is multiplied by $1/E$.

(c) if the threshold channel is neither an entrance nor an exit channel, the cross section:

(1) is smoothly varying if the threshold channel has a Coulomb repulsion,

(2) has a discontinuity in its $(l + 1)$th derivative, if the threshold channel is uncharged and has orbital angular momentum l.

An interesting extension of the channel elimination scheme has been given by Thomas (Th55). In this application only one channel is retained, the entrance channel. The resulting R matrix is one-dimensional and corresponds (for $R^0 = 0$) to the logarithmic derivative, f, which forms the basis of the work of Feshbach, Peaslee, and Weisskopf (Fe47). Application of this reduced $\mathcal{R}$ matrix to the region where the partial widths exceed the spacings, and to the *gross structure* problem is given by Thomas in his paper.

(b) *Sum Rules.* The analysis of experimental data using the approximation given by Eq. (110), or Eqs. (112) to (120) is aided by interpreting as far as possible, the $\gamma_{\lambda c}$ and the E_λ in terms of physical quantities. Using either the Teichmann-Wigner (Te52) prescription, $b_o = \rho G'/G$ (or the approximately equivalent, $\overline{S}_c = 0$, prescription), the surface region may be considered as physically within about 1 fermi of the sum of the nuclear radii of the two particles composing the alternative α. The E_0 of Eq. (110) will then be very close to the actual resonance energy. The $\gamma_{\lambda c}$ for this case are given by the left-hand side of Eq. (49); they have the general form of a transition probability, except, that as they connect wave functions defined in different spaces, difficulties in deriving general results can be expected. One general result has been given by Teichmann-Wigner (Te52)

$$\sum_{\lambda} \gamma_{\lambda s}\gamma_{\lambda t} = 0 \ (s \neq t) \qquad (142a)$$

$$= \infty \ (s = t)$$

(using the fact the left-hand side is related to an integral of Dirac's δ function). This expression may be interpreted to mean that the signs of $\gamma_{\lambda s}$ fluctuate at random so that Eq. (142a) may be true for all s and t.

Using heuristic arguments, Teichmann and Wigner (Te52) have given two further sum rules, which have proved very valuable in practice. The first is

$$\sum_{c}{}' \gamma_{\lambda c}^2 (b_c) \leqq (6\hbar^2 T/A)/(3\hbar^2 b^2 + 2MT/A)a_c^2 \qquad (142b)$$

Here b is the value of the boundary condition (if b varies from channel to channel, b^2 on the right-hand side is to be interpreted as $\langle b^2 \rangle$); A is the number of nucleons; T is the total kinetic energy, and M is the reduced nucleon mass. The prime on the sum denotes that the sum excludes highly excited levels.

Sum rule (142b) may be described in the following way (Wi49): The individual reduced width, $\gamma_{\lambda c}^2$, is the probability (multiplied by $\hbar^2 2M/a_c$) that, for the eigenstate X_λ, the nuclei of alternative c have separation r_c lying between a_c and $a_c + 1$. Hence, the sum over alternatives is simply the probability that r_c lies within a unit interval at the surface of the internal region. This depends on the boundary condition, for if $b = \infty$, the X_λ must vanish at the surface and the sum above also vanishes. If $b = 0$, this probability can be approximated as the ratio of the surface to the internal volume, i.e., $3/a_c$.

The next sum rule is the estimate of Bethe and of Feshbach, Peaslee, and Weisskopf (Fe47):

$$\gamma_{\lambda s}^2 \cong 3D/2\pi K a_c \qquad (142c)$$

where D = average level spacing and K is the average wave number of a particle in the nucleus. An interpretation of this in semiclassical terms has been given in Blatt and Weisskopf (Bl52); Teichmann-Wigner (Te52) give alternative deductions from reaction theory.

A final set of sum rules employs the *giant resonance* (independent particle) interpretation of nuclear reactions discussed by Lane, Thomas, and Wigner (La55). Here one designates a given channel c with two indices: r which labels the state of the residual nucleus and p the single particle state of the remaining nucleon. Then one finds that:

$$\sum_{rp} \gamma_{\lambda; rp} \gamma'_{\lambda; rp} \approx \langle \zeta_p^2 \rangle_{av} \delta_{\lambda\lambda} \qquad (143a)$$

$$\sum_{\lambda} r_{\lambda; rp} \gamma_{\lambda; r'p'} = \zeta_p^2 \delta_{rr'} \delta_{pp'} \qquad (143b)$$

where

$\zeta_p^2 = (a\hbar^2/2M)u_p^2(a)$, (with u_p the radial function of the particle p). The quantity ζ_p^2 is the single particle reduced width ($\approx \hbar^2/Ma^2$). For $r = r'$, $p = p'$ the above equation shows that the sum of the reduced widths for a given p group is the single particle reduced width, ζ_p^2.

(c) *Gamma-Ray Processes*. The preceding treatment, since it dealt with wave functions in configuration space, is restricted to particle processes, and does not as such include γ-ray emission. It is, however, straightforward to include such processes, using, for example, the semiclassical theory of radiation. The results can then be incorporated into the previous formalism by altering appropriately the meaning of the parameters and functions.

Let us first summarize the changes and then indicate their origin. We first define the γ-ray channels, c_γ, using as before the indices $c = (\alpha s l J M)$. The index α_γ now specifies that the channel consists of the pair: (a) definite nucleus J, π in a definite energy state, and (b) a photon of definite energy and definite character (electric or magnetic). The channel spin index, s_γ, now denotes the intrinsic angular momentum of the nucleus denoted by α_γ. Finally, the index l_γ is the multipolarity of the γ ray. With these formal identifications one finds that the angular distribution coefficient $B_L(\alpha s; \alpha' s')$ now has exactly the form given in Eq. (79) except that whenever a γ-ray channel occurs then the $\bar{Z}$ coefficient is to be replaced by the $\bar{Z}_1$ coefficient, where $\bar{Z}_1$ is defined as

$$\bar{Z}(l_1 J_1 l_2 J_2; s l) \rightarrow \bar{Z}_1(l_{1\gamma} J_1 l_{2\gamma} J_2; s_\gamma L)$$

$$\equiv (-)[(2l_{1\gamma} + 1)(2l_{2\gamma} + 1)(2J_1 + 1)(2J_2 + 1)]^{1/2}$$

$$\cdot [(1 + \pi_{1\gamma} \pi_{2\gamma}(-)^L)/2](l_{1\gamma} l_{2\gamma} 1 - 1 | L0)$$

$$\cdot W(l_{1\gamma} J_1 l_{2\gamma} J_2; s_\gamma L) \tag{144}$$

Here $\pi_{1\gamma}$ and $\pi_{2\gamma}$ are the parities of the γ ray :$(-)^{l_\gamma}$ for electric and $(-)^{l_\gamma + 1}$ for magnetic multipoles. [The $\bar{Z}_1$ coefficients differ in phase from the Z_1 coefficients originally defined by (Sh53) for precisely the reasons given in Section 2.C; see Eq. (70).]

For angular correlations involving γ rays, in particular $\gamma - \gamma$ correlations, a coefficient, F_ν, more specialized than $\bar{Z}_1$ is commonly used. The relation between these coefficients is

$$F_\nu(LL'j'j) = (-)^{j'-j} (2j + 1)^{-1/2} \bar{Z}_1(jLjL'; j'\nu) \tag{145}$$

Tabulations of this coefficient (for ν even) are given in Bi53a and Fe53b, the latter tabulation being quite extensive.

For the commonly occurring case where $l_{1\gamma} = l_{2\gamma}$ (and thus $L =$ even) the $\bar{Z}_1$ and $\bar{Z}$ coefficients are related by

$$\bar{Z}_1(l_1 J_1 l_1 J_1; sL) = \{[L(L + 1) - 2l_1(l_1 + 1)]/2l_1(l_1 + 1)\}$$
$$\bar{Z}(l_1 J_1 l_1 J_1; sL) \quad (146)$$

Next, one identifies the elements of the scattering matrix which refer to γ-ray channels, in the spectral form (one-level approximation), as

(a) The eigen phase shift is given as $\cot^{-1}[(E_r - E)/\Gamma^{1/2}]$.

(b) The elements of the eigenvectors $u_{c\gamma}^{J\pi k}$ are the (real) reduced matrix elements for the γ-ray transitions (normalized by $\Gamma^{-1/2}$). In the long wave length approximation, these terms are given by

$$u_{c\gamma}^{J\pi k} = (\Gamma^{-1/2})k^{L+1/2}a_{L\gamma} \quad (147)$$

where k is the wave number of the γ ray ($E_\gamma/\hbar c$), and L the multipolarity. The (real) constant, $a_{L\gamma}$, can be regarded simply as an energy independent parameter; it is related, however, to the reduced matrix element for the γ-ray transition.

In terms of the transition probability $T_E(L, m)$ and $T_M(L, m)$ of Blatt and Weisskopf (Bl52, p. 595), the relation is

$$a_{L\gamma} = [\hbar T_E(L,m)/(J_i L m_i m | J m_f)^2 i^L k^{2L+1}]^{1/2}$$

for electric transitions; for magnetic transitions $i^{-1}T_M(L,m)$ replaces $T_E(L,m)$. [Note that the wave functions used in calculating the matrix elements for $T(L,m)$ (Bl52, p. 598), must satisfy the phase conventions of Section 2.B, in order that $a_{L\gamma}$ be real.] The Wigner coefficient in this expression (corresponding to a nuclear transition from J_i to J) enters in order to convert the matrix elements into *reduced* matrix elements, i.e., to remove any dependence on magnetic quantum numbers.

Finally we indicate the origin of these changes, which arise from the nature of the photon. Because of the fact that the rest mass of the photon is zero, the spin is kinematically connected to the orbital motion, and in particular the total angular momentum for the photon has projection ± 1 along the direction of motion. This fact is expressed by the Wigner coefficient $(l_{1\gamma}l_{2\gamma} 1 - 1 | L0)$ (which replaces the previous statement that the orbital angular momentum had zero projection along the direction of motion which resulted in the Wigner coefficient $(l_1 l_2 00 | L0)$. Since the intrinsic angular momentum of the photon is coupled to its orbital angular momentum (which refers only to the photon since we neglect recoil and take the nucleus at rest), the channel spin thus becomes the J of the nucleus itself.

3. Total Cross-Section Measurements

A. *Experimental Techniques (see also Chapter V.A)*

(1) **General Relationship.** Determination of a total cross section at energy E involves ideally the measurement of only three quantities: the thickness n of the sample studied, the direct relative intensity I_0 of neutrons employed, and the relative intensity I transmitted through the sample. If sufficiently thin samples are employed, these quantities are related by the usual exponential law

$$I = I_0 e^{-n\sigma T}, \tag{148a}$$

i.e.,

$$\sigma_T = (1/n) \ln (I_0/I) \tag{148b}$$

(2) **Sample Considerations.** If an elemental sample is employed, the nuclear thickness n is obtained from the relation

$$n = (m/a)(N/A)$$

where m and a are the mass and cross-sectional area of the sample, respectively, A is its atomic weight, and N is Avogadro's number (6.0247×10^{23} grams/mole). Provided the sample is uniform in density, the error introduced by the measurement of n is usually very small. Frequently compounds, such as BeO, are compared to the elemental form (Be) to determine the cross sections of materials (in this case O) difficult to obtain as solids. Samples are usually of cylindrical shape and of diameter just sufficient to conveniently shield the detector from the finite sized source in the chosen geometry. The choice of sample thickness is usually governed by a compromise between counting statistics and multiple scattering. In general this places the transmission in the region of 60 to 70 per cent. However, the maximum and minimum cross section of resonances are often determined with samples of 80 to 90 per cent transmission. Since the cross section undergoes variations of a factor of 10 or more (in the fast neutron region), it is obvious that several sample thicknesses should be employed for a complete measurement of the resonance under investigation.

(3) **Neutron Sources.** In order to determine the properties of isolated resonances, it is desirable to have the over-all energy resolution considerably less than the natural width of the level in question.

Until recently this in general precluded the use of neutron sources other than (p, n), (d, n), and (α, n) reactions produced by *variable* energy accelerators of high stability. For the particular reaction appropriate to a given energy range (limited by the machine) see the general discussions of Chapter I. The reaction should be mono-energetic unless special techniques are employed to detect only transitions to a single state of the residual nucleus. (Improved time-of-flight techniques have made feasible the use of broad spectrum neutron sources for high resolution work; see Chapter IV.A.)

Several factors contribute to the over-all resolution obtained; the spread in energy of the charged particles incident upon the neutron producing target, the target thickness (or energy loss of the bombarding projectile), the Doppler broadening due to the thermal motion of the target and/or sample atoms, and the energy variation with angle of the neutrons produced by the reaction. When gas targets are necessary, an additional energy spread is introduced by the passage of the incident charged particles through the thin window (foil) sealing the bombarded gas from the accelerator vacuum system.

In principle, the resolution of the incident charged particles can be reduced to any desired value by first passing the particles through an electrostatic or magnetic analyzer with sufficiently narrow slits. In practice, this could result in such a low beam intensity that the experiment would become impossible. However, most present-day electrostatic accelerators can pass essentially all of their beam through slits giving resolution of 0.1 per cent in energy. It is, in fact, found that the measured resolution is usually a factor of at least 2 better (≤ 0.05 per cent) than the calculated value. This is due to the higher stability achieved by feedback control systems (He49, Jo57, Pa58).

Recently a method has been developed at Duke University (Pa58b) that reduces the beam energy spread still further. A vary-ing correction voltage is applied to the target which compensates the beam energy fluctuations. This reduces the spread to about 250 ± 120 ev, probably due to the ion source itself; i.e., it appears to be independent of accelerator voltage.

Most solid targets can be evaporated uniformly for thicknesses greater than 25 $\mu g/cm^2$. The limiting factor of this contribution to the over-all resolution is usually dictated by the yield of the reaction, the amount of beam current the target will withstand, and the efficiency of the neutron detectors.

Most gas targets used for neutron production employ foils equivalent to about 0.05 mil nickel. These will easily withstand 1/2 atmosphere pressure over an aperture of 1/4 inch diameter. Such foils, due to inhomogeneity and straggling, will give about 20 kev spread in energy for 1.35-Mev protons (Fo55). Very few neutron data have been taken to date with thinner foils, but practicality does not rule this out.

Doppler broadening is of the order of a few hundred ev. It can be lowered by cooling of the target and/or the sample. There are, however, attendant difficulties; cold surfaces tend to collect vapors more easily than hot ones so that a gradual thickening of the target is usually observed.

The energy variation with angle of the neutrons emitted by a reaction depends upon its own particular kinematics (Q-value, masses of incident, bombarded, emitted, and residual particles). Due to the finite geometry one must always use, the half angle subtended by the detector will usually be of the order $3°$. With most of the reactions commonly used, this contribution to the resolution need not be the limiting factor (see Chapter I.B.).

The over-all energy resolution will depend upon the manner in which the component resolutions are combined. This in turn will be influenced by the shape of the individual resolution functions. The slit opening imparts a triangular energy distribution of the charged particle beam (He49). Resolution due to the target thickness will be affected by the shape of the yield curve for the neutron producing reaction at the energy of interest. The thermal spread is Gaussian, and the angular variation depends upon the kinetics of the reaction. Often one then estimates the over-all energy resolution by taking the square root of the sum of the squares of the components. (This assumes all the components have Gaussian distribution.) Ultimately this can be checked by traversing a known resonance whose width is considerably less than the desired resolution. A useful standard for this purpose is the 585-kev S^{32} resonance whose natural width is known to be less than 1.5 kev (Pe50, Cr57). In the latter measurements of Cranberg a new technique of beam pulsing and swinging the target voltage about E_0 should prove very fruitful in the study of narrow resonances, the essential improvement being the reduced data collection time. (See also Chapter V.L., by H. W. Newson and J. H. Gibbons, which discusses high resolution work in the kev energy region.)

If the resolution cannot be made small compared to the level width, an estimate of the reduction in peak height can be obtained by averaging the theoretical cross section. Thus, if the level has a Breit-Wigner shape, the theoretical maximum will be reduced by the factor

$$f = \tan^{-1}(\Delta/\Gamma)/(\Delta/\Gamma) \tag{149}$$

where Δ is the resolution width and Γ is the natural width. Equation (149) assumes the energy distribution is square. For a Gaussian shape it becomes (Fe51)

$$f = 1.665(\Gamma/\Delta) \exp[0.693(\Gamma^2/\Delta^2)] \, \text{erfc}[0.833(\Gamma/\Delta)] \tag{150a}$$

where erfc is related to the error function (erf) by

$$\text{erfc} = (\pi/4)^{1/2}(1 - \text{erf}) \tag{150b}$$

In Eq. (150a) Δ is now the half-width of the Gaussian. Both resolution functions are shown in Fig. 1 as a function of Δ/Γ.

(4) **Detectors.** Neutron detectors are usually $B^{10}F_3$ gas counters or the recoil type. The former are quite useful below 0.5 Mev. Gas recoil counters (ionization and proportional), such a hydrogen, helium, methane (CH_4), and propane (C_3H_8), have been successful in the region of 0.1 to 3 or 4 Mev. In general all these counters have efficiencies between 10^{-2} and 10^{-3}; however, efficiencies up to the order of 10^{-1} can be obtained from Hornyak type buttons (Ho52) (ZnS in Lucite), anthracene and stilbene crystals, and liquid scintillators. These must, however, be used above approximately 2 Mev in order to discriminate favorably against γr ays. (See Appendix II.)

(5) **Background Correction.** D. Miller discusses background in great detail in Chapter V.A. It only needs to be emphasized here that with very thin targets, the effect of neutrons produced other than at the target can become quite important.

(6) **Single and Multiple Scattering.** Chapter V.A. gives formulas for estimating the *in-scattering* correction for neutrons scattered singly and multiply into the detector. Care must be taken in applying this correction, since the angular distributions of elasti-

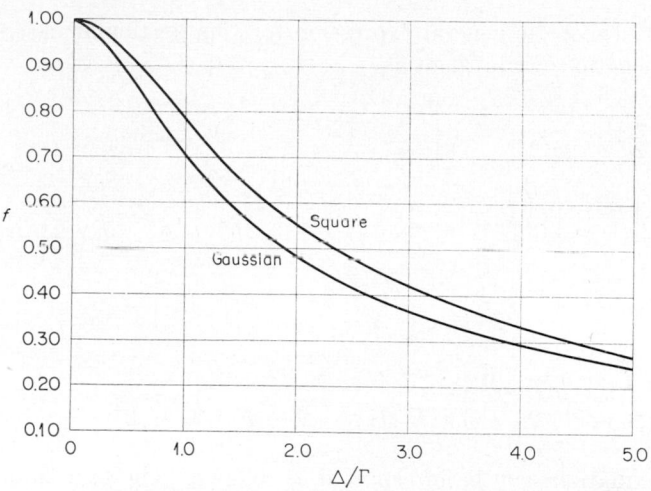

Figure 1. f, the ratio of the experimental to theoretical maximum cross section of a resonance, is shown as a function of the ratio of resolution to level width.   Both square and Gaussian resolution functions are illustrated.   Symbols are discussed in the text.

cally scattered neutrons may change rapidly and drastically as one traverses a resonance (often shifting from strong forward scattering to strong backward scattering, or the inverse).   Once the parameters of the level are determined, the differential cross section needed for this correction can easily be calculated to sufficient approximation

B. *Interpretation of Data*

Resonances observed in the measurement of neutron total interaction cross sections are due to levels of the compound nucleus. Their important parameters include the resonance energy E_0, the excitation energy in the compound nucleus E_x, the spin J, parity, π, and the total level width Γ.   Other quantities such as the various partial widths, Γ_n, $\Gamma_n{}'$, Γ_γ, Γ_p, Γ_α, ..., can usually be obtained by additional measurements of the corresponding partial cross section. It is the purpose in this section to illustrate the methods of analysis of measured total cross sections.

Assume first that there is only a single isolated level of sharp J_0, π_0.   Tails from the contribution of distant levels can then be lumped together with the potential scattering.   Equations (118)

and (119) give the general expression for this particular case. It is convenient to rewrite them as

$$
\sigma_n = \frac{4\pi\lambda_n^2}{(2a+1)(2b+1)} \left[\sum_{slJ \neq J_0} (2J+1) \sin^2 \xi_{nsl}^{'J\pi} \right.
$$

$$
+ (2J_0+1) \sum_{sl} \left| \sin \xi_{nsl}^{'J_0\pi_0} e^{-i\xi_{nsl}^{'J_0\pi_0}} + \frac{\frac{1}{2}\Gamma_{nsl}^{J_0\pi_0}}{(E_0 + \Delta - E) - \frac{1}{2}i\Gamma} \right|^2
$$

$$
+ (2J_0+1) \sum_{\substack{sl \\ s'l' \neq sl}} \frac{\frac{1}{4}\Gamma_{nsl}^{J_0\pi_0} \Gamma_{ns'l'}^{J_0\pi_0}}{(E_0 + \Delta - E)^2 + (\Gamma/2)^2} \right]
\tag{151}
$$

$$
\sigma_y = \frac{4\pi\lambda_n^2(2J_0+1)}{(2a+1)(2b+1)} \sum_{\substack{ss' \\ ll'}} \frac{\frac{1}{4}\Gamma_{ys'l'}^{J_0\pi_0} \Gamma_{nsl}^{J_0\pi_0}}{(E_0 + \Delta - E)^2 + \frac{1}{4}\Gamma^2}
\tag{152}
$$

These equations can be interpreted as follows: The first summation in Eq. (151) contains the contribution to the total cross section of all nonresonating partial waves with total angular momentum different from J_0. In the middle summation of Eq. (151) a square of the sum of two complex vector amplitudes appears. Squaring the first amplitude gives simply the nonresonant cross section due to the wave with $J = J_0$. The second amplitude squared is of the Breit-Wigner form and obviously the resonating portion of the cross section produced by incoming and outgoing waves *of the same l.* A cross term between the two amplitudes produces destructive interference in the cross section. It can be seen by inspection that *this interference in the total cross section can only occur between states that have the same channel spins, orbital angular momentum l, total angular momentum J_0, and parity π_0.*[17] The final summation is the resonance contribution from interference of the different l values which can combine with s to form J_0.[18] Equation (152) is the reaction cross-section and contains only resonance contributions.

The simplest practical case of interest is pure elastic scattering

[17] In order to clarify this important result, suppose neutrons incident upon a target nucleus of spin $b = 3/2^+$ from a resonance of $J = 1^+$. This state can be formed by combining s-waves ($l = 0$) with channel spin 1, and d-waves ($l = 2$) with channel spin 1 or 2. Thus, in this case there will be three distinct contributions to the interference.

[18] The parity selection rule, for states of sharp $J_0\pi_0$, restricts values of l to $l, l + 2, l + 4, \ldots$. At energies of a few Mev, the centrifugal barrier will in general make the contribution of waves $l + 2$ (or higher) small compared with l, except with respect to interference terms in $\sigma(\theta)$.

of neutrons by spin zero nuclei. In this case Eq. (151) can be simplified still further:

$$\sigma_n = 4\pi\lambda_n^2\left[\sum_{J\neq J_0} [(2J+1)/2]\sin^2\xi_l'^J\right.$$
$$\left.+ [(2J_0+1)/2]\sin^2(\beta_0 + \xi_l'^{J_0})\right] \quad (151a)$$

where

$$\beta_0 \equiv \tan^{-1}[(\Gamma_l^{J_0}/2)/(E_0 + \Delta - E)]$$

It can then be shown that the total cross section will have a maximum value at

$$E_{\max} = E_0 - (\Gamma_l^{J_0}/2)\tan\xi_l'^{J_0} \quad (153a)$$

and a minimum value at

$$E_{\min} = E_0 + (\Gamma_l^{J_0}/2)\cot\xi_l'^{J_0} \quad (153b)$$

provided that the energy variation of Γ_l, $\xi_l'^{J_0}$, and λ can be neglected (Ma40). If $\xi_l'^{J_0} < -\pi/2$, the minimum cross section will occur below the resonance energy. This condition will be true for $\Gamma_l \ll E_0$. For $\xi_l'^{J_0} > -\pi/2$ the converse holds true. But note carefully that if $\xi_l'^{J_0} = -\pi/2$, there will be no maximum at all, but a minimum at E_0. Figure 2 shows the effect of various values of ξ_l' on the shape of the resonance. Here the nonresonant scattering cross section of the partial waves not contributing to the resonance has been neglected.

Example I. The first observation of an *interference dip* in neutron total cross sections was made by Adair, Bockelman, and Peterson (Ad49a). Figure 3 shows the resonance in S^{32} occurring at a neutron bombarding energy of 108 kev—still a classic example in this field. At this low energy the nonresonant scattering will be nearly all s-wave. Therefore, the very fact that a dip occurs is sufficient evidence for an assignment of $J_0 = 1/2^+$ (since the ground state of S^{32} is 0^+). As a check, the maximum value, $\sigma_{\max}$, of the cross section (at 111 kev) should be $4\pi\lambda^2(2J_0+1)/(2a+1)$ $=4\pi\lambda^2$,[19] and the minimum value, $\sigma_{\min}$, should be zero. The theoretical

---

[19] Data on total cross sections are usually presented as a series of points plotted as a function of neutron energy *in the laboratory system*. The theory, of course, is derived in the system where the center-of-mass is at rest. Obviously the total cross section itself is independent of the reference frame. To calculate the theoretical values for comparison with the data, great care must be exercised. For example, the value of $4\pi\lambda_n^2$ in the center-of-mass system is given by

$$4\pi\lambda_n^2 \text{ (barns)} = 2.61 \ [(m+M)^2/M^2]E_{\text{lab}}^{-1}(\text{Mev})$$

where M is the target's nuclear mass and m is the mass of the neutron. Several errors in this particular calculation occur in the published literature.

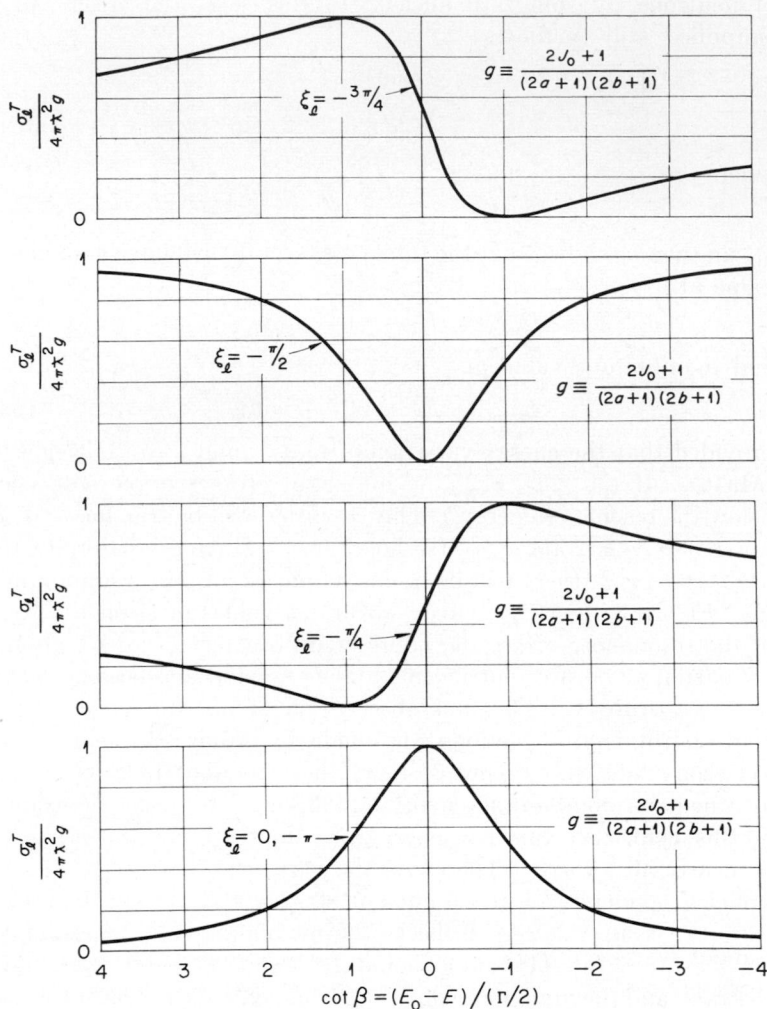

Figure 2. The effect on the total cross section of interference between resonance and potential scattering is shown for values of the potential phase shifts $\xi' = 0,\ -\pi/4,\ -\pi2,\ -3\pi/4,\ -\pi$. [$\sigma_l/4\pi\lambda^2 g$ is plotted as a function of $cot\ \beta = (E_0 - E)/(\Gamma/2)$ (see also F151)].

value for $\sigma_{\max}$ of 24.4 barns (corrected for isotopic abundance) is in good agreement with the observed value 21.5 ± 1 barns (corrected for the finite energy resolution). The minimum value $\sigma_{\min}$ occurs

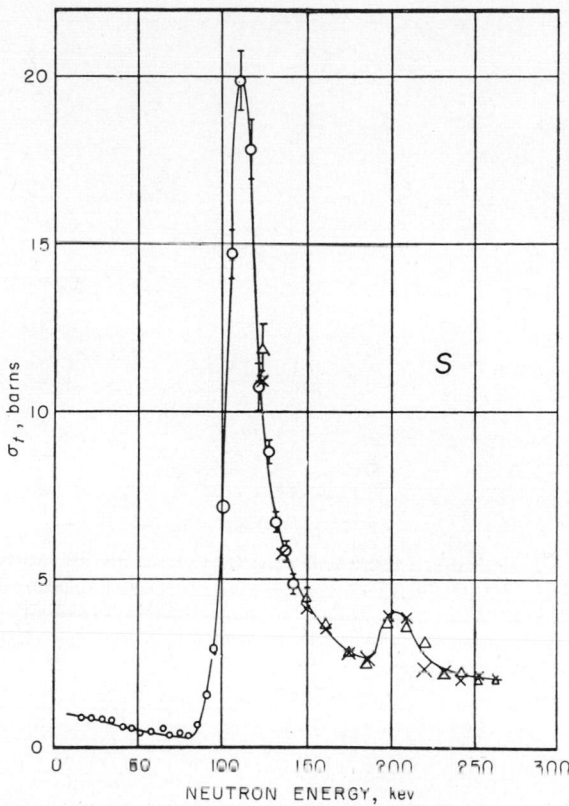

Figure 3. The total cross section of sulfur as a function of neutron energy (Ad49a); 108-kev resonance. (See also Pe50 for improved data.)

at about 80 kev with a magnitude of 0.3 barns; thus the s-wave nonresonant phase shift is about $-20°$.[20] The deviation of σ_{min} from zero can be explained by the contributions from neutron capture, p-wave nonresonance scattering, and the other isotopes of sulfur. Correcting the observed width of 19 kev for the finite energy resolution ($\sim$7 kev), the natural width of this level is found to be 18 kev.

[20] The sign of ξ_0' cannot always be determined from total cross-section data. For s-wave hard-sphere or potential scattering $\xi_0 = -kR$, and the negative sign for most light elements is confirmed from differential cross section measurements (Wi55a, Fo55), Li[7] being a notable exception (St51, Th56a, Wi56).

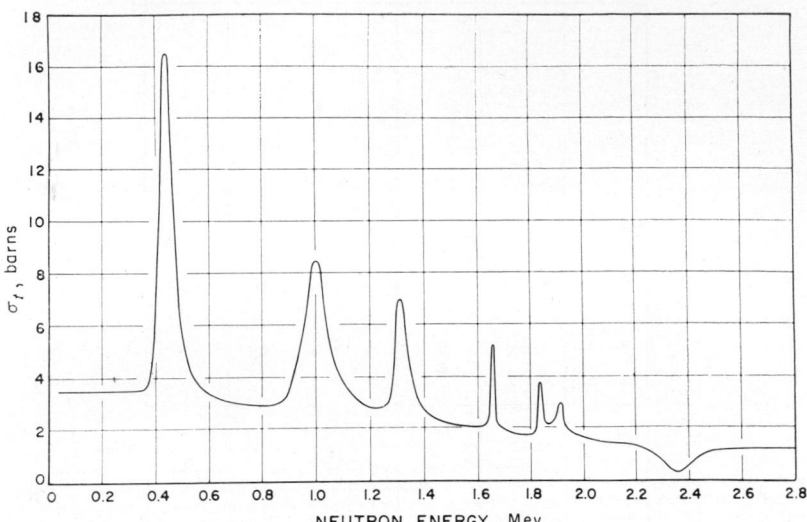

Figure 4. The total cross section of O^{16} (St58). (See also earlier data by Bo51.) At 2.37 Mev an inverted resonance is observed indicating the s-wave nonresonant phase shift is $\sim -\pi/2$. The nonzero cross section at resonance is a measure of the contribution of higher partial waves and exit channels other than elastic scattering (capture).

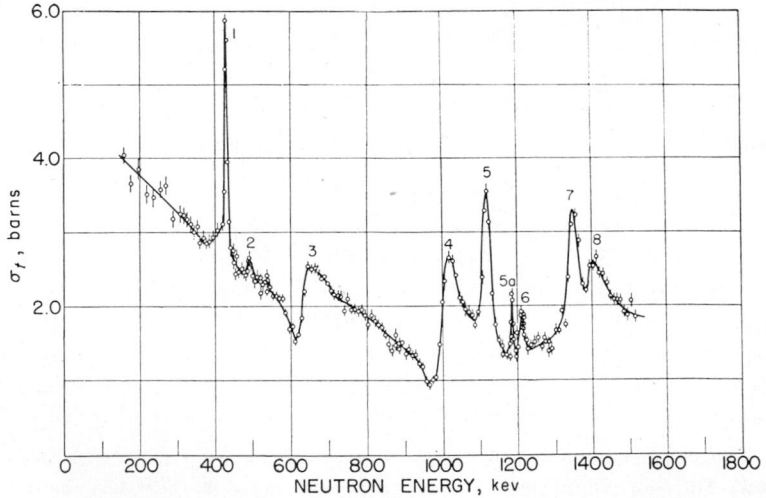

Figure 5. The total cross section of nitrogen as a function of neutron energy (Hi52).

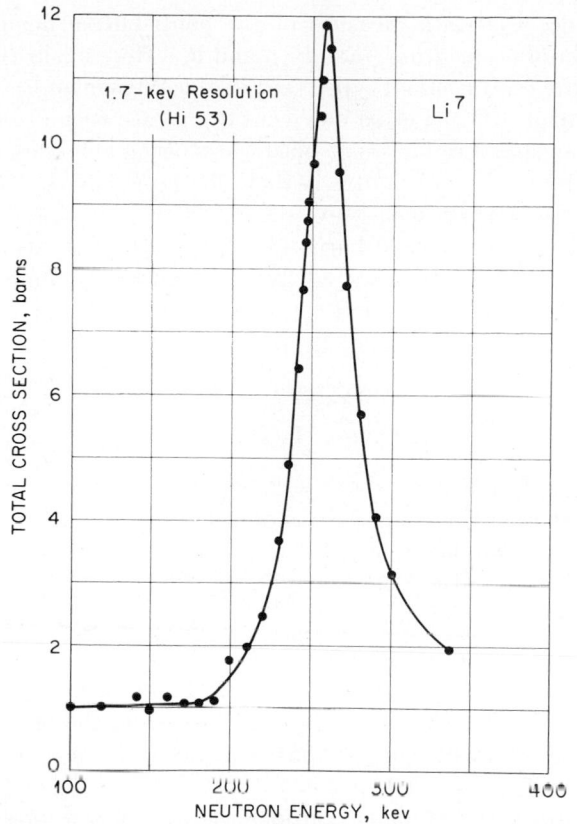

Figure 6. The total cross section of lithium as a function of neutron energy (Hi53); 256-kev resonance.

The reduced width γ_c^2 is 9 kev, or about 1 per cent of the Wigner single particle limit [Eq. (142b), with b_c set equal to 0].

Example II. Bockelman's data on O^{16} (Bo51, Ad49) indicate an *inverted resonance* at 2.37 Mcv incident neutron energy. (More recent data by Streibel, Darden, and Haeberli (St58) are shown in Fig. 4.) This dip indicates the potential phase shift is equal in magnitude and opposite in sign to the resonant phase shift (at E_0), viz., $-\pi/2$, hence the value of $J_0 = 1/2^+$ is assigned to this level (only the s-wave potential scattering would be sufficiently large at this energy to effect the cancellation). The residual cross section at resonance is thus a measure of the contribution from waves of higher orbital momentum, mainly p and d. Here again the reduced width of the level is about 1 per cent of the Wigner limit.

Example III. Let us now consider a case with *two open channels* in a nonspin zero nucleus; elastic scattering and proton emission from the interaction of neutrons with N^{14} (Jo50, Jo51, Hi52). The observed resonance at 0.64 Mev [see Fig. 5 (Hi52)], has a maximum (n, p) cross section of 0.20 barns (Jo50), a total cross section at the maximum of 2.6 barns preceded by an interference minimum of 1.5 barns (Hi52), and a measured total width of 43 kev (Hi52). Equation (152) gives for the peak (n, p) cross section

$$\sigma_p(\text{max}) = \frac{4\pi\lambda_n^2(2J_0 + 1)}{(2a + 1)(2b + 1)} \frac{\Gamma_n\Gamma_p}{(\Gamma_n + \Gamma_p)^2} \tag{154}$$

where $a = 1/2$, $b = 1$, and $4\pi\lambda_n^2 = 2.70$ barns at the resonance energy. Similarly the difference in cross section between the elastic scattering maximum and minimum will be

$$\sigma_n(\text{max}) - \sigma_n(\text{min}) = \frac{4\pi\lambda_n^2(2J_0 + 1)}{(2a + 1)(2b + 1)} \frac{\Gamma_n^2}{(\Gamma_n + \Gamma_p)^2} \tag{155}$$

From these data we find that $J_0 = 1/2$, $\Gamma_n = 36$ kev, $\Gamma_p = 7$ kev, and $l = 0$, the last conclusion being drawn from the observed interference dip [p-wave nonresonant scattering is negligible at this energy (Fo55)].

Example IV. Finally consider the case of a *p-wave resonance*, viz., the neutron interaction with Li^7 which has a strong resonance at 256 kev (Ad50, St51, Hi53). [Fig. 6 is the data of Hibdon (Hi53).] The nonresonant background total cross section is about one barn, the maximum value at resonance is 12 barns, and the width is 32 kev (Hi53). These facts are in agreement with the theoretical prediction for a $J_0 = 3$ resonance. Since the two possible channel spins are 1 or 2, s-wave formation is ruled out. This is confirmed by the absence of an interference minimum. Arguments based on the shape and width of the resonance indicate that it is most probably formed by p-waves (Ad50, St51). This has been verified from angular distribution measurements (Th56a, Wi55a).

Turner and Hibdon (Hi57) have developed a method of analyzing total cross sections of s-wave scattering resonances which makes use of a large fraction of the observed points, rather than just the maximum and minimum cross sections. This technique is quite useful when the levels are not completely resolved.

Interference between levels is sufficiently complex that differential cross sections are usually necessary for their interpretation in the fast neutron energy region. An example is given in Section 4-C.

4. Elastic Scattering Differential Cross-Section Measurements

A. Gas Recoil Techniques

(1) **Energy Distribution of the Recoils from Scattering of Monochromatic Neutrons.** A simple method exists for determining the differential cross sections of elastically and inelastically scattered neutrons. Baldinger, Huber, and Staub (Ba38) showed how the energy spectrum of the incident neutrons can be computed from the measured energy distribution of recoil particles in an ionization chamber on the assumption of isotropic scattering in the center-of-mass system. Barschall and Kanner (Ba40) further pointed out the important fact that the angular distribution of the scattered neutrons can be determined from the measurement of the energy distribution of the recoil particles. For monoenergetic neutrons the determination of the energy distribution of recoil nuclei becomes a method of measuring differential cross sections.

We limit ourselves, in the following, to elastic and inelastic scattering processes of neutrons. The relationships given can be extended to arbitrary reactions and also to relativistic energies (Ba54). It should be pointed out that when the end products are *both* charged particles, the total energy of the two (or more) particles is measured, unless the detector can differentiate between the pulses. Each neutron of mass m and energy E' scattered by a nucleus of mass M is evidently correlated with a recoil nucleus of definite energy. In contrast to the neutrons, these ionized recoils can be detected with ionization chambers, proportional counters, or scintillators. Let $f(E_2')$ be the measured energy distributions of recoils in the laboratory system. Consequently $f(E_2')dE_2'$ becomes the number of recoil nuclei of energy E_2' in the energy element dE_2' produced in the effective counting volume of a detector containing n nuclei by a bombardment of N neutrons. This number of recoil nuclei is the same as those neutrons scattered in the center-of-mass

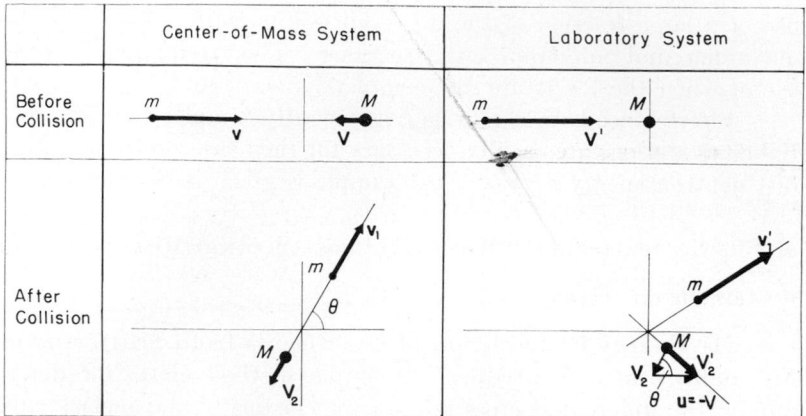

Figure 7. Representation of the scattering of neutrons.

system through angle θ into the element of solid angle $d\Omega = 2\pi \sin \theta d\theta = -2\pi d(\cos \theta)$. Accordingly

$$f(E_2')dE_2' = -nN\sigma(\theta)2\pi d(\cos \theta) \qquad (156)$$

where $\sigma(\theta)$ denotes the differential scattering cross section in the center-of-mass system. (The quantities in the laboratory system are distinguished by a prime from the corresponding quantity in the center-of-mass system.) The derivation of the relationship between E_2' and $\cos \theta$ becomes especially simple, Fig. 7, if the scattering is first considered in the center-of-mass system and then transformed to the laboratory system with the aid of the center-of-mass velocity $\mathbf{u}$. From the figure it follows that

$$V_2'^2 = V_2^2 + u^2 - 2V_2u \cos \theta$$

and therefore

$$E_2' = E_2 + (M/2)u^2 - MV_2u \cos \theta \qquad (157)$$

In the case of inelastic scattering, the customary case assumes implicitly that the neutron is emitted before the γ ray. From Eq. (157) the desired relationship between dE_2' and $d(\cos \theta)$ follows at once

$$dE_2' = -MV_2ud(\cos \theta) \qquad (158)$$

From this and Eq. (156) one obtains

$$\sigma(\theta) = f(E_2') \frac{MV_2 u}{2\pi nN} \tag{159}$$

The differential scattering cross section can thus be determined from a measurement of the energy distribution $f(E_2')$ of the recoil nuclei. According to Eq. (157), the energy E_2' of the recoil nucleus in the laboratory system for a given reaction is a linear function of $\cos \theta$. This fact in combination with Eq. (159) shows that the curves of $f(E_2')$ as a function of E_2' on the one hand, and of $\sigma(\theta)$ as a function

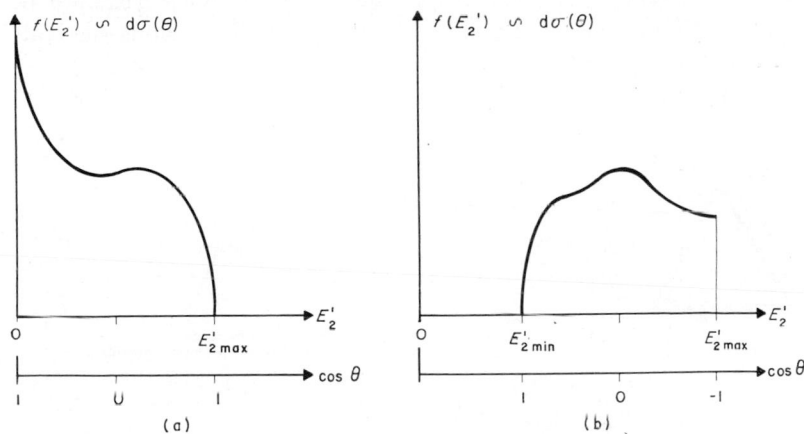

Figure 8. Connection between the scattering cross section in the center-of-mass system and the energy distribution of the recoil energy in the laboratory system. (a) Elastic scattering. (b) Inelastic scattering.

of $\cos \theta$ on the other hand, are identical to within a proportionality factor (compare Fig. 8). As mentioned at the outset, this simple relationship holds true quite generally (Ba54) (with appropriate changes in the proportionality factor). The recoil energy extends over an interval $2 MV_2 u$ (Eq. 157) from a minimum energy $E_{2\min}'$ up to a maximum energy $E_{2\max}'$. A simple qualitative explanation for this relationship can best be seen from a graphical construction (Fig. 9). [Graphical constructions have previously been given, see Chapter I.B and Ha49.] From momentum and energy conservation

$$m\mathbf{v}_1 + M\mathbf{V}_2 = 0$$

$$\tfrac{1}{2}mv_1^2 + \tfrac{1}{2}MV_2^2 = E + Q$$

where E is the total energy in the center-of-mass system before the collision and Q is the reaction energy, it follows, that the magnitude of the velocity V_2 of the recoil nucleus in the center-of-mass system is

$$V_2 = [2m(E + Q)/M(m + M)]^{1/2}$$

Therefore V_2 is independent of θ and the endpoint of V_2 lies on a circle. By vector addition of $\mathbf{V}_2$ and center-of-mass velocity $\mathbf{u}$, we obtain the corresponding laboratory velocity $\mathbf{V}_2'$. Thus the end-point of $\mathbf{V}_2'$ lies on a circle of radius V_2 the center of which is displaced by $\mathbf{u}$. In the case of elastic scattering (compare Fig. 9a)

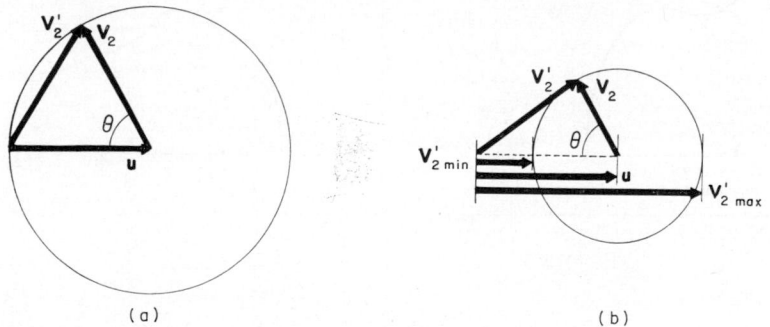

(a)   (b)

Figure 9. Graphical construction of the velocity of the recoil nuclei: (a) Elastic scattering; (b) Inelastic scattering.

$|\mathbf{u}|$ is just the same as V_2, so that the minimum energy becomes zero, occurring at $\theta = 0°$. In the case of inelastic scattering $|\mathbf{u}|$ has the same value as in the corresponding elastic scattering, but V_2 is now smaller $(Q < 0)$. Therefore recoil nuclei occur only at laboratory angles smaller than $90°$, and the velocities lie between V_{2min}' and V_{2max}' (compare Figs. 8b and 9b).

In order to use formulas (157) and (159) it is practical to express the quantities in terms of the reaction energy Q and the incident neutron energy E' in the laboratory system; that is

$$MV_2u = 2E' \frac{m}{m+M} \left[\frac{M}{m+M} \left(\frac{M}{m+M} + \frac{Q}{E'} \right) \right]^{1/2} \quad (160)$$

and

$$\frac{E_2'}{E'} = \frac{m}{m+M} \left(\frac{M}{m+M} + \frac{Q}{E'} \right) + \frac{mM}{(m+M)^2}$$

$$- \cos \theta \, \frac{2m}{m+M} \left[\frac{M}{m+M} \left(\frac{M}{m+M} + \frac{Q}{E'} \right) \right]^{1/2} \quad (161)$$

From these and Eq. (159) it follows for elastic scattering ($Q = 0$):

$$\sigma(\theta) = f(E_2')(E_{2max}'/4\pi nN) \quad (162)$$

where $\qquad\qquad E_{2max}' = E_2'(\cos \theta = -1)$

(2) **Gas Recoil Methods.** According to Eq. (159) the energy distribution of the recoil nuclei must be known for the calculation of the differential effective cross section. The existing measurements of such recoil energy spectra are based without exception on the ionization produced through the recoiling nuclei. This is the reason that only gaseous scattering bodies can be used for this method. Experimentally ion chambers (Ro49) and proportional counters are used for the measurement of recoil spectra. Gas recoil counters are considered in Chapter II A.

Through the ionization of the recoil nuclei in the gas, primary electric charges are produced. Both in the ion chamber and in the proportional counter charge must therefore be measured. The energy of the recoil nuclei can be calculated from the experimentally determined charge under the following conditions:

(a) knowledge of the energy per ion pair (w) of the scattering gas,

(b) no error of the quantity of charge through recombination and ballistic defects (Ba53a) of the measuring amplifier, and

(c) range of the recoil nuclei passing entirely within the counting volume of the chamber.

The energy per ion pair depends on the nature of the gas, the velocity of the ionizing particle, and the type of particle. Table II gives a collection of values for the energy per ion pair for different particles and gases. The values given denote an average energy

Table II. Energy per Ion Pair for Different Particles of Variable Energy

Ionized particle	Energy interval, Mev	Velocity interval, 10^8 cm/sec	A	95% A +5% CO_2	97% A +3% CO_2	95% A +5% Air	Energy per Ion Pair, ev						Ref.
							Air	N_2	O_2	H_2	He	Ne	
Heavy recoil atom:													
Po^{210}	0–0.10	0–0.21				115							(Ma45)
Po^{210}	0–0.10	0–0.21	118								123		(Je56)
ThC	0–0.12	0–0.225				100							(Ma45)
ThC	0–0.12	0–0.225								81			(St57a)
Po	0.10–0.17	0.21–0.27				66					60		(Ma45)
ThC′	0–0.17	0–0.27				89							(Ma45)
ThC′	0–0.17	0–0.27								68	55		(St57a)
Fission fragment:													
U^{233} heavy	0–56.6	0–8.7			28.2								(Le52)
U^{235} heavy	0–60.2	0–9.1			27.8								(Le52)
Pu^{239} heavy	0–65.2	0–9.6			27.5								(Le52)
Pu^{239} light	0–94.6	0–13.7			26.2								(Le52)
U^{235} light	0–94.5	0–14.0			26.5								(Le52)
U^{233} light	0–93.0	0–14.1			26.5								(Le52)
U^{235} heavy	0–17.5 / 0–66.9	0–49 / 0–9.6	28.8		27.5			39.9				39.8	(Sc56)
U^{235} light	0–22.4 / 0–98.9	0–6.75 / 0–14.2	27.7		26.7			39.2				38.6	(Sc56)

Light recoil atom:									
Li7	0–0.84	0–4.8	27.6						(Rh52)
Li7	0–0.84	0–4.81		25.4					(Je50)
Li7	0–1.015	0–5.3	27.4						(Rh52)
Li7	0.84–1.015	4.8–5.3	27.2						(Rh52)
α particle	0–0.33	0–4.0		25.5	38.4	39.6	35.2	36.5	(Gr44)
	0–0.9	0–6.6		25.5	37.8	39.0	34.6	36.5	(Gr44)
	0–1.4	0–8.2		25.5	37.2	38.4	34.1	36.8	(Gr44)
	0–1.47	0–8.4		25.5	38.6				(Je50)
	0–1.47	0–8.4		25.6					(Rh52)
	0–1.78	0–9.3		25.8					(Rh52)
	1.47–1.78	8.4–9.3		25.9					(Rh52)
	0–1.9	0–9.6		26.3	36.6	37.7	33.5	36.6	(Gr44)
	0–2.06	0–10.0		26.6	37.6				(Je50)
	1.47–2.06	8.4–10.0		26.6	35.5				(Je50)
	0–2.7	0–11.4		26.2	35.7	36.8	32.7	36.6	(Gr44)
	0–3.4	0–12.8		26.4	35.5	36.6	32.5	36.8	(Gr44)
	0–5.30	0–16.0		26.4	34.7	36.3			(Al47)
	0–5.30	0–16.0		26.25	35.5				(Je50)
	0–5.30	0–16.0		26.4		36.3	32.2		(Ha53)
	0–6.05	0–17.1		26.4	35.3				(Je50)
	0–6.77	0–18.1		26.4	35.1				(Je50)
	0–7.68	0–19.2		26.5	34.8				(Je50)

per ion pair in the case of total stopping of the ionizing particles. The energy interval, or respectively, the velocity interval, is listed.

An important question is the one concerning the dependence of the energy per ion pair on the velocity of the particle. The measurements under consideration here are rather sparse and partially in disagreement. In the region of natural α particles the measurements of Jesse and Sadauskis (Je50) show a variation of the energy per ion pair in argon of at most 1 per cent. Measurements of Gray (Gr44) exist for α-particle energies between 0.33 and 3.4 Mev and/or different gases relative to hydrogen. The rare gases He, Ne, and A show in this energy region the same energy per ion pair as hydrogen. For air, O_2, and N_2 on the other hand, the energy per ion pair relative to hydrogen is increased by about 10 per cent if the energy of the α particle decreases from 3.4 Mev to 0.33 Mev. Jesse and Sadauskis (Je50) determined, utilizing natural α particle, an increase in the energy per ion pair for air of around 2 per cent, if the α-particle energy is lowered from 7.680 Mev (RaC') to 5.298 Mev (Po).

For α particles from the $Li^6(n, \alpha)$ and $B^{10}(n, \alpha)$ reactions and Li^7 nuclei from the reaction $B^{10}(n, \alpha)Li^7$, different measurements exist for argon and (A + CO_2) mixtures. Jesse and Sadauskis (Je50) obtained in argon the same energy per ion pair as for Po-α-particles. Rhodes, Franzen, and Stephens (Rh52) and Hanna (Ha50) on the other hand obtained in a mixture (argon + few per cent CO_2) a distinct variation of the energy per ion pair. According to (Rh52) w is increased for α particles ($E_\alpha = 1.473$ and 1.778 Mev) about 2 per cent, for Li recoils ($E_{Li} = 0.841$ and 1.015 Mev) about 9 per cent relative to Po-α-particles.

For fission fragments, measurements by Leachman (Le52) and Schmitt and Leachman (Sc56) exist. The most probable fragments resulted in the following w values for argon relative to Po-α-particles given in Table III.

Table III

	U^{233}	U^{235}	Pu^{239}
$w_L/w_{P_0-\alpha}$	1.06	1.06	1.05
$w_H/w_{P_0-\alpha}$	1.13	1.11	1.10

Note: L, most probable light fragment; H, most probable heavy fragment.

Measurements of the energy per ion pair also exist for heavy recoil nuclei in different gases (Ma45, Je56, and St57a). They give values for w which are 2 to 4 times larger than the corresponding values for Po-α-particles.

In order to apply the gas recoil method to the measurement of angular distributions, it is necessary to know whether an important velocity dependence of the energy per ion pair exists for the recoil nuclei concerned. In the literature there are available measurements of Adair (Ad53), Fowler and Johnson (Fo55), and Sikkema, Pasma, and Barnveld (Si58). Adair observed that for oxygen recoils in CO_2 the total ionization and the recoil energy are proportional to one another in the region of 100 to 300 kev. These data show that in this energy region the energy per ion pair is independent of the recoil energy. In the work of Fowler and Johnson corresponding measurements of N recoils in nitrogen for recoil energies of 100 to 600 kev exist. The energy per ion pair is about 15 per cent greater for 100 kev recoils than for 600 kev. Sikkema finds for 300-kev Ne recoils a 10 per cent greater energy per ion pair than for 600-kev recoils. *This effect necessitates small corrections to the measured angular distributions.* Corrections for recoil energies smaller than about 300 kev are problematical.

The conditions mentioned under (b) and (c) are frequently not fulfilled simultaneously. Long ranges of the recoil nuclei often necessitate the use of a high chamber pressure and accordingly considerable recombination is present. For a parallel plate ionization chamber it is true that: so far as the mobility of charge remains constant when the region of decreasing F/p is considered (F = field strength, p = chamber pressure), then the reciprocal value of the measured charge is a linear function of the reciprocal field strength in accord with Jaffe's theory of column ionization (Wi58a). The saturation of charge can then be determined through the extrapolation $1/F \rightarrow 0$.

The wall effect of gas recoil counters has been tabulated by Rossi and Staub (Ro49) for the cases of parallel plate chambers with guard rings and cylindrical chambers with guard electrodes. The possibility of experimentally minimizing the wall effect by means of anticoincidence chambers exists. However, it should be noted that the counting volume of the chamber then becomes dependent upon the energy of the recoil nuclei.

(3) **Absolute Determination of the Differential Cross Section.** According to Eq. (159) the differential cross section is given by

$$\sigma(\theta) = f(E'_2)(MV_2u/2\pi nN)$$

The absolute determination of $\sigma(\theta)$ therefore requires the measurement of the energy distribution of $f(E'_2)$ of the recoil nuclei, the knowledge of the total number N of neutrons, and the number n of scattering nuclei in the counter volume. MV_2u can be calculated [Eq. (160)] from the incident neutron energy E', the reaction energy Q, and the scattering gas. The number of scattering nuclei n is given, in the case of a known counter volume (guard ring arrangement), by the gas pressure. The most difficult part of the absolute determination of $\sigma(\theta)$ is the measurement of the total number N of neutrons. This problem is given special consideration by J. E. Perry in Chapter IV.B.

A determination of the number of neutrons for the case of elastic scattering only can be circumvented, as long as the total cross section σ_T of the scattering process is known. It is true that

$$\sigma_T = \int \sigma(\theta)d\Omega = \frac{1}{nN} \int_0^{E_2'\text{max}} f(E'_2)dE'_2$$

From this N can be determined, i.e.,

$$N = \frac{1}{n\sigma_T} \int_0^{E_2'\text{max}} f(E)dE \tag{163}$$

In order to make use of this expression it is necessary, however, that the energy distribution of the recoils be known in the entire energy region from zero to $E'_{2\ \text{max}}$. The integral denotes the *total* number of measured recoils for a given measuring time. However, it is not essential that the neutron flux remain constant during this time, since variations occur at the same time for all angles. This property is one advantage of the gas recoil method. With Eq. (163) the differential cross section [Eq. (162)] now becomes

$$\sigma(\theta) = f(E'_2)E'_{2\ \text{max}} \ \sigma_T [4\pi \int_0^{E_2'\text{max}} f(E)dE]^{-1} \tag{164}$$

As a consequence of the background, e.g., noise in the measuring equipment, the energy distribution of the recoil nuclei can only be measured for energies greater than $E_2'^*$. For this reason the experimental information needed to determine N from Eq. (163) is missing. If a phase-shift analysis is made on the basis of the experimental recoil spectrum from $E_2'^*$ to $E_2'_{\text{max}}$ and of the total cross section σ_T, then the integral Eq. (163) is known. This furnishes by Eq. (164) the necessary transformation from the measured recoil spectrum $f(E_2')$ to the differential scattering cross section.

If, on the contrary, the total number of neutrons N of the scattering measurement is experimentally determined, then Eq. (163) furnishes a control of the phase-shift analysis; the analysis predicts an extrapolation of the recoil spectrum that in turn must predict N.

B. Solid Sample Techniques

Techniques used in the measurement of differential elastic scattering cross sections with solid samples are described in detail by M. Walt, Chapter V.B. Here the discussion will be limited to the special problems associated with high resolution work.

Fast neutron resonances (above 100 kev in energy) have been observed mainly in light nuclei ($A \gtrsim 40$) and at moderate energies (up to the order of 5 or 6 Mev). Thus it is apparent that the transformation of energies, plane angles, and solid angles from the laboratory to the center of mass system will be quite significant in this region. In the case of the neutron interaction with Li^6, for example, the laboratory energy of the elastically scattered neutrons will decrease by nearly a factor of 2 from $0°$ to $180°$. The laboratory angle of $90°$ will be displaced to $100°$ in the center-of-mass system, and the solid angle (or cross section) ratio will vary by a factor of 2 from $0°$ to $180°$. Chapter I.B lists general formulas for calculating these transformations. A useful tabulation of the plane and solid angle transforms has been carried out in the general nonrelativistic case by Marion (Ma57, Ma59).

The dependence of neutron detecting counters sensitivity with energy thus becomes a dependence with angle; the greater the variation, the greater the correction necessary to the data. An ideal detector would have a constant efficiency from $E_n(0°)$ down to $E_n(180°)$, below which it should drop rapidly to zero. Recoil proportional counters filled with hydrogen, methane, or propane approximate this characteristic and hence have proved useful in this field, despite their relatively low efficiencies (Wi55a, Fo55, Wi56, Th56a).

This neutron energy variation with angle also complicates the already difficult multiple scattering corrections. For example, when the angular distribution at an energy above the resonance value is desired, the multiple scattered neutrons will be reduced in energy, some to the resonance energy where the cross section is high. Furthermore, the angular distribution often changes rapidly as a resonance is traversed, reversing from strong forward peaking to large back scattering. Accordingly, the best corrections can only be made by machine calculations. [An approximate analytical solution has been employed by Fowler and Cohn (Fo58).] It is therefore desirable to keep these corrections small.

Effects of finite energy resolutions are discussed in the section on total cross sections [Section 2.A.(3)].

The correction for finite angular resolution has been discussed in detail by Rose (Ro53) and by Feingold and Frankel (Fe55).

C. Interpretation of Data

As indicated in Section 2.D.(5) there are two alternative methods of analyzing experimental data, (a) in terms of nuclear dispersion parameters, or (b) in terms of eigen phase shifts [see also Christy (Ch56)]. In cases of narrow resonances where Γ is small compared to the level spacing and the resonance energy, it is usually more convenient to use dispersion parameters. Here the most easily interpreted data consist of differential cross sections measured at a number of closely spaced neutron bombarding energies in the vicinity of the resonance and at several angles. Where the levels are broad, or overlapping, a general phase-shift analysis is usually simpler to interpret. Here the energy steps can be quite large, and the differential cross sections (at one energy) are measured at many angles. The problem in analyzing a narrow resonance is to determine which phase shift is undergoing a rapid energy variation. When the resonances are broad, however, the object is to fit the scattering at each energy by a set of phase shifts which are then slowly varying with energy. Both types of analysis are, of course, based on the same theory, but the techniques used to extract information from the experimental data are somewhat different.

Application of dispersion theory to narrow resonances can be considered a *cut and try* method. First of all, the J value can often be obtained from either total cross section data or the absolute magnitude of the anomaly observed in the differential measurements. At least it is usually possible to narrow the choice to two or at most three J values. Next the partial wave(s) contributing to the resonance can be inferred by the interference with nonresonant scattering. That is, for energies below 2 or 3 Mev the background scattering is predominantly s-wave (Wi55a, Fo55). If the angular distribution is isotropic, the resonance may involve s-waves, or $J = 0, 1/2$ levels. If there is a strong forward or backward scattering (which reverses as one traverses the resonance), the resonance is most probably p-wave. If the distribution is symmetric (or nearly symmetric) about $90°$, the resonance is most probably d-wave. Of course, there may be exceptions to these qualitative conclusions (see example II where the s-wave nonresonant scattering of Be^9 is channel-spin dependent).

Having selected tentative assignments of J_0 and l, the energy varying term given by $\beta_0 = \tan^{-1} [\frac{1}{2}\Gamma_{lJ_0}/(E_0 + \Delta - E)]$, and the associated parameters are inserted into the general expression for the angular distribution [Eq. (114)]. The calculated differential cross sections which result are then compared to the experimental data, the best fit giving the proper assignment.

Graphical and mechanical methods for the phase-shift analysis of angular distributions have been described by different authors, e.g., Laubenstein and Laubenstein (La51), Seagrave (Se53), Ashkin and Vasko (As53), and Clementel and Villi (Cl55). A very simple electrical analogue computer for construction of a phase-shift analysis has been reported by Baldinger (Ba52a).

All these methods are relatively simple as long as the channel spin is $\leq 1/2$ and only orbital angular momentum $l \leq 2$ contribute. For higher channel spins and orbital angular momenta a phase-shift analysis becomes greatly facilitated by use of electronic computers. In order to make full use of the method of Blatt and Biedenharn (Bl52a) (see Section 2.C.), the numerical tables of Price (Pr54), and Snowdon, Eisenbud, and Marshall (Sn58) for the expansion of angular distributions in terms of Legendre polynomials can be of great utility.

In this connection the method of Lustig and Blatt (Lu55) for charged particles is also of value. These authors determine first n proper moments through numerical integration of the angular distribution, and from these n simultaneous equations solve for the n desired phases. This method is advisable for data requiring a relatively large number of possible phases, particularly when electronic computers are unavailable.

Several examples illustrative of fitting data to the theory are given below. These include pure elastic scattering by zero spin and nonzero spin nuclei, two-channel reactions with nonzero spin nuclei, and interference between two overlapping levels.

Finally, a brief review is given of the phase-shift analyses of elastic scattering of neutrons by light nuclei. In this connection only the newest evaluations from the individual laboratories are given; the older phase determinations are considered with less emphasis. It should be noted that an appraisal of the accuracy of a phase-shift analysis is rather difficult. If all phases except one are held constant, then in some cases a change of this phase by a tenth of a degree, in other cases by ten degrees, can alter the agreement with the experimental data. For this reason an estimate of errors is not considered in general.

Example I. Pure Elastic Scattering by a Zero Spin Nucleus. The simplest possible (nontrivial) case arises when the only open channel for neutrons interacting with zero spin nucleus is elastic scattering. Actually this assumption is quite valid for fast neutrons and light nuclei. Capture is usually negligible at these energies (above 100 kev), inelastic scattering is limited by the high excitation energies of the first excited states, and charged particle emission frequently has a high threshold energy. If it is further assumed that only partial waves of $l = 0$ contribute to the nonresonant scattering [experimentally demonstrated to be approximately true up to 1.5 to 2.0 Mev for light nuclei (Wi55a, Fo55)], then the differential cross section [Eq. (114)] reduces to

$$\sigma_n(\theta) = \lambda_n^2 \sin^2 \xi_0' P_0(\cos \theta)$$

$$+ \lambda_n^2 (2J_0 + 1) \sum_{L=0} (0l00|L0)^2 \sin \xi_0' \sin \beta_0 \cos (\beta_0 + 2\xi_l' - \xi_0') P_1(\cos \theta)$$

$$+ (\lambda_n^2/2) \sin^2 \beta_0 \sum_{L=0}^{L_{\max}} \overline{Z}^2(lJ_0lJ_0; {}^1\!/_2 L) P_L(\cos \theta) \quad (165)$$

The well-known resonance in O^{17} at 442-kev neutron bombarding energy belongs in this category. High resolution total cross section measurements (Bo50, Ok55) show a peak height of 16.5 barns, a potential scattering contribution at resonance of 3.2 barns, and an observed width of 48 kev (Fig. 10). A spin assignment of $J_0 = 3/2$ gives a resonant contribution of 13.3 barns to σ_T, in excellent agreement with the experimental value for $\sigma_{\max} - \sigma_{\min}$. Since an interference dip does not appear, it can be concluded that the resonance is formed by p-waves, i.e., the level is $3/2^-$ (alternatively designated

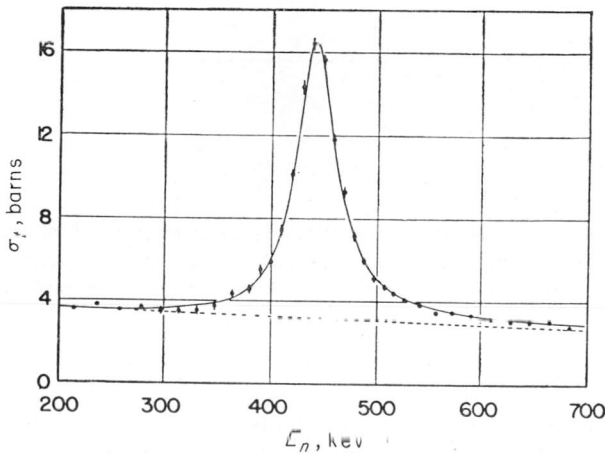

Figure 10. The total cross section of oxygen as a function of neutron energy (Ok55); 442 kev resonance.

$P_{3/2}$). The nonresonant phase shift ξ_0' can be determined from σ_H the background scattering (potential) shown as a dotted curve in Fig. 10. ξ_0' varies from $-36°$ at 300 kev to $-51°$ at 600 kev.[20] Since all the parameters of Eq. (165) are determined, the differential cross section can be calculated at any desired energy in the vicinity of the resonance

$$\sigma_n(\theta) = \lambda_n^2\{(\sin^2 \xi_0' + 2 \sin^2 \beta_0)P_0 + [4 \sin \xi_0' \sin \beta_0 \cos (\beta_0 - \xi_0')]P_1$$
$$+ (2 \sin^2 \beta_0)P_2\} \quad (166)$$

The potential and resonant contributions are symmetric with respect to E_0 (over the resonance region) and $90°$ (C.M.), but the inter-

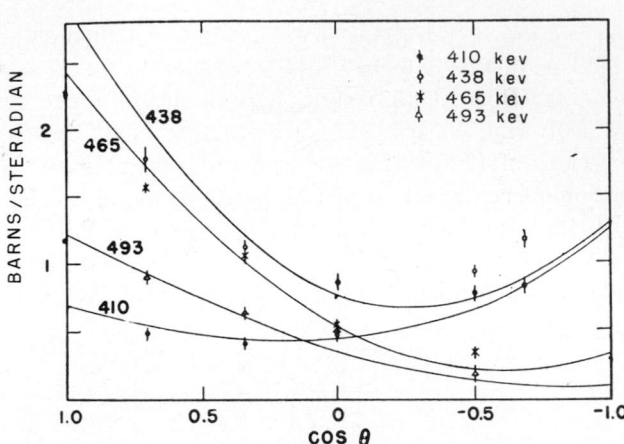

Figure 11. Differential elastic scattering cross sections for oxygen (Ok55), center-of-mass system.

ference (term P_1) between them is asymmetric with respect to both. This interference becomes zero at $\beta_0 - \xi_0' = \pi/2$, i.e., below resonance (420 kev). For lower energies, this term is negative and the scattering will be peaked in the backward direction. Above 420 kev it becomes positive, indicating more forward scattering. Including the effects of barrier penetration and level shift ($\gamma_n^2 = 113$ kev), the theoretical distributions calculated at 410, 438, 465, and 493 kev, when averaged over the experimental neutron energy spread, are seen to be in good agreement with the observed data [Fig. 11, (Ok55)]. The observed asymmetry gives a negative assignment to ξ_0', as selected above.

A second interesting example in this category is the 585-kev resonance in S^{32}. Early data on the total cross section (Pe50) indicated the resonance was probably $J = 3/2$ formed by either p- or d-wave neutrons. However, recent data (La59, private communication) on the angular distributions of neutrons scattered elastically in the vicinity of this resonance, show the presence of P_4 resonance terms, Fig. 12, indicating definite d-wave (or higher) formation. Analysis of the energy dependence of the Legendre coefficients gives a $J_0 = 5/2$, $l = 2$ assignment.

Example II. Pure Elastic Scattering by a Nonzero Spin Nucleus. The case of pure elastic scattering by a nonzero spin

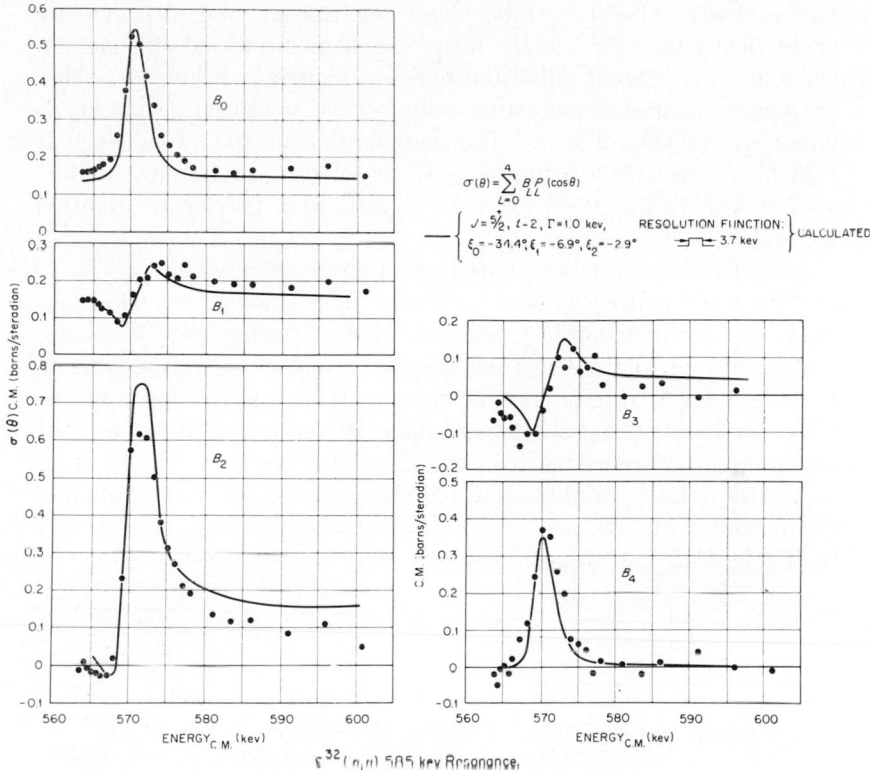

$$\sigma(\theta) = \sum_{L=0}^{4} B_L P_L (\cos\theta)$$

$$-\begin{cases} J = \frac{5}{2}, \ l-2, \ \Gamma = 1.0 \text{ kev}, \\ \xi_0 = -34.4°, \ \xi_1 = -6.9°, \ \xi_2 = -2.9° \end{cases}$$ RESOLUTION FUNCTION: $\qquad$ 3.7 kev $\Big\}$ CALCULATED

S^{32} (n,n) 585 kev Resonance.

Figure 12. Coefficients of a Legendre polynomial expansion for angular distributions of neutrons scattered elastically in the vicinity of the 585 kev S^{32} resonance (La59). Circles are experimental points, while the solid curves are theoretical for the parameters shown. (The coefficient B_L here is not that given in the text, but contains the factor $\lambda^2/(2a + 1)(2b + 1)$.)

nucleus introduces the complication of channel-spin mixing. Actually we have already discussed an even more general problem in Section 1.D.4, that of two levels, two channel spins, and two potential phase shifts. Let us now apply the results obtained there to the strong resonance in the neutron interaction with B^{11} at 430 kev (Bo50, Bo51).

The total cross-section data indicate that the resonance is $J_0 = 2$, probably formed by p-wave neutrons, although $J_0 = 3$ is not excluded (Bo50). Only elastic scattering and capture are energetically possible and the latter can be neglected at this energy. Off-resonance angular distributions for neutrons below ~ 1 Mev are nearly isotropic, indicating only s-wave potential scattering is important (Wi55a, Fo55). The contribution of the $(3-)$ level at 1.28 Mev varies from a phase shift β_{3-} of $0.1°$ at 200 kev to $3.5°$ at 700 kev (using the proper level shift and barrier penetration factors).

With these further simplifications, the expressions given in Section 1.D.4 can easily be evaluated. There are six contributions to the angular distribution: pure potential scattering, pure resonance scattering due to the $(2+)$ level, pure resonance scattering due to the $(3-)$ level, interference between potential scattering and the $(2+)$ level, interference between potential scattering and the $(3-)$ level, and interference between the $(2+)$ and $(3-)$ levels. In order to see the relative contributions of these terms, we have evaluated the formulas at 200, 430, and 700 kev, and tabulated the results in Table IV.

Table IV

	200 kev	430 kev	700 kev
Potential	$0.291\,P_0$	$0.228\,P_0$	$0.174\,P_0$
$(2+)$ resonance	$0.001\,P_0$	$0.360\,P_0$	$0.004\,P_0$
	$+0.001\,P_2$	$+0.252\,P_2$	$+0.003\,P_2$
$(3-)$ resonance	—	—	$0.001\,(P_0$
			$+P_2+P_4)$
Potential $-(2+)$ interference	$-0.016\,P_1$	$0.284\,P_1$	$0.031\,P_1$
Potential $-(3-)$ interference	$-0.001\,P_2$	$-0.004\,P_2$	$-0.019\,P_2$
$(2+)$ $-(3-)$ interference	—	—	$+(0.002\,P_1)$
			$\pm(0.001\,P_2)$

The resonances have arbitrary mixtures of channel spins, but for this table we have assumed the values which give the maximum contribution. It can be seen from this example that with experimental data no better than 5 per cent or so, the effect of the tail from the $(3-)$ level at 1280 kev is not observable.

At the two angles $\theta = \cos^{-1}(\pm 0.577)$ the Legendre polynomial $P_2(\cos\theta)$ is equal to zero, hence interference between s- and d-waves will have no effect at these angles. However, the interference between s- and p-waves will show up as a marked asymmetry if the ratio of the cross sections at these two angles is plotted as a function of neutron energy. Figure 13 shows that the experimental data (Wi55a) can be fitted by assuming a statistical mixture for the s-wave channel ($\xi'_{10} = \xi'_{20}$), and the resonance channel either all $s = 1$ or all $s = 2$ (experimentally indistinguishable).

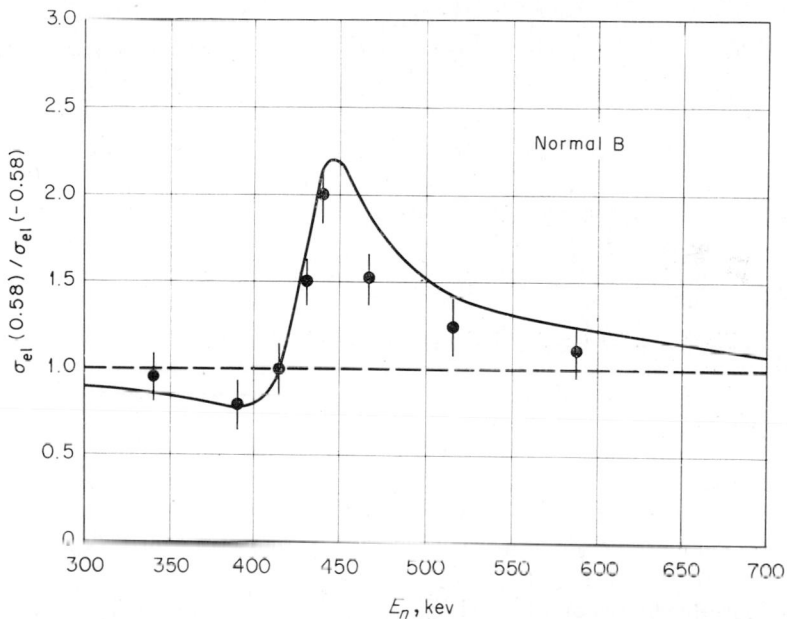

Figure 13. The measured center-of-mass differential cross section ratio for $cos\ \theta\ =\ 0.58$ to $cos\ \theta\ =\ -0.58$ for normal boron as a function of the incident neutron energy in the region of the 0.43-Mev resonance in B^{11}. The asymmetry calculated by assuming $J_0\ =\ 2,\ l\ =\ 1,\ \xi_{01}\ -\ \xi_{02}$, is shown as a solid curve, corrections being made for resolution and isotopic abundance (Wi55a).

A curious example in this category is the case of the 620-kev resonance for neutrons interacting with Be^9. Here the total cross-section assignment gives $J_0\ =\ 3$, probably formed by p-waves (Ad49, Bo50, Bo51, Wi55a); however, the angular distribution data show no asymmetry about 90° (C.M.). In fact, the data seem best fitted by assuming the s-wave potential scattering is all channel spin 1 (Wi55a).

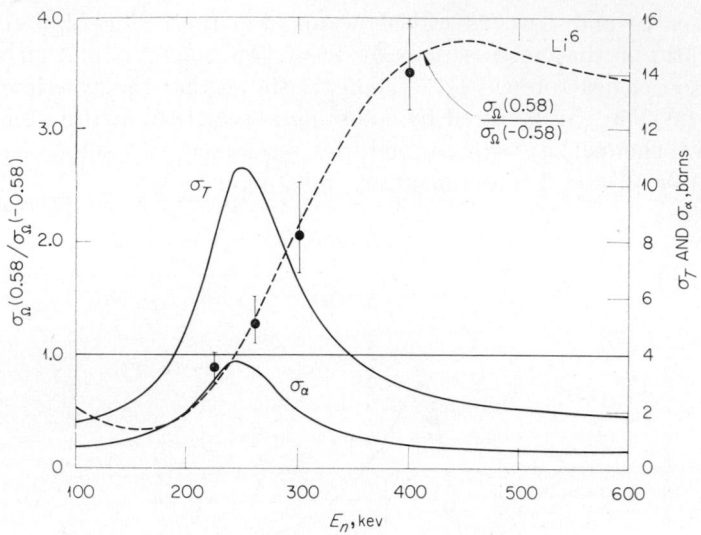

Figure 14. The ratio of the measured Li⁶ differential cross section for
$cos\ \theta = \pm\ 0.58$ as a function of the incident neutron energy.   The dotted curve is
theoretical (see text).   Solid curves are shown for calculated values of σ_T and
σ_α (Wi56).

**Example III.   Two Channel Reactions with Nonzero Spin
Nuclei.**   When the compound nucleus can decay by more than one
exit channel, the analysis is complicated only by the additional
unknown parameters introduced as partial widths.   This, of course,
necessitates more complete data, such as measurements of the various
partial cross sections.

A resonance at 255 kev for the interaction of neutrons with
Li⁶ was first observed in the $(n,\ \alpha)$ cross section (Bl55).   Total
cross-section measurements (Jo54) later gave the assignment of
$J_0 = 5/2,\ l = 1$ for this level.   The total width (C.M.) was found
to be 146 kev, with partial widths at E_0, $\Gamma_\alpha = 50$ kev, $\Gamma_n = 96$ kev.
Neutron barrier penetration and level shift effects are very appre-
ciable for this resonance and cannot be neglected.   The reduced
widths used for angular distribution calculations (Wi56) were $\gamma_n^2 =
1100$ kev, $\gamma_\alpha^2 = 50$ kev (Γ_α was assumed to be constant).   Thus the
angular distribution for elastically scattered neutrons becomes

$$H = (2 \sin^2 \xi'_{\frac{1}{2}0} + 4 \sin^2 \xi'_{\frac{3}{2}0})P_0 (\cos \theta) \qquad (167a)$$

$$N = \{1/4[(E_0 + \Delta - E)^2 + (\Gamma/2)^2]\}$$

$$\cdot \left[6\Gamma^2_{n\frac{3}{2}1} P_0(\cos \theta) + 6 \times \frac{84}{50} \Gamma^2_{n\frac{3}{2}1} P_2(\cos \theta) \right] \quad (167b)$$

$$I = \{1/[(E_0 + \Delta - E)^2 + (\Gamma/2)^2]^{1/2}\}$$

$$\cdot \left[6\Gamma_{n\frac{3}{2}1} \sin \xi'_{n\frac{3}{2}0} \cos \left(\xi'_{n\frac{3}{2}1} - \xi'_{n\frac{3}{2}1} \right) \right] P_1(\cos \theta) \quad (167c)$$

Figure 14 shows the ratio of the cross sections at $\theta = \cos^{-1}(\pm 0.58)$ as a function of neutron energy. The dotted curve, in agreement with the data, was calculated for a statistical mixture of s-wave potential scattering channel spins ($\xi'_{1/20} = \xi'_{3/20}$). Curves shown as solid lines were calculated from the same constants for σ_T and σ_α; they are in good agreement with the experimental data, when a constant nonresonant background contribution is added to σ_α (see Jo54).

Example IV.   Interference between Overlapping Levels. The total cross section of C^{12}, Fig. 15, shows the effect of interference between resonances at 2.95 and 3.6 Mev, both shown to be

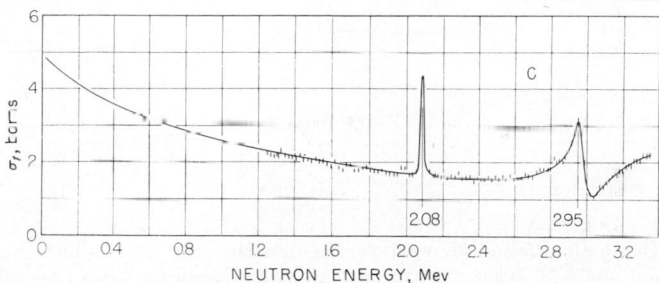

Figure 15. The total cross section of C^{12} as a function of neutron energy (Bo51).

$D_{3/2}$ levels (Bu55, Me54, Wi58). In order to fit the angular distribution data, using a general phase-shift expansion for spin zero nuclei (Me54), it is only necessary to express the total $D_{3/2}$ phase shift as

$$\tan \beta_{D_{3/2}} = \tan \beta_{2.95} + \tan \beta_{3.6}$$

where each β_R has the appropriate resonant energy, level width, and level shift.

This example shows the general superiority of a phase-shift expansion for analyzing complicated distributions. It is only necessary to lump all the contributions, resonant and nonresonant, of each partial wave to form a resultant phase shift to describe the interaction. The interference terms between partial waves then follow in a natural manner from the general expansion, Eq. (79).

(1) Summary Review of Phase-Shift Analyses for Light Nuclei

He$^4(n,n)$He^4: Corresponding to their great theoretical significance, the elastic scattering of neutrons and protons by helium has been investigated experimentally and theoretically by numerous laboratories (Ho58). The phase shifts of the proton-helium scattering with the application of Wigner and Eisenbud (Wi47) reaction theory and under certain other additional assumptions give a prediction of the phases for the neutron-helium scattering. In Fig. 16 these

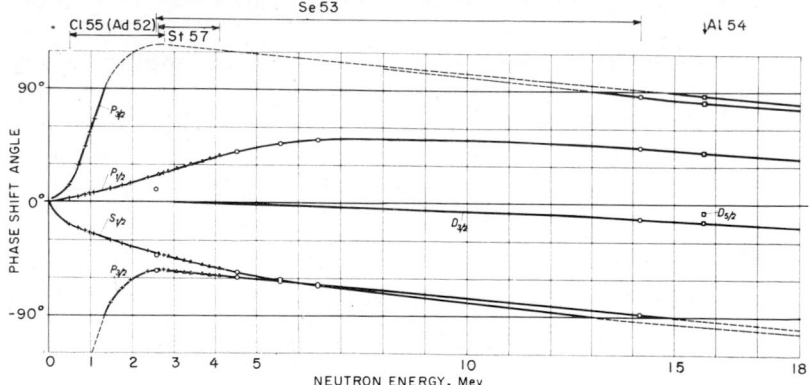

Figure 16. Phase-shift analysis He$^4(n,n)$He^4: + Phase-shift analysis of Clementel and Villi (Cl55) of the measurements made by Adair (Ad 52) with a proportional counter. △ Measurements by Striebel and Huber (St 57) with an ionization chamber. ○ Measurements by Seagrave (Se 53) with a proportional counter. □ Measurements by Alston *et al.* (A 154) made with a diffusion cloud chamber.

phases are indicated as solid curves, corresponding to the results of Seagrave (Se53). The conversion is based on the consideration of the level shift (about 1 Mev) in the mirror nuclei He^5 and Li^5 and the assumption that the logarithmic derivative of the wave function at the nuclear surface has the same value in both cases (Ad52). In this case the phase-shift analysis of Critchfield, Dodder, and Gammel (Do52, Cr49) was taken as a basis. The measurements of Seagrave

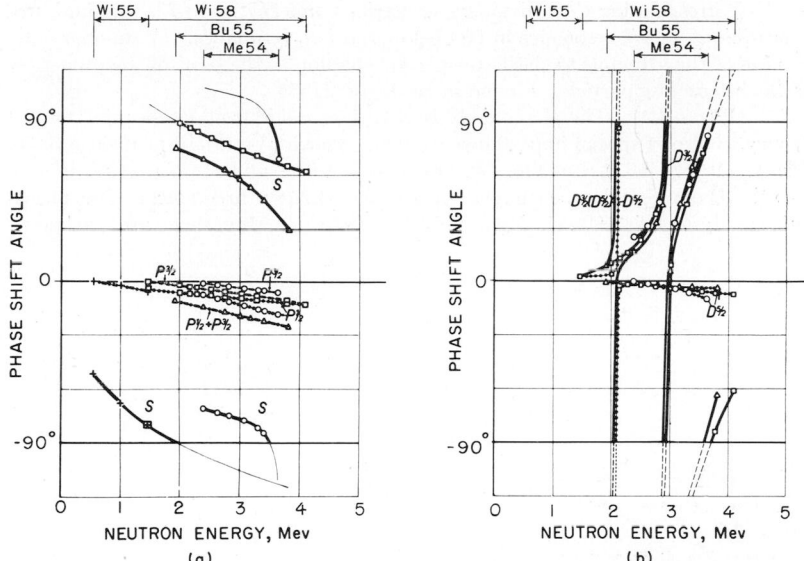

Figure 17.   Phase-shift analysis of $C^{12}(n,n)C^{12}$.   (a) S and P phase shifts.   (b) D phase shifts.   Willard, Bair, and Kington (Wi55a)—Solid sample technique.   Wills, Bair, Cohn, and Willard (Wi58)—solid sample technique. Budde and Huber (Bu55)—ion chamber.   Meier, Scherrer, and Trumpy (Me54) —solid sample technique.

(Se53), with 5 angular distributions between 2.6 and 14.3 Mev, agree exceptionally well with the phase behavior thus obtained, with the exception that the $P_{1/2}$ phase at 2.61 Mev is about 10° lower.   The new interpretation of Adair's (Ad52) measurements by Clementel and Villi (Cl55) result equally in very good agreement from 0.4 to 2.73 Mev *including* the $P_{1/2}$ phase.   The intermediate energy measurements of Striebel and Huber (St57) with 9 angular distributions between 2.61 and 4.09 Mev have all phase shifts in very good agreement with the p-He scattering.   Levintov (Le57u) also observed in polarization measurements of helium with D-D neutrons the $P_{1/2}$ phase at $E_n = 3.4$ Mev to be 30° and at $E_n = 2.75$ Mev to be $12° \pm 1°$; this latter measurement is in good agreement with the previously mentioned low value ($11 \pm 6°$) of Seagrave.   The polarization measurements at $E_n = 3$ Mev by White and Farley (Wh57) determine the polarization magnitude $P = 0.46 \pm 0.18$ of the neutrons scattered by helium through 90°. The phase value of the solid curve predicts $P = 0.2$ (Se53) (see however Pa58a). The two D-phases, $D_{3/2}$ and $D_{5/2}$, can be chosen equal in the case of the angular distribution of Seagrave (Se53) at $E_n = 14.3$ Mev, and correspond to the value for hard-sphere scattering with a radius of 2.9×10^{-13} cm.   At $E_n = 15.7$ Mev, however, Alston *et al.* (Al54) find best agreement with experiment for $D_{3/2} =$

$-14°$ (corresponding to hard-sphere scattering) and $D_{5/2} = -7°$, this indicates a possible $J = 5/2$ resonance in He^5 below the $D_{3/2}$ resonance. A summary discussion of the attempts to clarify the phase behavior on the basis of the properties of the interacting particles is found in Hodgson (Ho58).

C$^{12}(n,n)$C^{12}: The phase analysis of carbon, aside from its meaning for the theory, is also of special importance as an analyzer for polarized neutrons (Ba53, Me54, Mc56, Ha57). In Fig. 17a are plotted the S and P phases and in Fig. 17b the D phases. In the energy region of 2 to 4 Mev three independent phase-shift analyses exist (Bu55, Me54, Wi58). Below 2 Mev there are no known

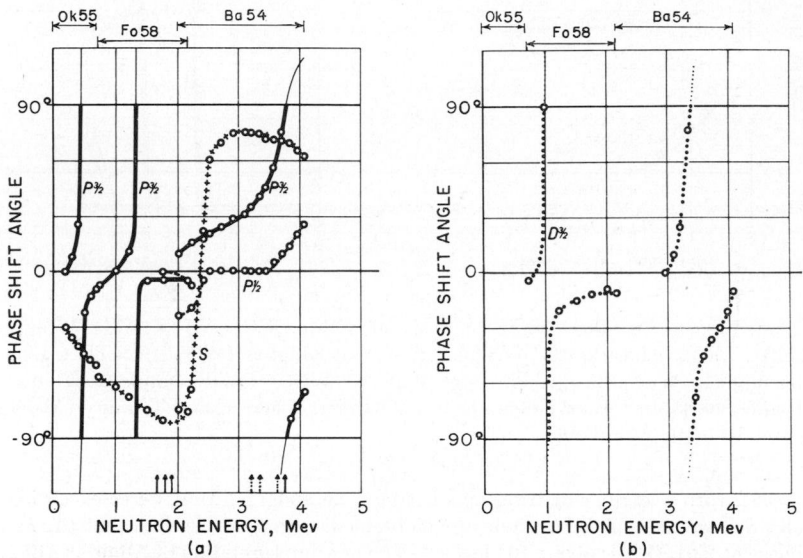

Figure 18. Phase-shift analysis of O$^{16}(n,n)$O^{16}. The measurements of Okazaki (Ok55), Fowler and Cohn (Fo58) are made by the solid sample technique. Those of Baldinger, Huber, and Proctor (Ba52b) with the gas recoil method. For discussion of arrows see text.

resonances in the total cross section (compare however Wi58). Willard *et al.* (Wi55a) find the S-phase sufficient for the three measured angular distributions and first use an additional P-phase of $5.7°$ at 1.5 Mev. The resonance at 2.08 Mev is interpretable in the measurements of Budde and Huber (Bu55) by either a $D_{3/2}$ or $D_{5/2}$ resonance. This resonance was shown with reasonable certainty to be a $D_{5/2}$ resonance in the measurements of Wills (Wi58). The agreement of the phase analyses from 2 to 4 Mev is generally quite good, yet the differences are quite large when one considers the use of carbon as an analyzer for polarized neutrons. The polarization results are extraordinarily sensitive to small phase

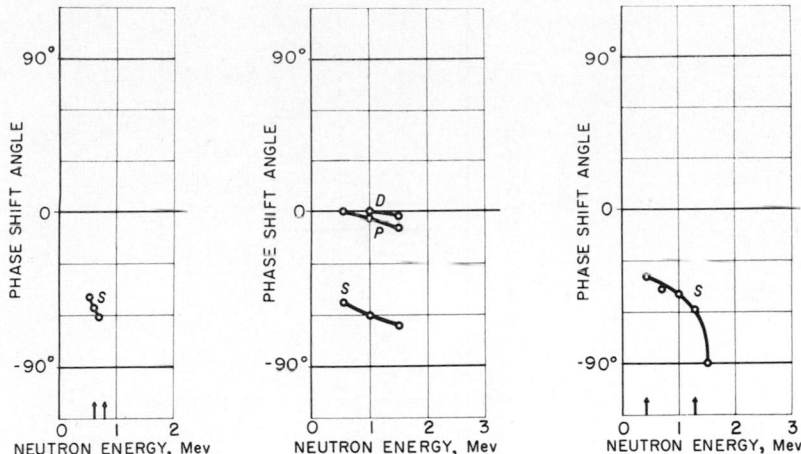

Figure 19. Potential scattering phase shifts of $Be^9(n,n)Be^9$.   Measurements by
Willard, Bair, and Kington (Wi55a) with the solid sample method.

Figure 20. Phase shift analysis of $B^{10}(n,n)B^{10}$ from measurements of Willard *et
al.* by the solid sample method (Wi55a).

Figure 21. Potential scattering phase shifts of $B^{11}(n,n)B^{11}$ from measurements of
Willard *et al.* (Wi55a) with the solid sample method.

changes.   The S-phase shift of Wills is in very good agreement with the theoretical phase behavior from a potential well with diffuse boundary (Fo58).

$O^{16}(n,n)O^{16}$:   (Compare here also the discussion of Example I and Fig. 10.)
Six angular distributions by Okazaki (Ok55) exist in the energy region of 0.2 to
0.7 Mev.   Their phase analysis confirms the assignment of $P_{3/2}$ to the resonance
at $E_n = 0.44$ Mev (Bo51).   The S-phase, as well as its extension by the phase
analysis of Fowler and Cohn (Fo58), is represented very well up to 2 Mev by hard-
sphere scattering with a radius of 5.6×10^{-13} cm (St58).   The P and D hard-
sphere scattering phases must be assumed to be zero.   Polarization experiments at
730 kev energy show that $-5°$ for the $D_{3/2}$ phase is in contradiction with the experiment (St58); there $D_{3/2}$ is equal to $0°$.   The two known narrow resonances
with $\Gamma \leq 7$ kev and $J \geq 3/2$ at 1.66 and 1.8 Mev (Bo51) as well as the broad $P_{1/2}$
resonance with $\Gamma = 30$ kev at 1.91 Mev are not shown in the phase analysis of
Fowler (Fo58).   These are designated in Fig. 18 with arrows.

The phase analysis of Baldinger *et al.* (Ba51) from 2 to 4 Mev are based on
15 angular distributions.   The agreement between his and Fowler's analysis is
satisfactory for the S and $D_{3/2}$ phase in the region of overlap around 2 Mev.   The
$P_{1/2}$ phase is difficult to appraise because of the neglected $P_{1/2}$ resonance at 1.91
Mev; while the $P_{3/2}$ phase agrees poorly at 2 Mev.

In the energy region of 3 to 4 Mev new measurements exist of the total
cross section for a resonance at 3.75 Mev (Wa57).   However, the three new levels

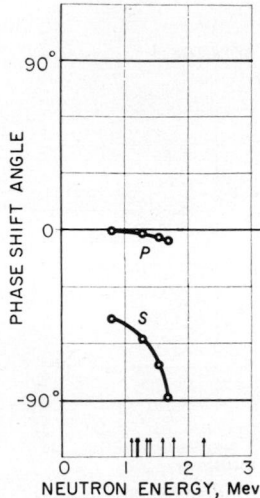

Figure 22. Potential scattering phase shifts of $N^{14}(n,n)N^{14}$ from measurements of Fowler and Johnson (Fo55) with the solid sample method supplemented by the gas recoil method (proportional counter).

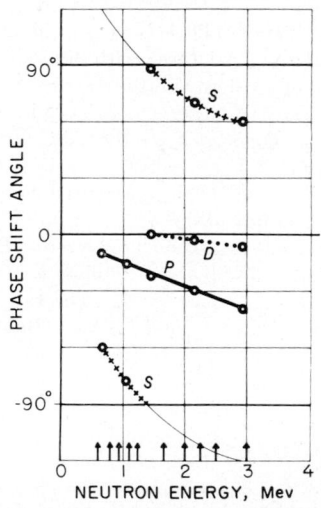

Figure 23. Potential scattering phase shifts of $F^{19}(n,n)F^{19}$ obtained by Wills, Bair, Cohn, and Willard (Wi58) with the solid sample method.

at 3.21, 3.43, and 3.63 neutron energy, which are found in the $C^{13}(\alpha,n)O^{16}$ reaction, are not evident in the total neutron cross section. These are accordingly indicated in Fig. 18 with dotted arrows.

The evaluation of the phases by Fowler and Cohn in the form of a phenomenological well with diffuse boundary and spin-orbit coupling appears quite promising (Fo58).

Be^9, B^{10}, B^{11}, N^{14}, F^{19}: In these nuclei the phase-shift analysis is rendered extraordinarily difficult because the target spin is different from zero. In Figs. 19 to 23 the values for hard-sphere scattering are presented. These phases are necessary in order to reproduce the angular distributions between resonances. For B^{10} however no resonances are known between 0.5 to 1.5 Mev (Bo51). In the other cases known resonances within the energy region considered are marked by arrows. Willard et al. (Wi55a) find for Be^9, B^{10}, and B^{11} that the observed S phases are generally larger than the predicted value of hard-sphere scattering [radius $= 1.40\ (A^{1/3} + 1) \times 10^{-13}$ cm.]. The observed P and D phases are on the other hand smaller than those thus calculated.

In the case of the 0.61 Mev resonance in Be^9, the hard-sphere scattering must be assumed spin dependent (S phase shift only channel spin 1) for best agreement with experiment. The best agreement in B^{11} (compare also in particular example II) at the 0.43 Mev resonance is given by the same authors with $J = 2, l = 1$, and either only channel spin 1 or only channel spin 2. The resonance at 1.28 Mev gives a choice of $J = 3, l = 2$ and a mixture of channel spins 1 and 2.

In F^{19} (Wi58) considerable interference probably occurs between the very close spaced resonances. This can change the given values of the hard-sphere scattering considerably.

In addition to the analysis of N^{14} by Fowler and Johnson (Fo55), Speiser (Sp54) has carried out an analysis of the scattering measurements of Huber and Streibel (Hu54a) made in the adjoining higher energy region.

References

(Ab52)   M. Abramowitz, Tables of Coulomb Functions, *A. M. S. No. 17, National Bureau of Standards Report* (1952).

(Ab54)   M. Abramowitz and P. Rabinowitz, *Phys. Rev.* **96,** 77 (1954).

(Ad49)   Adair, Barschall, Bockelman, and Sala, *Phys. Rev.* **75,** 1124 (1949).

(Ad49a)   Adair, Bockelman, and Peterson, *Phys. Rev.* **76,** 308 (1949).

(Ad50)   R. K. Adair, *Phys. Rev.* **79,** 1018 (1950).

(Ad52)   R. K. Adair, *Phys. Rev.* **86,** 155 (1952).

(Ad53)   R. K. Adair, *Phys. Rev.* **92,** 1491 (1953).

(Aj55)   F. Ajzenberg and T. Lauritsen, *Revs. Modern Phys.,* **27,** 77 (1955).

(Aj59)   F. Ajzenberg-Selove and T. Lauritsen, *Nuclear Phys.* **11,** 1 (1959).

(Aj60)   F. Ajzenberg-Selove, ed., *Nuclear Spectroscopy*, Academic Press, New York, 1960, Parts A and B.

(Al47)   F. Alder, P. Huber, and F. Metzger, *Helv. Phys. Acta* **20,** 234 (1947).

(Al54)   Alston, Crewe, Evans, Green, and Willmott, *Proc. Phys. Soc. (London)* **67A,** 657 (1954).

(As53)   J. Ashkin and S. H. Vosko, *Phys. Rev.* **91,** 1248 (1953).

(Ba38)   Baldinger, Huber, and Staub, *Helv. Phys. Acta* **11**, 245 (1938).

(Ba40)   H. H. Barschall and M. H. Kanner, *Phys. Rev.* **58**, 590 (1940).

(Ba52)   H. H. Barschall, *Revs. Modern Phys.* **24**, 120 (1952).

(Ba52a) E. Baldinger, *Helv. Phys. Acta* **25**, 446 (1952).

(Ba52b) Baldinger, Huber, and Proctor, *Helv. Phys. Acta* **25**, 142 (1952).

(Ba53)   E. Baumgartner and P. Huber, *Helv. Phys. Acta* **26**, 545 (1953).

(Ba53a) E. Baldinger and W. Haeberli, *Ergeb. exakt. Naturw.* **27**, 248 (1953).

(Ba54)   H. H. Barschall and J. L. Powell, *Phys. Rev.* **96**, 713 (1954).

(Ba58)   A. I. Baz', *Soviet Phys. JETP* **6**, 709 (1958).

(Bi51)   L. C. Biedenharn, "Tables of the Racah Coefficients," *Oak Ridge National Lab. Report* ORNL-1098, unpublished (1951).

(Bi52)   Biedenharn, Blatt, and Rose, *Revs. Modern Phys.* **24**, 248 (1952).

(Bi53)   L. C. Biedenharn, "Revised Z Tables of the Racah Coefficients," *Oak Ridge National Lab. Report* ORNL-1501, unpublished (1953). (Available from U. S. Department of Commerce Office of Technical Services, Washington 6, D. C., 1953; $1.00.)

(Bi53a) L. C. Biedenharn and M. E. Rose, *Revs. Modern Phys.* **25**, 729 (1953).

(Bi55)   Biedenharn, Gluckstern, Hull, and Breit, *Phys. Rev.* **97**, 542 (1955).

(Bi58)   L. C. Biedenharn and H. B. Willard, *Proc. Phys. Soc. (London)* **72**, 874 (1958).

(Bj35)   T. Bjerge and C. H. Westcott, *Proc. Roy. Soc. (London)* **150A**, 709 (1935).

(Bl51)   Bloch, Hull, Broyles, Bouricius, Freeman, and Breit, *Revs. Modern Phys.* **23**, 147 (1951).

(Bl51a) J. M. Blatt and L. C. Biedenharn, *Phys. Rev.* **82**, 123 (1951).

(Bl52)   J. M. Blatt and V. F. Weisskopf, *Theoretical Nuclear Physics*, Wiley, New York, 1952, Appendix B.

(Bl52a) J. M. Blatt and L. C. Biedenharn, *Revs. Modern Phys.* **24**, 258 (1952).

(Bl52b) J. M. Blatt and L. C. Biedenharn, *Phys. Rev.* **86**, 399 (1952).

(Bl54)   J. M. Blatt and L. C. Biedenharn, *Phys. Rev.* **93**, 1387 (1954).

(Bl55)   J. M. Blair and R. E. Holland, data reproduced in Hu55.

(Bl56)   C. Bloch, "Cours sur la Théorie des Réactions Nucléaires," Tomes I and II, *Centre d'Etudes Nucléaires de Saclay*, unpublished (1956).

(Bl57)   C. Bloch, *Nuclear Phys.* **4**, 503 (1957).

(Bo50)   C. K. Bockelman, *Phys. Rev.* **80**, 1011 (1950).

(Bo51)   Bockelman, Miller, Adair, and Barschall, *Phys. Rev.* **84**, 69 (1951).

(Br40)   G. Breit, *Phys. Rev.* **58**, 1068 (1940).

(Br57)   G. Breit, *Phys. Rev.* **107**, 1612 (1957).

(Br57a) G. E. Brown and C. T. DeDominicis, *Proc. Phys. Soc. (London)* **70A**, 668–681 (1957).

(Br59)   G. Breit, in *Handbuch der Physik*, S. Flügge, ed., Springer, Berlin, (1959) Vol. 41/1, p. 1.

(Br59a) G. E. Brown, *Revs. Modern Phys.* **31**, 893 (1959).

(Bu55)   R. Budde and P. Huber, *Helv. Phys. Acta* **28**, 49 (1955).

(Ch48)   R. F. Christy and R. Latter, *Revs. Modern Phys.* **20**, 185 (1948).

(Ch56)   R. F. Christy, *Physica* **22**, 1009 (1956).

(Ch58)   Chase, Klahr, and Temkin, "A Review of Phenomenological Descriptions for Neutron Induced Reactions," *Wright Air Development Center Report* WADC 58-79, unpublished (1958).

(Cl55) E. Clementel and C. Villi, *Nuovo cimento* **2**, 1121 (1955).

(Co35) E. U. Condon and G. H. Shortley, *Theory of Atomic Spectra*, Cambridge University Press, Cambridge, 1935.

(Cr49) C. L. Critchfield and D. C. Dodder, *Phys. Rev.* **76**, 602 (1949).

(Cr57) Cranberg, Beauchamp, and Levin, *Rev. Sci. Instr.* **28**, 89 (1957).

(DeW55) B. S. DeWitt, "The Operator Formalism in Quantum Perturbation Theory," *Univ. Calif. Radiation Lab. Report* UCRL-2884, unpublished (1955).

(Do52) D. C. Dodder and J. L. Gammel, *Phys. Rev.* **88**, 520 (1952).

(Ei48) L. Eisenbud, *Thesis*, Princeton University, unpublished (1948).

(Ei51) L. Eisenbud, *J. Franklin Inst.* **251**, 231 (1951).

(En57) P. M. Endt and C. M. Braams, *Revs. Modern Phys.* **29**, 683 (1957).

(En59) P. M. Endt and M. Demeur, Eds., *Nuclear Reactions*, North-Holland Publishing Co., Amsterdam, 1959.

(Fe47) Feshbach, Peaslee, and Weisskopf, *Phys. Rev.* **71**, 145 (1947).

(Fe51) Feld, Feshbach, Goldberger, Goldstein, and Weisskopf, Final Report of the Fast Neutron Data Project, *U. S. Atomic Energy Comm. Report* NYO-636, unpublished (1951).

(Fe53) B. T. Feld, "The Neutron," *Experimental Nuclear Physics*, Vol. II, Wiley, New York, 1953.

(Fe53a) Feshbach, Shapiro, and Weisskopf, "Tables of Penetrabilities for Charged Particle Reactions," *U. S. Atomic Energy Comm. Report* NYO-3077, NDA-15, B-5, unpublished (1953).

(Fe53b) M. Ferentz and N. Rosenzweig, "Table of F Coefficients," *Argonne National Lab. Report* ANL-5234, unpublished (1953).

(Fe55) A. M. Feingold and S. Frankel, *Phys. Rev.* **97**, 1025 (1955).

(Fe58) H. Feshbach, *Ann. Physics* **5**, 357 (1958).

(Fl48) S. Flügge, *Z. Naturforsch.* **9a**, 97 (1948).

(Fl51) S. Flügge, *Ergeb. exakt. Naturw.* **25**, 476 (1951).

(Fo55) J. L. Fowler and C. H. Johnson, *Phys. Rev.* **98**, 728 (1955).

(Fo58) J. L. Fowler and H. O. Cohn, *Phys. Rev.* **109**, 89 (1958).

(Fr53) B. E. Freeman and J. L. McHale, *Phys. Rev.* **89**, 223 (1953).

(Fr55) C. E. Froberg, *Revs. Modern Phys.* **27**, 399 (1955).

(Gi44) Gibert, Roggen, and Rossel, *Helv. Phys. Acta* **17**, 97 (1944).

(Gr44) L. H. Gray, *Proc. Cambridge Phil. Soc.* **40**, 72 (1944).

(Ha49) Hanson, Taschek, and Williams, *Revs. Modern Phys.* **21**, 635 (1949).

(Ha50) G. C. Hanna, *Phys. Rev.* **80**, 530 (1950).

(Ha53) W. Haeberli, P. Huber and E. Baldinger, *Helv. Phys. Acta* **26**, 145 (1953).

(Ha57) W. Haeberli and W. W. Rolland, *Bull. Am. Phys. Soc.* **2**, 234 (1957).

(He49) Herb, Snowdon, and Sala, *Phys. Rev.* **75**, 246 (1949).

(Hi52) Hinchey, Stelson, and Preston, *Phys. Rev.* **86**, 483 (1952).

(Hi53) C. T. Hibdon, private communication (1953) (see data in Hu55).

(Hi57) C. T. Hibdon, *Phys. Rev.* **108**, 414 (1957).

(Ho52) W. F. Hornyak, *Rev. Sci. Instr.* **23**, 264 (1952).

(Ho58)   P. E. Hodgson, *Adv. in Phys.* **7**, 1 (1958).

(Hu54)   R. Huby, *Proc. Phys. Soc.* (*London*) **67A**, 1103 (1954).

(Hu54a)   P. Huber and H. R. Streibel, *Helv. Phys. Acta* **27**, 157 (1954).

(Hu55)   D. J. Hughes and J. A. Harvey, "Neutron Cross Sections," *Brookhaven National Lab. Report* BNL-325, unpublished (Supt. Documents, U. S. Govt. Printing Office, Washington, D. C., 1955).

(Hu56)   D. J. Hughes and R. S. Carter, "Neutron Cross Sections, Angular Distributions," *Brookhaven National Lab. Report* BNL-400 (Supt. Documents, U. S. Govt. Printing Office, Washington, D. C., 1956).

(Hu58)   D. J. Hughes and R. B. Schwartz, *Revised Neutron Cross Sections*, BNL-325 (Hu55) (1958).

(Hu59)   M. H. Hull and G. Breit, in *Handbuch Physik*, S. Flügge, ed., Springer, Berlin, 1959, Vol. 41/1 p. 408.

(Ja51)   J. L. Jackson, *Phys. Rev.* **83**, 301 (1951).

(Je50)   W. P. Jesse and J. Sadauskis, *Phys. Rev.* **77**, 782 (1950).

(Je56)   W. P. Jesse and J. Sadauskis, *Phys. Rev.* **102**, 389 (1956).

(Jo50)   C. H. Johnson and H. H. Barschall, *Phys. Rev.* **80**, 818 (1950).

(Jo51)   Johnson, Petree, and Adair, *Phys. Rev.* **84**, 775 (1951).

(Jo54)   Johnson, Willard, and Bair, *Phys. Rev.* **96**, 985 (1954).

(Jo57)   Johnson, Judish, and Snyder, *Rev. Sci. Instr.* **28**, 942 (1957).

(Ka38)   P. L. Kapur and R. E. Peierls, *Proc. Roy. Soc.* (*London*) **166A**, 277 (1938).

(Kr55)   R. Krotkov, *Can. J. Phys.* **33**, 622 (1955).

(La51)   R. A. Laubenstein and M. J. W. Laubenstein, *Phys. Rev.* **84**, 18 (1951).

(La55)   Lane, Thomas, and Wigner, *Phys. Rev.* **98**, 693 (1955).

(La58)   A. M. Lane and R. G. Thomas, *Revs. Modern Phys.* **30**, 257ff (1958).

(La59)   R. O. Lane, private communication (1959).

(Le52)   R. B. Leachman, *Phys. Rev.* **87**, 444 (1952).

(Le57)   C. A. Levinson and M. K. Banerjee, *Ann. Physics* **2**, 471, 499 (1957).

(Le57a)   Levintov, Miller, and Shamshev, *Nuclear Phys.* **3**, 221 (1957).

(Lu55)   H. Lustig and J. M. Blatt, *Phys. Rev.* **100**, 777 (1955).

(Lu60)   H. Lustig, *Phys. Rev.* **117**, 1317 (1960).

(Lu60a)   H. Lustig, *Nuclear Phys.* to be published (1960).

(Ma40)   M. R. MacPhail, *Phys. Rev.* **57**, 669 (1940).

(Ma45)   B. S. Madsen, *Kgl. Danske Videnskab. Selskab Mat.-fys. Medd.* **23**, *Nr. 8* (1945).

(Ma57)   J. B. Marion and A. S. Ginzbarg, "Tables for the Transformation of Angular Distribution Data from the Laboratory System to the Center-of-Mass System," *U. S. Atomic Energy Comm. Report* NP-6241, unpublished (1957).

(Ma59)   Marion, Arnette, and Owens, "Tables for the Transformation between the Laboratory and Center-of-Mass Coordinate Systems and for the Calculation of the Energies of Reaction Products," *Oak Ridge National Lab. Report* ORNL-2574, unpublished (1959).

(Mc56)   McCormac, Steuer, Bond, and Hereford, *Phys. Rev.* **104**, 718 (1956).

(Me54)   Meier, Scherrer, and Trumpy, *Helv. Phys. Acta* **27**, 577 (1954).

(Mo33)   N. F. Mott and H. S. W. Massey, *The Theory of Atomic Collisions*, Oxford University Press, *London*, 1933, Chap. 2.

(Mo35)   P. B. Moon and J. R. Tillman, *Nature (London)* **135**, 904 (1935).

(Mo53)   P. M. Morse and H. Feshbach, *Methods of Theoretical Physics*, McGraw-Hill, New York, 1953.

(Mo58)   Monahan, Biedenharn, and Schiffer, "Tables of Neutron Penetrabilities and Shift Functions," *Argonne National Lab. Report* ANL-5846, unpublished (1958).

(Ne52)   T. D. Newton, *Can. J. Phys.* **30**, 53 (1952).

(Ok55)   A. Okazaki, *Phys. Rev.* **99**, 55 (1955).

(Os36)   Ostrofsky, Breit, and Johnson, *Phys. Rev.* **49**, 22 (1936).

(Pa58)   Parks, Newson, and Williamson, *Bull. Am. Phys. Soc.* **3**, 164 (1958).

(Pa58a) P. J. Pasma, *Thesis*, Groningen University, unpublished (1958).

(Pa58b) Parks, Newson, and Williamson, *Rev. Sci. Instr.* **29**, 834 (1958).

(Pc50)   Peterson, Barschall, and Bockelman, *Phys. Rev.* **79**, 593 (1950).

(Pr54)   P. C. Price, *Phil. Mag.* **45**, 237 (1954).

(Pr58)   F. W. Prosser, Jr., and L. C. Biedenharn, *Phys. Rev.* **109**, 413 (1958). Similar results have been obtained by Thomas (unpublished).

(Ra57)   J. Rainwater, in *Handbuch der Physik*, S. Flügge, ed., Springer, Berlin, 1957, Vol. 40.

(Re58)   C. W. Reich and M. S. Moore, *Phys. Rev.* **111**, 929 (1958).

(Rh52)   Rhodes, Franzen, and Stephens, *Phys. Rev.* **87**, 141 (1952).

(Ro49)   B. Rossi and H. Staub, *Ionization Chambers and Counters*, McGraw-Hill, New York, 1949.

(Ro53)   M. E. Rose, *Phys. Rev.* **91**, 610 (1953).

(Ro59)   Rotenberg, Bivins, Metropolis, and Wooten, Jr., *(3-j) and (6-j) Symbols*, The Technology Press, Cambridge, Massachusetts, 1959.

(Sc56)   H. W. Schmitt and R. B. Leachman, *Phys. Rev.* **102**, 183 (1956).

(Sc57)   J. P. Schiffer, "Tables of Charged Particle Penetrabilities," *Argonne National Lab. Report* ANL-5739, unpublished (1957).

(Se53)   J. D. Seagrave, *Phys. Rev.* **92**, 1222 (1953).

(Sh53)   Sharp, Kennedy, Sears, and Hoyle, "Tables of Coefficients for Angular Distribution Analysis, *Chalk River Report* CRT-556 or AECL-97, unpublished (1953) (revised 1954).

(Sh56)   Sharp, Gove, and Paul, "Graphs of Coulomb Functions," *Chalk River Report*, TPI-70 or AECL-268, unpublished (1956).

(Si53)   A. Simon and T. A. Welton, "A Note on the Maximum Total Cross Section for Resonance Reactions," *Oak Ridge National Lab. Report* ORNL-53-10-7, unpublished (1953).

(Si54)   A. Simon, "Numerical Table of the Clebsch-Gordan Coefficients," *Oak Ridge National Lab. Report* ORNL-1718, unpublished (1954).

(Si54a) Simon, Vander Sluis, and Biedenharn, "Tables of the Racah Coefficients," *Oak Ridge National Lab. Report* ORNL-1679, unpublished (1954).

(Si58)   C. P. Sikkema, *Thesis*, University of Groningen (1958).

(Sn58)   Snowdon, Eisenbud, and Marschall, "Analytical Representation of Angular Distribution Data," *J. Applied Phys.* **29**, 950 (1958).

(Sp54)   D. Speiser, *Helv. Phys. Acta* **27**, 427 (1954).

(St51)   P. H. Stelson and W. M. Preston, *Phys. Rev.* **84**, 162 (1951).

(St57)   H. R. Striebel and P. Huber, *Helv. Phys. Acta* **30**, 67 (1957).

(St57a) W. G. Stone and L. W. Cochran, *Phys. Rev.* **107**, 702 (1957).

(St58)   Striebel, Darden, and Haeberli, *Nuclear Phys.* **6**, 188 (1958).

(Te50)   T. Teichmann, *Phys. Rev.* **77**, 506 (1950).

(Te52)   T. Teichmann and E. P. Wigner, *Phys. Rev.* **87**, 123 (1952).

(Th51)   R. G. Thomas, *Phys. Rev.* **81**, 148 (1951).

(Th55)   R. G. Thomas, *Phys. Rev.* **97**, 224 (1955).

(Th56)   R. G. Thomas, "Lectures on Nuclear Reaction Theory," University of
         Mexico, (1956). (Our notation is chosen to agree with this reference
         as far as possible.) The notes on these lectures were written by J. E.
         Monahan; an extended version by Monahan has been circulated by
         the Argonne National Laboratory. See also the review article on
         "Nuclear Reactions," by A. M. Lane and R. G. Thomas, *Revs. Modern
         Phys.* **30**, 257 (1958).

(Th56a) Thomas, Walt, Walton, and Allen, *Phys. Rev.* **101**, 759 (1956).

(Tu58)   A. Tubis, "Tables of the Non-Relativistic Coulomb Wave Functions,"
         Los Alamos Scientific Lab. Report LA-2150, unpublished (1958).

(Vo58)   E. Vogt, *Phys. Rev.* **112**, 203 (1958).

(Wa57)   Walton, Clement, and Boreli, *Phys. Rev.* **107**, 1065 (1957).

(Wh57)   R. E. White and F. J. M. Farley, *Nuclear Phys.* **3**, 476 (1957).

(Wi31)   E. P. Wigner, *Group Theory and Its Application to the Quantum Me-
         chanics of Atomic Spectra*, translated by J. J. Griffen from the 1931
         German edition, with additions by the author, Academic Press, New
         York, 1959.

(Wi32)   E. P. Wigner, *Gott. Nach.* **31**, 546 (1932).

(Wi46)   E. P. Wigner, *Phys. Rev.* **70**, 15 (1946).

(Wi46a) E. P. Wigner, *Phys. Rev.* **70**, 606 (1946).

(Wi46b) E. P. Wigner, *Proc. Natl. Acad. Sci. U. S.* **32**, 302 (1946).

(Wi47)   E. P. Wigner and L. Eisenbud, *Phys. Rev.* **72**, 29 (1947).

(Wi48)   E. P. Wigner, *Phys. Rev.* **73**, 1002 (1948).

(Wi49)   E. P. Wigner, *Am. J. Phys.* **17**, 99 (1949).

(Wi49a) G. C. Wick, *Phys. Rev.* **75**, 1459 (1949).

(Wi51)   E. P. Wigner, *Ann. of Math.* **53**, 36 (1951).

(Wi52)   E. P. Wigner, *Ann. of Math.* **55**, 7 (1952).

(Wi52a) E. P. Wigner, *Am. Math. Monthly* **59**, 669 (1952).

(Wi55)   E. P. Wigner, *Phys. Rev.* **98**, 145 (1955).

(Wi55a) Willard, Bair, and Kington, *Phys. Rev.* **98**, 669 (1955).

(Wi55b) E. P. Wigner, *Am. J. Phys.* **23**, 371 (1955).

(Wi56)   Willard, Bair, Kington, and Cohn, *Phys. Rev.* **101**, 765 (1956).

(Wi58)   Wills, Jr., Bair, Cohn, and Willard, *Phys. Rev.* **109**, 891 (1958).

(Wi58a) F. Widder and P. Huber, *Helv. Phys. Acta* **31**, 601 (1958).

(Ya59)   Y. Yamaguchi, *Progr. Theoret. Phys.* **20**, Supplement 7, 1ff (1959).

(Yo58)   S. Yoshida, *Progr. Theoret. Phys.* **19**, 169 (1958).

The Theory of Polarization in Reactions and Scattering

T. A. WELTON

Oak Ridge National Laboratory, Oak Ridge, Tennessee

1. Introduction

There is, in principle, nothing complicated about the calculation of polarization effects in nuclear processes, but in practice the calculations can become very laborious. Within the past few years, however, it has become possible to systematize these calculations to a remarkable extent by the use of the now-familiar Racah techniques. The correct derivation of the necessary formulae nevertheless remains an annoyingly complex job, and available published material on the subject is beset with errors. It is the essential purpose of this chapter to give a coherent derivation of the pertinent formulae, so that the results can be used with ease and confidence. To this end, it is hoped that all necessary definitions are properly given so that the ambiguities which have plagued the literature will be avoided.

It is first necessary to define the problem more carefully. Given a projectile a' and a target A', which together form the alternative α of the assembled system, we suppose that dissociation occurs into an outgoing particle a and a residual system A, which form alternative α. For definiteness, it is assumed that the lower case letters are the lighter particles in either case. The treatment to be given will be explicitly non-relativistic, although most features can be taken over into a relativistic treatment without change. Parity conservation will be assumed so that weak interaction processes involving even slow electrons are excluded. Although photons are actually relativistic particles, the relevant formulae for the problems of radiative neutron capture and photo-neutron production will be given.

With these restrictions, which simplify the treatment considerably without appearing to seriously impair its utility, we must solve the following problem. Given the state of polarization of a' and A', what will be the polarization state of a and A? This question is, of course, to be answered in terms of the elements of the scattering matrix which describes the reaction.

It seems desirable to sketch the history of the subject at this stage, and give some of the relevant references, so as not to impede the development unduly. Apparently Schwinger (Sc46,Sc48) was the first to point out the possible importance of polarization studies in nuclear research, as well as give definite suggestions for obtaining and detecting polarized beams. Lepore (Le50) made detailed calculations based on the first of Schwinger's suggestions, namely that a neutron beam could be polarized and analyzed by scattering from helium. Wolfenstein (Wo49,Wo54,Wo56) has made extensive studies aimed largely at the special (but very important) problem of nucleon-nucleon scattering, and was the first to elucidate the question of possible complexity of angular distributions in polarization problems. Blin-Stoyle (Bl51) first made the very important observation that polarized neutrons should be a frequent product of nuclear reactions. This meant that by proper choice of the neutron-producing reaction, a strongly polarized beam could be obtained for use in the study of another reaction, a large intensity factor thereby being gained. Blin-Stoyle at the same time made a real beginning on a theory of reactions with arbitrary spins involved.

Blatt and Biedenharn (Bl52a) were first to give a complete account of the angular distribution (summed over spins) resulting from an unpolarized beam incident on an unpolarized target. They made use of the Racah techniques, which were quickly seen to be completely appropriate for the more complex problem involving polarized beams, when augmented by the concept of statistical tensors introduced by Fano (Fa52). This generalization was performed by Simon and Welton (Si53a,Si53b), so that general formulae were then available for calculating the final polarization state in terms of the initial polarization state. Simultaneously and independently, the general theory was given by Coester and Jauch (Co53) and by Satchler (Sa53). Devons and Goldfarb (De57) have recently given a most elegant and complete treatment of the general problem of angular correlations with polarization, which of course includes our problem as a special case. Other recent and very useful collections of results, which largely overlap with the material to follow, have been given by Goldfarb and Rook (Go59a) and by Baldin, Goldanskii, and Rozenthal (Ba61). For this reason, the treatment to follow is primarily aimed at making the complex formulae easily accessible and reliable, and to this end all derivations have been made afresh with extensive checks. The extension to the case of photon reactions was first correctly given by Morita, Sugie, and Yoshida (Mo54), and to Shirokov (Sh57) is due the relativistic generalization.

On the mathematical side, the general formulae only become useful with the availability of convenient tables of the Racah coefficients and the characteristic angular functions of the problem. The Racah coefficients have been tabulated by Biedenharn (Bi52), Simon, Vander Sluis, and Biedenharn (Si54a), and Obi, Ishidzu, Horie, Yanagowa, Tanabe, and Sato (Ob53,Ob54,Ob55). A recent and very useful tabulation is that of Rotenberg, Bivins, Metropolis, and Wooten (Ro59). A convenient modern reference for the general formalism of angular momentum theory is the book of Rose (Ro57), whose conventions will be largely adhered to in the following. All of the modern applications of angular momentum theory stem from the work of Wigner (Wi31) and Racah (Ra42a,Ra42b,Ra43).

2. Sketch of the Method

The method to be followed in the general derivation, although very simple in principle, becomes confusingly complex in detailed execution. It seems advantageous, therefore, to study a simple special case in some detail, in order to illustrate the concepts involved. The general derivation will then consist simply of a generalization and expansion of familiar ideas.

Consider the case first studied in detail by Lepore (Le50). A neutron beam incident on a helium nucleus is scattered through an angle θ. Given the polarization state of the incident beam, we wish to find the angular distribution and polarization state of the scattered particles. We assume that two odd-parity states (P states) are simultaneously resonant, but that all other states give zero contribution. More precisely, the contributing states have total angular momentum $3/2$ and $1/2$ ($^2P_{3/2}$ and $^2P_{1/2}$). The scattering will then be completely characterized by two phase shifts, $\delta_{3/2}$ and $\delta_{1/2}$. These are in turn related to the elements of the reaction matrix ($R = S - 1$) by

$$R_{3/2} = \exp(2i\delta_{3/2}) - 1 \tag{1a}$$

$$R_{1/2} = \exp(2i\delta_{1/2}) - 1 \tag{1b}$$

all other elements being zero.

We must choose a quantization axis for the angular momenta which enter the problem. This choice will of course not affect the final result, but convenience dicates the use of the incident beam direction as the z axis. The polarization state of the incident beam can be completely described (for the case of spin $1/2$, only) by specifying a *degree* and *direction* of polarization. The x axis will be chosen so that the polarization direction lies in the x-z plane.

The incident beam can be thought of as composed of two beams, incoherently combined. The first is completely unpolarized and has intensity I_0. The second is completely polarized in the specified direction and has intensity I_1. The degree of polarization, or fractional polarization, will be given by

$$f = I_1/(I_0 + I_1) \tag{2}$$

If the two neutron spin functions are designated by $N_{1/2}$ and $N_{-1/2}$, the following relations hold:

$$\sigma_z N_{\pm 1/2} = \pm N_{\pm 1/2} \tag{3}$$

A given incident neutron will have a spin function:

$$a_{1/2} N_{1/2} + a_{-1/2} N_{-1/2} \tag{4}$$

with

$$\left| a_{1/2} \right|^2 + \left| a_{-1/2} \right|^2 = 1 \tag{5}$$

A fully polarized beam will consist of a large number of neutrons, each with the same values for $a_{1/2}$ and $a_{-1/2}$. An unpolarized beam, on the other hand, will contain particles having all possible phases and magnitudes for $a_{1/2}$ and $a_{-1/2}$.

In order to specify the incident polarization state more precisely, we must study the effect produced on the spin function by σ_x and σ_y. Using the ordinary convention, we obtain

$$\sigma_x N_{\pm 1/2} = N_{\mp 1/2} \tag{6a}$$

$$\sigma_y N_{\pm 1/2} = \pm i N_{\mp 1/2} \tag{6b}$$

We can now construct a function of form (4) to describe a spin oriented at an angle α with the positive z axis and whose projection in the x-y plane makes an angle β with the positive x axis (measured in the direction of the positive y axis). This function must have value unity for the projection of the unit spin vector in this new direction, and it therefore satisfies

$$(\sigma_x \sin \alpha \cos \beta + \sigma_y \sin \alpha \sin \beta + \sigma_z \cos \alpha)\,(a_{1/2}N_{1/2} + a_{-1/2}N_{-1/2})$$
$$= a_{1/2}N_{1/2} + a_{-1/2}N_{-1/2} \quad (7)$$

By use of Eqs. (3), (6a), and (6b), we obtain

$$a_{1/2}e^{i\beta} \sin \alpha - a_{-1/2} \cos \alpha = a_{-1/2} \quad (8a)$$

$$a_{1/2} \cos \alpha + a_{-1/2}\, e^{-i\beta} \sin \alpha = a_{1/2} \quad (8b)$$

These two equations are easily seen to be consistent, and yield a value for the ratio of $a_{1/2}$ and $a_{-1/2}$. An arbitrary factor is adjusted to satisfy Eq. (5), with the result

$$a_{1/2} - e^{-i\beta/2} \cos \alpha/2 \quad (9a)$$

$$a_{-1/2} = e^{i\beta/2} \sin \alpha/2 \quad (9b)$$

The polarization state of a beam can now be represented by forming the following products of amplitudes:

$$a_{1/2}a^*_{1/2},\; a_{1/2}a^*_{-1/2},\; a_{-1/2}a^*_{1/2},\; a_{-1/2}a^*_{-1/2} \quad (10)$$

and averaging them over all the particles of the beam. These averages will be called the elements of the density matrix and will be designated by

$$\langle 1/2 | 1/2 \rangle, \qquad \langle 1/2 | -1/2 \rangle, \qquad \langle -1/2 | 1/2 \rangle, \qquad \langle -1/2 | -1/2 \rangle \quad (11)$$

The angular brackets serve to recall the matrix character of the quantities and also emphasize their nature as statistical averages.

The density matrix elements can be written in terms of averages over α and β, by use of Eqs. (9a) and (9b):

$$\langle 1/2 | 1/2 \rangle = \langle \cos^2 \alpha/2 \rangle \quad (12a)$$

$$\langle 1/2 | -1/2 \rangle = \langle e^{-i\beta} \sin \alpha/2 \cos \alpha/2 \rangle \quad (12b)$$

$$\langle -1/2 | 1/2 \rangle = \langle e^{i\beta} \sin \alpha/2 \cos \alpha/2 \rangle \quad (12c)$$

$$\langle -1/2 | -1/2 \rangle = \langle \sin^2 \alpha/2 \rangle \quad (12d)$$

In the future we write the density matrix in standard matrix notation as $\langle i|i'\rangle$ and label the rows by i and the columns by i'. Note that the matrix is Hermitean, a completely general property.

The density matrix for an unpolarized beam can now be formed by assuming that the direction (α,β) is uniformly distributed over the sphere. We immediately obtain

$$\langle i|i'\rangle = \tfrac{1}{2}\begin{pmatrix} 1 & 0 \\ 0 & 1 \end{pmatrix} = \tfrac{1}{2}\delta(i,i') \tag{13}$$

This is a special case of a general result. If the particles of the beam have spin i, with possible z components $-i, -i+1, \ldots\ldots i-1, i$, the density matrix for the unpolarized beam will clearly be

$$\langle i|i'\rangle = (2i+1)^{-1}\delta(i,i') \tag{14}$$

The trace (diagonal sum) is unity, and all spin projections are equally likely, with no correlations between different spin states.

The fully polarized case can be immediately written down by removing the averages in Eqs. (12), since α and β now have definite values:

$$\langle i|i'\rangle = \tfrac{1}{2}\begin{pmatrix} 1 + \cos\alpha & e^{-i\beta}\sin\alpha \\ e^{i\beta}\sin\alpha & 1 - \cos\alpha \end{pmatrix} \tag{15}$$

The trace is still unity (this is a general property!) since the average intensity is unity, as defined. Note carefully that if we set $\cos\alpha = 0$, we obtain equal probabilities for plus and minus z projections. We do *not* obtain an unpolarized beam, because of the correlations (off-diagonal elements).

The matrix for the actual incident beam can be obtained by combining Eqs. (13) and (15) in the correct proportions. Thus

$$\langle i|i'\rangle = I_0/(I_0 + I_1)\langle i|i'\rangle_0 + I_1/(I_0 + I_1)\langle i|i'\rangle_1 \tag{16}$$

$$= (1-f)/2\begin{pmatrix} 1 & 0 \\ 0 & 1 \end{pmatrix} + f/2\begin{pmatrix} 1 + \cos\alpha & e^{-i\beta}\sin\alpha \\ e^{i\beta}\sin\alpha & 1 - \cos\alpha \end{pmatrix} \tag{17}$$

It is clear that the density matrix for the incoherent combination of two beams is the average of the separate density matrices, weighted as the intensities. The coordinate system has already been chosen so that β is zero in Eq. (17), and we obtain:

$$\langle i|i'\rangle = \tfrac{1}{2}\begin{pmatrix} 1 + f\cos\alpha & f\sin\alpha \\ f\sin\alpha & 1 - f\cos\alpha \end{pmatrix} \tag{18}$$

The polarization problem can now be more concisely defined. We require the density matrix of the scattered beam at angle θ and azimuth φ in terms of the incident density matrix [Eq. (18)]. We must consider two incident wave functions, namely $N_{\pm 1/2}e^{ikz}$, and calculate the two corresponding scattered wave functions.

A word is necessary as to the definition of the wave vector k. In the assumed non-relativistic situation, z is the z displacement between the helium nucleus and the neutron. The quantity k is the magnitude of the momentum of *either* particle in the center-of-mass system. This definition remains appropriate even in relativistic problems, if the center-of-mass system is simply defined as the system in which the total momentum of the two particles is zero. The plane wave can be resolved into partial waves in the familiar way:

$$\exp(ikz) = \sum_l (2l + 1)i^l u_l(kr) P_l(\cos \theta) \tag{19}$$

with

$$u_l(kr) \rightarrow (2ikr)^{-1} [\exp(ikr - il \, \pi/2) - \exp(-ikr + il \, \pi/2)] \tag{20}$$

for $kr \gg l$.

Because of the complexity of the expressions to be dealt with, a new notation has been adopted for angular momentum quantities. The magnitude of a given angular momentum will be written as an italic letter, while the component of the same angular momentum along the quantization axis will be written as the corresponding roman letter. Thus, the familiar (l,m) will be replaced by (l,l) and (J,M) will be (J,J). It will be seen that the flexibility thus gained can be used to considerable advantage. It is unfortunate that the conventional notation, originally devised to allow treatment of simple problems with only a few angular momenta, should have been retained for the extraordinarily complex problems which are now routinely encountered. The imaginary unit will appear as i, and unfortunately only the context can distinguish this symbol from that for the total spin of the outgoing particle. In general the imaginary unit will appear in the final formulae only with no exponent and as a multiplying factor at the front of an expression. In such context, it will never be enclosed in parentheses.

In order to make use of the general formalism of angular momentum theory, it is convenient to write the $P_l(\cos \theta)$ in terms of the normalized spherical harmonics $Y_{\mathrm{l}l}(\theta,\phi)$. It is assumed for convenience that the usual choice of phases is made, so that Wigner's expression for the vector addition coefficients will apply. It follows that

$$P_l(\cos \theta) = [(4\pi)(2l + 1)^{-1}]^{1/2} Y_{l0}(\theta,\varphi) \tag{21}$$

The scattered wave function produced by an incident function $N_{i'}e^{ikz}$ can be calculated by multiplying Eq. (19) by $N_{i'}$ and rewriting the result as a sum of functions of definite J,J, and parity (II). Thus

$$N_{i'}Y_{l0} = \sum_{J=l-1/2}^{l+1/2} (l, \,^{1}/_{2}\, 0i'|\,Ji')\; C_{J,i'} \tag{22}$$

The quantity $(l_1 l_2\, l_1 l_2|\,ll)$ is the usual vector-addition coefficient (in an abbreviated notation) for combination of l_1 and l_2 to give l. The symbol $C_{J,\mathbf{J}}$ is the composite wave function for the system (spin variable and angles for arguments) with definite J and J. Note that its parity is $(-1)^l$.

Each function $C_{J,\mathbf{J}}$ has its appropriate asymptotic radial dependence, such that incoming and outgoing waves appear in the combination

$$\exp(2i\,\delta_J)\,\exp(ikr - il\,\pi/2) - \exp(-ikr + il\,\pi/2) \tag{23}$$

Note that $exp(2i\delta_J)$ is a very degenerate form (appropriate to the simple case here considered) of the scattering matrix, here in diagonal form

$$\exp(2i\delta_J) = S_J \tag{24}$$

In less abbreviated form, we can write

$$(J',\mathbf{J}'|S|J\mathbf{J}) = S_J\delta(J,J')\delta(\mathbf{J},\mathbf{J}') \tag{25}$$

where the δ-symbol is simply the Kronecker symbol. The peculiar simplicity of the case under consideration arises from the fact that only a half-unit of spin angular momentum is present. Thus, a state of definite parity can contain only a single orbital angular momentum. In general, if spin angular momentum i' is available initially, and i finally, then elements of the S-matrix may exist which join various (l,i) combinations having the same J,J, and parity. Thus the concept of the S-matrix must be extended to the set of quantities

$$(l'i'J'\mathbf{J}'\Pi'|S|liJ\mathbf{J}\Pi) = S_{J\Pi}(l'i';\; li)\,\delta(J,J')\,\delta(\mathbf{J},\mathbf{J}')\,\delta(\Pi,\Pi') \tag{26}$$

An element of this matrix then gives the amplitude of the outgoing wave with orbital and spin angular momenta l and i, assuming a unit amplitude incoming wave described by l' and i', with the two combined to give total angular momentum J. We defer further discussion until the full S-matrix is required for the general derivation.

By combination of Eqs. (19), (20), (21), (22), and (23), we can construct a solution of the wave equation which behaves at large r like $N_{\pm 1/2}e^{ikz}$ + outgoing wave. This solution is

$$N_{i'} \exp(ikz) + (4\pi)^{1/2} (2l + 1)^{1/2} \sum_l i^l (2ikr)^{-1} \exp(ikr - il\,\pi/2)$$

$$\times \sum_J (l\,^1/_2\,0i'|Ji')\,C_{J,i'}R_J \quad (27)$$

with $R_J = S_J - 1$. In this example, l is always unity, so that no summation over l appears. By use of the relation inverse to Equation (22), namely

$$C_{J,i'} = \sum_i (l^1/_2\,li|Ji')N_i Y_{l1} \quad (28)$$

the outgoing part of (27) can be written in a more useful form, namely

$$(4\pi)^{1/2} (2ikr)^{-1} \exp(ikr) \sum_{Ji} (2l + 1)^{1/2} R_J (l^1/_2\,0i')|Ji')$$

$$\times (l^1/_2\,li|Ji')\,N_i Y_{l1} \quad (29)$$

The incident beam will actually consist of a number of particles, each specified by two amplitudes, $a_{\pm 1/_2}$. The polarization properties of the beam are to be specified in terms of the density matrix defined in (10) and (11). The amplitude for a given final spin state N_i can be extracted from (29) by inspection, and we write

$$A_{i'1}(\Omega) = (4\pi)^{1/2} (2k)^{-1} \sum_{Jl} (2l + 1)^{1/2}$$

$$\times R_J (l^1/_2\,0i'|Ji')\,(l^1/_2\,li|Ji')\,Y_{l1}(\Omega) \quad (30)$$

If the two spin-state amplitudes for a typical incident particle are $a_{1/_2}$ and $a_{-1/_2}$, the corresponding spin function will be

$$\sum_{i'} a_{i'}N_{i'} \quad (31)$$

The resulting amplitude for spin state i in the outgoing wave at unit distance from the collision center will then be

$$\sum_{i'} A_{i'i}a_{i'} \quad (32)$$

The density matrix for the incident beam (assumed to be of unit intensity) will be

$$\langle i_1'|i_2'\rangle = \langle a_{i_1'}a^*_{i_2'}\rangle \quad (33)$$

while the resulting density matrix for the outgoing particles is formed by use of (32):

$$\langle i_1|i_2\rangle = \sum_{i_1'i_2'} \langle A_{i_1'i_1}a_{i_1'}A^*_{i_2'i_2}a^*_{i_2'}\rangle$$

$$= \sum_{i_1'i_2'} A_{i_1'i_1}A^*_{i_2'i_2}\langle i_1'|i_2'\rangle \quad (34)$$

Thus, the density matrix resulting from the reaction has been written as a linear combination of the elements of the density matrix of the incident beam. Note that the final density matrix does not have unit trace, since the outgoing beam does not have unit intensity. The differential scattering cross section can in fact be written as the trace of the final density matrix. Thus

$$d\sigma/d\Omega = \sum_{i,\, i_1',\, i_2'} A^*_{i_2'i}(\Omega) A_{i_1'i}(\Omega) \langle i_1' \,|\, i_2' \rangle \tag{35}$$

which can be further specialized to the case of an unpolarized incident beam, which satisfies Eq. (14), with $i = \frac{1}{2}$, $i = i_1'$, $i' = i_2'$. The final result will then be

$$d\sigma/d\Omega = \frac{1}{2} \sum_{i,\, i'} \left| A_{i'i}(\Omega) \right|^2 \tag{36}$$

which has a familiar appearance.

3. Elementary Evaluation

Some insight into the meaning and utility of the formalism to be introduced can be gained by considering the process of evaluating Equation (34) by elementary methods. We note that R_J fails to vanish only for $J = \frac{1}{2}$ and $J = \frac{3}{2}$, while $l = 1$. We must therefore consider terms in the sum of Eq. (30) with $l = 1$, 0, -1, i, $i' = \pm\frac{1}{2}$, and $J = \frac{1}{2}$, $\frac{3}{2}$. We thus find

$$A_{\frac{1}{2}\,\frac{1}{2}} = (3\pi/k^2)^{1/2}\, [R_{\frac{1}{2}}\, (1\ \tfrac{1}{2}\ 0\ \tfrac{1}{2}\,|\,\tfrac{1}{2}\ \tfrac{1}{2})(1\ \tfrac{1}{2}\ 0\ \tfrac{1}{2}\,|\,\tfrac{1}{2}\ \tfrac{1}{2})$$

$$+ R_{\frac{3}{2}}\, (1\ \tfrac{1}{2}\ 0\ \tfrac{1}{2}\,|\,\tfrac{3}{2}\ \tfrac{1}{2})\ (1\ \tfrac{1}{2}\ 0\ \tfrac{1}{2}\,|\,\tfrac{3}{2}\ \tfrac{1}{2})]Y_{10} \tag{37}$$

and similarly for the other three amplitudes. In an elementary evaluation, it is most convenient to insert numerical values at this stage. The required Wigner coefficients are of the type contained in the commonly available algebraic tables (Ro57, p. 224, for example). Similarly, explicit trigonometric expressions must be used for the spherical harmonics

$$Y_{10} = \left(3/4\pi\right)^{1/2} \cos\theta$$

$$Y_{11} = -\left(3/8\pi\right)^{1/2} \sin\theta\, e^{i\varphi} \tag{38}$$

$$Y_{1-1} = \left(3/8\pi\right)^{1/2} \sin\theta\, e^{-i\varphi}$$

The amplitudes of Eq. (37) then become

$$A_{1/2\,1/2} = (2k)^{-1}\,(R_{1/2} + 2R_{3/2})\,\cos\theta \tag{39a}$$

$$A_{1/2-1/2} = (2k)^{-1}\,(R_{1/2} - R_{3/2})\,\sin\theta\,e^{i\varphi} \tag{39b}$$

$$A_{-1/2+1/2} = -\,(2k)^{-1}\,(R_{1/2} - R_{3/2})\,\sin\theta\,e^{-i\varphi} \tag{39c}$$

$$A_{-1/2-1/2} = (2k)^{-1}\,(R_{1/2} + 2R_{3/2})\,\cos\theta \tag{39d}$$

We now assume that the incident density matrix is of the form of Eq. (18), and calculate the outgoing density matrix by Eq. (34), using Eqs. (39). There result

$$
\begin{aligned}
\langle {}^1\!/_2 | {}^1\!/_2 \rangle = {} & (8k^2)^{-1}\,[(|R_{1/2}|^2 + 4|R_{3/2}|^2 + 2R_{1/2}R^*_{3/2} \\
& + 2R_{3/2}R^*_{1/2})\,(1 + f\cos\alpha)\cos^2\theta + (-|R_{1/2}|^2 + 2|R_{3/2}|^2 \\
& + R_{1/2}R^*_{3/2} - 2R_{3/2}R^*_{1/2})\,f\sin\alpha\sin\theta\cos\theta\,e^{i\varphi} + (-|R_{1/2}|^2 \\
& + 2|R_{3/2}|^2 + R_{3/2}R^*_{1/2} - 2R_{1/2}R^*_{3/2})\,f\sin\alpha\sin\theta\cos\theta\,e^{-i\varphi} \\
& + (|R_{1/2}|^2 + |R_{3/2}|^2 - R_{1/2}R^*_{3/2} - R_{3/2}R^*_{1/2}) \\
& \times (1 - f\cos\alpha)\sin^2\theta] \tag{40}
\end{aligned}
$$

and three similar expressions.

These expressions contain all possible information on the differential cross section and outgoing polarization state for an arbitrarily polarized incident beam. To obtain less cumbersome expressions, we first calculate the cross section for an incident polarized beam, and then calculate the cross section and polarization state of the outgoing beam for an unpolarized incident beam. Thus the trace of the density matrix must first be calculated:

$$d\sigma/d\Omega = \sum_i \langle i | i \rangle$$

$$
\begin{aligned}
= {} & (4k^2)^{-1}\,\{|R_{1/2}|^2 + |R_{3/2}|^2\,(1 + 3\cos^2\theta) \\
& + (R_{1/2}R^*_{3/2} + R_{3/2}R^*_{1/2})\,(3\cos^2\theta - 1) \\
& + 3i\,(R_{1/2}R^*_{3/2} - R_{3/2}R^*_{1/2})\,f\sin\alpha\sin\theta\cos\theta\sin\varphi\} \tag{41}
\end{aligned}
$$

One essential feature of the polarization problem is illustrated in this expression. The incident beam is polarized by a fractional amount f, with the polarization oriented in the x-z plane. If $f = 0$, or if the polarization is longitudinal ($\alpha = 0$ or π), the differential cross

section becomes independent of azimuth (φ), as it must because of
the invariance of the total problem under rotation about the z axis.
If non-longitudinal polarization *is* present, the azimuthally dependent
term is proportional to $f \sin \varphi$, and it therefore vanishes if the scattering is in the plane which contains the initial polarization direction.
Thus, if it is desired to detect the polarization of a beam, it is convenient to measure the left-right asymmetry of scattering, the left
and right referring to two opposite azimuths in the plane perpendicular to the plane defined by the incident beam direction and the suspected polarization direction.

Another essential feature of the polarization problem is the interference character of the asymmetry term. *Two* non-vanishing
elements (at least) of the R-matrix are required, if the asymmetry
term is not to vanish. In the simple case here studied, the phase
shifts for the two R-matrix elements must differ for asymmetry to
exist, since

$$i(R_{1/2} R^*{}_{3/2} - R_{3/2} R^*{}_{1/2}) = 8 \sin (\delta_{1/2} - \delta_{3/2}) \sin \delta_{1/2} \sin \delta_{3/2} \quad (42)$$

In the general treatment to be given, more general (but completely
analogous) restrictions will be found.

As a check of the work, it is useful to integrate Eq. (41) over
angles to obtain the total cross section. We obtain

$$\sigma = \pi k^{-2} \left(\left| R_{1/2} \right|^2 + 2 \left| R_{3/2} \right|^2 \right) \quad (43)$$

which agrees with the result obtained by simpler methods.

The interference character of the asymmetry term, together
with the requirement of non-equality of the two interfering phase
shifts has a simple intuitive explanation. The polarization of the incident beam can produce an actual asymmetry only by virtue of an
interaction between the spin and orbital motions. Such a spin-orbit
interaction must manifest itself by causing states with the same l, but
different J, to have unequal phase shifts, as $\delta_{1/2}$ and $\delta_{3/2}$. It is unfortunately *not* intuitively clear why *both* phase shifts must be nonzero.

The other quantity to be calculated is the polarization of the
scattered beam, for the case of $f = 0$. (In the future we use f' and f
for the polarizations of the incident and scattered waves, respec-
tively.) By use of Equation (17), the quantities f, α, and β (α, β being the polarization orientation angles for the scattered beam) can be

found as functions of θ and φ from the elements of the density matrix. First, the total intensity will be given by Eq. (41) with $f = 0$. Next, the three quantities $f\, e^{i\beta} \sin \alpha (d\sigma/d\Omega)$, $f\, e^{-i\beta} \sin \alpha (d\sigma/d\Omega)$, and $f \cos \alpha (d\sigma/d\Omega)$ can be written as

$$(^1/_2)f\, e^{-i\beta} \sin \alpha (d\sigma/d\Omega) = \langle ^1/_2 | -^1/_2 \rangle \qquad (44\text{a})$$

$$(^1/_2)f\, e^{i\beta} \sin \alpha (d\sigma/d\Omega) = \langle -^1/_2 | ^1/_2 \rangle \qquad (44\text{b})$$

$$f \cos \alpha (d\sigma/d\Omega) = [\langle ^1/_2 | ^1/_2 \rangle - \langle -^1/_2 | -^1/_2 \rangle] \qquad (44\text{c})$$

Substitution from Eq. (40), with $f = 0$, yields

$$e^{-i\beta} \sin \alpha\, d\sigma/d\Omega = (2k)^{-2}\, 3(R_{3/2} R^*_{1/2} - R_{1/2} R^*_{3/2}) \sin \theta \cos \theta\, e^{-i\theta}$$

$$(45\text{a})$$

$$f\, e^{i\beta} \sin \alpha\, d\sigma/d\Omega = (2k)^{-2}\, 3(-R_{3/2} R^*_{1/2} \\ + R_{1/2} R^*_{3/2}) \sin \theta \cos \theta\, e^{i\varphi} \quad (45\text{b})$$

$$f \cos \alpha\, d\Omega/d\sigma = 0 \qquad (45\text{c})$$

From Eq. (45c), it is clear that $\cos \alpha = 0$, so that the polarization is perpendicular to the direction of the incident beam. Further, if $\sin \alpha$ is set equal to unity in Eq. (45b), we see that

$$f(d\sigma/d\Omega) = 3(2k)^{-2}\, i(R_{3/2} R^*_{1/2} - R_{1/2} R^*_{3/2}) \sin \theta \cos \theta \qquad (46)$$

$$\beta = \varphi + \pi/2 \qquad (47)$$

We therefore see that the fractional polarization is proportional to the same combination of amplitudes that determined the amount of asymmetry in the case of the scattering of a polarized beam. Finally, Eq. (47) in combination with $\alpha = \pi/2$ shows that the polarization direction is perpendicular to the plane defined by the directions of the incident beam and the scattered beam.

These results lead immediately to the original suggestion of Schwinger (Sc46), namely that the spin-orbit interaction in the scattering of neutrons by α-particles can be studied by scattering neutrons from helium. The scattered neutrons are then to be scattered again from helium, and the left-right asymmetry measured. The fractional asymmetry will be proportional to the product of two amplitudes of the form of Eq. (46). From a practical viewpoint, such an experiment would be quite difficult, but it does represent the prototype polarization experiment. The principal improvement required is the substitution of a charged-particle reaction as the producer of the polarized neutron beam. In this way, as pointed out by Blin-Stoyle (Bl51), very high intensities can be made available.

4. Tensor Moments

Several new concepts must be introduced before the projected general treatment can be undertaken. The first is the concept of the tensor moment, first introduced by Fano (Fa52). Although the incident and outgoing density matrices contain all possible information as to the polarization states, this information is nevertheless contained in very clumsy form. Some reformulation is necessary in which quantities with an obvious directional significance are displayed. Just as the polarization state of a beam with spin $1/2$ is described in terms of a scalar (the intensity) and a vector (the fractional polarization, together with its two orientation angles), so will a beam with higher spin be describable in terms of tensor quantities of integral rank up to and including $2i$. It is a simple matter to construct linear combinations of the elements of the density matrix which behave as such tensor quantities, it being convenient to make the tensors traceless and transforming as the so-called irreducible tensors (Ro57, p. 77).

Suppose we have a beam of particles each with spin i and amplitude a_i for a particular spin state. Suppose that a rotation of the coordinate system is made, with Euler angles (α, β, γ) (Ro57, p. 50). The wave function will be transformed in a known way, using the Wigner matrices $D_{i'i}^{i}(\alpha, \beta, \gamma)$ (Ro57, p. 52). Thus if

$$\chi = \sum_i a_i \chi_i \tag{48}$$

in the initial coordinate frame, χ can be rewritten in terms of new coefficients a'_i and the spin functions χ'_i appropriate to the new axes. Thus

$$\chi = \sum_i a'_i \chi'_i = \sum_i a'_i \sum_{i'} D^{i}_{i'i}(\alpha, \beta, \gamma) \chi_{i'} \tag{49}$$

which when equated to Eq. (48) yields a relation between a'_i and a_i:

$$a_i = \sum_{i'} D^{i}_{ii'}(P) a'_{i'} \tag{50}$$

where P has been introduced as a convenient abbreviation for the three Euler angles. The relation can be inverted by use of the rotation matrices for the inverse rotation (P^{-1}):

$$
\begin{aligned}
a'_{i'} &= \sum_i D^i{}_{i'i} (P^{-1}) a_i \\
&= \sum_i D^{i*}{}_{ii'} (P) a_i
\end{aligned}
\tag{51}
$$

The density matrix for the beam in the new axes can now be simply calculated in terms of the original density matrix:

$$
\langle i'_1 | i'_2 \rangle' = \sum_{i_1} \sum_{i_2} D^{i*}{}_{i_1 i_1'} (P) \, D^i{}_{i_2 i_2'} (P) \, \langle i_1 | i_2 \rangle
\tag{52}
$$

The complex conjugate of the D-function is simply expressed as (Ro57, p. 54)

$$
D^{i*}{}_{i_1 i_1'} (P^{-1}) = (-1)^{i_1' - i_1} D^i{}_{-i_1\ -i_1'} (P^{-1})
\tag{53}
$$

If this relation is introduced in Eq. (52), the Clebsch-Gordan series (Ro57, p. 58) for the product of two D-functions can be used to simplify the result. Thus

$$
\langle i'_1 | i'_2 \rangle' = \sum_{i_1} \sum_{i_2} \sum_{q,\,q,\,q'} D^q{}_{q,q'} (P)
$$
$$
(ii\,i'_2 - i'_1 | qq') \, (iii_2 - i_1 | qq) \, (-1)^{i_1' - i_1} \langle i_1 | i_2 \rangle
\tag{54}
$$

We multiply each side by $(-1)^{i\ -\ i_1'}(iii'_2 - i'_1 | rr')$ and sum over i'_1, i'_2, with the result

$$
\sum_{i_1' i_2'} (-1)^{i\ -\ i_1'} (iii'_2 - i'_1 | qq) \, \langle i'_1 | i'_2 \rangle'
$$
$$
= \sum_{q'} D^q{}_{q'q} (P) \sum_{i_1 i_2} (-1)^{i - i_1} (iii_2 - i_1 | qq') \, \langle i_1 | i_2 \rangle
\tag{55}
$$

It will be convenient to define the new quantities, first introduced by Fano (Fa52),

$$
T(qq) = (2i + 1)^{1/2} (2q + 1)^{-1/2} \sum_{i_1 i_2} (-1)^{i\ -\ i_1}(iii_2 - i_1 | qq) \, \langle i_1 | i_2 \rangle
$$
$$
= \sum_{i_1 i_2} (i\ q\ i_1 q | \ddot{i}i_2) \, \langle i_1 | i_2 \rangle
\tag{56}
$$

which will be called the tensor moments of the beam. Note that the elementary properties of the Wigner coefficients require q to be an integer, with $2i \geqslant q \geqslant 0$, as is intuitively required. Further, for given

q there are $2q + 1$ q-values. The total number of tensor components is therefore $(2i + 1)^2$, which is the same as the number of elements of the density matrix. Accordingly, specification of all the $T(qq)$ gives complete information about the density matrix. The explicit relation is easily found by multiplying Eq. (56) by $(-1)^{i - j_2}(iij_1, -j_2|qq)$ and summing over q and q. There results

$$\langle i_1|i_2\rangle = \sum_{qq} (-1)^{i - i_1} (iii_2 - i_1|qq)(2i + 1)^{-1/2} (2q + 1)^{1/2} T(qq)$$

$$= (2q + 1) (2i + 1)^{-1} \sum_{qq} (iqi_1q|ii_2) T(qq) \qquad (57)$$

The tensor moments have two obvious advantages as a method for describing polarization. First, they transform very simply under spatial rotations, as seen from Eq. (55)

$$T'(qq) = \sum_{q'} D^q{}_{q'q}(P) T(qq') \qquad (58)$$

Second, the values of T for small values of q correspond to elementary polarization properties of the beam. A third advantage, which will only subsequently become clear, is that the use of the $T(qq)$ considerably simplifies the formulae to be derived.

It is of interest to deduce quantitative relations between the $T(qq)$ and quantities of immediate physical interest. First, $T(00)$ is simply the intensity. Thus

$$T(00) = \sum_{i_1 i_2} (i0i_1 0|ii_2) \langle i_1|i_2\rangle = \sum_{i_1 i_2} \delta_{i_1 i_2} \langle i_1|i_2\rangle$$

$$= \sum_i \langle i|i\rangle \qquad (59)$$

The tensor moment of rank 1 is very simply related to the fractional polarization. Thus

$$T(1\ 1) = \sum_{i_1 i_2} - [2i(i + 1)]^{-1/2}[(i + i_2) (i - i_2 + 1)]^{1/2}$$
$$\times \delta(i_2, i_1 + 1) \langle i_1|i_2\rangle$$

$$T(1\ 0) = \sum_{i_1 i_2} [i(i + 1)]^{-1/2} i_2 \delta(i_1, i_2) \langle i_1|i_2\rangle$$

$$T(1 - 1) = \sum_{i_1} [2i(i + 1)]^{-1/2} [(i - i_2) (i + i_2 + 1)]^{1/2}$$
$$\times \delta(i_2, i_1 - 1) \langle i_1|i_2\rangle \qquad (60)$$

We consider the irreducible vector spin operators for a particle of the beam, namely (Ro57, p. 84)

$$S_0 = S_z$$

$$S_1 = -(2)^{-1/2} (S_x + iS_y) \tag{61}$$

$$S_{-1} = (2)^{-1/2} (S_x - iS_y)$$

If the wave function for one particle of the beam is written

$$\chi = \sum_i a_i \chi_i \tag{62}$$

the expectation of S_q will be

$$(\chi^* S_q \chi) = \sum_{i_1 i_2} a_{i_1} a^*_{i_2} (\chi^*_{i_2} S_q \chi_{i_1}) \tag{63}$$

If we average Eq. (63) over the particles of the beam, there results

$$\langle S_q \rangle \equiv \langle (\chi^* S_q \chi) \rangle = \sum_{i_1 i_2} (\chi^*_{i_2} S_q \chi_{i_1}) \langle i_1 | i_2 \rangle \tag{64}$$

which has a form similar to Eq. (60). The matrix elements of S_q which appear in Eq. (64) are well known (Ro57, p. 27):

$$(\chi^*_{i_2} S_0 \chi_{i_1}) = i_1 \delta(i_1, i_2)$$

$$(\chi^*_{i_2} S_1 \chi_{i_1}) = -2^{-1/2} [(i - i_1)(i + i_1 + 1)]^{1/2} \delta(i_2, i_1 + 1) \tag{65}$$

$$(\chi^*_{i_2} S_{-1} \chi_{i_1}) = 2^{-1/2} [(i + i_1)(i \quad i_1 + 1)]^{1/2} \delta(i_2, i_1 - 1)$$

If the relations in Eq. (65) are substituted in Eq. (64), comparison with Eq. (60) yields

$$T(1\ q) = [i(i + 1)]^{-1/2} \langle S_q \rangle \tag{66}$$

This relation is a special case of a more general relation, obtained by using an obvious analogy between the components of the irreducible tensor operators formed from (S_x, S_y, S_z) and the corresponding operators (spherical harmonics) formed from the rectangular coordinates (x, y, z). Consider the quantities

$$P(qq;\ x,y,z) = (x^2 + y^2 + z^2)^{q/2} Y_{qq}(\theta, \phi) \tag{67}$$

These are polynomials in x, y, and z, with each term of degree q, if θ and φ are related to x, y, and z in the usual way. The tensor moments can be written in general as

$$T(qq) = N(i,q) \langle P(qq;\ S_x, S_y, S_z) \rangle \tag{68}$$

where

$$N(i,q) = [4\pi(2i + 1)2^{2q}(2i - q)!]^{1/2}$$
$$\times [(2q + 1)(2i + q + 1)!]^{-1/2} \qquad (69)$$

The definition of (68) is rendered ambiguous by the non-commutation of S_x, S_y, and S_z. This difficulty is simply rectified by taking each term in (68) to be the average of the terms obtained by permuting the factors in all possible ways. Note that if $2i \gg q$, the situation becomes essentially classical, with $N(i,q)$ approximated by

$$N(i,q) \simeq [4\pi(2q + 1)^{-1}]^{1/2} [i(i + 1)]^{-q/2} \qquad (70)$$

In this limit, the non-commutativity of S_x, S_y, and S_z becomes negligible and the components of $T(qq)$ become precisely the spherical harmonics of the orientation angles of the spin vector, with a new normalization which depends only on q.

For completeness we give the explicit expressions for $T(2,q)$, which may occasionally be needed:

$$T(2\ 0) = A(i)\ (2/3)^{1/2}\ [i(i + 1)^{-1}\ \langle 3S_z{}^2 - S^2 \rangle$$

$$T(2 \pm 1) = \mp A(i)\ [i(i + 1)]^{-1}$$

$$\times \langle (S_x \pm iS_y)S_z + S_z(S_x \pm iS_y) \rangle$$

$$T(2 \pm 2) = A(i)[i(i + 1)]^{-1}\ \langle (S_x \pm iS_y)^2 \rangle \qquad (71)$$

with

$$A(i) = (^3/_8)^{1/2}\ (i^2 + i)^{1/2}\ (i^2 + i - {}^3/_4)^{-1/2} \qquad (72)$$

As will become apparent, the explicit expressions are seldom actually required to predict the result of an experiment, but are often convenient for making quantitative the concept of "degree of polarization" of a beam. These alternative expressions for the tensor moments are used in the work of Simon and Welton (Si53a, Si53b), but are there given with an incorrect normalization factor.

5. The Scattering Matrix in Other Representations

Another concept which becomes very convenient for the general derivation is that of the generalized scattering matrix. Ordinarily, the term "scattering matrix" is used in two rather different ways. In nuclear reaction theory, it is the set of coefficients which give the amplitudes of the various outgoing spherical waves when an incoming spherical wave of unit amplitude exists. The scattering matrix which we used in our illustrative example is of this character. In elementary-particle physics, on the other hand, the scattering matrix refers to the outgoing amplitude at specified angle which results from an incoming wave of unit amplitude at some other angle. An elegant derivation of the polarization formula can be given by attempting to unify these two treatments. This procedure has the additional advantage that the results are available to several fields of work.

Consider first the illustrative example given earlier in this chapter. The amplitude given by Eq. (30) can be rewritten in a more suggestive form, by using

$$Y_{ll'}(0) = [(4\pi)(2l + 1)^{-1}]^{-1/2}\delta_{0l'} \tag{73}$$

A new symbol $(\Omega'i'|R|\Omega,i)$ will be introduced, which is related to $A_{i'i}(\Omega)$ by

$$A_{i'i}(\Omega) = 2\pi k^{-1}(0,i'|R|\Omega,i) \tag{74}$$

so that

$$d\sigma/d\Omega = 4\pi^2 k^{-2}(2i + 1)^{-1} \sum |(0,i'|R|\Omega,i)|^2 \tag{75}$$

Combination of Eqs. (30), (73), and (74) yields as an expression for the new symbol

$$(0,i'|R|\Omega,i) = \sum_{JJll'} R_J(l\ ^1/_2\ l'i'|JJ)\ (l\ ^1/_2\ li|JJ) Y^*_{ll'}(0) Y_{ll}(\Omega) \tag{76}$$

At this point, the general property of the S-matrix described in Eq. (25) can be used to write (76) in a more elegant form (note that $R = S - 1$, so that Eq. (25) holds equally with R inserted for S). At the same time i and i', which are both equal to $^1/_2$ in the example can be used in Eq. (76) to replace $^1/_2$. Finally, an arbitrary direction Ω' can be inserted to replace the special direction 0. A formula of rather general appearance results:

$$(\Omega',i'|R|\Omega,i)$$

$$\sum_{JJ'JJ'll'} = Y^*_{ll'}(\Omega')\ (l'i'l'i'|J'J')\ (J'J'|R|J,J)\ (lili|JJ)\ Y_{ll}(\Omega) \tag{77}$$

where $l' = l = 1$, for the example under discussion. For a general reaction with $a' + A' \rightarrow a + A$, but still with zero spin for A' and A, the form of Eq. (77) must be augmented slightly. First, the arguments of the R-matrix on the left must include the designation of initial and final alternatives, α' and α. Second, the R-matrix on the right must include α' and α, as well as arbitrary values of l' and l, which must be summed over.

We accordingly rewrite Eq. (77) as

$$(\Omega',i'\alpha'|R|\Omega,i,\alpha) =$$

$$\sum(\Omega'|l'l')(l'i'l'i'|J'J')(\alpha'l'i'J'J'\Pi'|R|\alpha l iJJ\Pi)\ (l i l i|JJ)\ (ll|\Omega)\quad (78)$$

where the sum extends over $J,J',\mathsf{J},\mathsf{J}',l,l',\mathsf{l},\mathsf{l}',\Pi,\Pi'$. The complete expression has been written in such form as to emphasize that the structure of the relation is that of a transformation of an operator R from one representation (angles diagonal) to another representation (angular momenta diagonal). The angle–to–orbital-angular-momentum transformation functions $(ll|\Omega)$ have been written instead of the spherical harmonics for reasons of symmetry. The R-matrix is diagonal in J and J (equivalent to overall conservation of angular momentum) and in parity Π (corresponding to the assumption of parity conservation in all reactions considered). The sums over J',J', and Π' can then immediately be done to yield

$$(\Omega',i',\alpha'|R|\Omega,i,\alpha) =$$
$$\sum(\Omega'|l'l')(l'i'l'i'|JJ)\ R_{J\pi}(\alpha'l'i';\ \alpha l i)\ (l i l i|JJ)\ (ll|\Omega)\quad (79)$$

At this point, it should be noted that the differential cross section for going from Ω' and α' to Ω and α is obtained by a generalization of Eq. (75), namely

$$d\sigma/d\Omega = 4\pi^2 k'^{-2}(2i+1)^{-1}\sum_{ii'}\big|(\Omega',i',\alpha'|R|\Omega,i,\alpha)\big|^2\quad (80)$$

Here k' is the wave number for the *initial* system.

One last generalization is required, since a', A', a, and A can all have spins. We designate these spins and their projections along the quantization axis by $i',\mathsf{i}',I',\mathsf{I}',i,\mathsf{i},I,\mathsf{I}$, respectively, and extend the concept of the R-matrix to the following symbol:

$$(\Omega',i',I',\alpha'|R|\Omega,i,I,\alpha)\quad (81)$$

It has become conventional to introduce the "channel-spin" representation, in which i and I are combined to make a single effective channel spin s and similarly for the initial spins. It becomes necessary of course to sum over the possible values of these channel spins which are allowed by the usual rules of vector addition $(|i-I| \leq s \leq i+I)$. If we introduce the Wigner coefficients required for this new transformation, Eq. (79) must finally be replaced by

$$(\Omega',i',I',\alpha'\,|\,R\,|\,\Omega,i,I,\alpha) =$$

$$\sum(\Omega'\,|\,l'I')(i'I'i'I'\,|\,s's')(l's'l's'\,|\,JJ)$$

$$\times\; R_{JII}(\alpha'l's';\ \alpha ls)(lsls\,|\,JJ)(iIiI\,|\,ss)(ll\,|\,\Omega) \quad (82)$$

The generalized reaction matrix as introduced in (82) can be used in many applications. The formalism is relativistic, if a Lorentz transformation to a system of zero total momentum has been made. In this event, k' is the magnitude of the momentum of *one* reactant, and the coefficient $4\pi^2/k'^2$ used in obtaining the cross section must be modified suitably. Pions can be treated in initial and final states, if isotopic spin variables are included. Photons can likewise be included, if a suitable modification is made of the spin variables describing the photon. Certain general properties are common to all applications. These are:

(1.) The scattering matrix is unitary:

$$S^\dagger S - (R^\dagger + 1)(R + 1) = 1,\ \text{or}\ R^\dagger R = -(R^\dagger + R) \quad (83)$$

This is the condition of probability conservation for all possible superpositions of incident waves, and will be assumed in the following. In applying it, the relation is always taken as a matrix relation with sums or integrals over repeated variables, irrespective of representation. Thus:

$$\sum_{iI\alpha} \int d\Omega(\Omega',i',I',\alpha'\,|\,R^\dagger\,|\,\Omega,i,I,\alpha)(\Omega,i,I,\alpha\,|\,R\,|\,\Omega'',i'',I'',\alpha'')$$

$$= -[(\Omega',i',I',\alpha'\,|\,R^\dagger\,|\,\Omega'',i'',I'',\alpha'') + (\Omega',i',I',\alpha'\,|\,R\,|\,\Omega'',i'',I'',\alpha'')] \quad (84)$$

for example, where $R^\dagger$ denotes the quantity obtained by taking the complex conjugate of R and interchanging initial and final variables.

(2.) The scattering matrix is multiplied by ± 1 under space reflections, unless weak interactions are involved, since the overall description of a collision should not depend on whether left-handed or right handed axes are used. The form of Eq. (82) can be made to automatically satisfy this condition, since $(ll\,|\,\Omega)$ has odd or even parity according to whether l is odd or even. If then $R_{JII}(\alpha',l',s';\alpha ls)$ is taken to be zero unless $|l - l'|$ is even (odd), every term in Eq. (82) is multiplied by $+1(-1)$ under simultaneous reflection of Ω and Ω'. This condition will be assumed in all that follows. The multiplication factor is simply the product of the intrinsic parities of a, A, a', A'.

(3.) The scattering matrix is invariant under time reversal. In this context, time reversal signifies the interchange of initial and final states, as well as the reversal of sign of all spin projections. Thus

$$(\Omega,-i,-I,\alpha\,|\,R\,|\,\Omega',-i',-I',\alpha') =$$
$$\Sigma(\Omega\,|\,ll)(iI - i - I\,|\,ss)(lsls\,|\,JJ)R_{JII}(\alpha ls;\ a'l's')$$
$$\times\ (l's'l's'\,|\,JJ)(i'I' - i' - I'\,|\,s's')(l'I'\,|\,\Omega')$$
$$= \Sigma(\Omega'\,|\,l' - l')^*(i'I' - i' - I'\,|\,s' - s')$$
$$(l's' - l' - s'\,|\,J - J)R_{JII}(\alpha ls;\ \alpha'l's')$$
$$\times\ (ls - l - s\,|\,J - J)$$
$$\times\ (iI - i - I\,|\,s - s)(l - l\,|\,\Omega) \quad (85)$$

where dummy summation indices have been freely reversed in sign. If we take

$$(l\!l \mid \Omega) \;=\; Y_{l\!l}(\Omega) \tag{86}$$

then

$$(l\!l \mid \Omega)^* \;=\; (-1)^{l}(l - l \mid \Omega) \tag{87}$$

By use of Eq. (87), together with the usual relation

$$(l\!l \mid \Omega)^* \;=\; (\Omega \mid l\!l) \tag{88}$$

and the identity covering reversal of sign of angular momentum projections in the Wigner coefficients

$$(abab \mid cc) \;=\; (-1)^{a+b-c}(ab - a - b \mid c - c) \tag{89}$$

Eq. (85) can be rewritten as

$$(-1)^{i-\mathrm{i}+I-\mathrm{I}+i'-\mathrm{i}'+I'-\mathrm{I}'}(\Omega,-\mathrm{i},-\mathrm{I},\alpha \mid R \mid \Omega',-\mathrm{i}',-\mathrm{I}',\alpha')$$
$$= \Sigma(\Omega' \mid l'l')(i'I'i'I' \mid s's')(l's'l's' \mid JJ)$$
$$\times\ (-1)^{l+l'}R_{J\Pi}(\alpha ls;\ \alpha'l's')(lsls \mid JJ)(iIiI \mid ss)(l\!l \mid \Omega) \tag{90}$$

In order to obtain reasonable behavior (reciprocity) under time reversal, it is clearly sufficient that

$$R_{J\Pi}(\alpha ls;\ \alpha'l's') \;=\; R_{J\Pi}(\alpha'l's';\ \alpha ls) \tag{91}$$

so that Eq. (90) becomes a simple relation between the amplitudes for a reaction and its inverse

$$(-1)^{i-\mathrm{i}+I-\mathrm{I}+i'-\mathrm{i}'+I'-\mathrm{I}'}(\Omega,-\mathrm{i},-\mathrm{I},\alpha \mid R \mid \Omega',-\mathrm{i}',-\mathrm{I}',\alpha')$$
$$= \pi\Pi\pi'\Pi'(\Omega',\mathrm{i}',\mathrm{I}',\alpha' \mid R \mid \Omega,\mathrm{i},\mathrm{I},\alpha) \tag{92}$$

The product of π's is simply the product of the intrinsic parities of the four particles involved. Since only products of two matrix-elements are observable, reciprocity is not disturbed by this factor, but the reason for its appearance is not intuitively obvious. Wigner and Eisenbud (Wi47) in fact originally obtained the result that $R_{J\Pi}$ (as defined above, *not* as they defined it) is antisymmetric if $\pi'\Pi'\pi\Pi = -1$. Huby (Hu54) first pointed out the error in the older result. In explanation, it is perhaps sufficient to remark that a pseudoscalar wave function (spin 0, odd intrinsic parity) can be seen from relativistic considerations to reverse its sign under time reversal, whereas a scalar wave function remains unchanged. See also an article by Coester (Co51), who apparently first made this observation, using the methods of field theory.

(4.) The scattering matrix must transform in a simple manner under spatial rotations. That is, if the directions Ω and Ω' are simultaneously rotated

$$\Omega \rightarrow P\Omega$$
$$\Omega' \rightarrow P\Omega' \tag{93}$$

then a corresponding rotation of the spin functions specified by i, i', I, and I' will leave the R-matrix invariant. Thus, it is required that

$$\sum_{h,h',H,H'} D^{i}{}_{ih}(P)D^{I}{}_{IH}(P)D^{*i'}{}_{i'h'}(P)D^{*I'}{}_{I'H'}(P)$$

$$\times (P\Omega',h',H',\alpha'|R|P\Omega,h,H,\alpha) = (\Omega',i',I',\alpha'|R|\Omega,i,I,\alpha) \quad (94)$$

This condition clearly suffices to guarantee that all cross sections will be independent of the coordinate system used in their calculation. An elementary (but laborious) calculation of the left-hand side of Eq. (94), using Eq. (82) for R and the elementary properties of the Wigner coefficients and the D-functions, shows that Eq. (94) is indeed satisfied. The particular property of R_{JII} which is involved is simply its independence of J, the projection of J.
The R-matrix in the form of Eq. (82) will be the basis of all the work to follow.

6. The Density Matrix and Tensor Moments for Non–Zero Target Spin

In order to make possible the description of polarization in a state where two particles possess spin, a generalization must be made of the previously introduced concepts of the density matrix and its tensor moments. First a beam of particles with spin i' incident on target particles with spin I' will be represented by a set of amplitudes $a_{i'I'}$. We define the density matrix for the system as

$$\langle i'_1 I'_1 | i'_2 I'_2 \rangle = \langle a_{i_1'I_1} \cdot a^*{}_{i_2'I_2'} \rangle \quad (95)$$

In any imaginable experimental situation, no coherence is possible between the spin states for the two initial particles, and therefore

$$\langle i'_1 I'_1 | i'_2 I'_2 \rangle = \langle i'_1 | i'_2 \rangle \langle I'_1 | I'_2 \rangle \quad (96)$$

where the factors on the right are the previously defined elements of the density matrices for a' alone and A' alone. This product form clearly will not hold for the density matrix which results from a reaction, although this distinction seems not to have been uniformly made in the literature.

The intensity of the beam is again the diagonal sum of Eq. (96)

$$\sum_{i'I'} \langle i'I'|i'I' \rangle \quad (97)$$

An unpolarized beam of unit intensity incident on an unpolarized target will be represented by

$$\langle i'_1 I'_1 | i'_2 I'_2 \rangle = (2i' + 1)^{-1} (2I' + 1)^{-1} \delta(i'_1,i'_2) \delta(I'_1,I'_2) \quad (98)$$

Just as in the illustrative example given at the beginning, the essential problem will be to calculate the outgoing density matrix for a given direction in terms of the incoming density matrix for the direction of incidence. For convenience, these density matrices will be specified in terms of the tensor moments for the various particles involved, and we accordingly introduce a generalization of the tensor moment concept which is appropriate for a system of two particles. We write

$$T(qq;QQ) = \sum (iq_1q \mid ii_2) (IQI_1Q \mid II_2) \langle i_1I_1 \mid i_2I_2 \rangle \qquad (99)$$

This symbol has several useful properties:

(1). Under rotation P, the components of $T(qq;QQ)$ transform to new values given by

$$T'(qq;QQ) = \sum D^q{}_{q'q}(P) \, D^Q{}_{Q'Q}(P) \, T(qq';QQ') \qquad (100)$$

(2). If the density matrix satisfies (96), we have

$$T(qq;QQ) = T(qq) \, T(QQ) \qquad (101)$$

This relation is very useful for the case of a polarized beam incident on a polarized target.

(3). In most cases of experimental interest, we wish to know the tensor moments for *one* of the final particles, while ignoring the state of the other particle. Making an obvious definition, we obtain

$$\begin{aligned} T(qq) &= T(qq;00) \\ T(QQ) &= T(00;QQ) \end{aligned} \qquad (102)$$

Analogous expressions can be given for the tensor moments of one particle when partial information is available on the polarization state of the other particle. See, for example, the discussion of efficiency tensors in the paper of Coester and Jauch (Co53), and in the review article of Devons and Goldfarb (De57), and in Section 9 of this chapter.

7. General Derivation

We can now put all the pieces which have been developed together and obtain the desired general formula. Consideration of Eqs. (74) and (95), taking $\Omega' = 0$ for convenience, yields an expression for the outgoing density matrix at angular position Ω on the unit sphere, in terms of the density matrix for the initial system. Thus

$$\langle i_1 I_1 | i_2 I_2 \rangle = (2\pi/k')^2 \sum (0,i'_1,I'_1,\alpha' | R | \Omega, i_1, I_1, \alpha)$$
$$\times (0,i'_2,I'_2,\alpha' | R | \Omega, i_2, I_2, \alpha)^* \langle i'_1 I'_1 | i'_2 I'_2 \rangle \quad (103)$$

We now insert the expression (82) for the angular dependence of the R-matrix, and make use of Eq. (99) and its obvious inverse. The result is a rather long expression, with, however, a clearly marked structure:

$$T(qq;QQ) = (2\pi/k')^2 \sum (iqi_1q | \ddot{u}_2)(IQI_1Q | II_2)(i'q'i'_1q' | i'i'_2)$$
$$\times (I'Q'I'_1Q' | I'I'_2)(2q'+1)(2Q'+1)(2i'+1)^{-1}(2I'+1)^{-1}$$
$$\times (0 | l'_1 l'_1)(i'I'i'_1I'_1 | s'_1 s'_1)(l'_1 s'_1 l'_1 s'_1 | J_1 J_1) R_{J_1 \Pi_1}(\alpha' l'_1 s'_1; \alpha l_1 s_1)$$
$$\times (l_1 s_1 l_1 s_1 | J_1 J_1)(iI i_1 I_1 | s_1 s_1)(l_1 l_1 | \Omega)(0 | l'_2 l'_2)^*$$
$$\times (i'I'i'_2 I'_2 | s'_2 s'_2)(l'_2 s'_2 l'_2 s'_2 | J_2 J_2) R^*_{J_2 \Pi_2}(\alpha' l'_2 s'_2; \alpha l_2 s_2)$$
$$\times (l_2 s_2 l_2 s_2 | J_2 J_2)(iI i_2 I_2 | s_2 s_2)(l_2 l_2 | \Omega)^* T(q'q';Q'Q') \quad (104)$$

It will be more convenient to calculate the final tensor moments with respect to a set of axes which are simply oriented with respect to the final beam direction. We choose the new z axis along $\mathbf{k}$ and the new y axis along $\mathbf{k'} \times \mathbf{k}$, where $\mathbf{k'}$ and $\mathbf{k}$ are the initial and final relative momenta, respectively.* The Euler angles (α, β, γ) for this rotation of axes are $(\varphi, \theta, 0)$, where θ is the usual scattering angle and φ is the azimuth of scattering measured in the positive direction (from x to y). From now on, $T(qq; QQ)$ will denote the tensor moments in these new axes, and the transformation [Eq. (100)] with angles $(\varphi, \theta, 0)$ will be introduced into Eq. (104) for this purpose. The spherical harmonics appearing in (104) must further be written in terms of D-functions. We have, from Eqs. (73) and (86)

$$(0 | l'_1 l'_1) = (l'_1 l'_1 | 0)^* = [(4\pi)(2l'_1 + 1)^{-1}]^{-1/2} \delta_{0 l'_1}$$
$$(0 | l'_2 l'_2) = (l'_2 l'_2 | 0)^* = [(4\pi)(2l'_2 + 1)^{-1}]^{-1/2} \delta_{0 l'_1} \quad (105)$$

while from Eq. (86) and a well-known relation (Ro57, pp. 54 and 60)

$$(l_1 l_1 | \Omega) = (-1)^{l_1} [(4\pi)(2l_1 + 1)^{-1}]^{-1/2} D^{l_1}_{-l_1 0}(\varphi, \theta, 0)$$
$$(l_2 l_2 | \Omega)^* = [(4\pi)(2l_2 + 1)^{-1}]^{-1/2} D^{l_2}_{l_2 0}(\varphi, \theta, 0) \quad (106)$$

* The sign convention here adopted is such as to make all polarizations agree with the so-called "Basel convention."

Now, by combining Eqs. (104), (105), and (106), we obtain

$$T(qq;\ QQ) = (2k')^{-2} \sum D^q_{pq}\, D^Q_{PQ}\, D^{l_1}_{-1_10}\, D^{l_2}_{1_20}\, [(2l'_1 + 1)$$
$$\times (2l'_2 + 1)\, (2l_1 + 1)\, (2l_2 + 1)]^{1/2}\, (-1)^{l_1}\, \delta_{01'_1}\, \delta_{01'_2}\, (2q' + 1)$$
$$\times (2Q' + 1)\, (2i' + 1)^{-1}\, (2I' + 1)^{-1}\, (iqi_1p\,|\,ii_2)\, (IQI_1P\,|\,II_2)$$
$$\times (i'q'i'_1q'\,|\,i'i'_2)\, (I'Q'I'_1Q'\,|\,I'I'_2)\, (i Ii'_1I'_1\,|\,s'_1s'_1)\, (l'_1s'_1l'_1s'_1\,|\,J_1J_1)$$
$$\times (l_1s_1l_1s_1\,|\,J_1J_1)\, (iI\,i_1I_1\,|\,s_1s_1)\, (i'I'i'_2I'_2\,|\,s'_2s'_2)\, (l'_2s'_2l'_2s'_2\,|\,J_2J_2)$$
$$\times (l_2s_2l_2s_2\,|\,J_2J_2)\, (iIi_2I_2\,|\,s_2s_2)\, R_{J_1\Pi_1}\, (\alpha'l'_1s'_1;\alpha l_1s_1)$$
$$\times R^*_{J_2\Pi_2}\, (\alpha'l'_2s'_2;\alpha l_2s_2)\, T(q'q';Q'Q') \quad (107)$$

where the arguments of each D-function are $(\varphi,\theta,0)$. The Clebsch-Gordan series (Ro57, p. 58) for products of D-functions must now be used three times in succession. We first combine the two functions with total angular momenta l_1 and l_2, to give a series of functions with angular momentum l. We then combine q and Q to obtain k, and finally l and k are combined to obtain L. Thus

$$D^q_{pq}\, D^Q_{PQ}\, D^{l_1}_{-1_10}\, D^{l_2}_{1_20}$$
$$= \sum (qQpP\,|\,ka)\, (qQqQ\,|\,kb)\, (l_1l_2 - 1_11_2\,|\,ll)\, (l_1l_200\,|\,l0)\, D^k_{ab}\, D^l_{10}$$
$$= \sum (qQpP\,|\,ka)\, (qQqQ\,|\,kb)\, (l_1l_2 - 1_11_2\,|\,ll)\, (l_1l_200\,|\,l0)$$
$$\times (klal\,|\,LL)\, (klb0\,|\,LL')\, D^L_{LL'} \quad (108)$$

Equation (107) can then be written as

$$T(qq;\ QQ) = (2k')^{-2} \sum A(qqQQ;\ q'q'Q'Q';\ \Omega)\, T(q'q';\ Q'Q') \quad (109)$$

where

$$A(qqQQ;\ q'q'Q'Q';\ \Omega)$$
$$= \sum B(l_1s_1l_2s_2qqQQ;\ l'_1s'_1l'_2s'_2q'q'Q'Q';\ LLL'\, J_1J_2)$$
$$\times R_{J_1\Pi_1}\, (\alpha'l'_1s'_1;\alpha l_1s_1)\, R^*_{J_2\Pi_2}\, (\alpha'l'_2s'_2;\alpha l_2s_2)\, D^L_{L'L}\, (\varphi,\theta,0) \quad (110)$$

and the coefficients B contain a very large number of magnetic sums to be performed. Note that the T's contain all directional information on spins before and after the reaction. The A's contain a complete specification of the dynamics of the problem, through the elements of the R-matrix. Finally, the B's contain all geometrical information having to do with the intricacies of compounding angular momenta. This type of formulation was originally used by Blatt and Biedenharn (Bl52a) for the problem of the angular distribution produced by an unpolarized beam on an unpolarized target ($q = q' = Q = Q' = q = q' = Q = Q' = 0$). They brought to bear (as we shall) the powerful methods of Racah for evaluating the B-coefficients. We now write the full expression for B, preparatory to such evaluation:

$$B(l_1s_1l_2s_2qqQQ;\ l'_1s'_1l'_2s'_2q'q'Q'Q';\ LLL'\ J_1J_2)$$
$$= [(2l'_1 + 1)\ (2l'_2 + 1)]^{1/2}\ (2q' + 1)\ (2Q' + 1)\ [(2i' + 1)$$
$$\times\ (2I' + 1)]^{-1}\ (-1)^{l_1 + l_2} \sum_{lklpPab} (2l + 1)\ (l_2l00|l_l0)$$
$$\times\ (klb0|LL)\ (klal|LL')\ (qQqQ|kb)\ (qQpP|ka)$$
$$\times\ M(l_1l_2l'_1l'_2s_1s_2s'_1s'_2qQq'Q'J_1J_2llpP) \quad (111)$$

where M is an abbreviation for a complicated sum over magnetic quantum numbers, given by

$$M = \sum\ (iqi_1p|ii_2)\ (IQI_1P|II_2)\ (i'q'i'_1q'|i'i'_2)\ (I'Q'I'_1Q'|I'I'_2)$$
$$\times\ (i'I'i'_1I'_1|s'_1s'_1)\ (l'_1s'_10s'_1|J_1J_1)\ (l_1s_1l_1s_1|J_1J_1)\ (iIi_1I_1|s_1s_1)$$
$$\times\ (i'I'i'_2I'_2|s'_2s'_2)\ (l'_2s'_20s'_2|J_2J_2)\ (l_2s_2l_2s_2|J_2J_2)$$
$$\times\ (iIi_2I_2|s_2s_2)\ (l_1ll_1l|l_2l_2) \quad (112)$$

where the sum is over $i_1,i_2,I_1,I_2,i'_1,i'_2,I'_1,I'_2,s_1,s_2,s'_1,s'_2,J_1,J_2,l_1,l_2$. There are a very large number of obvious relations between these angular momentum components, set by the elementary property of the Wigner coefficients that the total magnetic quantum number is conserved in coupling two angular momenta. The number of relations is 13 and the number of quantum numbers listed above is 16, so that a three-fold summation is actually to be done.

The sum in Eq. (112) can be performed by the techniques of Racah (Ra42a,Ra42b,Ra43). Illustrations involving similar applications are to be found in the original article of Blatt and Biedenharn (Bl52a), the articles of Simon and Welton (Si53a,Si53b) and the article of Blatt, Biedenharn, and Rose (Bl52b). The algebra involved in the evaluation is elementary but lengthy, and great pains must naturally be taken to avoid error. Unfortunately, many possible mistakes cannot be detected by simple tests, but it is believed that the following results are reliable.

The sum is conveniently split into three separate sums by introduction of four additional Wigner coefficients, which are summed over the appropriate indices to make use of the ortho-normality properties of these coefficients.   Thus:

$$M(l_1 l_2 l'_1 l'_2 s_1 s_2 s'_1 s'_2 q Q q' Q' J_1 J_2 l l p P)$$

$$= [(2s_2 + 1)\ (2s'_2 + 1)]^{-1} \sum_{tt'tt'} (2t + 1)\ U(iI s_1 s_2 q Q p P t t)$$

$$\times\ U(i'I's'_1 s'_2 q' Q' q' Q' t' t')\ V(l_1 l_2 l'_1 l'_2 s_1 s_2 s'_1 s'_2 J_1 J_2 l t t' t t') \quad (113)$$

where

$$U(iI s_1 s_2 q Q p P t t)$$

$$= \sum_{i_1 i_2} (iIi_1 I_1 | s_1 s_1)\ (iI i_2 I_2 | s_2 s_2)\ (i q i_1 p | i i_2)\ (IQ I_1 P | I I_2)\ (s_1 t s_1 t | s_2 s_2) \quad (114)$$

and similarly for $U(i'I's'_1 s'_2 q' Q' q' Q' t' t')$.   The factor V is given by

$$V = \sum_{s_1 s'_1} (l'_1 s'_1 0 s'_1 | J_1 J_1)\ (l_1 s_1 l_1 s_1 | J_1 J_1)(l'_2 s'_2 0 s'_2 | J_2 J_2)$$

$$\times\ (l_2 s_2 l_2 s_2 | J_2 J_2)\ (l_1 l l_1 l | l_2 l_2)\ (s_1 t s_1 t | s_2 s_2)\ (s'_1 t' s'_1 t' | s'_2 s'_2) \quad (115)$$

The first U-factor describes the composition of the final spins, each with specified tensor moment, to obtain the tensor moments of the channel spin.   The second factor describes the same composition for the initial spins.   The V-factor describes the composition of initial channel-spin tensor moment with orbital angular momentum to obtain the contribution to a specified final channel-spin tensor moment with given orbital angular momenta, the whole process being assumed to occur through a definite pair of compound states.   The split into factors very much simplifies the evaluation, each factor being quite similar to a sum which is evaluated somewhere in one of the references given above.

The evaluation of any such sum of products of Wigner coefficients involves the repeated use of two identities, plus a certain amount of trial and error.   The two identities are the usual ortho-normality relation for the Wigner coefficients

$$\sum_a (abab | cc)\ (abab | dd) = \delta(c,d)\ \delta(c,d) \quad (116)$$

and one of the defining relations for the Racah coefficients

$(abab|ee)$ $(eded|cc)$

$$= \sum_f [(2e + 1) (2f + 1)]^{1/2} W(abcd;ef) (bdbd|ff) (afaf|cc) \quad (117)$$

In addition, the various symmetry relations for the Wigner coefficients (Ro57, p. 38) must be freely used. Each time (117) is used, a sum over a new angular momentum variable appears, with a single Racah coefficient and two new Wigner coefficients replacing two previous ones. As this process is continued, it will become possible to use Eq. (116). This will allow one sum over an angular momentum projection to be performed and two Wigner coefficients will disappear, leaving a Kronecker delta involving two angular momenta. One of the sums over auxiliary angular momenta can then be performed. Thus, in U or V, the number of Wigner coefficients finally remaining will be four less than the number initially present, although the number of Racah coefficients which have been introduced is not so simple to state in advance. To sketch the calculation, we number the Wigner coefficients in a term of the sum, from left to right, and make the convention that use of (117) replaces the two factors involved by two new factors in the order of (117) without further change in order or numbering. As permutations of the factors are specified, they will be renumbered so that at the beginning of each step the numbering is from left to right *at that time*. In addition the indices of the Wigner coefficients will be written schematically as (abc) and a permutation of indices will be indicated as $(abc) \rightarrow (acb)$, for example. Any required sign reversals for the projection quantum numbers will not be specified, since these are always obvious.

The steps will be abbreviated as follows:

Recouple (2,3)   means to apply (117) to factors 2 and 3.

(13425)   means to place the factors in the indicated order and renumber.

$(abc \rightarrow acb)_4$ means to rearrange the indices of factor 4 as indicated, and re-letter.

Sum (2,4)   means to perform the magnetic sum
which replaces factors 2 and 4 by a
Kronecker δ. The then available
summation over an auxiliary angular
momentum variable is to be performed. The summed Wigner coefficients are simply deleted and the
remaining coefficients are renumbered
without change in order.

With this notation, the evaluation of U can be described as follows:

1. (15234)
2. Recouple (1,2)
3. $(abc \rightarrow cba)_2$
4. (13245)
5. Recouple (2,3)
6. $(abc \rightarrow cab)_3$
7. $(abc \rightarrow acb)_4$
8. Sum (3,4)
9. (132)
10. $(abc \rightarrow bac)_2$
11. Recouple (2,3)
12. $(abc \rightarrow acb)_1$
13. Sum (1,2).

The result of this sequence of steps is

$U(iIs_1s_2qQqQtt)$

$$= (2s_1 + 1)^{1/2} (2s_2 + 1) (2t + 1)^{-1} [(2i + 1) (2I + 1)]^{1/2}$$

$$\times (-1)^{s_2 - i + I} (QqQq \,|\, tt) \sum_f (2f + 1) (-1)^{2f} W(iIs_2t;s_1f)$$

$$\times W(iIif;s_2q) \, W(QIqf;It) \quad (118)$$

The dependence on the projection quantum numbers is just that of a
simple Wigner coefficient, describing the coupling of angular momenta Q and q to obtain t. The multiplying factor, which is a function of the various angular momentum magnitudes, can be written
more conveniently in terms of the X-function of Fano and Racah
(Fa52).

The X-function is defined by

$$X\begin{pmatrix} abc \\ def \\ ghi \end{pmatrix} = (-1)^s \sum_j (2j+1) \ W(bdcg;ja) \ W(dbfh;je) \ W(gchf;ji) \tag{119}$$

where $s = a + b + c + d + e + f + g + h + i$.

For ease in typesetting, the symbol will be written on a line as $X(abc;def;ghi)$, but the square form is of great value in emphasizing the high degree of sym metry possessed by the symbol. The square can be reflected in the principal diagonal without change in value. If any two rows or columns are interchanged, the value of the symbol is multiplied by $(-1)^s$. Finally, the symbol vanishes unless every row and every column can form a possible triangle, in the sense of the vector model. It is often necessary to evaluate Eq. (119) for a special con bination of its variables. We have

$$X(abc;dec;ggO) = (-1)^{c+g-a-e} \ [(2c+1)(2g+1)]^{-1/2} W(abde;cg) \tag{120}$$

If (119) is used as a guide, the standard symmetry relations for the Racah coefficients can be used to put the sum of Eq. (118) into the standard form [Eq. (119)]. The final result is

$$U(iIs_1s_2qQqQtt)$$

$$= (2s_1+1)^{1/2} (2s_2+1) (2t+1)^{-1/2} [(2i+1) \ (2I+1)]^{1/2}$$
$$\times (qQqQ|tt) \ X(iIs_1;qQt;iIs_2) \tag{121}$$

A very important special case is that where one of the two particles is unpolarized. We then obtain, by use of Eq. (120),

$$U(iIs_1s_2q0q0lt) = (2s_1+1)^{1/2} (2s_2+1) (2q+1)^{-1}$$
$$\times (2i+1)^{1/2} (-1)^{I+q-i-s_2} W(is_1is_2;I,q) \ \delta(q,l) \ \delta(q,t) \tag{122}$$

The sum V can be evaluated by similar manipulations, the de-tailed procedure being specified as follows [the Wigner coefficients are numbered 1 through 7 in Eq. (115)]:

1. $(abc \rightarrow bac)_3$
2. (1273456)
3. Recouple $(3,4)$
4. (1423567)
5. $(abc \rightarrow cab)_1$
6. Recouple $(1,2)$
7. (1324567)
8. Recouple $(2,3)$

9. $(abc \rightarrow cba)_3$
10. (1253467)
11. Recouple $(3,4)$
12. $(abc \rightarrow bac)_3$
13. Recouple $(2,3)$
14. $(abc \rightarrow acb)_3$
15. $(abc \rightarrow acb)_7$
16. Sum $(3,7)$
17. $(abc \rightarrow cab)_3$
18. $(abc \rightarrow acb)_5$
19. Sum $(3,5)$
20. $(abc \rightarrow bac)_1$
21. (312)
22. Recouple $(1,2)$.

The result of these manipulations can be written as a quadruple sum of a set of terms, each of which is a product of three Wigner coefficients and six Racah coefficients. By use of the Racah symmetry relations, two of these sums can be written as X-functions, yielding

$$V(l_1 l_2 l'_1 l'_2 s_1 s_2 s'_1 s'_2 J_1 J_2 l t t' t t')$$
$$= (-1)^{l'_2 + l_1 + l_2 + t' + 1} (2J_1 + 1)(2J_2 + 1)[(2s'_2 + 1)$$
$$\times (2s_2 + 1)(2l_2 + 1)(2l + 1)^{-1}]^{1/2} \sum_{l'} (2l' + 1)^{1/2}$$
$$\times (l'_1 l'_2 00 | l'0) \sum_{f} (2f + 1)^{1/2} (-1)^{f} (t't't'0 | ff)$$
$$\times (flf - 1 | tt) \, X \, (l_1 s_1 J_1 ; l l f ; l_2 s_2 J_2) \, X(l'_1 s'_1 J_1 ; l' t f ; l'_2 s'_2 J_2) \quad (123)$$

The coefficient B can now be assembled, by referring to Eqs. (111), (112), (113), (121), and (123). The result is

$$B(l_1 s_1 l_2 s_2 q q Q Q ; l'_1 s'_1 l'_2 s'_2 q' q' Q' Q' ; L J_1 J_2 L L') = [(2i + 1)$$
$$\times (2I + 1)]^{1/2} [(2i' + 1)(2I' + 1)]^{-1/2} (2q' + 1)(2Q' + 1)$$
$$\times [(2l_1 + 1)(2l_2 + 1)(2l'_1 + 1)(2l'_2 + 1)]^{1/2} [(2s_1 + 1)(2s_2 + 1)$$
$$\times (2s'_1 + 1)(2s'_2 + 1)]^{1/2} (2J_1 + 1)(2J_2 + 1)(-1)^{l_1 + l_2}$$
$$\times (-1)^{l_1 + l'_2 + t'} \sum [(2l + 1)(2l' + 1)(2f + 1)]^{1/2} (2t' + 1)^{+1/2}$$
$$\times (-1)^{f} (-1)^{l} (l'_1 l'_2 00 | l'0) (l_1 l_2 00 | l0) \, X \, (i'I's'_1 ; q'Q't' ; i'I's'_2)$$
$$\times X(iIs_1 ; qQt ; iIs_2) \, X \, (l'_1 s'_1 J_1 ; l't'f ; l'_2 s'_2 J_2) \, X(l_1 s_1 J_1 ; l l f ; l_2 s_2 J_2)$$
$$\times (t't't'0 | ff) (flf - 1 | tt) (qQqQ | kb) (klb0 | LL) (q'Q'q'Q' | t't')$$
$$\times (klal | LL') (qQpP | tt) (qQpP | ka) \quad (124)$$

where the sum is to be performed over $ll'kftt'$abpPtt'. A number of these sums can be performed, using only simple properties of the Wigner coefficients. We number the last eight Wigner coefficients in Eq. (124) from 1 to 8 from left to right. Using the previous notation, we proceed as follows:

1. Sum (7,8)
2. $(abc \rightarrow cba)_2$
3. Sum (2,6).

We are left with four of the original eight coefficients and an expression to be summed over $ll'tt'$:

$$B = [(2i' + 1) (2I' + 1) (2q + 1) (2Q + 1)]^{-1/2}$$

$$\times [(2i + 1) (2I + 1) (2q' + 1) (2Q' + 1)]^{1/2}$$

$$\times F(l_1 l_2 s_1 s_2 J_1 J_2 LL; qQqQ) \, F(l'_1 l'_2 s'_1 s'_2 J_1 J_2 LL'; q'Q'q'Q') \quad (125)$$

where

$$F(l_1 l_2 s_1 s_2 J_1 J_2 LL; qQqQ)$$

$$= [(2J_1 + 1) (2J_2 + 1) (2l_1 + 1) (2l_2 + 1) (2s_1 + 1) (2s_2 + 1)$$

$$\times (2q + 1) (2Q + 1)]^{1/2} \sum_{lt} [(2l + 1) (2t + 1)]^{1/2} (-1)^{h + L}$$

$$\times (l_1 l_2 00 | l0) \, (ll0L | LL) \, (qQqQ | tL) \, X(iI s_1; qQt; iI s_2)$$

$$\times X(l_1 s_1 J_1; ltL; l_2 s_2 J_2) \quad (126)$$

By combining Eqs. (109), (110), and (125) we obtain our final general result:

$$T(qq;QQ) = (2k')^{-2} [(2i + 1) (2I + 1) (2q + 1)^{-1} (2Q + 1)^{-1}]^{1/2}$$

$$\times \sum R_{J_1 \Pi_1}(\alpha' l'_1 s'_1; \alpha l_1 s_1) \, R^*_{J_2 \Pi_2}(\alpha' l'_2 s'_2; \alpha l_2 s_2)$$

$$\times F(l_1 l_2 s_1 s_2 J_1 J_2 LL; qQqQ) \, F(l'_1 l'_2 s'_1 s'_2 J_1 J_2 LL'; q'Q'q'Q')$$

$$\times D^L_{L'L}(\varphi, \theta, 0) [(2i' + 1) (2I' + 1) (2q' + 1)^{-1}$$

$$\times (2Q' + 1)^{-1}]^{-1/2} T(q'q'; Q'Q') \quad (127)$$

For the purpose of studying the general properties of Eq. (127). it is convenient to introduce new quantities in place of the tensor moments. We write

$$M(qq;QQ) = (k)^{-1} [(2q + 1) (2Q + 1) (2i + 1)^{-1}$$

$$\times (2I + 1)^{-1}]^{-1/2} T(qq;QQ) \quad (128)$$

which agrees (except for the k^{-1}) with the normalization which is usually adapted for these quantities. Using an obvious notation, we now have the symmetric expression

$$M = (4kk')^{-1} \Sigma R_1 R_2{}^* F(1,2) F'(1,2) D^L{}_{L'L} M' \quad (129)$$

which will save effort in algebraic manipulations, although it must be considerably expanded for numerical evaluation.

By use of the rule for interchanging arguments of the X-function, as well as parity conservation and the properties of the Wigner coefficients, it is easy to show that

$$F(2,1) F'(2,1) = (-1)^{q + Q + q' + Q'} F(1,2) F'(1,2) \quad (130)$$

This allows Eq. (129) to be rewritten in a form which is more convenient for studying reality properties. Since 1 and 2 are dummy indices, we can write

$$M = (4kk')^{-1} \Sigma {}^{1}/{}_2 [R_1 R_2{}^* F(1,2) F'(1,2)$$

$$+ R_2 R_1{}^* F(2,1) F'(2,1)] D^L{}_{L'L} M' \quad (131)$$

which from (130) becomes

$$M = (4kk')^{-1} \Sigma {}^{1}/{}_2 [R_1 R_2{}^* + (-1)^{q + Q + q' + Q'} R_1{}^* R_2]$$

$$F(1,2) F'(1,2) D^L{}_{L'L} M' \quad (132)$$

It is clear from their definition that the tensor moments satisfy a simple reality condition, namely

$$M^*(qq;QQ) = (-1)^{q + Q} M(q - q;Q - Q)$$

and $\qquad T^*(qq;QQ) = (-1)^{q + Q} T(q - q;Q - Q) \quad (133)$

It is easily verified that Eq. (133) (assumed valid for both M and M') is consistent with Eqs. (129) and (130).

An important relation between a reaction and its inverse can be obtained from (129). Because R is symmetric (time reversal invariance), and since L and L' are dummies, we can write

$$M' = (4kk')^{-1} \Sigma R_1 R_2{}^* F(1,2) F'(1,2) D^L{}_{LL'} M \quad (134)$$

This can be used in discussing the relation between the angular distribution of *polarization* produced by *unpolarized* reactants and the angular distribution of *intensity* produced by *polarized* reactants in the inverse reaction. The symmetry explicitly displayed in Eqs. (129) and (134) was generally proved, in somewhat different form, by Satchler (Sa58).

We now specialize (127) to the case of greatest experimental interest, in which only the incident particle is polarized and the polarization of the residual nucleus is ignored ($Q = Q' = 0$). We further consider two especially interesting sub-cases, the first with $q' = 0$ and the second with $q = 0$. The abbreviation $T(qq)$ will be used for $T(qq;00)$ in the following. We require a special case of the X-function, easily obtained from Eq. (120):

$$X(aeb;f0f;cgd) = (-1)^{e+f-a-d} \, \delta(e,g)$$
$$\times \, [(2e+1)(2f+1)]^{-1/2} \, W(abcd;ef) \quad (135)$$

and thus obtain for $F(1,2) \, F'(1,2)$

$$F(1,2) \, F'(1,2) = (2J_1 + 1)(2J_2 + 1) \, [(2l_1+1)(2l_2+1)(2l'_1+1)$$
$$\times \, (2l'_2+1)(2s_1+1)(2s_2+1)(2s'_1+1)(2s'_2+1)(2q+1)$$
$$\times \, (2q'+1)(2I+1)^{-1}(2I'+1)^{-1}]^{1/2} \, \delta(q,L) \, \delta(q',L')$$
$$\times \, (-1)^{l_1 + l'_1 + I + I' - i - i' - s_2 - s'_2 + q + q'} \, W(is_1is_2;Iq)$$
$$\times \, W(i's'_1i's'_2;I'q') \sum_{ll'} \, [(2l+1)(2l'+1)]^{1/2} \, (l_1l_200 \,|\, l0)$$
$$\times \, (l'_1l'_200 \,|\, l'0)(lq0q \,|\, l_1q)(l'q'0q' \,|\, l_1q') \, X(l_1s_1J_1;lqL;l_2s_2J_2)$$
$$\times \, X(l'_1s'_1J_1;l'q'L;l'_2s'_2J_2) \quad (140)$$

and for $T(qq)$

$$T(qq) = (2k')^{-2} \, [(2q+1)(2i'+1)(2I'+1)]^{-1} \sum [(2i+1)(2i'+1)$$
$$\times \, (2q+1)(2q'+1)]^{1/2} \, (-1)^{I+I'-i-i'-s_2-s'_2} \, W(is_1is_2;Iq)$$
$$\times \, W(i's'_1i's'_2;I'q') \, G_q(J_1l_1s_1;L \; q;J_2l_2s_2) \, G_{q'}(J_1l'_1s'_1;L \; q';J_2l'_2s'_2)$$
$$\times \, \tfrac{1}{2} \, [R_1{}^*R_2 + (-1)^{q+q'}R_2{}^*R_1] \, D^L_{q'q} \, (\varphi,\theta,0) \, T(q'q') \quad (141)$$

The G-function is, to within a phase factor, that defined by Simon (Si53b), and is given by

$$G_q(J_1l_1s_1;L \; q;J_2l_2s_2) = [(2J_1+1)(2J_2+1)(2l_1+1)(2l_2+1)$$
$$\times \, (2s_1+1)(2s_2+1)(2q+1)]^{1/2} \, (-1)^{l_1}$$
$$\times \, \sum_l \, (2l+1)^{1/2} \, (l_1l_200 \,|\, l0)(lq0q \,|\, Lq) \, X(l_1s_1J_1;lqL;l_2s_2J_2) \quad (142)$$

The G-function, like the X-function, is best thought of with its variables put in a square array. Thus the first three form the top row, the next two form a middle row with the central position vacant, and the last three form the bottom row. The first and third rows and the first and third columns must then form possible triangles, and the four quantities which terminate the central row and column (l_1l_2Lq) must form a quadrilateral.

The formula (141), together with the definition (142), embodies the principal result of Simon (Si53b), but with correction of all known phase and normalization errors. Further specialization to the cases $q = 0$ and $q' = 0$ requires

$$G_0(J_1l_1s_1;L\ 0;J_2l_2s_2) = [(2J_1 + 1)\ (2J_2 + 1)\ (2l_1 + 1)$$

$$\times\ (2l_2 + 1)\ (2s_1 + 1)]^{1/2}\ (-1)^{L + s_1 - J_2}\ \delta(s_1,s_2)$$

$$\times\ (l_1l_200|\ L0)W(l_1J_1l_2J_2;s_1L) = (2s_1 + 1)^{1/2}\ \delta(s_1,s_2)$$

$$\times\ (-1)^{L + s_1 - J_2}\ \bar{Z}(l_1J_1l_2J_2;s_1L) \quad (143)$$

where $\bar{Z}$ is the function defined in Eq. (69) of Chapter V.E. Also needed is the usual specialization of the Racah coefficient

$$W(is_1is_2;I0) = (-1)^{i - I + s_1}\ [(2i + 1)\ (2s_1 + 1)]^{-1/2}\ \delta(s_1,s_2) \quad (144)$$

For the case $q' = 0$, we now have

$$T(qq) = (2k')^{-2}\ [(2i' + 1)(2I' + 1)]^{-1}\ (2i + 1)^{1/2}\ (2q + 1)^{-1/2}$$

$$\times\ \sum\ (-1)^{I - i + s' - s_2 - J_2 + L}\ \bar{Z}\ (l'_1J_1l'_2J_2;s'L)$$

$$\times\ W(is_1is_2;\ Iq)\ G_q(J_1l_1s_1;L\ q;J_2l_2s_2)$$

$$\times\ {}^1\!/_2[R_1{}^*R_2 + (-1)^qR_2{}^*R_1]\ D^L{}_{0q}\ (\varphi,\theta,0) \quad (145)$$

and for $q = 0$

$$T(00) = \frac{d\sigma}{d\Omega} = (2k')^{-2}\ [(2i' + 1)(2I' + 1)]^{-1}$$

$$\times\ \sum\ (-1)^{I' - i' + s - s'_2 - J_2 + L}\ [(2i' + 1)(2q' + 1)]^{1/2}$$

$$\times\ \bar{Z}\ (l_1J_1l_2J_2;\ sL)\ W(i's'_1i's'_2\ I'q')\ G_{q'}(J_1l'_1s'_1;L\ q';J_2l'_2s'_2)$$

$$\times\ {}^1\!/_2\ [R_1{}^*R_2 + (-1)^{q'}\ R_2{}^*R_1]\ D^L{}_{q'0}(\varphi,\theta,0)\ T(q'q') \quad (146)$$

Equation (145) is the general formula (with corrected phase and normalization) obtained by Simon and Welton (Si53a).

The D^L_{0q} can be written in terms of the usual spherical har-monics. Wigner (Wi31) has shown that

$$D^L_{q'q}(\varphi,\theta,\chi) = e^{-iq'\varphi} d^L_{q'q}(\theta) e^{-iqx} \qquad (147)$$

The $d^L_{q'q}$ is a polynomial of degree L in $\sin\theta$ and $\cos\theta$ with a simple symmetry property

$$d^L_{q'q} = (-1)^{q'-q} d^L_{qq'} = d^L_{-q-q'} \qquad (148)$$

If $q = 0$ in Eq. (147), we have (Ro57, p. 60)

$$D^L_{q'0}(\varphi,\theta,0) = (4\pi/2L+1)^{1/2} Y^*_{Lq'}(\theta,\varphi) \qquad (149)$$

and from Eqs. (148) and (149) we have

$$
\begin{aligned}
D^L_{0q}(\varphi,\theta,0) &= (4\pi/2L+1)^{1/2} (-1)^q Y^*_{Lq}(\theta,0) \\
&= (4\pi/2L+1)^{1/2} Y_{L-q}(\theta,0)
\end{aligned}
\qquad (150)
$$

Finally, it is convenient to introduce the ordinary associated Legendre polynomials, since the $(4\pi)^{1/2}$ in Eqs. (149) and (150) is present only to allow the introduction of the Y_{Lq}. We accordingly write

$$(4\pi/2L+1)^{1/2} Y_{Lq}(\theta,\varphi) = i^{|q|+q} [(L-|q|)!]^{1/2}$$
$$\times [(L+|q|)!]^{-1/2} P_L^{|q|}(\cos\theta) e^{iq\varphi} \qquad (151)$$

where $P_L^{|q|}(\cos\theta)$ is the Legendre's associated function of the first kind defined in Jahnke and Emde (Ja33, p. 111). Some care must be used with these functions, since the $P_L^{|q|}$ defined by some authors differs from the above by a factor $(-1)^q$.

Although present experimental techniques make it unlikely that the general D-functions will be needed in the near future, we give for completeness a summary of the properties of these functions. We have, from Eq. (147)

$$D^L_{q'q}(\varphi,\theta,0) = d^L_{q'q}(\theta) e^{-iq'\varphi} \qquad (152)$$

where the $d^L_{q'q}(\theta)$ are simply related to the Jacobi polynomials, the most general polynomials which are at the same time hypergeometric functions. We have

$$d^L_{q'q}(\theta) = [(L-q)!(L+q')!]^{1/2} [(L+q)!(L-q')!]^{-1/2}$$
$$\times [(q'-q)!]^{-1} (-1)^{q'-q} [(1+\cos\theta)/2]^{L-1/2(q'-q)}$$
$$\times [(1-\cos\theta)/2]^{1/2(q'-q)} {}_2F_1[(-L+q', -L-q;$$
$$q'-q+1; -(1-\cos\theta)/(1+\cos\theta)] \qquad (153)$$

for $q' \geq q$. For $q' < q$, Eq. (148) is used to interchange q and q', so that Eq. (153) can be used. Finally, the $_2F_1$ function is defined by the hypergeometric series:

$$_2F_1(a.b;c;z) = 1 + \frac{ab}{c1!}\,z + \frac{a(a+1)\,b(b+1)}{c(c+1)2!}\,z^2 + \cdots \quad (154)$$

When a and b are negative integers, as in Eq. (153), the series terminates as soon as the first zero factor appears in a numerator.

As a check on our work, it is useful at this point to consider Eq. (145) for the cases $q = 0$ (scattering of an unpolarized beam) and $q = 1$ (polarization resulting from an unpolarized beam). First, for $q = 0$, we obtain

$$T(00) = d\sigma/d\Omega = (2k')^{-2}\,[(2i'+1)\,(2I'+1)]^{-1}\sum(-1)^{s-s'}$$

$$\times \bar{Z}(l_1J_1l_2J_2;sL)\,\bar{Z}(l'_1J_1l'_2J_2;s'L)$$

$$\times \tfrac{1}{2}\,[R_1{}^*R_2 + R_2{}^*R_1]\,P_L\,(\cos\theta) \quad (155)$$

which is seen to be identical with that given by combining Eqs. (67), (68), and (69) of Chapter V.E. For simplicity, whenever $s_1 = s_2$ or $s'_1 = s'_2$ in the foregoing work, they have been replaced by s or s'.

It should be noted that we have made an arbitrary choice of phase in the definition of the R-matrix. The Wigner coefficients $(lsls\,|\,JJ)$ and $(iIiI\,|\,ss)$ which appear in Eq. (82) could each have had their first two arguments interchanged without altering any matter of principle. Each such change will, however, produce a change in the final formula [Equation (127)], but each such change can be compensated by introducing a factor $(-1)^{s+s'}$ in $R_{JII}(\alpha'l's';\alpha ls)$, which does not affect its symmetry.

The case $q = 1$ provides another useful check. We have

$$T(1\ 0) = (2k')^{-2}\,[(2i'+1)\,(2I'+1)]^{-1}$$

$$\times \sum(-1)^{I-i+s'-s_2-J_2+L}\,(3)^{-1/2}\,(2i+1)^{1/2}$$

$$\times \bar{Z}(l'_1J_1l'_2J_2;s'L)\,W(is_1is_2;I1)\,G_0(J_1l_1s_1;L\ 1;J_2l_2s_2)$$

$$\times \tfrac{1}{2}\,[R_1{}^*R_2 - R_2{}^*R_1]\,P_L(\cos\theta) \quad (156)$$

From the Wigner coefficients appearing in the definition of G_q, a useful relation is apparent

$$G_{-q}(J_1l_1s_1;L\ q;J_2l_2s_2) = (-1)^{l_1+l_2+L+q}\,G_q(J_1l_1s_1;L\ q;J_2l_2s_2) \quad (157)$$

The parity-conserving Wigner coefficient in the definition of $\bar{Z}$ requires that $l'_1 + l'_2 + L$ be even. In addition, parity conservation requires $l'_1 + l'_2 + l_1 + l_2$ to be even, so that the phase factor in Eq. (157) is simply $(-1)^q$. Consequently, $G_0 = 0$ if q is odd, and $T(1\ 0)$ vanishes identically.

For $T(1 \pm 1)$, we have

$$T(1\ 1) = T(1 - 1) = (2k')^{-2}\ [(2i' + 1)(2I' + 1)]^{-1}$$
$$\times \sum (-1)^{I - i + s' - s_2 - J_2 + L}\ (3)^{-1/2}\ (2i + 1)^{1/2}$$
$$\times \bar{Z}(l'_1 J_1 l'_2 J_2; s'L)\ W(is_1 i s_2; I1)\ G_1(J_1 l_1 s_1; L\ 1; J_2 l_2 s_2)$$
$$\times \tfrac{1}{2}[R_1^* R_2 - R_2^* R_1][L(L + 1)]^{-1/2}\ P_L^1(\cos \theta) \quad (158)$$

which is purely imaginary.

From Eq. (66) we have, remembering that the intensity of the beam is not unity, but rather $T(00) = d\sigma/d\Omega$:

$$T(1,q) = [i(i + 1)]^{-1/2} \langle S_q \rangle\ (d\sigma/d\Omega) \quad (159)$$

In order to gain agreement with previous formulae, we define the fractional polarization as

$$f = (i)^{-1}[|\langle S_1 \rangle|^2 + |\langle S_0 \rangle|^2 + |\langle S_{-1} \rangle|^2]^{1/2} \quad (160)$$

so that a beam which consists of a pure magnetic substate, of maximum projection in some direction, will have $f = 1$. From the definition [Equation (61)], and the results [Eqs. (156) and (158)], we see that

$$\langle S_z \rangle\ d\sigma/d\Omega = [i(i + 1)]^{1/2}\ T(1\ 0) = 0 \quad (161a)$$

$$\langle S_x \rangle\ d\sigma/d\Omega = -(2)^{-1/2} \langle S_1 - S_{-1} \rangle\ d\sigma/d\Omega$$
$$= (2)^{-1/2}\ [(i(i + 1)]^{1/2}\ [T(1\ 1) - T(1 - 1)] = 0 \quad (161b)$$

$$\langle S_y \rangle\ d\sigma/d\Omega = i(2)^{-1/2} \langle S_1 + S_{-1} \rangle\ (d\sigma/d\Omega)$$
$$= i(2)^{-1/2}\ [i(i + 1)]^{1/2}\ [T(1\ 1) + T(1 - 1)] \quad (161c)$$

We see that the outgoing beam is polarized in its y direction. The y axis for the outgoing beam was defined, prior to Eq. (105), to be in the direction of the vector $\mathbf{k}' \times \mathbf{k}$. We accordingly define f to be $i^{-1} \langle S_y \rangle$, so that

$$f(\theta)\ (d\sigma/d\Omega) = i[2(i + 1)\ (i)^{-1}]^{1/2}\ T(1\ 1) \quad (162)$$

This result is essentially identical with that obtained by Simon and Welton (Si53a), after correction of the phase error first noted by Huby (Hu54). We note the general result that the polarization ($q = 1$) produced by reaction of unpolarized particles must always be perpendicular to the scattering plane (assuming parity conservation!). The interference character of the polarization is clear, since $T(1\ 1)$ will vanish if R_1 and R_2 refer to the same set of quantum numbers. Thus, $T(1\ 1)$ will vanish unless two J values, or two different l or s values contribute.

8. Illustrative Examples

We first consider the experimentally interesting case of the production of a beam of polarized particles by a reaction involving only unpolarized incident particles. This illustrative example should demonstrate the correct usage of the concepts which we have taken so much trouble to introduce, and at the same time should yield a useful check of the formulae which we have derived. A byproduct will be some understanding of the saving in labor which is possible by use of our formulae. The derivation which has been given is after all rather complicated. The labor involved in a single polarization calculation scarcely justifies so much effort in derivation, the real saving being made only when such polarization calculations must be made frequently, with values of the various angular momenta which are not trivially small.

Consider the system discussed in Section 2, the scattering of neutrons by He^4. We need consider only one alternative ($n + \alpha \rightarrow n + \alpha$), one channel spin ($s' = s = {}^1/_2$), and one orbital angular momentum ($l' = l = 1$). The only non-vanishing elements of the R-matrix have $J = {}^1/_2$ or ${}^3/_2$ and $\Pi = -1$. The alternative and parity designations will be deleted, and we obtain

$$R_{1/_2}(1\ {}^1/_2;\ 1\ {}^1/_2) = \exp(2i\ \delta_{1/_2}) - 1$$
$$R_{3/_2}(1\ {}^1/_2;\ 1\ {}^1/_2) = \exp(2i\ \delta_{3/_2}) - 1 \tag{163}$$

with all other elements vanishing.

We have $i' = i = {}^1/_2$, $I' = I = 0$, so that the formulae specialized to $Q = 0$ will be used. The unpolarized state of the incident beam implies that $T(0\ 0) = 1$ and all other T-components vanish for the incident neutrons. We require the final $T(qq)$. The simplest is $T(0\ 0)$, the differential cross section, being given by Eq. (155):

$$d\sigma/d\Omega = (2k')^{-2}\ ^1/_2\ \{[\,|R_{1/_2}|^2\ \bar{Z}^2(1\ ^1/_2\ 1\ ^1/_2;\ ^1/_2\ 0)$$
$$+\ (R^*_{1/_2}\ R_{3/_2} + R^*_{3/_2}\ R_{1/_2})\ \bar{Z}^2(1\ ^1/_2\ 1\ ^3/_2;\ ^1/_2\ 0)$$
$$+\ |R_{3/_2}|^2\ \bar{Z}^2(1\ ^3/_2\ 1\ ^3/_2;\ ^1/_2\ 0)]\ P_0\ (\cos\theta)$$
$$+\ [\,|R_{1/_2}|^2\ \bar{Z}^2(1\ ^1/_2\ 1\ ^1/_2;\ ^1/_2\ 2)$$
$$+\ (R^*_{1/_2}\ R_{3/_2} + R^*_{3/_2}\ R_{1/_2})\ \bar{Z}^2\ (1\ ^1/_2\ 1\ ^3/_2;\ ^1/_2\ 2)$$
$$+\ |R_{3/_2}|^2\ \bar{Z}^2\ (1\ ^3/_2\ 1\ ^3/_2;\ ^1/_2\ 2)]\ P_2\ (\cos\theta)\} \quad (164)$$

Several features are immediately obvious. The interference term between $J = {}^1/_2$ and $^3/_2$ in the P_0 term vanishes, because the $(^1/_2, ^3/_2, 0)$ combination in $\bar{Z}(1\ ^1/_2\ 1\ ^3/_2;\ ^1/_2\ 0)$ cannot form a triangle. Similarly, the coefficient $|R_{1/}|^2$ does not enter the P_2 term. We list the relevant values of the $\bar{Z}$-coefficients obtained from Si54a and Si54b, or Ro59:

$$[\bar{Z}(1\ ^1/_2\ 1\ ^1/_2;\ ^1/_2\ 0)]^2 = 2$$
$$[\bar{Z}(1\ ^1/_2\ 1\ ^3/_2;\ ^1/_2\ 0)]^2 = 0$$
$$[\bar{Z}(1\ ^3/_2\ 1\ ^3/_2;\ ^1/_2\ 0)]^2 = 4$$
$$[\bar{Z}(1\ ^1/_2\ 1\ ^1/_2;\ ^1/_2\ 2)]^2 = 0$$
$$[\bar{Z}(1\ ^1/_2\ 1\ ^3/_2;\ ^1/_2\ 2)]^2 = 4$$
$$[\bar{Z}(1\ ^3/_2\ 1\ ^3/_2;\ ^1/_2\ 2)]^2 = 4$$

The differential cross section follows immediately:

$$d\sigma/d\Omega = (2k')^{-2}\ \{|R_{1/_2}|^2 + 2|R_{3/_2}|^2 + [R^*_{1/_2}R_{3/_2} + R^*_{3/_2}R_{1/_2}$$
$$+\ |R_{3/_2}|^2]\ (3\cos^2\theta - 1)\} \quad (165)$$

and is easily shown to be identical with that previously derived by an unsophisticated approach, and given in Eq. (41). The fractional polarization f must be set equal to zero to obtain this case.

We now calculate the polarization of the scattered neutron beam by use of Eqs. (158) and (162). We have

$$f(\theta)(d\sigma/d\Omega) = i(6)^{1/2}\ T(1\ 1)$$
$$= (6)^{1/2}\ ^1/_2\ (^2/_3)^{1/2}\ (2k')^{-2} \sum\ ^1/_2\ (R_1{}^*R_2 - R_1R_2{}^*)$$
$$\times\ (-1)^{-1/2 + L - J_2}\ W(^1/_2\ ^1/_2\ ^1/_2\ ^1/_2;\ 0\ 1)\ \bar{Z}(1\ J_1\ 1\ J_2;\ ^1/_2\ L)$$
$$\times\ G_1(J_1\ 1\ ^1/_2; L\ 1; J_2\ 1\ ^1/_2)\ [L(L + 1)]^{-1/2}\ P_L{}^1(\cos\theta) \quad (166)$$

Because of the required interference for $q = 1$, we must have either $J_1 = {}^1/_2$ and $J_2 = {}^3/_2$, or the reverse, and the indicated summation is simply over these two alternatives. Parity conservation and the triangular conditions in the $\bar{Z}$-coefficient restrict L to the single value (2) and we obtain

$$f(\theta)(d\sigma/d\Omega) = i(k')^{-2} \, {}^1/_2 \, (6)^{-1/2} \, P_2{}^1 \, (\cos \theta)$$

$$\times \, {}^1/_2 \, (R^*{}_{1/2}R_{3/2} - R^*{}_{3/2}R_{1/2}) \, W({}^1/_2 \, {}^1/_2 \, {}^1/_2 \, {}^1/_2; \, 0 \, 1)$$

$$\times \, \bar{Z} \, (1 \, {}^1/_2 \, 1 \, {}^3/_2; \, {}^1/_2 \, 2) \, G_1 \, ({}^1/_2 \, 1 \, {}^1/_2; \, 2 \, 1; \, {}^3/_2 \, 1 \, {}^1/_2) \quad (167)$$

The relevant W, $\bar{Z}$, and G-coefficients are

$$W({}^1/_2 \, {}^1/_2 \, {}^1/_2 \, {}^1/_2; \, 0 \, 1) = {}^1/_2$$

$$\bar{Z}(1 \, {}^3/_2 \, 1 \, {}^1/_2; \, 2) = (3 \cdot 4 \cdot 3 \cdot 2)^{1/2} \, (1 \, 1 \, 0 \, 0 | 2 \, 0) \, W(1 \, {}^3/_2 \, 1 \, {}^1/_2; \, {}^1/_2 \, 2)$$

$$= 6(2)^{1/2} \, ({}^2/_3)^{1/2} \, (12)^{-1/2}$$

$$= 2$$

$$G_1({}^3/_2 \, 1 \, {}^1/_2; \, 2 \, 1; \, {}^1/_2 \, 1 \, {}^1/_2) = (4 \cdot 2 \cdot 3 \cdot 3 \cdot 2 \cdot 2 \cdot 3)^{1/2} \, (-1)$$

$$\times \sum_l \, (2l + 1)^{1/2} \, (1 \, 1 \, 0 \, 0 | l \, 0) \, (l \, 1 \, 0 \, 1 | 2 \, 1)$$

$$\times \, X(1 \, {}^1/_2 \, {}^3/_2; \, l \, 1 \, 2; \, 1 \, {}^1/_2 \, {}^1/_2) = 12(10)^{1/2}$$

$$\times \, X(1 \, {}^1/_2 \, {}^3/_2; \, 2 \, 1 \, 2; \, 1 \, {}^1/_2 \, {}^1/_2) = 12(10)^{1/2} \sum_j \, (2j + 1)$$

$$\times \, W({}^1/_2 \, 2 \, {}^1/_2 \, 1; \, j1) \, W(2 \, {}^1/_2 \, 2 \, {}^1/_2; \, j1) \, W(1 \, {}^1/_2 \, {}^1/_2 \, 2; \, j \, {}^3/_2)$$

$$= 48(10)^{1/2} \, W({}^1/_2 \, 2 \, {}^1/_2 \, 1; \, {}^3/_2 \, 1) \, W(2 \, {}^1/_2 \, 2 \, {}^1/_2; \, {}^3/_2 1)$$

$$\times \, W(1 \, {}^1/_2 \, {}^1/_2 \, 2; \, {}^3/_2 \, {}^3/_2) = (6)^{1/2}$$

and the final result is

$$f(\theta)(d\sigma/d\Omega) = -3i(2k')^{-2} \, (R_{3/2}R^*{}_{1/2} - R^*{}_{3/2}R_{1/2}) \sin \theta \cos \theta \quad (168)$$

This is identical with Eq. (46), save for an apparent reversal of sign. The expression for β in Eq. (47), however, shows that the sense of polarization axis thus defined is opposite to the sense assumed in Eq. (168), so that a reversal in sign is actually required.

Another simple illustration of the use of the formalism is the calculation of the reaction of a polarized deuteron beam with tritium. This reaction was originally proposed by Galonsky, Willard, and Welton (Ga59) as a convenient way of testing the efficiency of a polarized source of charged particles, and was studied more extensively by Gold-farb (Go59b) who previously (Go58) had made a more general study of reactions involving polarized deuterons. In this reaction relatively slow deuterons react with tritons to give energetic neutrons. Because only the s-wave is involved for the deuteron, the reaction does not *produce* polarization. If, however, the incident beam is polarized, both anisotropy and polarization of the final neutrons will result.

The reaction is specified as follows:

$$
\begin{array}{llll}
i' = 1 & q' = 0, 1, 2 & J_1 = J_2 = {}^3/_2 & \\
I' = {}^1/_2 & Q' = 0 & l'_1 = l'_2 = 0 & s'_1 = s'_2 = {}^3/_2 \\
i = {}^1/_2 & q = 0, 1 & l_1 = l_2 = 2 & s_1 = s_2 = {}^1/_2 \\
I = 0 & Q = 0 & &
\end{array}
$$

The single element of R involved is

$$R = R_{3/2+} \, (d\mathrm{T} \; 0 \; {}^3/_2; \, n\alpha \; 2 \; {}^1/_2) \tag{169}$$

all other possibilities being ruled out by the resonance character of the reaction, and considerations of centrifugal barrier height.

We assume that the incident beam has been prepared by a polarizing device which possesses a single axis of polarization. The polarization state of the beam is described by giving the fractional populations of the three magnetic substates defined by choosing a quantization axis along the polarization axis of the source. Choosing this axis to be the direction of the incident beam, and denoting the fractional populations by f_1, f_0, f_{-1}, we have from Eqs. (66) and (71):

$$
\begin{aligned}
T(0 \; 0) &= 1 \\
T(1 \; 0) &= (2)^{-1/2} \, (f_1 - f_{-1}) \\
T(1 \pm 1) &= 0 \\
T(2 \; 0) &= (10)^{-1/2} \, (f_1 - 2f_0 + f_{-1}) \\
T(2 \pm 1) &= 0 \\
T(2 \pm 2) &= 0
\end{aligned} \tag{170}
$$

If desired, the tensor moments for other choices of the polarization axis can be obtained from Eq. (168) by transformation with the appropriate D matrices. Because l' is necessarily zero, however, this transformation will have trivial consequences, as will become apparent.

We first use Eq. (146) to obtain the differential cross section, remembering that $T(1\ 0)$ cannot contribute because $G_0(J_1 l'_1 s'_1; L\ 1; J_2 l'_2 s'_2)$ vanishes:

$$d\sigma/d\Omega = -(2k')^{-2}\,(12)^{-1/2}\,|R|^2$$
$$\times \{\bar{Z}(2\ ^3/_2\ 2\ ^3/_2;\ ^1/_2\ 0)\ W(1\ ^3/_2\ 1\ ^3/_2;\ ^1/_2\ 0)$$
$$\times G_0\,(^3/_2\ 0\ ^3/_2;\ 0\ 0;\ ^3/_2\ 0\ ^3/_2) + (10)^{-1/2}\,(f_1 - 2f_0 + f_{-1})$$
$$\times (5)^{1/2}\,\bar{Z}(2\ ^3/_2\ 2\ ^3/_2;\ ^1/_2\ 2)$$
$$\times G_0(^3/_2\ 0\ ^3/_2;2\ 2;\ ^3/_2\ 0\ ^3/_2)\ ^1/_2\,(3\ cos^2\theta - 1)\} \quad (171)$$

As observed by Galonsky *et al.*, this differential cross section is simply transformed by rotation when the polarization axis is rotated to an arbitrary direction. This is so because the initial *s*-wave precludes the introduction of any directional information from the beam direction. The reaction simply serves to convert deuteron polarization into a corresponding anisotropy of the angular distribution, through the agency of the spin-orbit interaction.

Numerical values for the functions required in Eq. (171) are

$$\bar{Z}(2\ ^3/_2\ 2\ ^3/_2;\ ^1/_2\ 0) = -2$$
$$\bar{Z}(2\ ^3/_2\ 2\ ^3/_2;\ ^1/_2\ 2) = 2$$
$$W(1\ ^3/_2\ 1\ ^3/_2;\ ^1/_2\ 0) = (12)^{-1/2}$$
$$W(1\ ^3/_2\ 1\ ^3/_2;\ ^1/_2\ 2) = ^1/_2\,(6)^{-1/2}$$
$$G_0(^3/_2\ 0\ ^3/_2;0\ 0;^3/_2\ 0\ ^3/_2) = 4$$
$$G_0(^3/_2\ 0\ ^3/_2;2\ 2;^3/_2\ 0\ ^3/_2) = 4$$

and the desired result becomes

$$d\sigma/d\Omega = ^1/_6\,(k')^{-2}\,|R|^2\,[1 - ^1/_4(f_1 - 2f_0 + f_{-1})$$
$$\times (3\cos^2\theta - 1)] \quad (172)$$

As a further illustration of these methods, we calculate the neutron polarization produced in the $T(d,n)\alpha$ reaction if the incident deuterons are polarized as previously specified. For this purpose, the fairly general formula [Eq. (141)] must be used. We require the final $T(1q)$, given the initial $T(1q')$ and $T(2q')$. Again the mediation of the reaction by an *s*-wave means that the initial spin quantization axis can be arbitrarily chosen along the incident beam direction. Any rotation of this initial spin state will simply result in simultaneous identical rotations of the final polarization state and angular distribution. We therefore again take the initial tensor moments to be given by Eq. (170).

Because only a single R-matrix element is non-zero, $q + q'$ must be even to avoid cancellation. so that only $T(1q')$ can enter. Thus

$$T(1q) = -(2k')^{-2} |R|^2 (6)^{-1/2} W(1/2 \; 1/2 \; 1/2 \; 1/2; 0 \; 1)$$
$$\times W(1 \; 3/2 \; 1 \; 3/2; 1/2 \; 1) \; G_q(3/2 \; 2 \; 1/2; 1 \; 1; 3/2 \; 2 \; 1/2)$$
$$\times G_0(3/2 \; 0 \; 3/2; 1 \; 1; 3/2 \; 0 \; 3/2) \; (2)^{-1/2} (f_1 - f_{-1}) \; D^1_{0q} \quad (173)$$

The single term $L = 1$ is allowed by the properties of the G-functions. The required numerical values are

$$W(1/2 \; 1/2 \; 1/2 \; 1/2; 0 \; 1) = 1/2$$

$$W(1 \; 3/2 \; 1 \; 3/2; 1/2 \; 1) = -1/12 \; (10)^{1/2}$$

$$G_0(3/2 \; 0 \; 3/2; 1 \; 1; 3/2 \; 0 \; 3/2) = 16(3)^{1/2} \; X(0 \; 3/2 \; 3/2; 0 \; 11; 0 \; 3/2 \; 3/2) = 4$$

$$G_{\pm 1}(3/2 \; 2 \; 1/2; 1 \; 1; 3/2 \; 2 \; 1/2) = -8(10)^{-1/2}$$

$$G_0(3/2 \; 2 \; 1/2; 1 \; 1; 3/2 \; 2 \; 1/2) = 4(10)^{-1/2}$$

$$D^1_{00} = \cos \theta$$

$$D^1_{0\pm 1} = \pm (2)^{-1/2} \sin \theta$$

and the $T(1q)$ become

$$T(1 \; 0) = (k')^{-2} |R|^2 \; 1/12 \; (3)^{-1/2} (f_1 - f_{-1}) \cos \theta$$
$$T(1 \pm 1) = \mp (k')^{-2} |R|^2 \; 1/6 \; (6)^{-1/2} (f_1 - f_{-1}) \sin \theta \quad (174)$$

Comparison with Eq. (61) immediately shows that the polarization must lie in the scattering plane, with $\langle S_x \rangle$ and $\langle S_z \rangle$ different from zero. (Note that the coordinate system for the outgoing beam is such that positive $\langle S_z \rangle$ signifies polarization in the direction of the outgoing beam, and positive $\langle S_x \rangle$ signifies polarization in the direction of increasing θ.) From Eq. (61), we obtain

$$2 \langle S_z \rangle \; (d\sigma/d\Omega) = (3)^{1/2} T(1 \; 0)$$
$$= 1/12 \; (k')^{-2} |R|^2 (f_1 - f_{-1}) \cos \theta$$

$$3 \langle S_x \rangle \; (d\sigma/d\Omega) = -(6)^{1/2} T(1 \; 1)$$
$$= 1/6 \; (k')^{-2} |R|^2 (f_1 - f_{-1}) \sin \theta \quad (175)$$

If transversely polarized neutrons are desired, θ should clearly be taken to be $\pi/2$. The fractional polarization can then be found by dividing by the expression (172) for $d\sigma/d\Omega$. with $\theta = \pi/2$. We obtain

$$2 \langle S_x \rangle = (f_1 - f_{-1}) \left(\frac{5}{4} - \frac{3}{4} f_0 \right)^{-1} \qquad (176)$$

All of these results agree with those of Galonsky et al., which in turn agree with the more general results of Goldfarb for the same problem. Although this illustrative example is quite simple, it should serve to make clear all of the problems encountered in a typical calculation.

9. General Polarization Experiments

We have so far considered only cases where $Q = 0$, so that any possible polarization of the residual nucleus is ignored in the measurement. It is, of course, a trivial modification to set $q = 0$ and find instead the polarization state of the residual nucleus. A somewhat more complicated situation obtains if simultaneous measurements of the polarization states of both final particles are attempted. Both the outgoing beam at some angle, and the recoil nuclei, in their corresponding direction, could be used as incident particles in scattering experiments sensitive to beam polarization. If $T(qq)$ and $T(QQ)$ are the separate tensor moments for the two beams in such an experiment, we can describe the experimental arrangement in terms of two detector efficiencies. We let d and D be the respective probabilities of obtaining a count in the appropriate detection system when one particle of a beam with the above tensor moments is incident.

It is convenient to express these detection efficiencies as

$$d = \sum_{qq} d(qq) \ T(qq) \ [T(00)]^{-1} \qquad (177)$$

with a similar set of coefficients $D(QQ)$ for the experiment on the recoil nuclei. These coefficients characterize the two detection systems completely. They can be calculated by use of our general formulae, if the detection involves a second scattering or reaction and the R-matrix for this reaction is known. Otherwise, an experimental determination of the coefficients may be possible. Another possibility is that the angular distribution of a secondary radiation emitted by the detected particle is observed, in which case the appropriate coefficients can be determined from elementary angular correlation theory, once the angular momentum and parity assignments for the initial and final states are known.

If the two detectors are simultaneously used, it is easy to show that the probability of recording a count, with one particle incident, becomes

$$P = \sum_{q q Q Q} d(qq) \, D(QQ) \, T(qq; QQ) \, [T(00;00)]^{-1} \qquad (178)$$

This relation provides the formal basis for designing a set of experiments to obtain full information concerning the R-matrix for a reaction. There are $(2i + 1)^2 \, (2I + 1)^2$ different combinations of q,q,Q, and Q, and this is the number of independent detector arrangements which can be used to obtain angular distributions, in conjunction with $(2i' + 1)^2 \, (2I' + 1)^2$ different incident beams (with independent polarization properties). Such a full set of experiments in principle gives maximum information about the R-matrix, although experiments of this complexity can scarcely be regarded as routine.

10. Photon Reactions

As indicated previously, a special case must be made of reactions in which photons enter, although much of the approach used in previous sections is applicable. The reactions which are of importance for the present treatment are the (γ,n) and (n,γ) reactions, with the possibility of an arbitrary elliptical polarization state for the single photon involved The problem of finding a convenient, yet rigorous, theoretical framework for the calculation has proven quite troublesome in the past, the reason being obvious enough. All treatments of nuclear reactions have utilized the many-body, non-relativistic Schrödinger equation as a basis, while the photon inevitably appears as a seemingly foreign, relativistic field theoretical object in the calculation. This conceptual difficulty has actually not been allowed to interfere with the work, the usual procedure being to think of the vector potential as a sort of wave function for the photon. Its vector character corresponds to unit spin for the photon and, if due provision is made for the transverse character of the vector potential, results for the various tensor moments can be obtained which are undoubtedly correct. This approach was used by Simon (Si53b), Spiers (Sp49), Lane and Thomas (La58), Devons and Goldfarb (De57), and by Morita, Sugie, and Yoshida (Mo54). The original formulae of Simon (Si53b) must be revised by correction of several unfortunate errors and inclusion of a result given by Kennedy and Sharp (Ke54) before they become useful. The material to follow consists first of an attempt to sketch what is hoped to be an adequate theoretical framework for the treatment of nuclear reactions which involve photons, and second of a sketch of the derivation of a set of formulae which include previous formulae as special cases and which are hoped to be free of error and ambiguity.

An adequate theoretical framework can be achieved by appeal to the formalism of relativistic field theory. Nothing like the complete formalism is required for our purpose, since we need only the result that there exists an R-matrix for every reaction, with properties already largely given. The R-matrix is therefore the unifying element in a treatment which would otherwise contain elements too diverse to be easily joined.

We have then only to postulate a form for the R-matrix which will allow an adequate description of an initial or final state involving a photon. A suitable form is

$$(\Omega',i',I',\alpha' \,|\, R \,|\, \Omega,i,I,\alpha) \tag{179}$$

as previously, with a change in interpretation. If, for example, a photon is the outgoing particle, then the index i is a three-valued quantity, with each of the associated three quantities playing the role of components of a vector amplitude, either on a rectangular or spherical basis. This vector amplitude is the quantity which properly plays the role usually assigned to the vector potential.

To develop the theory further, we note that the transversality of the radiation field is contained in the statement that the vector which we have defined is perpendicular to a unit vector, with components Ω_i, in the direction of the outgoing particle. Thus, for an (n,γ) reaction

$$\sum_{i=-1}^{1} (1\ 1\ i\ -\ i | 0\ 0)\ \Omega_{-i}(\Omega',i',I',\alpha' \,|\, R \,|\, \Omega,i,I,\alpha) = 0 \tag{180}$$

where the spherical basis has been used, and the Wigner coefficient is required to form the scalar product. The work for a (γ,n) reaction is completely analogous and will not be separately given.

We must use an expansion for R, analogous to Eq. (82), which will automatically satisfy the transversality condition, Eq. (180).

For this purpose, the conventional transverse vector spherical harmonics must be introduced. We use j for the total angular momentum (spin *plus* orbital) of a given vector harmonic, and introduce a subscript p, which is zero for a magnetic multipole and unity for an electric multipole. The required transformation functions from the (jjp) representation to the (Ω,i) representation (vector spherical harmonics) are

$$(jj0|\Omega i) = (j1j - ii|jj)(jj - i|\Omega) \tag{181}$$

$$(jj1|\Omega i) = 2^{-1/2}(2j + 1)^{-1/2}[(j + 1)^{1/2}(j-11j-ii|jj)$$
$$\times (j-1\,j-i|\Omega) + (j)^{1/2}(j + 1\,1j-ii|jj)(j + 1\,j-i|\Omega)] \tag{182}$$

It is easily verified that Eqs. (181) and (182) satisfy the transversality condition, analogous to Eq. (180)

$$\sum_i (11i - i|00)\,\Omega_{-i}(jjp|\Omega i) = 0 \tag{183}$$

and that the $(jjp|\Omega i)$ are orthonormal with respect to j,j, and p when summed over i and integrated over Ω. Simon (Si53b) has written the vector spherical harmonics in more compact form as follows:

$$(jjp|\Omega i) = 2^{-1/2}\sum_l \epsilon(ljp)(j1-11|l0)(l1j-ii|jj)(lj-i|\Omega) \tag{184}$$

where

$$\epsilon(jj0) = \epsilon(j+1j1) = \epsilon(j-1j1) = 1$$

and $\epsilon(l\,jp)$ vanishes otherwise.

The required expansion of the R-matrix, analogous to Eq. (82) is clearly

$$(\Omega',i',I',\alpha'|R|\Omega,i,I,\alpha)$$
$$= \sum (\Omega'|l'l')(i'I'i'I'|s's')(l's'l's'|JJ)R_{JII}(\alpha'l's';\alpha jp)$$
$$\times (jIjI|JJ)(jjp|\Omega,i) \tag{185}$$

Instead of combining i and I to form s and then combining l and s to form J, as in Eq. (82), we effectively combine i and l to form j, and then combine j and I to form J. The coefficients R_{JII} are amplitudes for an incident wave, specified by l' and s' (compounded to form J) to yield an outgoing wave of definite multipolarity, specified by j and p (compounded with I to form J). It is easily verified that the general requirements for the R-matrix, as set forth at the end of Section 6, are all satisfied, and we therefore proceed with confidence to an evaluation of the final tensor moments in terms of the initial moments.

Although the concept of the tensor moment can be readily taken over for the description of the polarization state of a photon beam, some discussion is necessary if proper account is to be taken of the transversality condition. A simple way of proceeding is to augment the two transverse vector spherical harmonics by including a third, longitudinal, harmonic with $p = 2$, say. The transversality condition is then completely equivalent to the following two conditions, added to the conventional treatment of particles with unit spin:

A. $R_{J\pi} = 0$ for $p = 2$

B. If a photon is *incident*, and its spin angular momentum is quantized with respect to its direction of motion, the state with zero projection is absent.

Condition A of course means that no longitudinally polarized photons can result from a reaction, but we are free to use all existing mathematical machinery appropriate to the treatment of a non-relativistic particle with unit spin. We accordingly define three amplitudes a_1, a_0, and a_{-1} for the components of the "wave-function" of a photon corresponding to the three possible projections of spin angular momentum along the direction of motion (positive z direction). We define a density matrix as in Section 2:

$$\langle i_1 | i_2 \rangle = \langle a_{i_1} a^*_{i_2} \rangle \tag{186}$$

with, of course, the understanding that the matrix has zeros along its middle row and middle column. We have, in fact, a four-element density matrix, but the connection with our previous work is simple only if the nine-element form is assumed.

We then define the tensor moments by Eq. (56), thus obtaining (formally) *nine* different quantities

$$T(qq) = \sum_{i_1 i_2} (1qi_1q | 1i_2) \langle i_1 | i_2 \rangle \tag{187}$$

for $0 \leq q \leq 2$ and $-q \leq q \leq q$. Actually, only five of these quantities are nonvanishing, and only four (as intuitively required) are independent. Thus

$$T(00) = \langle 1 | 1 \rangle + \langle -1 | -1 \rangle \tag{188}$$

$$T(10) = 2^{-1/2} [\langle 1 | 1 \rangle - \langle -1 | -1 \rangle] \tag{189}$$

$$T(2 \pm 2) = 4(^3/_5)^{1/2} \langle \mp 1 | \pm 1 \rangle \tag{190}$$

$$T(20) = 10^{-1/2} [\langle 1 | 1 \rangle + \langle -1 | -1 \rangle] = 10^{-1/2} T(00) \tag{191}$$

and $T(qq) = 0$, otherwise.

Physically, $T(00)$ is (as before) the intensity and $T(10)$ is proportional to the fractional polarization along the beam direction. If $\langle -1 | -1 \rangle = 0$, the beam is completely *circularly* polarized in the right hand sense, while, for $\langle 1 | 1 \rangle = 0$, the beam is completely circularly polarized in the left hand sense. Thus if we define f_c as the fraction of *right circular polarization* in the beam ($f_c = -1$ for full *left* circular polarization), we can write

$$T(10) = 2^{-1/2} f_c T(00) \tag{192}$$

The quantity $T(20)$ is redundant, because of the transversality requirement, and is always to be calculated by multiplying $T(00)$ by $10^{-1/2}$. The two quantities $T(2 \pm 2)$, on the other hand, specify the linear polarization, if any. To show this, we introduce two new amplitudes, which are clearly the x and y components of the vector amplitude. Thus

$$a_1 = -2^{-1/2}(a_x + ia_y)$$
$$a_{-1} = 2^{-1/2}(a_x - ia_y) \tag{193}$$

and $T(2 \pm 2)$ becomes

$$T(2 \pm 2) = -2(^3/_5)^{1/2} \{ \langle a_x a_x^* \rangle - \langle a_y a_y^* \rangle \mp i \langle a_y a_x^* \rangle \mp i \langle a_x a_y^* \rangle \} \tag{194}$$

For a beam which is a mixture of unpolarized and circularly polarized radiation, $T(2 \pm 2)$ clearly vanishes. If, on the other hand, the radiation contains a linearly polarized component described by

$$a_x = a \cos \chi$$
$$a_y = a \sin \chi \tag{195}$$

then

$$T(2 \pm 2) = -2(^3/_5)^{1/2} |a|^2 e^{\pm 2i\chi}] \tag{196}$$

Since in this case $T(00) = |a|^2$, we can clearly write in general

$$T(2 \pm 2) = -2(^3/_5)^{1/2} e^{\pm 2i\chi} f_L T(00) \tag{197}$$

where f_L is the fractional content of linearly polarized radiation in the beam and χ is the azimuth of the polarization direction, measured from the x axis in the direction of the y-axis.

If we now combine the R-matrix expansion [Eq. (185)] with the definition of the tensor moments, we obtain an expression similar to Eq. (109)

$$T(qq;QQ) = (2k')^{-2} \sum A(qq\zeta Q;q'q'Q'Q';\Omega)\, T(q'q';Q'Q') \quad (198)$$

where

$$A(qqQQ;q'q'Q'Q';\Omega)$$
$$= \sum B(j_1p_1j_2p_2qq\zeta Q;l'_1s'_1l'_2s'_2q'q'Q'Q';LLL'J_1J_2)$$
$$\times R_{J_1\Pi_1}(\alpha'l'_1s'_1;\alpha j_1p_1)\, R^*_{J_2\Pi_2}(\alpha'l'_2s'_2;\alpha j_2p_2)\, D^L{}_{L'L}(\varphi,\theta,0) \quad (199)$$

and

$$B = (2q'+1)(2Q'+1)\,[(2i'+1)(2I'+1)]^{-1}$$
$$\times [(2l'_1+1)(2l'_2+1)]^{1/2} \sum (i'q'i'_1q'|i'i'_2)(I'Q'I'_1Q'|I'I'_2)$$
$$\times (i'I'i'_1I'_1|s'_1s'_1)(i'I'i'_2I'_2|s'_2s'_2)(l'_1s'_10s'_1|J_1J_1)(l'_2s'_20s'_2|J_2J_2)$$
$$\times \sum [(2l_1+1)(2l_2+1)]^{1/2}(-1)^h\,(l_1l_200|l0)(l_1l_2-l_1l_2|ll)$$
$$\times (lqlp|jj)(lq0q|jq)\,\epsilon(j_1l_1p_1)\,\epsilon(j_2l_2p_2)$$
$$\times (1qi_1p|1i_2)(l_11l_1i_1|j_1j_1)(l_21l_2i_2|j_2j_2)(I\zeta I_1P|I\Pi_2)$$
$$\times (j_1Ij_1I_1|J_1J_1)(j_2Ij_2I_2|J_2J_2)(jQjP|LL')(iQqQ|LL) \quad (200)$$

The evaluation of (200) follows along lines similar to those sketched for our previous general result [Eq. (127)], and will not be completely described. One new type of summation is required, as pointed out by Kennedy and Sharp (Ke54). We have in (200) a summation over an unobservable orbital angular momentum of a photon, and it is reasonable to expect that this quantity can be eliminated. We consider the sum

$$\sum_{\substack{l_1l_2l\\l_1l_2l\\i_1i_2p}} (-1)^h\,[(2l_1+1)(2l_2+1)]^{1/2}\,(l_1l_200|l0)(l_1l_2-l_1l_2|ll)(lqlp|jj)$$

$$\times (lq0q|jq)(1qi_1p|1i_2)(l_11l_1i_1|j_1j_1)$$
$$\times (l_21l_2i_2|j_2j_2)\,\epsilon(j_1l_1p_1)\,\epsilon(j_2l_2p_2)$$
$$= \sum_{l_1l_2l} [(2l_1+1)(2l_2+1)]^{1/2}\,(l_1l_200|l0)(lq0q|jq)\,\epsilon(j_1l_1p_1)\,\epsilon(j_2l_2p_2)$$
$$\times C(l_1l_2lj_1j_2jqq) \quad (201)$$

The sum $C(l_1 l_2 l j_1 j_2 jqq)$ is easily done, yielding

$$C = (-1)^{l + l_2} [(3(2j + 1)(2l + 1)(2j_1 + 1)]^{1/2}$$

$$\times X(l_1 1 j_1; l q j; l_2 1 j_2) (j_1 j j_1 j | j_2 j_2) \quad (202)$$

so that (201) becomes

$$[3(2j + 1)(2j_1 + 1)]^{1/2} (j_1 j j_1 j | j_2 j_2) \sum_{l_1 l_2 l} [(2l_1 + 1)$$

$$\times (2l_2 + 1)(2l + 1)]^{1/2} (-1)^{l_1}(l_1 l_2 00 | l0)(l q 0 q | j q) \epsilon(j_1 l_1 p_1)$$

$$\times \epsilon(j_2 l_2 p_2) X(l_1 1 j_1; l q j; l_2 1 j_2) \quad (203)$$

Kennedy and Sharp give, with some change in notation, and correction of an apparent misprint, an expression for the sum which appears in (203). Thus (203) becomes

$$[(3)(2j_1 + 1)(2j_2 + 1)]^{1/2} (-1)^{j_1 + j_2} (j_1 j_2 - j_1 j_2 | jj)$$

$$\times E_q(j_1 p_1; j_2 p_2; jq) \quad (204)$$

where

$$E_0 = \frac{1}{2} (-1)^{j_1 + 1} (2q + 1)^{-1/2} [1 + (-1)^{j_1 + j_2 + j + q + p_1 + p_2}$$

$$\times (11 - 11 | q0)(j_1 j_2 1 - 1 | j0) \quad (205a)$$

$$E_1 = E_{-1} = 0 \quad (205b)$$

$$E_2 = (-1)^{j_1 + j_2 + j + p_1 + p_2} E_{-2}$$

$$= \frac{1}{2} (-1)^{j_1 + p_2} (2q + 1)^{-1/2} (j_1 j_2 11 | j2)\delta(q,2) \quad (205c)$$

If (204) is now substituted in Eq. (200), the remaining sums over angular momentum projections can be done by the methods previously explained. The coefficient B becomes

$$B = [(2i' + 1)(2I' + 1)(2q' + 1)^{-1}(2Q' + 1)^{-1}]^{-1/2}$$

$$\times [(3)(2I + 1)(2q + 1)^{-1} (2Q + 1)^{-1}]^{1/2}$$

$$\times F(l'_1 l'_2 s'_1 s'_2 J_1 J_2 L L'; q' Q' q' Q')$$

$$\times H(j_1 j_2 p_1 p_2 J_1 J_2 L L; q Q q Q) \quad (206)$$

where F is defined by Eq. (126) and

$$H(j_1 j_2 p_1 p_2 J_1 J_2 LL; qQqQ) = [(2J_1 + 1)(2J_2 + 1)$$
$$\times (2j_1 + 1)(2j_2 + 1)(2q + 1)(2Q + 1)]^{1/2} \sum_j (2j + 1)^{1/2}$$
$$\times (-1)^{j + L + q} E_q(j_1 p_1; j_2 p_2; jq)(jQqQ|LL)$$
$$\times X(j_1 I J_1; jQL; j_2 I J_2) \quad (207)$$

The corresponding formula for the case of photon in and particle out is obtained by an obvious set of interchanges

$$B = {}^3\!/_2\, [(3)(2I' + 1)(2q' + 1)^{-1}(2Q' + 1)^{-1}]^{-1/2}$$
$$\times [(2i + 1)(2I + 1)(2q + 1)^{-1}(2Q + 1)^{-1}]^{1/2}$$
$$\times F(l_1 l_2 s_1 s_2 J_1 J_2 LL; qQqQ)$$
$$\times H(j'_1 j'_2 p'_1 p'_2 J_1 J_2 LL'; q'Q'q'Q') \quad (208)$$

For the case of photon in and photon out, we obtain

$$B = {}^3\!/_2\, [(3)(2I' + 1)(2q' + 1)^{-1}(2Q' + 1)^{-1}]^{-1/2}$$
$$\times [(3)(2I + 1)(2q + 1)^{-1}(2Q + 1)^{-1}]^{1/2}$$
$$\times H(j_1 j_2 p_1 p_2 J_1 J_2 LL; qQqQ)$$
$$\times H(j'_1 j'_2 p'_1 p'_2 J_1 J_2 LL'; q'Q'q'Q') \quad (209)$$

The factor ${}^3\!/_2$ at the beginning of Eqs. (208) and (209) is required to allow for the fact that the transversality condition allows only 2 possible polarization states for an incident photon, whereas the factor $3(=2\cdot1 + 1)$ enters the formalism in a natural way, as the degeneracy factor for an incident "particle" of unit spin. It should be noted that this factor follows in a simple fashion from the rules we have laid down, if the relation (191) is used, and we now make the convention that the redundant $T(20)$ for the photon beam is to be set equal to zero in all calculations using Eq. (198) and the following formulae.

Although we have given the general results for completeness, it will be more useful in practice to simplify Eqs. (206), (208), and (209) to the case of unpolarized target and residual nucleus ($Q = Q' = 0$). All that is necessary is to replace the F-function by the G-function defined in Eq. (142) and the H-function by a simpler function. Thus

$$F(l_1l_2s_1s_2J_1J_2LL;q0q0) = (-1)^{L+I+q-i-s_2}$$
$$\times [(2I+1)(2q+1)]^{-1/2} W(is_1is_2;Iq)$$
$$\times G_q(J_1l_1s_1;L \ q;J_2l_2s_2) \, \delta(q,L), \quad (210)$$

and

$$H(j_1j_2p_1p_2J_1J_2LL;q0q0) = (-1)^{L+I-j_1-J_2+q}$$
$$\times [(2J_1+1)(2J_2+1)(2j_1+1)(2j_2+1)(2q+1)(2I+1)^{-1}]^{1/2}$$
$$\times E_q(j_1p_1j_2p_2;Lq) \ W(j_1J_1j_2J_2;IL) \, \delta(q,L) \quad (211)$$

We can illustrate the use of these formulae, and simultaneously support their validity, by applying them to the case of radiative capture of slow neutrons by some target nucleus. We assume the incident neutron beam to be partially polarized and the target to be unpolarized. Thus, the tensor moments for the incident beam will vanish except for

$$T(00) = 1$$
$$T(10) = f_n(3)^{-1/2} \quad (212)$$

where f_n is the fractional polarization. The polarization has been assumed to be in the positive beam direction. No loss of generality is involved, since only zero neutron orbital angular momentum contributes, and a spatial rotation of the polarization is equivalent to the same rotation of the final angular distributions.

It will be convenient to assume that the photon emitted on neutron capture is magnetic dipole, and the interaction will be assumed to be strongly resonant. Thus, we have only a single value of J (and Π), $l'_1 = l'_2 = 0$, $j_1 = j_2 = 1$, and $p_1 = p_2 = 0$. The target nucleus is unpolarized and the polarization of the residual nucleus is ignored, so that $Q = Q' = 0$. Since $q' = 0$ or 1, the selection rules force us to consider only $q = 0$ or 1.

The R-matrix now has only four non-vanishing elements, with the two possible channels designated by the letters n and γ. Since $l'_1 = l'_2 = 0$, s' must have the single value J, and we accordingly have

$$R_{J\Pi}(n0J;n0J) = R_{11}$$
$$R_{J\Pi}(n0J;\gamma10) = R_{12}$$
$$R_{J\Pi}(\gamma10;n0J) = R_{21}$$
$$R_{J\Pi}(\gamma10;\gamma10) = R_{22} \quad (213)$$

The two R's with incident photon have been added for completeness. Such a two-dimensional R-matrix can always be written as

$$R = U^{-1}(e^{2i\Delta} - 1)U \tag{214}$$

where U is a simple real rotation matrix (characterized by a single rotation angle η), and Δ is a diagonal phase-shift matrix. We write

$$e^{2i\Delta} = \begin{pmatrix} e^{2i\delta_1} & 0 \\ 0 & e^{2i\delta_1} \end{pmatrix} \tag{215}$$

and further note that only one δ (δ_1, say) will be near $\pi/2$ (except by coincidence), while $e^{2i\delta_2}$ can be taken as unity. Thus

$$\begin{pmatrix} R_{11} & R_{12} \\ R_{21} & R_{22} \end{pmatrix} = 2ie^{i\delta}\sin\delta \begin{pmatrix} \cos\eta & -\sin\eta \\ \sin\eta & \cos\eta \end{pmatrix}\begin{pmatrix} 1 & 0 \\ 0 & 0 \end{pmatrix}\begin{pmatrix} \cos\eta & \sin\eta \\ -\sin\eta & \cos\eta \end{pmatrix}$$

$$= 2ie^{i\delta}\sin\delta \begin{pmatrix} \cos^2\eta & \sin\eta\cos\eta \\ \sin\eta\cos\eta & \sin^2\eta \end{pmatrix} \tag{216}$$

In order to make connection with the elementary Breit-Wigner formula, we note that if $E \simeq E_0$ (E_0 = the resonance energy), we will have the relations

$$\delta = \tan^{-1}\frac{\Gamma/2}{E_0 - E}$$

$$2ie^{i\delta}\sin\delta = i\Gamma/(E_0 - E + i\,\Gamma/2)$$

$$\Gamma_\gamma = \Gamma\sin^2\eta$$

$$\Gamma_n = \Gamma\cos^2\eta$$

$$\Gamma_\gamma + \Gamma_n = \Gamma \tag{217}$$

We now use Eqs. (198), (199), (206), (210), and (211) to calculate the tensor moments of the outgoing photon beam. The selection rules are easily seen to require $q = q' = L$, so that the two non-vanishing photon tensor moments are given by

$$T(00) = (d\sigma/d\Omega) = (2k')^{-2}\left|R_{J\text{II}}(n0J;\gamma10)\right|^2$$

$$\times B(10100000;0J0J0000;000JJ)D^0{}_{00}(\varphi,\theta,0) \tag{218}$$

$$T(10) = 2^{-1/2}f_c\,(d\sigma/d\Omega) = (2k')^{-2}(3)^{-1/2}f_n\left|R_{J\text{II}}(n0J;\gamma10)\right|^2$$

$$\times B(10101000;0J0J1000;100JJ)D^1{}_{00}(\varphi,\theta,0) \tag{219}$$

The two B-coefficients are given from (206) by

$$B(10100000;0J0J0000;000JJ) = (2J + 1) [(2)(2I' + 1)]^{-1} \quad (220)$$

$$B(10101000;0J0J1000;100JJ) = (2J + 1) [(2)(2I' + 1)]^{-1}$$

$$\times 4(3)^{1/2} [J(J + 1) + (1/2)(3/2) - I'(I' + 1)]$$

$$\times [J(J + 1)(1/2)(3/2)]^{-1/2} [J(J + 1) + (1)(2) - I(I + 1)]$$

$$\times [J(J + 1)(1)(2)]^{-1/2} \quad (221)$$

We require $D^1_{00}(\varphi,\theta,0)$ and $D^0_{00}(\varphi,\theta,0)$. By use of Eqs. (149) and (151), we obtain

$$D^0_{00} = 1$$
$$D^1_{00} = \cos \theta \qquad (222)$$

The final formulae can now be assembled, with the help of Eqs. (213), (216), and (217). We obtain

$$d\sigma/d\Omega = (2k')^{-2} (2J + 1) [(2)(2I' + 1)]^{-1}$$

$$\times \Gamma_n\Gamma_\gamma [(E - E_0)^2 + \Gamma^2/4]^{-1} \quad (223)$$

$$f_c = 1/4 (2)^{1/2} f_n \cos \theta [J(J + 1) + (1/2)(3/2) - I'(I' + 1)]$$

$$\times [J(J + 1)(1/2)(3/2)]^{-1/2} [J(J + 1) + (1)(2) - I(I + 1)]$$

$$\times [J(J + 1)(1)(2)]^{-1/2} \quad (224)$$

The result for the differential cross section [Eq. (223)] is im-mediately recognizable as the correct Breit-Wigner form, with the required isotropic angular distribution. The result for the fractional circular polarization [Eq. (224)] has a maximum value proportional to the neutron polarization. The angular distribution for f_c with an arbitrary neutron polarization direction can, of course, be obtained by a simple rotation of the $\cos \theta$.

11. Selection Rules and Complexity of Angular Distributions

The formulae which we have derived possess a number of general features which are quite useful. Many of these features have already been stated or implied, and others are apparent from the illustrative examples, but remain to be explicitly formulated. The first complete statement of the so-called selection rules for reactions with polarization was given by Simon (Si53b), who generalized the concise treatment of Blatt and Biedenharn (Bl52a). We first consider reactions in which *one* initial particle and *one* final particle are unpolarized. Angular information is supplied to the reaction by the tensor moments for the incoming and outgoing beams. The reaction is mediated through one or more compound states with specified total angular momenta and orbital angular momenta. The resulting angular distribution will possess a complexity (maximum value of the sum of the exponents of sin θ and cos θ in a single term of the distribution) which must be less than some upper limit set by the ranks of the highest nonvanishing tensor moments and the relevant angular momenta.

To begin, the complexity of a given term of Eq. (141) is just L, the angular momentum parameter entering $D^L_{q'q}$. Consider the term in the sum which describes the interference between two R-matrix elements, $R_{J_1\Pi_1}(\alpha'l'_1s'_1;\alpha l_1s_1)$ and $R_{J_2\Pi_2}(\alpha'l'_2s'_2;\alpha l_2s_2)$. We seek the largest value of L entering the coefficient of $R_1{}^*R_2$. One obvious requirement is imposed by one triangle condition in the G-functions, namely

$$|J_1 - J_2| \leq L \leq J_1 + J_2 \tag{225}$$

The definition of the G-function [Eq. (142)] requires

$$\begin{aligned} ||l_1 - l_2| - q| &\leq L \leq l_1 + l_2 + q \\ ||l'_1 - l'_2| - q'| &\leq L \leq l'_1 + l'_2 + q' \end{aligned} \tag{226}$$

so that the values of L resulting from the interference between two transitions, 1 and 2, will satisfy

$$\begin{aligned} L &\leq J_1 + J_2 \\ L &\leq l_1 + l_2 + q \\ L &\leq l'_1 + l'_2 + q' \end{aligned} \tag{227}$$

Two of these inequalities can be slightly tightened. If 1 and 2 refer to compound states of the same parity, then parity conservation requires $l_1 + l_2$ and $l'_1 + l'_2$ to be even. If now q = 0, the definition of the G-function requires $q + L$ to be even. We therefore see that if q is even (odd) and q' is odd (even), L is even (odd), and $l'_1 + l'_2 + q'$ is odd (even). It therefore follows that if $q + q'$ is odd, and q = 0, $L < l'_1 + l'_2 + q'$, the equality being no longer possible. A symmetrical result, of course, holds with primed and unprimed quantities interchanged.

Another useful rule is similarly obtained if $q = q' = 0$. In this case, $q + L$ and $q' + L$ must both be even, so that $q + q'$ must be even for a non-vanishing result to be obtained. It is this rule, stemming directly from parity conservation, which forbids the production of a longitudinally polarized beam by an unpolarized incident beam.

All the above rules are directly applicable to the case of reactions involving photons. Care must, however, be taken to avoid confusion of the term polarization as herein used with the term as customarily used in optics. Thus, a *longitudinally* polarized (in our sense) photon beam possesses *circular* polarization (in the conventional optical sense). If, for example, we consider the case in which a photon beam is produced by a reaction with unpolarized particles, we see that no circular polarization of the photon beam can result ($q' = q' = q = 0, q = 1$). It is, however, a simple matter for *linear* polarization ($q = 2, q = \pm 2$) to be so produced.

All of the preceding rules can be generalized to the case of $Q, Q' \neq 0$ by reference to the general formulae previously obtained [Eqs. (126) and (127)]. Thus

$$L \leq J_1 + J_2$$

$$L \leq l_1 + l_2 + q + Q \qquad (228)$$

$$L \leq l'_1 + l'_2 + q' + Q'$$

the possibility of equality in the last relation is removed if $\Pi_1 = \Pi_2$, $q = Q = 0$, and $q + Q + q' + Q'$ is odd, and similarly with interchange of primed and unprimed quantities. If $q = Q = q' = Q' = 0$, it follows immediately that $q + Q + q' + Q'$ must be even.

The last point to be mentioned is that, since for $q + Q + q' + Q'$ odd the R-matrix elements must appear in the combination $R_1^*R_2 - R_2^*R_1$, considerable restriction is placed on the conditions under which polarization can be obtained. Thus, if it is desired to obtain a polarized neutron beam from an unpolarized particle beam, we have $q = 1, q = \pm 1, q' = Q' = Q = q' = Q' = Q = 0$. Only interference terms of the above form can therefore enter. As originally discussed by Simon and Welton (Si53a,Si54c), there accordingly exist several alternatives. These are:

(1.) The reaction may involve an accidental overlapping of two distinct resonances, so that a high cross section results.

(2.) The reaction may involve a single resonance plus interfering potential amplitudes for other J,Π combinations. If these interfering amplitudes are sufficiently large, an adequate yield of polarized neutrons may result.

(3.) The reaction may involve a single resonance with several possible initial or final channel spins or orbital angular momenta. Considerations of barrier height unfortunately often prevent this mechanism from being useful.

References

(Ba61)   Baldin, Goldanskii, and Rozenthal, *Kinematics of Nuclear Reactions* (English Translation), Pergamon Press, London, 1961.

(Bi52)   L. C. Biedenharn, "Tables of Racah Coefficients," *Oak Ridge National Laboratory Report* ORNL-1098, unpublished (1952).

(Bl51)   R. J. Blin-Stoyle, *Proc. Phys. Soc. (London)* **64A**, 700 (1951).

(Bl52a)   J. M. Blatt and L. C. Biedenharn, *Revs. Modern Phys.* **24**, 258 (1952).

(Bl52b)   Blatt, Biedenharn, and Rose, *Revs. Modern Phys.* **24**, 249 (1952).

(Co51)   F. Coester, *Phys. Rev.* **84**, 1259 (1951).

(Co53)   F. Coester and J. M. Jauch, *Helv. Phys. Acta* **26**, 3 (1953).

(De57)   S. Devons and L. Goldfarb, "Angular Correlations," in *Handbuch der Physik*, Vol. 42, S. Flügge, ed., Springer, Berlin, 1957.

(Fa52)   U. Fano, *National Bureau of Standards Report* No. 1214 (1952).

(Ga59)   Galonsky, Willard, and Welton, *Phys. Rev. Letters* **2**, 349 (1959).

(Go58)   L. J. B. Goldfarb, *Nuclear Phys.* **7**, 622 (1958).

(Go59a)   L. J. B. Goldfarb and J. R. Rook, *Nuclear Phys.* **12**, 494 (1959).

(Go59b)   L. J. B. Goldfarb, *Nuclear Phys.* **12**, 657 (1959).

(Hu54)   R. Huby, *Proc. Phys. Soc. (London)* **67A**, 1103 (1954).

(Ja33)   E. Jahnke and F. Emde, *Tables of Functions with Formulae and Curves*, B. G. Teubner, Leipzig, 1933.

(Ke54)   J. M. Kennedy and W. T. Sharp, *Phys. Rev.* **95**, 440 (1954).

(La58)   A. M. Lane and R. G. Thomas, *Revs. Modern Phys.* **30**, 257 (1958).

(Le50)   J. V. Lepore, *Phys. Rev.* **79**, 137 (1950).

(Mo54)   Morita, Sugie, and Yoshida, *Prog. Theoret. Phys.* **12**, 713 (1954).

(Ob53)   Obi, Ishidzu, Horie, Yanagowa, Tanabe, and Sato, *Ann. Tokyo Astron. Observ., Second Series III* No. 3, **89** (1953).

(Ob54)   Obi, Ishidzu, Horie, Yanagowa, Tanabe, and Sato, *Ann. Tokyo Astron. Observ., Second Series IV* No. 1, **1** (1954).

(Ob55)   Obi, Ishidzu, Horie, Yanagowa, Tanabe, and Sato, *Ann. Tokyo Astron. Observ., Second Series IV* No. 2, **77** (1955).

(Ra42a)   G. Racah, *Phys. Rev.* **61**, 186 (1942).

(Ra42b)   G. Racah, *Phys. Rev.* **62**, 438 (1942).

(Ra43)   G. Racah, *Phys. Rev.* **63**, 367 (1943).

(Ro57)   M. E. Rose, *Elementary Theory of Angular Momentum*, Wiley, New York, 1957.

(Ro59)   Rotenberg, Bivins, Metropolis, and Wooten, *The 3-j and 6-j Symbols*, Technology Press, Cambridge, Mass., 1959.

(Sa53)   G. R. Satchler, *Proc. Phys. Soc. (London)* **66A**, 1081 (1953).

(Sa58)   G. R. Satchler, *Nuclear Phys.* **8**, 65 (1958).

(Sc46)   J. Schwinger, *Phys. Rev.* **69**, 681 (1946).

(Sc48)   J. Schwinger, *Phys. Rev.* **73**, 407 (1948).

(Sh57)   M. I. Shirokov, *Zhur. Eksperiment. i Teoret. Fiz.* **32**, 1022 (1957).

(Si53a) A. Simon and T. A. Welton, *Phys. Rev.* **90**, 1036 (1953).

(Si53b) A. Simon, *Phys. Rev.* **92**, 1050 (1953).

(Si54a) Simon, Vander Sluis, and Biedenharn, "Tables of the Racah Coefficients," *Oak Ridge Laboratory Report* ORNL-1679, unpublished (1954).

(Si54b) A. Simon "Numerical Table of the Clebsch-Gordan Coefficients," *Oak Ridge National Laboratory Report* ORNL-1718, unpublished (1954).

(Si54c) A. Simon and T. A. Welton, *Phys. Rev.* **94**, 943 (1954).

(Sp49)   J. A. Spiers, *Directional Effects in Radioactivity*, National Research Council of Canada, Ontario, 1949.

(Wi31)   E. P. Wigner, *Gruppentheorie*, Friedrich Vieweg und Sohn, Braunschweig, 1931; also translated by J. J. Griffen, Academic Press. New York, 1950.

(Wi47)   E. P. Wigner and L. Eisenbud, *Phys. Rev.* **72**, 29 (1947).

(Wo49)   L. Wolfenstein, *Phys. Rev.* **75**, 1664 (1949).

(Wo54)   L. Wolfenstein, *Phys. Rev.* **96**, 1654 (1954).

(Wo56)   L. Wolfenstein, *Ann. Rev. Nucl. Sci.* **6** (1956).

Polarization of Neutrons in Reactions and Scattering

W. Haeberli

University of Wisconsin, Madison, Wisconsin

1. Introduction and Summary

In the study of neutron-producing reactions (Chapters I.C, I.D, I.E) the incident charged particles as well as the target nuclei are usually unpolarized, i.e. their spins are randomly oriented in space. The outgoing neutrons, however, are in general *polarized* because of the strong spin-orbit coupling in nuclear reactions. This was pointed out first by Wolfenstein in 1948 for the specific case of the D-D reaction (Wo49). His suggestion was based on a paper by Konopinski and Teller (Ko48) who had shown that the interpretation of the D-D reaction cross section requires a large amount of *p*-wave interaction with strong spin-orbit coupling.

Since conventional neutron detectors measure the number of neutrons irrespective of their spin orientation, special arrangements have to be used to detect the polarization. For slow neutrons the transmission through magnetized iron is known to depend on the orientation of the spin relative to the direction of magnetization and consequently can be used to detect (or "analyze") the polarization of a beam. For fast neutrons nuclear elastic scattering is commonly used as a polarization-analyzer. In this method use is made of the fact that in the presence of spin-orbit coupling neutrons with spin up are preferentially scattered to one side of the incident beam, those with spin down to the other. Thus, if there are more "up" than "down" neutrons in the beam, the flux scattered to one side will be higher than the flux scattered through the same angle to the other side. The ratio of right- to left-scattered flux clearly depends on *two* quantities: on the degree of polarization in the incident beam; and on the extent to which the scattering is sensitive to the spin orientation of the neutrons, i.e. the "analyzing power" of the scatterer. The two quantities cannot be separated experimentally. Consequently one has to use as a scatterer a nucleus for which the analyzing power can be calculated. This is possible for some light nuclei where the resonance parameters are known from the analysis of total and differential cross sections. The characteristics of different light nuclei as polarization-analyzers are summarized in Section 5.

The idea to detect the presence of polarization in a beam of neutrons by resonance scattering was originally proposed by Schwinger. He pointed out already in 1946 (Sc46) that the scattering of neutrons by helium shows evidence for a large spin-orbit splitting in the p-state, and that for neutron energies near 1 Mev n-He^4 scattering should be a good polarization analyzer. One now knows that this is the case over a much wider energy range, because the widths and the splitting of the $P_{1/2}$ and $P_{3/2}$ levels in He^5 were subsequently found to be much larger than had first been assumed.

The first experiments which showed that nucleons produced in a reaction are polarized, and that the polarization can be detected by resonance scattering, were reported in 1952. Bishop, Preston, Westhead, and Halban (Bi52) discovered the polarization of protons from the D-D reaction by scattering from helium. At about the same time Huber and Baumgartner (Hu53,Ba53) and Ricamo (Ri53,Ri53a) observed the polarization of D-D neutrons. These experiments used scattering by carbon as polarization analyzer.

It turned out to be quite difficult to obtain reliable values for the neutron polarization because of the very indirect way in which the analyzing power of the scatterers had to be deduced. This has remained one of the serious problems in polarization experiments. In principle the analyzing power of a scatterer can be obtained directly from a double scattering experiment, i.e. two successive scatterings by the same nucleus. However, for reasons of intensity and background, double scattering of neutrons is not feasible. A different approach to this problem was proposed by Barschall (Ba56) who pointed out that the polarization of neutrons produced in a reaction can, in certain cases, be measured directly if the inverse reaction rather than a scattering is used for analysis. This method is discussed in more detail in Section 2. Another possibility is to look for scatterers for which the analyzing power can be calculated accurately. This is the case for small-angle scattering from heavy nuclei which was suggested as a polarization analyzer by Schwinger (Sc48). In this case the spin-orbit coupling is provided by the electromagnetic interaction of the neutron magnetic moment with the Coulomb field of the nucleus. An attempt to use small-angle scattering was made by Longley, Little, and Slye (Lo52) in one of the first polarization experiments. The method has rarely been used because it is very difficult to carry out observations at scattering angles in the order of one degree. A recent experiment is described in Section 6.

In practice almost all results on the polarization in neutron-producing reactions have been obtained by scattering from light nuclei. Scattering from He^4, C^{12}, and O^{16} is most often used because for light spinless nuclei the resonance parameters are least uncertain. The polarization of the outgoing neutrons has been measured most extensively for the $Li^7(p, n)Be^7$ and for the $D(d, n)He^3$ reaction. The neutron energy interval covered by these and other investigations extends almost continuously from about 0.2 Mev to over 20 Mev. Over much of this range the polarization is relatively small (in the order of 0.2), but at certain energies values as high as 0.6 have been found. In some cases the measurement of the polarization of emitted neutrons has helped in the interpretation of the reaction mechanism. Results on the polarization in neutron-producing reactions are summarized in Section 4.

Information on the scattering of polarized neutrons from light nuclei is collected in Section 5. Except for scattering from deuterium this section essentially concerns resonance scattering. No separation is made between nuclei for which the analyzing power is known primarily from calculations, and nuclei for which the analyzing power was found by scattering neutron beams of known polarization.

Experiments on the scattering of polarized neutrons from intermediate and heavy elements (Section 6) have mainly been motivated by the interest in the optical model of the nucleus. Measurements for a large number of elements have been reported with polarized neutrons of energies between 0.4 and 3.2 Mev. The polarization is found to change systematically with atomic weight, indicating the need for a spin-orbit term in the optical potential.

A recent article by Faissner (Fa59) provides an excellent summary of work on polarization in nuclear scattering. A number of shorter summaries can be found in the "Proceedings of the International Symposium on Polarization Phenomena of Nucleons" (Pr61). Earlier reviews are those of Blin-Stoyle and Grace (Bl57) and of Wolfenstein (Wo56).

The theory of polarization in reactions and scattering is treated by Welton in the preceding chapter.

2. Definitions and Principles of Measurement

In all experiments with polarized fast neutrons reported to date the neutrons were produced in nuclear reactions in which *unpolarized* targets were bombarded with *unpolarized* charged particles from an accelerator. The present discussion will be limited to this situation. As was shown in the preceding chapter (Chapter V.F), the polarization $\mathbf{P}_1$ of the outgoing neutrons is normal to the reaction plane, i.e. normal to the plane established by the momentum vectors $\mathbf{k}_1$ and $\mathbf{k}'_1$ of incident and outgoing beams (Fig. 1). Consequently the polarization may be written as

$$\mathbf{P}_1 = P_1 \mathbf{n}_1 \tag{1}$$

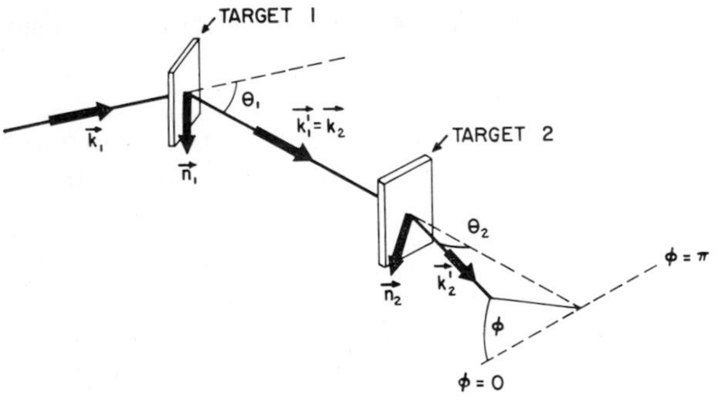

Figure 1. Geometry of fast-neutron polarization experiments. An unpolarized charge particle beam from an accelerator is incident in the direction $\mathbf{k}_1$. Neutrons emitted by the first target in the direction $\mathbf{k}_1'$ form the incident beam $\mathbf{k}_2$ of the second target. Reaction products emitted by the second target in the direction $\mathbf{k}_2'$ are detected. The vectors $\mathbf{n}_1$ and $\mathbf{n}_2$ are in the direction of $\mathbf{k}_1 \times \mathbf{k}_1'$, and $\mathbf{k}_2 \times \mathbf{k}_2'$, respectively. ϕ is the angle between $\mathbf{n}_1$ and $\mathbf{n}_2$. [It should be noted that Welton (Chapter V.F) uses primes to denote *incoming* channels, while primes here denote *outgoing* channels. Thus, whereas the direction of positive polarization is taken as the direction of $\mathbf{k} \times \mathbf{k}'$, positive polarization in Welton's chapter is in the direction of his $\mathbf{k}' \times \mathbf{k}$.]

where n_1 is a *unit* vector normal to the reaction plane. The degree of polarization P_1 is defined as

$$P_1 = (N_+ - N_-)/(N_+ + N_-) \qquad (2)$$

where N_+ and N_- are the numbers of neutrons with spin parallel and antiparallel to n_1, respectively. A different sign convention for the polarization results, depending on whether n_1 is chosen in the direction of $k_1 \times k'_1$, or opposite to it. Both definitions have been used extensively in the literature. In this article the polarization is called positive when a majority of the spins point in the direction $k_1 \times k'_1$. This agrees with the convention adopted at the International Symposium on Polarization Phenomena of Nucleons of 1960 in Basel (see Si60).

For a given reaction the polarization P_1 of the outgoing neutrons depends on the bombarding energy E_1 and on the reaction angle θ_1. The angular dependence $P_1(\theta_1)$ can be expressed in the form [Equations (158) and (162) of Chapter V.F]:

$$P_1(\theta_1) \cdot \sigma(\theta_1) = \sum_{L=1}^{L_{max}} a_L P_L^{(1)}(\theta_1) \qquad (3)$$

where $\sigma(\theta_1)$ is the differential reaction cross section and $P_L^{(1)}(\theta_1)$ is the associated Legendre polynomial:

$$P_L^{(1)}(\theta) = \sin \theta \, \frac{dP_L(\cos \theta)}{d(\cos \theta)}. \quad \text{The}$$

coefficients a_L depend in a complicated way on the matrix elements of the reaction.

There are, however, a number of simple "selection rules" which frequently are useful. They are listed below (Si53; Bl57, p. 591).

(a) If the largest effective values of the incident orbital angular momentum, final orbital angular momentum and total angular momentum are l, l', and J, then L_{max} in (3) must be less than or equal to $2l$, $2l'$, and $2J$. In addition, all L's must be even if the interfering states have the same parity.

(b) If only s-waves are effective in either the formation or the decay of the intermediate nucleus, there can be no polarization.

(c) If only levels of the compound nucleus having $J = 0$ or $1/2$ are effective, there will be no polarization unless interference arises between $J = 1/2$ states of opposite parity.

(d) If only channel spin 0 is effective for the final channel spin, the polarization vanishes.

(e) If there is no spin-orbit coupling, the polarization is zero.

(f) Polarization results from interference of different subchannels (i.e. partial waves or final channel spins) contributing to the reaction. Therefore if there is only a single nonzero element of the reaction matrix, the polarization will vanish.

These rules are analogous to the well known Eisner-Sachs rules for the complexity of angular distributions (see Sa53).

The usual way to observe the polarization of neutrons is to scatter them from a second target. It is convenient here to consider the more general case that instead of an elastic scattering a reaction can take place in the second target. The arrangement is shown schematically in Fig. 1. The vectors $\mathbf{k}$ and $\mathbf{k}'$ are *unit* vectors in the direction of incident and outgoing beam, respectively, and subscripts are used to distinguish between the two reactions. The momentum vector $\mathbf{k}'_2$ of particles emerging from the second target is described in spherical coordinates with respect to $\mathbf{k}_2$ as polar axis. The azimuthal angle φ is the angle between $\mathbf{n}_1$ and $\mathbf{n}_2$:

$$\cos \varphi = \mathbf{n}_1 \cdot \mathbf{n}_2 \tag{4}$$

where $\mathbf{n}_1 = \mathbf{k}_1 \times \mathbf{k}'_1$, and $\mathbf{n}_2 = \mathbf{k}_2 \times \mathbf{k}'_2$ are unit vectors normal to the reaction planes.

From the general theory it is known that if the neutron beam from the first target is polarized, the differential cross section in the second reaction depends not only on the scattering angle θ_2 but also on the azimuthal angle φ. The azimuthal variation is one in $\cos \varphi$ of amplitude proportional to the polarization P_1 of the incident beam:

$$\sigma(\theta_2,\varphi) = \sigma(\theta_2)[1 + P_1 A_2(\theta_2) \cos \varphi] \tag{5}$$

This equation may also be expressed in the form[1]

$$\sigma(\theta_2,\varphi) = \sigma(\theta_2)[1 + \mathbf{P}_1 \cdot \mathbf{A}_2(\theta_2)] \tag{6}$$

where $\mathbf{A}_2(\theta_2)$ is defined as $\mathbf{A}_2(\theta_2) = \mathbf{n}_2 A_2(\theta_2)$. In (5) and (6) $\sigma(\theta_2)$ is the differential cross section in the second reaction for an *unpolarized* incident beam. $A_2(\theta_2)$ is the amplitude of the azimuthal variation for a completely polarized incident beam. The quantity A_2 is called the asymmetry in the reaction. Frequently the term "analyzing power" is used instead, since the magnitude of A_2 determines how effective a detector of the incident polarization the reaction is. It was shown by Blin-Stoyle (Bl52; see also Sa58,Bi59) that A_2 may also be

---

[1] Equation (6) is more general than (5) since it applies even if $\mathbf{P}_1$ is not normal to $\mathbf{k}_2$, as may be the case, for instance, when magnetic fields are present between targets 1 and 2.

interpreted as the polarization in the inverse reaction, i.e. A_2 is equal to the polarization which would result in the outgoing neutron beam $(-\mathbf{k}_2)$ in the *inverse* reaction, the incident beam $(-\mathbf{k}'_2)$ being unpolarized.

Of particular practical interest is the case that the second reaction is an elastic scattering process. In this case there is no distinction between the reaction and its inverse. Consequently the neutron polarization P which results when an initially unpolarized beam is scattered elastically is equal to the amplitude of azimuthal variation A observed with a completely polarized beam; neutron energy, scattering angle, and target being the same.[2] Customarily the symbol A_2 of (5) is then replaced by P_2 and the quantity is referred to as "the polarization in the scattering" even though in practice it is the asymmetry that is being observed. For reactions the distinction between P and A must be maintained, because there is no reason to assume that, for instance, the polarization of $Li^7(p,n)Be^7$ neutrons is the same as the asymmetry which would be obtained in the same reaction if the incident protons were polarized.

In Fig. 1 the position of the neutron detectors is not shown. The detectors are placed such as to measure at a fixed scattering angle θ_2 the flux I_0 and I_π for azimuthal angles equal to $\varphi = 0$ and $\varphi = \pi$, respectively. These two counter positions are frequently labeled R (right) and L (left). We choose to call $\varphi = 0$ the "right" position, i.e., the right is the side reached by two scatterings in the same sense. The intensity ratio

$$r = I_0/I_\pi = I_R/I_L \tag{7}$$

will be called the *right-left ratio*.[3] From Eqs. (6) and (7) it follows that

$$r = (1 + P_1P_2)/(1 - P_1P_2) \tag{8}$$

where A_2 has been replaced by P_2. From this follows the well-known expression for the polarization product P_1P_2 in terms of the measured counting rates:

[2] Wolfenstein (Wo56) gave a simple, instructive derivation of this statement for the case of scattering from a spinless target. The argument makes use of the fact that in this special situation to conserve total angular momentum and parity the spin orientation of the neutrons is conserved in the scattering.

[3] Sometimes r is referred to as the "right-left asymmetry." However, this term is also used to denote the quantity P_1P_2 (Wo56).

$$P_1 P_2 = \frac{I_0 - I_\pi}{I_0 + I_\pi} = \frac{I_R - I_L}{I_R + I_L} = \frac{r - 1}{r + 1} \tag{9}$$

The measurement of either P_1 or P_2 is straightforward if one of the two quantities is known. The usual procedure is first to measure P_1 for a given reaction by using a scatterer for which the analyzing power P_2 can be calculated (Section 5). Once the source polarization P_1 is known, the reaction may be used to measure the polarization in the scattering from other nuclei.

Barschall (Ba56) proposed a method for measuring the polarization of reaction products which eliminates the need for a scatterer of known polarization. Instead of a scattering the *inverse reaction* is used for analysis. If, for instance, the polarization of $C^{13}(\alpha,n)O^{16}$ neutrons is to be measured, the azimuthal asymmetry of alpha particles in the $O^{16}(n,\alpha)C^{13}$ reaction is observed. Since the asymmetry in a reaction is equal to the polarization in the inverse reaction, and the two successive reactions are chosen to be the inverse of each other, P_1 and A_2 of (5) are equal to each other, i.e., the azimuthal asymmetry depends only on the square of the polarization. This, of course, presumes that in both reactions the same center-of-mass angle between the neutron and the α particle is chosen; and that the velocity of the neutron relative to the O^{16} nucleus is the same in both reactions. For a given bombarding energy both conditions are satisfied for at most *one* reaction angle. If the polarization of particle d produced in the reaction $a + b \rightarrow c \rightarrow d + e$ is to be studied, the proper angle ψ_1 in the laboratory system between incident particles of energy E_a and the direction of emission of d is given by (Ba56):

$$\cos \psi_1 = \frac{[E_a (m_b + m_e) + Q(m_c + m_e)]}{2\sqrt{\dfrac{m_a m_e}{m_d}} E_a(E_a m_b + Q m_c)} \tag{10}$$

where Q is the energy released in the reaction. The experiment is possible if $0 < \cos \psi_1 < 1$.

For Barschall's method to be applicable, the product nucleus must be stable and available in sufficient quantity. The reaction cross section and the polarization must be reasonably large since the counting rate and the asymmetry depend on the *square* of these quantities. The method has recently been applied to the $T(p,n)He^3$

reaction (see Section 4). Other methods must be used to determine the sign of polarization.

One of the main difficulties in neutron polarization experiments is the intensity problem. In angular distribution measurements ring geometries are sometimes used to improve counting rates. To some extent the same method is applicable here. When the ring is mounted in the usual manner (coaxially with the charged particle beam; see Fig. 1b, Chapter V.B), the polarization does not average out. Rather $\cos \varphi = \mathbf{n}_1 \cdot \mathbf{n}_2 = -1$ for neutrons scattered from all elements of the ring. Therefore, according to Eq. (5), the observed quantity is the differential cross section multiplied by a factor $[1 - P_1 P_2(\theta_2)]$ where P_1 is the polarization of the neutrons incident on the ring, and $P_2(\theta_2)$ the polarization in the scattering from the ring material. The separate measurement of $\sigma(\theta_2)$ and $P_2(\theta_2)$ would require, for instance, the use of two different reactions producing neutrons of the same energy but different polarization, or the use of magnetic fields to change the direction of the polarization vector $\mathbf{P}_1$.

Brinkman (Br61) recently suggested that the ring geometry could be used to measure the source polarization P_1, provided $\sigma(\theta_2)$ and $P_2(\theta_2)$ for the ring material are known. Measurements would be made for two different angles θ_2 for which P_2 should differ as much as possible. The neutron polarization P_1 would be found from the observed ratio of counting rates and the *calculated* ratio of solid angles subtended by the counter in the two positions. So far the ring geometry has not been used.

3. Experimental Techniques

The experimental problems in neutron polarization measurements are very similar to those which arise in the measurement of the angular distribution of scattered neutrons (Chapters V.B and V.E). While polarization experiments are simpler in that they require only *relative* intensity measurements, the precision required of the right-left ratio is high. For the discussion of techniques it is convenient to divide the experiments into two groups: (a) experiments in which the scattered neutrons are detected; (b) experiments in which the recoil nuclei are detected, the neutrons being unobserved. The second group mostly concerns the scattering from helium. Experiments in which the recoil nuclei are observed in *coincidence* with the scattered neutrons are included under (a).

A. *Detection of the Scattered Neutrons*

(1) **Typical Arrangement.** A typical arrangement is shown in Fig. 2. It was used by the Wisconsin group for the scattering of 1-Mev polarized neutrons from intermediate and heavy elements (C158). The proton beam from an electrostatic generator bombarded a lithium target. Neutrons emitted at angle $\psi_1 = 50°$ with respect to the proton beam were incident on a scattering sample. Those neutrons which were scattered through angle ψ_2 were detected with a cylindrical proportional counter. The detector was shielded from direct source neutrons by a paraffin collimator. The counter was mounted upon a support which could be rotated about the axis of the sample. The intensity of the scattered neutrons was determined by measuring the number of counts obtained with the sample in position and by subtracting from this the number of counts obtained during a corresponding run with the sample removed. Right-left intensity ratios were obtained by alternately carrying out this procedure for right and left scatterings. Background counts averaged 20 to 40 per cent of the sample-in counts for scattering angles ψ_2 of 55° and 90°. Counting rates were in the order of a few counts per second. For example, with a 6-μa beam on a 100-kev thick lithium target, 10 counts per second were obtained for 90°-scattering of 1-Mev neutrons from Cu, which at this angle and energy has a scattering cross section of 0.18 barns/steradian.

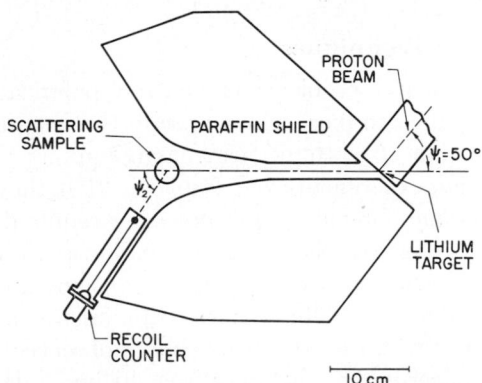

Figure 2. Arrangement used in polarization experiments with Li^7 $(p,n)Be^7$ neutrons of 1-Mev energy (C158).

Other arrangements differ from that shown in Fig. 2 in several
ways.   In many experiments two counters have been used to measure
simultaneously scattering to the left and to the right.   With increasing neutron energy the distance between target and scatterer is increased.   The distance is about 30 cm for 1-Mev neutrons (Cl58)
and 70 cm for neutrons of 3 Mev (Ba53,Me54).   A different arrangement of the shield was used in an experiment which employed the
pulsed-beam time-of-flight method (Cr59), where the target-to-scatterer distance was very small, the scatterer-to-detector distance large.
In many recent experiments the arrangement of Fig. 2 has been modified by the addition of a solenoid between first and second target to
allow reversal of the neutron spin.   Other variations in experimental
techniques are much the same as those which occur in angular distribution experiments.

(2) **Scatterers.**   The scattering samples are usually in the form
of cylinders with axes normal to the scattering plane.   Typically the
diameter of the sample may be one-third to one-half of a neutron
mean free path.   The height of the sample may exceed its diameter
several times since the spread in azimuthal angle can easily be taken
into account.

Precautions to be taken in the preparation of solid scatterers
are discussed in Chapter V.A.   Special problems arise only when
gases or liquefied gases are used.   Scattering from oxygen and from
helium are of particular interest.   For work with liquid oxygen[4]
small Dewars which contribute little to the scattering have been used
(Ok55).   They consist of a thin-walled metal can surrounded with a
styrofoam jacket.   Rather than using a second identical Dewar for
background measurements the same can should be used to eliminate
effects of moisture condensing on the styrofoam.

For scattering from helium, gaseous as well as liquid samples
have been used.   Baicker and Jones (Ba60) used liquid helium contained in a can of 5-cm diameter, surrounded by a vacuum jacket.
A radiation shield of 0.1-mm thick copper which was held at liquid
air temperature surrounded the helium container.   A loss rate of

[4] Oxygen is conveniently liquefied in the laboratory by passing the gas
through a coil of $1/_4$-inch diameter copper tubing which is submerged in liquid
nitrogen. The tubing ends in a needle valve which is partially open. With high
pressure ($\sim$100 atm) oxygen in the copper tube a steady flow of liquid oxygen at
a rate of 0.1 to 0.2 liter per minute emerges from the valve.

12 cm³ of liquid helium per hour was reported for this Dewar. The number of neutrons scattered by the wall material was about 50 per cent of the number scattered by the helium. Dewars with thinner walls have been described by Wh55 and Ni55. Containers like those described by Marshall (Ma55) may also be suitable.

In a recent polarization experiment Cranberg (Cr59) used a scatterer of helium gas at a pressure of 360 atmospheres. The container was a spherical steel shell of 3.8 cm diameter and 0.8 mm wall thickness. Neutrons scattered by the helium were distinguished from those scattered by the container by means of the pulsed-beam time-of-flight technique (Chapter IV.A). A different technique was employed by Pasma (Pa58). Neutrons scattered by helium were counted in coincidence with the recoil α particles. The helium scatterer consisted of a stainless steel cylinder filled with a mixture of 90 per cent helium and 10 per cent xenon to a total pressure of 17 atmospheres. Gas scintillations caused by recoil α particles were detected by a photomultiplier with quartz envelope, while the scattered neutrons were detected with liquid scintillators. Despite the coincidence technique, shielding had to be employed. An improved system of the same type has been described by Dubbeldam and Walter (Du62,Wa62). Their gas scintillator (95% He, 5% Xe) operated at a pressure of 160 atmospheres (see also Ru58). They avoided the need for quartz windows by coating the inside of the cell with a wavelength shifter. A "fast-slow" coincidence system with a resolving time in the fast channel of about 10^{-8} sec was used. In order to obtain even higher efficiency, Perkins and Simmons in a recent experiment (Pe61) replaced the gaseous scintillator by a scatterer of liquid helium, making use of the observation (Th59,Fl59) that helium in the liquid state scintillates as well.

The method of detecting scattered neutrons in coincidence with recoil nuclei has also been applied to scattering by carbon (St59) and by deuterium (Br59,Bu59). The scatterers consisted of deuterated benzene (C_6D_6) to which an activator was added. The preparation of deuterated benzene has been described in detail by Brüllman *et al.* (Br58).

(3) **Detectors.** For a discussion of neutron detectors and of techniques which are used to distinguish between elastically and inelastically scattered neutrons we refer to Chapter V.B. A comment may be made about the relative advantages of using two detectors to measure simultaneously left- and right-scattered flux, compared to

the single-detector arrangement of Fig. 2. If a single counter is used it has to be moved from side to side a number of times during each measurement. The individual runs have to be monitored by either a monitor counter or a beam current integrator. The use of two counters obviously allows faster data collection, but requires the construction and handling of more equipment. The counters still have to be interchanged in order to compensate for the difference in counter efficiency. An important advantage in using two counters is that no beam monitor is necessary. The duration of the measurements and the difference in counter efficiency cancel entirely if the right-left ratio is taken as

$$ r = \sqrt{\frac{I_{R,1}}{I_{L,1}} \frac{I_{R,2}}{I_{L,2}}} \tag{11} $$

where the subscripts 1 and 2 label the particular detector, and L and R refer to their position.

(4) **False Asymmetries.** In order to avoid instrumental asymmetries, it is important that the scatterer-to-detector distance and the scattering angle be identical for scattering to the left and to the right. This statement needs clarification for the case that two counters are used. It is not particularly important that counters 1 and 2 are set to precisely the same distance and scattering angle, since this type of asymmetry cancels when the geometric mean of the right-left ratios with interchanged detectors is taken according to (11). Rather, the crucial requirement is that the position of a *given* counter when it is set to detect right-scattering be exactly symmetric to the position of the *same* counter when it is set to detect left-scattering. In other words, whether one or two counters are used the problem is only one of accurately interchanging left and right. The accuracy with which this interchange can be carried out depends much on the methods used. The simplest procedure is to keep neutron shield and target stationary and to move the detectors from left to right. To keep the distance from scatterer to detector constant presents a relatively simple mechanical problem. However, asymmetries caused by slight differences in the angular setting can be serious in cases where the differential scattering cross section varies rapidly with angle. Precise definition of the angle is difficult because the detectors frequently cover an angular interval of 10 degrees or more, and their

effective centers may not be known accurately. One method which establishes the angular scale to about 0.5 degree is to observe the counting rate as a function of angular position as the detector is moved through the neutron-shadow of the scatterer (Me54,Cl58). The position where the transmission reaches a minimum is taken as the $\psi_2 = 0$ position. The accuracy of this method is not always sufficient, as may best be illustrated by an example. Suppose that 3-Mev polarized D-D neutrons ($P_1 = -0.11$) are scattered from tantalum through $45°$. If P_2 is to be correct to ± 0.05, the instrumental asymmetries must be less than 1 per cent. Since the scattering cross section of tantalum at this angle varies by 8 per cent per degree, the scattering angle on the two sides must be equal to within $0.13°$, i.e. the zero point of the angular scale must be correct to $\pm 0.06°$.

This accuracy can be approached by another technique, first employed by the Virginia group (Mc56). Instead of reversing the vector $\mathbf{A}_2 = A_2\mathbf{n}_2$ [Eq. (6)] by moving a given counter from the left to the right, the incident polarization vector $\mathbf{P}_1 = P_1\mathbf{n}_1$ is reversed. To accomplish this, the complete assembly of scatterer, detectors, and shield is rotated from $+\psi_1$ to $-\psi_1$, the rotation taking place about an axis which is normal to the scattering plane and passes through the neutron-producing target. Errors in the position of the detectors average out provided the assembly is rotated exactly about the effective center of the neutron-producing target. High accuracy can be achieved in those cases where the target-to-scatterer distance is large and the target spot is accurately defined. Another method which gives similar accuracy is to rotate the assembly of scatterer and detectors about the axis defined by the centers of the neutron-producing target and the scatterer.

Besides counter misalignment, an important cause of instrumental asymmetry is the variation with reaction angle of the cross section in the neutron-producing reaction. Because of this variation the number of incident neutrons is larger on one side of the scatterer than on the other, causing the effective center of the scatterer to shift toward the left or the right. Consequently, the left and the right counter have a different solid angle, a different amount of attenuation of the scattered neutrons in the scatterer, and a different mean scattering angle. Corrections which compensate for these effects can in most cases be evaluated without much difficulty. Additional asymmetries of a similar nature arise from the variation of neutron energy with reaction angle ψ_1 because in general the scattering cross section and the counter efficiency are energy-dependent.

A very elegant method by which asymmetries of this kind can be avoided entirely was proposed and first used by Hillman, Stafford, and Whitehead (Hi56). The polarization vector $\mathbf{P}_1$ was reversed by means of a magnetic field in the region between first and second target. The field was along the direction of motion of the neutrons, and was produced by an air core solenoid through which the neutrons passed. The solenoid current was chosen such that the neutron spin precessed through 90°, so that depending on the sense of current flow the polarization vector became parallel or opposite to the vector $\mathbf{n}_1 \times \mathbf{k}_1$ (Fig. 1). Consequently, the second reaction plane was placed perpendicular to the first. The asymmetry was measured by reversing the solenoid current, the counters remaining fixed. This eliminates all false asymmetries, provided the accelerator beam and the detectors are properly shielded from magnetic fields. For non-relativistic neutrons the number of *ampere-turns* required is equal to

$$H \cdot l = 0.94 \cdot 10^5 \cdot \sqrt{E} \qquad (12)$$

where E is the neutron energy in Mev.

The solenoid method was first applied to small-angle scattering of 95-Mev neutrons from uranium (Hi56). Recently, Dubbeldam *et al.* (Du59) described a solenoid of length $l = 80$ cm for measurements on 3-Mev neutrons. According to the above formula the required field strength is about $H = 2000$ amp/cm.

Instead of a longitudinal field a transverse field parallel to the first reaction plane can also be used (Hi56). In this case the second reaction plane is chosen co-planar with the first and measurements are taken alternately with no field and with a field of sufficient strength to reverse the polarization vector. The necessary field strength is twice that given by Eq. (12). This disadvantage is partially offset by the fact that an iron core magnet can be used.

(5) **Corrections.** Corrections for instrumental asymmetries have already been mentioned. In addition, corrections for the finite angular resolution, for the spread in neutron energy, and for multiple scattering of the neutrons in the sample must be considered. The multiple scattering problem is treated in detail by Walt in Chapter V.B for the case that the neutrons incident on the scatterer are unpolarized. If the incident neutrons are polarized the multiple-scat-

tered flux depends on the azimuthal angle, i.e. it exhibits a right-left asymmetry. The calculation of this asymmetry involves so-called triple scattering parameters (see Fa59 and Wo56) which in general are not known. For the sake of simplicity the asymmetry is usually neglected altogether, and the number of multiple scattered neutrons as a function of scattering angle is calculated as in Chapter V.B. There is good evidence that the correction computed in this way is too large (Cl58,El62). It appears that the right-left asymmetry of multiple scattered neutrons is in the same direction as for single scattered neutrons, but of smaller magnitude.

The multiple scattering correction becomes particularly complicated for scattering from light nuclei because of the variation of the scattering cross section with energy, and the variation of the energy of scattered neutrons with scattering angle. It is therefore desirable to keep the fraction of multiple scattered neutrons low. The optimum size of the scatterer depends on the experimental conditions. How small an amount of scattering material can be used is limited to a large extent by the background.

An approximate calculation of the multiple scattering correction has been presented by Brüllmann et al. (Br59). Their treatment includes scatterers which consist of a binary mixture of nuclei.

The correction for finite angular resolution, arising from the finite sizes of scatterer and detectors, can be found by a method outlined by McCormac et al. (Mc56). Also, the finite-geometry correction which Meier et al. (Me54) applied to differential cross section measurements can be modified to include polarization.[5]

A correction for the energy spread of the neutrons needs be applied only when P_1 as well as P_2 varies over the energy spread of the beam. If, for instance, P_1 can be considered constant, the energy spread is simply taken into consideration by replacing P_2 in (9) with the weighted mean, $\overline{P_2(E)}$, where the weight is proportional to the product of reaction cross section and scattering cross section.

---

[5] The correction can be expressed as a factor γ by which the observed ratio $(I_R - I_L)/(I_R + I_L)$ has to be multiplied to give the corrected P_1P_2. From Me54 one finds

$$\gamma = 1 - [2k_1P_2' + k_2P_2'' + 2k_2P_2'(\sigma'/\sigma)]/2P_2$$

where σ is the (unpolarized) scattering cross section. P_2, σ, and their derivatives with respect to angle are evaluated at ψ_2. The moments k_1 and k_2 are given in Me54 for a particular geometry.

B. Detection of the Recoil Nuclei

With scattering samples in the gaseous state the recoil-nucle can be observed instead of the scattered neutrons. Scattering from helium is of particular interest because this nucleus is an excellent polarization analyzer. The recoil method was first applied to polarization studies by Levintov, Miller, and Shamshev (Le57) and independently by White and Farley (Wh57). The relation between the energy E' of the recoiling nucleus and the energy E_n of the incident neutrons is

$$E' = 4E_n \frac{mM}{(m + M)^2} \cos^2 \psi' = 2 \frac{mM}{(m + M)^2} (1 - \cos \theta) \quad (13)$$

M and m are the masses of the target nucleus and the neutron, respectively, ψ' is the laboratory angle of the recoil nucleus with respect to the incident neutron beam, and θ is the center-of-mass scattering angle. Also useful is the relation between recoil angle and center-of-mass scattering angle:

$$\psi' = (\pi - \theta)/2 \quad (14)$$

Clearly, the azimuthal angle of the recoil differs from the azimuthal angle of the scattered neutrons by π.

The technique which Levintov *et al.* and White *et al.* used to measure the azimuthal asymmetry of helium recoils is notable for its simplicity. Helium filled proportional counters of a diameter which was small compared to the range of the recoil α particles were used. Recoils nearly parallel to the counter axis were selected by accepting only the largest counter pulses. Right-left axymmetries were measured by taking alternate measurements for the two counter positions shown in Fig. 3. For neutron energies above 2.5 Mev the polarization in n-He^4 scattering is highest for a center-of-mass angle of 135°. This large scattering angle is favorable to the detection of recoils, since more than half of the neutron energy is transferred to the recoil. A particular advantage of the recoil method is that no shielding is required. For low neutron energies there are no background problems. With higher energy a background arises from reactions in the counter walls and wire supports.

To improve the counting rate Levintov *et al.* operated seven closely-packed counters in parallel. The counters each had a diam-

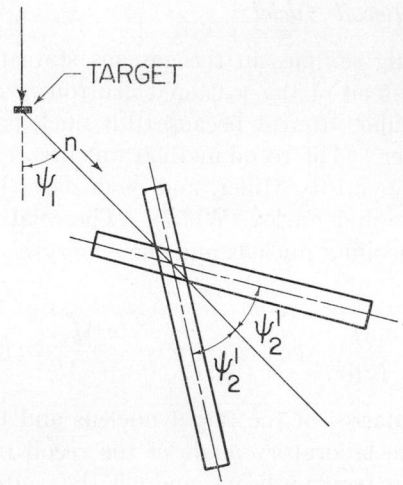

Figure 3. **A**rrangement of Levintov *et al.* (Le57) and of White and Farley (Wh57) in which recoil α particles in a long, helium-filled proportional counter are detected. The counting rate is measured for the two counter positions shown. The angle which the counter axis makes with the direction of the incident neutrons is labeled ψ_2'.

eter of 0.7 cm and were 7 cm long. The helium pressure was chosen such that the range of recoils moving parallel to the counter axis was 4.4 cm. The active volume of the counter was about 10 cm from the target. The counting rate depended strongly on the bias of the counting circuit, i.e. on the accepted spread in recoil angle. With the bias set to accept recoils in an angular interval of ±10 degrees, 35 counts per minute were recorded when the counters were 10 cm from a source of 3.5-Mev neutrons of source strength 3×10^7 per second per steradian.[6]

Levintov *et al.* used their equipment to measure the polarization of neutrons from the $D(d,n)He^3$ and the $T(d,n)He^4$ reaction (Le57a, Le58). To relate the neutron polarization to the observed right-left ratio requires integration over the counter volume of the number of recoil α particles which cause pulses above a certain height. The

[6] For comparison it may be noted that Pasma's arrangement which was described in Section A gave about 20 counts per minute (Pa58a). However, while in Pasma's experiment conditions of source strength and spread in scattering angle were similar to Levintov's, his spread in the reaction angle ψ_1 was much smaller.

necessary numerical integrations are complicated because the principle of the counter results in large wall effects and because the
spread in reaction angle and in scattering angle is relatively large.
For the same reasons it is difficult to predict accurately how much
false asymmetry is caused by the variation of neutron flux and neutron energy across the counter.

A helium recoil counter in which recoils nearly parallel to the
counter wire were selected on the basis of the pulse *shape* has been
used by Ot-Stavnov (Ot59). References to other counters based on
the same principle are given in a paper by Facchini *et al.* (Fa59a).

4. Polarization in Reactions

A. The $D(d,n)He^3$ Reaction

The early experiments by Huber and Baumgartner (Ba53,
Hu53), by Ricamo (Ri53,Ri53a) and by Longley, Little, and Slye
(Lo52) showed that for bombarding energies below 1 Mev D-D neu-
trons are partially polarized. Since then more accurate measure-

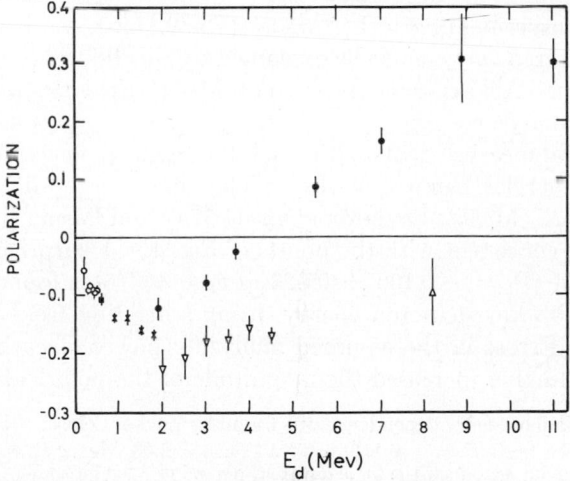

Figure 4.   Polarization of neutrons from the $D(d,n)He^3$ reaction as a function of bombarding energy.   The data are by: O Pa58, ■ Me54, × Le57a, ∇ Ba60,
△ Da59, and apply to laboratory angles of 47°, 50°, 49°, 40°, 34°, respectively;
and ● Du61, for a center-of-mass angle of 45°.   In the measurements of Du61 for
$\theta_1 = 45°$, the laboratory angle varied between $\psi_1 = 36°$ at 1.9 Mev and $\psi_1 = 32°$ at 11.0 Mev.

ments have been carried out, and the energy range has been extended to a deuteron energy of 11 Mev. The largest amount of data is for reaction angles near $\theta_1 = 45°$. Figure 4 shows the results obtained with "thin" targets. The measurements below 2 Mev are those of Pasma (Pa58), Meier *et al.* (Me54), and Levintov *et al.* (Le57a). A measurable polarization is already found for a deuteron energy of 0.2 Mev. Toward higher energies the magnitude of the polarization increases and seems to approach a maximum near 2 Mev. Below 2 Mev bombarding energy, there is excellent agreement between the different measurements, particularly if one considers that quite different techniques have been used.

The experiments of Baicker and Jones (Ba60) and of Daehnick (Da59) suggested that the polarization does not change greatly as the bombarding energy is increased from 2 to 8.2 Mev. However, an entirely different behavior was found in a very recent experiment by Dubbeldam and Walter (Du61). Their results for a center-of-mass reaction angle $\theta_1 = 45°$ (corresponding to laboratory angles ψ_1 between 36° and 32°) indicate that the polarization changes sign at 4 Mev[7] and continues to increase to $P_1 = 0.30 \pm 0.05$ at $E_d = 11.0$ Mev. Measurements at other angles (Da59,Du61, see below) show that the discrepancy cannot be explained by the difference in angle of observation. All experiments (except Me54) used scattering from helium as analyzer.

Several measurements with thick targets have been reported for deuteron energies below 1.8 Mev. The thick target data of Mc-Cormac *et al.* (Mc56), Levintov *et al.* (Le57a), and Pasma (Pa58a) are reasonably consistent with the points of Fig. 4. A surprisingly large polarization ($P_1 = -0.106 \pm 0.023$ at $\theta_1 = 46°$) was found by Kane (Ka59) at 93 kev deuteron energy, using scattering from carbon as analyzer. Errors in the assumed analyzing power of carbon would only have further increased the magnitude of the polarization. The

---

[7] A similar energy dependence was found by Zucker (Zu61). For $\theta \sim 51°$ ($\psi_1 = 40°$) he finds $P = -0.118 \pm 0.014$ ($E_d = 2.03$ Mev), $P = -0.094 \pm 0.015$ ($E_d = 2.53$ Mev), and $P = -0.054 \pm 0.015$ ($E_d = 2.89$ Mev). Scattering by helium was used for analysis. A helium filled proportional counter the axis of which was parallel to the neutron beam served as a radiator. Two sets of collimating vanes ("venetian blinds") were adjacent to the counter so that recoil α particles of the desired recoil angle could leave the counter on the left and right and could be detected by scintillation counters. At other angles some of Zucker's results agree poorly with those of Du61.

significance of this measurement for the analysis of the D-D reaction has been discussed by Rook and Goldfarb (Ro61b).

The angular dependence of polarization has been measured by Meier *et al.* (Me54) and by McCormac *et al.* (Mc56) at deuteron energies between 0.5 and 0.9 Mev and by Dubbeldam and Walter (Du61) at five energies between 1.9 and 8.9 Mev. The dependence on angle can be represented by

$$P(\theta) = [\sigma(\theta)]^{-1}[A \sin (2\theta) + B \sin (4\theta) + \ldots \ldots] \quad (15)$$

This equation follows from Eq. (3), where only even values of L are included because the identity of the colliding particles requires that $P(\theta) = -P(\pi - \theta)$. The analysis of the D-D reaction by Beiduk, Pruett, and Konopinski (Be50) showed that the variation of the cross section with energy can be entirely attributed to the energy variation of the barrier penetrability for deuterons of different orbital angular momentum. For deuteron energies up to about 300 kev only s- and p-waves are effective. Above 300 kev d-waves become important, and above 2 Mev f-waves have to be considered. Correspondingly in (15), A should be the only important term up to 300 kev; A and B should be sufficient up to 2 Mev. Actually, within the accuracy of the experiments, A and B were found to be sufficient even for the highest energy measured (Du61). Other than near 4 Mev, where A changes sign, the first term always is the most important one; i.e., $P(\theta)$ has a single maximum between 0 and π. The fact that the first term in Eq. (15) dominates, and the observed shape of the energy dependence of A for $E_d \leq 2$ Mev agree with what Fierz (Fi52) predicted for the case that the nucleon-nucleon tensor force mainly provides the spin-orbit coupling in the reaction (see Ha60).

B. The $T(p,n)He^3$ Reaction

For a bombarding energy of 1.40 Mev and a neutron emission angle of $\psi_1 = 50°$ Willard, Bair, and Kington (Wi54) found no polarization ($P_1 = 0.01 \pm 0.04$). Artemov, Vlasov, and Samoïlov (Ar59) made measurements for proton energies up to 9.9 Mev using the inverse reaction method (see Section 2). A cell filled with He^3 served as the radiator of a proportional counter telescope. The intensity of protons from the $He^3(n,p)T$ reaction for different angles ψ_2 to the right and the left was measured for several bombarding energies

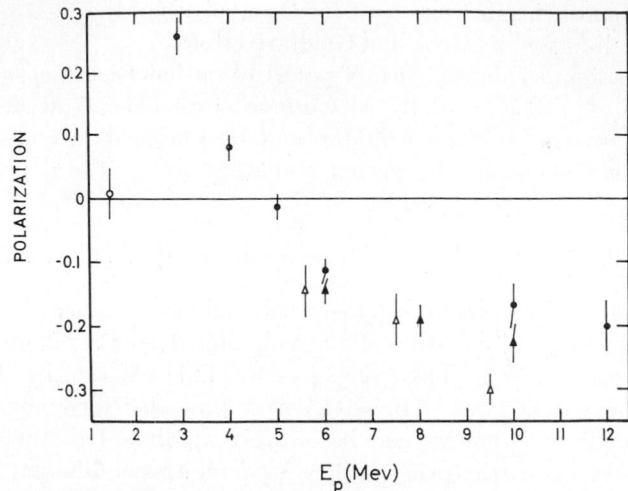

Figure 5.   Polarization of neutrons from the $T(p,n)He^3$ reaction as a function of proton energy.[8]   The data are by: O Wi54, △ Ar59, ▲ Wa61, and apply to laboratory angles of 50°, 40°, 40°, respectively;   and ● Wa62, with a center-of-mass angle of 45°.   In the measurements of Wa61 for $\theta_1 = 45°$, the laboratory angle varied between $\psi_1 = 33°$ at 2.9 Mev and $\psi_1 = 35°$ at 12.0 Mev.

and reaction angles ψ_1 of the first reaction.   For $E_p = 9.9$ Mev a reaction angle of 16.5° has to be chosen to satisfy the conditions of Barschall's method [Eq. (10)].   For this angle the polarization was found to be quite small so that the asymmetry was difficult to measure.   The largest effect was observed for neutrons emitted at $\psi_1 = 40°$ ($\theta_1 = 50°$) and most measurements were performed at this angle. At this angle the neutrons had an energy of 7.72 Mev rather than the required 8.85 Mev.   However, the inverse reaction technique is still applicable provided the polarization changes slowly with energy. The results of the experiment justified this assumption.

More extensive measurements have very recently been reported by Walter *et al.* (Wa61) who used scattering from He^4 for analysis.   Their results for $\psi_1 = 40°$ (Fig. 5) are in reasonable agree-

[8] For the results of Ar59 which were obtained with the inverse reaction method, the energies quoted are 0.6 Mev below the proton energies in the first reaction, to take into account that the energies in first and second reaction are mismatched by about 1.2 Mev.   In plotting the results of Ar59, the sign was chosen to agree with that of Walter's measurements (Wa61).

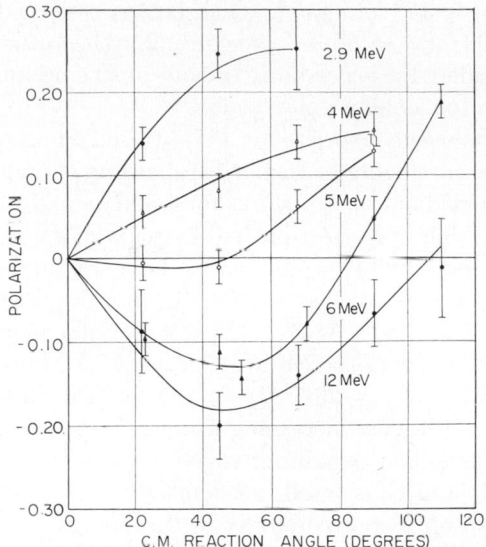

Figure 6.   Polarization of neutrons from the $T(p,n)He^3$ reaction as a function of center-of-mass angle for various proton energies.   The figure is by Walter et al. (Wa62).

ment with those of Artemov et al. (Ar59).   The points for a center-of-mass angle $\theta_1 = 45°$ ($\psi_1 = 33°$ to $35°$) show that the polarization is fairly large also near 3 Mev proton energy.

The polarization angular distributions of Walter et al. (Wa61) are shown in Fig. 6.   Between 6 and 12 Mev the angular dependence appears to change very slowly.   Measurements of the angular dependence were also made in the inverse reaction experiment of Artemov et al. (Ar59).   Their results are consistent with those of Fig. 6.

C. The $T(d,n)He^4$ Reaction

Measurements have been reported for deuteron energies between 0.1 and 0.3 Mev by Pasma (Pa58,Pa58a) and at 1.8 Mev by Levintov, Miller, and Shamshev (Le58).   Helium was used as analyzer in both cases.   At the lower energies no polarization was found ($P_1 \lesssim 0.05$) for neutron emission angles of $\psi_1 = 45°$ and $\psi_1 = 90°$.   At 1.8 Mev the recoil method was used to obtain results for five angles of neutron emission between 45° and 135°. The largest observed polarization[9] was 0.12 ± 0.03 for $\psi_1 = 67.5°$. According to the authors their values are to be considered a lower limit because instrumental asymmetries tended to give too small a polarization.

In a very recent experiment Perkins and Simmons (Pe61) extended the measurements to higher bombarding energies. For $E_d = 5$ Mev they carried out observations for reaction angles between $\psi_1 = 15°$ and 120°. The polarization had extrema of $P_1 = 0.26$ at $\psi_1 = 30°$ and $P_1 = -0.43$ at $\psi_1 = 90°$. For these two angles, the neutron polarization was measured at several bombarding energies between 1.8 Mev and 7.7 Mev. At 30° the polarization increases steadily from $P_1 = -0.05$ for $E_d = 1.8$ Mev ($E_n = 17.5$ Mev) to $P_1 = 0.64$ for $E_d = 7.7$ Mev ($E_n = 23.7$ Mev). At 90° the values were $P_1 = -0.16$ at $E_d = 1.8$ Mev increasing in magnitude to $P_1 = -0.54$ at $E_d = 6$ Mev and then remaining constant up to the highest energy measured. Helium was used as analyzer. Since the analyzing power is known only approximately in this energy region (Pe61), no uncertainties are quoted for the neutron polarization. However, the values of P_1P_2 were large ($P_1P_2 = 0.43 \pm 0.03$ at $E_d = 6$ Mev, $\psi_1 = 90°$), so that independent of P_2, one knows that the reaction provides high energy neutrons of appreciable polarization. The large polarization of protons from the $He^3(d,p)$ reaction (Br61a) confirms the results of Perkins and Simmons, since one would expect the polarization of the outgoing nucleons in the $T(d,n)$ and in the $He^3(d,p)$ reactions to be of similar magnitude.

It has been pointed out (see Chapter V.F) that in the $T(d,n)$ reaction a large neutron polarization results even at very low bombarding energies if the incident deuterons are polarized. An ion source which produces a 0.01-microampere beam of partially polarized deuterons has recently been built at the University of Basel (Ba60a).

D. The $Li^7(p,n)Be^7$ Reaction

The $Li^7(p,n)Be^7$ reaction is discussed by Gibbons and Newson in Chapter I.E. For proton energies between threshold (1.881 Mev) and 3.1 Mev the polarization of the outgoing neutrons has been

---

[9] The sign is not known since in Le58 the direction of positive polarization is not defined.

investigated extensively by Barschall's group at Wisconsin. Results
for a neutron emission angle $\psi_1 = 50°$ are shown in Fig. 7 together
with the measurements at higher energies of Cranberg (Cr59) and
of Baicker and Jones (Ba60). The polarization analyzers used were
Mg^{24}, Li^6, and Li^7 for neutron energies below 0.38 Mev (Da61), O^{16}
between 0.35 and 3.1 Mev (Ok55,St58,Au61), and He^4 above 3 Mev
(Cr59,Ba60).

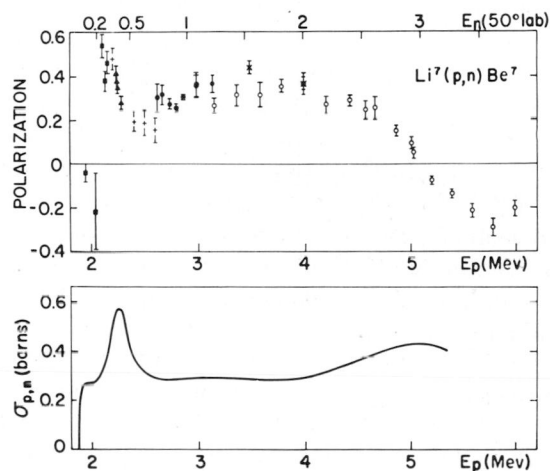

Figure 7. Polarization of neutrons from the $Li^7 (p,n)Be^7$ reaction as a function of proton energy for a laboratory angle $\psi_1 = 50°$. The neutron energy scale
is indicated at the top of the figure. Scattering from the following nuclei was
used for polarization analysis: ■ Mg^{24}, Li^6, Li^7 (Da61); + O^{16} (Au61); ▲ O^{16}
(Ok55); ● O^{16} (St58); ○ He^4 (Ba60); × He^4 (Cr59). In the lower half of the figure the $Li^7(p,n)Be^7$ total cross section (Gi59) is shown.

After the early work by Adair, Darden, and Fields (Ad54,Ad54a)
and by Willard, Bair, and Kington (Wi54), there remained the question whether in the vicinity of 2.1 Mev the polarization varies rapidly
with energy or not. Later measurements (Ok55,St58) were consistent with almost constant polarization from 2.2 to 3.1 Mev, but
the addition of the very recent results by Darden, Donoghue, and
Kelsey (Da61) and by Austin et al. (Au61) now gives a more complete
picture. Figure 7 shows a rapid rise of the polarization between 2
and 2.1 Mev, followed by a peak just below 2.2 Mev. The energy

spread in these measurements was in the order of 30 kev.[10] The polarization seems to pass through a minimum at 2.5 Mev and then rises slowly to a value of about 0.35. Above 4 Mev it decreases and changes sign at 5 Mev. For comparison the $Li^7(p,n)Be^7$ total cross section (Gi59) is also shown. It is apparent that the variation in the polarization near 2.2 Mev is associated with the well-known resonance at 2.25 Mev. The variation near 5 Mev is probably connected with the resonance which occurs in the $Li^7(p,n)$ cross section at this energy.

For proton energies above 4 Mev the measurements (Ba60) did not discriminate against neutrons to the first excited state of $Be.^7$ The intensity of this group relative to the ground state group is probably about 20 per cent (Ba60). Cranberg (Cr59) found an upper limit of about 0.15 for the polarization of neutrons to the first excited state of Be^7 at 3.48-Mev proton energy.

Measurements for reaction angles other than 50° are not nearly as extensive. Austin et al. (Au61) reported an angular distribution at 2.6-Mev proton energy. Between laboratory angles of 30° and 85° the polarization increases from 0.136 ± 0.02 to 0.204 ± 0.043 and then drops sharply to 0.036 ± 0.045 and 0.016 ± 0.043 at 105° and 115°, respectively. Measurements have also been reported at reaction angles of 30° and 70° with proton energies of 2.2 Mev and 2.6 Mev (Au61) and at 35° with four proton energies between 3.5 and 5 Mev (Cr59). In a very recent experiment (Be62) the angular dependence of the polarization was determined for seven proton energies between 4 and 10 Mev. Neutrons to the ground state and the first excited state of Be^7 were counted with approximately equal efficiency. Above 4.7 Mev the magnitude of the polarization was less than 0.20 for all angles measured ($\psi_1 = 20°$ to 110°).

The interpretation of the $Li^7(p,n)$ reaction in terms of the level structure of Be^8 is discussed in Chapter I.E. Recently Austin et al. (Au61) did further work on the explanation of the differential cross section and the polarization. They found that the set of levels which Macklin and Gibbons (Ma58) used to fit the total cross section gives poor agreement with the observed angular distributions and polarization. They obtained better agreement by adding a 2^+ level of

---

[10] Very detailed results with greater statistical accuracy and better energy resolution by Elwyn and Lane (El62) indicate that the polarization maximum ($P = 0.59$) occurs at $E_p = 2.18$ Mev.

channel spin $S = 2$ at 3.2 Mev, and by appropriately adjusting the hard-sphere phases.

E. The $Be^9(p,n)B^9$ Reaction

Kelsey, Donoghue, and Darden (Ke60) recently measured the polarization in this reaction for bombarding energies between 2.29 and 4.34 Mev, i.e., 0.23 to 2.28 Mev above threshold. The reaction angle was $\psi_1 = 50°$. Lithium, oxygen, and carbon were used as scatterers. The detectors were biased to exclude neutrons from the three-body breakup. The results were consistent with a polarization of less than 0.1 throughout the energy range investigated.

For proton energies between 4.5 and 5.3 Mev and $\psi_1 = 45°$, Cranberg (Cr61) detected a small polarization of the neutrons ($|P| \leq 0.1$).

F. The $C^{12}(d,n)N^{13}$ Reaction

For $E_d > 2$ Mev the angular distribution of neutrons from the $C^{12}(d,n)N^{13}$ reaction is peaked forward with a maximum at about 20° (El59). Analysis in terms of the stripping theory shows that the final state is formed by capture of a proton with one unit of angular momentum. Newns (Ne53) first suggested that nucleons produced in a stripping reaction should be polarized.

The polarization of ground-state neutrons was measured by Haeberli and Rolland (Ha57) in the deuteron energy range from 2 to 3.6 Mev. Scattering from carbon was used for analysis. The angular distribution of polarization for $E_d = 2.8$ and 3.0 Mev is shown in Fig. 8. The values are based on the analyzing power calculated by Wills et al. (Wi58; see Section 5). All values are lower by about 20 per cent if the calculations of Meier et al. (Me54) are used instead. Additional measurements were made for a neutron emission angle of $\psi_1 = 20°$. The results were 2.0 Mev (-0.34 ± 0.14); 2.2 Mev (-0.11 ± 0.07); 2.63 Mev (-0.28 ± 0.015); 3.14 Mev (-0.38 ± 0.02); 3.54 Mev (-0.32 ± 0.04), where the first number is the deuteron energy at the center of the target and the second number gives the polarization. The sign of polarization is opposite to that predicted by Newns (Ne53) but agrees with more recent theoretical work (Ne58,Ro61a) and with the sign found in the $C^{12}(d,p)C^{13}$ reaction (Al59).

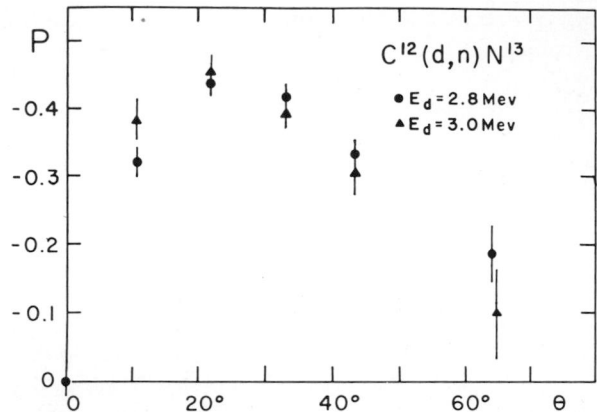

Figure 8. Polarization of neutrons from the $C^{12}(d,n)N^{13}$ reaction as a function of center-of-mass angle of neutron emission for bombarding energies 2.8 and 3.0 Mev (Ha57).

An appreciable neutron polarization has also been found by Budzanowski *et al.* (Bu61) with deuterons of 12.9 Mev. The different neutron groups were not distinguished from one another.

5. Polarization in Scattering from Light Nuclei

This section chiefly concerns *resonance scattering* of neutrons. For unpolarized neutrons this topic is discussed in Chapter V.E where it is shown how the observed angular distributions can be reduced to scattering phase shifts which may in turn be interpreted in terms of virtual excited states of the compound nucleus. If the phase shifts are known, the polarization can be calculated by means of the formulae given in the preceding chapter (V.F).

The phase shifts are best known for scattering from He^4, C^{12}, and O^{16}. These nuclei have no spin so that for a given incident orbital angular momentum l there are only two phase shifts, namely those for $J = l \pm \frac{1}{2}$. Furthermore, the phase shifts are real since it can be assumed that elastic scattering is the only process. For target nuclei with spin, or in the case that inelastic scattering and reactions take place, the phase shift analysis is more complicated and correspondingly more uncertain. Since practically all polarization measurements are based on calculated values of the polarization in the scattering from spinless nuclei, the formula for this special case is given below. The polarization is most conveniently expressed as (Ba53):

$$P = - \frac{2\text{Im}(g^*h)}{|g|^2 + |h|^2} \tag{16}$$

where $g = (1/k)\sum_l P_l(\cos\theta)[(l+1)\sin\delta_l^+ e^{i\delta_l^+} + l\sin\delta_l^- e^{i\delta_l^-}]$

$h = (1/k)\sum_l P_l^{(1)}\sin(\delta_l^+ - \delta_l^-)e^{i(\delta_l^+ + \delta_l^-)}$

The denominator in eq. (16) is the differential scattering cross section. The coefficients P_l and $P_l^{(1)}$ are the Legendre polynomials $[P_0 = 1, P_1 = \cos\theta, P_2 = (3\cos^2\theta - 1)/2, etc.]$, and the associated polynomials defined in Section 2, respectively.[11] The phase shifts δ_l^+ for $J = l + \frac{1}{2}$ and δ_l^- for $J = l - \frac{1}{2}$ are functions of energy. From Eq. (16) it is apparent that the polarization vanishes when $\delta_l^+ = \delta_l^-$ for all values of l; i.e. when there is no spin-orbit coupling. Of course the other selection rules listed in Section 2 apply as well.

To find the quantities g and h, graphical methods are sometimes used (see Ri60). Equation (16) may also be expressed in the form of Eq. (3). Explicit formulae for the coefficients a_L are listed in Me54.

It was pointed out in Chapter V.E that the accuracy of a phase-shift analysis is rather difficult to estimate, because the errors in the individual phases are correlated in a complicated way. Correspondingly very little is known about the uncertainty of the computed polarizations. One indication that errors may be large arises from parallel experiments with protons, in which case double-scattering experiments have been performed to check the computed polarization. In spite of the higher accuracy of the differential cross section measurements, the polarization has been found to be in error by as much as a factor of two for proton scattering from carbon (Ev60, To60). For scattering from helium the calculated polarization appears to be within about 10 per cent of the correct value (Ju56, Sc58,Ph59).

Because for neutrons double-scattering experiments are not feasible, other methods must be used to test the accuracy of the calculated polarizations. In some cases the polarization P_1 of neutrons from a given reaction has been measured with two different

[11] In Equation (16), Im stands for "imaginary part of" and g^* is the complex conjugate of g.

scatterers or with the same scatterer for more than one scattering angle. The degree of consistency of the results gives an indication of the magnitude of the errors in the calculated polarization P_2. In particular, of course, no asymmetry should be observed at those angles and energies where P_2 is predicted to be zero. Also the predicted variation of the polarization P_2 with energy near a scattering resonance can be tested if the neutron-producing reaction has no resonances, since in this case P_1 can be assumed to be approximately constant so that P_1P_2 should follow the predicted $P_2(E)$.

For most light nuclei the phase-shift analysis is so uncertain that the polarization cannot be predicted. This leaves the possibility of measuring the polarization using a neutron source for which P_1 is known. Such experiments have been reported, among others, for scattering from deuterium at a number of different neutron energies.

A. Scattering from Deuterium

The asymmetry in the scattering of polarized neutrons from deuterium has been studied for neutron energies between 1 Mev and 3.9 Mev. Darden, Kelsey, and Donoghue (Da60) made measurements for center-of-mass scattering angles of 70°, 110°, and 140° with 1-Mev neutrons from the $Li^7(p,n)$ reaction. A small positive polarization ($\sim 0.09 \pm 0.05$) was found for all angles. The measurements by Cranberg (Cr59) at 2.1 Mev covered the angular range from $\theta_2 = 45°$ to $\theta_2 = 138°$. The polarization was found to be less than 0.07, in agreement with a measurement by Darden et al. (Da60) at $E_n = 2.0$ Mev, $\theta_2 = 110°$. Brüllmann, Gerber, Meier, and Scherrer (Br59) measured the asymmetry in n-d scattering with D-D neutrons of 3.27-Mev energy for six scattering angles between $\theta_2 = 53°$ and $\theta_2 = 161°$. The scattered neutrons were detected in coincidence with the recoil deuterons in a deuterated organic scintillator. The same technique was used by Bucher, Beverly, Cobb, and Hereford (Bu59) for neutron energies of 2.3, 3.1, and 3.9 Mev. All of these experiments agree with each other within the uncertainties and indicate that the polarization is at most a few per cent. Although most values are consistent with zero polarization, positive values occur more frequently than negative ones. The early experiment by White et al. (Wh58) in which a large polarization was found near 2 and near 3 Mev is inconsistent with the more recent results.

The polarization in n-d scattering and in p-d scattering should be of comparable magnitude. Polarizations less than 0.1 were found in p-d scattering for proton energies of 3.4 Mev (Sh60) and 10 Mev (Br60). The latter experiment covered the angular range from $\theta_2 = 40°$ to $\theta_2 = 130°$.

B. Scattering from Helium

Neutron-helium scattering is discussed in Chapter V.E and more extensively in a review paper by Hodgson (Ho58). The polarization calculated from the phase shifts is shown in Figs. 9 and 10 as a function of neutron energy in the laboratory system. The curves are labeled by the scattering angle in the center-of-mass system. In Fig. 10 the laboratory angles are given in parentheses.

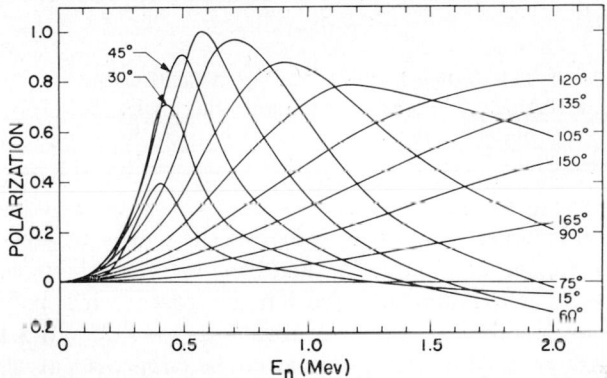

Figure 9. Polarization in the scattering of neutrons by He^4 for neutron energies below 2 Mev. The labels refer to the center-of-mass scattering angle.

The polarization calculations are based on the solid lines of Fig. 16, Chapter V.E, i.e. s- and p-wave phase shifts derived from the p-He^4 phase shifts (Se53). The $d_{3/2}$-phase shift was included, but the $d_{5/2}$-phase was assumed to be zero. For high neutron energies the results agree well with the calculations of Levintov $et\ al.$ (Le57), but near 1 Mev their results differ significantly from those given here.

It is apparent from Figs. 9 and 10 that helium is an excellent polarization analyzer. The polarization varies relatively slowly with energy due to the large widths of the two P-states involved. The

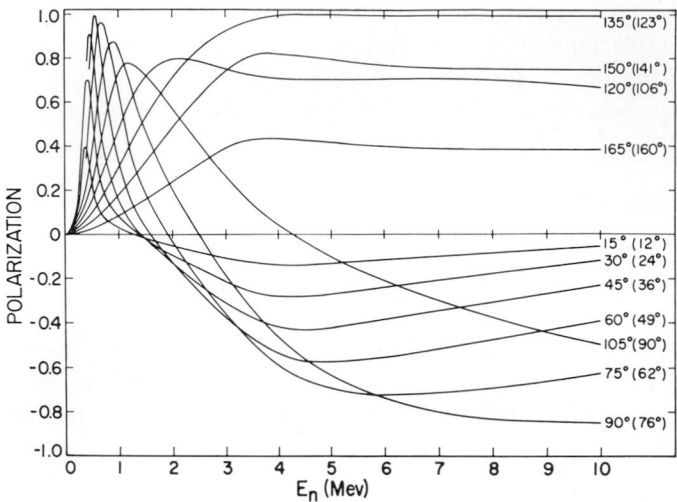

Figure 10. Polarization in the scattering of neutrons by He⁴ for neutron energies below 10 Mev. The labels give the scattering angle. The first number refers to the center-of-mass system. The number in parentheses indicates the laboratory angle.

polarization is large.   By proper choice of the scattering angle, values of 0.75 or higher are found for neutron energies above 0.4 Mev. The angle of maximum polarization increases with bombarding energy, being about $\theta_2 = 90°$ at 1 Mev and $\theta_2 = 135°$ at 4 Mev and higher.   Above 8 Mev the polarization is large also at 90°.   For $E_n > 10$ Mev, see Le57 and Pa58.

    Little is known about the magnitude of the uncertainty of the calculated polarization.   The discrepancy in the determination of

    [12] It now appears likely that the $p_{1/2}$-phase shift derived from the p-He⁴ phases is correct.   The lower $p_{1/2}$-phase received strong support from an experiment (Le57) in which the polarization at 2.45 Mev was compared to the polarization at 4.11 Mev.   However, the conclusion reached in this paper seems to be incorrect because of numerical errors in the calculation of the curves in Fig. 7 of Le57.   The actual value of R in Fig. 8 of Le57 is a much slower function of δ_1^-, and leads to an unreasonably low value of the $p_{1/2}$ phase shift of about $-3°$. Also, new angular distribution measurements (Au60) support the n-He⁴ phase shifts derived from the p-He⁴ phases.   See also Pi59.

the $p_{1/2}$-phase shift at E_n = 2.6 Mev has been mentioned already in Chapter V.E.[12] The magnitude of the d-wave phase shifts is still very uncertain. This causes considerable uncertainty in the calculated polarization for neutron energies above 10 Mev but no quantitative estimates of the errors have been made. For lower neutron energies Levintov *et al.* (Le57) performed an experiment to check the results of the phase-shift analysis. They scattered D-D neutrons of 3.4-Mev energy from helium and observed the right-left asymmetry for seven scattering angles between θ_2 = 68° and θ_2 = 135°. The observed asymmetry as a function of angle confirmed the essential features of the phase analysis. Also near 1.2-Mev neutron energy the polarization in the Li$^7(p,n)$Be^7 reaction measured with a helium analyzer (Ba60,Se60) agreed well with experiments in which oxygen was used as analyzer (Au61). However, it should be pointed out that the accuracy of these tests is not very high. From all information available one estimates that below 6 Mev the uncertainty in P is about ΔP = 0.1 near the maximum of the polarization *vs.* angle curve, and about twice as large where the polarization changes rapidly with angle.

C. Scattering from Lithium

The neutron total cross section of both lithium isotopes shows a strong p-wave resonance at 225-kev neutron energy. The total width is 32 kev for the resonance in Li^7 and 100 kev for Li^6 (Wi56). The heavier lithium isotope was first used as polarization analyzer by Willard, Bair, Cohn, and Kington (Wi56a). Darden, Kelsey, and Donoghue (Da61,Da61a) calculated the polarization for scattering through θ_2 = 96° on the assumption that all of the non-resonant cross section arises from s-wave scattering with channel spin 2 (Th56). Measurements of the asymmetry in the scattering of Li$^7(p,n)$ neutrons by Li^7 between 0.25 and 0.4 Mev (Da61) support this assumption, since lower asymmetries would have been expected if part of the s-wave scattering is of channel spin 1 (Wi56). The results of Darden's group at Notre Dame (Da61a) indicate that above 0.4 Mev the calculated analyzing power of Li^7 is unreliable.

Extensive experimental results on n-Li^7 polarization have very recently been obtained by Elwyn and Lane (La61,El62) using

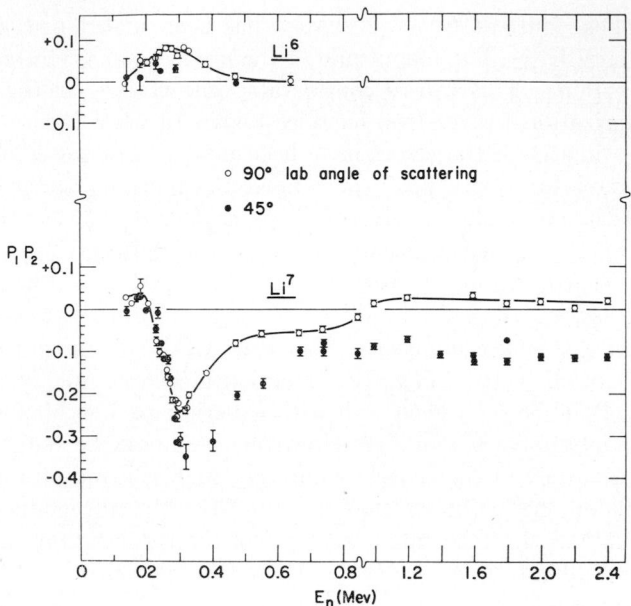

Figure 11. The product of the polarization P_1 of $Li^7(p,n)Be^7$ neutrons at ψ $= 51°$, and the polarization P_2 in the elastic scattering of neutrons by Li^6 and Li^7 for scattering angles $\psi_2 = 45°$ and $\psi_2 = 90°$. The measurements are by Elwyn and Lane (La61, El62).

$Li^7(p,n)$ neutrons.   Their results for P_1P_2 are shown in Fig. 11, where P_1 is the polarization of $Li^7(p,n)Be^7$ neutrons at $\psi_1 = 51°$ and P_2 is the polarization in the elastic scattering of neutrons by Li^7 for scattering angles of $\psi_2 = 45°$ and $\psi_2 = 90°$.   Comparison between Fig. 11 and Fig. 7 shows that with increasing neutron energy P_2 ($\psi_2 = 45°$) goes from $P_2 \sim -0.8$ at $E_n = 0.4$ Mev, to an almost constant value of $P_2 \sim -0.35$ for neutron energies between 0.8 and 2.4 Mev.

Darden et al. (Da61) also discussed the polarization in the scattering from Li^6.   The calculation is complicated by the presence of the competing (n,α) reaction.   From asymmetry measurements similar to those in the upper part of Fig. 11 they concluded that the non-resonant s-wave interaction is stronger for antiparallel spins than for parallel spins.

For recent measurements on both lithium isotopes see also La61a.

D. Scattering from Carbon

Scattering from carbon was employed in the first polarization experiments of Huber and Baumgartner (Hu53,Ba53) and of Ricamo (Ri53,Ri53a), but at the time the correct interpretation of the resonance structure of $C^{12} + n$ was not known.   In the meantime it has been well established that there is a broad d-wave resonance at $E_n = 3.67$ Mev, interfering with a narrower resonance at 2.95 Mev. Both resonances form compound states of total angular momentum $J^\pi = {}^3/_2{}^+$ as was suggested already by the energy dependence of the total cross section (Bo51).

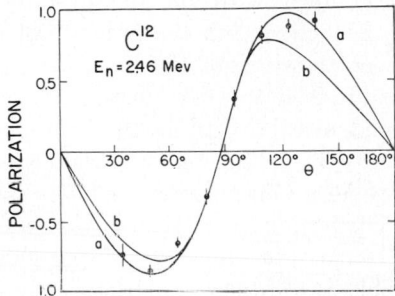

Figure 12. Angular dependence of the polarization in the scattering of 2.46-Mev neutrons by C^{12}.   Curve (a) is calculated from the phase shifts of Meier *et al.* (Me54), curve (b) from the phase shifts of Wills *et al.* (Wi58). The points were obtained from observation of the right-left asymmetry when neutrons from the $C^{12}(d,n)N^{13}$ reaction were scattered by a sample of graphite (Ha57).   In plotting the points the polarization of the neutrons was arbitrarily assumed to be -0.36.

In the energy region between 2 and 4 Mev, three phase shift analyses have been reported.   They are summarized in Fig. 17 of Chapter V.E.   They agree qualitatively and show that the scattering is dominated by potential $s_{1/2}$ and resonant $d_{3/2}$ scattering.   However, the three sets of phase shifts yield quite different amounts of polarization.   This is caused in part by the difference in the magnitude of the $p_{3/2}$-phase shift.   If no p-wave were present, the differential cross section $\sigma(\theta)$ would be symmetric about $90°$, and the polarization $P(\theta)$ would be proportional to $\sin(2\theta)/\sigma(\theta)$; i.e. it would be point-symmetric about $\theta = 90°$.   This is very close to what has been found experimentally.   The points of Fig. 12 show the polarization angular dependence which was measured by Haeberli and Rolland (Ha57) with 2.46-Mev neutrons from the $C^{12}(d,n)N^{13}$ reaction. Similar measurements have been reported by McCormac et al. (Mc56, Mc57). The solid curves are calculated (a) for the phase shifts of Meier, Scherrer, and Trumpy (Me54), and (b) for the phase shifts of the Oak Ridge group (Wi58). The small p-wave phase shifts which occur in these two analyses account quantitatively for the observed shift of the $P = 0$ point away from 90°. The measurements are not consistent with the large $p_{3/2}$ phases of Budde and Huber (Bu55).

The experimental points of Fig. 12 agree best with the polarization predicted from the phase shifts of Meier et al. Satisfactory agreement is also obtained with the phase shifts of Wills et al., since it must be kept in mind that the ordinate of the experimental points contains the polarization of the incident neutrons as an unknown scale factor. Indeed the two phase shift solutions of Me54 and Wi58 are nearly identical except for the s-wave phase shift which differs by almost 30°. The effect on the total cross section is small because in the energy region in question the phase shift is near $-90°$. Also the angular distributions are almost the same. However, a large difference occurs in the extension of the phase shifts to low energies. In the analysis of Meier et al. the s-wave phase shift is too small to account for the total cross section at $E_n \sim 1$ Mev and one must assume that the tail of the $J^{\pi} = 3/2^+$ resonance at 3.7 Mev makes up the difference. On the other hand, in the analysis of Wills et al. the assumption was made that the $d_{3/2}$ phase is correctly given by a Breit-Wigner two-level formula. This leads to a small $d_{3/2}$ phase at low energies and requires a correspondingly larger s-wave phase shift. Measurements by Striebel and Haeberli (St57) of the polarization in n-C^{12} at lower energies helped to clarify this question. The experiments were carried out with $Li^7(p,n)$ neutrons of 0.4, 1.0, and 1.4 Mev.[13] For $E_n = 1$ Mev the results were $P = -0.02 \pm 0.02$ at $\theta_2 = 59°$, $P = 0.09 \pm 0.02$ at $\theta_2 = 95°$, and $P = 0.12 \pm 0.04$ at $\theta_2 = 129°$. This requires a d-wave splitting of $\delta_2^+ - \delta_2^- = -1.4 \pm 0.4$ degree, which agrees with the value calculated from the Breit-Wigner formula taking into account in the usual way the variation of level width and level shift with energy (Chapter V.E). Similarly at 0.4 Mev and 1.4 Mev the measured d-wave splittings were

[13] More extensive results have recently been reported by Elwyn and Lane (El62). See also Cr61.

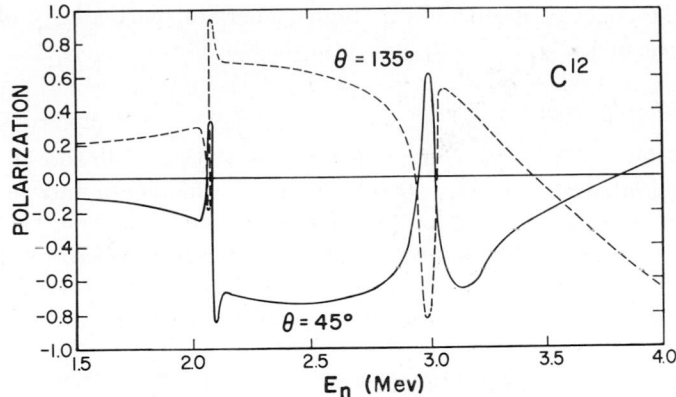

Figure 13. Polarization in the scattering of neutrons by C^{12} for center-of-mass
angles $\theta_2 = 45°$ and $\theta_2 = 135°$ (Wi58).

-0.1 ± 0.2 degree and -5 ± 1 degree, respectively. These results,
together with the observation that at 0.5 Mev and 1.0 Mev the angular distributions are isotropic (Wi55) definitely support the phase
shift solution of Wi58. The p-wave splittings (e.g. 1.9 ± 0.4 degree
at 1 Mev) are consistent with the extension to lower energies of the
phases of Meier (Me54) and of Wills (Wi58).

Calculated values of the polarization for scattering angles
$\theta_2 = 45°$ and $\theta_2 = 135°$ are shown in Fig. 13. The curves are from
Wi58. The characteristic symmetry $[P(\theta) \approx -P(\pi - \theta)]$ caused by
the dominant even-parity scattering is evident for all energies. The
resonances at 2.08 Mev and at 2.95 Mev are seen to cause rapid fluctuations in the polarization. Between 2.2 and 2.8 Mev the polarization
is large and nearly constant, which makes carbon a convenient
analyzer. For $\theta_2 = 45°$ the polarizations computed from the phase
shifts of Me54 are larger in magnitude by an amount which increases
from 0.13 at 2.2 Mev to 0.27 at 2.8 Mev and which is about 0.14 at 3.2
Mev (Bu59a,Du60).

Bucher *et al.* (Bu59a) and Dubbeldam et al. (Du60) made use of
partially polarized D-D neutrons to measure the polarization in
scattering from carbon relative to the polarization in scattering from
helium. At 2.2 Mev the measurements are consistent with the values
of Fig. 13. From 3.2 to 3.8 Mev the magnitude of the calculated
polarization of Fig. 13 appears to be too low. This is not surprising,

since the effect of resonances at higher energies, particularly of the resonance at 4.1 Mev, was neglected in the analysis.

E. Scattering from Oxygen

Below 1.5 Mev the neutron total cross section of O^{16} shows three well-separated resonances. The total angular momenta and parities of the corresponding states in O^{17} are $J^{\pi} = {}^3/_2{}^-$, ${}^3/_2{}^+$, and ${}^3/_2{}^-$ (Chapter V.E). Figure 14 shows the polarization for two angles of scattering. For comparison the total cross section is also shown. The polarization was calculated from the phase shifts which the Wisconsin

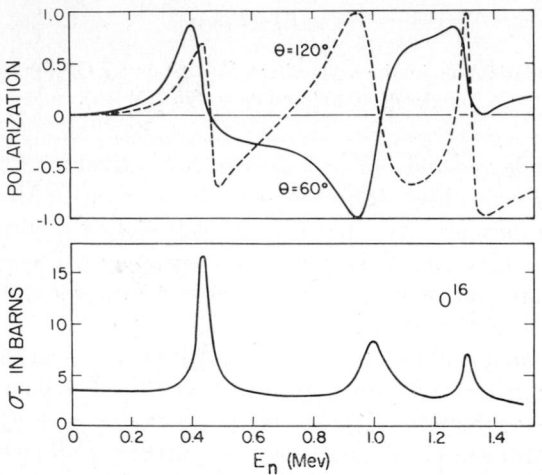

Figure 14. Polarization in the scattering of neutrons by O^{16} for center-of-mass angles $\theta_2 = 60°$ and $\theta_2 = 120°$. The calculations are based on the phase shifts of St58. The lower portion of the figure shows the oxygen total cross section (St58) for comparison.

group (Ok55,St58) obtained from the analysis of total and differential scattering cross sections. The $\theta_2 = 60°$ curve has a maximum error of ± 0.1 near 0.7 Mev and ± 0.15 near 1.2 Mev and probable errors somewhat less than half as large (St58). The uncertainties are appreciably smaller near 0.95-Mev neutron energy but become larger above 1.4 Mev. For neutron energies above 1.6 Mev the phase shifts are not known well enough for a reliable polarization calculation.

At $\theta_2 = 90°$ the polarization is large at the 0.44-Mev resonance and in the vicinity of 1.4 Mev. A curve[14] of $P(90°)$ $vs.$ E_n up to E_n = 1.5 Mev is given in a paper by Austin $et~al.$ (Au61).

Some of the features of the polarization calculations have been checked by experiments. Striebel et al. (St58) confirmed that the polarization at $\theta_2 = 60°$ changes sign close to 1-Mev neutron energy and approaches zero again near 1.4 Mev. Also the values of $P_1P_2(\theta_2)$ which they found in the scattering of 0.965-Mev neutrons through $\theta_2 = 58°$, $90°$, and $128°$ were consistent with the calculated $P_2(\theta_2)$. See also El62.

F. Scattering from Magnesium

The total cross section of Mg^{24} has an 8-kev wide resonance at 83-kev neutron energy (Ne59). The total angular momentum and parity of the level is $J^\pi = {}^3/_2{}^-$. Since the potential scattering can be assumed to be almost entirely of zero angular momentum, the polarization is easily calculated. For scattering through 90° the polarization is large ($P > 0.4$) for neutron energies between about 70 and 90 kev. For higher energies the wide ($\Gamma = 75$ kev) ${}^1/_2{}^-$ resonance at 260 kev has been found to produce very large polarization (El62). The isotope Mg^{25} (10.1 per cent abundance) has resonances at 80 and 105 kev (Ne59) which complicate the use of magnesium as polarization analyzer. See also La61a.

G. Other Light Nuclei

Seagrave, Cranberg, and Simmons (Se60) investigated the polarization in the scattering from T and He^3 at neutron energies of 1.1 Mev and 2.15 Mev for scattering angles between $\theta_2 = 83°$ and $\theta_2 = 137°$. Within the uncertainties (± 0.03 to ± 0.12) no polarization was detected.

Measurements on Be^9 have been reported between 0.5 and 2.4 Mev for $\psi_2 = 45°$ and $\psi_2 = 90°$ (El62). $Li^7(p,n)$ neutrons were

---

[14] The spikes which appear in this curve just above 1 Mev are surprising since at 90° one expects very small polarization where d-wave (resonance) scattering interferes with s-wave (potential) scattering. The p-wave phase shifts are very small. The spikes arise from the particular circumstance that in this part of the resonance the $s_{1/2}$ and $d_{3/2}$ phase shifts are equal. This causes complete destructive interference and makes even a very small p-wave phase shift dominate.

used. The energy resolution was sufficiently good to observe in detail the variation of the polarization caused by the 0.62-Mev resonance. The maximum polarization is less than 0.3 in the energy range covered. Similar measurements were also carried out for scattering from boron. In addition, measurements for several elements have been reported with D-D neutrons of 3.2-Mev energy (Mc57,St59). The polarization in the scattering from Be^9 was found to be negative for forward angles with a minimum of $P = -0.32 \pm 0.06$ at $\theta_2 = 60°$, and positive for back angles with a maximum of $P = 0.6 \pm 0.1$ at $\theta_2 = 109°$.

6. Scattering by Intermediate and Heavy Nuclei

A. Experiments Connected with the Optical Model

The first measurements of the polarization in the scattering of neutrons from intermediate and heavy elements were carried out by Adair *et al.* at Wisconsin (Ad54). Neutrons of 0.4-Mev energy were scattered from a number of elements ranging in atomic weight from that of copper to that of bismuth. Shortly before, Feshbach, Porter, and Weisskopf had shown that the neutron total cross section as a function of atomic weight and energy is well reproduced by a neutron-nucleus interaction in the form of a square potential well with absorption. The optical model in this early form did not contain a spin-orbit term. Since the shell model had shown the importance of spin-orbit forces it was expected that they would be effective in the scattering as well. Adair pointed out that the only reasonably direct way to determine the presence of spin-orbit coupling in the optical model is by polarization experiments. He found that the polarization was largest for elements near $A = 100$. This agreed with the behavior which was expected from a spin-orbit term in the potential, the variation near $A = 100$ being caused by the splitting of the p-wave giant resonance in this region. The results suggested a spin-orbit term of about -1.5 (l·s) Mev, i.e., a spin-orbit energy of the same sign and similar magnitude as that required by the shell model (Ad54).

In the last few years measurements of this type have been considerably extended. The results of the Wisconsin group (Cl58) at 0.38 and 0.98 Mev are shown in the upper part of Fig. 15. The

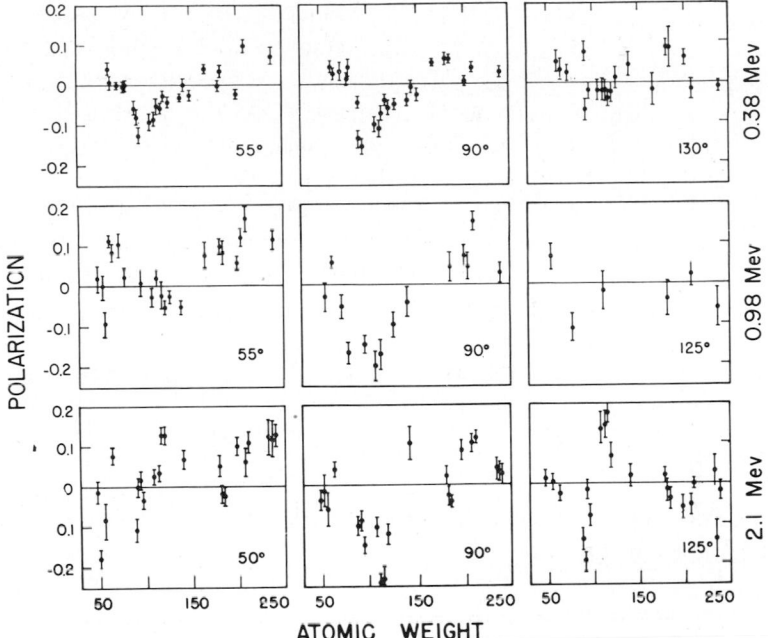

Figure 15. Polarization in the scattering by intermediate and heavy elements as a function of atomic weight for three angles of scattering. The data for neutron energies of 0.38 Mev and 0.98 Mev are by Cl58. The data at 2.1 Mev are by Cranberg (see Ro60).

polarization depends on atomic weight in a smooth way, at least for the scattering angles 55° and 90°. The polarization of the incident Li^7(p,n)Be^7 neutrons ($\psi_1 = 50°$) was assumed to be $P = 0.38$ for $E_n = 0.38$ Mev and $P = 0.30$ for $E_n = 0.98$ Mev. The bottom part of Fig. 15 shows very recent results obtained by Cranberg at Los Alamos for a neutron energy of 2.1 Mev (see Ro60). For energies between 0.38 and 2.1 Mev the polarizations are of similar magnitude. A slight increase is noted with increasing bombarding energy. In a series of measurements at the University of Virginia (Mc57,St59, He61), in which D-D neutrons of 3.2 Mev were scattered from heavy elements, polarizations up to 0.5 ± 0.1 were found. Similar experiments have been reported by Remund (Re56). See also Br61b for measurements as a function of neutron energy between 0.4 and 1.3 Mev.

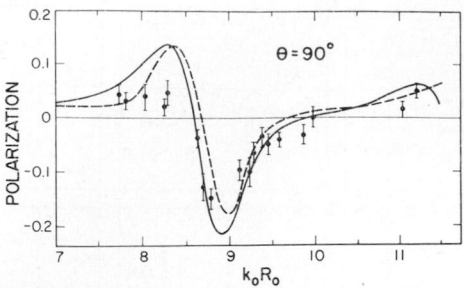

Figure 16. Optical model calculations by Nemirovskiĭ (Ne59a) of the polarization in the scattering by intermediate and heavy elements. The potential used is given in the text. The abscissa is $k_0 R_0$, where $k_0 = (1/\hbar)\sqrt{2mV_0}$. The dashed and the solid lines were computed for neutron energies of 0.25 Mev and 0.5 Mev, respectively, and a scattering angle of 90°. The measurements are those of Cl58 at 0.38 Mev.

These observations clearly demonstrate that a realistic optical model must include spin-orbit coupling. A number of calculations have been reported of the polarization of the scattered neutrons. For 0.38-Mev neutron energy a square potential well to which a uniform spin-orbit term was added gave too large a variation of the polarization with atomic weight (Ok55). While the measurements at 90° (Fig. 15) show only a dip at $A = 100$, the calculations also predicted two pronounced peaks. Thomas made calculations with a square well in which the spin-orbit coupling was placed at the nuclear surface (see Cl58). The spin-orbit coupling and the absorption parameters of the potential were varied over a wide range but it was not possible to find parameters which at the same time reproduced the polarization and the total cross section as a function of atomic weight. This failure of the square well model is not surprising because the rounding of the well is known to be essential to account quantitatively for the measured cross sections (see Chapter V.C).

Recently Nemirovskiĭ (Ne59a) compared the data at 0.38 and 0.98 Mev with calculations in which a spin-orbit term of the Thomas type was added to a potential well with a diffuse surface (Saxon well). The potential was

$$V(r) = V_c(1 + i\,\zeta) + V_s \tag{17}$$

where

$$V_c = -V_0/[1 + \exp\{(r - R_0)/a\}]$$
$$V_s = -(\kappa/r)(dV_c/dr)\cdot(\mathbf{s}\cdot\mathbf{l})$$
$$V_0 = 50 \text{ Mev}$$
$$a = 0.65\cdot10^{-13} \text{ cm}$$
$$\zeta = 0.05$$
$$\kappa = 2.8 \cdot 10^{-27} \text{ cm}^2$$
$$R_0 = (1.16A^{1/3} + 0.36) \cdot 10^{-13} \text{ cm}$$

The results for $E_n = 0.25$ Mev and 0.5 Mev, $\theta_2 = 90°$, are shown in Fig. 16, together with the measurements at 0.38 Mev. In the calculation compound elastic scattering was included assuming that inelastic scattering is negligible. Measured points which correspond to nuclei with a large deformation were omitted from the graph. Calculations were also made for $\theta_2 = 55°$ and $\theta_2 = 130°$. The agree-

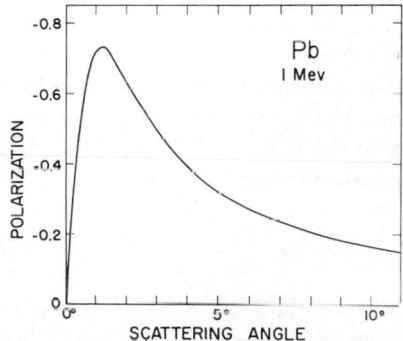

Figure 17. Polarization in Mott-Schwinger scattering. The curve was computed for scattering of 1-Mev neutrons by lead.

ment between theory and experiment is satisfactory except that for $\theta_2 = 55°$ the first maximum in the calculated polarization is entirely absent in the experiment. If the absorption parameter ζ is increased to 0.1 the fit becomes worse. The strength of the spin-orbit coupling which was used for these calculations is approximately the same as is required by the shell model (Ne59a).

Calculations were also made by Nemirovskiǐ for a neutron energy of 1.25 Mev. The comparison with the measurements at 0.98 Mev is complicated by the fact that the amount of compound elastic scattering is not known. The agreement for 90°-scattering is satisfactory, but for scattering through 55° there is no agreement for elements heavier than selenium. A calculation for 2.1-Mev neutrons has been made by Hodgson (Ho61).

Bjorklund reported attempts (Bj59) to fit the 1-Mev polarization data with a potential (Bj58) which differed from that of (17) in that the absorption was assumed to take place on the nuclear surface. No agreement could be obtained. The reasons for this difficulty, which was encountered also with the data at 3.2 Mev (Mc57), are not clear. For the case of *proton* scattering the measured polarization is well reproduced by potentials with either surface absorption or uniform absorption (Bj59,Ro59,Bl59,Ro60,No60,Ro61).

Faissner (Fa59) and Rodberg (Ro60a) discussed the relation between the angular distribution and the polarization in the optical model and showed that the polarization is proportional to the derivative of the scattering cross section, i.e. the polarization is zero at the minima and maxima of the cross section. The arguments are based on the observation that because of the spin-orbit part of the potential the diffraction pattern for spin-up neutrons is shifted in angle with respect to the pattern for spin-down neutrons. From this also follows a formula by which the depth of the spin-orbit potential can be estimated from the observed polarization (Ro60a).

B. Mott-Schwinger Scattering

Schwinger pointed out (Sc48) that a large polarization arises in small-angle scattering of neutrons from heavy nuclei. The same effect had been predicted earlier by Mott (Mo29) for the scattering of electrons. In Mott-Schwinger scattering the spin-orbit force is of electromagnetic rather than of nuclear origin. In the rest system of the neutron a magnetic field is produced by the Coulomb field of the nucleus moving past the neutron. An interaction $\mathbf{\mu} \cdot \mathbf{B}$ arises between this field $\mathbf{B}$ and the magnetic moment $\mathbf{\mu}$ of neutron. Since the direction of the field $\mathbf{B}$ is associated with the orbital angular momentum vector $\mathbf{l}$, and the magnetic moment $\mathbf{\mu}$ is associated with the neutron spin $\mathbf{s}$, the interaction is of the form $\mathbf{l} \cdot \mathbf{s}$.

The electromagnetic interaction is weak and practically does not affect the neutron total cross section (Sc48). Because of the long range of the Coulomb field, the largest effects arise for small scattering angles. For unpolarized neutrons the differential scattering cross section is modified by the addition of a contribution proportional to $\cot^2(\theta/2)$. The contribution amounts to about 2 barns/ steradian for scattering from lead through one degree. A rise of the predicted magnitude has indeed been observed in scattering from lead and from uranium (Vo56,Al56; see also Al57). For scattering angles of a fraction of a degree the screening of the nucleus by atomic electrons has to be taken into account (Ko60,Sc48).

Schwinger calculated the polarization of the scattered neutrons in Born approximation. The nuclear Coulomb field was assumed to be that of a point charge of magnitude Ze and the nuclear part of the scattering was assumed to be spin-independent. The polarization results from interference between nuclear and electromagnetic scattering and is given by (Sc48, see also Sa56)

$$P(\theta) = \frac{-2\gamma \, \cot \, (\theta/2) \, \cdot \, \mathrm{Im}\mathfrak{F}(\theta)}{|\mathfrak{F}(\theta)|^2 + \gamma^2 \cot^2 (\theta/2)} \tag{18}$$

where $\mathfrak{F}(\theta)$ is the nuclear scattering amplitude and $\gamma = \mu Ze^2/Mc^2 \approx 1.46Z \cdot 10^{-16}$ cm. The denominator of (18) is the scattering cross section. Within the restricted angular range of interest here, $\mathfrak{F}(\theta)$ can be replaced by $\mathfrak{F}(0)$. According to the familiar "optical theorem," $\mathrm{Im}\mathfrak{F}(0)$ is equal to $k\sigma_T/4\pi$, so that the polarization can be calculated from the measured forward scattering cross section and the total cross section. Figure 17 shows the polarization for 1-Mev neutrons scattered from lead. The cross sections were taken from Wa54 and Da55. The polarization reaches a maximum at 1.2° and for large angles falls off as $1/\theta$.

The observation of Mott-Schwinger scattering is difficult. Background problems are severe because the detector needs to be very close to the direct beam. The angular spread must be small and the detector must be positioned very accurately. The first attempt to use Schwinger scattering as polarization analyzer gave inconclusive results (Lo52). The effect was first clearly demonstrated by Voss and Wilson at Harwell in the scattering of 100-Mev neutrons from uranium (Vo56). Gorlov, Lebedeva, and Morosov (Go58) at the Atomic Energy Institute in Moscow succeeded in observing the effect at 3.6 Mev neutron energy. The D-D reaction served as the neutron source. A lead scatterer was placed at 45° with respect to the deuteron beam, about 60 cm from the target. The collimator was conical, with an aperture near the source of 0.15 x 1.2 cm, and an aperture of 1.2 x 1.2 cm near the scatterer. A stilbene detector 2×2 cm was placed 60 cm from the scatterer at angles from -4 to $+4$ degrees. The observed asymmetry was 1.37 ± 0.04 for $2°$-scattering and 1.12 ± 0.04 for $4°$-scattering. They deduced a value $P = (-)0.192 \pm 0.02$ for the polarization of D-D neutrons at $E_d = 1$ Mev and $\psi_1 = 45°$, assuming for the Schwinger polarization the values of Baz' (Ba56a). From the measurements with helium as analyzer one expects $P = -0.14$ at this energy and angle.

The interest in Mott-Schwinger scattering lies in the fact that the polarization can be calculated from measured cross sections, thus avoiding the complications of a phase shift analysis. A large polarization can result even at very low neutron energies (Ma61).

References

(Ad54)   Adair, Darden, and Fields, *Phys. Rev.* **96,** 503 (1954).

(Ad54a)   R. K. Adair, *Phys. Rev.* **96,** 709 (1954).

(Al56)   I. A. Aleksandrov and I. I. Bondarenko, *Zhur. Eksptl. Teoret. Fiz.* **31,** 726 (1956); *Soviet Phys. J.E.T.P.* **4,** 612 (1957).

(Al57)   I. A. Aleksandrov, *Zhur. Eksptl. Teoret. Fiz.* **33,** 294 (1957); *Soviet Phys. J.E.T.P.* **6,** 228 (1958).

(Al59)   R. G. Allas and F. B. Shull, *Phys. Rev.* **116,** 996 (1959).

(Ar59)   Artemov, Vlasov, and Samoĭlov, *Zhur. Eksptl. Teoret. Fiz.* **37,** 1183 (1959); *Soviet Phys. J.E.T.P.* **10,** 841 (1960).

(Au61)   Austin, Darden, Okazaki, and Wilhelmi, *Nuclear Phys.* **22,** 451 (1961).

(Au62)   S. M. Austin, H. H. Barschall, and R. E. Shamu, *Phys. Rev.* **126,** 1532 (1962).

(Ba53)   E. Baumgartner and P. Huber, *Helv. Phys. Acta* **26,** 545 (1953).

(Ba56)   H. H. Barschall, *Helv. Phys. Acta* **29,** 145 (1956).

(Ba56a)   A. I. Baz', *Zhur. Eksptl. Teoret. Fiz.* **31,** 159 (1956); *Soviet Phys. J.E.T.P.* **4,** 259 (1957).

(Ba60)   J. A. Baicker and K. W. Jones, *Nuclear Phys.* **17,** 424 (1960).

(Ba60a)   Baumgartner, Brown, Huber, Rudin, and Striebel, *Phys. Rev. Letters* **5,** 154 (1960).

(Be50)   Beiduk, Pruett, and Konopinski, *Phys. Rev.* **77,** 622 (1950).

(Be62)   Benenson, May, and Walter, *Nuclear Phys.,* **32,** 510 (1962).

(Bi52)   Bishop, Preston, Westhead, and Halban, *Nature (London)* **170,** 113 (1952).

(Bi59)   L. C. Biedenharn, *Nuclear Phys.* **10,** 620 (1959).

(Bj58)   F. Bjorklund and S. Fernbach, *Phys. Rev.* **109,** 1295 (1958).

(Bj59)   F. Bjorklund, in *Proceedings of the International Conference on the Nuclear Optical Model,* Florida State University Studies, Number 32, Tallahassee, 1959, p. 1.

(Bl52)   R. J. Blin-Stoyle, *Proc. Phys. Soc. (London)* **65A,** 452 (1952).

(Bl57)   R. J. Blin-Stoyle and M. A. Grace, in *Handbuch der Physik*, S. Flügge, Ed., Springer, Berlin, 1957, Vol. 42, p. 555.
(Bl59)   W. A. Blanpied, *Phys. Rev.* **113**, 1099 (1959).
(Bo51)   Bockelman, Miller, Adair, and Barschall, *Phys. Rev.* **84**, 69 (1951).
(Br58)   Brüllmann, Gerber, and Meier, *Helv. Chim. Acta* **41**, 1831 (1958).
(Br59)   Brüllmann, Gerber, Meier, and Scherrer, *Helv. Phys. Acta* **32**, 511 (1959).
(Br60)   Brolley, Putnam, Rosen, and Stewart, *Phys. Rev.* **117**, 1307 (1960).
(Br61)   II. Brinkman, *Ilelv. Phys. Acta, Supplementum* **6**, 166 (1961).
(Br61a)   R. I. Brown and W. Haeberli, *Bull. Am. Phys. Soc.* **6**, 307 (1961).
(Br61b)   Brown, Ferguson, and White, *Nuclear Phys.* **25**, 604 (1961).
(Bu55)   R. Budde and P. Huber, *Helv. Phys. Acta* **28**, 49 (1955).
(Bu59)   Bucher, Beverly, Cobb, and Hereford, *Nuclear Phys.* **13**, 164 (1959).
(Bu59a)   Bucher, Beverly, Cobb, and Hereford, *Phys. Rev.* **115**, 961 (1959).
(Bu61)   Budzanowski, Grotowski, Niewodniczański, Nurzyński, and Slapa, *Helv. Phys. Acta, Supplementum* **6**, 215 (1961).
(Cl58)   Clement, Boreli, Darden, Haeberli, and Striebel, *Nuclear Phys.* **6**, 177 (1958).
(Cr59)   L. Cranberg, *Phys. Rev.* **114**, 174 (1959).
(Cr61)   L. Cranberg, *Ilelv. Phys. Acta, Supplementum* **6**, 311 (1961).
(Da55)   Darden, Perkins, and Walton, *Phys. Rev.* **100**, 1315 (1955).
(Da59)   W. W. Daehnick, *Phys. Rev.* **115**, 1008 (1959).
(Da60)   Darden, Kelsey, and Donoghue, *Nuclear Phys.* **16**, 351 (1960).
(Da61)   Darden, Donoghue, and Kelsey, *Nuclear Phys.* **22**, 439 (1961).
(Da61a)   Darden, Kelsey, and Donoghue, *Helv. Phys. Acta, Supplementum* **6**, 269 (1961).
(Du59)   Dubbeldam, Jonker, and Heemskerk, *Nucl. Instr. and Methods* **4**, 234 (1959).
(Du60)   Dubbeldam, Jonker, and Boersma, *Nuclear Phys.* **15**, 452 (1960).
(Du61)   P. S. Dubbeldam and R. L. Walter, *Nuclear Phys.*, **28**, 414 (1961).
(El59)   Elwyn, Kane, Ofer, and Wilkinson, *Phys. Rev.* **116**, 1490 (1959).
(El62)   A. J. Elwyn and R. O. Lane, *Nuclear Phys.*, **31**, 78 (1962).
(Ev60)   J. E. Evans and M. A. Grace, *Nuclear Phys.* **15**, 646 (1960).
(Fa59)   H. Faissner, *Ergebnisse der Exakten Naturw.* **32**, 180 (1959).
(Fa59a)   Facchini, Gatti, and Pellegrini, *Nuclear Instr. and Methods* **4**, 221 (1959).
(Fi52)   M. Fierz, *Helv. Phys. Acta* **25**, 629 (1952).
(Fl59)   Fleishman, Einbinder, and Wu, *Rev. Sci. Instr.* **30**, 1130 (1959).
(Gi59)   J. H. Gibbons and R. L. Macklin, *Phys. Rev.* **114**, 571 (1959).
(Go58)   Gorlov, Lebedeva, and Morosov, in *Conference on Nuclear Reactions at Low Energies*, Moscow, 1958, p. 93.
(Ha57)   W. Haeberli and W. W. Rolland, *Bull. Am. Phys. Soc.* **2**, 234 (1957).
(Ha60)   W. Haeberli, *Helv. Phys. Acta, Supplementum* **6**, 149 (1961).
(He61)   F. L. Hereford, *Helv. Phys. Acta, Supplementum* **6**, 303 (1961).
(Ili56)   Hillman, Stafford, and Whitehead, *Nuovo Cimento* **4**, 67 (1956).
(Ho58)   P. E. Hodgson, *Advances in Physics* **7**, 1 (1958).

(Ho61)   P. E. Hodgson, *Proceedings of the Rutherford Jubilee International Conference*, Paper C3/10.

(Hu53)   P. Huber and E. Baumgartner, *Helv. Phys. Acta* **26**, 420 (1953).

(Ju56)   A. C. Juveland and W. Jentschke, *Z. Physik* **144**, 521 (1956).

(Ka59)   P. P. Kane, *Nuclear Phys.* **10**, 429 (1959).

(Ke60)   Kelsey, Donoghue, and Darden, *Bull. Am. Phys. Soc.* **5**, 404 (1960).

(Ko48)   E. J. Konopinski and E. Teller, *Phys. Rev.* **73**, 822 (1948).

(Ko60)   V. M. Koprov, *Zhur. Eksptl. Teoret. Fiz.* **38**, 639 (1960); *Soviet Phys. J.E.T.P.* **11**, 459 (1960).

(La61)   R. O. Lane, private communication (1961).

(La61a)   Lane, Elwyn, and Langsdorf, *Bull. Am. Phys. Soc.* **6**, 430 (1961).

(Le57)   Levintov, Miller, and Shamshev, *Nuclear Phys.* **3**, 221 (1957).

(Le57a)   Levintov, Miller, Tarumov, and Shamshev, *Nuclear Phys.* **3**, 237 (1957).

(Le58)   Levintov, Miller, and Shamshev, *Zhur. Eksptl. Teoret. Fiz.* **34**, 1030 (1958); *Soviet Phys. J.E.T.P.* **7**, 712 (1958).

(Lo52)   Longley, Little, Jr., and Slye, *Phys. Rev.* **86**, 419 (1952).

(Ma55)   L. Marshall, *Rev. Sci. Instr.* **26**, 614 (1955).

(Ma58)   R. L. Macklin and J. H. Gibbons, *Phys. Rev.* **109**, 105 (1958).

(Ma61)   B. Margolis, *Nuclear Phys.* **22**, 498 (1961).

(Mc56)   McCormac, Steuer, Bond, and Hereford, *Phys. Rev.* **104**, 718 (1956).

(Mc57)   McCormac, Steuer, Bond, and Hereford, *Phys. Rev.* **108**, 116 (1957).

(Me54)   Meier, Scherrer, and Trumpy, *Helv. Phys. Acta* **27**, 577 (1954).

(Mo29)   N. F. Mott, *Proc. Roy. Soc. (London)* **124A**, 425 (1929).

(Ne53)   H. C. Newns, *Proc. Phys. Soc. (London)* **66A**, 477 (1953).

(Ne58)   H. C. Newns and M. Y. Refai, *Proc. Phys. Soc. (London)* **71A**, 627 (1958).

(Ne59)   Newson, Block, Nichols, Taylor, and Furr, *Ann. Phys. (New York)* **8**, 211 (1959).

(Ne59a)   P. E. Nemirovskiĭ, *Zhur. Eksptl. Teoret. Fiz.* **36**, 588 (1959); *Soviet Phys. J.E.T.P.* **9**, 408 (1959).

(Ni55)   V. O. Nicolai, *Rev. Sci. Instr.* **26**, 1203 (1955).

(No60)   J. S. Nodvik and D. S. Saxon, *Phys. Rev.* **117**, 1539 (1960).

(Ok55)   A. Okazaki, *Phys. Rev.* **99**, 55 (1955).

(Ot59)   P. S. Ot-Stavnov, *Zhur. Eksptl. Teoret. Fiz.* **37**, 1815 (1959); *Soviet Phys. J.E.T.P.* **10**, 1281 (1960).

(Pa58)   P. J. Pasma, *Nuclear Phys.* **6**, 141 (1958).

(Pa58a)   P. J. Pasma, Thesis, Groningen (1958).

(Pe61)   R. B. Perkins and J. E. Simmons, *Phys. Rev.* **124**, 1153 (1961).

(Ph59)   G. C. Phillips and P. D. Miller, *Phys. Rev.* **115**, 1268 (1959).

(Pi59)   G. Pisent and C. Villi, *Nuovo Cimento* **11**, 300 (1959).

(Pr61)   *Proceedings of the Symposium on Polarization Phenomena of Nucleons*, *Helv. Phys. Acta, Supplementum* **6** (1961).

(Re56)   A. E. Remund, *Helv. Phys. Acta* **29**, 545 (1956).

(Ri53)   R. Ricamo, *Helv. Phys. Acta* **26**, 423 (1953).

(Ri53a)   R. Ricamo, *Nuovo Cimento* **10**, 1607 (1953).

(Ri60)   H. T. Richards, in *Nuclear Spectroscopy*, F. Ajzenberg-Selove, *ed.* Academic Press, 1960, Part A, p. 133.

(Ro59)   L. Rosen, in *Proceedings of the International Conference on the Nuclear Optical Model*, Florida State University Studies, Number 32, Tallahassee, 1959, p. 72.

(Ro60)   L. Rosen, in *Proceedings of the International Conference on Nuclear Structure*, University of Toronto Press, Toronto, 1960, p. 185.

(Ro60a) L. S. Rodberg, *Nuclear Phys.* **15,** 72 (1960).

(Ro61)   Rosen, Brolley, and Stewart, *Phys. Rev.,* **121,** 1423 (1961).

(Ro61a) D. Robson, *Nuclear Phys.* **22,** 34 (1961).

(Ro61b) J. R. Rook and L. J. Goldfarb, *Nuclear Phys.* **27,** 79 (1961).

(Ru58)   C. Rubbia and M. Toller, *Nuovo Cimento* **10,** 410 (1958).

(Sa53)   R. G. Sachs, *Nuclear Theory*, Addison Wesley, Cambridge, 1953, p. 316.

(Sa56)   J. T. Sample, *Can. J. Phys.* **34,** 36 (1956).

(Sa58)   G. R. Satchler, *Nuclear Phys.* **8,** 65 (1958).

(Sc46)   J. Schwinger, *Phys. Rev.* **69,** 681 (1946).

(Sc48)   J. Schwinger, *Phys. Rev.* **73,** 407 (1948).

(Sc58)   M. J. Scott, *Phys. Rev.* **110,** 1398 (1958).

(Se53)   J. D. Seagrave, *Phys. Rev.* **92,** 1222 (1953).

(Se60)   Seagrave, Cranberg, and Simmons, *Phys. Rev.* **119,** 1981 (1960).

(Sh60)   Shafroth, Chalmers, Strait, and Segel, *Phys. Rev.* **118,** 1054 (1960).

(Si53)   A. Simon and T. A. Welton, *Phys. Rev.* **90,** 1036 (1953).

(Si60)   Sign Convention for Particle Polarization, *Nuclear Phys.* **21,** 696 (1960).

(St57)   H. R. Striebel and W. Haeberli, *Bull. Am. Phys. Soc.* **2,** 234 (1957).

(St58)   Striebel, Darden, and Haeberli, *Nuclear Phys.* **6,** 188 (1958).

(St59)   Steuer, Bucher, and Hereford, in *Comptes Rendus du Congres International de Physique Nucléaire*, Dunod, Paris, 1959, p. 545.

(Th56)   Thomas, Walt, Walton, and Allen, *Phys. Rev.* **101,** 759 (1956).

(Th59)   E. H. Thorndike and W. J. Schlaer, *Rev. Sci. Instr.* **30,** 838 (1959).

(To60)   Tombrello, Burloutaud, and Phillips, *Phys. Rev.* **119,** 761 (1960).

(Vo56)   R. G. P. Voss and R. Wilson, *Phil. Mag.* **1,** 175 (1956).

(Wa54)   M. Walt and H. H. Barschall, *Phys. Rev.* **93,** 1062 (1954).

(Wa62)   Walter, Benenson, Dubbeldam, and May, *Nuclear Phys.* **30,** 292 (1962).

(Wh55)   E. A. Whalin, Jr. and R. A. Reitz, *Rev. Sci. Instr.* **26,** 59 (1955).

(Wh57)   R. E. White and F. J. M. Farley, *Nuclear Phys.* **3,** 476 (1957).

(Wh58)   White, Chisholm, and Brown, *Nuclear Phys.* **7,** 233 (1958).

(Wi54)   Willard, Bair, and Kington, *Phys. Rev.* **95,** 1359 (1954).

(Wi55)   Willard, Bair, and Kington, *Phys. Rev.* **98,** 669 (1955).

(Wi56)   Willard, Bair, Kington, and Cohn, *Phys. Rev.* **101,** 765 (1956).

(Wi56a) Willard, Bair, Cohn, and Kington, *Bull. Am. Phys. Soc.* **1,** 54 (1956).

(Wi58)   Wills, Bair, Cohn, and Willard, *Phys. Rev.* **109,** 891 (1958).

(Wo49)   L. Wolfenstein, *Phys. Rev.* **75,** 342 (1949).

(Wo56)   L. Wolfenstein, *Ann. Rev. Nuclear Sci.* **6,** 43 (1956).

(Zu61)   M. S. Zucker, Thesis, Wisconsin (1961).

Neutron Nonelastic Collision Cross Sections

R. C. ALLEN,[1] *Los Alamos Scientific Laboratory, Los Alamos, New Mexico*

R. E. CARTER, *Los Alamos Scientific Laboratory, Los Alamos, New Mexico*

H. LYNDON TAYLOR, *Texas Instruments Incorporated, Dallas, Texas*

1. Introduction

The neutron nonelastic collision cross section is defined as the cross section for all neutron interactions other than elastic scattering. Its magnitude is equal to that of the total cross section minus the elastic scattering cross section. Like the total cross section it does not refer to a particular type of interaction but rather to a sum of interactions. In most cases it is the cross section for the removal, by a process other than elastic scattering, of neutrons of a given energy. The components of the nonelastic collision processes include inelastic scattering, capture, reactions such as (n, p) and (n, α) and the neutron multiplicative reactions such as fission and (n, xn). In general, over a large part of the fast neutron energy region, capture processes and reactions such as (n, p), (n, α), and (n, xn) are rather small and the main components of nonelastic interactions are inelastic scattering and, in some cases, fission.

By the mid 1930's the elastic and nonelastic interactions of fast neutrons with various materials were being extensively studied. Auger (Au33) observed proton recoils in a cloud chamber and suggested that the increase in the number of short recoils associated with the placement of certain materials near the neutron source might be due to inelastic scattering. Dunning and his co-workers (Du34,

---

[1] Now at Atomics International, Canoga Park, California.

Du35, Du35a), with Ra-α-Be and Rn-α-Be neutron sources, were conducting some ring scattering and total cross section measurements. Also, by observing the attenuation of neutrons by spheres of different thicknesses placed around the source, the possibility of inelastic scattering was demonstrated experimentally. Danysz *et al.* (Da34) studied the activation of several elements by Rn-α-Be neutrons with and without intermediate lead and gold absorbers. The presence of the absorbers increased the activities of silver and iodine and this was attributed to nuclear collisions in which part of the neutron energy was emitted in the form of γ rays. Ehrenburg (Eh35) continued this type of experiment and made an extensive study with silver as the absorber. Lea (Le35) detected the γ rays emitted by material placed near a Po-α-Be source and concluded that nuclear excitation seemed to be the most plausible cause. Collie and Griffiths (Co36) placed spheres around Rn-α-Be sources and observed the activities of external threshold detectors. In some cases the activities induced with the spheres around the source were greater than those with the source alone, and this was attributed to inelastically scattered neutrons. Seaborg *et al.* (Se37) conducted an experiment in which the neutrons were slowed down before detection. By observing neutrons of all energies, the transmission of materials placed around the Ra-α-Be source remained near unity while at the same time the γ rays from the materials were observed. In this manner it was demonstrated that γ rays were definitely due to inelastic scattering. By adding other absorbing materials, these experimenters also showed that the excitation of the γ rays was a function of the neutron energy. Aoki and his collaborators (Ao37, Ao39, Ki39, Wa39, Wa40), with D-D neutrons in the 2-3 Mev energy region, made measurements of the γ rays and neutron angular distributions both by ring scattering methods and by moving the detector around the scatterer. Grahame and Seaborg (Gr38), with threshold detectors, measured absorption and inelastic scattering cross sections by observing the decrease in activity of the detectors when cylinders of material were placed around a Ra-α-Be source. With a 2.5-Mev D-D neutron source, Hudspeth and Bonner (Hu38) studied inelastic scattering in lead by observing proton recoils in a cloud chamber. MacPhail (Ma40), with D-D neutrons from 2.3 to 2.8 Mev, demonstrated the presence of resonances in neutron total cross sections. Dunlap and Little (Du41) put a thick lead sphere around a 2.5-Mev D-D neutron source and measured the spectrum of inelastically scattered neutrons with a cloud chamber placed at 90°. Barschall and Ladenburg (Ba42) studied the elastic and inelastic scattering of 2.5 Mev neutrons by several elements by analyzing recoil α particles in an ion chamber.

From this incomplete summary, it is evident that prior to World War II there were many experimental approaches to the study of the interactions of fast neutrons with various materials. In general, however, the results pertaining to nonelastic processes were difficult to interpret and the cross sections were not very accurate.

The establishment of the Manhattan Project gave great impetus to many phases of fast neutron physics research. Some early Los Alamos work (Ma46, Ol46, Ba47, Ba47a) consisted of measuring the scattering of neutrons by circular discs of material placed half way between the neutron source and the neutron detector, and of measuring the back scattering from circular discs with the detector between the source and the scatterer. Several neutron energies up to 3 Mev were used. From the proton recoil distributions in the detectors these experimenters were able to get considerable information about the elastic scattering, inelastic scattering, and transport cross sections. Other Los Alamos experimenters (Ha46) were studying capture and inelastic scattering by placing different neutron sources in the center of thick spheres and observing the transmissions. The interpretation of the inelastic scattering results, however, was somewhat uncertain. Concurrently, in Chicago (Sz48), measurements were being made on the nonelastic collision cross sections of several elements by measuring the decrease in the counting rate of a U^{238} fission threshold detector when thick spheres of material were placed around Ra-α-Be and Ra-α-Be neutron sources. Although multiple scattering corrections were attempted, the results of these experiments were inconclusive. In Italy, Amaldi *et al.* (Am46) were measuring total, nonelastic collision, and elastic scattering cross sections.

Although during the war years new techniques and improvements of older methods resulted in better measurements of neutron interaction cross sections, it is significant to note that techniques for the measurements of nonelastic collision and elastic scattering cross sections had not been well established.

However, shortly after the war, when better detectors and sources were available, several groups began using what is now known as *the sphere method*. The ideas of compensation of elastically scat-

tered neutrons and the reciprocity theorem (Ph49, Be52) whereby the
source is located outside and the detector inside of the sphere brought
about the use of this method for measuring nonelastic collision cross
sections with asymmetrical monoenergetic neutron sources. In this
method the counting rates of an energy dependent neutron detector
are observed with and without a spherical shell of material around the
detector. With ideal geometrical conditions (Section 2.A), and only
elastic scattering, the attenuation of the primary neutron beam by that
part of the sphere between the source and the detector is exactly compensated by the neutrons elastically scattered into the detector by the
remainder of the sphere. In this case there is no net effect due to
elastically scattered neutrons, (i.e., $T = 1$), and this is the significance
of spherical geometry. If other reactions can occur, the transmission,
which is the ratio of the counting rates with and without the sphere,
is dependent to a large extent on these other interactions, the nonelastic collision cross section. Early measurements were made by
Gittings *et al.* (Gi49) with a 14-Mev D-T neutron source and threshold
activation detectors. Phillips *et al.* (Ph49, Ph52) extended the
14-Mev measurements and made some valuable contributions to the
understanding of some of the corrections involved in the sphere
method. The work of Bethe, Beyster, and Carter (Ca53, Be55a,
Be56a) (hereinafter referred to as BBC), which discusses the analysis
of data obtained from sphere transmission experiments, extended the
reliable use of this method to a wide range of neutron energies and
experimental conditions. A large part of this article deals with a
detailed discussion of the sphere method, the detectors developed for
this experiment, the relationship between the nonelastic collision
cross section and the observed transmission, and the final cross
sections.

     A second approach to the determination of nonelastic collision
cross sections which has been developed in the past few years is that
of measuring the total cross section and subtracting from it the measured total elastic scattering cross section. By definition, this difference is the nonelastic collision cross section. In general, this method
is not as accurate as the sphere method but has produced some valuable results. Since the experimental techniques involved in measuring
the total and elastic scattering cross sections are discussed elsewhere
in this book (Chapters V.A and V.B), only the nonelastic results are
included in this chapter.

A third approach is the measurement of all the nonelastic collision cross section components. This method yields considerably more information than the others but is also more difficult. Inelastic scattering, for instance, has been studied by analyzing recoil distributions in cloud chambers, photographic plates, scintillation crystals and proportional counters; by observing the γ rays associated with inelastic scattering; and by measuring the activations of isomeric states. Recent advances in neutron and γ-ray time-of-flight techniques have brought about major improvements in the inelastic scattering measurements. Since this approach is becoming more important and the trend is toward the measurement of the specific interactions, this chapter will include some results obtained by this approach which correspond to the nonelastic collision cross sections determined by the other methods. The experimental techniques involved in measuring these quantities, however, will not be discussed here as several are described elsewhere in this book[2] (see Chapters IV and V).

The notation used to describe the interactions discussed above is as follows (see the Appendix). Since we are dealing only with neutron reactions, and the bombarding energy E is always a parameter, the subscript n and the argument E will be omitted and understood. The total cross section is σ_T. The total elastic scattering cross section is σ_n and refers to scattering in which the neutron energy is conserved in the center-of-mass-system. The differential elastic scattering cross section is given by $\sigma_n(\theta)$, where θ is the C. M. angle, and

$$\sigma_n = \int_\Omega \sigma_n(\theta) d\Omega$$

The elastic transport cross section is

$$\sigma_{et} = \int_\Omega \sigma_n \psi \, (1 - \cos \psi) d\Omega$$

where Ψ is the laboratory angle, and the transport cross section

$$\sigma_{tr} = \sigma_X + \sigma_{et}$$

where σ_X, the nonelastic collision cross section, is

$$\sigma_X = \sigma_T - \sigma_n$$

[2] Previous summaries of the measurement techniques and results of elastic scattering, inelastic scattering and nonelastic collision cross sections have been written by Barschall (Ba52), Freeman (Fr56), and Cranberg, Day, Rosen, Taschek, and Walt (Cr56).

The inelastic scattering cross section is $\sigma_{n'}$. The inelastic scattering cross section for the direct excitation of a given state of energy E_j in a target nucleus is $\sigma_{n'}(E_j)$. (The total probability of excitation of a given level may be greater because of cascade γ-ray decay from more highly excited states.) In the discrete energy level region,

$$\sigma_{n'} = \sum_j \sigma_{n'}(E_j)$$

The differential inelastic scattering cross section for the direct excitation of a given level with the neutron emerging at angle θ is

$$\sigma_{n'}(E_j,\theta)$$

and

$$\sigma_{n'}(E_j) = \int_\Omega \sigma_{n'}(E_j,\theta) d\Omega$$

The capture cross section is denoted by σ_γ and the fission cross section by σ_f.

2. The Sphere Method

In principle, the sphere transmission method works as follows: If an isotropically emitting neutron source is surrounded by a spherical shell of material which can only elastically scatter the neutrons, then the number of neutrons transmitted through this shell will be identically the same as the number emitted by the source. Therefore, the transmission measured by a detector at a large distance will be unity. However, if some of the neutrons are absorbed by the nuclei of the shell, the transmission will be less than one, and it might be assumed that the observed transmission is a function of the absorption cross section only.

This would be true if all of the neutrons traveled through the spherical shell along radial paths unless they suffered a nonelastic collision, and in that case the transmission would be a simple function of the nonelastic cross section, namely,

$$T = \exp[-\Sigma_X(r_2 - r_1)] \tag{1}$$

where r_2 = outer radius, r_1 = inner radius, $\Sigma_X = N_0\sigma_X$ = macroscopic nonelastic cross section in cm^{-1}.

It is clear, however, that if the elastic scattering properties of the nuclei of the sphere can produce much of an increase in path length through the shell, Eq. (1) will be only an approximation to the correct description of the physical picture. However, there are two general conditions in which Eq. (1) will not be very much in error: (a) if the thickness of the shell is so small that

$$T = 1 - \Sigma_X(r_2 - r_1) \tag{2}$$

is applicable, or (b) if the elastic transport cross section

$$\sigma_{et} = \int_\Omega \sigma_n \psi(1 - \cos\psi)d\Omega \tag{3}$$

is small compared to σ_X.

These conditions severely limit the use of Eq. (1) because, as will be shown in the next section, the transmission of a shell thin enough to satisfy condition (a) is, in general, so large that it prohibits accurate cross section measurements. Condition (b) restricts one to situations in which the nonelastic cross section is about one-half of the total cross section, and in which the elastic scattering is peaked strongly in the forward direction. Then an elastic scattering acts about like no scattering at all. Therefore, condition (b) limits one to incident neutron energies of several Mev, where the nonelastic cross sections are no longer very dependent on neutron energy.

Except for MacGregor's minor modifications and extensions (Ma57), the analytical methods developed by BBC have established the methods now in general use for interpreting sphere transmission measurements. Therefore the development in the next section will follow closely that given in these references. Since these papers are available in the literature, the details of the algebra will be avoided, and the physical picture of what a neutron does in a macroscopic sphere will be emphasized.

A. Thin Shell

The thin shell analysis seems particularly instructive, because not only can one keep the mathematics easily in hand, but also, since the average neutron does not have many collisions in the shell, the physical picture can be kept fairly clearly in mind. In this section it will be assumed that a point, isotropic, monoenergetic neutron source is placed at the center of a spherical shell whose nuclei have infinite mass. Then the elastic scattering changes only the direction of motion of the neutron. The second assumption is that only non-

elastic processes render a neutron undetectable, but all such processes
do.   This is the characteristic of an ideal threshold detector.

In the linear (first order) approximation, no neutron has more
than one collision, which may be either elastic or nonelastic, and so
the transmission is of the form

$$T = 1 - (a\Sigma_n + b\Sigma_X)D \tag{4}$$

where a and b are constants, and

$$D = r_2 - r_1$$

But, since $T = 1$ in the absence of nonelastic scattering, $a = 0$.
Thus the transmission is a function of the nonelastic cross section
alone.

In the second order approximation, the path lengthening effect
first appears.   The computation of the expected transmission to
order D^2 requires obtaining and adding two terms: (a) The fractional
number of neutrons whose first collision is nonelastic, namely,

$$N_1 = \sigma_X/\sigma_T[1 - \exp(-\Sigma_T D)] = \Sigma_X D - \frac{1}{2}(\Sigma_X \Sigma_T D^2) \tag{5}$$

and (b) The fractional number of neutrons whose first collision is
elastic, but whose second collision is nonelastic.   From Fig. 1, the
integral to be performed to obtain this term is

$$N_2 = \int_\Omega \int_{r_1}^{r_2} \Sigma_n(\psi)dr \, d\Omega \, \Sigma_X \, Y(r,\psi) \tag{6}$$

where $\Sigma_X \, Y(r,\psi)$ is the probability that the elastically scattered neutron will be scattered nonelastically before escaping from the shere.
In order to evaluate this expression, the following two simplifying
assumptions are made:

(a)   Instead of the explicit angular distribution for elastic
scattering, isotropic scattering is assumed, with σ_{et} [(Eq. 3)] as the
appropriate cross section for elastic scattering.   This has been shown
to give quite accurate results, and will be discussed further in Section
2.B.

(b)   The shell is thin, not only compared to a mean free path,
but compared to its radius, i.e., $D \ll r_2$.
Equation (6) then gives (BBC):

$$N_2 = \frac{1}{2}\Sigma_X \Sigma_{et} D^2 L \tag{7}$$

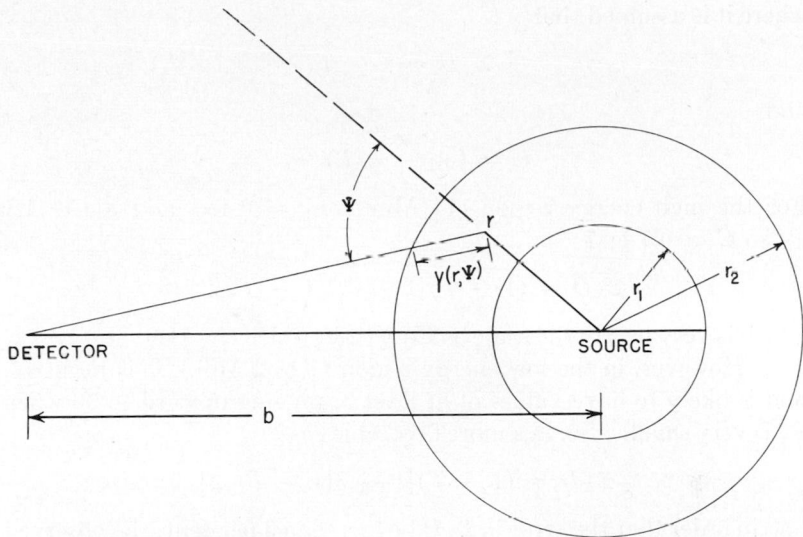

Figure 1. Geometry used for the analysis of sphere transmission measurements.

where

$$L = [^3/_2 + \ln(2r_2/D)] = 3 \text{ to } 4 \tag{8}$$

Adding Eqs. (5) and (7), the transmission is

$$T - 1 - \Sigma_X D[1 - {}^1/_2(\Sigma_{tr} - \Sigma_{et}L)D] \tag{9}$$

Now, generally, up to incident neutron energies of 3 or 4 Mev,

$$\sigma_{et} > {}^1/_2\sigma_n > {}^1/_4\sigma_{tr}.$$

So, if $L = 4$, the bracketed term in Eq. (9) will be >1, and a curve of the transmission $vs.$ thickness (D) does not have the form of an exponential $[(T = \exp(-\Sigma_X D)]$ but bends downward, instead of up. This means that an elementary analysis (linear or exponential) of thin shell transmission gives too large a value for σ_X. The magnitude of the likely error can be estimated simply, and will be done for two energy regions; (a) about 14 Mev, and (b) about 1 to 2 Mev.

In order to make a quantitative estimate, Eq. (9) can be rewritten as

$$\Sigma_X D = (1 - T)[1 + C(1 - T)/2]$$

where it is assumed that

$$\Sigma_X D \approx 1 - T$$

and

$$C = (\sigma_{\text{tr}} - \sigma_{\text{et}}L)/\sigma_X$$

For the high energy region (14 Mev), $\sigma_{\text{et}} \approx 0.1\sigma_X$ and $\sigma_{\text{tr}} \approx 1.1$ σ_X so $C = 0.7$ and

$$\Sigma_X D = (1 - T)[1 + 0.7(1 - T)/2]$$

which is very nearly the same as Eq. (1), in which $C = 1.0$.

However, in the low energy region (1 to 2 Mev), C is negative, and is likely to have values of at least 3, ranging upward to 30 when σ_X is very small. So, in a more favorable case,

$$\Sigma_X D = (1 - T)[1 - 3(1 - T)/2]$$

and in order that the error in $\Sigma_X D$ be less than 5 per cent, the observed transmission must be high enough such that

$$4(1 - T)/2 < 0.05$$

or

$$(1 - T) < (0.05 \times 2/4 = 0.025)$$

A transmission of 0.97, accurate enough to yield a reliable cross section, is very difficult to obtain. Since this is a relatively favorable value for C in this energy region, it is clear that there is no practicable sphere which can be considered *thin* when the nonelastic cross section is less than about one-half as large as the transport cross section.

Therefore, the exponential relationship between transmission and nonelastic cross section is only an approximation, and must be so regarded. There are indeed conditions under which the exponential does not cause more than 5 per cent error in the nonelastic cross section, but these conditions must be evaluated in a quantitative way.

An important point brought out by the details of this thin shell analysis (BBC) is that the average length of path for a neutron which has been elastically scattered isotropically is almost independent of the radius, r, at which the initial scattering occurs. This means that the chance of making a second collision which is nonelastic, for

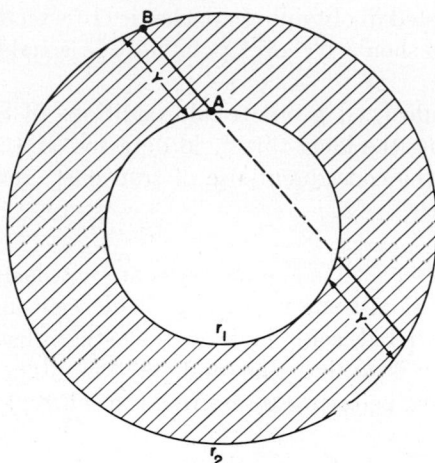

Figure 2. Paths of neutrons colliding at outer and inner edges of a thin spherical shell.

example, is independent of how near the first collision was to the outer edge of the sphere. This can be seen in Fig. 2, where A and B represent the two extreme points of collision for a typical neutron. If the first collision occurs at A, the neutron still has to traverse the distance Y (either forward or backward) in order to escape from the shell. If the collision occurs at B, the $\sim$50 per cent going forward have no material to traverse, but the 50 per cent going backward have $2Y$ to traverse. So in each case the average thickness yet to be traversed is Y. The results of this argument help in understanding the properties of the escape probabilities introduced in the next section.

Now that it has been demonstrated that the neglect of elastic scattering in the sphere can lead to large errors, even for very thin shells, an expression will be derived in the next section which is valid for all neutron energies and any shell thickness.

B.   Multiple Scattering Analysis

This is just an extension of the thin shell computation, but now a neutron must be followed through more than one elastic collision in order to obtain the probability of its making a nonelastic collision before escaping from the sphere. However, the implication is made that one is interested in obtaining nonelastic cross sections, and so the shell transmission should be correspondingly reasonable, for example, $0.9 \geqq T \geqq 0.5$.

Again the idealized geometrical conditions of Section 2.A are assumed, including the ideal threshold detector, and isotropic elastic scattering, with the consequent use of transport cross sections, i.e.,

$$\sigma_{tr} = \sigma_{et} + \sigma_X$$

As for the thin shell, some neutrons are nonelastically scattered on their first collision, some make one elastic collision and then are nonelastically scattered, some make two elastic collisions, and so on. The problem then is to find the total fraction of the neutrons non-elastically scattered before escaping from the sphere, and this is equal to $(1 - T)$.

Let a neutron start from the source. At some point in the sphere it may make a collision. If it does, it will be either non-elastic or elastic. If nonelastic, the neutron is "lost," and contributes to $(1 - T)$. If the collision is elastic, then one of two things can happen: (a) it can escape from the sphere without making a second collision of any kind, and P_1 is defined as the average probability for this escape, or (b) it can make a second collision, with a proba-bility of $(1 - P_1)$. So, since the number of first collisions in the shell is

$$(1 - T_0) = 1 - \exp(-\Sigma_{tr}D) \tag{11}$$

the number of first nonelastic collisions is [Eq. (5)]

$$N_1 = (\sigma_x/\sigma_{tr})(1 - T_0) \tag{12}$$

and the number of nonelastic collisions following only one elastic collision is

$$N_2 = (\sigma_{et}/\sigma_{tr})(1 - T_0)(1 - P_1)(\sigma_X/\sigma_{tr}) \tag{13}$$

Then defining P_2 as the average escape probability for a neutron whose first two successive collisions have been elastic, the number of non-elastic collisions following these two elastic ones is:

$$N_3 = (1 - T_0)(\sigma_{et}/\sigma_{tr})^2(1 - P_1)(1 - P_2)\sigma_X/\sigma_{tr} \tag{14}$$

This process can be continued, and all of the terms added to give

$$1 - T = N_1 + N_2 + N_3 + \ldots + N_m \tag{15}$$

It is clear that the escape probabilities become exceedingly difficult to compute exactly, but, as was pointed out in Section 2.A, the probability of escape from a shell after a collision is not very dependent on the location of the point of scattering. Therefore, the successive P's are not very much different. This is less true for a thick shell than a thin one, but is always approximately correct (BBC). In addition, the spatial distribution of successive collisions tends towards a stable, limiting form, the normal mode distribution, and this is obtained after only a very few collisions. As a consequence of these two conditions, it is a good approximation to assume all of the above escape probabilities to be equal, i.e.,

$$P_1 = P_2 = P_3 = \ldots = P_m \tag{16}$$

and when the terms are summed, according to Eq. (15), one obtains

$$1 - T = (1 - T_0)\, \sigma_X/(\sigma_X + \sigma_{et}P_m) \tag{17}$$

Except for the ideal geometrical conditions, and the use of the transport cross section, Eq. (16) is the only simplifying assumption leading to Eq. (17). It is not necessary to make even this latter assumption, because both P_1 and P_2 have been computed (BBC), and one can use P_m (normal mode) in place of P_3 and higher. The summing still can be performed fairly simply, but of course a much more complicated looking formula [Eq. (20)] results.

Equation (17), in addition to giving fairly accurate answers, has the further advantage that it allows a simple physical interpretation. The first term is the total number of first collisions in the shell, and hence can be considered the *source* term. Then there are two mechanisms by which these neutrons can be removed from the shell, namely, nonelastic scattering, and escape following an elastic collision. The second term therefore gives the fraction which is lost by nonelastic scattering, and it is only this fraction which actually represents neutrons that are undetectable.

The inverted form of Eq. (17) is

$$T = T_0 + (1 - T_0)\, \sigma_{et}P_m/(\sigma_X + \sigma_{et}P_m) \tag{18}$$

which also allows a simple physical interpretation, and in addition lends itself more simply to a discussion of some of the corrections to be applied because of finite geometrical conditions (see Section 2.C).

The escape probabilities (P_1, P_2, etc.) are of the form

$$P_n = \int_\Omega \int_{r_1}^{r_2} f_n(r)\Sigma_n(\psi)dr\ d\Omega \exp[-\Sigma_{\mathrm{tr}}Y(r,\psi)] \div \int_{r_1}^{r_2} f_n(r)\Sigma_n dr \quad (19)$$

where $f_n(r)$ is the flux of neutrons at radius r, and $f_n(r)\Sigma_n(\psi)dr\ d\Omega$ is the number scattered at r, into $d\Omega$ at angle ψ. Then

$$\exp[-\Sigma_{\mathrm{tr}}Y(r,\psi)]$$

(see Fig. 1) is the probability of escaping from the sphere without suffering any more collisions. For P_1, for example, $f_1(r)$ is the exponential distribution

$$\exp[-\Sigma_{\mathrm{tr}}(r - r_1)]$$

of the unscattered neutrons.

In order to test the validity of Eq. (16), computations were made of the spatial distributions within a spherical shell of first, second,

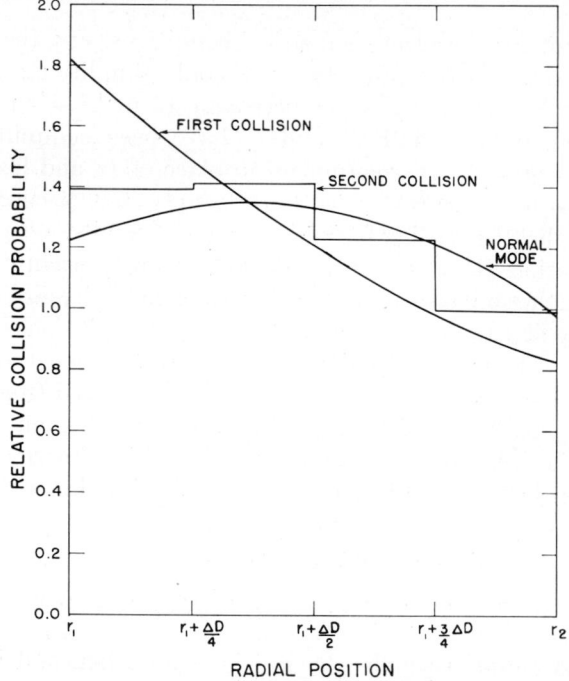

Figure 3. Radial distribution of first, second, and normal mode collisions in a shell with $\Sigma_{\mathrm{tr}}D = r_1/r_2 = 0.8$.

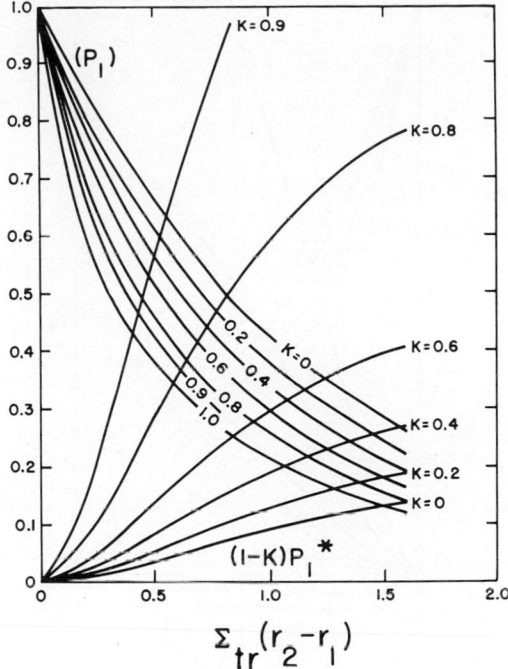

Figure 4. P_1, escape probability from a spherical shell after the first elastic collision. Shell thickness is in transport mean free paths.

and normal mode type collisions. Figure 3 shows these three distributions in a sphere with

$$r_1/r_2 = \Sigma_{tr}(r_2 - r_1) = 0.8$$

The two points demonstrated by these curves are:

(a) There are no large differences among the three curves, except at the inner edge of the spherical shell.

(b) The second-collision distribution has a shape very much like that for many collisions (normal mode), so the third collision distribution is expected to be represented quite accurately by the normal mode distribution. When the escape probabilities (Eq. 19) are computed from the three collision distributions of Fig. 3, the following values are obtained for P_1, P_2, and P_m, respectively: 0.319, 0.322, 0.329.

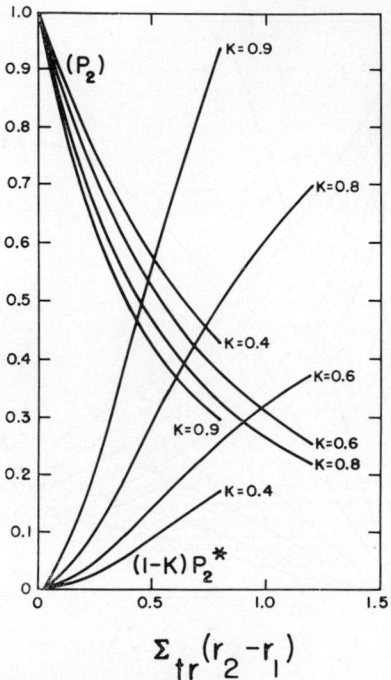

Figure 5. P_2, escape probability from a spherical shell after the second elastic
collision. Shell thickness is in transport mean free paths.

Since the arguments leading to Eq. (16) are supported by these
numerical values for the P's, it is reasonably certain that this assumption does not lead to large errors in obtaining nonelastic cross sections.
However, in many circumstances it is desirable to eliminate even
these small errors, and so, instead of Eq. (16), the following assumptions are made: (a) $P_1 \neq P_2 \neq P_3$, and (b) $P_3 = P_4 = \ldots = P_m$.
Then, making these substitutions into the infinite series of Eq. (15),
and summing the terms,

$$1 - T = (1 - T_0)(\sigma_X/\sigma_{tr}) \left\{ 1 + (\sigma_{et}/\sigma_{tr})(1 - P_1) \right.$$

$$\left. + (1 - P_1)(1 - P_2)\sigma_{et}{}^2/[\sigma_{tr}(\sigma_X + \sigma_{et}P_m)] \right\} \quad (20)$$

For convenience, curves of P_1, P_2, and P_m are given in Figs. 4, 5,
and 6, and these, with interpolation, cover most of the usual region of
interest for nonelastic cross section measurements ($K = r_1/r_2$). On

the same figures there are curves of $(1 - K)P_n^*$, which are explained in Section 2.C, where the correction due to finite source-to-counter distances is discussed.

Equation (20) is based on the use of the transport cross section to describe the interactions between the neutrons and the nuclei of the shell, and except for this assumption should be very nearly exact.

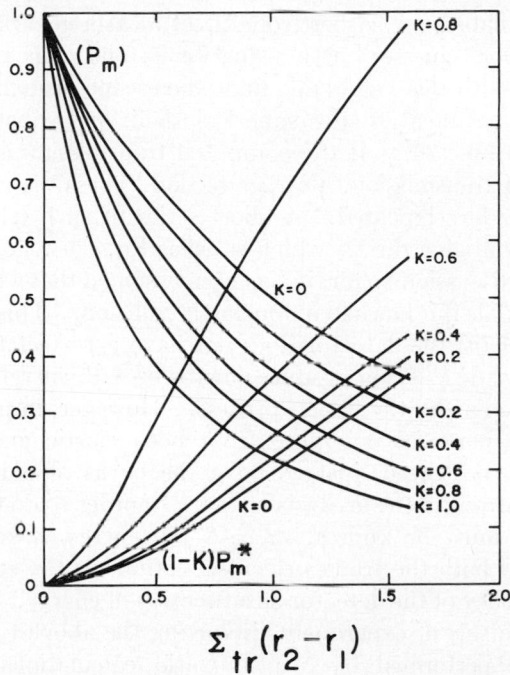

Figure 6. P_m, escape probability from a spherical shell after a normal mode type elastic collision. Shell thickness is in transport mean free paths.

Therefore, a test of the accuracy obtained by using Eq. (20) should also constitute a measure of the validity of using transport cross sections. Both MacGregor (Ma57) and BBC made this test by computing the expected transmission by means of Monte Carlo calculations, and comparing these results with Eq. (20). At 14 Mev, the former finds that the two methods agree to within 0.1 per cent in nonelastic cross section. At lower neutron energies, the latter find that the two methods agree to about 1 per cent. Therefore, if geometrical conditions are ideal (Section 2.A), Eq. (20) can be used with confidence, and in general the accuracy of derived nonelastic cross sections is determined by the uncertainty in the measured transmission, and the knowledge of the other parameters, such as σ_{et}.

One obtains σ_X from a measured transmission, T, and Eqs. (20) or (17) as follows: One obtains σ_{et} from the literature (and it is generally available now, either from direct measurements or by interpolation). One "guesses" at a value for σ_X and adds this to σ_{et} to obtain σ_{tr}. With this value, one finds the escape probabilities (Figs. 4, 5, and 6) pertinent to the spherical shell, and substitutes these numbers into Eq. (20). If the computed transmission is larger than the measured transmission, a larger second "guess" is made for σ_X, and the procedure repeated. A short series of such trial and error calculations will give the σ_X which satisfies Eq. (20).

In the discussion so far, it has been assumed that a neutron is no longer detectable if it has had a nonelastic collision. This assumption is not valid if (a) the detector does not have a perfect threshold, or (b) the nonelastic collision produces neutrons with energies above the threshold, such as by the fission process. However, in principle, the paths of the neutrons emerging from both elastic and nonelastic collisions can be traced, just as have the paths of only elastically scattered neutrons in the analysis so far. In order to do this, though, more details must be known, such as the energy spectrum of the neutrons, and both the transport cross sections of the sphere nuclei, and the efficiency of the detector as a function of energy.

The analysis of experiments involving the above types of processes can be performed by Monte Carlo calculations, but these usually require large amounts of time on a computer. The simplest procedure which is still accessible by analytical methods is to break all neutron spectra into groups, and to follow each group through the sphere and into the detector. The general features of this method have been discussed (BBC) and used by these authors to analyze some transmission measurements with three different detectors of both fissionable and nonfissionable spheres. E. R. Graves (Gr55) has performed some similar measurements with 14-Mev neutrons, and has also used a *long counter* to obtain the neutron multiplication factor of the sphere. Then with the data from both a threshold detector and the flat response detector, some information about the components of the nonelastic process, such as σ_f, $\sigma_{n'}$, $\sigma(n, 2n)$, was obtained.

C. Corrections

In the previous sections, the assumptions have been made that the geometrical conditions are ideal, including that the neutron counter is a perfect threshold detector, and that the source emits neutrons isotropically. In this section the types of corrections necessary for finite geometry are discussed and, in Section 3, the threshold detector problem is explored.

In the previous section, in order to simplify the discussion and the computation of the sphere transmission, the isotropic source has been placed at the center of the sphere. Phillips *et al.* (Ph49, Ph52) have discussed placing the sphere around the detector instead, and have shown for some special cases that the number of neutrons transmitted is the same. Bethe (Be52) has made a general proof of the same fact, with the restrictions that (a) the source and detector both be isotropic, nonabsorbing, and of the same size and shape, (b) the cross section for elastic scattering of a neutron in the sphere be independent of whether or not it has already been elastically scattered, and (c) the detector efficiency be independent of the number of elastic scatterings before detection. Under these conditions, then, the statement concerning this interchangeability of source and detector, the reciprocity theorem, is as follows: if a detector be placed at the center of a hollow sphere, and a source outside, the number of neutrons detected is the same as would be detected if the positions of the source and detector were interchanged. This is a very useful theorem, because not many neutron sources are isotropic, whereas most neutron detectors of interest can be made so. This means that sphere transmission experiments can be performed with the detector inside of the sphere, and it is only necessary that the neutron intensity due to the external source be reasonably constant throughout the solid angle containing the sphere. As will be noted later in this section, small corrections can be made if the intensity and/or energy vary across the diameter of the sphere.

Below, we will list the corrections which must be considered in evaluating a sphere transmission experiment; however, they can be made negligible by proper choice of experimental conditions. For simplicity, these corrections are discussed separately, and with the source inside of the sphere, but always with the reciprocity theorem in mind, because its validity is not decreased by any of the geometrical factors, and energy loss on elastic collisions only modifies the theorem to the extent that the elastic scattering cross section changes with energy.

(1) Obliquity Effect (Finite Source-to-Counter Distance). If the source and detector are separated by a distance which is very large compared to the radius of the spherical shell, then the probability of detecting a nonscattered neutron is the same as the probability of detecting a neutron which has been only elastically scattered, because the detector subtends the same solid angle for both groups of neutrons. In this case, the transmission equation [Eq. (20)] of Section 2.B is equal to the corresponding ratio of observed counting rates. However, if this separation distance is comparable with the sphere radius, the average distance that an elastically scattered neutron travels, after its last collision, in reaching the detector will not be equal to the distance between source and detector. So, in the transmission formula, terms corresponding to the detection of elastically scattered neutrons will have to be corrected for this effect. Collie and Griffiths (Co36), Graham and Seaborg (Gr38), Phillips and Graves (Ph49, Ph52), Bethe (Be52), and BBC have all discussed the obliquity factor. The magnitude of the correction will depend upon the relative intensities of the two groups of neutrons (unscattered and elastically scattered) and this is a function of the actual transmission, and of the ratio of the nonelastic cross section to the transport cross section. For example, at 14 Mev, most of the detected neutrons have come directly from the source, so the correction is small, as both Phillips (Ph49, Ph52) and MacGregor (Ma57) have noted.

This can be seen, as can the magnitude of the correction at lower neutron energies, by the use of Eq. (18) in the two following cases.

(a) 14 Mev: let $\sigma_{et}/\sigma_{tr} = 0.5$. Then if $T_0 = 0.5$, P_m (Fig. 6) is between about 0.3 and 0.6. If the larger value is chosen, the maximum effect occurs. Substituting $P_m = 0.6$ into Eq. (18)

$$T = 0.5 + 0.5(0.6/1.6) = 0.5 + 0.188 = 0.688.$$

If the elastically scattered neutrons (second term) have even a 5 per cent larger solid angle for detection than the unscattered ones, the error in σ_X is only about 3 per cent.

(b) About 1 Mev: let $\sigma_{et}/\sigma_{tr} = 0.90$. Then if $T_0 = 0.5$, P_m is between the limits given in case (a), so

$$T = 0.5 + 0.5(0.54/0.64) = 0.5 + 0.422 = 0.922.$$

If the second term, which corresponds to the elastically scattered neutrons, is increased by 5 per cent, the accompanying error in σ_x is about 30 per cent. This 5 per cent increase in the relative solid angle seems large, but this is about the magnitude of the effect if the distance between the source and detector is one sphere diameter, which is not an unusual distance for sphere transmission measurements with a monoenergetic external source. Therefore, since the error can be large, the correction factors $(1 - K)P_n{}^*$ are given in Figs. 4, 5, and 6 along with the escape probabilities.

The escape probabilities defined by Eq. (19) imply that a non-scattered and an elastically scattered neutron are detectable with the same probability, viz, that the source and detector are infinitely far apart. If, instead, the detector is at a distance b from the source, the relative probability for a scattered neutron to escape and enter the detector is

$$\overline{P_n} = \int_\Omega \int_{r_1}^{r_2} f_n(r)dr\Sigma_n(\psi)d\Omega[1 - (r^2/b^2)\sin^2\psi]^{-1/2} \exp[-\Sigma_{tr}\, Y(r,\psi)]$$
$$\div \int_{r_1}^{r_2} f_n(r)\,\Sigma_n\, dr \quad (21)$$

This can be evaluated, in principle, just as Eq. (19) has been. But in order to simplify the calculations (BBC), Eq. (21) was expanded in a series to give the following:

$$\overline{P_n} = \int_\Omega \int_{r_1}^{r_2} f_n(r)dr\Sigma_n(\psi)d\Omega \exp[-\Sigma_{tr}\, Y(r,\psi)]\,\{1 + (r^2/2b^2)\sin^2\psi + ..\}$$
$$\div \int_{r_1}^{r_2} f_n(r)\,\Sigma_n\, dr \quad (22)$$

in which the first term is just the pure escape probability of Eq. (19), and the higher order terms represent the corrections because r/b is finite. If Eq. (22) is integrated, we can indicate it as:

$$\overline{P_n} = P_n + P_n{}^*/2b^2 + \ldots \quad (23)$$

If escape from the normal mode collision distribution is computed in this way, the simplified transmission Eq. (18) has the form

$$T = T_0 + (1 - T_0)\,\sigma_{et}\,\overline{P_m}/(\sigma_x + \sigma_{et}P_m) \quad (24)$$

where the escape probability in the numerator refers to the detection of the neutrons, but the escape probability in the denominator refers only to the probability of getting out of the sphere.

Inserting the equivalent of Eq. (23) into Eq. (24) gives:

$$T = T_0 + (1 - T_0) \left[\sigma_{et}/(\sigma_X + \sigma_{et}P_m) \right]$$
$$[P_m + P_m{}^*/2b_{tr}{}^2 + \dots] \quad (25)$$

into which the value of b in transport mean free paths ($b_{tr} = b/\lambda_{tr}$) is to be substituted. When this is done, the $P_m{}^*$'s are obtained from Fig. 6. If the more general equation (20) is used to analyze the transmission measurement, $P_1{}^*$ and $P_2{}^*$ (Figs. 4 and 5) are inserted in the inverted form in an analogous way. Note that $(1 - K)P_1{}^*$, $(1 - K)P_2{}^*$, $(1 - K)P_m{}^*$ are given in the figures. They are expressed this way for convenience in plotting, so that $(1 - K)$ factors must be divided out before insertion into Eq. (25) or the counterpart of Eq. (20); $(K = r_1/r_2)$.

(2) **Finite Counter Size.** In Sections 2.A and 2.B, it has been assumed that the central source is a nonabsorbing isotropic point. If in practice it is not a point, there are three effects which can lead to errors in the analysis:

(a) The neutron flux at a detecting point in space is not specified exactly by a simple $1/4\pi b^2$ relation between source center and detector.

(b) Many of the neutrons do not travel along radii, but pass through the spherical shell obliquely. Hence, the probability of a first collision is increased.

(c) Because of (b), the spatial distribution of first collisions is not exponential with radius, so the first collision escape probability is not given exactly by P_1 [Eq. (19)]. However, since the location of the collision does not affect the subsequent probability of escape very much, this effect is quite small.

Therefore, if (c) be neglected, the correction for finite source size (or counter size, if reciprocity be used) can be resolved into the first two effects, which can be computed separately. That is, one must compute the flux at the detecting point with no sphere, and the corresponding flux with a sphere around the source, so that, if all other corrections are ignored

$$T_{obs} = T + (\text{correction terms}) = (\phi_1 + \phi_2)/\phi_3$$

Here, from Fig. 7,

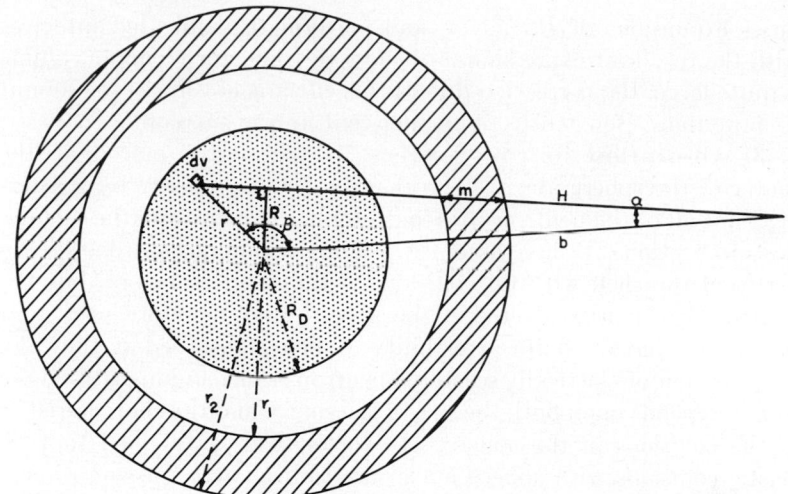

Figure 7. Geometry used in computing corrections due to finite detector (source) size.

$$\phi_1 = (Q/V_D) \int_0^{V_D} \exp(-\Sigma_{tr}m)/4\pi H^2 \, dV$$

= flux of neutrons at b which have made no collisions

$$\phi_2 = Q[1 - (1/V_D) \int_0^{V_D} \exp(-\Sigma_{tr}m) \cos \alpha/4\pi H^2 \, dV]$$

$$\cdot \sigma_{et}P_n/(\sigma_X + \sigma_{et}P_m)$$

= flux of neutrons at b which have made one or more elastic collisions

$$\phi_3 = (Q/V_D) \int_0^{V_D} (4\pi H^2)^{-1} \, dV$$

= flux of neutrons at b with no sphere around the source

where Q = total source strength; V_D = total source (detector) volume; and dV = element of source (detector) volume; and

$$H^2 = b^2 + r^2 - 2rb \cos \beta$$

$$m = (r_2^2 - R^2)^{1/2} - (r_1^2 - R^2)^{1/2}$$

$$R = r \sin (\alpha + \beta)$$

If the detector (source) is not very large compared to the inside diameter of the spherical shell ($R_D < 0.1 \, r_1$), it is possible to make series expansions of H and m, and perform the indicated integrals with the resultant expressions. Unless the detector (source) volume is quite large, the correction due to this effect is not likely to amount to more than a few tenths of one per cent in transmission.

(3) **Absorption in the Source.** If the source placed at the center of the sphere absorbs (or changes neutron energy by scattering), not all of the neutrons produced by it will behave as the calculations in Section 2.B have assumed. The fraction of neutrons escaping from the shell with no collisions is the same as before, but the neutrons which are scattered in the sphere, and therefore can enter the source, have a finite probability of being absorbed if they do. The fraction of elastically scattered neutrons which impinges upon the source depends upon both the size of the source and the characteristics of the collisions in the sphere. However, if it is assumed that all elastic collisions with sphere nuclei are isotropic (this assumption is included with the use of the transport cross section) this latter effect can be neglected. Then the absorption in the source can be treated as though it increases the transport cross section of the sphere nuclei in a way which is proportional to the scattering cross section, namely:

$$\sigma_{tr}' = \sigma_X + \sigma_{et}(1 + \Sigma_s')$$

where Σ_s' includes both the macroscopic absorption cross section of the source and the probability that a neutron elastically scattered in the spherical shell will enter the source.

This newly defined expression, σ_{tr}', can be substituted in place of σ_{tr} in the derivation of the transmission equation. It is clear that the effect of this absorption in the source is to decrease the observed transmission, so the derived nonelastic cross section of the sphere nuclei will be too large. However, most sources only scatter, and do not actually absorb neutrons, so a central source is not likely to have a big effect on the observed transmission.

If the detector is placed at the center of the sphere, neutron absorption in it also decreases the flux of neutrons available for detection, and so a similar kind of error results in the derived nonelastic cross section. The correction in this case can be treated as outlined above for the central source, but is likely to be negligible unless the actual nonelastic cross section is very small, or the transmission of the detector is small.

(4) **Nonisotropic Detector.** If the central source does not emit isotropically, the flux of nonscattered neutrons escaping from the sphere is a function of the angle between the detector and some fixed arbitrary axis, whereas those neutrons elastically scattered before escape from the sphere will in general emerge with a different (more isotropic) angular distribution. Therefore, the ratio of unscattered to scattered neutrons is a function of this angle, and the true transmission could be obtained only by performing a complete angular integration with the detector.

If a transmission measurement is made with the detector inside of the sphere, any angular asymmetry in its efficiency will cause a similar effect. However, if the angular efficiency has been measured, and the asymmetry is not large, the counter can usually be oriented with respect to the source position so that most of the error is averaged out. Small additional corrections (BBC) can be applied if necessary to reduce any residual errors.

(5) **Nonisotropic Source.** Most sources of monoenergetic neutrons are anisotropic, not only in intensity, but also in energy. The magnitude of the anisotropy is usually so large that it is not possible to surround the source with the sphere and then make corrections. Instead, one invokes the reciprocity theorem, and surrounds the detector. Then it is only necessary that the sphere subtend a small enough angle at the source that the variations are not large across its diameter. With this condition, and knowing the variation with angle of the neutron flux intensity, corrections can be made.

However, if the energy of the source neutrons changes rapidly with angle, and if in addition the nonelastic cross section is a strong function of energy, the computation of the corrections may be quite uncertain. In cases of this sort, the best geometrical conditions must be used.

Since the characteristics of the source, detector, sphere, and its nuclear cross sections all determine the corrections which must be made, there is no simple analytical procedure. Instead, after quantities relating to these characteristics have been measured, a numerical computation of the correction factors is made (BBC).

(6) **Energy Loss.** If the threshold of the detector is not close to the energy of the primary neutron, some nonelastic collisions may leave the neutron above the threshold. Then the observed trans-

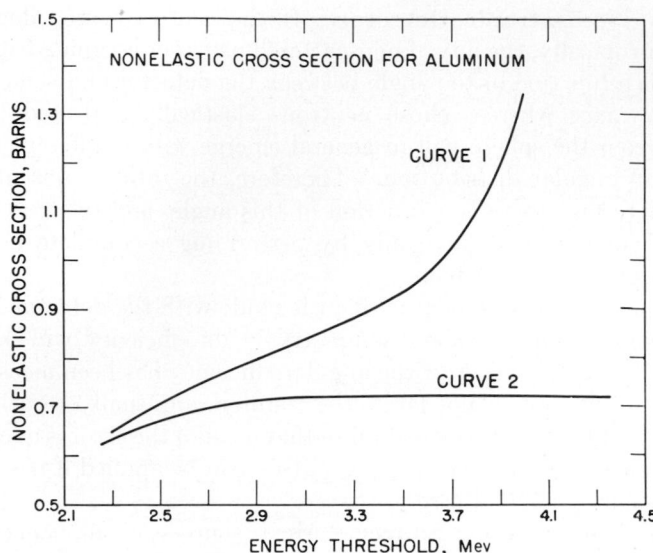

Figure 8. Apparent nonelastic cross section of Al for 4.5-Mev incident neutrons *vs.* counter bias. Curve 1, no correction for energy loss during elastic collisions; Curve 2, energy loss corrected by Monte Carlo calculations.

mission is too high, and too low a value is obtained for the nonelastic cross section.   On the other hand, if the threshold is very close to the energy of the primary neutron, some elastic collisions reduce the neutron's energy so that its detectability is reduced.   This effect makes the observed transmission too small, and the derived nonelastic cross section is too large.   An approximate analytical method for making corrections for this effect was discussed and used in BBC for elements no lighter than aluminum.   However, both BBC and MacGregor *et al.* (Ma57) performed Monte Carlo calculations to study the energy loss in more detail, and found that the analytical method tends to overcompensate, and thus a relatively large error can result, especially for such light elements as beryllium and carbon. However, if no correction for elastic scattering energy loss is made, the cross section for these lighter elements can be in error by as much as 50 per cent (Ma57).

Figure 8 shows the kinds of corrections which have been found necessary for aluminum by Beyster *et al.* (BBC) by means of Monte Carlo computations.

D. Summary

The sphere technique for measuring neutron nonelastic cross sections was started in the middle 1930's, was used a little during the 1940's, but except for a very few workers fell into disrepute because of the difficulty of understanding the information which it produced. During the early 1950's there was renewed interest in the method because it seemed potentially powerful for obtaining nonelastic cross sections, which at that time were almost entirely unmeasured.

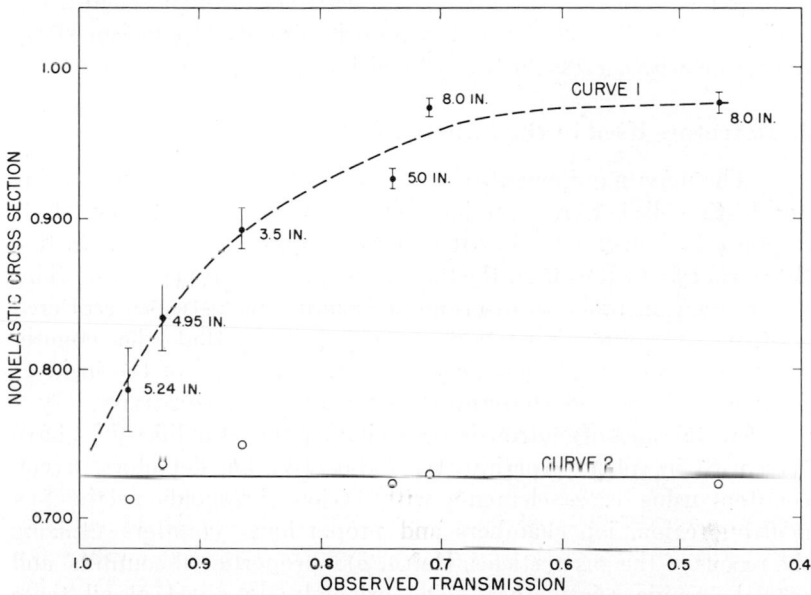

Figure 9. Nonelastic cross section of Fe for various sphere sizes (U^{238} detector and fission spectrum source). Curve 1 is computed from Eq. (1), $T = \exp(-\Sigma_x D)$. Curve 2 is computed from Eq. (20) with corrections for finite geometry. Statistical uncertainties are indicated on Curve 1.

At the present time, the sphere method can be used to obtain non-elastic cross sections to accuracies of a few percent for almost all of the elements, and at most neutron energies [MacGregor *et al.* (Ma57) quote uncertainties of 1 to 4 per cent at 14 Mev]. However, since a relatively large amount of material is required to make a practicable sphere, not all separated isotopes can be measured.

The computational methods have been developed sufficiently now so that most of the residual uncertainty is due to the usual experimental factors, such as statistical fluctuations in the measured transmission.   Therefore, even though it is reasonable to make qualitative arguments about the cancellation of the elastic scattering, one is usually not justified in using Eq. (1) for analyzing a transmission measurement.   Figure 9 shows the magnitude of the error which can easily be introduced by applying the exponential formula.

Not only the gross nonelastic cross sections can be obtained by measurements of the transmission of neutrons through spheres, but with specialized detectors and appropriate analysis one can study the details with success (Sections 3 and 4).

3. Detectors Used in the Sphere Method

The main requirement of a neutron detector used in measuring nonelastic collision cross sections by the sphere method is that its response be known and that it be much more efficient for detecting the primary neutrons than the inelastically scattered neutrons.   This is necessary in order to discriminate against inelastically scattered neutrons.   Another important requirement is that the counter response be reasonably independent of the direction of the incident neutrons.   Also the detector must have a low γ-ray sensitivity.

Several types of neutron detectors having these qualifications have been used in sphere experiments; radioactivation detectors, fission counters using those elements with fission thresholds in the fast neutron region, ion chambers and proportional counters utilizing the recoils of the gas particles, $He^3(n, p)T$ proportional counters, and special organic scintillators.   The principles involved in all these detectors, as well as the details of He^3 counters, are discussed elsewhere in this book (Chapters II, III, and IV) and will not be dealt with in this article.   Only some special applications of importance to sphere measurements will be discussed.

A. Radioactivation and Fission Detectors

Some of the reactions that have been used in sphere measurement detectors are: $P^{31}(n, p)Si^{31}$, $Al^{27}(n, p)Mg^{27}$, and $Cu^{63}(n, 2n)Cu^{62}$, which have thresholds at about 1.6, 2.6, and 10.8 Mev, respectively. These detectors are insensitive to γ rays and the thresholds do not

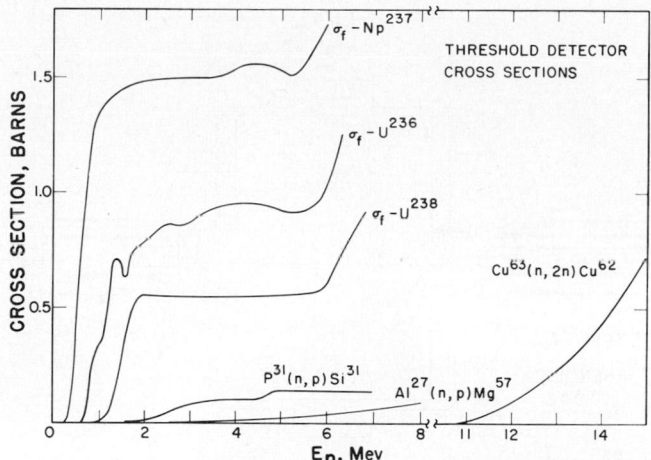

Figure 10. Cross sections for threshold detector reactions.

drift. The main disadvantages of these reactions are: the slowly rising nature of the cross sections obscures the threshold definitions; the fixed thresholds limit the energy range in which these detectors can be used effectively; and the samples must be counted after the irradiations.

The use of fission counters removes the objection to measuring the response of the detector after the irradiation is completed, but the other disadvantages of fixed threshold detectors are not eliminated. Fissionable nuclei which have thresholds in the fast neutron region and which have been used in counters are Np^{237}, U^{236}, and U^{238}. The thresholds are near 0.2, 0.6, and 1.0 Mev, respectively. These detectors are, however, relatively inefficient. The cross sections for some of these fixed-threshold detectors are shown in Fig. 10. (See also Chapters III.E and IV.C.)

B. Proportional Counter

The low efficiency and fixed threshold disadvantages of the detectors mentioned above are both eliminated by the use of gas recoil proportional counters. One such counter[3] is shown in Fig. 11.

[3] This counter was developed by R. C. Allen, Los Alamos Scientific Laboratory.

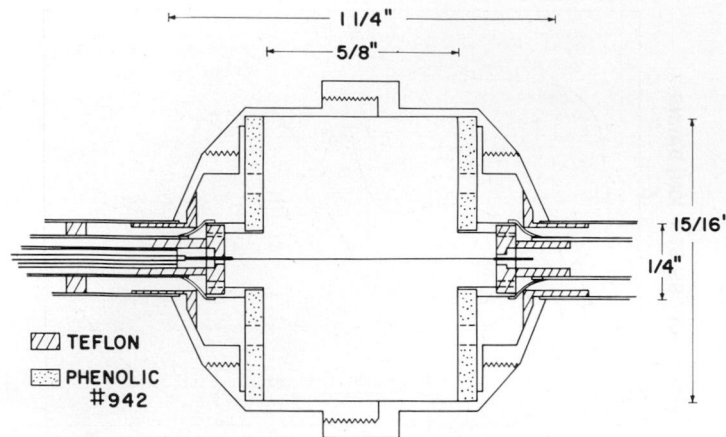

Figure 11. Small volume high pressure proportional counter.

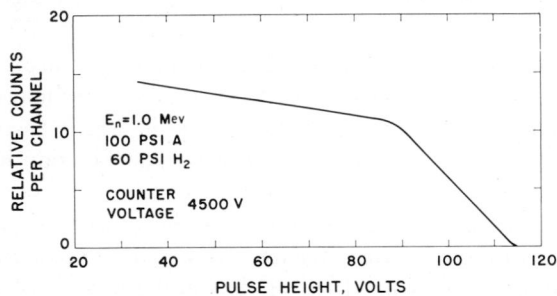

Figure 12. Recoil pulse-height distribution for hydrogen-filled proportional counter.

The main features of this counter are its small size and the use of field tubes (Co51). The field tubes are connected to the counter walls by partially conducting disks which in this case were made of a phenolic. By putting the appropriate voltage on the field tubes the distortion of the electric field at the ends of the counter is minimized. This results in a more uniform multiplication along the central wire and therefore a more idealized pulse height distribution. The stainless steel central wire is 2.5×10^{-3} cm in diameter. The counter is operated at pressures up to 300 psi, which requires a counter voltage of up to 5 kv to obtain a multiplication of about 10. Under these operating conditions the counter response varies less than 5 per cent

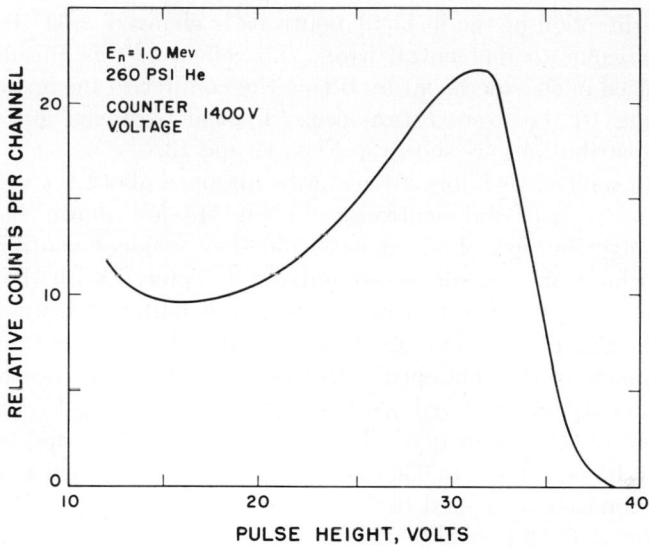

Figure 13. Recoil pulse-height distribution for helium-filled proportional counter.

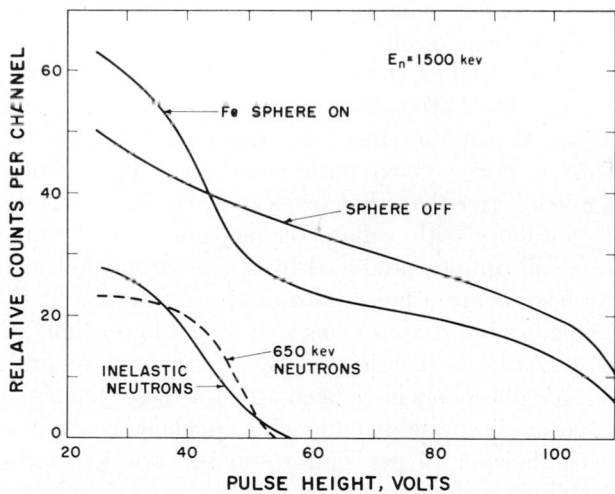

Figure 14. Pulse-height distributions obtained with iron sphere around counter showing presence of inelastically scattered neutrons.

as the direction of the incident neutrons is changed ±80° from the perpendicular to the central wire. The effect of this anisotropy is minimized in an experiment by tilting the counter to the angle corresponding to the average response. Typical hydrogen and helium recoil distributions are shown in Figs. 12 and 13.

In some cases information can be obtained about the spectra of inelastically scattered neutrons. In Fig. 14 are shown the pulse height distributions obtained with 1500-kev incident neutrons with and without an iron sphere around the detector. With the sphere on, the presence of lower energy neutrons is definitely indicated. The pulse-height distribution of these inelastically scattered neutrons corresponds to that obtained with 650-kev neutrons, indicating that the inelastically scattered neutrons are a monoenergetic group of neutrons of 650 kev energy. This is, of course, just as expected since the first level in iron is at 850 kev. In this manner the sphere method can in some cases be used to determine nuclear levels (Al57) and the inelastic scattering involving these levels, and thus gives some information about this component of the nonelastic collision cross section.

C. Organic Scintillators

Another type of detector[4] developed for sphere experiments involves the use of organic scintillators. These scintillators utilize the light pulses from recoil protons for detecting neutrons and the light pulses from Compton electrons for detecting γ rays. In each case the light pulse is proportional to the range of the particle and to the ionization density produced by the particle in the scintillator (Bi51, Ta51). For a given path length, the pulse from a recoil proton is much larger than that from an electron. Thus, by using a spherical scintillator with a diameter dependent on the range of the maximum recoil protons produced by the neutrons under study, it is possible to have neutron pulses two or three times larger than γ-ray pulses. This form of detector has a practical lower limit of about 3 Mev because, for lower energies, the sphere size becomes prohibitively small. Plastic phosphors have been used for these spheres since there is no variation in pulse height with incident neutron direction. (Anthracene shows a 15 per cent response variation and therefore is undesirable as a sphere detector.)

[4] This type of counter was developed by McCrary, Taylor, Bonner (Mc54, Ta55) at The Rice University.

Since the counting rate is proportional to the volume of the scintillator used, it is convenient to use more than one sphere for neutrons of energy between 3 and 7 Mev. In this case, it is necessary to separate the spheres by an electron absorbing material in order to

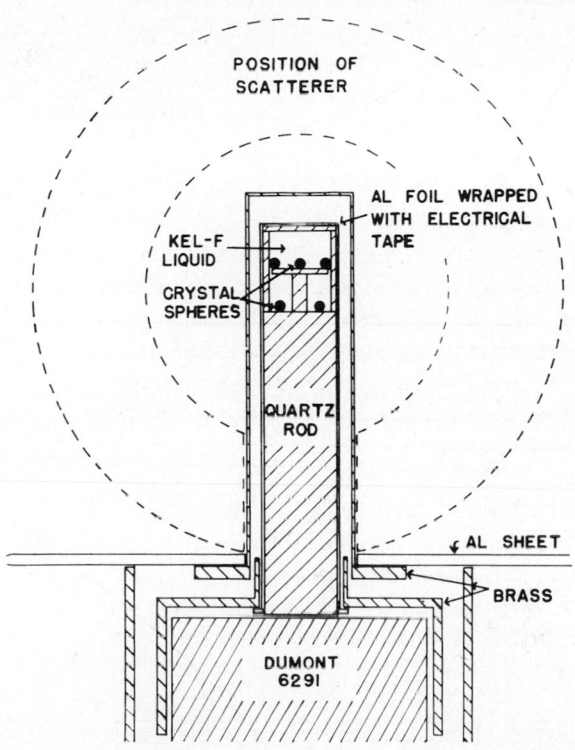

Figure 15. Diagram of 3.5 Mev neutron detector showing scintillators, silica light pipe, and position of the scattering sample.

reduce the probability of an electron traversing more than one scintillation sphere. The intervening material should not contain hydrogen since recoil protons produced in it would adversely affect the pulse height distribution curve of the detector. The electron absorbent must also serve as an optical coupling to acheive uniform response from all scintillating spheres. Taylor *et al.* (Ta55) immersed the spheres in Kel-F fluid ($Cl_3F_3C_6$) while Beyster *et al.* (Be55a) separated the spheres by quartz plates.

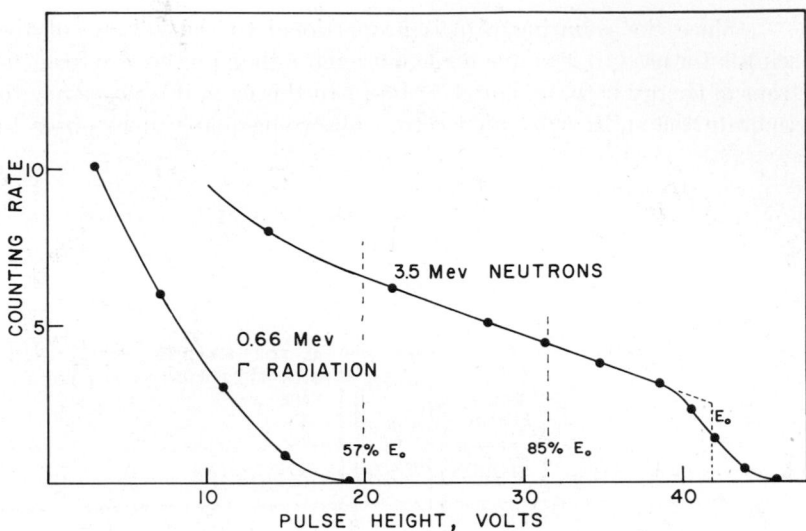

Figure 16. Pulse-height distribution for 3.5-Mev neutrons in eight 1.5-mm diameter scintillators and pulse-height distribution of γ rays of maximum effective energy.

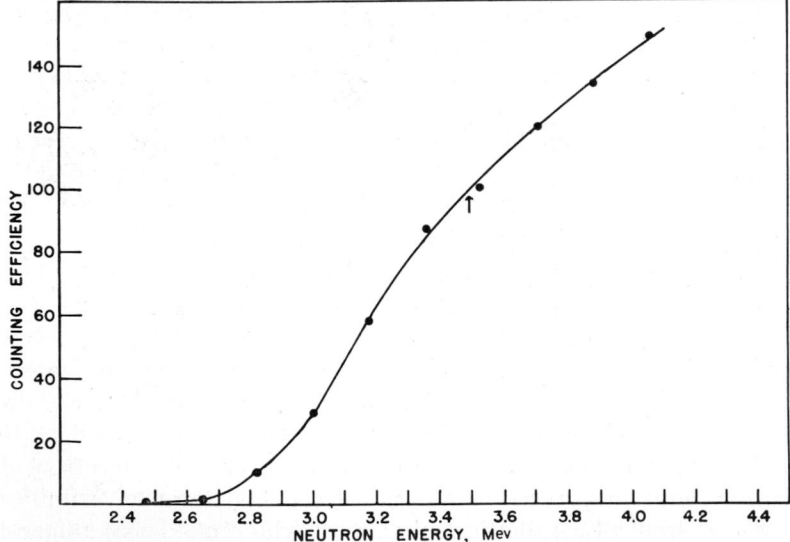

Figure 17. Relative efficiency of detection as a function of neutron energy for the detector biased at 85 per cent energy for 3.5-Mev neutrons.

It is usually necessary to pipe the light pulse from the scintillator at the center of the scattering sphere to the photomultiplier tube outside the scatterer. The most frequently used light pipe is a silica rod wrapped with aluminum foil. (Lucite has the disadvantage of containing hydrogen.)

Figure 15 shows the arrangement of the 3.5-Mev detector used by Taylor *et al.* (Ta55). Eight 1.5-mm diameter spheres were used for 3.5-Mev neutrons, four 2.5-mm diameter spheres for 4.7-Mev neutrons, one 6.5-mm diameter sphere for 7.1-Mev neutrons, and one 10-mm sphere for 12.7- and 14.1-Mev neutrons. For 14-Mev neutrons, discrimination against γ rays could be achieved with a larger sphere but a 10-mm diameter was used because of the size limitation of the scattering spherical shell.

Figure 16 shows the pulse-height distribution curve for the 3.5-Mev neutron detector. The dashed extrapolation at E_0 indicates how the maximum pulse height was determined. The per cent energy bias points were then calculated from the known pulse-height, range, and energy interrelationships.

Figure 17 shows the measured efficiency curve for detecting neutrons of different energies with the bias set at the pulse height estimated for neutrons of 85 per cent of the energy of the incident 3.5-Mev neutrons. The efficiency curve is used with the differential elastic scattering cross section and the angular energy distribution of the neutron source to correct the measured sphere transmissions for the effects of the loss of energy in elastic scattering and the angular energy variation of the neutron source.

4. Nonelastic Collision Cross Sections

A. Partial Summary of Cross Sections

Considerable information is now available on neutron nonelastic collision cross sections. Representative data are given in Tables I through VIII and in Figs. 18 through 24. No attempt has been made to include all the known results, but the figures contain most of the known measurements with monoenergetic neutrons for the elements aluminum, iron, copper, silver, tin, lead, and bismuth in the energy range 0 to 30 Mev. All of the cross sections except those of Rosen and Stewart (Ro57) and Ahn and Roberts (Ah57) were determined either by the sphere method or by the total minus elastic method.

Table I. 1.0-Mev Nonelastic Collision Cross Sections[a]

Element	Al54 Al57	Wa 54	Be55a	Be56	Po56	Ba56
C			0.0 ± 0.04		0.4 ± 0.2	
Na			-0.01 ± 0.03		0.2 ± 0.1	
Al	0.36 ± 0.10					
Ti		0.1		0.17 ± 0.07		
Fe		0.4	0.41 ± 0.03	0.49 ± 0.06	0.3 ± 0.1	
Co		0.2			0.1	
Ni		0.1				
Cu		0.3	0.21 ± 0.04	0.06 ± 0.03	0.2 ± 0.1	
Zn		0.3	0.10 ± 0.06			
Se		0.7				
Sr		0.7				
Zr		0.4		0.13 ± 0.04		
Nb		0.7				
Mo		1.1				
Ag		2.1	1.80 ± 0.20	1.72 ± 0.20		

Cd		1.4	1.04 ± 0.08	1.04 ± 0.07	1.0 ± 0.2
In		0.4			
Sn		0.7	0.06 ± 0.05		0.4 ± 0.2
Sb		0.8			0.7 ± 0.3
Te		0.6			
Ba		0.2			
Ce		0.1			
Hf		2.1			
Ta		2.2			
W		2.2		2.25 ± 0.30	2.6 ± 0.8
Au		1.5	1.80 ± 0.25	1.75 ± 0.20	
Hg		0.9			1.5 ± 0.4
Pb^{206}		0.2			
Pb	0.30 ± 0.10	0.3	0.21 ± 0.03		0.2 ± 0.1
Bi	0.19 ± 0.10	0.1	0.12 ± 0.03		0.1
Th		1.8			
U				1.80 ± 0.25	1.6 ± 0.5
U^{235}	2.65 ± 0.35			2.70 ± 0.30	
U^{238}	1.57 ± 0.20				
Pu^{239}	2.57 ± 0.35				1.7 ± 0.3

a Refer to text for discussion of references

Table II. 1 to 3-Mev Nonelastic Collision Cross Sections[a]

Ele-ment	Be56 1.77 Mev	Be56 2.5 Mev	St57 2.5 Mev	Ma58 2.6 Mev
Be				0.27 ± 0.10
C		0.05 ± 0.05		
Na			0.53 ± 0.26	
Mg			0.77 ± 0.25	
Al	0.15 ± 0.03	0.38 ± 0.05	0.96 ± 0.17	
P			0.7 ± 0.2	
S			0.54 ± 0.21	
Cl			0.6 ± 0.3	
Ca			0.4 ± 0.2	
Ti	0.55 ± 0.05	0.79 ± 0.06		
Cr			1.4 ± 0.3	
Fe	0.73 ± 0.04	1.04 ± 0.05	1.16 ± 0.12	
Co			1.40 ± 0.11	
Ni		0.80 ± 0.06	0.83 ± 0.12	
Cu		1.27 ± 0.06	1.58 ± 0.15	
Zn		1.30 ± 0.10	1.88 ± 0.15	
Se			1.88 ± 0.17	
Zr	0.60 ± 0.05	1.16 ± 0.06		
Mo			1.9 ± 0.3	
Ag		2.08 ± 0.12	2.1 ± 0.2	
Cd	1.55 ± 0.10	1.92 ± 0.12	2.2 ± 0.2	
Sn	0.72 ± 0.04	1.37 ± 0.07	1.65 ± 0.3	
Sb			1.9 ± 0.2	
Te			2.0 ± 0.35	
I			1.96 ± 0.25	
Ba			1.6 ± 1.0	
Ta		2.90 ± 0.35		
W		2.66 ± 0.30	2.6 ± 0.25	
Au	2.20 ± 0.17	2.76 ± 0.20		
Hg			2.6 ± 0.3	
Pb		0.71 ± 0.06	1.7 ± 0.3	
Bi	0.40 ± 0.04	0.75 ± 0.06	0.7 ± 0.3	
U		3.20 ± 0.30		
U^{235}		3.25 ± 0.30		

[a] Refer to text for discussion of references.

Table III. 3 to 4-Mev Nonelastic Collision Cross Sections[a]

Element	Be56 3.25 Mev	Ta55 3.5 Mev	Ma58 3.5 Mev	Ha57 3.7 Mev
Be			0.43 ± 0.08	
Al	0.53 ± 0.05	0.68 ± 0.05		
Ti	0.98 ± 0.07	1.24 ± 0.05		
Cr		1.14 ± 0.04		
Fe	1.09 ± 0.07	1.14 ± 0.04		
Ni		1.48 ± 0.04		
Cu		1.45 ± 0.04		
Zr	1.44 ± 0.08			2.1 ± 0.3
Mo				2.3 ± 0.3
Ag		2.03 ± 0.07		
Cd	1.95 ± 0.12			
Sn	1.73 ± 0.09	2.00 ± 0.09		
Au	2.63 ± 0.15			
Pb		1.58 ± 0.07		
Bi	1.33 ± 0.07	1.73 ± 0.06		

[a] Refer to text for discussion of references.

Measurements made prior to the work of Gittings *et al.* (Gi49) have not been included and only a minimum amount of editing has been done.

In many cases the experimental measurements do not give the total nonelastic collision cross sections. Counter resolution, for instance, often makes it difficult to distinguish between elastically scattered neutrons and inelastically scattered neutrons which have lost only a small amount of energy. Thus in presenting cross sections the limitations of the measuring techniques and resulting restrictions on the cross sections must be discussed. For this reason a brief description of each of the references is presented.

(1) **Gi49, Ph52.** These were early Los Alamos sphere experiments done with 14.5-Mev and 14.15-Mev neutrons, respectively, produced by the D-T reaction. Several activation threshold detectors were used, but only the results obtained with copper detectors, with an effective threshold at about 12.5 Mev, are included. The cross sections were determined from the exponential transmission equation [Eq. (1)]. Phillips *et al.*, however, discuss some of the multiple scattering and distance corrections.

Table IV. 4 to 6-Mev Nonelastic Collision Cross Sections[a]

Element	Be55a 4.0 Mev	Wa55 4.1 Mev	Pa56 4.1 Mev	Ma58 4.1 Mev	Be55a 4.5 Mev	Ta55 4.7 Mev	Ma58 5.0 Mev
Be	0.62 ± 0.03[b]	0.6 ± 0.1		0.51 ± 0.07			0.60 ± 0.07
C	0.04 ± 0.04	0.08 ± 0.1					
Na			0.57				
Mg			0.78 ± 0.20				
Al	0.75 ± 0.04	0.7 ± 0.2	0.78 ± 0.20		0.72 ± 0.04	0.70 ± 0.05	
Cl			0.90 ± 0.20				
Ti	1.28 ± 0.07	1.2 ± 0.2			1.18 ± 0.07	1.32 ± 0.06	
Cr						1.32 ± 0.03	
Fe	1.42 ± 0.05	1.5 ± 0.2	1.58 ± 0.3		1.33 ± 0.05	1.38 ± 0.05	
Ni	1.35 ± 0.10				1.50 ± 0.06	1.54 ± 0.06	
Cu	1.60 ± 0.05		1.68 ± 0.25		1.60 ± 0.05	1.69 ± 0.04	
Zn	1.69 ± 0.06[b]	1.7 ± 0.2	1.58 ± 0.3		1.81 ± 0.10		
Zr	1.56 ± 0.05	1.8 ± 0.2			1.59 ± 0.07		
Ag	2.05 ± 0.10				2.02 ± 0.10	2.14 ± 0.07	
Cd	2.06 ± 0.10	2.1 ± 0.2	2.3 ± 0.3		2.12 ± 0.12		
Sn	2.09 ± 0.07	2.1 ± 0.2	2.11 ± 0.3		2.18 ± 0.06	2.33 ± 0.07	
Sb			2.13 ± 0.3				
Ba			2.2 ± 0.4				
Ta		2.7 ± 0.2					
W	2.60 ± 0.20	2.4 ± 0.3			2.60 ± 0.20		
Au	2.75 ± 0.15	2.7 ± 0.3			2.70 ± 0.15		
Hg			3.36 ± 0.3				
Pb	1.86 ± 0.10	1.9 ± 0.3	1.72 ± 0.3		2.02 ± 0.14	2.25 ± 0.07	
Bi	1.98 ± 0.09	2.2 ± 0.3	1.14 ± 0.40		2.19 ± 0.08	2.39 ± 0.06	

[a] Refer to text for discussion of references.
[b] The neutron energy was 4.07 Mev.

Table V. 6 to 9-Mev Nonelastic Collision Cross Sections[j]

Element	Ma58 6.0 Mev	Be56 7.0 Mev	Ta55 7.1 Mev	Ba57 7 Mev	Bo56 8.2 Mev	Ba57 8 Mev
Be	0.73 ± 0.06	0.60 ± 0.04		0.62 ± 0.04[a]		0.60 ± 0.03[f]
C		0.17 ± 0.03				
Mg						
Al		0.86 ± 0.05		0.92 ± 0.06[b]		0.94 ± 0.04[g]
S		1.14 ± 0.07	0.74 ± 0.05	0.91 ± 0.06[c]		0.94 ± 0.04[h]
KCl		1.12 ± 0 11				
Ca		1.14 ± 0 07				
Ti		1.30 ± 0.06	1.21 ± 0.04			
Cr			1.22 ± 0.04			
Fe		1.41 ± 0.07	1.35 ± 0.04			
Ni		1.48 ± 0.06	1.33 ± 0.06			
Cu		1.54 ± 0.06	1.37 ± 0.05	1.57 ± 0.06[d]	1.46 ± 0.06	1.55 ± 0.03[g]
Zn		1.61 ± 0.10				
Zr		1.70 ± 0.08			1.94 ± 0.07	1.71 ± 0.03[i]
Ag		2.00 ± 0.10	2.01 ± 0.07			
Cd		2.05 ± 0.10				
Sn		2.00 ± 0.10	2.12 ± 0.06	2.01 ± 0.05[e]	1.99 ± 0 07	1.96 ± 0.04[g]
Ta		2 50 ± 0.20				
W		2 45 ± 0.20				
Au		2 50 ± 0.15				
Pb		2.38 ± 0.15	2.67 ± 0.07	2.42 ± 0.06[d]	2.45 ± 0 09	
Bi		2.38 ± 0.14	2.66 ± 0.07		2.46 ± 0 09	2.57 ± 0.05[i]

[a] Neutron energy, 7.0 Mev.
[b] Neutron energy, 6.7 Mev.
[c] Neutron energy, 7.3 Mev.
[d] Neutron energy, 7.2 Mev.
[e] Neutron energy, 7.4 Mev.
[f] Neutron energy, 8.0 Mev.
[g] Neutron energy, 8.3 Mev.
[h] Neutron energy, 8.1 Mev.
[i] Neutron energy, 8.4 Mev.
[j] Refer to text for discussion of references.

Table VI. 9 to 14-Mev Nonelastic Collision Cross Sections[g]

Element	Ba57 9 Mev	Bo56 9.8 Mev	Ba57 11.0 Mev	Ba57 12 Mev	Ta55 12.7 Mev
Be	0.61 ± 0.05[a]		0.56 ± 0.04[c]		0.49 ± 0.08
C					0.56 ± 0.10
Mg	0.98 ± 0.03[a]		1.00 ± 0.03	0.96 ± 0.05[d]	
Al	1.00 ± 0.03[b]		1.07 ± 0.03	1.00 ± 0.05[e]	1.06 ± 0.07
Ti					1.17 ± 0.06
Cr					1.26 ± 0.07
Fe					1.36 ± 0.05
Ni					1.35 ± 0.05
Cu	1.55 ± 0.03[a]	1.46 ± 0.06	1.55 ± 0.04	1.53 ± 0.06[d]	1.49 ± 0.05
Zr	1.69 ± 0.03[b]		1.78 ± 0.05	1.72 ± 0.05[e]	
Ag		1.99 ± 0.07			1.75 ± 0.10
Sn	1.94 ± 0.04[a]	1.98 ± 0.07	1.97 ± 0.05	2.02 ± 0.07[f]	1.97 ± 0.09
Pb		2.74 ± 0.09			2.58 ± 0.09
Bi	2.58 ± 0.05[b]	2.60 ± 0.09	2.57 ± 0.06	2.51 ± 0.08[e]	2.47 ± 0.14

[a] Neutron energy, 9.6 Mev.
[b] Neutron energy, 9.5 Mev.
[g] Refer to text for discussion of references.

[c] Neutron energy, 11.2 Mev.
[d] Neutron energy, 12.5 Mev.

[e] Neutron energy, 12.8 Mev.
[f] Neutron energy, 12.6 Mev.

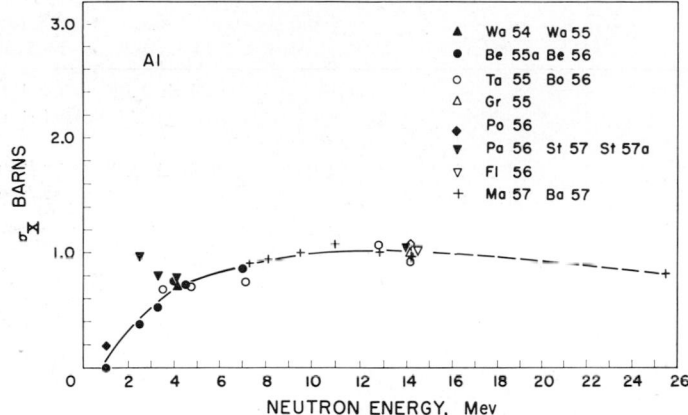

Figure 18. Neutron nonelastic collision cross sections.

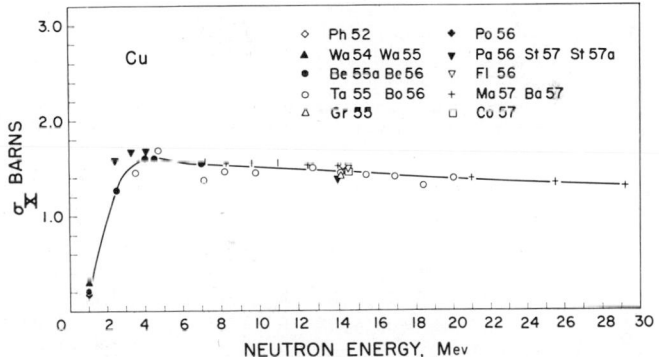

Figure 19. Neutron nonelastic collision cross sections.

(2) **Al54, Al57, Al57a.** The sphere method was used with 1-Mev neutrons. The neutron detector was the proton recoil counter discussed in Section 3.B. The data were analyzed by the BBC method.

The U^{235}, U^{238}, and Pu^{239} cross sections do not include inelastic scattering involving levels of 150 kev or lower. All the other results are the total nonelastic collision cross sections.

(3) **Wa54, Wa55.** The primary interest in these experiments was the angular distribution of elastically scattered neutrons. A proton recoil detector, either a proportional counter or a scintillator,

Table VII. 14-Mev Nonelastic Collision Cross Sections[a]

Element	Gi49 14.5 Mev	Ph52 14.2 Mev	Gr55 14.1 Mev	Ta55 14.1 Mev	F156 14.5 Mev
Be				0.37 ± 0.08	0.64 ± 0.02
B					0.64 ± 0.04
B^{10}		0.69 ± 0.10			
C		0.76 ± 0.04	0.601 ± 0.006	0.51 ± 0.08	0.73 ± 0.02
N		0.79 ± 0.05			0.82 ± 0.02
O					0.85 ± 0.03
F					
Mg					0.95 ± 0.04
Al		1.06 ± 0.05	1.00 ± 0.01	0.91 ± 0.05	1.02 ± 0.02
Si					1.02 ± 0.06
P					1.13 ± 0.03
S					1.15 ± 0.03
KCl					1.20 ± 0.03
Ca					1.36 ± 0.02
Ti				1.17 ± 0.04	
Cr				1.33 ± 0.04	
Fe		1.45 ± 0.02	1.27 ± 0.04	1.38 ± 0.03	1.38 ± 0.02
Co					
Ni				1.45 ± 0.05	
Cu		1.51 ± 0.06	1.42 ± 0.04	1.44 ± 0.04	1.48 ± 0.02
Zn			1.46 ± 0.03		1.58 ± 0.02
Se					1.77 ± 0.06
Zr					
Ag			1.82 ± 0.02	1.78 ± 0.05	
Cd		1.89 ± 0.06	1.95 ± 0.05		1.92 ± 0.03
Sn			1.96 ± 0.05	1.82 ± 0.06	1.85 ± 0.02
Sb					2.06 ± 0.04
Te					
I					2.11 ± 0.06
Ba					
Ta					
W					2.48 ± 0.03
Au		2.51 ± 0.04	2.44 ± 0.02		
Hg					2.65 ± 0.04
Pb	2.29 ± 0.29	2.56 ± 0.05	2.49 ± 0.02	2.52 ± 0.09	2.54 ± 0.05
Bi		2.56 ± 0.05	2.53 ± 0.02	2.50 ± 0.07	2.59 ± 0.03

[a] Refer to text for discussion of references.

St57a 14 Mev	Ma57 14.2 Mev	Co57 14.5 Mev	Ba57 14 Mev	Ro57 Ah57 14 Mev	Element
	0.49 ± 0.02			0.42 ± 0.07	Be
					B
	0.56 ± 0.06				B[10]
0.63 ± 0.05	0.56 ± 0.02		0.55 ± 0.03[b]		C
					N
					O
	0.83 ± 0.05				F
0.96 ± 0.08	0.99 ± 0.02				Mg
1.04 ± 0.06	0.97 ± 0.02				Al
					Si
					P
1.08 ± 0.08	1.14 ± 0.04				S
					KCl
					Ca
	1.33 ± 0.03				Ti
					Cr
1.29 ± 0.07	1.36 ± 0.03	1.36 ± 0.08			Fe
	1.37 ± 0.03				Co
1.38 ± 0.05	1.38 ± 0.03				Ni
1.40 ± 0.05	1.49 ± 0.02	1.45 ± 0.09	1.52 ± 0.03[c]		Cu
1.37 ± 0.07	1.58 ± 0.03				Zn
1.57 ± 0.08					Se
	1.72 ± 0.03			1.0 + 0.2	Zr
	1.90 ± 0.04				Ag
1.84 ± 0.06	1.91 + 0.03				Cd
1.81 + 0.08	1.90 ± 0.03	2.09 ± 0.16	1.87 ± 0.07[d]		Sn
1.87 ± 0.08	1.96 ± 0.03				Sb
2.00 ± 0.10					Te
1.88 ± 0.16					I
1.90 ± 0.17					Ba
				2.0 ± 0.4	Ta
2.35 ± 0.14	2.40 ± 0.05				W
	2.42 ± 0.04				Au
2.8 ± 0.3	2.43 ± 0.04				Hg
2.42 ± 0.08	2.56 ± 0.03	2.57 ± 0.16			Pb
2.40 ± 0.09	2.56 ± 0.04		2.59 ± 0.05[e]	2.4 ± 0.4	Bi

[b] Neutron energy, 14.2 Mev.
[c] Neutron energy, 14.0 Mev.
[d] Neutron energy, 14.5 Mev.
[e] Neutron energy, 13.9 Mev.

Table VIII. 14 to 30-Mev Nonelastic Collision Cross Sections[a]

Element	Bo56 15.5 Mev	Bo56 17.0 Mev	Bo56 18.5 Mev	Bo56 20.0 Mev	Ba57 21.0 Mev	Ba57 25.5 Mev	Ba57 29.2 Mev
Be						0.38 ± 0.05	
C					0.49 ± 0.04	0.44 ± 0.04	0.45 ± 0.04
Mg					0.78 ± 0.05	0.78 ± 0.05	0.76 ± 0.05
Al						0.81 ± 0.05	
Ti						1.08 ± 0.06	
Fe						1.21 ± 0.07	
Cu	1.43 ± 0.06	1.40 ± 0.06	1.30 ± 0.06	1.39 ± 0.06	1.39 ± 0.07	1.33 ± 0.07	1.30 ± 0.07
Zr				1.65 ± 0.07		1.58 ± 0.08	
Ag	1.70 ± 0.07	1.81 ± 0.07	1.68 ± 0.07				
Sn	1.92 ± 0.07	1.96 ± 0.07	1.77 ± 0.07		1.72 ± 0.08	1.77 ± 0.08	1.83 ± 0.10
Pb	2.56 ± 0.09	2.44 ± 0.09	2.35 ± 0.09		2.44 ± 0.10	2.56 ± 0.10	2.60 ± 0.10
Bi	2.34 ± 0.09	2.34 ± 0.09	2.36 ± 0.09			2.43 ± 0.10	

[a] Refer to text for discussion of references.

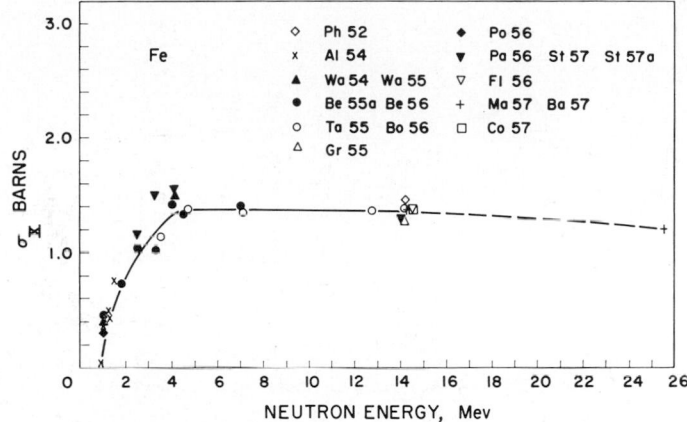

Figure 20. Neutron nonelastic collision cross sections.

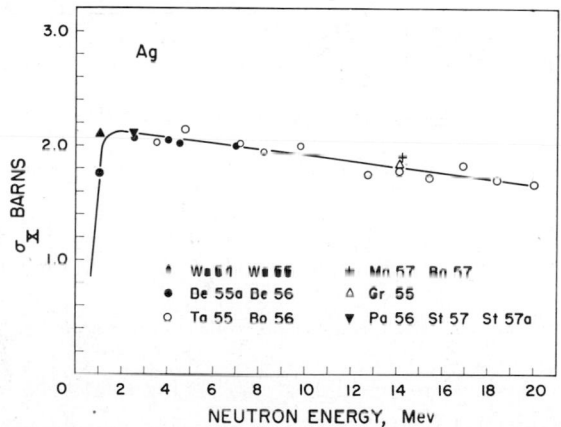

Figure 21. Neutron nonelastic collision cross sections.

was moved about cylindrical samples and the angular distributions were measured and the nonelastic collision cross sections determined by subtracting the elastic from the total cross sections.   In the 1-Mev experiment, two detector bias settings were used.   The efficiency for 0.9-Mev neutrons was 0.6 and 0.4 relative to the efficiency for 1.0-Mev neutrons for the low and high biases, respectively.   The high bias data were reported, although except for tungsten, both biases gave the same results.   In the 4.1-Mev experiment, three detector

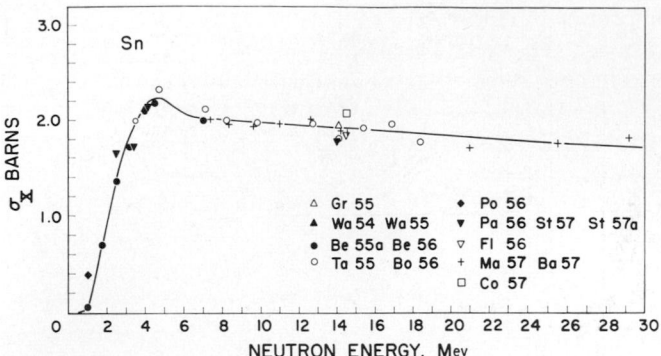

Figure 22. Neutron nonelastic collision cross sections.

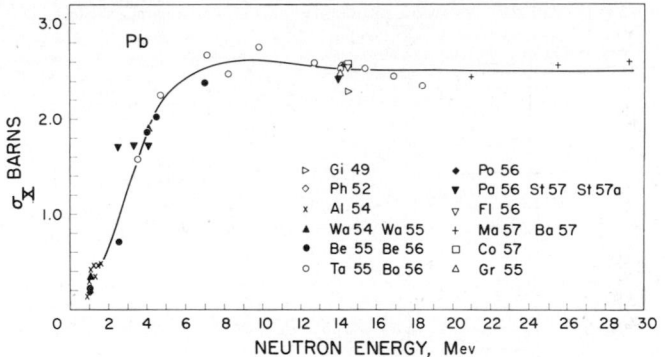

Figure 23. Neutron nonelastic collision cross sections.

biases were used, with the highest bias being relatively 50 per cent effective for 3.8-Mev neutrons.

(4) **Gr55.** Nonelastic cross sections were measured for 14-Mev neutrons by observing the transmission of spheres of various materials placed around a D-T source. The stilbene detector was biased to give 50 per cent efficiency for 12-Mev neutrons. The forward elastic scattering at this energy reduces multiple scattering corrections and none were made in this experiment.

(5) **Be55, Be55a, Be56.** Sphere measurements were performed at neutron energies of 1.0, 1.77, 3.25, 4.0, 4.5, and 7.0 Mev with proportional counters and scintillators as detectors. The BBC analysis was, of course, used. The total nonelastic collision cross sections

were determined by extrapolation from values obtained at several biases. Since the data in reference Be55a are later results than the data in reference Be55 the values in this latter reference have not been included in this summary. Angular distributions of elastically scattered neutrons were also measured in the work of reference Be56, but the resulting nonelastic collision cross sections have not been listed.

(6) **Ta55, Bo56.** The sphere method was used with 3.5, 4.7, 7.1, 8.2, 12.7, 14.1, 15.5, 17.0, 18.5, and 20.0-Mev neutrons. The neutron counter was the scintillator described in this chapter (Section 3.C) adjusted for relative detection efficiencies similar to that shown in Fig. 17. The BBC corrections were applied to the data.

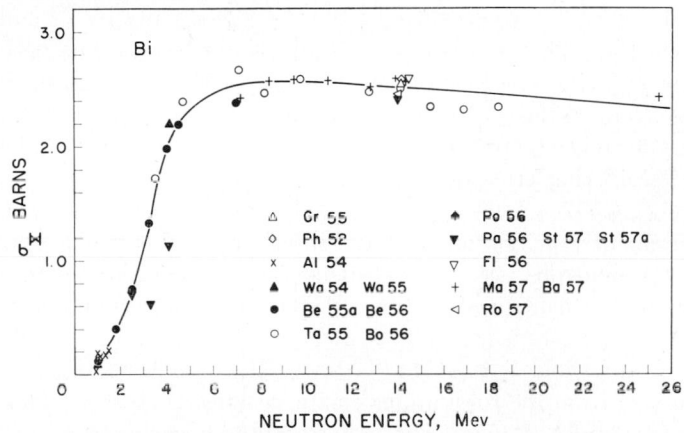

Figure 24. Neutron nonelastic collision cross sections.

(7) **Pa56, St57, St57a.** Phosphorus, aluminum and copper threshold activation detectors were used with the sphere method for 2.5, 3.3, 4.1, and 14-Mev neutrons. Some multiple scattering corrections have been made.

(8) **Po56.** Photoneutron sources Na-γ-D$_2$O, La-γ-Be, and Na-γ-Be, giving respectively, 0.3, 0.77, and 1.0-Mev neutrons were placed inside spheres of various materials. The transmissions of the spheres were measured with hydrogen or helium recoil ionization chambers. The cross sections were computed with some multiple scattering corrections. Some information about inelastically scattered neutrons was also obtained.

(9) **Fl56.** Nonelastic collision cross sections were measured by the sphere method with the sphere surrounding a 14-Mev neutron source. A stilbene crystal was used as the neutron detector. The cross sections were determined from the flat transmissions observed in the 9 to 12-Mev region. No corrections were applied.

(10) **Ba56.** A He^3 neutron spectrometer was used to study the spectra of 0.5 to 1.0-Mev neutrons scattered inelastically by U^{238}. From sphere measurements, the nonelastic collision cross sections were determined with the BBC method. The low-lying levels in U^{238} (Cr58) were not completely resolved, however, and the results are only lower limits.

(11) **Ha57.** Ring geometry was used to measure the angular distribution of 3.7-Mev neutrons scattered elastically by Zr and Mo. The neutron detector was a scintillator similar to the one described in Section 3.C. The bias setting was chosen high enough so that no effects from inelastically scattered neutrons were detected. The nonelastic collision cross sections were computed from the total minus elastic scattering cross sections.

(12) **Co57.** This experiment also dealt with ring geometry measurements of the angular distribution of elastically scattered 14.5-Mev neutrons. A trans-stilbene crystal or a liquid scintillator was used as a neutron detector. Particular effort was made to discriminate against inelastically scattered neutrons and the effective detector threshold was at 14.0 Mev. The nonelastic results were determined from the total minus elastic scattering cross sections.

(13) **Ma57, Ba57.** The sphere method was used to measure nonelastic collision cross sections for 7, 8, 10, 11, 13, 14, 21, 25, and 29-Mev neutrons. An organic scintillator was used as a neutron detector. The values obtained at several biases were extrapolated to give the total nonelastic collision cross sections. BBC corrections have been applied.

(14) **Ma58.** A pulsed-beam time-of-flight technique was used to measure the angular distribution of 2.6, 3.5, 4.1, 5.0, and 6.0-Mev neutrons scattered elastically by beryllium. The inelastically scattered neutrons were completely resolved and some scattering information was obtained. The nonelastic collision cross sections were computed by subtracting the elastic scattering cross sections from the total cross sections, which were also measured.

(15) **Ro57, Ah57.** Nuclear emulsion detectors were used to

measure the energy and angular distributions of neutrons from the interaction of 14-Mev neutrons with beryllium, zirconium, tantalum, and bismuth. Neutrons of energy less than 12 Mev were considered as due to nonelastic events with the σ_{2n} process occurring whenever energetically possible. The nonelastic collision cross sections were determined by adding $\sigma_{n'}$ and σ_{2n}, and it was assumed that the cross sections for other processes were negligible.

B. Components of Nonelastic Collision Cross Sections

As stated in the introduction, one method of determining nonelastic collision cross sections is to measure all of the component cross sections. A large number of experiments have been performed in the study of the various components, but only in a very few cases is the information complete enough to determine the nonelastic collision cross sections.

The experiments of Rosen and Stewart (Ro57) and Ahn and Roberts (Ah57), as discussed in Section 4.A, are examples of determining the nonelastic collision cross sections by measuring the components.

Graves (Gr55, Gr58) has extended the sphere method and has made measurements at 14 Mev both on the transmission of primary energy neutrons with an energy dependent detector and on the total neutron multiplication with a flat response detector. By combining these results, nonelastic collision cross sections and limits on some of the nonelastic components were determined. The energy spectra of inelastically scattered neutrons have also been studied with a stilbene neutron spectrometer.

The nonelastic components have also been measured for the nucleus U^{238} in the 1-Mev neutron energy region. The nonelastic components are inelastic scattering, capture, and fission. The

Table IX. Components of Nonelastic Collision Cross Sections of U^{238}

E_n (kev)	$\sigma_{n'}$ (barns)	σ_f (barns)	σ_γ (barns)	σ_x (barns)
550	1.7 ± 0.2	0.01	0.14	1.8 ± 0.2
1000	2.0 ± 0.4^a	0.015	0.10	2.1 ± 0.4
2000	2.4 ± 0.2^a	0.56	0.05	3.0 ± 0.3

[a] Does not include inelastic scattering involving levels within 250 kev of the primary neutron energy.

capture cross sections (Ro55) and the fission cross sections (He57) have been known for some time. Recent measurements using the pulsed-beam time-of-flight techniques (Cr58) have yielded considerable information about the level structure of the U^{238} nucleus and the energy and angular distributions of inelastically scattered neutrons. A summary of the results of all these measurements is given in Table IX.

References

(Ah57) Se Hee Ahn and J. H. Roberts, *Phys. Rev.* **108,** 110 (1957).
(Al54) R. C. Allen, *Phys. Rev.* **95,** 637(A) (1954).
(Al57) R. C. Allen, *Phys. Rev.* **105,** 1796 (1957).
(Al57a) R. C. Allen, *Nuclear Sci. and Eng.* **2,** 787 (1957).
(Am46) Amaldi, Bocciarelli, Cacciapuoti, and Trabacchi, *Nuovo Cimento* **3,** 203, (1946); *Fundamental Particles and Low Temperatures*, Phys. Soc., London, 1947, Vol. 1.
(Ao37) H. Aoki, *Proc. Phys. Math. Soc. Japan* **19,** 369 (1937).
(Ao39) H. Aoki, *Proc. Phys. Math. Soc. Japan* **21,** 232 (1939).
(Au33) P. Auger, *Compt. rend.* **196,** 170 (1933).
(Ba42) H. H. Barschall and R. Ladenburg, *Phys. Rev.* **61,** 129 (1942).
(Ba47) Barschall, Manley, and Weisskopf, *Phys. Rev.* **72,** 875 (1947).
(Ba47a) Barschall, Battat, Bright, Graves, Jorgensen, and Manley, *Phys. Rev.* **72, 881** (1947).
(Ba52) H. H. Barschall, *Revs. Modern Phys.* **24,** 120 (1952).
(Ba56) R. Batchelor, *Proc. Phys. Soc. (London)* **69A,** 214 (1956).
(Ba57) Ball, MacGregor, and Booth, *Univ. Calif. Reports* UCRL-5014 and UCRL-5144, unpublished (1957).
(Be52) H. A. Bethe, *Los Alamos Sci. Lab. Report* LA-1428 (1952).
(Be55) Beyster, Henkel, and Nobles, *Phys. Rev.* **97,** 563 (1955).
(Be55a) Beyster, Henkel, Nobles, and Kister, *Phys. Rev.* **98,** 1216 (1955).
(Be56) Beyster, Walt, and Salmi, *Phys. Rev.* **104,** 1319 (1956).
(Be56a) Bethe, Beyster, and Carter, *J. Nuclear Energy* **3,** 207, 273 (1956); *J. Nuclear Energy* **4,** 3, 147 (1957).
(Bi51) J. B. Birks, *Phys. Rev.* **84,** 364 (1951).
(Bo56) T. W. Bonner and J. H. Slattery, *Bull. Am. Phys. Soc.* **1,** 175 (1956); and private communication.
(Ca53) R. E. Carter and J. R. Beyster, *Phys. Rev.* **90,** 389 (1953).
(Co36) C. H. Collie and J. Griffiths, *Proc. Roy. Soc. (London)* **155A,** 434 (1936).
(Co51) A. L. Cockroft and S. C. Curran, *Rev. Sci. Instr.* **22,** 37 (1951).
(Co57) Coon, Davis, Felthauser, and Nicodemus, private communication (1957).
(Cr56) Cranberg, Day, Rosen, Taschek, and Walt, *Progress in Nuclear Energy*, Pergamon, London and New York, 1956, Vol. 1, Series 1, p. 107.
(Cr58) L. Cranberg and J. S. Levin, *Phys. Rev.* **109,** 2063 (1958).
(Da34) Danysz, Rotblat, Wertenstein, and Zyw, *Nature (London)* **134,** 970 (1934).

(Du34)   J. R. Dunning, *Phys. Rev.* **45**, 586 (1934).
(Du35)   Dunning, Pegram, and Fink, *Phys. Rev.* **47**, 325(A) (1935).
(Du35a)   Dunning, Pegram, Fink, and Mitchell, *Phys. Rev.* **48**, 265 (1935).
(Du41)   H. F. Dunlap and R. N. Little, *Phys. Rev.* **60**, 693 (1941).
(Eh35)   W. Ehrenburg, *Nature (London)* **136**, 870 (1935).
(Fl56)   N. N. Flerov and V. M. Talyzin, *Atomic Energy (USSR) (English Translation)* **4**, 617 (1956).
(Fr56)   J. Freeman, *Progr. Nuclear Phys.*, **5**, 38 (1956).
(Gi49)   Gittings, Barschall, and Everhart, *Phys. Rev.* **75**, 1610 (1949).
(Gr38)   D. C. Grahame and G. T. Seaborg, *Phys. Rev.* **53**, 795 (1938).
(Gr55)   E. R. Graves and R. W. Davis, *Phys. Rev.* **97**, 1205 (1955).
(Gr58)   E. R. Graves, private communication (1958).
(Ha46)   A. O. Hanson, *Los Alamos Sci. Lab. Report* LA-276, unpublished (1946).
(Ha57)   H. S. Hans and S. C. Snowden, *Phys. Rev.* **108**, 1028 (1957).
(He57)   R. Henkel, *Los Alamos Sci. Lab. Report* LA-2114, unpublished (1957).
(Hu38)   E. Hudspeth and T. W. Bonner, *Phys. Rev.* **53**, 928(A) (1938).
(Ki39)   Kikuchi, Aoki, and Wakatuki, *Proc. Phys. Math. Soc. Japan* **21**, 410 (1939).
(Le35)   D. E. Lea, *Proc. Roy. Soc. (London)* **150A**, 637 (1935).
(Ma40)   M. R. MacPhail, *Phys. Rev.* **57**, 669 (1940).
(Ma46)   Manley, Agnew, Barschall, Bright, Coon, Graves, Jorgensen, and Waldman, *Phys. Rev.* **70**, 602 (1946).
(Ma57)   MacGregor, Ball, and Booth, *Phys. Rev.* **108**, 726 (1957).
(Ma58)   Marion, Levin, and Cranberg, *Bull. Am. Phys. Soc.* **3**, 165 (1958).
(Mc54)   McCrary, Taylor, and Bonner, *Phys. Rev.* **94**, 808(A) (1954).
(Ol46)   P. Olum, "Evaluation of Scattering Data," *Atomic Energy Comm. Report* MDDC-353 unpublished (1946).
(Pa56)   M. V. Paschnik, *Proc. Intern. Conf. Peaceful Uses Atomic Energy, Geneva* **2**, 3 (1956).
(Ph49)   D. D. Phillips, *Atomic Energy Comm. Report* AECU-404, unpublished (1949).
(Ph52)   Phillips, Davis, and Graves, *Phys. Rev.* **88**, 600 (1952).
(Po56)   Kh. R. Poze and N. P. Glazkov, *J. Exptl. Theoret. Phys. (U.S.S.R.)* **3**, 745 (1956).
(Ro55)   B. Rose, *Atomic Energy Research Establ. Report* NP/R 1743, unpublished (1955).
(Ro57)   L. Rosen and L. Stewart, *Phys. Rev.* **107**, 824 (1957).
(Se37)   Seaborg, Gibson, and Grahame, *Phys. Rev.* **52**, 408 (1937).
(St57)   V. I. Strizhak, *J. Exptl. Theoret. Phys. (U.S.S.R.)* **4**, 769 (1957).
(St57a)   V. I. Strizhak, *J. Nuclear Energy* **5**, 253 (1957).
(Sz48)   Szilard, Bernstein, Feld, and Ashkin, *Phys. Rev.* **73**, 1307 (1948).
(Ta51)   Taylor, Jentschke, Remley, Eby, and Kruger, *Phys. Rev.* **84**, 1034 (1951).
(Ta55)   Taylor, Lönsjö, and Bonner, *Phys. Rev.* **100**, 174 (1955).
(Wa39)   Wakatuki and Kikuchi, *Proc. Phys. Math. Soc. Japan* **21**, 656 (1939).
(Wa40)   Wakatuki and Kikuchi, *Proc. Phys. Math. Soc. Japan* **22**, 430 (1940).
(Wa54)   M. Walt and H. Barschall, *Phys. Rev.* **93**, 1062 (1954).
(Wa55)   M. Walt and J. R. Beyster, *Phys. Rev.* **98**, 677 (1955).

Excitation Functions for Neutron Inelastic Scattering

JANET B. GUERNSEY,
Wellesley College, Wellesley, Massachusetts

DAVID A. LIND,
University of Colorado, Boulder, Colorado

1. Introduction

The bombardment of nuclei with fast neutrons may give rise to two kinds of scattering: one in which the outgoing neutron has the same energy as the incident neutron, designated elastic scattering, and one in which the energy of the outgoing neutron is less than the bombarding energy, designated inelastic scattering. It is the second process which will be of interest in this article.

If the energy of an incident neutron is greater than that of an excited state in the target nucleus, the target may be left in this excited state, the scattered neutron going off with an energy equal to its incident energy minus the excitation energy of the target. The target nucleus then decays back to its ground state, usually by the emission of one or more γ rays. For bombarding energies of a few Mev this process predominates over other inelastic processes (e.g., neutron radiative capture). It should be noted that an incoming neutron of energy E may interact to form a compound nucleus with the subsequent emission of a neutron of equal energy, E. In this case we have *compound elastic scattering*, as differentiated from *shape elastic scattering*. The cross section for this process may be of the same order of magnitude as for inelastic scattering. Experimentally, the two types of elastic scattering are hard to separate, although they may be differentiated in part by a study of the angular distribution of the scattered neutrons.

For neutron energies above about 10 Mev, the $(n, 2n)$ reaction competes favorably with the (n, n') reaction. Thus, the energy region of interest in the study of inelastic scattering is from just below the energy of the first excited state of the target nucleus to about 5 Mev. In this energy region, the cross section, $\sigma_{n'}$, for the (n, n') reaction is expected to approach the value $(\sigma_T - \sigma_n)$ where σ_T is the total scattering cross section, and σ_n the cross section for elastic scattering. Here $\sigma_{n'}$ is the sum of the cross sections for the excitation of individual levels in the target.

Experimentally one detects the inelastic scattering process by observing either the inelastically scattered neutrons or the de-excitation γ radiation. Ideally, if the energy and total yield of scattered neutron groups could be measured precisely, both the energy of the excited state and the absolute cross section for its formation could be determined. Excitation functions ($\sigma_{n'}$ vs. E_n) should provide a good check on the theory. Note, however, that the yield of scattered neutrons is dependent on the scattering angle, thus the determination of an absolute value for $\sigma_{n'}$ depends on a knowledge of the differential cross sections. In fact, the angular distribution of scattered neutrons may provide a more sensitive check on the theory than does the excitation function. The accumulation of data on excitation functions is, however, much easier. Measurements of this angular dependence have been made with good accuracy for some elements at a few bombarding energies (Cr56). Fast neutron spectrometers using time-of-flight and coincidence techniques have been developed for determining the energies of scattered neutrons. Some work has been done using photographic plate techniques (Ro53, We56). Methods of neutron detection are discussed in Section 2.B. Techniques for the measurement of γ radiation following inelastic scattering are discussed briefly in Section 2.A and in more detail in Chapter V.K. Detection of conversion electrons and of metastable state excitation is discussed in Sections 2.D and 2.E.

Section 3 deals with the determination of absolute values for inelastic scattering cross sections. Corrections to γ-ray yields and counter and neutron flux calibration are discussed in Section 3. A brief resume of current theories of inelastic scattering is given in Section 4. These theories are discussed in detail in Chapters V.C., V.D., and V.E.

Section 5 presents representative experimental data for both light and heavy nuclei, together with excitation functions calculated from theory. These data are interpreted in the light of the theory in Section 4.

2. Experimental Techniques

A. General Remarks

The determination of excitation functions for inelastic scattering to different levels in the target nucleus requires a monoenergetic source of neutrons which is variable in energy over a range of a few tens of kilovolts to several Mev. Most of the work done to date has used the $Li^7(p, n)Be^7$ or the $T(p, n)He^3$ reaction, with a Van de Graaff electrostatic accelerator as a proton source. The first excited state of Be^7 has an energy of 0.434 Mev and above the threshold for neutron emission to this level the $Li^7(p, n)Be^7$ reaction yields two groups of neutrons, which complicates cross section measurements. Some work has been done using the $D(d, n)He^3$ reaction, and isolated cross section values have been obtained using 14-Mev neutrons from the $T(d, n)He^4$ reaction. The first three reactions can be used to good advantage, since thin targets of Li, T, and D are readily available, and the reaction thresholds are such that neutrons in the desired energy range can be obtained. Neutron yield from lithium is superior to that from tritium, but the higher threshold for the reaction (1.88 Mev as against about 1 Mev for T) limits the maximum neutron energy available with a given accelerator. The Li reaction is accompanied by a rather large yield of γ rays which may introduce undesirable background effects. At very low neutron energies, these reactions give two groups of neutrons in the forward direction, as discussed in Chapter I.B. Thus, for the excitation of very low levels, it may be desirable to use some other reaction. The spread in neutron energy is determined by the energy spread of the bombarding protons, by the thickness of the target, and by the angular spread of the scattering sample. Thus, with thin targets and detectors of high resolving power, it is possible to obtain excitation functions with a resolution of a few kilovolts. This is desirable, particularly in examining inelastic scattering from light or medium-weight nuclei with a view to determining possible resonance structure.

B. Gamma-Ray Detectors

Methods for the detection of γ rays following inelastic scattering fall into two categories: those which require a considerable amount of scattering material, and those which require only a small

amount and are thus suitable for the examination of separated isotopes. Here again if absolute cross sections are to be evaluated, it
is necessary to know the angular dependence of the γ rays, or the total
yield. Thus, an ideal arrangement should allow angular measurements to be made, or should have an acceptance angle of essentially
4π. Techniques for the detection of γ rays for both closed and open
geometries are discussed in detail in Chapter V.K.

C. Detection of Inelastically Scattered Neutrons

(1) **Transmission Experiments.** Detection of the inelastically scattered groups of neutrons requires that the detector discriminate fairly sharply between neutrons of different energies. The use
of biased detectors to observe neutrons transmitted through the
scattering sample provides information on the yield of neutrons in an
energy interval determined by two settings of the detector bias
(Wa54). These experiments are particularly effective for those elements whose first excited state is several hundred kev above the
ground state and whose levels are fairly well separated. It is clear
that cross sections derived from experiments of this type represent
total nonelastic cross sections. They are useful for comparison with
inelastic cross sections determined by other methods in energy regions
where inelastic scattering is the predominant process and for setting
an upper limit to the value of $\sigma_{n'}$. The energy resolution of experiments of this type is not good enough to provide detailed information
on excitation functions. The sphere transmission method is discussed in detail in Chapter V.H.

(2) **Time-of-Flight Methods.** Successful measurements of
inelastically scattered neutron yields and angular distributions have
been made by Cranberg and others (Cr55, Cr56, Mu56, El57), using
a pulsed neutron beam and a time-of-flight method. This method
employs a shielded plastic scintillator and a time-to-pulse-height
converter (We56) for the separation of neutron groups with different
energies. For bombarding energies of a few Mev, background problems are not too troublesome, and good results should be obtainable
from which to calculate inelastic excitation functions. This method
is discussed in Chapter IV.A. It is particularly applicable to elements with widely spaced level structure. A similar setup has been
used by Day and Lind (Li57) to detect γ rays from inelastic scattering, using a NaI(Tl) crystal as detector (see Chapter V.K).

(3) **Photographic Plates.** Various other techniques have been used to detect scattered neutrons. Photographic plate methods (Ro53), while tedious, have the advantage of allowing angular distribution measurements to be made at all chosen angles simultaneously. These experiments have been performed at several bombarding energies in the 14-Mev region (We56, Ro53, Ro55). Application to the determination of excitation functions should be possible, since the energy resolution of these detectors is good. A detailed discussion of photographic plate techniques is found in Chapter II.D. Other methods of neutron spectroscopy, e.g., recoil proportional counters, are also discussed in detail in Chapters II and III.

D. Coincidence Techniques

Coincidence techniques have been used with some success, particularly where cascading γ radiation gives a false measure of the inelastic cross section. The yield of de-excitation γ rays from a particular level in the target nucleus will be the sum of those produced by direct excitation of the level and those produced in cascade with radiation from higher excited levels. A comparison of the yield of γ rays from the level under observation with the yield in coincidence with those of other energies will give a measure of the direct excitation of the particular state (Ro58). A discussion of this method is given in Chapter V.Q. It is especially useful in cases where two cascade γ rays have so nearly the same energy that they are unresolved by the crystal spectrometer (see, for example, discussion of Ta excitation function, Section 5).

E. Metastable State Excitation

Metastable states in some nuclei are excited by neutron inelastic scattering. Since these states generally have an angular momentum very different from that of the ground state, their excitation functions should be of interest in interpreting theory. The method is to bombard with a constant flux of neutrons for a time long compared to the mean life of the excited state, then to remove the neutron beam and to observe the de-excitation radiation (see Chapter V.K). An excitation function for gold, determined by this method, is presented in Section 5. A variation of the above method is used for metastable states in the mμsec range. A fast coincidence circuit with variable delay time has been used in conjunction with a pulsed neutron source to determine the mean life of the 1.72-Mev level of Zr^{90} (Kl59). In this case, the 0.51-Mev radiation from the pair internal conversion of the 0^+ excited state is observed with a scintillation crystal. The excitation function for this state has been obtained in part by this method.

F. Electron Detection

A possible method for detecting excitation by neutron inelastic scattering from low-lying levels in heavy elements is to count internal conversion electrons. High conversion ratios for these elements make γ-ray de-excitation difficult to observe. Low counting rates, poor electron energy resolution, and background problems have so far defeated attempts to make such measurements. Malmfors (Ma58) has described a trochoidal focusing spectrometer with a solid angle greater than 14 per cent of the sphere and a resolution of less than one per cent in electron energy at 1 Mev. This would be admirably suited to such work, especially with pulsed beams. It may also be noted in this connection that several experiments (Li55, Gu56) have produced excitation functions for iodine by detecting γ rays produced in the iodine of the NaI(Tl) scintillation detector itself. Here we have essentially a 4π geometry, and excitation functions can be obtained with good resolution. This method suggests the possibility of using, for conversion electron detection, scintillation crystals loaded with a small amount of the element to be investigated. To date, experiments of this type have not been successful, mainly because of the difficulty of incorporating a reasonable amount of foreign material into a scintillator without destroying its light-output properties. This method should be particularly successful for heavy elements where the internal conversion ratio is high.

3. Measurement of Absolute Cross Sections

A. Absolute Calibration for γ-ray Detection

The calculation of absolute values for $\sigma_n{}'$ involves a knowledge of both the total excitation of the state and the incident neutron flux. For measurements of de-excitation γ radiation, the measurement of total excitation is dependent upon several factors.

(1) **Spectrum Analysis.** If more than one γ ray is detected by the spectrometer, some method must be devised by which the spectrum may be analyzed. Methods of spectral analysis and background subtraction are discussed in detail in Chapter V.K. It should be remarked that scintillation spectrometers are at present capable of resolving accurately at most a few γ rays of different energies in the same spectrum. A resolution of better than 10 per cent is difficult to achieve below 1 Mev. Relative yield curves are determined with reasonable accuracy once techniques for spectral analysis have been developed.

(2) **Detector Calibration.** Absolute calibration of the detector must be done for the entire range over which γ-ray energies are to be measured. This may be calculated or performed experimentally. γ-Ray spectra produced in scintillation crystals are generally complex, and total yield is usually determined by finding the number of counts under the photoelectric peak of the spectrum. It is then necessary to know the ratio of photopeak counts to total counts in order to determine the true γ-ray yield. Calculations of this photopeak efficiency have been made for point sources (Ma54, Be55) and serve as a check on calculations for distributed γ-ray sources. Efficiency calculations must be made for individual γ-ray energies and for individual geometries. These involve a knowledge of Compton and pair-production cross sections for the detecting crystal, as well as the cross section for the production of photoelectrons. Day (Da56) has made calculations for rings of various sizes of the number of pulses produced in a right circular cylinder of NaI-(Tl) by a known source of γ radiation distributed throughout the ring. He finds experimentally that, for γ-ray energies between 0.5 and 2.8 Mev, the logarithm of the photopeak efficiency is a linear function of the logarithm of the γ-ray energy to within 2 per cent.

Absolute efficiency can be determined experimentally, provided one has available a radioactive source of known strength. The energy of the calibrating γ ray should be nearly the same as that of the experimental one, and its position and distribution should approximate the geometry of the experiment. For the large-crystal, ring geometries, a solution containing a known amount of radioactive material is placed in a can the size and shape of the scatterer, in the position of the scatterer, and the efficiency determined directly (Da56). The corrections to be discussed below must of course be applied to the determination of absolute yield. For the thin-crystal techniques, absolute efficiency is more easily calculated and can be checked experimentally to a first approximation with a point source placed an appropriate distance from the detector (Gu56). For time-of-flight techniques, calibration is effected experimentally by placing a radioactive source of known strength at the position of the scatterer and observing the pulse height spectrum. In every case, an attempt is made to have the energy of the calibrating source near that of the γ ray to be calibrated unless the efficiency of the counter as a function of γ-ray energy is known. Absolute efficiency of the detector will represent an uncertainty of at best 2 or 3 per cent in absolute cross section values.

(3) **Neutron Flux Determination.** The problem of determining neutron flux accurately is discussed in Chapter IV.B. Two methods are in wide use for inelastic scattering experiments. The absolute neutron flux can be calculated from the target thickness, proton beam, and the known cross section for the reaction producing the neutrons. These calculations of course will be only as accurate as the published cross section values. They may also be unreliable because of the difficulty of insuring that the measured beam current represents the true current. A second method is to use a flat response neutron detector, such as the McKibben *long counter*, calibrated with a standard Pu-, Po-, or Ra-α-Be source, or by a reaction whose cross section is known. The long counter can also be calibrated by comparison with a recoil proportional counter, which can be made absolute (see Chapter III.A). It should be noted that in the experimental setup the neutron monitor should be placed far enough away from the scatterer to eliminate effects of neutrons scattered from the material under investigation. Corrections may have to be made for room-scattered neutrons. Neutron flux measurements can be accurate to about 5 per cent.

(4) **Energy Resolution.** In calculating absolute cross sections for use with excitation functions, particularly where it is desired to examine resonance structure, account must be taken of the energy resolution of the neutron source. For reactions giving monoenergetic neutrons, the spread in neutron energy will be given by the angular spread of the scattering sample, the target thickness and the energy spread of the bombarding particles. The latter is quite small (a few kev) in electrostatic accelerators using magnetic or electrostatic

analyzers.   In principle, the target thickness may also be made quite small.   The limitation on this is the obtainable neutron flux, which must be large enough to give a reasonable signal-to-noise ratio at the detector.   For elements with small inelastic cross sections and for angular distribution measurements, this may seriously limit the energy resolution of the results.   A transmission measurement of a narrow resonance in a total cross section, such as the 588-kev resonance in sulfur or the 2.08-Mev resonance in carbon, is perhaps the best method of determining the experimental neutron energy spread.

B. Absolute Calibration for Neutron Detectors

Absolute values of cross sections for neutron detection techniques depend as before on a knowledge of absolute detector efficiency and of neutron flux.   Flux determinations are as discussed above. Some methods of neutron detector calibration are discussed in the following paragraphs.

(1) **Transmission Techniques.** For the determination of nonelastic cross sections, the absolute efficiency of the detector need not be known, since measurements with and without scatterer will yield cross sections directly.   If the detector counts neutrons of all energies, the total cross section is obtained.   If the detector has a sharp cut-off just below the bombarding energy, this method gives an accurate measure of the elastic cross section only.   The nonelastic cross section is then determined by subtraction.   For energy regions in which inelastic scattering is the predominant process, these measurements provide a good check on cross sections determined by other methods.   It should be noted that detectors used for this technique must fulfill the requirement that they be insensitive to γ rays.

(2) **Time-of-Flight Techniques.** Spectrum analysis for time-of-flight detectors depends on both the energy resolution of the neutron beam and the time resolution of the detector.   The former is important at low energies and the latter at high energies (Cr56a). Plastic scintillators are in widest use for these experiments because of their short pulse duration.   The absolute efficiency of these detectors is determined experimentally by comparison with a long counter or proton telescope.   These detectors need not be insensitive to γ rays, since these are separated from the neutron groups by the time-of-flight method.

Cross sections for inelastic scattering have been determined experimentally by comparison with the known differential (n, p) elastic scattering cross section (Cr55). The scattering sample is replaced by a polyethylene scatterer of an appropriate size, and the yield of scattered neutrons is observed at such an angle that their energy is the same as that of the neutrons inelastically scattered from the sample. If the angular distribution of scattered neutrons is known, the total inelastic cross section can be calculated.

(3) **Photographic Plate Techniques.** Measurements may be made of both neutron flux and neutron energy through the use of photographic emulsions. For neutron energies up to 14 Mev, proton recoils in the emulsion give an unambiguous count of the number of neutrons per cm^2 in a given energy interval. This requires knowledge of the concentration of hydrogen in the emulsion (which depends upon the humidity of the laboratory) and of the solid angle of acceptance for proton recoils. Corrections must be made for shrinkage of the emulsion during processing, for the attenuation of neutrons in the emulsion, for proton recoil tracks leaving the emulsion and for (n, p) reactions in the emulsion (Ro53). It may be noted that only a representative number of tracks need be counted to give a good indication of the number and energy distribution of the incident neutrons. If plates from the same batch are used to measure both incident and scattered flux, correction factors for absolute efficiency of the detector can be eliminated, as is the case with transmission measurements. This method is not useful for low energy neutrons.

C. Corrections to Data

Several corrections must be made to the raw data in determining absolute cross sections. The uncertainty in these corrections limits the accuracy of absolute cross sections to, at best, ± 8 per cent. In cases where several corrections must be made, absolute cross sections may be in error by as much as a factor of 2.

(1) **Angular Distribution.** As has been suggested before, the angular distribution of the emitted γ rays or neutrons must be known in order to determine the total yield. Thus, measurements made with *good* geometry should be accompanied by angular distribution measurements. It should be noted that, while the statistical model predicts symmetry about 90°, this is not the case for direct interactions (see Section 5). Thus, angular distributions should be measured through

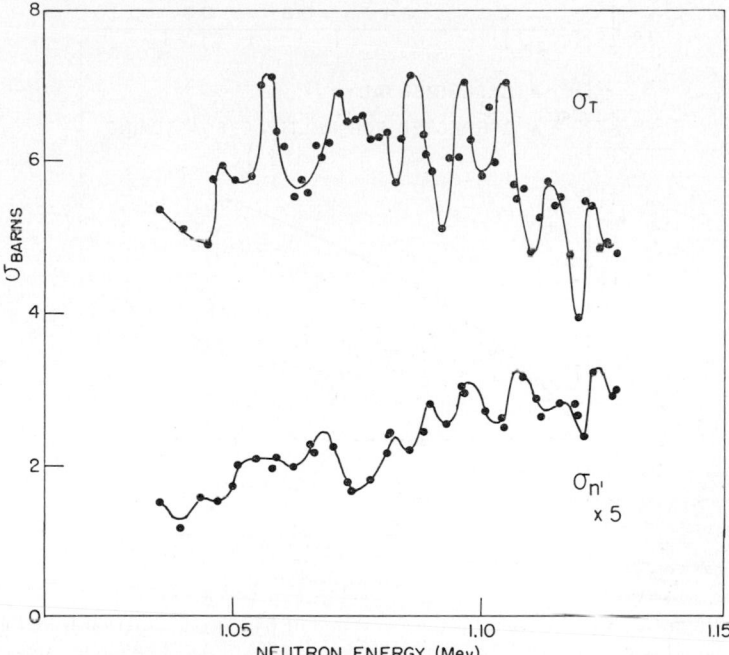

Figure 1. Elastic and inelastic cross sections for zirconium (Gu56). Comparison shows essentially the same resonance structure. The neutron energy resolution is about 3 kev for the total cross section measurement; about 20kev for the inelastic measurement.

as large an angle as possible to obtain a true value for the integrated cross section. Such measurements have been made with good precision for a number of elements (Cr56b, Cr58, Li55).

Gamma-ray measurements made with ring scatterers often cover an angular range of acceptance of about $90° \pm 45°$ with respect to the incident neutron direction, and those made with small thin crystals cover an angular range of almost $180°$; thus, angular distribution corrections will not be so important with these methods.

(2) **Multiple Scattering.** Another correction that must be considered for geometries in which there is a considerable amount of scattering material, is the effect of multiple scattering in the sample. A neutron, once having suffered an elastic collision, may not be scattered out directly, but may undergo one or more further collisions

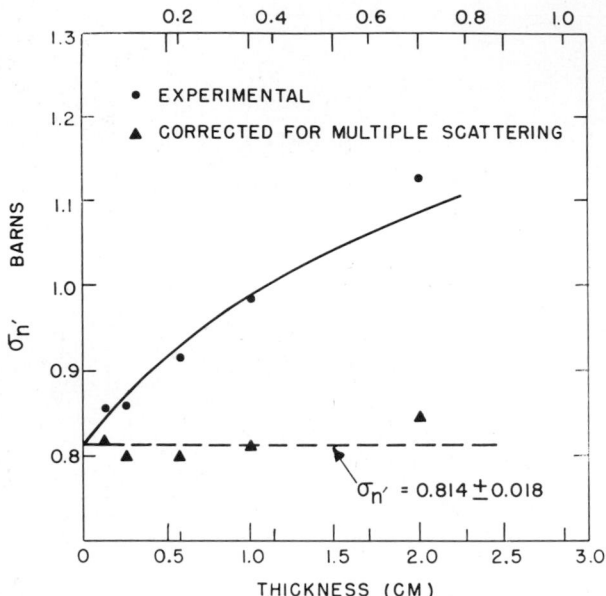

Figure 2. Cross section for the excitation of 847-kev γ radiation from Fe^{56} as measured with rings of different axial thickness (Da56). The circles give cross sections calculated from neutron flux and γ-ray yield, corrected for attenuation and for one additional scattering after the first. The triangles give these cross sections after correction for multiple neutron scattering. The solid curve shows the theoretical variation of the γ-ray yield caused by multiple scattering.

before leaving the sample. This process has the effect of increasing the neutron flux through the scatterer. Particularly in the case of light and medium-weight elements, where resonance structure is evident in the total cross section, this may appear as spurious structure in the inelastic cross section. Figure 1 shows comparable structure in the total and inelastic cross sections for zirconium. Inelastic measurements were done with ring geometry in which a considerable amount of scatterer was used. It is thus possible that the resonance structure observed is in part a reflection of resonances in the elastic scattering of the incident neutrons. The effect of multiple scattering in light nuclei is compensated for to some extent by the degradation in energy of the scattered neutrons.

If a neutron, having suffered an inelastic encounter, has enough energy to be scattered inelastically several more times, the subse-

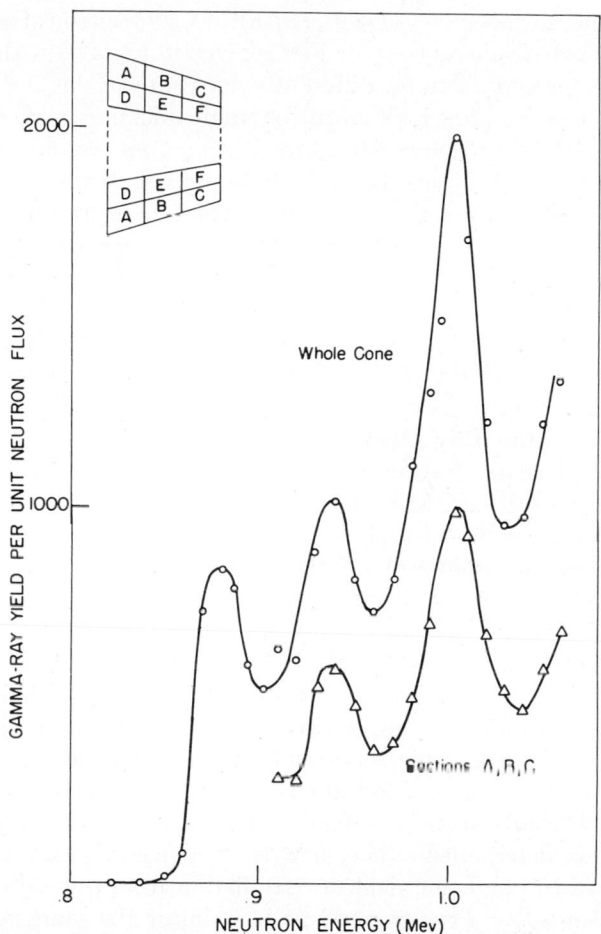

Figure 3. Cross section for the excitation of 847-kev radiation from Fe^{56} near threshold, using scattering rings of different radial thickness (Gu55). Ring sections used are indicated on the diagram. Resonance structure is observed to be somewhat diminished in the thinner cone. Calculated yield ratio *thick ring/thin ring* for the peak at 1 Mev is 1.58, while the experimental value is 1.74.

quent yield of γ radiation will be anomalously large. Absolute cross sections calculated from γ-ray yields must then be corrected for this effect. Multiple scattering corrections have been calculated and also determined experimentally, using different sizes and shapes of scatterer for the ring geometry (Da56, Gu55). A comparison of corrected and uncorrected values of $\sigma_{n'}$ for Fe^{56} is given in Fig. 2. It should be noted that the correction for different values of axial thickness of the scattering ring is appreciable even for small thicknesses of scatterer. A comparison of resonance structure in the cross section of Fe^{56} is given in Fig. 3. It is seen that, for a 50 per cent decrease of radial thickness of the scatterer, the resonance structure is preserved. This appears also to be the case for a decrease in the axial thickness. Yield corrections for multiple scattering are given in La57 and Da56. Since multiple scattering corrections and corrections for neutron beam attenuation in the sample tend to cancel, satisfactory results may be obtained in the ring geometry by making no correction for either effect.

(3) **Gamma-Ray Absorption.** Another correction that must be made in the case of γ-ray detection is for the self-absorption of the γ rays in the scattering sample. Day (Da56) has performed transmission experiments which show that this correction may be calculated with an uncertainty of as little as 1 or 2 per cent. The correction becomes important for large scattering samples and for samples of any thickness at low γ-ray energies. For the detection of low-energy radiation with the thin-crystal technique, the scattering sample is usually chosen to be infinitely thick to the γ rays (Gu56), thus making the absorption calculation easier. Kiehn and Goodman (Ki54) have devised a method by which counter efficiency and self-absorption are measured simultaneously for the ring geometry. The γ-ray yield from neutron bombardment of a conical can filled with iron shot is determined. The shot is then coated with a known amount of Mn^{54} and the yield of γ radiation from the source determined. Since the γ ray from Mn^{54} has almost the same energy as that from inelastic scattering from iron, the true yield from the inelastic scattering can be determined by comparison. This technique can also be used for thin-crystal measurements of low-lying levels, using a scatterer in powder form, mixed with a known amount of radioactive material, such as Co^{57}.

(4) **Internal Conversion.** Gamma rays from low-lying levels in heavy nuclei are known to have large internal conversion coefficients. Thus, corrections to γ-ray yields from these levels must be made. These coefficients are extremely energy sensitive and are not too well known for very low-energy γ rays. Quoted cross sections

for low-lying levels are apt to be in error by as much as a factor of 2. Internal conversion coefficients have been calculated by Rose (Ro55a) for K and L conversions by both electric and magnetic multipole radiation.

(5) **Excitation of Higher Levels.** As indicated above, especially for elements with a rotational level structure, the excitation of levels higher than the one under observation will result in cascade transitions that will increase the γ-ray yield of the level being studied. Correction for this effect may be made experimentally using coincidence techniques (see Section 2.D) or may be calculated, providing excitation functions for the higher levels, and branching ratios, are known. The γ-ray yield curve for the 137-kev radiation from tantalum shows this effect clearly [see Section 5.B(2).]

4. Elements of Theory

A. Hauser-Feshbach Theory

At the present time there are several models which may serve to explain the interaction of fast neutrons with nuclei. The statistical model of compound nucleus formation should be particularly applicable to isotopes of medium to high mass number. The excitation energy of the compound nucleus, which is just the incident neutron energy plus the binding energy of the captured neutron, is then great enough so that the density of levels is large and the statistical model should apply. This model assumes that there exist resonance levels with all J-values which it is possible to excite. The cross section for the formation of the compound nucleus by an incident neutron of energy E is given by Hauser and Feshbach (Ha52) as:

$$\sigma_c = \Sigma_l \sigma_c{}^{(l)} = \Sigma_l (2l + 1) \pi \lambda^2 T_l(E) \tag{1}$$

where $\sigma_c{}^{(l)}$ is the cross section for incoming partial waves of angular momentum l, λ the wavelength of the incoming neutron, and $T_l(E)$ the transmission coefficient or penetration factor for the target nucleus for waves of this l and λ. The values of $T_l(E)$ are directly related to the shape, depth, and radius of the potential well with which the incoming neutron interacts. (See Chapters V.C and V.J; the $T_l(E)$ are tabulated in Chapter V.C.)

The probability that a neutron will be emitted into a particular exit channel will again depend on the penetrability $T_l(E')$, where E'

is the energy of the emitted neutron. This probability will depend upon the number of competing channels open and upon the spin and parity of the excited state of the residual nucleus. The cross section for the excitation of a particular level in the target will be the product of σ_c and the cross section for emission to this state. Thus, the shape of the excitation curve as a function of bombarding neutron energy, particularly near the threshold for a given level, should be sensitive to the angular momentum and parity of both the excited level and the ground state of the target. The importance of obtaining accurate experimental excitation functions is evident.

The transmission coefficients $T_l(E)$ may be calculated in several ways. The *black nuclear* model assumes a strong interaction in which the neutron immediately forms a compound nucleus, and its motion is integrated into a collective motion of the whole nucleus. The *cloudy crystal ball* model, based on experimental evidence for nuclear shell structure, permits the bombarding nucleon to exist for some time as an individual particle before being absorbed into the compound nucleus. The *shape* of the excitation function is quite insensitive to the method of calculation of $T_l(E)$, although the calculated values of $\sigma_{n'}$ may be quite different. Calculations made for Pb^{207} show that both models may be fitted to the experimental data (St55) by proper choice of parameters (Ol56).

B. Direct Interaction

For light nuclei and for nuclei with large deformation from spherical shape, the above model is not expected to give good results. In the first case, at least for low bombarding energies, the assumption of overlapping levels in the compound nucleus is no longer valid, and resonance theory may be more applicable. In the second case, the deformation of the potential well may lead to a surface interaction with the excitation of rotational levels of predictable energies. This will be true particularly for those isotopes which lie midway between the closed-shell nuclei (Bo53). The wave function for the interaction is expressed as a sum of amplitudes corresponding to various states of the target nucleus and the incident particle, giving a set of coupled equations for the amplitudes corresponding to surface excitation of the target nucleus. A strong angular dependence in the scattering is expected (Yo56). The excitation function should rise slowly near threshold, with absolute values of cross section becoming comparable

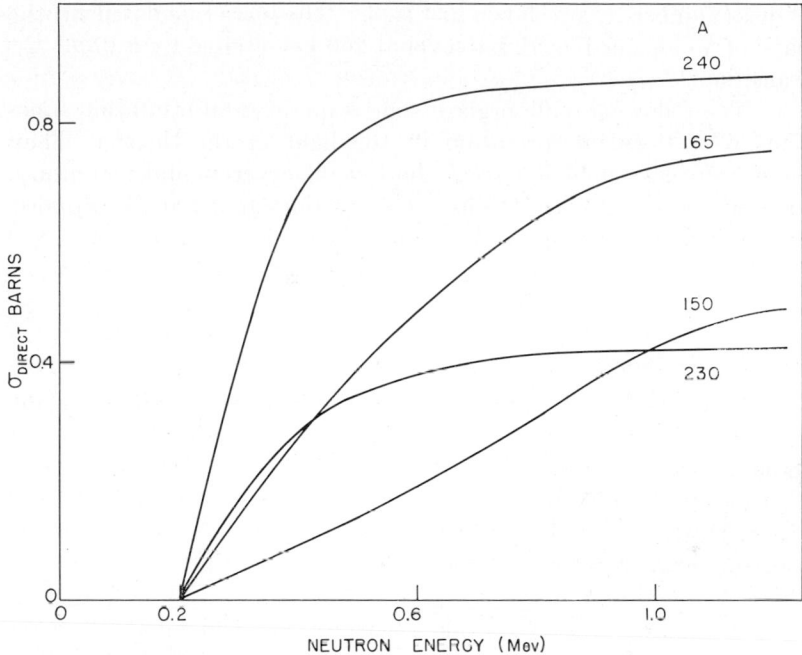

Figure 4. Theoretical direct interaction cross sections for inelastic neutron scattering for four values of A. (Br55). These are calculated assuming a 200-kev first excited level with spin 2^+ and ground state 0^+.

to those for compound nucleus formation at energies 0.5 to 1 Mev above threshold.   Calculations of excitation functions for rotational states have been made by Chase and Wilets (Ch57).   Experimental work done recently on U^{238} indicates that compound nucleus formation is the dominant process up to a few Mev bombarding energy (Cr58) but gives some evidence of the presence of a direct interaction.

For high bombarding energies or for light nuclei, excitation of a single particle in the target nucleus may occur as a result of a direct interraction between the incident neutron and a single nucleon in the target nucleus.   The magnitude of this effect is expected to be small compared with resonance formation of the compound nucleus but may be appreciable between resonances.   The presence of this type of interaction should give rise to an anisotropic angular distribution of the scattered neutrons.   Curves calculated by Brink (Br55) for four values of mass number A, are shown in Fig. 4. These are calculated on the basis of an assumed low-lying level at 200 kev excited by a $0^+ \rightarrow 2^+$ transition.

The following section gives some experimental excitation functions with their interpretation in the light of the theory. They have been chosen to illustrate the several experimental techniques in current use and to point out the corrections that must be applied before theoretical comparisons can be made.

5. Experimental Results

A. Light Elements

Compound nucleus formation in the light and medium-weight nuclides exhibits a strong resonance structure, with widely spaced resonances in the very light elements. Excited levels in the target nucleus are also likely to be widely spaced, making detection of individual level excitation readily observable and unambiguous. Here γ-ray detection is favored, since self-absorption in the scattering sample is at a minimum.

(1) **Iron.** One of the first elements to yield information on inelastic scattering excitation functions was Fe^{56}, with a first excited level at 850 kev. The yield of γ radiation from this level is large, and its excitation as a function of neutron energy therefore is easily

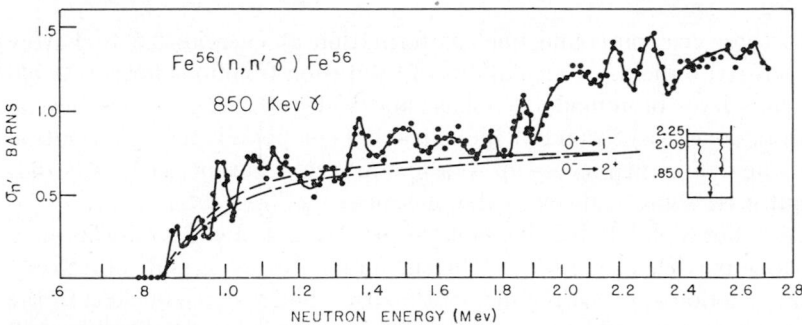

Figure 5. Cross sections for the production of γ rays from the 850-kev level in Fe^{56} by inelastic neutron scattering (Ki54). Absolute values were calculated from measurements of neutron flux and γ-ray yield. Corrections have been made for γ-ray and neutron attenuation, but not for multiple scattering. Data were obtained using a ring geometry.

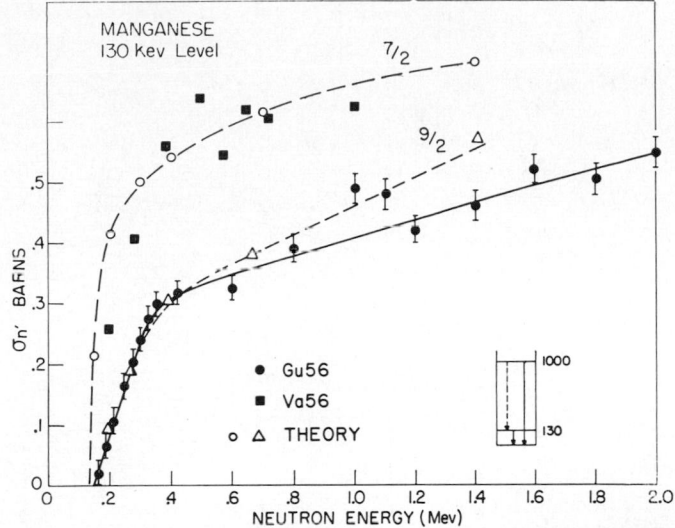

Figure 6. Cross section for the production of γ rays from the 128-kev level in Mn[55] (Va56, Gu56). Absolute values were obtained from γ-ray yield and neutron flux. Both sets of data were obtained using thin scatterers; thus, corrections for neutron attenuation and multiple scattering were unnecessary.

determined. Figure 5 shows the results of Kiehn and Goodman (Ki54) obtained using a ring geometry and a NaI(Tl) detector. The presence of strong resonance structure is evident, as is the general shape agreement with Hauser-Feshbach theory. Above 2 Mev the rise in the yield curve gives evidence of the contribution of the next excited state, at 2.09 Mev, which cascades through the 850-kev level, thus adding to the yield of the latter radiation. The resonance structure and absolute cross section are in agreement with the work of other experimenters (Fr55, Va56). The initial rise of the yield curve is compared with a *black nucleus* calculated curve, with good agreement in shape and absolute value. Here the calculated curves for different spin and parity assignments are so similar that definite assignment cannot be made. Absolute values for cross section were obtained by the method explained in Section 3.B(3), but were not corrected for multiple scattering.

(2) **Manganese.** Figure 6 gives data on the low-lying level of Mn[55] obtained by two different methods. The M.I.T. data were taken using the thin-crystal technique (Gu56), while the Wisconsin

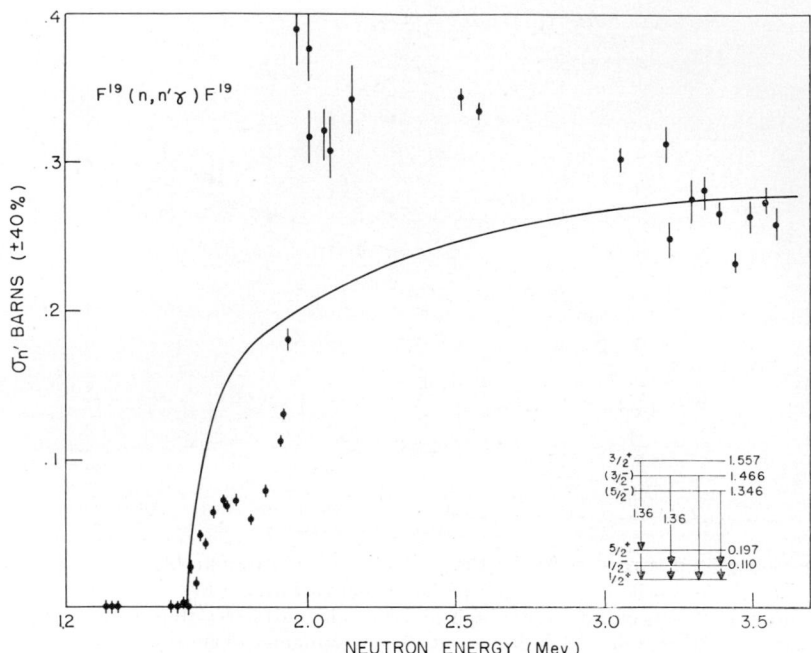

Figure 7. Cross section for the production of γ rays from two excited levels in F^{19} by inelastic neutron scattering (Fr57). Data were obtained using a ring geometry. The level scheme shows two de-excitation γ rays of energy 1.36 Mev; these were detected simultaneously. Absolute values were obtained from γ-ray yield and neutron flux. Corrections have been made for γ-ray and neutron attenuation but not for multiple scattering. Solid curve is Hauser-Feshbach calculation.

data were obtained in a closed geometry γ-ray detection scheme using a thin scatterer (Va56). In neither case has a correction been made for multiple scattering, since only a small amount of scattering material was used. The dashed curves represent Hauser-Feshbach excitation functions calculated assuming a *black nucleus*. The two sets of data, while they disagree in absolute value, show a similar slope for the initial rise of the yield curve. This would point to a spin assignment of $9/2^+$ for the first excited state in this element. The shape of the excitation function depends, however, on the spectrum and energy spread of the incident neutrons; thus, the comparison may not be reliable. Freeman (Fr55) has reported a second excited state in Mn^{55} at 0.98 Mev, which decays 95 per cent to the 128-kev level. Thus, one might expect to see a distinct rise in the yield at about 1 Mev. That this is not the case points either to competition in the excitation of the two levels or to a large angular momentum change between the ground state and the second level, and thus a slowly rising excitation.

The disagreement in absolute values arises from the difficulty in making neutron and γ-ray attenuation corrections to the data. These corrections are, at best, made semi-empirically and thus may be expected to give results which differ by a small factor. The absence of resonance structure might be interpreted as indicating that resonant formation of a compound nucleus is not present, or it might be explained in terms of lack of multiple scattering in the sample. The total cross section for Mn^{55} shows a pronounced resonant structure (Hu55).

(3) **Fluorine.** Figure 7 shows the yield function for the excitation of two levels simultaneously (Fr57). The data represented here were obtained using a ring geometry and NaI(Tl) spectrometer. As is seen by the level scheme, the de-excitation γ rays from the 1.56-Mev level to the 0.197-Mev level, and those from the 1.47 to the 0.11-Mev level have essentially the same energy and thus are detected simultaneously. The solid curve in the figure represents a Hauser-Feshbach calculation for the two levels simultaneously, assuming the spin assignments shown on the level scheme. It is clearly seen that the experimental points cannot be explained in the light of statistical theory. For bombarding energies up to 3 Mev the density of levels in the compound nucleus of so light an element cannot be great enough for statistical theory to apply. Above 3 Mev, experimental data represent a better fit, but this is perhaps fortuitous. Freeman (Fr57) has also attempted to apply Hauser-Feshbach theory to her results on the excitation of the 2.79-Mev level in this element but concludes that experimental results cannot be fitted to curves of this type.

The experimental curve of Fig. 7 shows a pronounced dip at about 1.8 Mev. The total cross section for F^{19} shows a large resonance at about 2 Mev (Wi58). The sharp rise in the inelastic cross section at this bombarding energy may be a reflection of this resonance caused by multiple scattering in the sample, or it may be true resonance formation of the compound nucleus.

(4) **Oxygen.** Figure 8 shows the excitation function for the production of 6.1-Mev γ radiation from the second excited level of oxygen (Pr57). Here the bombarding energy is well above the threshold for inelastic scattering from this level. Data were taken using a ring geometry. In this energy region, it is necessary to make

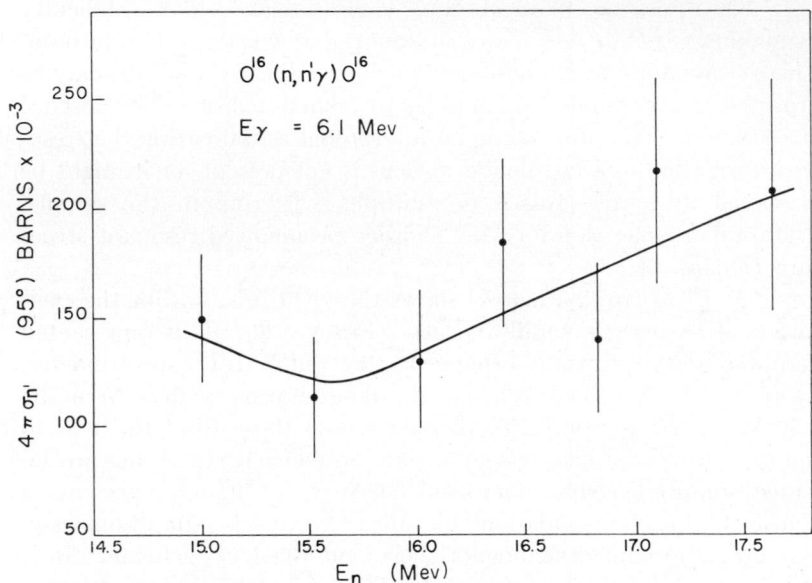

Figure 8. Cross section for the production of 6.1-Mev γ rays from the second excited state in O^{16} by inelastic neutron scattering (Pr57). Data were obtained using a ring geometry. Absolute values were calculated from γ-ray yield and neutron flux. Corrections have been made for γ radiation from $O^{16}(n, p)N^{16}$. At these neutron energies, corrections for γ-ray and neutron attenuation are not significant.

corrections for the competing (n, p) reaction. It is seen that cross section values in this region do not differ radically from those for other light elements at much lower bombarding energies. The inelastic cross section is, however, small with respect to calculated values for compound nucleus formation (Be57). This is to be expected, because of the alternative modes of decay available to the compound nucleus at this excitation energy.

B. Heavy Elements

For these elements, the level structure is likely to be closely spaced, with good probability of cascades between excited levels. The unambiguous interpretation of γ-ray spectra becomes more difficult in this region of the periodic chart. Agreement with statistical theory, however, is expected to be better.

(1) **Iodine.** Figure 9 shows the excitation function for the lowest lying level, at 60 kev, in I^{127}. Data were taken by the thin-crystal technique, using the iodine of the scintillation crystal as

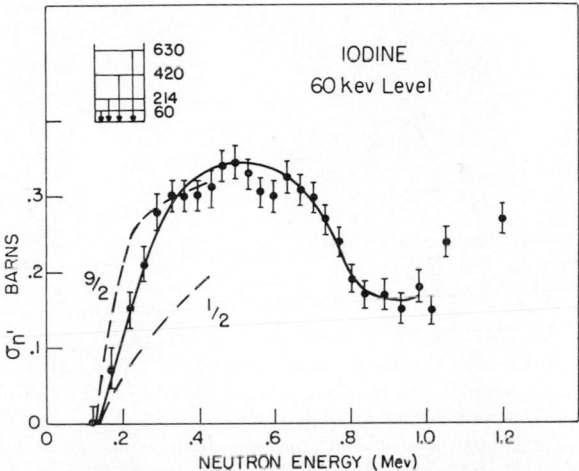

Figure 9. Cross section for the production of γ radiation from the 60-kev level in I^{127} (Gu56). Data were obtained using a thin NaI(Tl) crystal as detector, with the iodine of the crystal as scatterer. Absolute values of cross section were calculated from γ-ray yield and neutron flux. Corrections were made for the escape of γ radiation from the crystal but not for neutron attenuation or multiple scattering. The crystal thickness was 1.8 mm. The effect of competition in the excitation of higher levels is evident. Dashed curves were calculated from Hauser-Feshbach theory using *black nucleus* penetration factors (Va56).

scatterer (Gu56). Thus, absorption and attenuation corrections did not need to be made, although correction for escape of γ rays from the crystal was included. The bombarding neutron energy covered a range large enough to excite the first few levels of the nucleus under investigation. Since this element consists of a single isotope and there are few, if any, cascade transitions, the excitation of a single

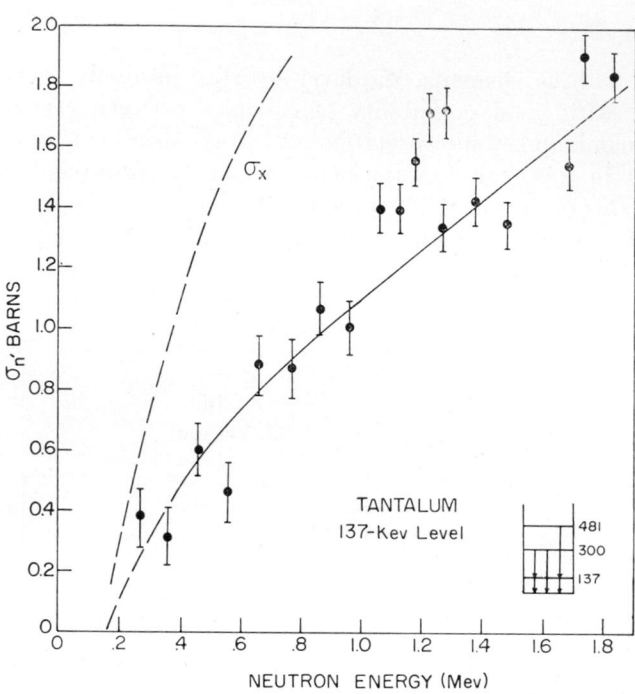

Figure 10. Cross section for the production of 137-kev γ radiation from Ta[181] by inelastic neutron scattering (Gu56). Data were taken with a thin crystal detector. Cross section values were calculated from γ-ray yield and neutron flux. Corrections have been made for γ-ray attenuation and internal conversion. Included in the γ-ray yield is unresolved 163-kev cascade radiation from the 300-kev level. This and cascades from higher levels cause the yield of γ radiation to continue to increase with increasing neutron energy. The dashed curve is the assumed total nonelastic cross section for this element (Be57).

level in competition with other levels can be studied readily from these data. Two pronounced dips in the yield curve are observed just above 0.4 Mev and 0.6 Mev, indicating the onset of competition in the excitation of the 0.43-Mev and the 0.63-Mev levels, respectively. Above 0.7-Mev bombarding energy, the effect of competition is clearly seen in the sharp decrease in excitation of the 60-kev level. Lind (Li58) has observed seven levels in iodine between 0.6 and 1.2 Mev, which would account for this large decrease. These results are consistent with those of Van Loef and Lind (Va56). They are also in agreement with data taken using a ring geometry

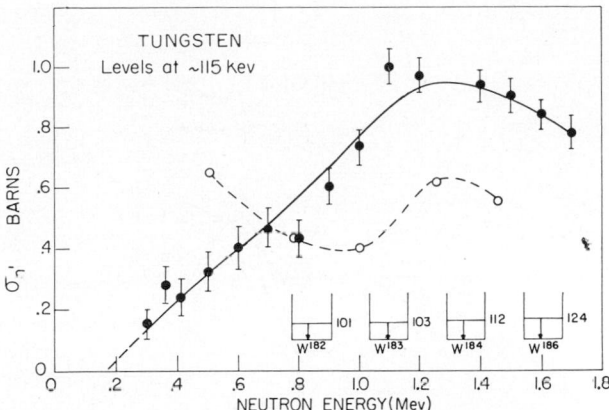

Figure 11. Cross section for the production of 115-kev γ radiation from natural tungsten by inelastic neutron scattering (Gu56). Data were taken with a thin crystal detector. Cross section values were calculated from γ-ray yield and neutron flux. Corrections have been made for γ-ray attenuation and internal conversion. The effects of competition from the excitation of higher levels is seen clearly. The dashed curve is the relative cross section for natural tungsten, measured by the same technique, taken from Fig. 12 and normalized at 0.8 Mev.

and a large NaI(Tl) crystal, with a glass cone filled with iodine crystals as scatterer (Gu55). The plotted Hauser-Feshbach curves were calculated by Van Loef using strong-coupling penetration factors (Va56) and well parameters consistent with the total excitation observed for the first four levels. Here again it is difficult to make excited level spin assignments on the basis of the shape of the experimental curve near threshold, although the general shape agreement suggests that compound nucleus formation is the dominant process. For heavy elements a comparison of the *total* inelastic cross section with the theoretical cross section for the formation of a compound nucleus may be the most significant theoretically since the details of the excitation of individual levels will be unimportant.

(2) **Tantalum.** The excitation function for the lowest-lying level in another monoisotopic element is shown in Fig. 10. These data were taken using the thin-crystal technique. Ta^{181} is known to have a rotational level scheme (Mc55). The de-excitation of higher levels differs from that of iodine in that there are cascade transitions between its excited levels, with rather large cascade-to-crossover ratios. Here the effect of competition in the excitation of higher

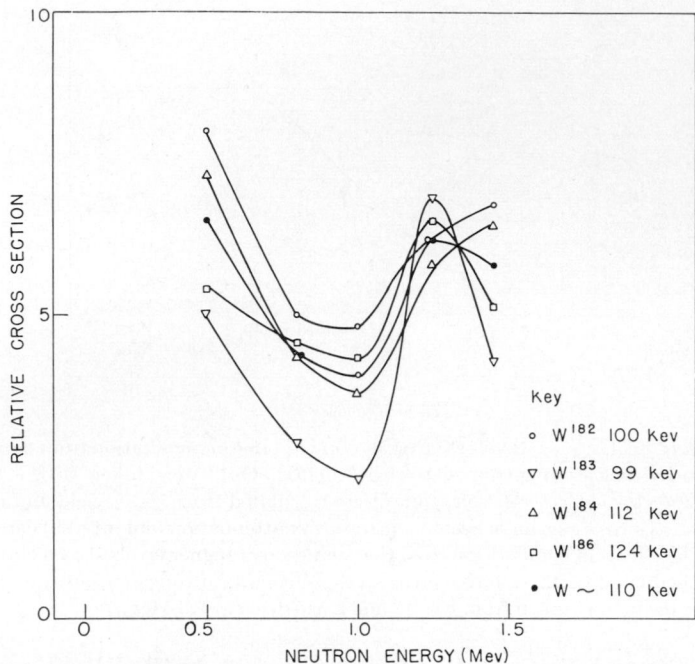

Figure 12. Relative cross section for the production of γ radiation from the first excited states in the four isotopes of tungsten and from natural tungsten by inelastic neutron scattering (Si57). Data were obtained using a thin crystal detector, normalized to neutron flux.

levels is obscured by the population of the lowest level through cascade. Unfortunately, the situation is further complicated by the finite resolution of the detecting equipment. The cascade from the second level to the first has an energy of 163 kev and is not resolved from the 137-kev radiation under observation. Thus, that portion of the excitation of the 300-kev level which decays by cascade is counted twice. The continued rise of the yield with increasing neutron energy is interpreted as indicating that the curve represents the excitation of all levels which it is energetically possible to excite. The dashed curve gives the total nonelastic cross section assumed on the basis of the statistical model from data obtained above 4 Mev (Be57). This is seen to be substantially higher in cross section value and in threshold slope. Certainly the possibility of some direct interaction in the excitation of this nucleus should be considered.

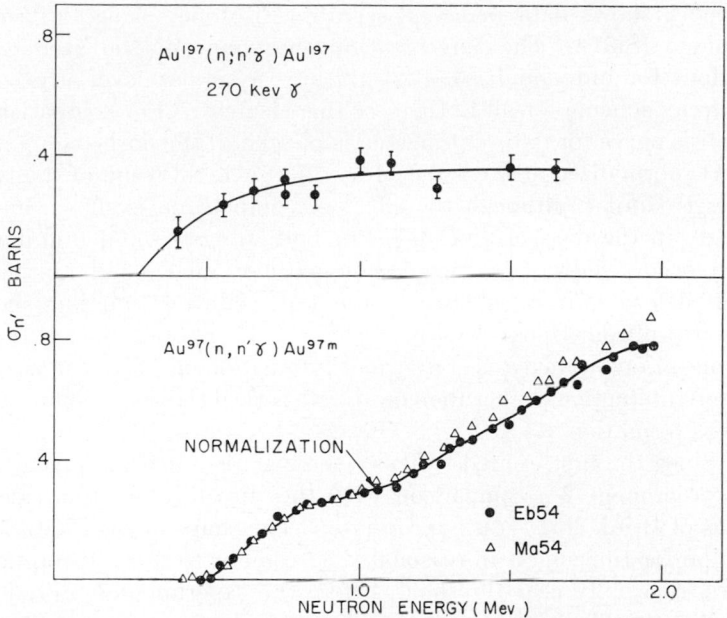

Figure 13. *Lower Figure.* Cross section for the production of γ radiation from Au^{197m} by inelastic neutron scattering (Eb54, Ma54). Data were taken by bombarding scatterer, removing it from the neutron beam, and observing the decay of the metastable state. Corrections have been made for residual activity of the sample after bombardment and for internal conversion. Absolute values were obtained for the Los Alamos data (Ma54) from γ-ray yield and neutron flux. The M.I.T. data (Eb54) are normalized to the Los Alamos data at the point indicated. *Upper Figure.* Cross section for the production of 270-kev radiation from Au^{197} by inelastic neutron scattering (Gu56). Data were obtained using a thin crystal detector. Absolute values were calculated from γ-ray yield and neutron flux. Corrections have been made for γ-ray attenuation and internal conversion.

(3) **Tungsten.** For comparison it is interesting to look now at the excitation of an element that has several isotopes. Figure 11 shows the combined excitation of the lowest lying levels in the four isotopes of tungsten, obtained by the thin-crystal technique (Gu56). Here the effects of both competition from higher level excitation and of cascades to the first level are noticeable. The pronounced dip in the vicinity of 0.8 Mev probably arises from competition of higher levels which do not decay by cascade to the lowest level, while the subsequent rise may be caused by still higher levels which do cascade.

Figure 12 shows data taken on separated isotopes using the same technique (Si57). The agreement in the shape of the excitation functions for individual isotopes indicates a similar level structure and decay scheme for all isotopes of this element. For comparison, Sinclair's curve for natural tungsten is plotted in the dashed curve of Fig. 11, normalized at $E_n = 0.8$ Mev. The general trend of the two curves is similar, although the effect of competition is shown more strongly in the data of Sinclair. For both tungsten and tantalum, which occur midway between magic-number nuclei and are thus largely deformed from spherical shape, the excitation functions show a departure from Hauser-Feshbach shape. This points toward their interpretation on the basis of a surface interaction or a direct nucleon-nucleon interaction, rather than on the statistical theory of compound nucleus formation.

Since the first excited states of the even isotopes are given the spin assignment 2^+, comparison with the direct interaction calculations of Brink (Fig. 4) is appropriate. The shape of the excitation function for tungsten is in reasonable agreement with the theoretical curves, especially near threshold, before the experimental curve has exhibited the effects of competition and cascade transitions.

(4) **Gold.** An example of the excitation of a metastable state is given in the lower curve of Fig. 13. The M.I.T. data are relative values (Eb54) normalized to the absolute cross section curve obtained at Los Alamos (Ma54). The method of obtaining data was described in Section 2.E. For comparison, the upper curve shows the excitation function for the 270-kev level in gold, observed by using a thin crystal (Gu56). Cross sections are seen to be of the same order of magnitude and to have similar shapes up to a bombarding energy of 1 Mev. The excitation of the isomeric state rises again above 1.2 Mev. This may be caused by excitation of higher levels that cascade through the metastable level. Agreement in the shape of these curves at threshold with Hauser-Feshbach predictions is fairly good; thus, there seems to be evidence that compound nucleus formation may be the predominant mechanism here. The absolute values for inelastic scattering cross sections are very much smaller than the nonelastic value of 2.7 barns at a neutron energy of 4 Mev given by Walt and Beyster (Wa56) from threshold detection experiments. The decay scheme for gold is complicated with five or six levels below 1 Mev; and the excitation functions given are for single levels. Thus, the

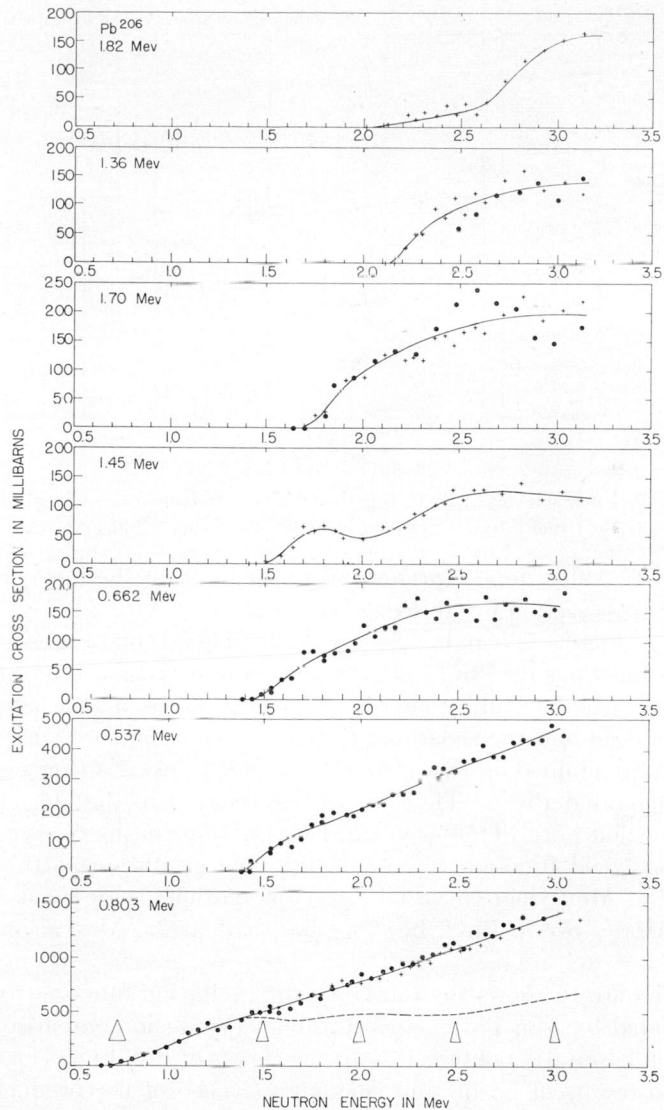

Figure 14. Cross sections for the production of γ rays from Pb^{206} by inelastic neutron scattering (Da56a, Li58). Data were obtained using a ring geometry. Cross section values are referred to 100 per cent isotopic abundance. Circles represent data taken by Day *et al.* (Da56a) and crosses represent data taken at a later time (Li58).

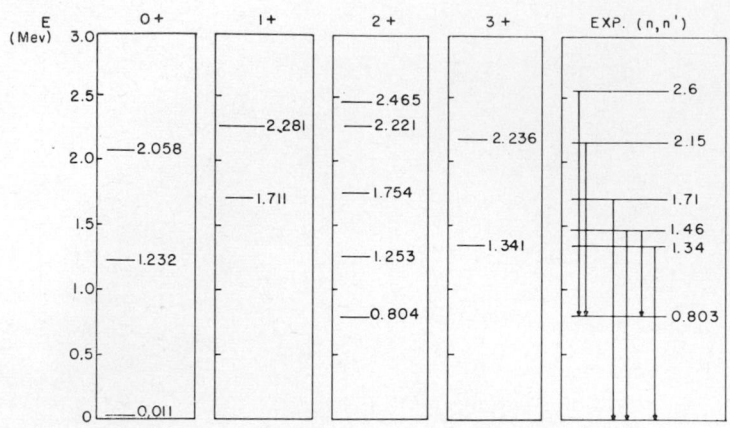

NUCLEAR ENERGY LEVELS FOR Pb^{206}

Figure 15. Energy levels of Pb^{206}, together with γ-ray transitions observed experimentally by neutron inelastic scattering (Tr58).

nonelastic value must represent an upper limit on the inelastic scattering cross section for all levels in this element.

(5) **Lead.** There has been considerable speculation about excitation functions for Pb^{206}. This nuclide is of particular interest, since it lies close to the doubly magic Pb^{208}. Work has been done using both natural lead and the separated isotope. Figure 14 shows excitation functions obtained by Day *et al.* (Da56a, Li58), using a ring geometry and separated Pb^{206}. These should be referred to the level scheme of True and Ford (Tr58) given in Fig. 15. The dashed curve on the 803-kev yield function represents the true excitation of this level. The 1.82-Mev yield curve may have a spurious component from a 1.77-Mev γ ray in Pb^{207}, but the sharp rise at 2.6 Mev is probably true Pb^{206} excitation.

Figure 16 shows the total inelastic excitation function for Pb^{206} calculated by Van Patter and Rothman (Va58) in comparison with the total excitation obtained from the curves of Fig. 14. The experimental results of Kiehn and Goodman (Ki54) for the production of the 803-kev γ ray are also plotted on this figure. These values have been corrected for the isotopic abundance of Pb^{206}. The theoretical curve, calculated on the basis of a *black nuclear* model, is seen to rise more sharply at threshold than the experimental curves. This might be interpreted to mean that compound nucleus formation is not the

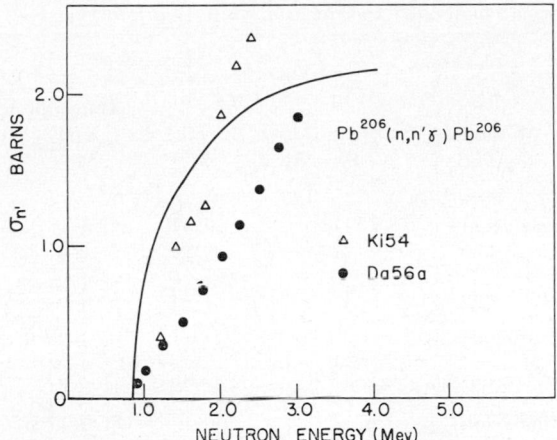

Figure 16. Total inelastic cross section for the production of γ radiation from Pb[206] by neutron inelastic scattering. The solid curve (Va58) is calculated from Hauser-Feshbach theory, using a *black-nuclear* model, for the first eleven levels in this isotope. Los Alamos data (Da56a) represent total γ-ray yield from inelastic scattering. M.I.T. data (Ki54) represent experimental data on the production of 803-kev γ radiation only. Discrepancy in absolute values may arise from correction factors applied to the raw data. All experimental values are referred to 100 per cent isotopic abundance.

only interaction taking place at these bombarding energies. The discrepancy in absolute values of experimental cross sections may arise in the correction factors applied to the raw data. It should be remarked that recent calculations by Ford (Fo58) at Los Alamos using the Hauser-Feshbach model and the best available values of T_l give cross sections in reasonable agreement with the experimental ones in every case.

Yasuno (Ya56) has calculated a theoretical curve for the excitation of the 803-kev level in Pb[206] assuming that rotational levels are the only excited levels. The slope of his curve below 2 Mev is more nearly in agreement with the experimental evidence, although his absolute values of cross section are lower than the experimental ones. There appears to be evidence to support either the statistical or the direct interaction theory. One might conclude that both modes of excitation are possible. This would support the interpretation given by Cranberg (Cr58) of his angular distribution measurements on U[238]. He finds evidence of both types of interaction, with compound nucleus formation predominant.

Table 1.   Information about Experimental Excitation Functions*

Element	Method of observation	E, excited state, Mev	E_γ, obs. Mev	Range of NBE, Mev	E spread of bombarding neutrons (kev)
$_3$Li^7	Ring geom	0.478	0.478	0.5–1.7	20
$_5$B^{10}	Ring geom	0.717	0.72	1.0–5.2	30–40
$_5$B^{11}	Ring geom	2.14	2.14	2.4–3.2	40
C^{12}	Phot emul	C$^{12}(n,n')3\alpha$ reaction		12.3–20.0	80–150
$_7$N^{14}	Ring geom	2.31	2.30	3.4–5.0	50–150
$_8$O^{16}	Ring geom	6.14	6.1	14.9–17.6	50–150
$_9$F^{19}	Thin scat, large crys det	0.110	0.110	0.2–1.8	50–200
	"	0.197	0.197	0.2–1.8	50–200
	Ring geom	1.35	1.24	1.3–3.6	70
	Ring geom	1.47	1.36	1.3–3.6	70
	Ring geom	1.56	1.36	1.3–3.6	70
	Ring geom	2.79	2.59	3.1–3.6	70
$_{11}$Na^{23}	Ring geom	0.440	0.440	0.5–1.2	
	Ring geom	2.08	2.08	2.1–2.9	
	Ring geom	2.39	2.39	2.5–3.0	
	Ring geom	0.440	0.440	0.5–3.5	50–100
	Ring geom	2.05	1.61	1.8–3.4	50–100
			2.05	1.9–2.5	
	Ring geom	2.37	1.90	2.4–3.4	50–100
			2.37	2.4–3.4	
	Ring geom	2.70	2.70	2.7–3.4	50–100
	Ring geom	2.96	2.96	3.0–3.4	50–100
$_{13}$Al^{27}	Ring geom	0.847	0.847	0.8–2.8	25
	Ring geom	1.025	1.025	1.0–2.8	25
	Ring geom	2.23	2.23	2.2–2.7	25
	Ring geom	0.843	0.843	2.4–4.5	100
	Ring geom	1.01	1.01	2.4–4.5	100
$_{14}$Si^{28}	Ring geom	1.78	1.78	1.7–3.0	50
$_{14}$Si^{29}	Ring geom		2.02	2.2–3.0	50
			2.41	2.4–3.0	50

* See p. 1522 for the list of abbreviations used.

Basis of determining abs values	Corrections to exptl data	Estimated reliability ±%	Ref.	Element
γ yield, NF	Iso abund	21	Fr55a	$_3Li^7$
γ yield, NF	γ atten	10	Da60	$_5B^{10}$
γ yield, NF	Iso abund; γ & N atten	30	Li58	$_5B^{11}$
NF, emul thickness	N atten; ang dist	18	Fr55b	$_6C^{12}$
γ yield, NF	γ & N atten	50	Fr57	$_7N^{14}$
γ yield, NF	$O^{16}(n,p)N^{16}$	30	Pr57	$_8O^{16}$
Rel vals only			Va56	$_9F^{19}$
Rel vals only			Va56	
Det effy; N yield comp with known $\sigma_{n'}$		40	Fr57	
"		40	Fr57	
"		40	Fr57	
"		40	Fr57	
Det effy, NF			Fr58	$_{11}Na^{23}$
Det effy, NF			Fr58	
Det effy, NF			Fr58	
γ yield, NF	γ & N atten	30	Li58	
γ yield, NF	γ & N atten	30	Li58	
γ yield, NF	γ & N atten	30	Li58	
γ yield, NF	γ & N atten	30	Li58	
γ yield, NF	γ & N atten	30	Li58	
Comp with Fe(n,n)Fe* $\sigma_{n'}$	γ + N atten	20	Ki54	$_{13}Al^{27}$
"	γ + N atten	20	Ki54	
"	γ + N atten	20	Ki54	
NF, det effy	γ atten; induced activity	20	Mo56	
NF, det effy	"	20	Mo56	
γ yield, NF	Iso abund; γ + N atten	30	Li58	$_{14}Si^{28}$
γ yield, NF	"	30	Li58	$_{14}Si^{29}$
γ yield, NF	"	30	Li58	

(*continued*)

Table I (Continued)

Element	Method of observation	E, excited state, Mev	$E\gamma$, obs. Mev	Range of NBE, Mev	E spread of bombarding neutrons (kev)
$_{14}Si^{30}$	Ring geom		2.20	2.3–3.0	50
$_{19}K^{39}$	Ring geom	2.52	2.52	2.5–4.0	20
	Ring geom	2.81	2.81	2.7–4.0	20
	Ring geom	3.05	3.05	3.0–4.0	20
	Ring geom	3.59	3.59	3.7–4.0	20
$_{24}Cr$	Ring geom	1.44	1.44	1.4–2.7	25
$_{25}Mn^{55}$	Thin cryst	0.130	0.130	0.1–2.0	25
	Thin scat, large crys det	0.130	0.128	0.2–1.2	150
	Ring geom	0.979	0.853	1.0–1.25	20
$_{26}Fe$	Ring geom	0.85	0.85	0.8–2.7	25
	Ring geom	0.833	0.833	0.9–1.2	20
	Ring geom	0.84	0.84	3.3–5.0	100
$_{28}Ni$	Ring geom	1.33	1.33	1.3–2.7	25
	Ring geom	1.47	1.47	1.3–2.7	25
$_{39}Y^{89}$	Thin samp, MSE	0.91(16s)	0.91	0.8–1.8	60–90
$_{40}Zr$	Ring geom	0.93	0.93	0.8–2.4	25
$_{40}Zr^{90m}$	Ring geom	1.77	0.511^a	1.7–3.6	50
$_{40}Zr^{90}$	Ring geom; PBT with enr targ	2.18	2.18	2.18–4.0	50
	"	2.745	0.42	3.1–3.6	50
			2.30	3.1–3.6	50
	"	3.07	0.88	3.1–3.6	50
	"	3.29	3.29	3.4–3.7	50
$_{40}Zr^{91}$	"	1.20	1.20	1.25–2.25	20–30
	"	1.46	1.46	1.46–3.6	20–30
$_{40}Zr^{92,94}$	"	1.48	0.56	1.5–2.2	20–30
$_{40}Zr^{91,92,94}$	"	0.92	0.92	0.9–4.0	20–30
$_{41}Nb^{93}$	Thin crys	0.74	0.736	0.75–1.8	30

Basis of determining abs values	Corrections to exptl data	Estimated reliability $\pm\%$	Ref.	Element
γ yield, NF	"	30	Li58	$_{14}Si^{30}$
γ yield, NF	Iso abund; γ + N atten.	30	Li58	$_{19}K^{39}$
γ yield, NF	"	30	Li58	
γ yield, NF	"	30	Li58	
γ yield, NF	"	30	Li58	
Comp with Fe(n,n)Fe $\sigma_{n'}$	γ & N atten	20	Ki54	$_{24}Cr$
γ yield, NF	γ atten	50	Gu56	$_{25}Mn^{55}$
γ yield, NF	γ & N atten, mult scat	15	Va56	
Det effy, NF		20	Fr55	
DCA		20	Ki54	$_{26}Fe$
Det effy, NF		20	Fr55	
Det effy, NF	γ atten, induced activity		Mo56	
Comp with Fe(n,n')Fe $\sigma_{n'}$	γ + N atten	20	Ki54	$_{28}Ni$
"	γ + N atten	20	Ki54	
Calibrated γ + N dets	2nd N group from Li(p,n)-Be	20	Sw55	$_{39}Y^{89}$
Comp with Fe(n,n)Fe $\sigma_{n'}$	γ + N atten	30	Gu56a	$_{40}Zr$
γ yield, NF	Iso abund; γ + N atten	30	Kl59	$_{40}Zr^{90m}$
γ yield, NF	Iso abund; γ + N atten	30	Li58	$_{40}Zr^{90}$
γ yield, NF	"	30	Li58	
γ yield, NF	"	30	Li58	
γ yield, NF	"	30	Li58	
γ yield, NF	"	30	Li58	
γ yield, NF	"	30	Li58	$_{40}Zr^{91}$
γ yield, NF	"	30	Li58	
γ yield, NF	"	30	Li58	$_{40}Zr^{92,94}$
γ yield, NF	"	30	Li58	$_{40}Zr^{91,92,94}$
Comp with Fe(n,n')Fe* $\sigma_{n'}$			Ro57	$_{41}Nb^{93}$

(*continued*)

Table I (*Continued*)

Element	Method of observation	E, excited state, Mev	$E\gamma$, obs. Mev	Range of NBE, Mev	E spread of bombarding neutrons (kev)
	Thin crys	0.96	0.957	0.75–1.8	30
$_5Rh^{103}$	Thin crys	0.300	0.300	0.3–1.1	30
$_{49}In^{115}$	Ring geom	0.91	0.91	0.9–2.0	50–75
	Ring geom	1.11	1.11	1.1–2.0	50–75
	Ring geom	1.29	1.29	1.3–2.0	50–75
	Ring geom	1.42	0.49	1.4–2.0	50–75
			1.42	1.4–2.0	50–75
$_{49}In^{115m}$	MSE of thin foils	0.335	0.335	0.3–5.5	100
$_{53}I^{127}$	NaI(Tl) crys used as scat	0.062	0.062	0.1–0.7	150
	"	0.208	0.208	0.2–1.2	150
	"	0.418	0.418	0.45–1.2	150
	"	0.632	0.632	0.63–1.2	150
	Thin crys used as scat	0.06	0.06	0.1–1.2	25
	Ring geom	0.208	0.208	0.3–1.6	30
	Ring geom	0.375	0.375	0.4–1.6	30
	Ring geom	0.418	0.418	0.4–1.6	30
	Ring geom	0.612	0.612	0.61–1.6	30
	Ring geom	0.646	0.646	0.64–1.6	30
	Ring geom	0.744	0.744	0.75–1.6	30
	Ring geom	0.928	0.928	0.95–1.6	30
	Ring geom	1.03	1.03	0.95–1.6	30
	Ring geom	1.09	1.09	1.08–1.6	30
	Ring geom	1.222	1.222	1.3–1.6	30
	Ring geom	1.398	1.398	1.4–1.6	30
$_{56}Ba^{137m}$	Thin samp, MSE	0.661(2.6m)	0.661	0.5–3.0	60–90
$_{73}Ta^{181}$	Thin crys	0.137^b	0.137	0.2–1.8	25
$_{74}W$	Thin crys	0.115^b	0.115	0.3–1.7	25
Sep isos	Thin crys	0.115^b	0.099 to 0.124	0.5–1.5	

Basis of determining abs values	Corrections to exptl data	Estimated reliability $\pm\%$	Ref.	Element
Fe(n,n')Fe* $\sigma_{n'}$			Ro57	
Comp with Ta(n,n')Ta* $\sigma_{n'}$		20	Ro57	$_{45}$Rh^{103}
γ yield, NF	Iso abund; γ + N atten	30	Li58	$_{49}$In^{115}
γ yield, NF	"	30	Li58	
γ yield, NF	"	30	Li58	
γ yield, NF	"	30	Li58	
γ yield, NF	"	30	Li58	
Det effy, NF	γ atten; int conv; β-decay to Sn	30	Ma54a Eb54	$_{49}$In^{115m}
Det effy, NF	γ escape from crys		Va56	$_{53}$I^{127}
Det effy, NF	γ escape from crys		Va56	
Det effy, NF	γ escape from crys		Va56	
Det effy, NF	γ escape from crys		Va56	
Det effy, NF	γ escape from crys	20	Gu56	
γ yield, NF	γ + N atten	20	Li58	
γ yield, NF	γ + N atten	20	Li58	
γ yield, NF	γ + N atten	20	Li58	
γ yield, NF	γ + N atten	20	Li58	
γ yield, NF	γ + N atten	20	Li58	
γ yield, NF	γ + N atten	20	Li58	
γ yield, NF	γ + N atten	20	Li58	
γ yield, NF	γ + N atten	20	Li58	
γ yield, NF	γ + N atten	20	Li58	
γ yield, NF	γ + N atten	20	Li58	
γ yield, NF	γ + N atten	20	Li58	
Calibrated γ + N dets	2nd N group from Li(p,n)Be	20	Sw55	$_{56}$Ba^{137m}
γ yield, NF	Int conv	50	Gu56	$_{73}$Ta^{181}
γ yield, NF	Int conv	50	Gu56	$_{74}$W
Rel vals only	Int conv		Si57	Sep isos

(*continued*)

Table I (Continued)

Element	Method of observation	E, excited state, Mev	$E\gamma$, obs. Mev	Range of NBE, Mev	E spread of bombarding neutrons (kev)
$_{78}$Pt	Thin crys	0.33	0.33	0.4–1.8	25
$_{79}$Au^{197}	Thin crys	0.27	0.27	0.4–1.6	25
$_{79}$Au^{197m}	MSE of thin foils	0.279(7.5s)	0.279	0.4–5.5	100
$_{80}$Hg^{199m}	Thin samp, MSE	0.527(44m)	0.159	0.4–2.0	60–90
$_{82}$Pb	Ring geom	0.803	0.803	1.2–2.7	25
$_{82}$Pb^{206}	Ring geom	0.803	0.803	0.7–3.2	50–100
	Ring geom	1.34	0.535	1.4–3.1	50–100
	Ring geom	1.46	0.662	1.45–3.1	50–100
			1.45	1.45–3.1	
	Ring geom	1.73	1.731	1.6–3.1	50–100
	Ring geom	1.83	1.83	2.1–3.1	50–100
	Ring geom	2.25	1.36	2.1–3.1	50–100
$_{90}$Th^{232}	PBT, thin samp	0.715	0.665	0.7–1.6	100–125
	PBT, thin samp	0.790	0.610	0.65–1.6	100–125
			0.740		
			0.790		
	PBT, thin samp	1.035	0.965	1.0–1.6	100–125
			1.035		
	PBT, thin samp	1.100	1.106	1.0–1.6	100–125
$_{92}$U^{238}	PBT, thin samp enriched	0.654	0.610	0.6–1.6	100–150
	"	0.710	0.666	0.5–1.6	100–150
	"	0.725	0.728	0.5–1.6	100–150
	"	0.900	0.850	0.85–1.6	100–150
			0.900		
	"	1.010	1.010	0.96–1.6	100–150
	"	1.080	1.080	1.1–1.6	100–150
	"	1.210	1.210	1.2–1.6	100–150
	"	1.430	1.430	1.2–1.6	100–150

[a] Annihilation.

[b] And higher.

Basis of determining abs valnes	Corrections to exptl data	Esti-mated reli-ability $\pm\%$	Ref.	Element
γ yield, NF	Int conv	50	Gu56	$_{78}$Pt
γ yield, NF	Int conv	50	Gu56	$_{79}$Au^{197}
NF, det effy	γ atten, int conv		Ma54a Eb54	$_{79}$Au^{197m}
Calibrated γ + N dets	2nd N group from Li(p,n)Be	20	Sw55	$_{80}$Hg^{199m}
Comp with Fe(n,n)Fe* $\sigma_{n'}$	γ + N atten	20	Ki54	$_{82}$Pb
γ yield, NF	Iso abund; γ + N atten	30	Li58	$_{82}$Pb^{206}
γ yield, NF	"	30	Li58	
γ yield, NF	"	30	Li58	
γ yield, NF	"	30	Li58	
γ yield, NF	"	30	Li58	
γ yield, NF	"	30	Li58	
γ yield, NF	Iso abund; γ + N atten	30	Li58	$_{90}$Th^{232}
γ yield, NF	"	30	Li58	
γ yield, NF	"	30	Li58	
γ yield, NF	"	30	Li58	
γ yield, NF	Iso abund; γ + N atten	50	Li58	$_{92}$U^{238}
γ yield, NF	"	50	Li58	
γ yield, NF	"	50	Li58	
γ yield, NF	"	50	Li58	
γ yield, NF	"	50	Li58	
γ yield, NF	"	50	Li58	
γ yield, NF	"	50	Li58	
γ yield, NF	"	50	Li58	

C. Conclusions

For reference, Table I gives available experimental excitation curves, together with the methods by which the data were obtained, and, where possible, the correction factors that have been applied in obtaining absolute values of inelastic cross section. Much work is now in progress toward refining techniques for observing yield functions and toward their theoretical interpretation. As more nearly exact experimental evidence becomes available, it should be possible not only to determine level structure and decay schemes unambiguously, but also to approach more closely an understanding of the mode of interaction in terms of such parameters as nuclear well depth, absorption, and deformation.

Abbreviations Used in Table I

γ	γ ray
abs	absolute
ang dist	angular distribution
atten	attenuation
comp	comparison
crys	crystal
DCA	direct calibration including attenuation factors for neutrons and γ rays
det, dets	detector, detectors
det effy	detector efficiency
E	energy
emul	emulsion
exptl	experimental
enr targ	enriched target
geom	geometry
int conv	internal conversion
iso abund	isotopic abundance
MSE	metastable state excitation
mult scat	multiple scattering
N	neutron
NBE	neutron bombarding energy
NF	neutron flux
obs	observed
PBT	pulsed-beam technique
phot emul	photographic emulsion
rel vals	relative values
samp	sample
scat	scatterer
sep isos	separated isotopes

References

(Be55)   M. J. Berger and J. A. Daggett, *Phys. Rev.* **99**, 663 (1955).
(Be57)   J. R. Beyster, "Predictions of Fast Neutron Scattering Data with a Diffuse Surface Potential Well," *Los Alamos Sci. Lab. Report* LA-2099 (1957).
(Bo53)   A. Bohr and B. R. Mottelson, *Dan. Mat. Fys. Medd.* **27**, No. 16 (1953).
(Br55)   D. M. Brink, *Proc. Phys. Soc. (London)* **68A**, 994 (1955).
(Br55a)   J. E. Brolley and J. L. Fowler, *Revs. Modern Phys.* **28**, 103 (1956).
(Ch58)   D. M. Chase, L. Wilets, and Edmonds, *Phys. Rev.* **110**, 1080 (1958).
(Cr55)   L. Cranberg and J. S. Levin, *Phys. Rev.* **100**, 434 (1955).
(Cr56)   L. Cranberg and J. S. Levin, *Phys. Rev.* **103**, 343 (1956).
(Cr56a)   Cranberg, Frye, Nerensson, and Rosen, *Phys. Rev.* **103**, 662 (1956).
(Cr56b)   Cranberg, Day, Rosen, Taschek, and Walt, *Progr. Nuclear Energy* **1**, 107 (1956).
(Cr58)   L. Cranberg and J. S. Levin, *Phys. Rev.* **109**, 2063 (1958).
(Da56)   R. B. Day, *Phys. Rev.* **102**, 767 (1956).
(Da56a)   Day, Johnsrud, and Lind, *Bull. Am. Phys. Soc.* **1**, 56 (1956).
(Da57)   R. B. Day and D. A. Lind, *Bull. Am. Phys. Soc.* **2**, 32 (1957).
(Da60)   R. B. Day, and M. Walt, *Phys. Rev.* **117**, 1330 (1960).
(Eb54)   A. A. Ebel and C. Goodman, *Phys. Rev.* **93**, 197 (1954).
(El57)   Elwyn, Glasoe, Landon, and Oleksa, *Bull. Am. Phys. Soc.* **2**, 357 (1957)
(Fo58)   K. Ford, private communication (1958).
(Fr55)   Joan M. Freeman, *Phil. Mag.* **46**, 12 (1955).
(Fr55a)   Freeman, Lane, and Rose, *Phil. Mag.* **46**, 17 (1955).
(Fr55b)   Frye, Rosen, and Stewart, *Phys. Rev.* **99**, 1375 (1955).
(Fr57)   Joan M. Freeman, *Phil. Mag.* **2**, 628 (1957).
(Fr58)   J. M. Freeman and J. H. Montague, *Nuclear Phys.* **9**, 181 (1958).
(Gu55)   J. B. Guernsey, unpublished results (1955).
(Gu56)   J. B. Guernsey and A. Wattenberg, *Phys. Rev.* **101**, 1516 (1956).
(Gu56a)   J. B. Guernsey and C. Goodman, *Phys. Rev.* **101**, 294 (1956).
(Ha52)   W. Hauser and H. Feshbach, *Phys. Rev.* **87**, 366 (1952).
(Hu55)   D. J. Hughes and J. A. Harvey, "Neutron Cross Sections," *Brookhaven Natl. Lab. Report* BNL-325 (1955), and Supplement No. 1 (1957).
(Ki54)   R. M. Kiehn and C. Goodman, *Phys. Rev.* **95**, 987 (1954).
(Kl59)   Kloepper, Day, and Lind, *Phys. Rev.* **114**, 204 (1959).
(La57)   Langsdorf, Lane, and Monahan, *Phys. Rev.* **107**, 1077 (1957).
(Li55)   D. A. Lind and J. J. Van Loef, *Phys. Rev.* **99**, 621 (1955).
(Li57)   Lind, Day, and Kloepper, *Bull. Am. Phys. Soc.* **2**, 309 (1957).
(Li58)   Lind, Day, and Kloepper, *Phys. Rev.*, 1958 data to be published.
(Ma54)   Maeder, Miller, and Wintersteiger, *Helv. Phys. Acta* **27**, 3 (1954).
(Ma54a)   Martin, Diven, and Taschek, *Phys. Rev.* **93**, 199 (1954).
(Ma58)   K. Malmfors, *Arkiv Fys.* **13**, 237 (1958).
(Mc55)   McClelland, Mark, and Goodman, *Phys. Rev.* **97**, 1191 (1955).
(Mo56)   Ira L. Morgan, *Phys. Rev.* **103**, 1031 (1956).
(Mu56)   Muehlhause, Bloom, Wegner, and Glasoe, *Phys. Rev.* **103**, 720 (1956).
(Ol56)   S. Oleksa, *Phys. Rev.* **101**, 1035 (1956).

(Pr57)   Prud'homme, Sattar, Bostrom, and Morgan, *Bull. Am. Phys. Soc.* **2,** 308 (1957).

(Ro53)   L. Rosen, *Nucleonics* **11,** No. 7, 32; No. 8, 39 (1953).

(Ro55)   L. Rosen and L. Stewart, *Phys. Rev.* **99,** 1052 (1955).

(Ro55a)   M. E. Rose, in K. Siegbahn, ed., *Beta- and Gamma-ray Spectroscopy*, Interscience, New York, 1955.

(Ro57)   Rothman, Van Patter, Dubey, Porter, and Mandeville, *Phys. Rev.* **107,** 155 (1957).

(Ro58)   Rothman, Van Patter, Nath, and Mandeville, *Bull Am. Phys. Soc.* **3,** 18 (1958).

(Si57)   R. M. Sinclair, *Phys. Rev.* **107,** 1306 (1957).

(St55)   P. H. Stelson and E. C. Campbell, *Phys. Rev.* **97,** 1222 (1955).

(Sw55)   C. P. Swann and F. R. Metzger, *Phys. Rev.* **100,** 1329 (1955).

(Tr58)   W. W. True and K. Ford, *Phys. Rev.* **109,** 1675 (1958).

(Va56)   J. J. Van Loef and D. A. Lind, *Phys. Rev.* **101,** 103 (1956).

(Va58)   D. M. Van Patter and M. A. Rothman, private communication (1958).

(Wa54)   M. Walt and H. H. Barschall, *Phys. Rev.* **93,** 1062 (1954).

(Wa56)   M. Walt and J. R. Beyster, *Phys. Rev.* **98,** 279(A) (1956).

(We56)   Weber, Johnstone, and Cranberg, *Rev. Sci. Instr.* **27,** 166 (1956).

(Wi58)   Wills, Bair, Cohn, and Willard, *Phys. Rev.* **109,** 891 (1958).

(Ya56)   M. Yasuno, *Progr. Theoret. Phys.* **15,** 568 (1956).

(Yo56)   M. Yoshida, *Proc. Phys. Soc. (London)* **69A,** 668 (1956).

Statistical-Model Theory of Neutron Reactions and Scattering

H. GOLDSTEIN
Nuclear Development Corporation of America, White Plains, N.Y.

1. Introduction

Conceived in the late 1930's, the statistical theory of the nucleus flourished most vigorously in the 1940's under V. Weisskopf and his group (Fe49, Fe51, Bl52a), and was displaced as a valid picture of the nucleus in the face of contrary evidence in the early 1950's.

Yet a presentation of the statistical theory for fast-neutron reactions has more than mere antiquarian interest today. For a certain class of reactions, such as (n,n'), (n,p) and (n,α), induced by high-energy neutrons in medium-weight nuclei it remains the most complete and easily accessible description of the reaction presently available. More generally, in order to be able to identify and assess effects arising out of more sophisticated pictures, such as the optical model (Chapter V.C) and direct interaction (Chapter V.D), one must first know what the predictions from the statistical model would have been. It is therefore intended to discuss here as much as the statistical theory as is needed for these two applications.

The statistical model was of course never at any time supposed to apply to all types of nuclear reactions. It eschews any description of resonance phenomena, and in fact is particularly aimed at situations in which the resonances are so closely spaced compared to their width that at any one incident neutron energy a statistical average of the levels is excited. The detailed assumptions involved are elaborated below.

2. Assumptions of the Statistical Theory

The statistical theory is based upon a number of assumptions:

(a) *Compound Nucleus Formation.* It is assumed first that the Bohr picture of a nuclear reaction holds: The incident nucleon initially forms a compound nucleus which lasts for a time long compared to the nucleon period within the nucleus. The compound nucleus then decays into one or another of the various reaction channels.

(b) *Continuum of Compound Nucleus Levels.* The excitation of the compound nucleus corresponding to the incident nucleon energy is taken to be so high that the levels formed overlap strongly, forming a continuum. It is indeed assumed that the overlapping is so extensive that for each incident energy so many states of given quantum numbers, such as J, parity, etc., are formed that a *statistical average* is obtained over all possible phases among the states.

(c) *Independence Hypothesis.* The mode of decay of the compound nucleus is taken to be independent of its method of formation, but to depend only on the quantum parameters of the system— E, J, parity, etc., and the properties of the particular decay channel involved. This independence assumption enables the cross section for a given mode of decay to be factored into the cross section for formation of the compound nucleus times the probability for the compound nucleus to decay by the given route.

The previous statistical averaging hypothesis further ensures that in the probability for decay in any one channel the interference terms between states of various l or J will cancel out, since the phases between states will be random. Hence, the separate, say J- or spin-, contributions will be additive in cross section rather than in scattering amplitudes. We can thus speak of the cross section for a process resulting in a final state summarized by quantum numbers β, and write it in the form

$$\sigma(\alpha,\beta) \;=\; \sigma_c(\alpha)P(\alpha,\beta) \tag{1}$$

Here $\sigma_c(\alpha)$ is the probability for forming the compound nucleus and $P(\alpha,\beta)$ is the probability for decay into the β state. The cross section for a given reaction, say inelastic scattering, would then be obtained by summing (1) over all states α and β consistent with the reaction.

Friedman and Weisskopf (Fr55) have pointed out that while the independence hypothesis should unquestionably be valid in the isolated resonance region, it is on particularly shaky grounds when the continuum of compound nucleus levels, postulated in assumption (b), is formed.   If the levels of the compound nucleus are far apart compared to their width only one level can be excited at a given energy and there is no interference with other states.   Such a level is practically a "pure" quantum state, whose properties must necessarily depend only on the "good" quantum numbers describing it. But if the levels overlap widely, then what is formed in the continuum is a mixture of a number of states with unspecified phases between them.   These phases should initially depend on the method of forming the compound nucleus, and there is no guarantee that the probability of decay by a given mode does not depend on the phases.   It is hoped, however, that the requirement of assumption (b) that very many states be excited will lead to a distribution of compound nucleus states at the time of decay which is independent of the mode of formation.

As is well known, there is considerable experimental evidence that the compound nucleus assumption (a) has only limited validity. Nuclear reactions can take place by other than compound nucleus formation (e.g., by direct interaction).   Even where an incoming nucleon eventually shares its energy with the target nucleus to form a compound nucleus, it may initially move as an independent particle in the potential of the target nucleus (optical model).   The validity of the independence hypothesis [assumption (c)] has received much less experimental attention.   As far as the meager available evidence goes [summarized by Kinsey (Ki57), LeCouteur (Le59), and Douglas and MacDonald (Do59)] it would appear that under conditions when both assumptions (a) and (b) hold, then the decay of the compound nucleus is indeed independent of the mode of formation.

The three assumptions discussed so far can be considered as adequate foundation for a statistical model of nuclear reactions. They are all that's needed, for example, in the treatment of reactions leading to a discrete number of well separated final states.   We shall call a theory involving only these assumptions the *partial statistical model*.   The term *"complete statistical model"* or just *"statistical model"* will be reserved to a theory in which two further assumptions are made:

(d) *Continuum of Final States*.   In each accessible mode of decay (inelastic scattering, charged particle reactions, fission, etc.) the states of the residual system form a continuum of levels, similar to that assumed for the compound nucleus. For each mode of decay there are thus many channels available, corresponding to the various final states. In contrast elastic scattering involves only one channel, or at most two if spin-flipping can occur without change of energy. It seems, therefore, reasonable to assume:

(e) *Absence of Compound Elastic Scattering.* The compound nucleus has so many open channels available, that the probability that it decays by emitting a single particle of the same type and energy as the incident particle is taken to be negligible.

Elastic scattering thus does not take place through the intermediary of a compound nucleus, but occurs in the statistical model only as the diffraction of the incident nucleon beam by the target nucleus. Predictions of the angular distribution of elastic scattering on the basis of the statistical model have been made (Fe51), but inasmuch as these have been superseded almost entirely by the quite different results of the optical model they will not be further discussed here.

Solely for convenience in calculating the cross section for formation of the compound nucleus it is customary, following Weisskopf, to use a simplified nuclear model based on the following two auxiliary assumptions:

(i) The nuclear interaction potential extends only to a sharply defined nuclear radius R and is zero beyond it.

(ii) Despite the postulated prompt formation of the compound nucleus it is assumed that *immediately* inside the nuclear radius the incoming nucleon travels as an independent particle in a square potential well. Crudely this well is of such a depth that the top of the Fermi distribution for the nucleons already in the nucleus is just below the top of the well. The only purpose of this assumption is to provide boundary conditions for the outside wave function at the nuclear surface. As will be seen many of the predictions of the theory are reasonably independent of the assumed depth of the interior well.

3. General Predictions of the Statistical Theory

A. The Cross Section for Compound Nucleus Formation

The nuclear model discussed above makes no provision for spin-orbit coupling, or any other dependence of the nuclear forces on spin. Under these conditions it can be shown that the predictions from the statistical model are then the same as if the particles and nuclei involved had zero spin. In words, the argument goes something as follows. Since the scattering amplitudes do not depend on spin or total angular momentum, but at most only on orbital angular momentum l for an unpolarized incident beam, the particle spins and J can enter in only in the enumeration of the number of possible quantum states with given l. But this is clearly independent of the way in which one counts the states, and it might just as well be done entirely in terms of l only, without mention of the other angular momentum numbers.

The expressions for the various cross sections on the basis of the statistical model have been derived in a number of places, notably Fe49 and Bl52a; it will suffice here to sketch the main outlines of the derivations. Outside the nucleus there will be a wave function associated with the incident particle at energy E determined by the wave equation

$$\nabla^2 \psi + [k^2 - (2\mu/\hbar^2)V(r)]\psi = 0, \quad r \geq R \tag{2}$$

Here k is the wave number the particle would have in the absence of any potential:

$$k = 1/\lambda = (2\mu E)^{1/2}/\hbar \tag{3}$$

μ is the reduced mass, and V is the external, nonnuclear, potential of the target. For a neutron V would be zero; for a charged particle it would be a Coulomb field or some screened version thereof.

The incident part of the wave function can be written as a series:

$$\psi_{\text{inc}} = (2kr)^{-1} \sum_l (2l + 1)i^{l+1}[u_l^-(r) - u_l^+(r)]P_l(\cos\theta) \tag{4}$$

The radial wave functions u_l^- and u_l^+ are such that at large distances from the target they correspond to incoming and outgoing spherical waves respectively. For neutrons, for example, the asymptotic forms of u_l^- and u_l^+ are

$$u_l^{\pm}(r) \rightarrow e^{\pm ik(r - l\pi/2)} \tag{5}$$

The total wave function must differ from (4) only in the magnitude of the outgoing part of the wave function, and so can be written as

$$\psi = (2kr)^{-1} \sum (2l + 1)i^{l+1}[u_l^-(r) - \eta_l u_l^+(r)]P_l(\cos\theta) \tag{6}$$

where η_l is the complex scattering amplitude. The difference between ψ and ψ_{inc} will be the elastically scattered wave:

$$\psi_S = (2kr)^{-1} \sum_l (2l + 1)i^{l+1}(1 - \eta_l)u_l^+(r)P_l(\cos \theta) \qquad (7)$$

The elastic scattering cross section, here designated as σ_S, can be evaluated from (7) by calculating the scattered current divided by the incident flux, with the result that

$$\sigma_S = (\pi/k^2) \sum_l (2l + 1)|1 - \eta_l|^2 \qquad (8)$$

On the basis of assumption (e), the statistical model provides that the loss of particles from the state at incident energy E must all correspond to compound nucleus formation, since compound elastic scattering will not occur. Hence, the cross section for formation of the compound nucleus is determined by the ratio of the absorbed current to the incident flux. In turn, the absorbed current can be found from ψ, (6), and will consist of an incoming current, determined by the u^- part, minus an outgoing current, determined from the u^+ term. The result is

$$\sigma_c = (\pi/k^2) \sum_l (2l + 1)(1 - |\eta_l|)^2 \qquad (9)$$

Except for the identification of (9) as the compound nucleus cross section the statistical model has not been used in the preceding. The specific values of η_l will clearly depend, however, on the assumptions of the model. Before indicating the procedure for evaluating the η_l's it is convenient to introduce a different terminology, based on the fact that the u_l radial wave functions are solutions of a one-dimensional problem with effective potential

$$U(r) = V(r) + \frac{\hbar^2}{2\mu r^2} l(l + 1)$$

Thus u_l^- can be looked on as the one-dimensional wave function incident on the barrier U from the right and u_l^+ would correspond to a wave travelling away from the barrier (cf. Fig. 1). In accordance with the statistical model assumptions, the wave function immediately to the left of R corresponds only to a wave travelling only to the left, i.e., the transmitted wave. For $r \geq R$ the wave function is the sum of an incident and reflected wave:

$$u_l = u_l^- - \eta_l u_l^+$$

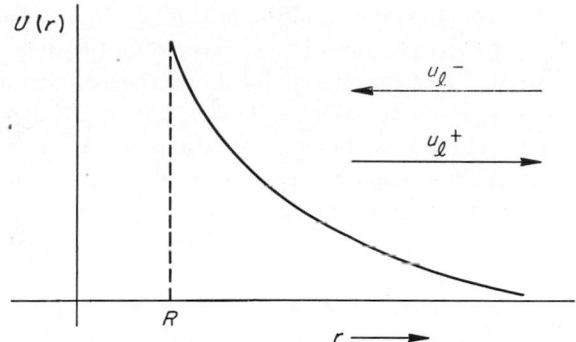

Figure 1. The one-dimensional barrier for calculating transmission coefficients.

with reflection coefficient η_l^2 and transmission coefficient

$$T_l = 1 - |\eta_l|^2 \tag{10}$$

Hence σ_c can also be written as

$$\sigma_c = \sum_l \pi \lambda^2 (2l + 1) T_l(E) \tag{11}$$

The transmission coefficients T_l are frequently referred to in the literature as *penetrabilities*.

The values of η_l, and therefore T_l, can be determined in the usual manner, by matching wave functions and first derivative at the boundary $r = R$. In particular, the matching condition can be expressed solely in terms of the logarithmic derivative

$$f_l = R \left[\frac{1}{\mu} \frac{du}{dr} \right]_{r=R}$$

The statistical model requires that just inside the nucleus the wave function be that of an incoming wave

$$u \sim e^{-iKr}$$

where K is the wave number corresponding to the assumed internal potential. The logarithmic derivative required at the boundary is therefore

$$f_l = iKR \equiv -iX. \tag{12}$$

The subsequent evaluation of η_l, and T_l, is then straightforward although (especially for charged particles) often very tedious.

Clearly, f_l, will be in general a function of l, E, X, R, and the charges of the incident particle and target. For neutrons the only variables are l, kR, and X. The functional forms of the penetrabilities for neutrons have been given in Bl52a, and extensive graphs will be found in Fe51. With charged particles evaluation of the T_l's requires lengthy numerical calculations: Shapiro (Fe53) has given extensive tables for the strict statistical model assumed here. Modifications of the penetrabilities in the framework of the optical model will be discussed below.

At very high energies T_l clearly goes to unity (and η_l goes to zero); the incident energy is so large compared to the barrier that there is complete transmission and zero reflection. For very small energies the penetrabilities for neutrons go as

$$T_l(x,X) \rightarrow \left[\frac{(l-1)!}{(2l-1)!} \right]^2 \frac{xX}{X^2 + l^2} (2x)^{2l}, \ l \geq 1 \tag{13}$$

When $l = 0$, the low energy behavior of T_0 is

$$T_0(x,X) \rightarrow 4x/X \tag{14}$$

Hence for all l, T_l varies as $E^{l+1/2}$ for small E. Especially at higher angular moments the penetrability is very small at low energies and then rises rapidly to unity when x reaches the vicinity of l. Indeed for high angular momenta a first crude approximation to T_l is a unit step function with the break at $x = l$. This picture can be used to obtain a limiting sum for the series in (11) at high energies where many angular momentum terms are present. The penetrabilities can then be taken as unity for all l through a limiting value L, where $L = x \equiv R/\lambda$ and zero for higher l, so that

$$\sigma_c = \pi\lambda \sum_{l=0}^{L} (2l + 1) = \pi\lambda^2(L + 1)^2 = \pi(R + \lambda)^2 \tag{15}$$

On the other hand at low energies the $l = 0$ term predominates and $\sigma_c(E)/\pi R^2$ decreases with increasing energy as $4/xX$. As the energy increases the ratio $\sigma_c(E)/\pi R^2$ approaches an asymptotic value of unity, independent of X. Figure 2, taken from Bl52a shows the energy behavior of the cross section for compound nucleus formation as calculated in more detail.

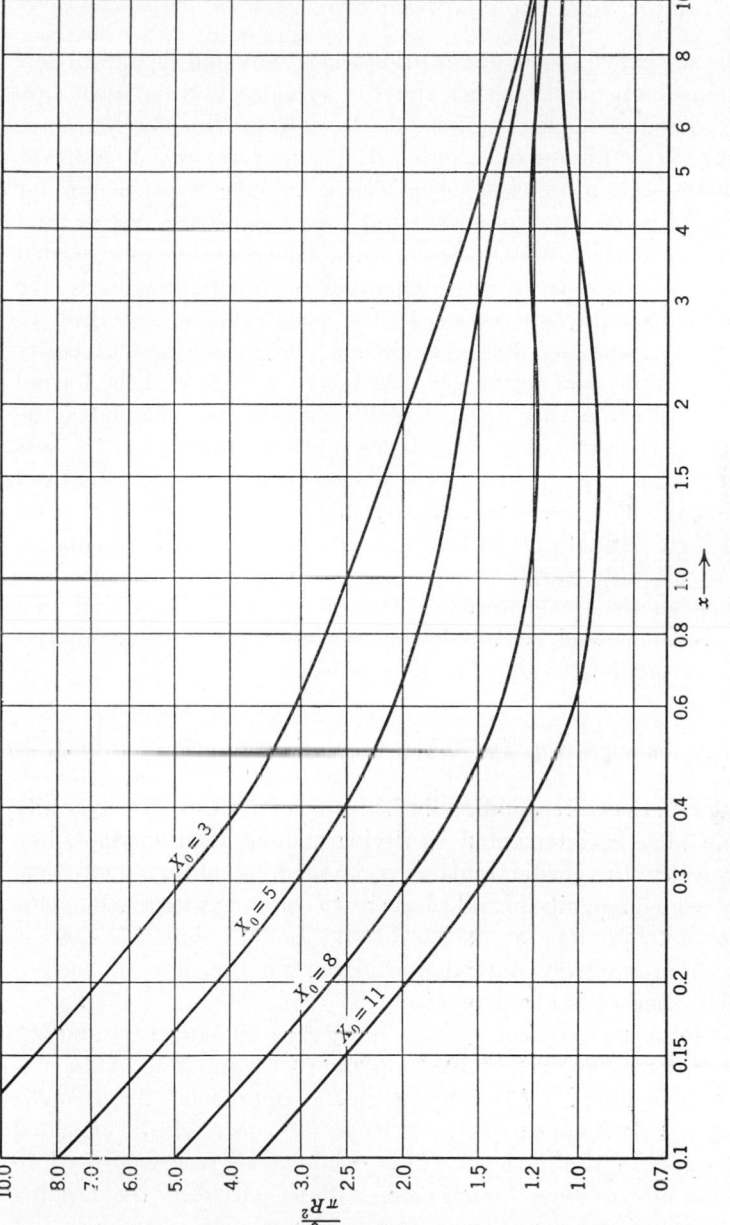

Figure 2. Cross section for the formation of the compound nucleus by neutrons. The abscissa is $x = kR = 0.218\epsilon^{1/2}R$ if ϵ is given in Mev, R in 10^{-13} cm. $X_0 = K_0R$ and is roughly equal to the nuclear radius in units of 10^{-13} cm. (Reproduced with permission from J. M. Blatt and V. F. Weis kcpf, *Theoretical Nuclear Physics*, John Wiley & Sons, 1952.)

B. *The Inelastic Scattering and Total Cross Sections*

The statistical model assumption that compound elastic scattering is vanishingly small implies that the cross section for formation of the compound nucleus, σ_c, is identical with the reaction cross section σ_R. In addition to σ_c or σ_R the total cross section involves σ_S the cross section for elastic scattering, i.e., the cross section for scattering without change of energy in the center-of-mass system (and in principle scattering without spin flip). To calculate σ_c one needed only the absolute value of η_l which could be directly related to the easily visualized physical concept of a penetrability, T_l. For σ_S the complete expression for η_l is needed and in a form not easily susceptible to physical argument. As has been indicated the formal procedure for evaluating η_l is straightforward: one calculates the logarithmic derivative of ψ, (6), at the nuclear surface $r = R$, sets it equal to the value assumed by the statistical model, (12), and solves for η_l. The result will clearly involve the values of u^- and u^+, and their derivatives, at the nuclear surface, with l, kR, and X being the ultimate variables. It would be pointless to reproduce the rather lengthy final formulae; they are reproduced in Fe49 and Bl52a. But it should be noted, that for $kR = x \gg 1$ (in practice $x > 8$), the predicted value for σ_S approaches

$$\sigma_S \to \pi(R + \lambda)^2 \tag{15a}$$

identical with the corresponding limiting form (15) for σ_c. Physically the result may be interpreted as saying that at high energies, i.e., short wavelength, elastic scattering is predominantly small-angle and is of such a magnitude and phase as to combine with the incident wave so as to produce a shadow in the forward direction. As is familiar from ordinary optical considerations the area of such a diffraction shadow is given precisely by (15a).

The total cross section σ_T is given by the sum of $\sigma_c \equiv \sigma_R$ and σ_S; Fig. 4.4 in Chapter VIII of Bl52a portrays the predicted values as functions of x and X. At high energies σ_T approaches $2\pi(R + \lambda)^2$ which at first sight appears to be twice as large as might be expected from the area of the nucleus. This result arises from the need to include the shadow cross section along with σ_R. By now the paradox and its resolution have become familiar from many examples not only in neutron scattering but in optics and acoustics, and no further comment is needed.

So far nothing has been said of the value of the parameter K, the wave number for the assumed potential. If we use the picture of a square well for the potential then the internal wave number is given by

$$K = (K_0^2 + k^2)^{1/2}$$

where $$K_0 - (2\mu V)^{1/2}/\hbar$$

V being the depth of the well. Originally Weisskopf (Fe49, Bl52a) presented arguments that V should be identified with the top of the Fermi gas distribution for the A particles contained in the nucleus. This predicts a well about 25 Mev deep, and a value of K_0 of about 1.0×10^{13} cm^{-1}. It is tempting nowadays to identify the internal potential of this statistical model with the single-particle potential of the optical model (see Chapter V.C). The best estimates of the well depth (at least real part) are now of the order of 50 Mev (Fe60), corresponding to K_0 about 1.4×10^{13} cm^{-1}. In any case the predictions of the statistical model are nearly independent of K or K_0 except at very low energies where the statistical model is not to be believed in anyhow.

C. Strength Functions

An important parameter in the optical model of the nucleus is the *strength function*

$$S_\nu = \bar{\Gamma}_{n\nu}/\bar{D}_\nu \tag{16}$$

where $\Gamma_{n\nu}$ and D_ν are resonance neutron widths and separations respectively, the bars denote averaging over many resonances, and the subscript ν refers to some set of distinguishing quantum numbers such as l and J. The optical model predictions of the value of S_ν differ radically from those of continuum or statistical model, and it is therefore of some interest to indicate what the statistical model does say about the strength function.

The connection between the resonance phenomena implicit in the strength function definition and the statistical model can be obtained by mathematically averaging the resonance structure over many overlapping levels, as was done by Feshbach and Weisskopf (Fe49). The same results can however be obtained, or at least made plausible, by an argument originated by Weisskopf.[1]

Even where levels overlap $\Gamma_{n\nu}$ preserves its meaning as $\hbar$ times the probability per unit time of a state of the ν type decaying by emission of a neutron. We may consider the process by imagining the neutron wave packet inside the nucleus incident on the surface $1/P$ times per unit time. But in the same interval the number of times it escapes is $\Gamma_{n\nu}/\hbar$. Hence the neutron transmission coefficient from inside to outside, denoted by T_ν' is

$$T_\nu' = P\Gamma_{n\nu}/\hbar$$

It is next observed that for a number of well known systems— particle in a well, Bohr orbits, etc.—when there are many stationary states possible the particle period P is related to the average spacing of levels by $\bar{D}_\nu$ by

$$P = 2\pi\hbar/\bar{D}_\nu$$

Hence $$\bar{\Gamma}_{n\nu}/\bar{D}_\nu = \bar{T}_\nu'/2\pi \tag{17}$$

Further, the average transmission coefficient $\bar{T}_\nu'$ can, by a time reversal argument, be identified with the penetrabilities T calculated above for the statistical model. At low energies such that $x \ll X$, the expression for T reduce to (cf. Bl52a, p. 360)

$$T_l = (4k/K_0)v_l \tag{18}$$

where v_l is a rational function of x and X for each l.

From the theory of resonances (cf. Chapter V.E) it can also be noted that the width $\Gamma_{n\nu}$ can be written as

$$\Gamma_{n\nu} = 2kRv_l\gamma_\nu \tag{19}$$

where γ_ν is the energy independent "reduced width." Historically, a differently defined reduced width was introduced by experimenters for the case of $l = 0$ neutrons. The reduced width $\Gamma_{n_0}^0$ as this simply Γ referred to some convenient reference energy E_0, conventionally 1 ev. Since $v_l = 1$ for $l = 0$ neutrons $\Gamma_{n_0}^0$ is related to Γ_{n_0} by

$$\Gamma_{n_0}^0 = [k(E_0)/k(E)]\Gamma_{n_0} \tag{20}$$

---

[1] Breit (Br59) has given a detailed discussion of the relationship between Weisskopf's simplified physical picture and the more abstract arguments given e.g., by Teichman and Wigner (Te52).

The "reduced strength function" S_0^0 would then be given by

$$S_0^0 \equiv (\bar{\Gamma}_{n_0}^0/D_0) = [k(E_0)/k(E)](\bar{\Gamma}_{n_0}/D_0)$$

$$= (2/\pi)[k(E_0)/K_0] \tag{21}$$

$$= (2/\pi)(E_0/V)^{1/2} \tag{22}$$

where V is the potential corresponding to K_0. If $E_0 = 1$ ev and $V \sim 50$ Mev, then the statistical model predicts through (22) that S_0^0 is about 1×10^{-4}, completely independent of the nucleus.

The convention for the strength functions of higher angular momenta levels has not yet been fixed by practice. Many define the reduced width for l neutrons as

$$\Gamma_{nl}^0 = [k(E_0)/(kv_l)_E]\Gamma_{nl} \tag{23}$$

which has the advantage that the statistical model prediction for the corresponding reduced strength function is identical with (22):

$$S_l^0 = (2/\pi)(E_0/V)^{1/2} \tag{24}$$

With this manner of reducing the measured neutron widths the predicted strength function on the basis of the statistical model has the value of $\sim 1 \times 10^{-4}$ apparently independent of nuclear mass or size or neutron angular momentum. The nuclear radius does however enter in determining v_l used in (23).

A reduced strength function can also be defined in terms of the reduced width γ_ν, favored by many theorists. Here the statistical model prediction would be

$$\bar{\gamma}_\nu/\bar{D} = 1/\pi K_0 R \tag{25}$$

which is also independent of neutron angular momentum but would exhibit an explicit dependence on nuclear radius R. Finally it should be mentioned that a number of theorists employ a reduced width γ^2 related to γ by

$$\gamma^2 = \gamma R \tag{26}$$

The corresponding strength function has the predicted value

$$\overline{\gamma_\nu^2}/\bar{D} = 1/\pi K_0 \tag{27}$$

Unlike the previous definitions, this strength function has dimensions, that of a length. According to the statistical model its universal value should be about 0.45×10^{-13} cm.

4. Reaction Cross Sections in the Partial Statistical Model

A. Cross Sections Integrated Over All Angle

Consider a reaction on a target nucleus specified by an incident particle at energy E and an emergent particle at energy E'. It is assumed that the conditions—compound nucleus formation, statistical continuum of compound nucleus levels, and independence hypothesis—of the partial statistical model hold (cf. Section 2). Then the cross section for this reaction, integrated over all solid angle of the emergent particle is given by

$$\sigma(\alpha|\alpha') = \pi\lambda^2 \sum_{J,j,l,j',l'} \frac{2J+1}{(2i+1)(2I+1)} \frac{T^J_{\alpha'j'l'} T^J_{\alpha jl}}{\sum\limits_{\alpha'',j'',l''} T^J_{\alpha''j''l''}} \qquad (28)$$

when

$I \;=\;$ target nucleus spin
$i \;=\;$ incident particle spin
$l \;=\;$ orbital angular momentum of the incident particle
$j \;=\;$ channel spin of the incident particle $(j = I + i = J - l)$
$l' \;=\;$ orbital angular momentum of the emerging particle
$j' \;=\;$ channel spin of the emergent particle $(j' = J - l')$
$\alpha \;=\;$ channel designation for the initial system of incident particle and target nucleus; it includes energy of incident particle, type (neutron, proton, etc.), and state of excitation of target nucleus
$\alpha' \;=\;$ channel designation for the final system of emergent particle and residual nucleus; it includes type and energy of emergent particle and excitation of residual nucleus
$T \;=\;$ penetrability

The sums in (28) are not unrestricted; they are subject to the conservation laws, for example, of energy and parity. Conservation of angular momenta and the definitions of the channel spins require that terms be included in the sums only when

$$|J - l| \leq j \leq J + l$$
$$|I - i| \leq j \leq I + i$$
$$|J - l'| \leq j' \leq J + l'$$
$$|I' - i'| \leq j' \leq I + i'$$

The summation over the double primed quantities in the denominator represents a sum over all possible ways in which it is permissible for the compound nucleus to decay when the decay represented by $\alpha'j'l'$ can occur. Thus if the reaction considered is a neutron inelastic scattering leading to an excited state E_1, the sum contains all terms arising from *elastic* scattering with the given J and l, all possible ways of inelastic scattering from the stated level consistent with J and parity—including the j', l' term, all possible inelastic scattering from levels other than E_1 consistent with J, parity and total energy, all possible channels with outgoing charged particles again under the same conditions and finally all radiative transitions satisfying the same conditions.[2]

The derivation for (28), either in the general form stated or applied to specific situations, has been given by a number of authors. The first derivations, nearly simultaneous, were by Wolfenstein (Wo51) and by Hauser and Feshbach (Ha52). Subsequently proofs have been given in Feld *et al.* (Fe51), Lane and Thomas (La58), and Feshbach (Fe60a). The derivations are all quite elaborate and in most cases the physical content is lost sight of in the overwhelming mass of formalism. For the present purposes it may be sufficient to describe in a general manner the physical origin of the various terms in (18). The factor

$$(2J + 1)/[(2i + 1)(2I + 1)]$$

is easily recognized as a statistical weight factor representing a sum over projections of J and an averaging over projections of i and I (only unpolarized reactions are considered). It appears as the end result of considerable manipulation of angular momentum factors. The term $\pi\lambda^2 T^J_{\alpha jl}$ derives from the cross section for formation of the compound nucleus by a particle α with the quantum numbers J, j, and l. Finally, the remainder represents the probability that the compound nucleus so formed will decay by emission of a particle α', orbital angular momentum l and channel spin j'. This can most simply be seen by remembering from the discussion in Section 3.C that the penetrabilities T are proportional to the widths for decay of the given state. Thus in (28) the factor $T^J_{\alpha'j'l'}/\sum\limits_{\alpha''j''l''} T^J_{\alpha''j''l''}$

is the same as the ratio of probabilities $\Gamma'/\Sigma\Gamma''$, where the sum in the denominator consists of Γ' plus the widths of all possible modes of decay competing with Γ'. Each term in the main summation is a product of a cross section for formation times a probability for decay.

---

[2] The penetrabilities to be used for the radiative capture terms will be discussed later in this section.

In the absence of spin-orbit interactions the penetrabilities should involve l only, independent of j and J. If the incident and emerging particles are neutrons (or any spin $1/2$ particles) then j can at most have two values, $j_{1,2} = I \pm 1/2$. Under these circumstances, the sums over j and j' can be performed explicitly and the cross section represented as a sum over l of the contributions from the various J values possible at each l:

$$\sigma(\alpha|\alpha') = \frac{\pi\lambda^2}{2(2I+1)} \sum_l T_{\alpha l} \sum_j \frac{\epsilon^J_{j,l'}(2J+1) \sum_{l'} \epsilon^J_{j',l'} T_{\alpha'l'}}{\sum_{l''} \epsilon^J_{j'',l''} T_{\alpha''l''}} \tag{29}$$

Here $\epsilon^J_{j,l}$ is a quantity such that

$$\epsilon^J_{j,l} = 2 \text{ if } J \text{ is such that both channel spins satisfy}$$
$$|J - l| \leq j \leq (J + l),$$
$$= 1 \text{ if } J \text{ is such that only one of the channel spins satisfies}$$
$$\text{the above inequality, and}$$
$$= 0 \text{ for all other values of } J.$$

Thus $\epsilon^J_{j,l}$ automatically includes the degeneracy of T with j, and restricts the angular momentum quantum to those permitted by the definition of the channel spins. Parity conservation must still be additionally included. It should be remembered that α includes the energies of the particle and nuclear states involved.

The original model on which (28) was formulated assumed that the penetrabilities would be obtained from the black nucleus picture as described in Section 3.A. This is not an inevitable consequence of the model, however, and more sophisticated pictures can be employed. It is customary now to take the penetrabilities, or their near cousins, the cross sections for compound nucleus formation, from some complex potential calculation (cf. Chapter V.C). Compilations of such penetrabilities are scarce. Monahan, Biedenharn, and Schiffer (Mo58) have issued one tabulation based on a simple square well, which is now considered unrealistic. Beyster, Walt, and Salmi (Be56) used a diffuse-edge well, but their choices of Z and E are too widely spaced to permit easy interpolation, especially in view of the non-smooth way the well parameters varied. More recently Campbell, Feshbach, Porter, and Weisskopf (Ca60) have issued a more extensive compilation using similar potentials but different parameters. Spin-orbit potentials (for which T would be dependent on J as well as l) were not included. There is great need for detailed and systematic calculation of the T's using a complex potential model complete enough to describe known interactions properly, over a wide range of parameters, and for both neutrons and charged particles. Failing that, there should at least be available a sufficiently complete and sophisticated machine code in some generally usable language that could be accepted as a standard.

Where radiative capture is present, the penetrabilities involved are obtained from the corresponding widths by the relation

$$T_\gamma^J = 2\pi(\bar{\Gamma}_\gamma/\bar{D}^J) \tag{30}$$

$\bar{D}^J$ is the average level spacing at the incident energy E for given J. Equation (30) is the counterpart of the corresponding relation for neutron widths discussed in Section 3.C on strength functions, and is essentially the relation used in the derivation of (28) to replace widths by penetrabilities. To be consistent, there should be a term T_γ^J for each initial radiative transition for which parity and total angular momentum considerations are satisfied. In practice it is assumed that the sum radiation width for all transitions involved with a given J is independent of J. Similar approximations are often used for example if fission reaction competition is present, the fission channels being represented by a single fission width, independent of energy. Calculations in this manner for inelastic scattering, radiative capture and fission in U^{235} have been calculated by Rae, Margolis, and Troubetzkoy (Ra58). It might also be remarked that the competition of a charged particle reaction, in the absence of detailed penetrabilities, often has to be represented by a single energy-dependent width, sometimes chosen so that the experimental charged particle cross section is consistently described by the calculation.

One further assumption lies buried in the derivation of (28) or (29). The terms in the summation are ratios of products and sums of widths. As the formula is used the widths are interpreted as average widths over statistical distribution of levels in the compound nucleus. Actually the averaging sign occurs over products and ratios of widths. It is implicitly assumed that these can be replaced by products and ratios of average widths. Where only a few channels of decay are available, for example elastic scattering and radiative capture at low energies, it is known that as a result of the fluctuations in the elastic width the assumption breaks down badly (cf. Chapter V.M, Section 3). What occurs at high energies is not known, although it is felt that where there are sufficient channels for decay of the compound nucleus such fluctuation phenomena are probably not significant (cf. the discussion by Feshbach, Fe60a, p. 664f.).

Fluctuation phenomena manifest themselves in another way—when the number of levels excited at one time in the compound nucleus is not enough to satisfy the condition of a statistically independent distribution. Suppose, for example that the excitation of many levels is brought about by using an incident beam of particles distributed over an energy band. If the band width is not large enough too few levels may be excited to provide a complete statistical averaging. As the average energy is varied the cross section will then show fluctuations corresponding to fluctuations in the properties—number, widths, interferences—of the levels excited at any specific average energy. Thus, the cross section predicted by (28) should therefore be a smooth averaged variation about which the observed cross section fluctuates to a greater or lesser extent. There have been a number of qualitative discussions [e.g., Ericson (Er60)] of these fluctuations, but very little is known quantitatively. Feshbach and collaborators (unpublished) have shown that for certain simplified models the variance of the fluctuation distribution can be very large. At any rate the existence of these fluctuations must make one cautious of interpreting any deviation from the average predictions of the statistical model as indicating the presence of some different mode of nuclear interaction.

B. Angular Distribution of Reaction Products

Carried several steps backward, the derivation of (28) involves the differential cross section in angle, given as

$$\sigma(\alpha \,|\, \alpha', \Omega) = \left(\frac{\lambda^2}{4}\right) \sum_{J,j,l,j',l',L} \frac{(-1)^{j'-j}}{(2i+1)(2I+1)} \frac{T^J{}_{\alpha jl} T^J{}_{\alpha'j'l'}}{\sum\limits_{\alpha''j''l''} T^J{}_{\alpha''j''l''}}$$

$$\times \bar{Z}(lJlJ;jL)\bar{Z}(l'Jl'J;j'L)P_L(\cos\theta) \quad (31)$$

The $\bar{Z}$ factors are angular momentum quantities that arise from the decomposition of incident plane wave into states of given quantum numbers, J, l, j, parity, of the decay of the intermediate system into final states j' and l', and of the squaring of the overall wave function and subsequent expansion into Legendre polynomials $P_L(\cos\theta)$. The circumstance that the indices l, J or l', J repeat in the $\bar{Z}$ factors arises from the statistical averaging assumption in which interference between different states in the compound nucleus is taken to average out. As a result when the cross section is formed involving the products of wave functions, only those terms are retained involving products with the same l and J values. The same cancellation of interference terms means that no polarization can result from the reaction and since the incident beam is assumed unpolarized the cross section depends only on the polar angle. In terms of Clebsch-Gordan and Racah W coefficients the $\bar{Z}$ factors are given as

$$\bar{Z}(lJlJ; jL) = (2l + 1)(2J + 1)(ll00|L0)W(lJlJ; jL) \qquad (32)$$

Here $(ll00|L0)$ is the Clebsch-Gordan coefficient for the coupling of two states l, $m_l = 0$ to form the angular momentum L, $m_L = 0$. The $\bar{Z}$ factors are those used by Lane and Thomas (La58), they are connected to the Z factor introduced by Blatt and Biedenharn (Bl52) through a different choice of time-reversal convention:

$$\bar{Z}(lJlJ; jL) = i^{-L}Z(l_1Jl_2J; jL) \qquad (32a)$$

One of the properties of the $Z(l_1Jl_2J; jL)$ factors is that they vanish unless $l_1 + l_2 + L$ is even. In the case of (30) this means that the only nonvanishing terms in the L summation are those for which $2l + L$ is even, i.e., L is even. In turn L even implies that the *angular distribution must be symmetric around* $90°$. Clearly this symmetry arises from the cancellation of interference terms for that is what led to the common l indices in the $\bar{Z}$ factors. But this conclusion can be seen more directly and physically. The angular dependence of each l term on the initial or final wave function goes as $P_l(\cos\theta)$. The statistical cancellation assumption means that in the product wave function only products of terms of the same l remain, i.e., the angular distribution can only contain terms of the form $P_l^2(\cos\theta)$, which assures the symmetry about $90°$.

Numerous compilations of Clebsch-Gordan, W, and Z coefficients exist. For present purposes the most useful are probably those of Biedenharn and Simon (Bi54), the range of L from 0 to 8, probably as high as needed, but the channel spin is limited to 3 or less. For higher values the tables of Racah coefficients published by Obi *et al.* (Ob55), would prove helpful.

5. Reaction Cross Sections in the Complete Statistical Model

A. *Cross Sections Integrated Over All Angle*

In the complete statistical model it is assumed that there is a continuum of residual states available having a statistical distribution of quantum numbers. One of these states corresponds to elastic scattering, but its contribution is negligible and need not be particularly singled out. The cross sections under these conditions can most directly be obtained by summing the formulas of the preceding section over the continuum of states of interest. Since energy is now a continuous variable we will display it explicitly. For simplicity competing decay channels corresponding to radiative transition or fission will be ignored, so that the index α refers only to the particle type, e.g., neutron, proton, alpha particle, etc. Parity considerations can be safely ignored, since the continuum is assumed to have equal populations of both parities in all states.

Under these conditions consider the cross section for particle α with energy E for reactions leading to particles α' with energy E' and dE'. The residual nucleus will be left in states of energy $\epsilon' = E - E' - Q$, where Q is the reaction energy involved. For inelastic scattering, where target and residual nucleus are the same, Q is of course zero. The density of levels at excitation ϵ' with spin I' will be designated as $\omega_{\alpha'}(I', E')$. The cross section of interest involves a sum over all the residual spins I' at ϵ' consistent with angular momentum conservation conditions. Equation (28) then becomes:

$$\sigma_{\alpha,\alpha'}(E; E')dE' = \pi \lambda^2 \sum_{J,j,l} \frac{2J + 1}{(2i + 1)(2I + 1)}$$

$$\frac{T^J_{\alpha j l}(E) \sum_{J'l'I'} T^J_{\alpha'j'l'}(E')\omega_{\alpha'}(I', \epsilon')dE'}{\sum_{\alpha''j''l''I''} \int_0^{E-Q} dE'' \, T^J_{\alpha''j''l''}(E)\omega_{\alpha''}(I'',\epsilon'')d\epsilon''} \quad (33)$$

with the cross section now written in the standard notation.

To reduce (33) to the form familiar in the literature two further assumptions must be made. The first is that the density function

ω has a factorable spin dependence and that this dependence is in fact just $2I + 1$:

$$\omega(I', \epsilon') = (2I' + 1)\omega(\epsilon') \tag{34}$$

The nature and limitations of this assumption will be discussed later on. Equation (34) permits immediate evaluation of the sums over I' and I''. For fixed j' and i' the values of I' must lie between $|j' - i'|$ and $j' + i'$, and simple enumeration then shows that

$$\sum_{I'} (2I' + 1) = (2j' + 1)(2i' + 1) \tag{35}$$

In both numerator and denominator of (33) the sums over j' and j'' are then of the form

$$\sum_{j'} (2j' + 1)\, T^J_{\alpha'j'l}(E')$$

To perform the sums the second assumption must be made that the penetrabilities do not depend on j' or J but only on l. Where spin-orbit potentials are important this assumption is manifestly incorrect, but is inevitably made in view of present ignorance of the j-dependence of the penetrabilities. The T's can then be taken outside the summations, which for fixed l' and J can now be performed as in (35).

$$\sum_{j'} (2j' + 1) = (2l' + 1)(2J + 1) \tag{36}$$

Equation (36) now takes the form

$$\sigma_{\alpha,\alpha'}(E;\, E')dE' = \pi\lambda^2 \sum_{l,j,J} (2J + 1)\, T_{\alpha l}(E)$$
$$\frac{\sum_{l'} (2i' + 1)(2l' + 1)\, T_{\alpha'l'}(E')\omega_\alpha(\epsilon')dE'}{\sum_{\alpha''} (2i'' + 1) \int_0^{E-Q} \sum_{l''} (2l'' + 1)\, T_{\alpha''l''}(E'')\omega_{\alpha''}(\epsilon'')d\epsilon''} \tag{37}$$

Two further summations can be performed, that over j and J. At constant j and l the summation over J leads, by direct enumeration, to

$$\sum_j (2J + 1) = (2l + 1)(2j + 1)$$

and finally the sum over all states of j yields

$$\sum_j (2j + 1) = (2i + 1)(2I + 1)$$

The summations over j and J therefore reduce simply to[3]

$$\sum_{j,J} \frac{(2J + 1)}{(2i + 1)(2I + 1)} = (2l + 1) \qquad (38)$$

The penetrabilities in the reduced form of (37) now occur only in the combinations $\sum_l (2l + 1)T_l$, which may be recognized from (11) as being proportional to the cross section for formation of the compound nucleus, σ_c. With this substitution (37) takes on the familiar form

$$\sigma_{\alpha,\alpha'}(E; E')dE' = \sigma_{c,\alpha}(E) \frac{(2i' + 1)E'\sigma_{c,\alpha'}(E')\omega_{\alpha'}(\epsilon')dE'}{\sum_{\alpha''}(2i'' + 1)\int_0^{E-Q} E''\sigma_{c,\alpha''}(E'')\omega_{\alpha''}(\epsilon'')d\epsilon''} \qquad (39)$$

where $\sigma_{c,\alpha}(E)$ is the cross section for formation of the compound nucleus by incident particles α at energy E. The total cross section for the reaction α,α', $\sigma_{\alpha,\alpha'}(E)$, can of course be obtained by integrating (39) over E' from 0 to $E - Q$.

Equation (39) has been derived at length from (33) in order to emphasize the explicit introduction of the two assumptions not necessarily inherent in the statistical model. Of the disregard of possible j-dependence of the penetrabilities there is little more that can be said. However the assumed spin-dependence of the level density in (34) calls for some discussion. Various models of the nucleus have been employed to yield conclusions about the level density. Bloch (Bl54) has pointed out that on general grounds the models examined so far lead to a spin dependence of the form

$$\omega \propto \exp[-I^2/2\sigma^2] - \exp[-(I + 1)^2/2\sigma^2] \qquad (40)$$

where σ^2 is an energy dependent parameter that is rather large compared to unity at low excitations and decreases slowly with energy. Equation (40) can be rearranged into the form

$$\omega \propto 2 \exp\left(-\frac{1}{8\sigma^2}\right) \sinh\left(\frac{I + 1/2}{2\sigma^2}\right) \exp\left[-\frac{(I + 1/2)^2}{2\sigma^2}\right] \qquad (41)$$

[3] There is an obvious misprint on p. 311 of La58 where this summation is stated to be unity.

For $2\sigma^2 \gg I + 1/2$ this may be approximated well enough by

$$\omega \propto \left(\frac{2I + 1}{2\sigma^2}\right) \exp\left[-\frac{(I + 1/2)^2}{2\sigma^2}\right] \qquad (42)$$

Only for the stronger requirement $2\sigma^2 \gg (I + 1/2)^2$ does (42) reduce to the simple spin-dependence $(2I + 1)$ of (34). Values of $2\sigma^2$ quoted empirically (Bloch (Bl54), Douglas and MacDonald (Do59), and Hibdon (Hi59)) are the order of 5–10 for excitations in the 7–14 Mev range. Hence the exact spin-dependence (42) could begin to deviate from the approximation (34) even for I as low as 2 or 3. But with the more complete form of (42) the sums over I' and I'', (35) cannot be performed, and the reduction of (33) can go little further. There is no reason why in any particular case (33) cannot be used where these two assumptions are expected to be invalid, and the analysis of experiments should not automatically be based on the simpler form (39).

Equation (39) was originally derived (We40) by much simpler considerations going back to the fundamental assumptions of the statistical model. Since this derivation is more frequently referred to in the textbooks, it may be well to review the procedure briefly here. Details will be found in Blatt and Weisskopf (Bl52a, Chapter VIII). The problems introduced by the two assumptions discussed above are side-stepped by disregarding spins completely. Where only one type of reaction can occur (39) under these conditions reduces to

$$\sigma_{\alpha,\alpha'}(E; E')dE' = \sigma_{c,\alpha}(E) \frac{E'\sigma_{c,\alpha'}(E')\omega_{\alpha_c}(\epsilon')dE'}{\int_0^{E-Q} E''\sigma_{c,\alpha'}(E'')\omega_{\alpha'}(\epsilon'')d\epsilon''} \qquad (43)$$

To derive this form one writes the cross section as a product of a cross section for forming the compound nucleus times the probability for decay in the desired manner:

$$\sigma_{\alpha,\alpha'}(E; E')dE' = \sigma_{c,\alpha}(E)P(E', dE') \qquad (44)$$

If $\Gamma(E)$ is the width for decay of the compound nucleus to a state with emitted energy E', then $P(E', dE')$ can be represented as the ratio of the $\Gamma(E')$ times the number of states at E' in range dE' to the total decay width Γ:

$$P(E', dE') = \frac{\Gamma(E')\omega_\alpha(\epsilon')dE'}{\Gamma} = \frac{\Gamma(E')\omega_\alpha(\epsilon')dE'}{\int_0^{E-Q} \Gamma(E'')\omega_\alpha(\epsilon'')d\epsilon''} \qquad (45)$$

The widths for *decay* of the compound nucleus are now related to the cross section for *formation* of the compound nucleus by an incident particle of energy E', through a reciprocity theorem which states that

$$\Gamma(E') = f(E_i)\,\sigma_{c,\alpha}(E')E' \tag{46}$$

Here $f(E_c)$ is a function only of the compound nucleus and its excitation energy E_c. Equation (46) is the counterpart of (30) linking $\bar{\Gamma}^J$ and the penetrabilities T^J; the function $f(E_c)$ thus involves such quantities as the level spacing in the compound nucleus. Application of (46) for $\Gamma(E')$ leads to a probability

$$P(E', dE') = \frac{\sigma_{c,\alpha'}(E')E'\omega_{\alpha'}(\epsilon')dE'}{\int_0^{E-Q}\sigma_{c,\alpha'}(E'')E''\omega_\alpha(\epsilon'')dE''} \tag{47}$$

which on substitution in (44) immediately leads to the simplified cross section (43).

To use (39) it is necessary to know the functional form of σ_c, the cross section for formation of the compound nucleus, and $\omega(\epsilon)$ the density of energy levels. Historically, values of σ_c obtained from the black nucleus model were employed, as described in Section 3.A. It has now become customary to take σ_c from the predictions of the complex potential mode, either as directly computed or as obtained in terms of the penetrabilities. For high energies there is in fact little difference in the energy variation of σ_c on the two models, although the deviations can become important at low excitations.

The use of the cross sections σ_c borrowed in this way is not, however, without conceptual difficulties. In (39) the first $\sigma_{c,\alpha}(E)$ represents the formation of the compound state by the particle α at energy E incident upon the target nucleus invariably in its ground state. The other σ_c cross sections employed however were derived from consideration of the inverse reaction to form the same compound nucleus. They therefore represent the cross section formation of the compound state by the particle α' at energy E' incident upon an *excited* residual nucleus. The excitation will be all the higher the smaller E'. However all of the σ_c cross sections so far calculated have referred to an unexcited target nucleus. In the black nucleus model such fine distinctions are washed out, but this need not be so with the complex potential model where some variation of the effective potential parameters should be expected with nucleus excitation energy. That the distinction is not without significance may be noted from the fact that with a target nucleus in the ground state σ_c at low energies contains a high proportion of compound elastic scattering. But when the initial nucleus is highly excited the compound nucleus has so many ways to decay that compound elastic scattering must be a negligible part of σ_c.

Considerations of nuclear level density today almost comprise a separate domain of nuclear physics, and it is impossible to describe here the current status of the subject in any detail. Some brief orientation may prove helpful, however. From the derivation of (39) it is clear that what is wanted for ω is the density of states of given total angular momentum and not the density of *all* states at the given excitation energy. By using a model of the nucleus that envisaged a Fermi gas of nucleons in a box Bethe (Be37) showed that the dependence of the level density ω on excitation energy should go as

$$\omega \propto E^{-2} \exp[2(aE)^{1/2}] \tag{48}$$

There have been many refinements on Bethe's original model, in recent years, for example by Bloch (Bl54) and Ross (Ro57), taking different forms for the potentials the nucleons move in and including nucleon-nucleon interactions. But the energy dependence so predicted remains as given in (48). About the most important improvement is an empirical correction to E in the exponent to account for the observed level density changes between even and odd nucleus. Newton (Ne56), elaborating an old suggestion of Hurwitz and Bethe (Hu51), has suggested that E in the exponent should be replaced by

$$E^* = E - c\delta \tag{49}$$

where δ is the pairing energy of the last pairing of the last neutrons or protons, and is roughly $22A^{-1/2}$ Mev. The factor c is zero for odd-odd, $1/2$ for odd-even, and 1 for even-even.

With the level density ω, (48), so modified, the energy-dependence of the emitted particles predicted by (39) is

$$\sigma_{\alpha,\alpha'}(E; E') \propto E'\sigma_{c,\alpha}(E')\epsilon^{-2} \exp[2(a\epsilon)^{1/2}] \tag{50}$$

where here

$$\epsilon = E^* - Q - E' = E - c\delta - Q - E'$$
$$\equiv \bar{E} - E' \tag{51}$$

It often happens that the emitted particle energies E' are small compared to $\bar{E}$. The exponent can then be expanded as

$$2[a(\bar{E} - E')]^{1/2} = 2(a\bar{E})^{1/2}[1 - (E'/2\bar{E})] = 2(a\bar{E})^{1/2} - (a/\bar{E})^{1/2}E'$$

Further in the ϵ^{-2} term E' can be neglected compared to $\bar{E}$. The E'-dependence of $\sigma_{\alpha,\alpha'}$ thus reduces to

$$\sigma_{\alpha,\alpha'}(E; E') \propto \sigma_{c,\alpha}(E')E' \exp\left[-E'/(\bar{E}/a)^{1/2}\right] \tag{52}$$

Equation (52) predicts that $\sigma_{\alpha,\alpha'}(E')/\sigma_{c,\alpha}(E')$ is a Maxwellian with a temperature τ given by

$$\tau = (\bar{E}/a)^{1/2} \tag{53}$$

Experimentally, the temperature can be found from the slope of a suitable plot of $\sigma_{\alpha,\alpha'}$:

$$\tau^{-1} = -\frac{d}{dE'}\left(\ln\frac{\sigma_{\alpha,\alpha'}}{E'\sigma_{c,\alpha}}\right) \tag{54}$$

Many of the older analyses ignored the variation of $\sigma_{c,\alpha}(E')$ with E', but this is surely a worse approximation than making use of one of the calculated cross sections.

It must be emphasized that (52) and (53) are justified on the basis of (50) only if E' is small compared to the maximum excitation energy of the residual nucleus $\bar{E}$. It does not involve much more complexity to analyze the experiment on the basis of (50) or at least insure that the conditions presupposed in (52) are satisfied. There is nothing particularly sacred in the level density form (48) either; the models on which it is based are clearly simplifications of the actual nuclei. A number of other models and modifications often semi-empirical, have been proposed (e.g., Newton (Ne56), Lang and LeCouteur (La54), Cameron (Ca58) but most of these have been concerned with reproducing the variation of ω with nucleur species rather than with excitation energy. In the final analysis the validity of (48) probably depends on the constancy with excitation energy of the constant a derived from experiment. LeCouteur and Lang have recently analysed a variety of experiments at excitation energies ranging from a few Mev to 100 Mev and Fig. 3 is a reproduction of the plot of a vs. A obtained by them from all sources. The agreement in the a values among the various experiments is remarkably good. Similar values of a have been obtained by Thom-

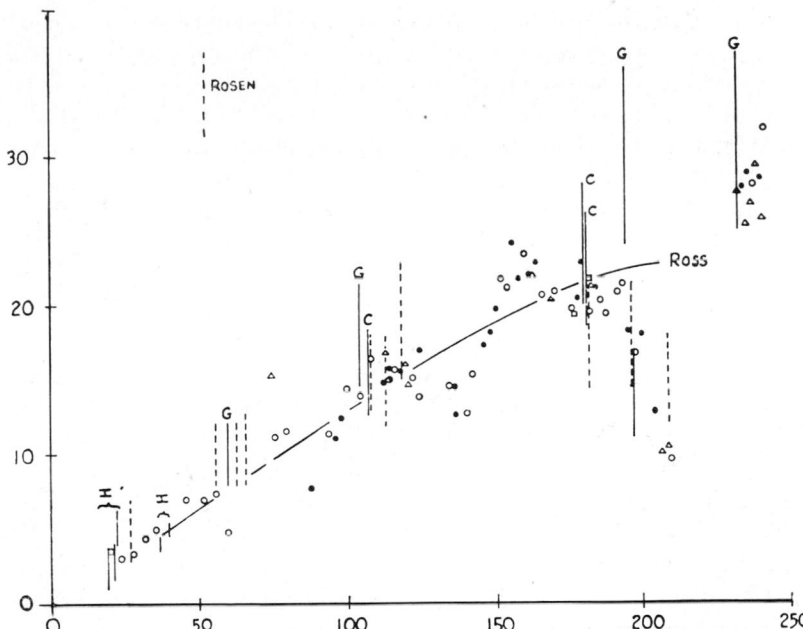

Figure 3. Estimate of a deduced from experiments of Gross (G) at 190 Mev, Cranberg and Levin (C) at 6 Mev, Rosen and Stewart and Graves and Rosen, and from heavy ion experiments (H), shown with their experimental errors. Values deduced from measured nuclear level spacings at neutron binding energy are shown for comparison (O, ●, △, □). The curve represents Ross' estimate from levels of individual particles in a potential well. From LeCouteur (Le59).

son (Th60) from analysis of neutron inelastic scattering spectra from many elements with neutrons of 4 to 7 Mev [quoted by Ericson (Er60)].

One last point may be made. The "temperature" τ defined by (54) is a purely empirical constant derived from the analysis of experiments. It is often confused with a thermodynamic temperature t occurring in many of the currently popular nuclear models. Only for the most simplified of models—the original Bethe picture—are the two the same.

B. Angular Distribution of Reaction Products

In principle the angular distribution on the complete statistical model picture can be calculated by introducing into (31) the same modifications that led from (28) to (33). The sums over I' and I'' cannot be performed without knowledge of the dependence of the level densities on spins. If the ansatz of (34) is made, i.e., a $(2I + 1)$-dependence, then it can be shown, cf. Lane and Thomas (La58. p. 312), that the properties of the $\bar{Z}$ coefficients are such that the only non-vanishing term in the L expansion is for $L = 0$, i.e., the distribution is isotropic. It is important to note that σ is isotropic only if the (34) approximation is made; it does not follow from the correct distribution (40).

This result is surprising and somewhat disconcerting, for it was felt that where there is a statistical averaging of states both in the compound and final nuclei there should be no preferred direction left. Ericson and Strutinski (Er59) and Ericson (Er60a) however have given a classical argument in the limit of high angular momenta to show that conservation of angular momentum still imposes a preferred direction and that the angular distribution should be peaked symmetrically in the backward and forward directions. Douglas and MacDonald (Do59) have carried out a "brute-force" evaluation of the angular distribution on the basis of the spin-dependence of (42) for the specific reactions $Cu^{63}(n,p)$ and $Fe^{54}(n,p)$ with 14 Mev neutrons. The sums over the $\bar{Z}$ coefficients were evaluated explicitly. The calculated angular distributions are of course symmetric, since this is ensured by the statistical averaging over states in the compound nucleus. But anisotropies between $0°$ and $90°$ were obtained as high as 1.9 for $2\sigma^2$ of 5 or less. Comparison with experiment indicated smaller anisotropies, corresponding to larger values of $2\sigma^2$.

It has often been fashionable to interpret any deviation in the angular distribution of reaction products from isotropy as indicative of reaction modes other than compound nucleus formation. The predicted anisotropies on the basis of a complete statistical model should be a warning of the dangers of this procedure. Even where the observed angular distributions show assymmetries about $90°$ it is not safe to conclude the presence, for example, of direct interaction. It has already been pointed out that an incomplete statistical mixture of states in the compound nucleus leads to apparent fluctuations in the total cross sections. These fluctuations would show up in the angular distributions as assymmetries about $90°$. Only if the assymmetry does not fluctuate with incident energy, i.e., is a smooth and persistent function of energy, is it good evidence for processes not involving compound nucleus formation.

C. Cascade Reactions

If the residual nucleus in a two-body reaction is left in a sufficiently excited state as to be above the binding energy for another particle then de-excitation may occur by emission of this particle. The overall reaction would thus appear to be a three body reaction, but can be treated on the statistical model basis as a succession of two body reactions. A typical example is the $(n,2n)$ reaction. Let us suppose that neither charged particle nor photon emission can compete with neutron emission whenever this is energetically possible. The sum of the (n,n') and $(n,2n)$ cross sections, will therefore always be σ_c. If a neutron is emitted from the compound nucleus with an energy $E' \geq E - E_n$, where E_n is the separation energy of a neutron from the residual nucleus, then the excitation energy of the residual nucleus will be less than E_n, and we will have pure inelastic scattering. If, however, $E' < E - E_n$. emission of a second neutron takes place. The $(n,2n)$ cross section is therefore proportional to

$$\sigma_{n,2n}(E) \propto \int_0^{E-E_n} E'\sigma_c(E')\omega(E - E')dE' \tag{55}$$

Correspondingly the (n,n') cross section is proportional to

$$\sigma_{n,n'}(E) \propto \int_{E-E_n}^{E} E'\sigma_c(E')\omega(E - E')dE' \tag{56}$$

and the rate of cross sections is:

$$\frac{\sigma_{n,2n}(E)}{\sigma_{n,n'}(E)} = \frac{\int_0^{E-E_n} E'\sigma_c(E')\omega(E - E')dE'}{\int_{E-E_n}^{E} E'\sigma_c(E')\omega(E - E')dE'} \tag{57}$$

An approximate expression for this ratio is sometimes obtained by using (52) for the integrands, further neglecting the variation of $\sigma_c(E')$ with E'. Since E is usually much greater than τ, $\exp[-E/\tau]$ is further neglected compared to $\exp[-(E - E_n)/\tau]$ (57) then reduces to

$$\frac{\sigma_{n,2n}(E)}{\sigma_{n,n'}(E)} = \frac{e^\rho}{1 + \rho} - 1 \tag{58}$$

where
$$\rho = \frac{E - E_n}{\tau}$$

and

$$\sigma_{2n,n}(E) = \sigma_c(E) \{1 - \exp[-(E - E_n)/\tau](\tau + E - E_n)/\tau\} \quad (59)$$

The approximations involved in this calculation are so large, however, that it is not fair to blame the statistical model for any deviation of experiment from (58) or (59).

The spectrum of neutrons observed in the sum of the (n_2,n') and $(n,2n)$ reactions can also be deduced. A very simple picture is to assume the first neutrons come off with one temperature τ, and all the second neutrons with some other temperature τ_2, neglecting the variation of $\sigma_c(E')$ with E'. The total spectrum, which is that of the nonelastic cross section in the absence of competing reactions, can then be written as:

$$\sigma_{nX}(E; E') = \sigma_{nX}(E)\{[\tau_1{}^2E'/(1 + \alpha)] \exp(-E'/\tau_1)$$
$$+ [\alpha\tau_2{}^2E'/(1 + \alpha)] \exp(-E'/\tau_2)\} \quad (60)$$

where

$$\alpha = [\sigma_{n,2n}(E)]/[\sigma_{n,n'}(E)]$$

Here $\sigma_{nX}(E)$ can either be set equal to the calculated σ_c or taken from experiment.

It is easy to formulate the spectrum in a fashion that is more rigorous, at least in the framework of the statistical model. Let $P(E|E - \epsilon)$ be the probability that the emission of the fast neutron leaves the residual nucleus at an energy in unit range $d\epsilon$. Further let $N_2(\epsilon,E')$ be the number of second neutrons emitted from this residual nucleus at energy E' in unit range. Then the spectrum of second neutrons must be proportional to

$$\sigma_{n,2n}(E; E') \propto \int_{E_n+E'}^{E} P(E|E - \epsilon)N_2(\epsilon,E')d\epsilon \quad (61)$$

From (39)

$$P(E|E - \epsilon) \propto (E - \epsilon)\sigma_c(E - \epsilon)\omega(\epsilon)$$

and similarly

$$N_2(\epsilon,E') \propto E'\sigma_c(E')\omega(\epsilon - (E' + E_n))$$

so that:

$$\sigma_{n,2n}(E; E') \propto E'\sigma_c(E') \times$$
$$\int_{E_n+'E}^{E} (E - \epsilon)\sigma_c(E - \epsilon)\omega(\epsilon)\omega(\epsilon - (E' + E_n))d\epsilon \quad (62)$$

Equation (62) leads to the approximation involved in (60) only if N_2 is taken as a Maxwellian with a temperature τ_2 independent of ϵ, and if $E - E_n \gg \tau_2$ so that the lower limit of the integral can be neglected.

Feshbach (Fe51) has calculated a number of $(n,2n)$ spectra from (62) neglecting the variation of σ_c with energy but using various forms for ω. LeCouteur (Le52, Le59, Le59a) has examined the spectra where successive cascades can take place; in colorful language, when the incident particle brings in so much energy that the compound nucleus can successively boil off a number of nucleons. He has ingeniously employed statistical arguments to obtain the spectra if the individual nucleons emitted have a Maxwellian energy distribution with a temperature dependent on the excitation energy of the emitting nucleus. The approximate result then is that the spectrum has the form

$$(E')^{5/11} \exp\left(-E'/\tau^*\right)/\sigma_c(E')$$

where τ^* is a temperature different from the single nucleon emission temperature. Reasonably good agreement is obtained with the results of high energy evaporation experiments. Douglas and MacDonald (Do59) have examined the angular distribution of the cascade particles in an (n,np) reaction by a complicated calculation that uses the correct spin-dependence of level density but is otherwise based on the successive-emission picture.

The spectrum of neutron-capture gamma rays can be calculated in the complete statistical model picture if the photons are considered as "particles" with penetrabilities derived from the individual radiation widths on the basis of (30). This was originally done for the distribution of the initial photon emitted after capture by Weisskopf and Margolis in Section VIII of Fe51. More recently the complete spectrum of the cascade photons has been calculated by Troubetzkoy (Tr61) in this fashion. The detailed agreement obtained with the observed spectra of some heavy nuclei such as Au is remarkably good.

References

(Be37) H. A. Bethe, *Revs. Modern Phys.* **9**, 69 (1937).

(Be56) J. R. Beyster, R. G. Schraudt, M. Walt, and E. W. Salmi, "Predictions of Fast Neutron Scattering Data with a Diffuse Surface Potential Well," *Los Alamos Scientific Laboratory Report* LA-2099 (1956).

(Bi54) L. C. Biedenharn and A. Simon, "Revised Z Tables of Racah Coefficients," *Oak Ridge National Laboratory Reports* ORNL-1501 (1952) and ORNL-1501 Supplement (1954).

(Bl52) J. M. Blatt and L. C. Biedenharn, *Revs. Modern Phys.* **24**, 258 (1952).

(Bl52a) J. M. Blatt and V. F. Weisskopf, *Theoretical Nuclear Physics*, Wiley, New York, 1952.

(Bl54) C. Bloch, *Phys. Rev.* **93**, 1094 (1954).

(Br59) G. Breit, in *Handbuch der Physik*, S. Flügge, ed., Springer, Berlin, 1952, Vol. 41/1, p. 195.

(Ca58) A. G. W. Cameron, *Can. J. Phys.* **36**, 1040 (1958).

(Ca60) E. J. Campbell, H. Feshbach, C. E. Porter, and V. F. Weisskopf, "Some Optical Model Calculations," *M. I. T. Laboratory for Nuclear Science Technical Report* 73, unpublished (1960).

(Do59) A. C. Douglas and N. MacDonald, *Nuclear Phys.* **13**, 382 (1959).

(Er59) T. Ericson and V. Strutinski, *Nuclear Phys.* **8**, 284 (1958) and **9**, 689 (1959).

(Er60) T. Ericson, in *Proceedings of the International Conference on Nuclear Structure*, D. A. Bromley and E. W. Vogt, eds., University of Toronto Press, Toronto, 1960, Section 7.3, p. 697.

(Er60a) T. Ericson, *Nuclear Phys.* **17**, 1250 (1960).

(Fe49) H. Feshbach and V. F. Weisskopf, *Phys. Rev.* **76**, 1550 (1949).

(Fe51) B. T. Feld, H. Feshbach, M. L. Goldberger, and V. F. Weisskopf "Final Report of the Fast Neutron Data Project," *U. S. Atomic Energy Commission Report* NYO-636, unpublished (1951).

(Fe53) H. Feshbach, M. M. Shapiro, and V. F. Weisskopf, "Tables of Penetrabilities for Charged Particles," *U. S. Atomic Energy Commission Report* NYO-3077 (*NDA Report* 15B-5), unpublished (1953).

(Fe60) H. Feshbach, in *Nuclear Spectroscopy*, F. Ajzenberg-Selove, ed., Academic Press, New York, 1960, Part B, p. 1033.

(Fe60a) H. Feshbach, in *Nuclear Spectroscopy*, F. Ajzenberg-Selove, ed., Academic Press, New York, 1960, Part B, p. 625.

(Fr55) F. L. Friedman and V. F. Weisskopf, in *Niels Bohr and the Development of Physics*, Pergamon Press, London, 1955, p. 134.

(Ha52) W. Hauser and H. Feshbach, *Phys. Rev.* **87**, 366 (1952).

(Hi59) C. T. Hibdon, *Phys. Rev.* **114**, 179 (1959).

(Hu51) H. Hurwitz and H. A. Bethe, *Phys. Rev.* **81**, 898 (1951).

(Ki57) B. B. Kinsey, in *Handbuch der Physik*, S. Flügge, ed., Springer, Berlin, 1957, Vol. 40, p. 202.

(La54) J. M. B. Lang and K. J. LeCouteur, *Proc. Phys. Soc.* (*London*) **67**A, 586 (1954).

(La58) A. M. Lane and R. G. Thomas, *Revs. Modern Phys.* **30**, 257 (1958).

(Le52)   K. J. LeCouteur, *Proc. Phys. Soc.* (*London*) **65A**, 718 (1952).
(Le59)   K. J. LeCouteur, in *Nuclear Reactions*, P. M. Endt and M. Demeur, eds., North-Holland, Amsterdam, 1959, Vol. 1, p. 318.
(Le59a) K. J. LeCouteur and D. W. Lang, *Nuclear Phys.* **13**, 32 (1959).
(Mo58)   J. E. Monahan, L. C. Biedenharn, and J. P. Schiffer, "Tables of Neutron Penetrabilities and Shift Functions," *Argonne National Laboratory Report* ANL-5856, unpublished (1958).
(Ne56)   T. D. Newton, *Can. J. Phys.* **34**, 804 (1956).
(Ob55)   S. Obi, T. Ishidzu, H. Horie, S. Yanagawa, Y. Tanabe, and M. Sato, *Annals of the Tokyo Astronomical Observatory*, Second Series, **3**, 89 (1953), **4**, 3 (1954), and **4**, 72 (1955).
(Ra58)   E. B. Rae, B. Margolis, and E. S. Troubetzkoy, *Phys. Rev.* **112**, 492 (1958).
(Ro57)   A. A. Ross, *Phys. Rev.* **108**, 720 (1957).
(Te52)   T. Teichman and E. P. Wigner, *Phys. Rev.* **87**, 123 (1952).
(Th60)   D. B. Thomson, Los Alamos Scientific Laboratory, unpublished data (1960).
(Tr61)   E. S. Troubetzkoy, *Phys. Rev.*, to be published (1961).
(We40)   V. F. Weisskopf and D. H. Ewing, *Phys. Rev.* **57**, 472 and 935 (1940).
(Wo51)   L. Wolfenstein, *Phys. Rev.* **82**, 690 (1951).

Gamma Radiation from Neutron Inelastic Scattering

J. M. Freeman

Atomic Energy Research Establishment, Harwell, England

1. Introduction

When neutron inelastic scattering occurs as a result of fast neutron bombardment of a nucleus, the residual nucleus is left in one of its excited states. Unless the excitation of this state is so high that particle emission is energetically possible, the nucleus will usually decay to its ground state, either directly or by a cascade process, with the emission of γ rays. A study of this γ radiation can therefore provide information about the nature and decay properties of the state, as well as giving a measure of the probability of inelastic neutron scattering to this particular state.

If the energy of the bombarding neutrons is such that only a few levels of the target nuclei are excited, the observed γ-ray spectrum can usually be analyzed into its individual energy components. The energies of the excited states cannot be inferred directly from such an analysis because of the possibility that some of the γ rays are due to cascade decay, but if the level positions are not already known from other work, one can deduce them by gradually increasing the neutron bombarding energy from a low value and observing the threshold for excitation of each new γ ray in turn. Since the cross section for inelastic scattering to a particular level usually rises quite rapidly from the threshold, the latter can be determined to within a few tens of kilovolts. This gives an approximate value for the level energy. The mode of decay of each level can then be deduced from the observed γ-ray energies, and accurate measurements of these latter give precise values for the level energies. If a number of cascade transitions are occurring, γ-γ coincidence measurements can also be used to assist in working out the level and decay scheme. Gamma-ray energies can be measured with greater accuracy than is at present possible for neutron group measurements, so that the γ-ray detection method of studying (n, n') reactions not only provides data on decay schemes, but is also very useful for more precise level determinations and for the resolution of closely spaced levels. Finally, measurements of the absolute yield of γ rays from a given level allow the deduction of the cross section for the inelastic scattering process leading to this level, and the excitation function can also be determined (see Chapter V.I).

As the neutron bombarding energy is increased, more and more levels of the target nucleus can of course be excited and the γ-ray spectrum becomes correspondingly complex and difficult to analyze into its separate components. Moreover, once the initial neutrons attain an energy greater than the binding energy of a neutron in the target nucleus ($\sim$10 Mev), levels can be excited which decay by emission of another neutron rather than by direct γ radiation. In this $(n, 2n)$ reaction the final nucleus, with neutron number one less than that of the target nucleus, may also be left in one of its excited states, emitting its own characteristic γ rays. Because the density of levels in the target nucleus increases with excitation energy, the $(n, 2n)$ process, once energetically possible, competes quite strongly with (n, n') reactions to the less numerous bound levels. At this stage, therefore, the total γ-ray spectrum tends to show a continuum except perhaps at the lowest γ-ray energies (Sc53, Sc57).

Studies of γ radiation following neutron inelastic scattering are thus most profitably pursued at neutron bombarding energies up to a few Mev only, for the investigation of the lowest half-dozen or so levels of a particular nucleus. Light and medium-weight nuclei are in general the easiest to study since their level spacings are large enough to allow resolution of the γ rays. Heavy nuclei usually have more closely spaced levels; they present a problem in absorption of the radiation within the sample, and, moreover, internal conversion often occurs to such an extent that γ radiation cannot be observed from low-lying levels. Nevertheless, some useful experiments with heavy nuclei have been carried out, particularly with Bi and the isotopes of Pb, for which the proximity of the doubly-closed shell makes the level spacings unusually large for heavy nuclei.

The method of exciting nuclear levels for decay studies by neutron inelastic scattering has some advantages over that of excitation by charged particle scattering. In the latter case the Coulomb barrier limits investigations to light nuclei, except for quite low-lying levels which can be excited by Coulomb excitation. Moreover, with neutrons one can excite and observe each level in turn, just a little above the threshold for its excitation, so that the γ-ray spectrum is not complicated by radiation due to the decay of higher levels; with charged particles higher bombarding energies are required, even for light elements, and competing reactions may also occur which contribute to the complexity of the γ-ray spectrum. On the other hand, in neutron work the background problems are more serious, and angular distribution measurements are quite difficult.

The availability during the past few years of satisfactory neutron sources and γ-ray detectors has allowed a variety of experiments to be carried out on the γ rays from inelastic scattering. The $D(d, n)$ reaction has been a useful source of 2.5-Mev neutrons and it has also allowed investigations up to 6 or 7 Mev. Some work has been done with 14-Mev neutrons from the $T(d, n)$ reaction. For threshold measurements, and for observation of the γ rays as a function of neutron energy, the $T(p, n)$ reaction, produced by protons from an electrostatic generator, has proved the most satisfactory and flexible source. The $Li^7(p, n)$ reaction is also useful, particularly for lower energy neutrons.

The detection and measurement of the γ rays in the early experiments was done with ion chambers or Geiger counters and absorbers (Le35, Ki35, Se37, Be50, Gr51). More recently the development of crystal scintillators together with suitable photomultiplier tubes has provided a more satisfactory method of γ-ray observation. These detectors are however still far from ideal for work with neutrons; the problems associated with the detectors are discussed in Section 2.

The best experimental arrangement for the γ-ray investigations depends on the amount of material available for the scattering sample, on whether low or high energy levels are being excited in the target nuclei, and on the nature of the experimental room and the associated background problems. If a large enough room or one with thin walls is available, an *open geometry* system is best; this is an arrangement in which the shielding and extraneous material in the neighborhood of the scattering and detecting apparatus are kept to a minimum. The problem of room background is discussed in Section 3.A. In a very confined room a *closed geometry*, that is a totally shielded system, gives better results (see Section 3.C). Of the open geometry systems the ring geometry arrangement, in which the scatterer is in the form of an annulus, is the most efficient. For maximum counting rates with a given neutron source and detector position, the ring should be placed around either the source or detector. Except for the case of a $T(d, n)$ 14-Mev source, which is approximately isotropic for low-energy deuterons, the placing of the ring around the detector is more convenient. The ring geometry method is discussed in detail in Section 3.A. A neat and useful method for investigating low energy γ rays from small samples is the thin crystal technique described in Section 3.B(2). Other methods particularly suitable for the study of enriched isotopes are dealt with in Section 3.B(1), and also in Section 3.D, where the very promising time-of-flight method is described. Section 3.E discusses the special case of isomeric levels.

The quantities of interest for study are (a) γ-ray energies and relative intensities, (b) the thresholds for excitation of the γ rays, (c) γ-n and γ-γ coincidences, (d) angular distributions of the γ rays, (e) excitation functions and cross sections, (f) level and decay schemes deduced from some of the above data and other experiments. The topics (b) and (e), that is, excitation functions, thresholds, and cross sections are dealt with in detail in Chapter V.I and are mentioned only briefly here; the other items just listed are discussed in Section 3 (experimental methods), Section 4 (the detector calibration and a list of suitable γ-ray calibration sources), Section 5 (coincidence measurements and the deduction of level and decay schemes), and Section 6 (angular distribution measurements).

2. Gamma-Ray Detectors

A. Sodium Iodide Crystals

For the study of γ radiation following neutron inelastic scattering a detector having good efficiency and good energy resolution is required. The most satisfactory instrument available at present is the thallium-activated sodium-iodide scintillation crystal (denoted by NaI (Tl) or sometimes just NaI), used in conjunction with a selected photomultiplier tube. Its application to $(n, n'\gamma)$ work was first reported by Grace *et al.* (Gr52). In most experiments the crystal takes the form of a cylinder or rectangular block with a cross sectional area of a few square centimeters and a thickness in the range 1 mm to about 5 cm, chosen according to the energies of the γ rays to be studied. The energy resolution obtainable for the full-energy peak is about 8 per cent (full width at half height) for 500-kev γ rays, and varies as $1/\sqrt{E\gamma}$. The intrinsic efficiency for production of a pulse in the full-energy peak approaches 100 per cent for low-energy γ rays ($\sim$100 kev) but falls off considerably for γ rays exceeding an Mev or so (see Chapter V.I).

A general limitation to the usefulness of NaI(Tl) crystals arises from the complicated and energy-dependent spectral shapes which they give even for monoenergetic radiation, particularly in the case of γ rays with energies appreciably greater than 1 Mev, where both Compton and pair-production processes contribute (He57). This feature leads to difficulties in the analysis of composite spectra.

Apart from the spectral shape problem, which is met in any γ-ray spectroscopy work, the NaI crystal introduces special difficulties in neutron work because of its sensitivity to neutrons. Even when the crystal is shielded from the primary source, neutrons reach it by elastic and inelastic scattering from the sample under investigation, and in addition it is difficult to exclude from the crystal all neutrons which have been scattered from various parts of the room and associated apparatus. Fast neutrons can produce several background effects in the NaI crystal: (a) neutron capture, leading to prompt γ-ray emission plus subsequent β-emission from Na^{24} or I^{128}; the latter, with a half-life of 25 minutes, is the more prominent and produces a continuous background spectrum which varies in intensity according to the amount of neutron irradiation which has occurred during the previous hour or so; (b) inelastic scattering by the sodium or iodine nuclei of the crystal, leading to γ-ray emission characteristic of the levels of Na^{23} and I^{127}; (c) sodium recoils from neutron scattering.

The capture process is usually not very serious unless the experiment has to be done in a small room, which can produce a rather high flux of degraded neutrons, or unless there is some injudiciously placed hydrogenous material close to the crystal, so that many low-energy neutrons can reach the crystal. Recoiling sodium nuclei produce no background except in the very low energy part of

the spectrum (Sz58). The effect (b) due to inelastic scattering is
however quite serious, particularly in the case of iodine which has
many levels available for excitation. The γ rays below 1 Mev,
observed by Van Loef and Lind (Va56) and by Day (Da56) in the
neutron bombardment of iodine, are given in Table I. For comparison the γ rays following Coulomb excitation of iodine are also listed.
Except for those attributed to a capture reaction, each γ-ray peak
begins to appear as the neutron energy reaches the threshold for excitation of the corresponding level (all the γ-ray transitions are believed
to go direct to the ground state in iodine); the peak usually rises to a
maximum with increasing neutron energy and then begins to fall off
again in intensity as competition from higher levels sets in. The
sodium of the NaI crystal does not contribute so strongly to the inelastic scattering effects since it has only one excited state (440 kev)
below 2 Mev (Bu57, Fr58).

Table I. Gamma Rays from Iodine[a]

Neutron bombardment E_γ (kev)		Coulomb excitation E_γ (kev)
(Va56)	(Da56)	(Da56a)
31 ± 2[b]		
62 ± 2	58	60 ± 2
145 ± 5[b]	138[b]	
208 ± 2	204	208 ± 7
390 ± 10	396	392 ± 8
435 ± 4	441	438 ± 10
632 ± 6	634	631 ± 10
750 ± 20	742	751 ± 25
950 ± 20		941 ± 50

[a] Other references: Gu54, Ki54a, Wo56, Mo56, He56, Li57.
[b] Due probably to capture.

The types of background spectra obtained from a NaI crystal
in an inelastic neutron scattering experiment are illustrated in Fig.
1. These curves were obtained by Day (Da56) with a ring geometry
arrangement to be described in Section 3.A. The neutron bombarding energies are indicated on these curves. A carbon scatterer,
producing only elastic scattering at these energies, was used except
for the curve marked "no scatterer" which illustrates the effect due
to neutrons scattered from the room and various parts of the appa-

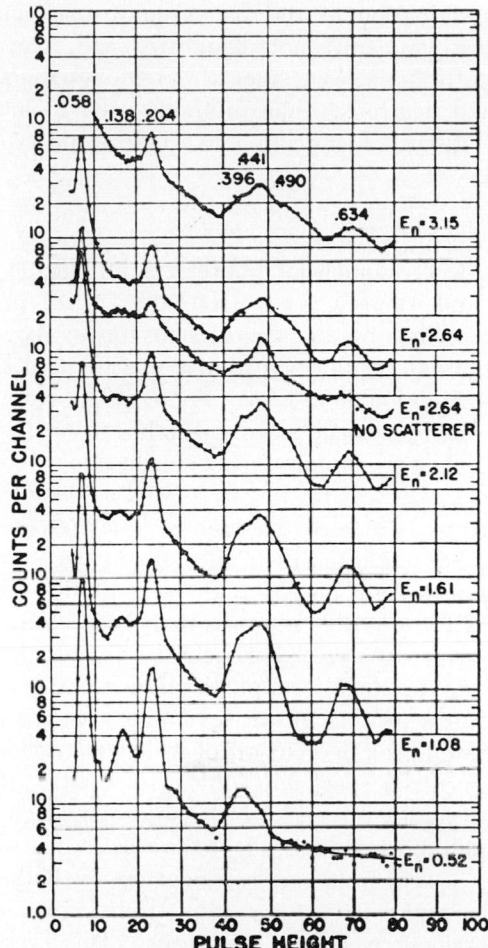

Figure 1. NaI(Tl) pulse-height distributions, in the γ-ray energy range below 1 Mev, produced by neutrons of the energies shown. Photopeak energies are given in Mev above the top curve. The ordinate changes by a factor 10 for each neutron energy (Da56).

ratus. In the energy range above 1 Mev the γ-ray spectra for the higher neutron energies show a fairly smooth continuum corresponding to a number of unresolved γ rays due to iodine with some contributions from sodium.

The determination of the background spectrum appropriate to a particular experiment is not straightforward; one cannot simply remove the scattering sample since this removes the source of some of the scattered neutrons. The methods used to meet these difficulties will be discussed in Section 3, where some typical NaI data will be given.

B. Organic Scintillators

In cases where somewhat poorer resolution and efficiency can be tolerated, and where a γ ray from the (n, n') process is being studied at neutron bombarding energies not too far above the threshold for its excitation, an organic scintillator can be used as the detector instead of a sodium iodide crystal. Some of the more objectionable background troubles associated with the latter are thereby avoided. The organic detector can produce scintillations due to Compton electrons from γ rays scattered in it, as well as responding to proton recoils caused by scattered neutrons. The response of organic phosphors depends on the nature of the ionizing particles (Bi51, Br56), and for energies up to a few Mev the scintillation response due to recoil electrons from γ rays is more than twice that due to proton recoils of the same energy. Consequently, for neutron energies not too far above the threshold for a particular level, the γ rays following inelastic neutron scattering to this level give rise to a pulse distribution, the Compton peak and cut-off of which are well separated from the scattered neutron spectrum (unless, of course, the γ rays are considerably degraded in energy by cascades through lower levels). The background above the cut-off of the elastic neutron spectrum is due partly to γ rays from neutron capture by hydrogen nuclei in the scintillator and partly to γ rays from capture and inelastic scattering in various parts of the apparatus. It is a smooth and slowly-varying spectrum, more easily allowed for than the background arising with a NaI crystal.

In Fig. 2 an example is given of the use of a stilbene crystal for measuring the γ rays following excitation of the 478-kev level of Li^7 by inelastic neutron scattering. A ring geometry arrangement (to be described in Section 3.A) was used. Curve A is the spectrum obtained in the crystal when a lithium scatterer was bombarded with 720-kev neutrons. Curve B shows a background run, for the same number of neutrons, with the scatterer removed, and the broken curve

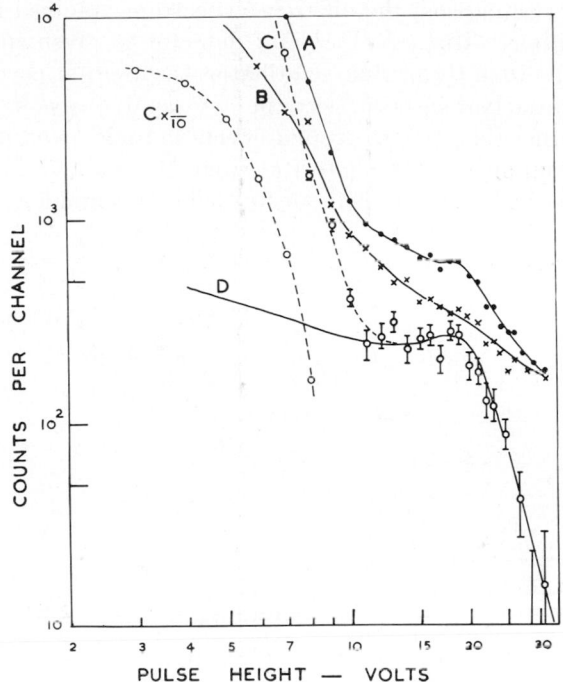

Fig. 2. Stilbene crystal spectra with 720-kev neutrons bombarding lithium. Curve A, lithium in; curve B, lithium out; curve C (open circles), difference; curve D, 178 kev γ ray spectrum from Be⁷ (Fi33).

C (open circles) represents the difference. The full curve D is a 478-kev γ-ray spectrum (from a Be⁷ source), fitted to curve C at one point. It demonstrates that the Compton spectrum of the γ rays from the Li reaction is clean above the scattered neutron cut-off.

The organic phosphor is useful even for examining a complicated spectrum. This is illustrated in Fig. 3a which shows the spectrum obtained with a plastic scintillator 2 inches in diameter and 2 inches long following the bombardment of a sodium ring with 3-Mev neutrons. The background obtained with a carbon ring has been subtracted. The arrows indicate the positions of extrapolated end-points of Compton spectra due to γ rays from Na²³. The full curve shows the spectral shape due to a RdTh γ-ray source (2.615 Mev) adjusted to fit the highest energy (2.64 Mev) component of the spectrum. For comparison, the difference spectrum obtained under the same conditions with a NaI crystal detector is given in Fig. 3b. The spectrum from the organic scintillator was useful in checking that the peaks in the NaI spectrum were in fact due to γ rays from the Na scatterer rather than to background effects in iodine, and it was also used to obtain an upper limit to the intensity of a 2.71-Mev γ ray, the asymmetrical shapes of NaI spectra being unsuitable for showing

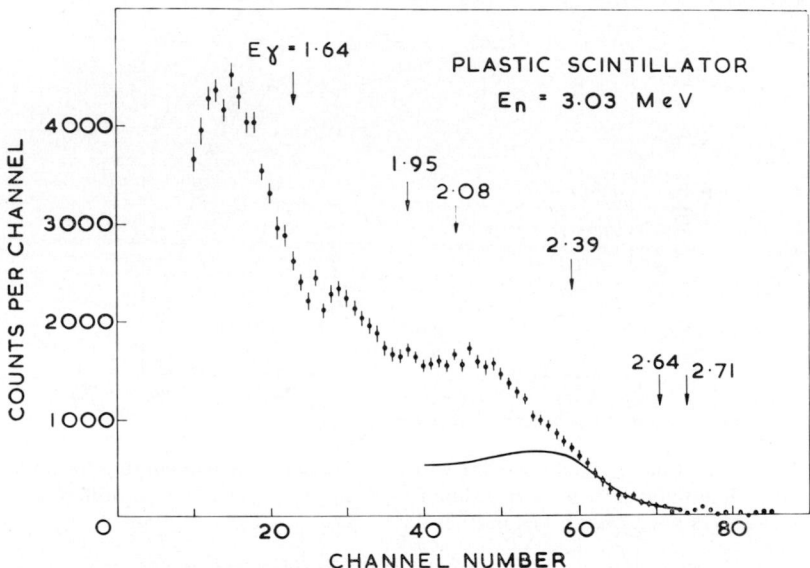

Figure 3a. Plastic scintillator spectrum of γ rays from $Na^{23}(n, n')$ obtained with 3-Mev neutrons and a ring geometry arrangement. The background has been subtracted. The full curve shows the *shape* of a 2.615-Mev spectrum from a RdTh source adjusted to fit a 2.64-Mev Compton edge (Fr58).

up a small higher energy component in the presence of the 2.64-Mev peak. Some further examples and discussion of the use of organic phosphors for γ-ray detection in (n, n') reactions have been given by Fr55, Fr56, and El54. More extensive use of these phosphors would seem to be justified. However most experimenters have preferred to use only the somewhat more versatile NaI(Tl) crystal; the work to be described in subsequent Sections here is therefore mainly concerned with NaI detectors.

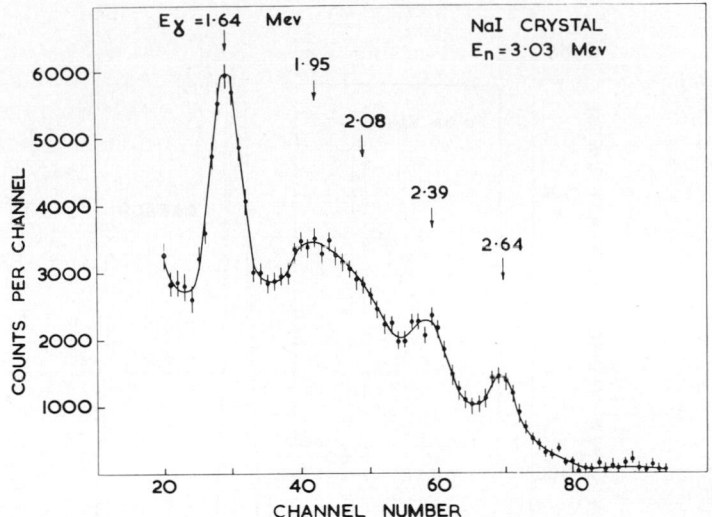

Figure 3b. NaI crystal spectrum of γ rays from $Na^{23}(n, n')$ obtained under the same conditions as for Fig. 3a. The background from a carbon scatterer has been subtracted (Fr58).

C. Other Techniques

Our ideal detector would have (a) good efficiency over the whole γ-ray energy range, (b) good resolution, (c) a single peak for a single γ-ray energy, and (d) a very low response to neutrons. The invention of such a device would allow a great advance in work in many fields. The NaI crystal fulfills the first requirement, at least in the lower energy range, and also the second, but falls short of the other two criteria; the organic scintillator offers a tolerably low neutron response over a limited range of energies, but is rather inadequate in other respects. So far most attempts to improve on this situation have concentrated on modifying a NaI detector in such a way that the neutron-induced background is overcome at the expense of efficiency. To this end some form of coincidence measurement is introduced, for example, (a) selection of those γ-ray pulses which are in coincidence with inelastically scattered neutrons recorded in another detector, (b) effective collimation of the neutron source by use of the associated particle technique, (c) avoidance of scattered neutron effects by a time-of-flight method. These methods are discussed in

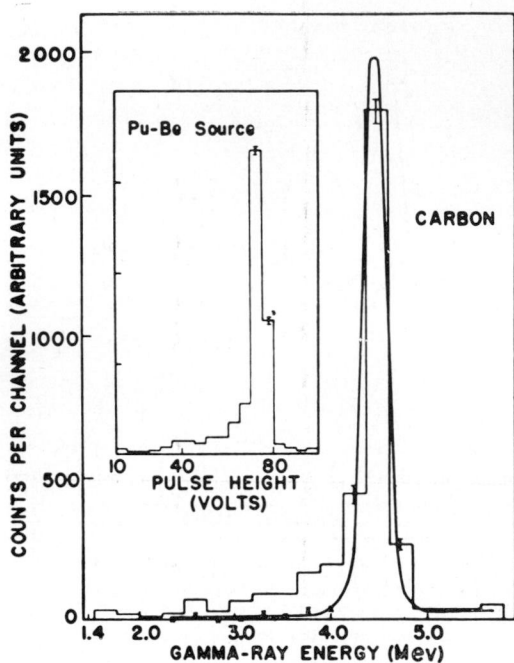

Figure 4. Pulse-height distribution of γ rays due to 14-Mev neutron bombardment of carbon, detected with a 3-crystal pair spectrometer. The smooth curve shows the spectrum corrected for radiative loss and electron escape. Insert: spectrum from a Pu-α-Be source of the same 4.4-Mev γ rays (Ba55).

Sections 3 and 4. A device suitable for the study of harder γ rays is the three-crystal pair spectrometer which gives a single peak for a given γ-ray energy, and which can discriminate against backgrounds. The peak is obtained from the detection of electron-positron pairs due to γ rays stopped in a central NaI crystal, when the two associated annihilation quanta are simultaneously recorded in two auxiliary NaI crystals flanking the main detector diametrically. Thus a three-fold coincidence is required to allow pulses from the center crystal to be analyzed. The use of this instrument for studying the γ radiation from carbon under 14-Mev neutron bombardment has been described by Battat and Graves (Ba55). The spectrometer was placed 26 cm in front of $T(d, n)$ source, immediately behind which was located a graphite ring scattering sample; a tungsten bar provided shielding of the center crystal from the direct neutron beam. Figure 4 shows the resulting pulse-height distribution (spectrum with scatterer in minus spectrum with scatterer out). The crosses represent the net result after correction for radiative loss and electron escape, obtained by normalization from Pu-α-Be data (see inset). The very good discrimination against neutron induced background is apparent. However, like the other coincidence techniques, the three-crystal spectrometer has low efficiency.

3. Experimental Methods

A. Ring Geometry

When adequate material is available for the scattering sample, an efficient arrangement for the study of γ rays from the (n, n') process is that illustrated in Fig. 5. The scatterer is in the form of an annulus surrounding the scintillation detector, which may be a sodium iodide crystal or an organic phosphor. The scatterer receives neutrons emitted at a small angle (about 5° to 7°) with respect to the direction of the accelerator beam which is producing neutrons in a suitable gas or solid target. A cone of polyethylene, lead, or tungsten shields the crystal detector from the neutron source. The scale given

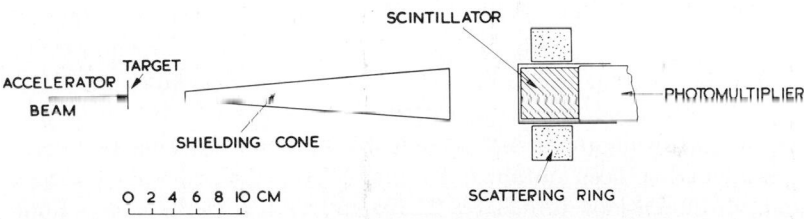

Figure 5. Ring geometry arrangement for studying γ rays from neutron inelastic scattering.

in Fig. 5 indicates the dimensions used in a typical experiment with neutrons of energies up to a few Mev. The useful radial thickness of the scattering ring varies between a few cms and about 1 mm according to the material and the energy of the γ rays to be detected, self-absorption being the limitation. For monitoring purposes a neutron detector such as a BF_3 long counter is placed in a convenient position one to two meters away from the neutron source, at an angle of between 45° and 90°; for absolute flux determinations this monitor can be compared, after the experiment, with an absolutely calibrated long counter set up to receive neutrons emitted in the direction normally taken up by the scatterer.

The target assembly, and the supports for the detector, scattering ring, and cone, are made as small and light as possible to minimize the amount of extraneous scattering material in the vicinity of the experiment. This is necessary in order to keep down the background counts in the crystal detector. For the same reason it is advisable to keep the whole system as far from thick floors and walls as possible. The intensity of the background in the absence of the scattering ring is very dependent on the size and wall thicknesses of the experimental room. Some theoretical estimations of the neutron flux scattered back to the source by the walls of a laboratory have been made (Bi50, Ma51). For example, with some simplifying assumptions it can be shown that, for the case of a spherical room of radius a with a neutron source of strength S at its center, the room having non-absorbent walls of thickness t in which the primary neutron has a mean free path l, the flux of neutrons returning to the source is of the order $St/4\pi a^2 l$. If there is an opening or one thin wall in the experimental room, the returning flux is considerably reduced (by a factor of the order of l/t). In a very large room air scattering becomes important; an experimental investigation of this (Gl54) has shown that the flux due to air scattering returning to a point distant r from an isolated source S follows the relation $\pi S/16\lambda r$ where λ is the mean free path of the neutrons in air.[1] In a practical case, a worthwhile reduction in room background in a ring geometry experiment has been obtained by going from a thick-walled target room, of dimensions 40 feet by 22 feet by 12 feet, with a light floor and pit below the target, to a situation where the neutron source was 10 feet from the ground in a large thin-walled area. The type of experimental arrangement in which shielding and extraneous scattering material are kept to a minimum is referred to as an *open geometry* system. For a further discussion of this topic see Chapter IV.F.

With the ring geometry the mean angle of observation of the γ rays with respect to the neutrons incident on the scattering ring is a little under 90°; the angular range of acceptance due to the dimensions

---

[1] The author is grateful to Dr. R. M. Sinclair for drawing her attention to the literature on room backgrounds, as well as for a general discussion and comments on the manuscript of this review.

of the ring and crystal is usually about 90°. The spread in energy of the incident neutrons is determined partly by the effective thickness of the target for the (p, n) or (d, n) source, and partly by the range of angles over which the scattering ring receives neutrons from the source. For targets in common use, with thicknesses equivalent to 20 kev or more, the target thickness is the major factor in determining the energy spread.

The pulses from the photomultiplier associated with the crystal detector are fed through a stabilized linear amplifier to a pulse-height analyzer. If the latter is of a type such as the Hutchinson-Scarrott analyzer, with an average dead time of some hundreds of microseconds, then this very often sets the limit to the experimental counting rate when a NaI crystal is used.

As pointed out in Section 2.A, a sodium iodide detector gives a complicated background spectrum, due mainly to γ rays produced in the crystal itself by neutrons scattered into it either from the scattering ring or from the room and associated apparatus; a smaller contribution comes from unwanted γ radiation produced externally. To reproduce this background spectrum one needs to reproduce all the neutron scattering in the absence of the γ rays from inelastic scattering in the sample. For studies in the energy range up to a few Mev, a fair approximation to this condition is obtained by replacing the scattering sample with a similar ring of carbon; the latter, at neutron energies below 4.4 Mev (the energy of the first excited state in carbon), gives only elastic neutron scattering. The importance of using a suitable scatterer for the background run is illustrated in Fig. 6. Here the uppermost curve A is the spectrum obtained in a good geometry system with a ring of the material under investigation (Na^{23}). The lowest curve C is the spectrum, taken for the same total neutron flux, with the ring scatterer removed; this represents the background due to scattering from the room and various parts of the apparatus. The center curve B is the corresponding spectrum obtained when an equivalent carbon ring replaced the sodium ring; this shows the room background plus the additional background due to elastic neutron scattering from the ring sample. Neutrons of energy 3.9 Mev were used for this experiment (Fr58). The γ-ray spectrum due to sodium is quite complex; some of the full-energy peaks are indicated.

The mass of carbon for the background run should be chosen to give the same amount of elastic scattering into the crystal as is pro-

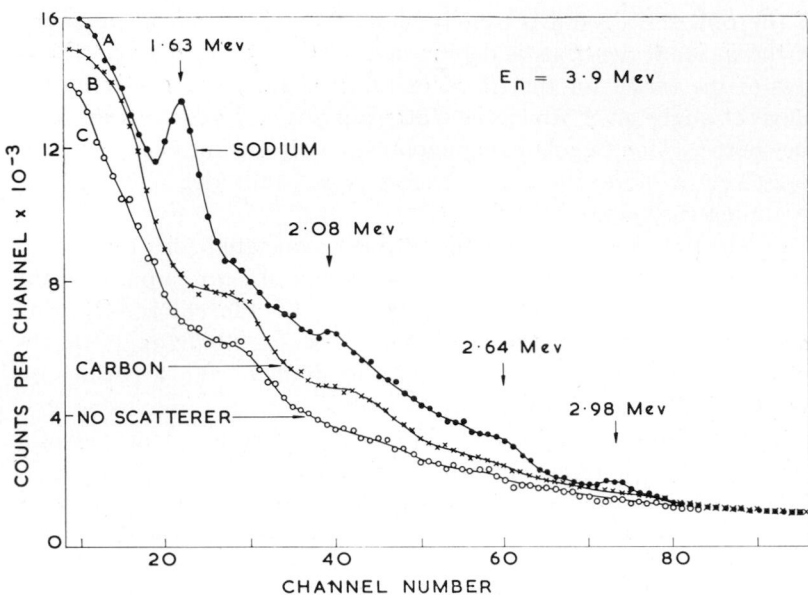

Figure 6. NaI(Tl) spectra in the γ-ray energy range indicated by the arrows, obtained with 3.9-Mev neutrons for: *A*, sodium ring; *B*, carbon ring; *C*, no scattering ring. The neutron flux was the same for each run (Fr57a).

duced by the sample under investigation.   The amount required can be estimated roughly with the aid of published data on total and differential scattering cross sections, but rapid variations of these with neutron energy introduce practical difficulties.   Moreover, this procedure does not reproduce the background conditions *exactly* because (a) the energy of neutrons scattered from carbon is not quite the same as for a target material with a different nuclear mass, and (b) allowance has not been made for neutrons scattered inelastically from the sample into the crystal; these latter neutrons, however, are in many cases sufficiently degraded in energy to be unable to induce γ-ray emission in the NaI crystal in the energy region under consideration.   When possible, the best criterion that the correct conditions have been chosen for the background run is an examination of the shape obtained for the spectrum due to an isolated γ ray from the scattering sample, after subtraction of the background spectrum (normalized to the same number of neutron monitor counts).   This

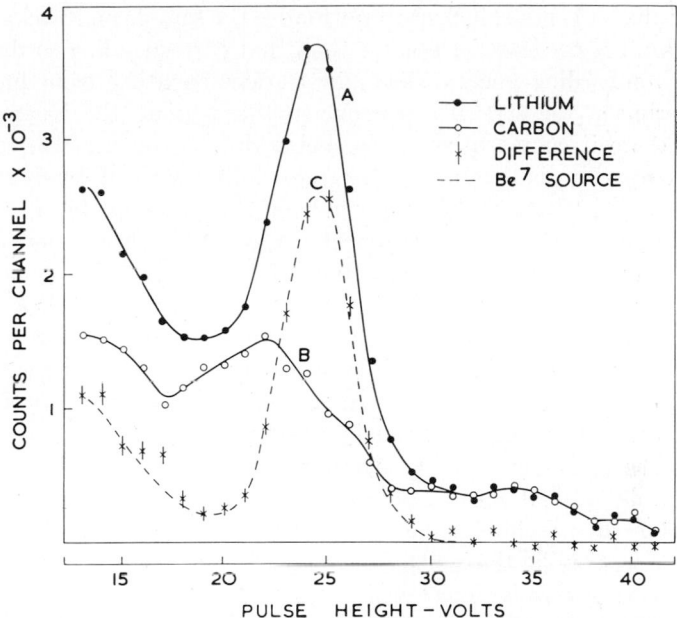

Figure 7. NaI(Tl) spectra in the γ-ray energy range 250 to 800 kev for a lithium ring (curve *A*), and a carbon ring (curve *B*), bombarded by 1.2-Mev neutrons. The crosses represent the difference spectrum and the broken curve *C* (which has been normalized to fit the difference spectrum at the peak) is due to 478-kev γ rays from a Be[7] source (Fr55).

can be compared with the predicted shape obtained from measurements with radioactive sources in the same geometry. Figure 7 shows, by way of example, the spectrum (curve *A*) obtained with 1.2-Mev neutrons bombarding a lithium ring and exciting the 478-kev level of Li[7]. Curve *B* is the corresponding spectrum obtained with a carbon ring, and the crosses represent the difference spectrum. The broken curve *C* is a spectrum due to the same 478-kev radiation from a Be[7] source; it has been normalized to fit the crosses at the peak and the good fit over the entire curve demonstrates that the background has been correctly allowed for. An alternative method of checking the background correction is the selection of a prominent peak in the background spectrum which can be compared with that obtained in the sample run (see, for example, the peak at a pulse height of about 34 volts in the spectra *A* and *B* of Fig. 7). It should however be noted that it is not sufficient to normalize the sample and background spectra at γ-ray energies greater than that corresponding to the neutron bombarding energy since no γ rays resulting from inelastic scattering in the crystal can occur in this region; the background level there is comparatively low, being due to capture γ rays, and the comparison is therefore a very insensitive one. A further practical point is that the use (reported once or twice in the literature) of Perspex, or any other material containing hydrogen as well as carbon for the background run is inadvisable, since it can produce considerably degraded neutrons which have an enhanced probability of inducing capture reactions in a sodium iodide crystal. If the crystal shows appreciable activity when the neutron source is turned off, then due allowance must be made for the irradiation history and the times of the sample and background runs.

The ring geometry arrangement is suitable for absolute cross section determinations. The γ-ray yield is obtained from measurements of the absolute efficiency of the detector, with corrections for self-absorption in the scattering ring and for internal conversion. The neutron flux is determined with the aid of an absolutely-calibrated neutron detector, or from the known yield of the reaction providing the source; consideration has to be given to the effect of attenuation and multiple scattering in the sample. The problems of absolute cross section determinations are discussed in Chapter V.I.

For further details of the ring geometry technique the reader is referred to Da56, Fr55, and Ki54. For accounts of experiments using this method see also Ro53, Ki54a, Ki54b, Gu54, Ro54, Th54, Ra54, Ba55, Be55, Fr55a, Fr55b, Gr55, Ro55, Ra55, Mo56, Fr56, Fr57, Li57, Pr57, Fr58, Ha59, and Ho59.

B. Small Sample Techniques

(1) **Study of Enriched Isotopes.** The ring geometry method requires an appreciable quantity of material for the scattering sample, usually a few hundred grams. When only small amounts are available this method is not practicable; however several alternative techniques have been successfully used in this case. With the production now in gram quantities of many electromagnetically enriched isotopes, the interpretation of the γ rays from polyisotopic elements under fast neutron bombardment has become feasible and is of considerable

interest.   A number of nuclear levels have already been identified for the first time by this means.

A straightforward open geometry system suitable for small sample studies is illustrated in Fig. 8; this shows the arrangement used by Sinclair (Si55).   The background with this system is fairly large compared with γ radiation from the sample, so that accurate measurements of yields and thresholds are not possible.   However for the comparison of spectra from samples having different isotopic enrichments, but being otherwise identical, the arrangement provides a very satisfactory method of attributing the various γ-ray peaks to

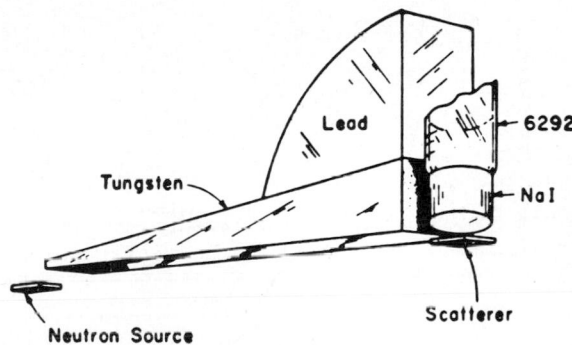

Figure 8. Experimental arrangement for the study of small samples.   The source-to-scatterer distance is 10 inches (Si55).

the correct isotopes.   Figure 9 shows the pulse-height distributions obtained by Sinclair for tellurium samples, each of weight about 4 grams, enriched to 80 per cent or more in the isotope indicated. From these curves the γ rays with energies 0.68, 0.76, and 0.83 Mev can immediately be assigned to the isotopes with masses 126, 128, and 130 respectively.   For other work using this method see Si55, Si56, Gr56, and Si57.   For early experiments using the same geometry see Sc53 and Sc53a.

Some experimenters, working in a confined target room with correspondingly high background effects, have preferred to dispense with shielding of the crystal in order to place the scattering sample directly in front of the neutron source, with the crystal detector close to it.   In this way Beghian et al. have made measurements for a number of elements, including enriched Fe^{54} and Fe^{56}; their γ-ray

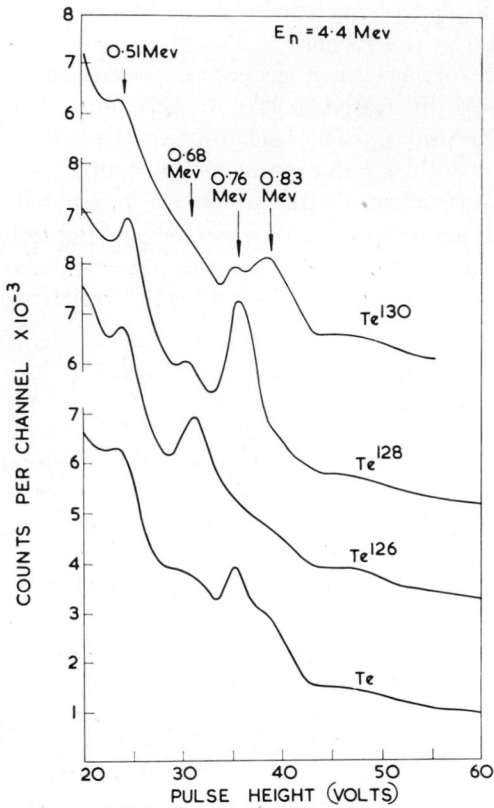

Figure 9. Gamma-ray spectra obtained with the apparatus of Fig. 8 for: (a) normal tellurium; (b) Te^{126}; (c) Te^{128}; (d) Te^{130} (Si56).

studies were supplemented by observations of the corresponding neutron groups with a stilbene crystal (El54, Be55a, Be56).

An interesting method for the study of γ rays from small samples, including enriched isotopes, has been developed by Faust *et al.* (Fa55, Sc55, Sh57). One feature is the elimination of some of the background by the associated-particle technique: the reaction D(d, n)He^3 is used as a source and the forward-emitted neutrons (2.6 Mev) are selected by detecting the corresponding He^3 particles in a thin KI(Tl) crystal, after magnetic analysis. Only those events in the γ-ray detector are analyzed which are in coincidence with He^3 counts. The other feature is the γ-ray detector, which consists of a

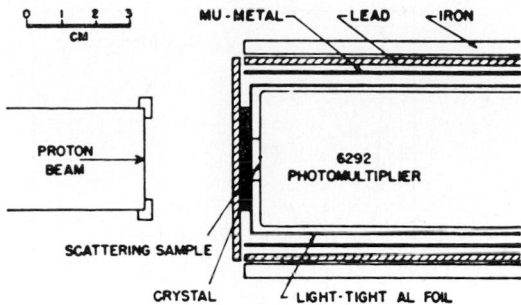

Figure 10. Thin crystal geometry for the investigation of low-energy γ rays (Gu56).

5-inch diameter by 3-inch long NaI crystal with a 1-inch diameter hole drilled along its central axis to accommodate the scattering sample. The neutrons reach the scatterer after passing through a hole in a tungsten shield. This arrangement gives almost 4π acceptance of γ rays from the sample. Thus all the cascade γ rays following a particular inelastic scattering event have a fair chance of being stopped in the crystal, and some pulses are obtained corresponding to the individual energies (Lu54, Sh57a). Provided the observed spectra are not too complicated, it is possible to infer from them the level and decay scheme for the nuclei of the scattering sample. The background spectrum due to scattered neutrons is obtained as usual by substituting a carbon scatterer. This method has been applied to the study of the isotopes Fe^{54}, Fe^{56}, and Fe^{57} by the use of enriched Fe_2O_3 samples weighing 4 or 5 grams (Sh57).

Other methods suitable for the study of small samples of enriched isotopes are the closed geometry system and the particularly successful time-of-flight technique. These methods are discussed in Sections 3.C and 3.D.

(2) **The Thin Crystal Method.** For the investigation of low-energy γ rays ($\sim$200 kev or less) following inelastic scattering, only a thin layer of the scattering sample is effective because of the strong probability of self-absorption of the γ rays within the scatterer. For the heavier elements in particular, not more than about a millimeter thickness of material is useful. Hence for a given neutron flux the observable γ-ray yield is much less than in the case of harder γ rays. However the low-energy γ rays are also much more easily

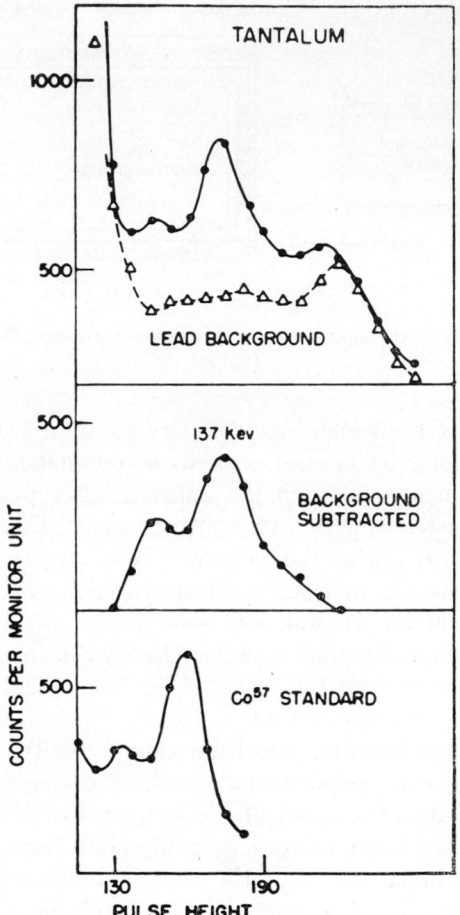

Figure 11. Pulse-height spectrum obtained with a tantalum scatterer in the apparatus of Fig. 10. The 124-kev radiation from a Co[57] source is shown for comparison (Gu56).

stopped in a sodium iodide crystal, and only a thin layer on the surfaces exposed to the γ rays is effective in their detection. On the other hand the neutron-induced background depends on the volume of the crystal; thus a thin crystal with a large surface-to-volume ratio gives a good signal-to-background effect, and can be placed in the direct neutron beam, close to the source. Guernsey and

Wattenburg (Gu56) have investigated the properties of thin NaI crystals for this application and have found for example that, for 124-kev γ radiation, a 1-mm thick crystal has a resolution about the same as that of a 3-cm thick crystal and a detection efficiency only 3 or 4 times less. The experimental arrangement used by Guernsey and Wattenburg for inelastic scattering investigations is shown in Fig. 10. A NaI crystal 1 mm thick and 2.5 cm² in area, and the photomultiplier tube to which it was cemented, were enclosed in a thin light-tight aluminum case and a cylindrical shield of lead, iron, and mu-metal. The scattering sample, effectively of infinite thickness with respect to attenuation of the γ rays under investigation, was placed immediately in front of the crystal, and was backed by a $1/_8$-inch thick lead disc which could stop low-energy γ rays although it was transparent to the neutrons. The positions of this lead disc and of the sample could be reversed, in which situation the γ rays from the sample were absorbed, but the background in the crystal was unaltered. A subtraction of the spectra obtained before and after this reversal thus gave the required spectrum of γ rays produced in the sample. The curves obtained in this way for tantalum (137-kev level), together with a comparison 124-kev spectrum due to Co^{57} are given in Fig. 11. This technique allows the measurement of absolute yields and cross sections. (Further details are given in Chapter V.I.)

A geometrical arrangement similar to that of Fig. 10, with somewhat thicker crystals and samples, has been used by Rothman et al. (Ro57) to study γ rays up to 960 kev (in Rh^{103} and Nb^{93}). Absolute cross sections could not be estimated directly in this case but relative yields were obtained.

C. Closed Geometry

In the open geometry experiments described in the preceding sections the amount of shielding material in the vicinity of the apparatus is kept to a minimum. However, in a situation where it is not possible to have the neutron source well away from thick walls and floors, the scattered neutron flux in the room can cause very serious background problems in an unshielded arrangement. The use of a very thin NaI crystal to avoid this is only possible in the study of low-energy γ rays. In general, shielding of the source offers a reasonable solution in such a case. The system must be carefully designed

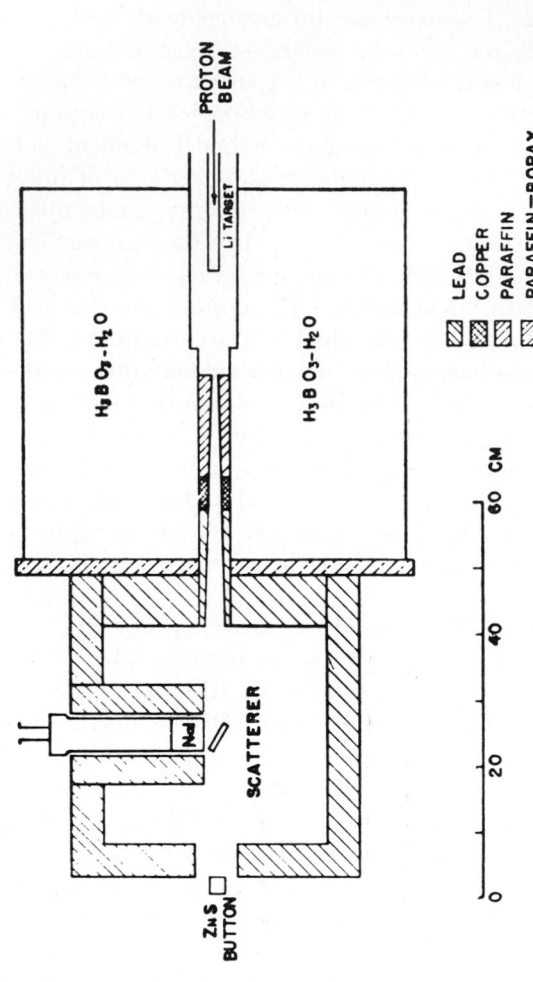

Figure 12. Shielded system (closed geometry) for studying γ rays from neutron inelastic scattering (Va56).

to keep degraded neutrons from reaching the sample and crystal detector. (The general problem of neutron collimation and shielding is discussed in Chapter IV.E.) A satisfactory arrangement developed by Van Loef and Lind (Va56) for (n, n') studies is illustrated in Fig. 12. The $Li^7(p, n)$ source was situated inside a 60-cm barrel, filled with boric acid and water, which served to slow down and capture most of the unwanted neutrons. The forward beam of neutrons was collimated by paraffin and copper cylinders forming a conical hole with an apex at the target. A lead cylinder at the end of the collimator acted as a shield without seeing the primary neutron beam. The scattering samples were discs, about 4 cm in diameter and 1 cm thick, placed at an angle of 60° to the beam direction, in a chamber enclosed by 5-cm thick lead walls. The sodium iodide crystal detector had additional shielding. A ZnS and lucite button was used for monitoring the beam. This apparatus was used successfully, with neutron bombarding energies up to 1.8 Mev, for studying the γ rays from Fe, Mn, I, and F, including excitation functions and absolute yields. In the confined target room available to the experimenters, this system gave an appreciably lower background than was attainable with an open geometry arrangement in the same situation, but it did not give as favorable a signal-to-background ratio as has been obtained in the best open (ring) geometry systems discussed in Section 3.A. However the shielded system had the advantage of being readily adaptable to angular distribution measurements (see Section 6).

D. The Time-of-Flight Technique

A promising method which discriminates against the prompt neutron-induced background in a NaI detector, and which at the same time allows small scattering samples to be used, has recently been developed by Day and Lind (Da56b, Da57). It is based on Cranberg's suggestion that the neutron time-of-flight be used to distinguish between γ rays due to inelastic scattering in the sample, and the background due to neutrons scattered from the sample into the detector. The experimental arrangement is shown schematically in Fig. 13. The scatterer, in the form of a disc, is placed about 4 cm from a pulsed neutron source (the $T(p, n)$ reaction in a tritium gas target) so that it receives neutrons emitted in the forward direction. The NaI detector is situated about 18 cm from the scatterer, in the

90° direction, and is shielded from direct neutrons by a tungsten wedge. With this geometry the γ rays produced in the scattering sample, as a result of a given pulse of primary neutrons of energy 1 or 2 Mev, reach the detector about 10^{-8} sec before the neutrons scattered by the sample begin to arrive there. It is arranged that only those pulses from the crystal are analyzed which occur at the times corresponding to γ-ray arrival. A typical time spectrum obtained as a result of bombarding a 4.3-gm sample of Zr^{94} with 1.71-Mev neutrons is given in Fig. 14a; time is increasing from right to left. The groups of pulses due to γ rays and to scattered neutrons are shown for each

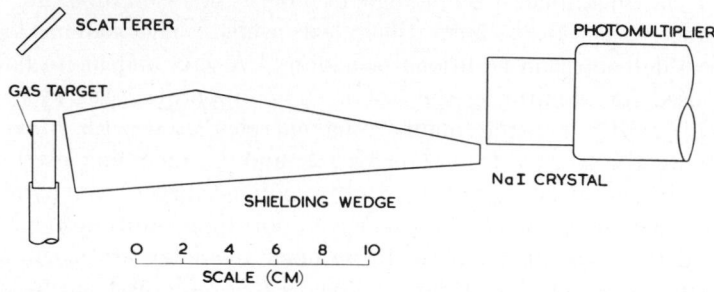

Figure 13. Experimental arrangement for observing γ rays following neutron inelastic scattering with a pulsed neutron source and a time-of-flight technique. (Da56b, Da57).

half of the radio-frequency cycle which produced the pulsed neutrons by sweeping the proton beam across a slit before it reached the tritium target. Two single-channel analyzers were adjusted to cover only those peaks in the time spectrum corresponding to γ-ray arrival, and the pulses from these were used to gate a pulse-height analyzer which displayed pulses from the NaI crystal detector. The resulting gated spectrum is shown in Fig. 14b; the upper and lower curves represent runs with and without the scattering sample in position (note that the ordinate scale is logarithmic). The spectra give evidence for peaks corresponding to γ rays with energies 0.92, 0.56, and 0.39 Mev from Zr^{94}. The thresholds for excitation of these and higher energy γ rays were observed and the Zr^{94} level scheme thereby deduced; samples of Zr^{90} and Zr^{92} were similarly studied (Da57). The level schemes obtained in this way are shown in Fig. 15 which illustrates well the value of this technique for the investigation of separated isotopes.[2]

In comparing this method with the simpler small-sample method described in Section 3.B we note that in the present case the loss of efficiency involved in the withdrawal of the detector from the sample to a distance of about 20 cm is more than compensated for by the location of the sample only 4 cm from the neutron source. This,

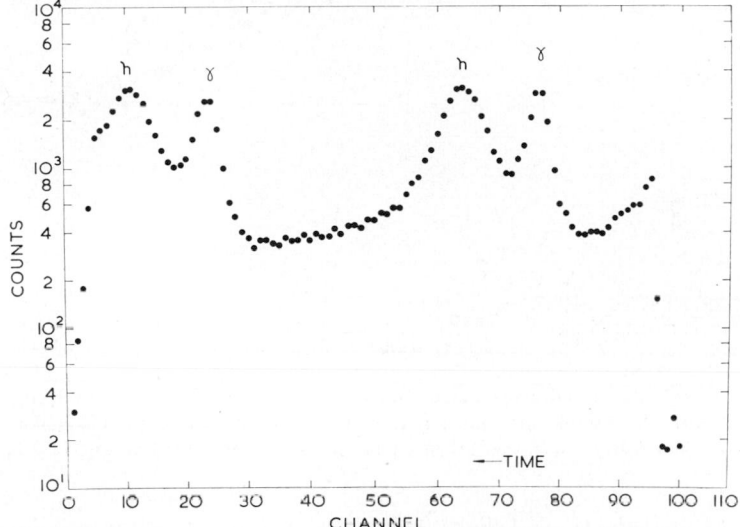

Figure 14a. Time spectrum for Zr[94] bombarded with 1.71-Mev pulsed neutrons; time is increasing from right to left, and one channel is equivalent to about 0.8 mμsec (Da56b, Da57).

plus the reduction in background level, results in a good signal-to-background ratio. Moreover in the time-of-flight method the background spectrum, due mainly to room-scattered neutrons, can be fairly well reproduced by taking a run with the scattering sample removed, whereas in the other method the background effect due to the scatterer is not so simply obtained. Another advantage of the geometry of Fig. 13 plus the time-of-flight technique is the reduction in background from radioactive samples (such as Th[232] and U[238]).

[2] The author is grateful to Dr. R. B. Day for sending these results in advance of publication and also for reading and offering comments on this review.

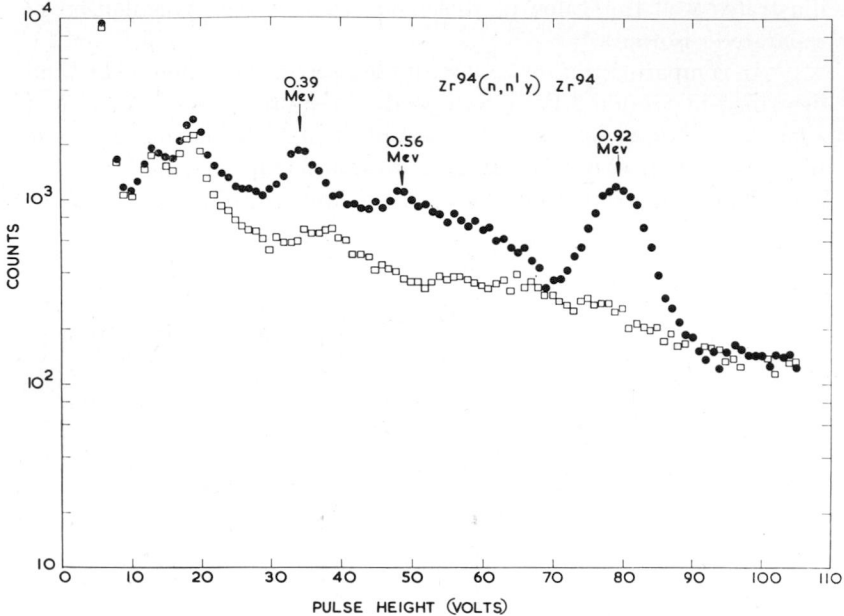

Figure 14b. Gated pulse-height spectra of γ rays. The upper curve was taken with the sample in; the γ-ray energies corresponding to the peaks are shown. The lower curve was taken with the sample out (Da56b, Da57).

Use of the time-of-flight technique to eliminate neutron-induced backgrounds has also been reported by Schrader *et al.* (Sc57). The γ-ray spectra due to 14-Mev neutrons incident on ring scatterers of various materials were obtained; these spectra were in general found to show some structure below 2 Mev, with a continuum above 2 Mev. An interesting observation was the fact that with a lead scatterer all the γ-ray lines observed could be identified with transitions in Pb^{206} or Pb^{207}, suggesting that the predominant contribution was from γ rays following $(n, 2n)$ reactions.

In the experiments just described the neutron time-of-flight technique has been used simply to remove the unwanted neutron-induced background; all the γ rays resulting from inelastic scattering are recorded. In order to select only those γ rays corresponding to excitation of a given level of the scattering nucleus one would have to use a separate neutron detector to resolve the inelastically scattered

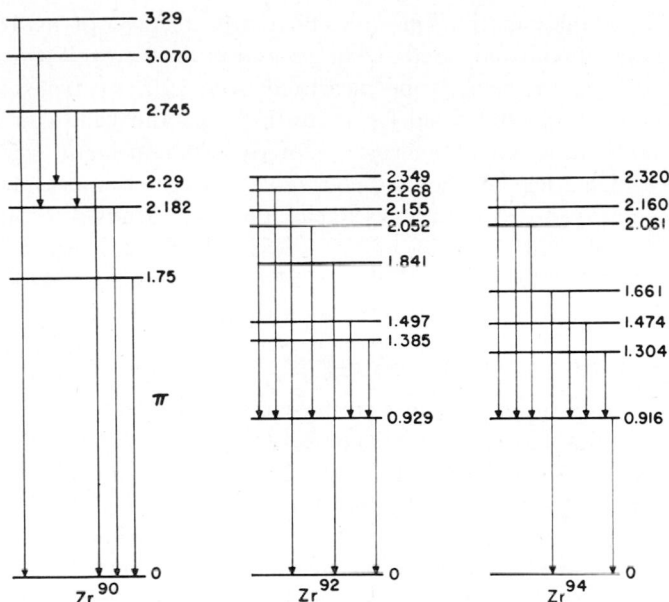

Figure 15. Level and decay schemes of the isotopes of zirconium, derived from γ-ray observations using the time-of-flight technique (Da57).

neutron groups by their time-of-flight. The γ-ray detector could then be placed close to the scatterer and those pulses in coincidence with a selected inelastic neutron group could be analyzed. Such an experiment would assist in interpreting a complicated level scheme in which a number of cascade decays were occurring. It would however be rather difficult because of low counting rates.

E. Excitation of Isomeric States

For a number of nuclei which have a fairly low lying level with a spin differing by several units from the spins of all lower levels, the de-excitation of this level by γ radiation may be delayed by seconds or even hours. Such levels can be excited directly by neutron inelastic scattering because the barrier factor for neutron penetration into the nucleus is quite small even when the angular momentum is greater than zero. In such cases the γ radiation following the inelastic process can be studied after the neutron irradiation has ceased,

and the troublesome background effects due to prompt neutron reactions are thereby avoided. The cross section for excitation of an
isomeric level can usually be measured even with neutron energies
quite close to the threshold for excitation, and the yield can be followed as a function of energy. Moreover the inelastic scattering
to those higher levels which happen to decay to the isomeric state can
also be observed. A number of nuclei have been studied in this way,
for example: Cd^{111} (Fr53), Pb^{207} (St55), In^{115} and Au^{197} (Co48,
Eb54, Ma54), Hg^{199} and Ba^{137} (Sw54). For further discussion of
excitation functions for isomeric states see Chapter V.I.

4. Calibration of the Gamma-Ray Detector

For calibration of the scintillation detector in terms of γ-ray
energies, suitable radioactive sources of γ rays of known energy are
used. Care has to be taken to check the possibility of rate-dependent
gain shifts in the photomultiplier or amplifier systems (Be55b), since
the counting rates in the neutron scattering experiments are often
quite large. Under satisfactory conditions the energies of γ rays
following inelastic neutron scattering can be measured by means of a
sodium iodide crystal with a standard deviation of 1 per cent or less.
This allows a more accurate determination of nuclear level positions
than is possible at present from neutron energy measurements.

The spectral shapes obtained for the γ rays from standard
sources are also necessary for the analysis of complex spectra: the
contribution of each γ ray in the spectrum is determined by fitting
the appropriate standard shape, beginning with the highest energy
peak, and *peeling off* each γ ray in turn. To give the correct standard
shapes, the radioactive sources should be placed in the same mean
position, relative to the crystal detector, as is normally occupied by
the scattering sample. Moreover the sources should be such as to
give the same average Compton scattering as the sample. The
spectral shapes are particularly sensitive to these factors in the case
of γ rays with energies of about 2 Mev or greater. Interpolations
between standard shapes corresponding to different energies can be
adopted when required.

Another possibility which must be allowed for when the scattering sample is close to the detector (as in the ring geometry method
for example) is that of coincident detection of two γ rays in cascade,
leading to a sum peak which may be mistaken for a cross-over transi-

tion.   The magnitude of this effect, which may amount to several per cent in some cases, can be calculated or determined experimentally with a suitable standard source of coincident γ rays.   An easy method to confirm the existence of a sum peak is to observe the change in intensity as a function of the source-to-detector distance l: the variation will be approximately as l^4 for a sum peak and as l^2 for a crossover peak.

Table II.   Some Gamma-Ray Sources Suitable for Energy and Spectral Shape Calibrations (Adopted values as given by Ma60)

Source	Eγ (Mev)	Half-life
Am^{241}	0.05958	458 years
Co^{57}	0.12198	268 days
Ce^{141}	0.1455	32 days
In^{114m}	0.1903	50 days
Hg^{203}	0.27912	47 days
Cr^{51}	0.321	28 days
Au^{198}	0.41176	2.7 days
Be^7	0.4780	54 days
Cs^{137}	0.6616	28 years
Nb^{95}	0.764	35 days
Mn^{54}	0.835	314 days
Zn^{65}	1.114 and 0.51094	244 days
Sc^{46}	1.118 and 0.892	84 days
Na^{22}	1.2736 and 0.51094	2.6 years
Co^{60}	1.3325 and 1.1727	5.2 years
K^{42}	1.52 and 0.32	12.8 hours
Al^{28}	1.78	2.3 min
Y^{88}	1.841 and 0.900	105 days
Sb^{124}	2.088, 1.692, and 0.605	60 days
Mn^{56}	2.12, 1.80, and 0.85	2.6 hours
Ce^{144}(Pr^{144})	2.18, 1.48, and 0.69	290 days
RdTh (ThC″)	2.6142	1.9 years
Na^{24}	2.754 and 1.368	15 hours
S^{37}	3.13	5 min
Pu-α-Be ⎱		24,000 years
Ra-α-Be ⎰ Be$^9(\alpha,n\gamma)$C^{12}	4.432	1,622 years
Po-α-Be		138 days

For the measurement of the absolute efficiency of the detector radioactive sources of known strength are used. The best procedure is to make these sources in the same geometrical form and size as the scattering sample and in such a way that the attenuation is the same. Details of absolute calibration methods and the necessary corrections for cross section determinations are discussed in Chapter V.I.

In Table II are listed some γ-ray sources which have been found useful for energy calibration of the detector and for spectral analysis. Some additional sources as well as representative spectral distributions are given in a catalogue prepared by Heath (He57). In addition to these sources there are quite a number of reactions which can be used to produce strong monoenergetic γ rays; these are particularly useful for filling in gaps between the energies available from radioactive nuclei. Examples are $(p, \alpha\gamma)$ reactions in Na^{23} (giving a 1.63-Mev γ ray) and in Be^9 (3.57-Mev γ ray), and $(p, p'\gamma)$ or $(n, n'\gamma)$ reactions in F^{19} (0.110 and 0.197 Mev), V^{51} (0.325 Mev), Zr^{92,94} (0.92 Mev), Si^{28} (1.78 Mev), and S^{32} (2.24 Mev).

5. Coincidence Measurements

A. Gamma-Gamma Coincidences

We have seen that the study of γ rays from inelastic scattering at one neutron energy only does not allow one to deduce uniquely

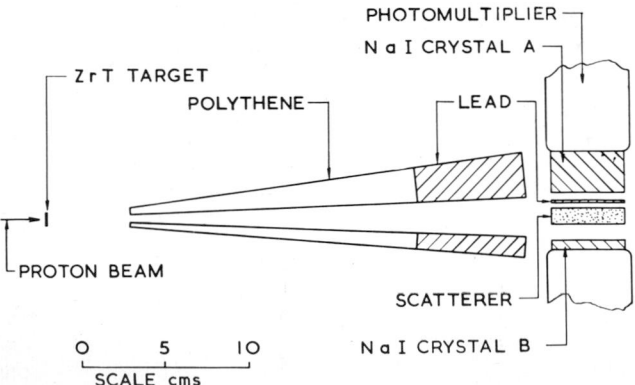

Figure 16. Experimental arrangements for γ-γ coincidence measurements (Fr56).

the level positions of the target nucleus.   This latter information may be obtained from observation of the thresholds for excitation of the γ rays, from measuring the energies of the inelastic neutron groups, or from other data such as radioactive decay or charged particle reactions.   The latter data are not always available, and the threshold and neutron measurements may not be precise enough if there are closely-spaced levels.   In some such cases additional infor-

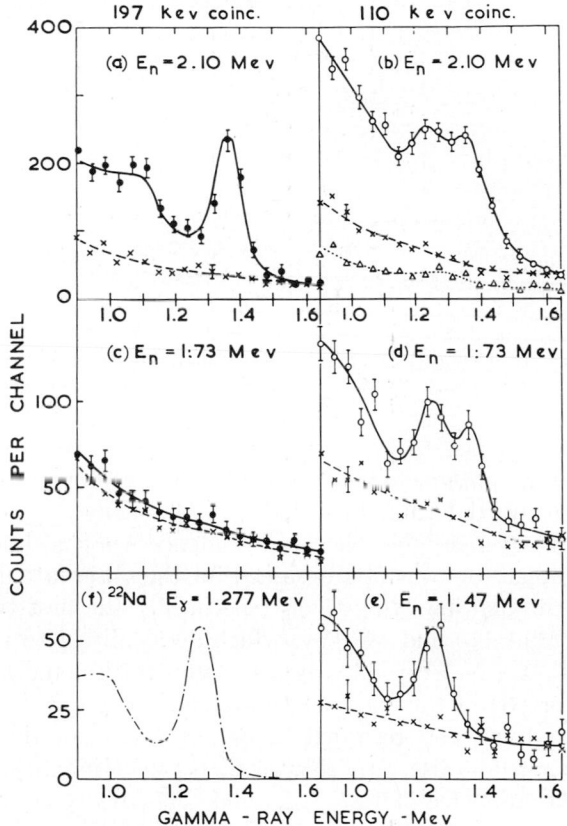

Figure 17. Gamma-ray spectra from F^{19} in coincidence with 197-kev radiation (full curves (a) and (c)), and with 110-kev radiation (full curves (b), (d), and (e)), for the neutron energies indicated. Broken curves represent similar runs with a carbon scatterer; the dotted curve in (b) shows the random rate; curve (f) is a calibration spectrum from a Na^{22} source (Fr56).

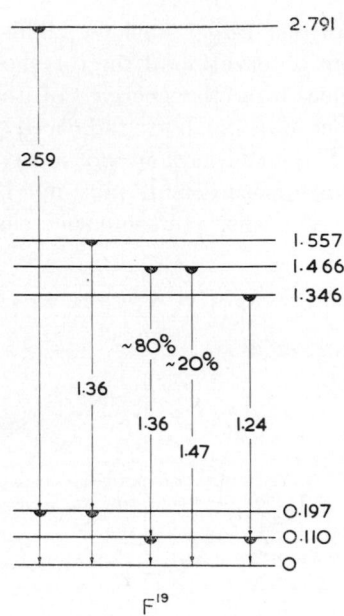

Figure 18. Level and decay scheme of F^{19} deduced from ring geometry and coincidence experiments. Level and γ-ray energies are given in Mev (Fr56, Fr57).

mation may be obtained from γ-γ coincidence measurements, which also assist in the determination of the decay scheme.

An arrangement suitable for coincidence work is shown in Fig. 16. This apparatus was first designed for the observation of γ rays cascading through low-lying levels (specifically the first two excited states of F^{19} at 110 and 197 kev, which decay direct to the ground state), so that a NaI crystal only a few mm thick could be used for one detector (B) of the coincidence system. The other crystal (A) was 2.5 cm thick and recorded harder γ rays from the scatterer, which was a teflon disc. (A ring-geometry experiment had already revealed the existence of 1.24, 1.36, and 1.47-Mev γ radiation from the F^{19} ($n, n'\gamma$) reaction.) Pulses were selected from crystal B if they occurred in one of the two photopeaks corresponding to 110 and 197-kev radiation; the pulses from crystal A arriving in coincidence with each of these photopeaks were displayed in turn on a gated pulse-height analyzer. With a resolving time of about 0.5 μsec the random

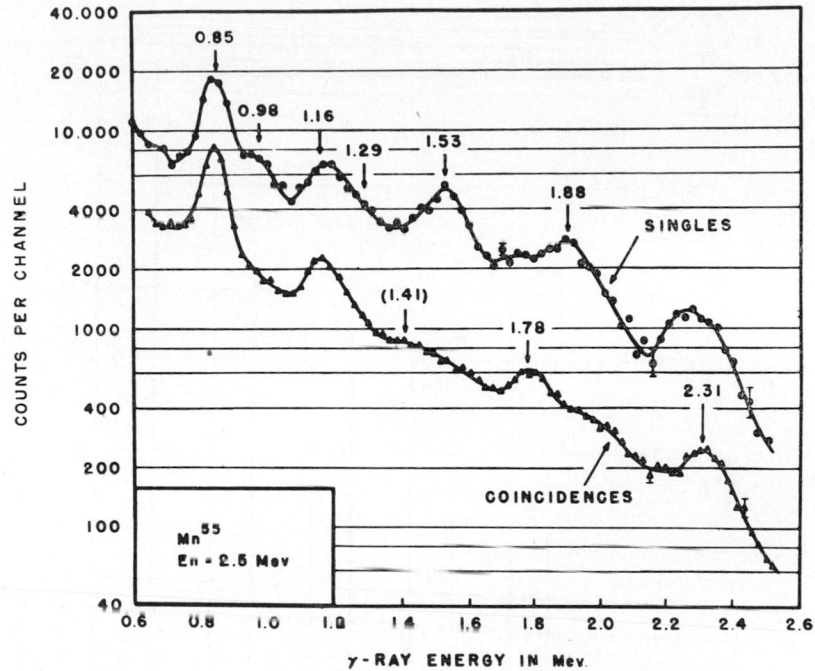

Figure 19. Single-crystal spectrum and spectrum in coincidence with 128-kev γ rays obtained from the bombardment of Mn⁵⁵ with 2.5-Mev neutrons (Ro58).

rate was quite small; a more serious background arose from genuine coincidences due mainly to Compton-scattered γ rays from crystal A reaching crystal B. This effect was greatly reduced by a 2-mm thick lead absorber placed between the scattering sample and crystal A; this stopped the soft scattered γ rays from reaching B, while having a negligible effect on the harder γ rays coming from the scatterer to A. Typical coincidence spectra are shown in Fig. 17 for the neutron bombarding energies indicated. Curve (a) shows that there are 1.36-Mev γ rays going to the 197-kev state; (b) shows both 1.36 and 1.24-Mev γ rays going to the 110-kev state. This then suggests the existence of three levels, at 1.56, 1.47, and 1.35 Mev. The coincidence spectra below the effective 1.56-Mev level threshold (curves c and d) and below the effective 1.47-Mev level threshold (curve e) confirm this deduction. The F¹⁹ level scheme deduced from these and ring geometry measurements is shown in Fig. 18. The

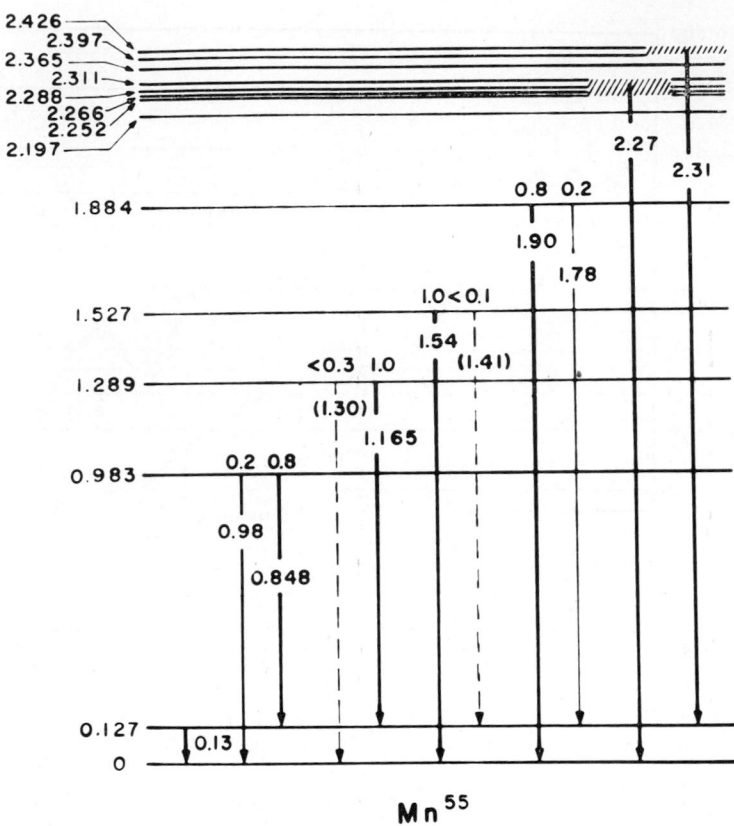

Mn^{55}

Figure 20. Decay scheme for Mn^{55} deduced from observations of γ-γ coincidence following inelastic neutron scattering. The branching ratios shown above the γ-ray transitions are preliminary figures (Ro58).

coincidence experiments were vital in revealing the complexity of the 1.36-Mev radiation as well as in putting upper limits (of less than 10 per cent) on some of the unobserved transitions.

An experimental arrangement similar to that of Fig. 16, but with a thicker crystal *B*, has recently been applied to a study of γ rays in the energy range 1.6 to 2.6 Mev from Na$^{23}(n, n'\gamma)$ in coincidence with transitions from the first excited state (440 kev). Although more difficult than the F^{19} experiment, because of the background due to double-scattering events of various kinds, it has successfully revealed a number of cascade transitions to the 440-kev level (Fr58).

Gamma-gamma coincidences following inelastic neutron scattering have also been observed by Beghian et al. (Be56) for the case of Mn,[55] the spectrum of γ rays cascading through the first excited state at 128 kev being recorded. The sample and the two crystal detectors were placed, unshielded, close to a D(d, n) source, and a 1-mm thick crystal was used for detecting pulses in the 128-kev peak. The same reaction has recently been studied further by Rothman et al. (Ro58) with a geometrical arrangement similar to that of Fig. 16. Typical single crystal and coincidence spectra obtained by them are shown in Fig. 19, and the preliminary decay scheme deduced from their results is given in Fig. 20.[3]

B. Neutron-Gamma Coincidences

The possibility of selecting for observation those γ rays in coincidence with a given inelastic neutron group, chosen by its time-of-flight, has already been mentioned (Section 3.D), but such an experiment has not yet been performed. A less ambitious coincidence experiment is that of analyzing all the pulses from the γ-ray detector which are in coincidence with counts in a neutron detector, both detectors being fairly close to the scattering sample (time separation of the inelastically scattered neutrons is not then involved). Such an experiment has been described by Garrett et al. (Ga53) in studies of γ rays from Al, Fe, Mg, and Cu. By this method much of the objectionable background in the sodium iodide detector was removed. A shielded target and detector system was used, and care was taken to prevent inelastic scattering or Compton scattering from the sodium iodide crystal into the organic scintillator which served as the neutron detector. The complimentary procedure of recording a neutron spectrum in coincidence with pulses in the photopeak of a selected γ ray has also been reported [1.43-Mev γ ray from chromium (Sh54)].

With the development of milli-microsecond coincidence equipment, the n-γ coincidence method shows promise of considerable versatility. Its use has been described recently by Naggiar et al. (Na57, Sz58) for the study of the angular distribution of inelastic neutrons associated with a particular level of the scattering nucleus.

[3] The author is indebted to Dr. D. M. Van Patter for sending these preliminary results in advance of publication.

Fast pulses are taken from both γ-ray and neutron counters, and co-incidences between them (resolving time $\sim 10^{-8}$ sec) are used to open a gate on a pulse-height analyzer, into which are fed slower pulses obtained from one of the dynodes of the photomultiplier used for the γ-ray detector. The intensity of the γ-ray peak corresponding to the level under consideration is then a measure of the relative intensity of inelastic neutron emission to that level (if higher states which can decay to that level are also excited, the neutron emission to these levels will also be included). If the neutron counter is now rotated about the scatterer, then the angular distribution of the neutron group with respect to the direction of the γ-ray detection is obtained. Measurements on iron and iodine (of the NaI crystal) have been made in this way.

6. Angular Distribution Measurements

The measurement of the angular distributions of the γ rays following neutron inelastic scattering, with respect to the direction of the primary neutrons, is clearly of considerable interest for comparison with theory, for assistance in deducing level spins, and for deriving

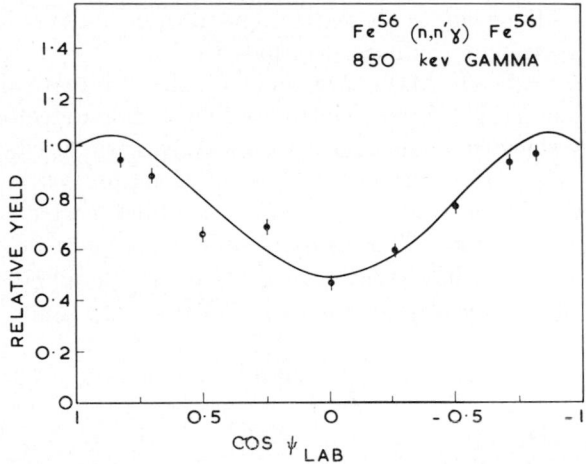

Figure 21. Angular distribution of the 850-kev γ rays from Fe^{56} at a neutron bombarding energy of 1.77 Mev. The curve is a least-squares fit to the experimental points corrected for angular resolution of the detector and finite size of the scatterer (Va56).

inelastic scattering cross sections.   However it is technically difficult because of the NaI background effect, and for this reason very little experimental work of this type has yet been done.   In the open geometry systems discussed in Section 3, any movement of the crystal detector relative to the rest of the apparatus is liable to place it in a different background flux, the nature and effects of which are difficult to predict.   Some experiments have been done with the ring geometry arrangement by moving the γ-ray detector along the axis of the scattering ring.   In this way the crystal remains within the shadow of the shielding cone.   The method has the disadvantage that the detection efficiency varies with angle, but a correction for the variation can be calculated.   Day and Walt (Da56) report having measured the angular distribution of several γ rays in this way.   For an account of a recent experiment using this technique, see Ho59.

Van Loef and Lind (Va56) have used a closed geometry (shielded) system, as discussed in Section 3.C, to measure the angular distribution of the 850-kev γ rays from the first excited state of Fe^{56}. The NaI detector was placed about 8 cm from a cylindrical scatterer of diameter 2 cm and length 4 cm and could be rotated between angles of 25° and 160° with respect to the neutron beam.   The counting rate above the 850-kev photopeak was used as a monitor of the neutron-induced background; no angular dependence of the latter was found.   The angular distribution obtained for the 850-kev γ rays is shown in Fig. 21.   The curve represents a least-squares fit to the experimental points, corrected for angular resolution.   The result shows symmetry about 90° and a $P_4(\cos\theta)$ term consistent with an assignment of 2^+ for the first excited state of Fe^{56}.   The experimental curve was compared with a theoretical expression derived by Satchler (Sa54) on the basis of the statistical model; this expression was later corrected and fairly good agreement with the experimental curve was then obtained (Sa56).

The time-of-flight technique, which allows discrimination against the neutron-induced background by time-separation of the γ rays, offers a promising method for the investigation of angular distributions.   Cranberg and Levin (Cr56) have made some measurements on titanium, iron, and nickel with this technique.   They used a shielded plastic scintillator as the detector, and observed the relative intensities of the γ-ray peaks as well as the neutron groups in their time spectra as the detector was rotated about the scattering sample.   This procedure did not allow discrimination between γ rays of different energies but was quite satifactory for investigating cases where only one level of the target nucleus was being excited by inelastic scattering. An extension of the method used by Day and Lind (see Section 3.D) would allow more complicated cases to be studied.

References

(Ba55)   M. E. Battat and E. R. Graves, *Phys. Rev.* **97,** 1266 (1955).
(Be50)   Beghian, Grace, Preston, and Halban, *Phys. Rev.* **77,** 286 (1950).
(Be55)   Beghian, Hicks, and Milman, *Phil. Mag.* **46,** 924 (1955).
(Be55a) Beghian, Hicks, and Milman, *Phil. Mag.* **46,** 963 (1955).
(Be55b) Bell, Davis, and Bernstein, *Rev. Sci. Instr.* **26,** 726 (1955).
(Be56)   Beghian, Hicks, and Milman, *Phil. Mag.* **1,** 261 (1956).
(Bi50)   M. B. Biram and J. H. Tait, *Atomic Energy Research Establ.* (*Gt. Brit.*) *Report* T/R563 (1950).
(Bi51)   J. B. Birks, *Proc. Phys. Soc.* (*London*) **64A,** 874 (1951).
(Br56)   F. D. Brooks, *Progr. in Nuclear Phys.* **5,** 252 (1956).
(Bu57)   W. W. Buechner and A. Sperduto, *Phys. Rev.* **106,** 1008 (1957).
(Co48)   S. G. Cohen, *Nature* (*London*) **161,** 475 (1948).
(Cr56)   L. Cranberg and J. S. Levin, *Phys. Rev.* **103,** 343 (1956).
(Da53)   R. B. Day, *Phys. Rev.* **89,** 908 (1953).
(Da56)   R. B. Day, *Phys. Rev.* **102,** 767 (1956).
(Da56a) Davis, Divatia, Lind, and Moffat, *Phys. Rev.* **103,** 1801 (1956).
(Da56b) R. B. Day, "Proceedings of the Gatlinburg Conference," *Oak Ridge Natl. Lab. Report* ORNL-2309, p. 90 (1956).
(Da57)   R. B. Day and D. A. Lind, private communication and *Bull. Am. Phys. Soc.* **2,** 32 (1957).
(Eb54)   A. A. Ebel and C. Goodman, *Phys. Rev.* **93,** 197 (1954).
(El54)   Eliot, Hicks, Beghian, and Halban, *Phys. Rev.* **94,** 144 (1954).
(Fa55)   Faust, Scherrer, and Allison, *Phys. Rev.* **98,** 224 (1955).
(Fr53)   Francis, McCue, and Goodman, *Phys. Rev.* **89,** 1232 (1953).
(Fr55)   Freeman, Lane, and Rose, *Phil. Mag.* **46,** 17 (1955).
(Fr55a) J. M. Freeman, *Phil. Mag.* **46,** 12 (1955).
(Fr55b) J. M. Freeman, *Phys. Rev.* **99,** 1446 (1955).
(Fr56)   J. M. Freeman, *Phil. Mag.* **1,** 591 (1956).
(Fr57)   J. M. Freeman, *Phil. Mag.* **2,** 628 (1957).
(Fr57a) J. M. Freeman and J. H. Montague, unpublished results (1957).
(Fr58)   J. M. Freeman and J. H. Montague, *Nuclear Phys.* **9,** 181 (1958).
(Ga53)   Garrett, Hereford, and Sloope, *Phys. Rev.* **92,** 1507 (1953).
(Gl54)   D. W. Glasgow, *Hanford Works Report* HW-32086 (1954).
(Gr51)   Grace, Beghian, Preston, and Halban, *Phys. Rev.* **82,** 969 (1951).
(Gr52)   Grace, Lemmer, and Halban, *Proc. Phys. Soc.* (*London*) **65A,** 456 (1952).
(Gr55)   G. L. Griffith, *Phys. Rev.* **98,** 579 (1955).
(Gr56)   G. L. Griffith, *Phys. Rev.* **103,** 643 (1956).

(Gu54)   J. B. Guernsey and C. Goodman, *Phys. Rev.* **95**, 636 (1954).

(Gu56)   J. B. Guernsey and A. Wattenberg, *Phys. Rev.* **101**, 1516 (1956).

(Ha59)   H. E. Hall and T. W. Bonner, *Nuclear Phys.* **14**, 295 (1959).

(He56)   Heymann, Lindström, and Neuert, *Z. Naturf.* **11A**, 919 (1956).

(He57)   R. L. Heath, "Scintillation Spectrometry; Gamma-Ray Spectrum Catalogue," *Phillips Petroleum Co. (Idaho Falls) Report* IDO-16408 (1957).

(Ho59)   H. Hosoe and S. Suzuki, *J. Phys. Soc. Japan* **14**, 699 (1959).

(Ki35)   Kikuchi, Aoki, and Husimi, *Proc. Phys.-Math. Soc. Japan* **17**, 369 (1935).

(Ki54)   R. M. Kiehn and C. Goodman, *Phys. Rev.* **93**, 177 (1954).

(Ki54a)   R. M. Kiehn and C. Goodman, *Phys. Rev.* **95**, 636 (1954).

(Ki54b)   R. M. Kiehn and C. Goodman, *Phys. Rev.* **95**, 989 (1954).

(Le35)   D. E. Lea, *Proc. Roy. Soc. (London)* **150A**, 637 (1935).

(Li57)   Lind, Day, and Kloepper, *Bull. Am. Phys. Soc.* **2**, 309 (1957).

(Lu54)   D. C. Lu and M. L. Wiedenbeck, *Phys. Rev.* **94**, 501 (1954).

(Ma51)   M. E. Mandl, *Atomic Energy Research Establ. (Gt. Brit.) Report* T/R727 (1951).

(Ma54)   Martin, Diven, and Taschek, *Phys. Rev.* **93**, 199 (1954).

(Ma60)   J. B. Marion, "Nuclear Reaction Graphs," *U. S. Atomic Energy Comm. Report* (1960).

(Mo56)   I. L. Morgan, *Phys. Rev.* **103**, 1031 (1956).

(Na57)   V. Naggiar, *International Conference on Neutron Interactions*, Columbia Univ., New York, September 1957.

(Pr57)   Prud'homme, Sattar, Bostrom, and Morgan, *Bull. Am. Phys. Soc.* **2**, 308 (1957).

(Ra54)   Rayburn, Lafferty, and Hahn, *Phys. Rev.* **94**, 1641 (1954).

(Ra55)   Rayburn, Lafferty, and Hahn, *Phys. Rev.* **98**, 701 (1955).

(Ro53)   B. Rose and J. M. Freeman, *Proc. Phys. Soc. (London)* **66A**, 120 (1953).

(Ro54)   M. A. Rothman and C. E. Mandeville, *Phys. Rev.* **93**, 796 (1954).

(Ro55)   Rothman, Hans, and Mandeville, *Phys. Rev.* **100**, 83 (1955).

(Ro57)   Rothman, Van Patter, Dubey, Porter, and Mandeville, *Phys. Rev.* **107**, 155 (1957).

(Ro58)   Rothman, Van Patter, Nath, and Mandeville, *Bull. Am. Phys. Soc.* **3**, 18 (1958); also *Progress Report of the Bartol Research Foundation, Franklin Institute*, NYO-6461, 4 (1958).

(Sa54)   G. R. Satchler, *Phys. Rev.* **94**, 1304 (1954).

(Sa56)   G. R. Satchler, *Phys. Rev.* **104**, 1199 (1956).

(Sc53)   Scherrer, Theus, and Faust, *Phys. Rev.* **89**, 1268 (1953).

(Sc53a)   Scherrer, Theus, and Faust, *Phys. Rev.* **91**, 1476 (1953).

(Sc55)   Scherrer, Faust, and Allison, *Phys. Rev.* **98**, 224 (1955).

(Sc57)   Schrader, Benveniste, and Zenger, *Bull. Am. Phys. Soc.* **2**, 309 (1957).

(Se37)   Seaborg, Gibson, and Grahame, *Phys. Rev.* **52**, 408 (1937).

(Sh54)   Shapiro, Scherrer, Allison, and Faust, *Phys. Rev.* **95**, 751 (1954).

(Sh57)   P. Shapiro and R. W. Higgs, *Phys. Rev.* **108**, 760 (1957).

(Sh57a)   P. Shapiro and R. W. Higgs, *Rev. Sci. Instr.* **28**, 939 (1957).

(Si55)   R. M. Sinclair, *Phys. Rev.* **99**, 1351 (1955).

(Si56)   R. M. Sinclair, *Phys. Rev.* **102,** 461 (1956).

(Si57)   R. M. Sinclair, *Phys. Rev.* **107,** 1307 (1957).

(St55)   P. H. Stelson and E. C. Campbell, *Phys. Rev.* **97,** 1222 (1955).

(Sw54)   C. P. Swann and F. R. Metzger, *Phys. Rev.* **95,** 636(A) (1954).

(Sz58)   Szteinsznaider, Roclawski-Conjeaud, Naggiar, and Phillips, *J. phys. radium* **19,** 54 (1958); also *Compt. rend.* **245,** 668 (1957).

(Th54)   L. C. Thompson and J. R. Risser, *Phys. Rev.* **94,** 941 (1954).

(Va56)   J. J. Van Loef and D. A. Lind, *Phys. Rev.* **101,** 103 (1956).

(Wo56)   E. A. Wolf, *Phil. Mag.* **1,** 102 (1956).

Neutron Cross Sections in the kev Region

H. W. Newson, *Duke University, Durham, North Carolina*

and

J. H. Gibbons, *Oak Ridge National Laboratory, Oak Ridge, Tennessee*

1. Introduction

Soon after the discovery of neutron-induced radioactivity by Fermi and his collaborators, it was shown that the radiative capture processes took place at very low neutron energies and were highly energy-sensitive. Theoretical understanding of the indicated resonances resulted from the compound nucleus picture of Bohr and the development of the one-level dispersion formula by Breit and Wigner. By 1937 when Bethe reviewed the problem (Be37a) the theory had been so well developed that his discussion is still pertinent even though all the experimental measurements he discussed are obsolete. This review treated the compound nucleus statistically and emphasized the importance of the average level spacing of the compound nuclei formed by neutrons (see Section 5.G). The theoretical considerations reviewed by Bethe indicated that this *average spacing should change very slowly among the heavier elements ($A \geq 80$)*. This rule was in agreement with the rather sparse experimental evidence available at the time and in general with the much better data obtained during the next decade.

A second rule may also be formulated from Bethe's arguments and the data available at that time. The inverse lifetime of a heavy compound nucleus for γ-ray emission, that is $\Gamma_\gamma/\hbar$ should *not vary greatly from nucleus to nucleus or from level to level of the same compound nucleus*. The third rule may be formulated by combining the previous two; it is then easy to show (see Chapter V.M) that the *capture cross section, averaged over a wide enough energy range to include many resonances, should be a smooth, slowly varying function of mass number.*

A fourth rule developed more slowly. Arguments were put forth that the dimensionless quantity now known as the *strength function* was a universal constant with a value of about 10^{-4} (Be37a,Fe47). *This rule predicts (Bl52) that all total neutron cross sections averaged over an energy interval much greater than the average spacing, D, should be monotonically decreasing functions of neutron energy and should change little from element to element except for a dependence on the nuclear radius.*

During the last ten years serious exceptions were discovered to all of these rules. Barschall (Ba52) showed that total cross sections did not by any means decrease monotonically with energy after the effects of individual resonances had been averaged and hence the strength function was *not* a universal constant. Similarly Hughes *et al.* (Hu53) showed that the average capture cross section (near 1 Mev) went through minima at the magic numbers 50, 82, and 126 and, hence that one or both of the other rules had been violated. Newson and Rohrer (Ne54) showed that the average level spacings for most of the magic and near magic compound nuclei fall between 1 and 100 kev, several hundred times the spacings of the normal heavy compound nuclei, thus invalidating the first rule. Exceptions to the second rule are discussed in Chapter V.M.

These rules are still valuable guides (with certain exceptions) and must be considered theoretical successes. However if the rules had proved to be perfectly accurate, the future of neutron physics and particularly that in the kev region would have been bleak. The results of almost any fast neutron cross section measurement could have been predicted from a few sample measurements mostly at low energies and a few high energy measurements (above the kev region) would have been sufficient to verify the predictions. Furthermore, if equations derived from such very general considerations were completely valid, little could be learned about the structure of nuclei or the nature of nuclear forces by the methods of neutron physics. This would have been particularly true of work in the kev region for which experimental methods had not been developed at the time when the rules were formulated.

Up to energies of a few hundred kev, neutron physics is now largely concerned with violations of the above rules; that is, with variations of strength functions, capture functions, and average spacings as a function of nucleon numbers and angular momenta for intermediate, magic, and normal heavy nuclei. For higher energy neutrons it is not generally feasible to measure these specific quantities, but models may be tested by comparing measured cross section curves to theoretical predictions. A very considerable improvement in compound-nucleus models has already resulted from such work and further improvements are anticipated.

2. Interpretation of Experiments

In interpreting a neutron cross section curve of any sort, it is desirable whenever possible to identify the spins and parities (J^{π}) of the individual levels which are observed as resonances. We have defined the kev region (1 to 150 kev) so that, in general, only elastic scattering contributes appreciably (i.e., more than a few per cent) to the total cross section. The levels of the compound nucleus which cause the observation of resonances in a cross section curve can in general be assigned as to spin and parity, J^{π}, by inspection if the resolution is sufficiently high. Even if the resolution is so poor that no individual resonances are recognizable, one can still interpret the cross section curve in terms of an averaged parameter, the strength function previously referred to, and hard sphere or potential scattering which, unlike resonance scattering, is a slowly varying function of energy. The theoretical basis necessary for these interpretations will now be reviewed briefly.

A. The Breit-Wigner Formula

The reader is referred to a complete discussion of the resonance formalism given in Chapter V.E. In this section we present only a few remarks concerning effects in the kev range. The dispersion-theory formula, already familiar from atomic physics, was first applied to single-nuclear energy levels by Breit and Wigner (Br36) and Bohr (Bo36) and extended to many levels by Wigner and Eisenbud (Wi47). The single-level formula was re-derived in a form particularly useful to the experimentalist by Feshbach, Peaslee, and Weisskopf (Fe47). In their notation the s-wave scattering cross section (in the kev region) may be written as the sum of the effects of the two possible channels corresponding to total angular momentum $J = I \pm \frac{1}{2}$;

$$\sigma_n = \sigma_n(I + \tfrac{1}{2}) + \sigma_n(I - \tfrac{1}{2}) \cong \sigma_T \qquad (1)$$

where

$$\sigma_n(I \pm \tfrac{1}{2}) = \pi \lambda^2 g_{\pm} \left| \frac{i\Gamma_{\pm}}{(E - E_{\pm}) + i\Gamma_{\pm}/2} + (\exp 2ikr_{\pm}) - 1 \right|^2 \quad (2)$$

The symbols k and λ are the wave number and Dirac wave length, respectively; $E_{\pm}$ gives the resonance energies of the nearest resonances to the neutron energy, E, in each channel; $\Gamma_{\pm}$ indicates corresponding neutron widths; the $kr_{\pm}$ are phase shifts which change slowly with energy and are not usually the same for both channels.[1] The statistical weight factor, $g_{\pm} = (2J + 1)/2(2I + 1)$, is double-valued except when the spin of the target nucleus, $I = 0$. Otherwise $g_{\pm} = \tfrac{1}{2} \pm [2(2I + 1)]^{-1}$.

The use of $r_+ \neq r_-$ in the neighborhood of each resonance takes account of resonance-resonance interference to some extent since r includes the coherent effects of the nearby resonances, but it is obvious that (2) is not general enough to describe all resonances which may be expected to occur in the lower kev region. Methods for analysis of these more complicated cases (Wi47) have been developed recently (Bo62).

If a resonance is very well separated from its neighbors in all channels or if $I = 0$, Eq. (1) reduces to the familiar form:

$$\sigma_T \approx \sigma_n = \frac{\sigma_0}{1 + x^2} + \sigma_0 \tan 2kr' \left(\frac{x}{1 + x^2} \right) + 4\pi\lambda^2 \sin^2 kr' \quad (2a)$$

When (2a) applies the subscript $\pm$ is dropped except for the statistical weight factor. $x \equiv 2(E - E_0)/\Gamma$ and $\sigma_0 \equiv 4\pi g_{\pm}\lambda^2 \cos^2 2k_0 r$. The third term in (2a) may include the effects of interference with neighboring resonances in the same channel and should not be confused with the potential scattering as defined by Feshbach, Porter, and Weisskopf (Fe54).

In addition, p- or d-wave resonances ($l = 1$ or 2) will sometimes be observed which add incoherently to the effects of s waves as given in (1), although (2) still holds. Clearly g_J can assume two or more values for these higher angular momentum interactions. The scat-

---

[1] The use of the undefined shift kr rather than the potential phase shift kr' makes (2) an approximate multilevel formula, since some account is taken of coherent additions of neighboring resonances. Except for interpretation of the cross section near a particular resonance, r' should be written instead of r.

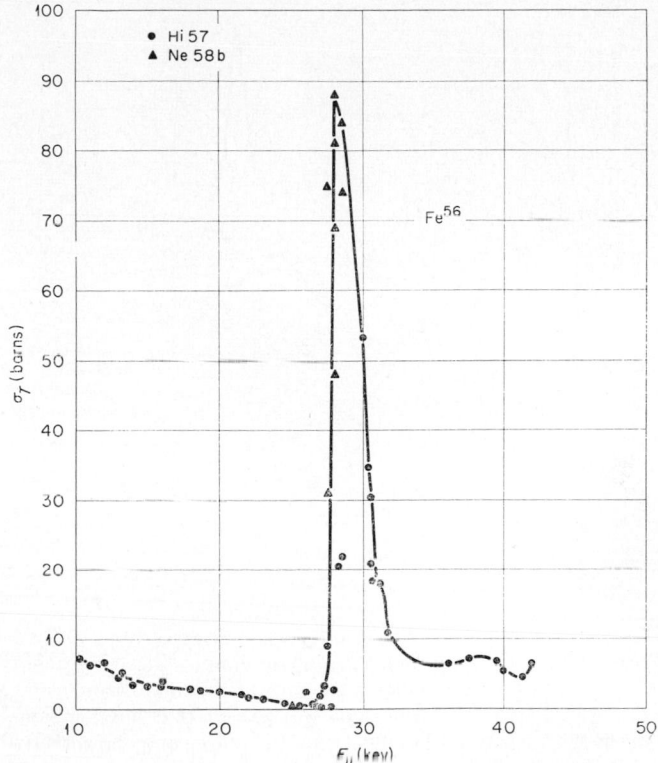

Figure 1. The total cross section of iron near the resonance at 28 kev. The dots were measured with pure Fe^{56} (Hi57) and the triangles with natural Fe (Bi57). The peak cross section is very near the theoretical maximum.

tering cross section for such a resonance in the kilovolt region may be obtained from (2) by setting $r \cong 0$:

$$\sigma_n \cong \sigma_0/(1 + x^2) \cong 4\pi g \lambda^2 \Gamma_n^2/[4(E - E_0)^2 + \Gamma^2], \; l \neq 0 \quad (3)$$

p- and d-wave resonances in the kev region are usually narrow enough that interference with tails of neighboring resonances are not important. The approximation $r = 0$ when $l \neq 0$ breaks down at high energy, but should usually be valid in the kev region. Thus the observation of interference in the low kev region is sufficient evidence to assign a resonance to s-wave neutrons. It is shown later that for a *given reduced width*, the corresponding observed width, Γ_n, decreases

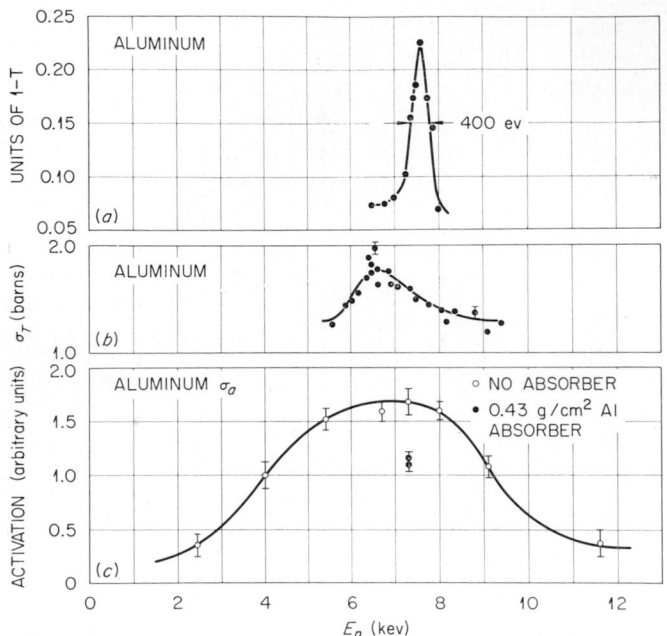

Figure 2. A low energy resonance in aluminum. The circles on the lower curve (c) were measured (Ro54) by activating an aluminum sample at 120°; the solid points were measured in the same way except that another sample of Al, 0.43 g/cm² in thickness, was placed between the source and the activated sample (Ro54). The middle curve (b) is a total cross section measured (with a very thick sample) at 120° with a 2 × 20° opening. The upper curve which is a plot of 1-T rather than cross section was measured at 160° with an 0.5° opening, (Bi57). The width at half maximum (after allowing for potential scattering) gives a good indication of the neutron energy spread.

rapidly for increasing values of l, the angular momentum of the neutron. Thus the approximation $\Gamma = \Gamma_n + \Gamma_\gamma \approx \Gamma_n$ which is generally valid for observable s-wave resonances in the kev region may not be true for p- or d-wave resonances. This effect is particularly important in the interpretation of resonances leading to observable capture cross sections. Since λ and the Γ's are more slowly varying functions than $(E - E_0)$, (3) describes a nearly symmetric peak for p- or d-wave resonance (for $E_0 \gg \Gamma$) with maximum cross section, $\sigma_0 = 4\pi g\lambda^2 \Gamma_n/\Gamma \approx 4\pi g\lambda^2$ for nearly all total cross sections. On the other hand (2) and (2a) contain the asymmetric interference term (since x

changes sign at the resonance energy) and there will be a minimum as well as a maximum for s-wave resonances. However, $\sigma_{max} - \sigma_{min} = 4\pi\lambda^2 g$; the minimum cross section σ_{min} goes to zero when $g = 1$ and $l_{neutrons} = 0$ (Fig. 1).

With the help of the Breit-Wigner formula the resonances of a perfectly resolved total cross section curve may be assigned a J value since (assuming $\Gamma \approx \Gamma_n$), $\sigma_{max} - \sigma_{min} = (4\pi\hbar^2/2mE_0)(2J + 1)/2\cdot(2I + 1)$, and J is the only unknown parameter (m is the reduced mass of the neutron). The parity of the level is the same as that of the target nucleus if the shape of the resonance indicates an s-wave (even parity) interaction. On the other hand a symmetric peak probably indicates a p-wave (odd parity) and therefore a different parity from the target.

Resonances due to d-wave ($l = 2$) and higher angular momentum neutrons are certainly present but it is quite unlikely that they are observable in the kev region. This is simply because the large centrifugal barrier factor causes the width in almost all cases to be unobservably small. *Thus the resonances observed in kev total cross sections are restricted to those whose J's are within $\frac{3}{2}$ (usually only $\frac{1}{2}$) units of angular momentum from the value of the target nucleus ground state spin.*

Neutron capture in the kev region is weak compared to elastic scattering and in general does not contribute appreciably to the total cross section in the neighborhood of a detectable resonance; however the effect is large enough to measure. Figure 2 shows the capture cross section of aluminum which was measured by means of the induced radioactivity following neutron capture. The one-level formula for this peak is:

$$\sigma_{n\gamma} = \frac{\pi\lambda^2 g_J \Gamma_n \Gamma_\gamma}{(E - E_0)^2 + \Gamma^2/4} \tag{4}$$

Note that the maximum possible σ_0 occurs when $\Gamma_n = \Gamma_\gamma = \Gamma/2$, and $E = E_0$; the condition $\Gamma_n \gg \Gamma_\gamma$ which nearly always holds in the kev region leads to a small capture section. This effect will become more clear if we integrate (3) and (4) over the resonance region since it is this integrated cross section which determines the detectability of a narrow resonance when a very thin sample is used for the measurement. These *resonance integrals* for scattering and capture respectively are:

$$\Sigma_{sc} = 2\pi^2\lambda^2\Gamma_n{}^2/\Gamma \cong 2\pi^2\lambda^2\Gamma_n \tag{5}$$

and

$$\Sigma_\gamma = 2\pi^2\lambda^2\Gamma_n\Gamma_\gamma/\Gamma \cong 2\pi^2\lambda^2\Gamma_\gamma \tag{6}$$

The indicated approximations, which are nearly always valid in the kev region when $l = 0$, show that capture detectability is determined by the quantity Γ_γ and is independent of the total width $\Gamma \cong \Gamma_n$. On this basis we can understand a comparison of capture and scattering in Fig. 2; the very weak resonance at 7 kev which was almost lost (Ro54) in the potential scattering background in early total-cross-section measurements (Fig. 2b) is easily detected by capture with even poorer resolution (Fig. 2c). More recent total cross section data (Bi57) with better resolution is shown in Fig. 2a.

Total cross sections in the kev region cannot be interpreted nearly so simply if appreciable inelastic scattering occurs. In this case

$$\sigma_{max} - \sigma_{min} = 4\pi g\lambda^2\Gamma_n/(\Gamma_n + \Gamma_n' + \Gamma_\gamma)$$

and if, for instance, the neutron enters as a p-wave and departs inelastically as an s-wave so that $\Gamma_n' \gg \Gamma_n$, $\sigma_{max} - \sigma_{min}$ may drop to an extremely low value compared to $4\pi\lambda^2 g$. Such considerations enter into the interpretation of, for instance, the fluorine total cross section above the inelastic scattering threshold at 109 kev, but in general resolvable resonances in the kev region are at energies less than the inelastic threshold.

B. Widths

The quantity, $\Gamma = \Gamma_n + \Gamma_\gamma$, the width at half maximum of the resonance term in the Breit-Wigner formula, is interpreted as inversely proportional to the mean lifetime of the state of the compound nucleus, $\tau = \hbar/\Gamma$. The partial widths are also interpretable, in complete analogy to radioactive decay, as proportional to the partial decay rates for neutron emission or γ-ray emission respectively. In the kev region the approximation $\Gamma = \Gamma_n$ is nearly always valid for resonances wide enough to be detected by present transmission techniques. Hence in total cross section measurements, one may determine only Γ_n, while Γ_γ is measurable only when the capture cross section is determined independently.

Consider the probability of escape of a neutron from a square potential well if it has sufficient energy to escape as a free particle. On each collision with the surface, the probability of its escape (Bl52) is $v_l 4kK/(K + k)^2 \cong 4v_l k/K = P$, where $K \gg k$ are the neutron wave numbers inside and outside the well respectively, and v_l is the probability of passing a centrifugal barrier. For neutrons (assuming a square well potential)

$$v_0 = 1$$
$$v_1 = k^2 R^2/(1 + k^2 R^2) \tag{7}$$
$$v_2 = k^4 R^4/(9 + 3k^2 R^2 + k^4 R^4)$$

where R is the well radius and $k^2 R^2 \approx E_{\text{C.M.}}$ (Mev) $A^{2/3}/8$. If f is the fraction of the time an actual compound nucleus spends in the single particle configuration where a neutron may escape as a free nucleon, the mean lifetime is $t/fP = \hbar/\Gamma_n$ where $t = 2mR/K\hbar$ is the mean time between collisions with the nuclear surface for a neutron traveling only on the nuclear diameter. Then $\Gamma_n = \hbar Pf/t = (4f\hbar kv_l/K) \cdot (Kh/2mR) = (2\hbar^2/mR)kv_l f$. The rigorous treatment leading to the sum rule of Teichman and Wigner (Tc52) gives nearly the same result:

$$\Gamma_n/\Theta^2 = \Gamma_W = (3\hbar^2/2mR)kv_l \tag{8a}$$

Γ_W is the greatest width (corresponding to the shortest lifetime), which a resonance may have. In actual compound nuclei $\Theta^2 \ll 1$, and the observed widths of the resonances will, in general, be very much narrower than this so-called Wigner limit. The quantity Θ^2 varies over wide limits. It is greater than 0.3 (Ne57,Ma58) for the very wide 2^- level in Be^8 which is principally responsible for the emission of neutrons near the threshold of the $Li^7(p,n)Be^7$ reaction (see Chapter I.E), about 0.05 for the 100-kev p-wave resonance in $F(n,n)$, and about 7×10^{-7} for the 1.45-ev resonance in $In^{115}(n,n)$. If the fluorine resonance were ascribed to d-wave neutrons rather than p-wave, then $\Theta^2 \approx 2.6$, and therefore this resonance cannot be due to d waves.

For low-energy neutrons it is convenient to define the *reduced width* of a level as

$$\Gamma_n^l = \Gamma_n v_l^{-1}(E_1/E_0)^{1/2} = \Gamma_n v_l^{-1}\lambda_0/\lambda_1 \tag{9a}$$

where λ_1 is the Dirac wavelength of a 1-ev neutron and λ_0 is that of a resonance neutron. Equation (9a), for s-wave neutrons, reduces to the familiar expression

$$\Gamma_n^0 = \Gamma_n(E_1/E_0)^{1/2} \tag{9b}$$

where the standard energy, $E_1 = 1$ ev. The original definition of Teichman and Wigner (Te52)

$$\gamma_l^2 = \Gamma_n v_l^{-1} \lambda_0/2 = \Gamma_n^l \lambda_1/2 = 2.3\Gamma_n^l \, 10^{-10} \tag{10}$$

(which is usually expressed in ev $\times$ cm) is more commonly used in fast-neutron work.[2] The first definition, Eq. (9a), is the most useful for slow neutron resonances and will be adopted for our discussion. Under this definition the Wigner limit on the reduced width may be expressed as:

$$\Gamma_n^l/f = \Gamma_W^i = \Gamma_W(E_1/E_0)^{1/2}v_l^{-1} = 20A^{-1/3}\,\text{kev} \tag{8b}$$

when the nuclear radius, $R = 1.35\,A^{1/3}10^{-13}$ cm. It will be noted that both definitions simply eliminate the specific dependence of Γ_n on the neutron wave length and barrier penetration probability. Since experimental values of reduced widths are extremely sensitive to the correct assignment of neutron angular momentum, it is worthwhile to use the index l in Eqs. (8) and (10). The reduced width varies over wide limits from resonance to resonance in the same spectrum and the study of this distribution is of considerable current interest.

We shall call the quantity

$$S_{J,0} \equiv \Sigma\Gamma_n^0(J)/(E_2 - E_1) \tag{11}$$

the (experimental) strength function for neutron angular momentum $l = 0$, and compound nucleus spin J where $(E_2 - E_1)$ is the energy interval over which the reduced widths of individual resonances have been measured and summed in (11). Since the average spacing, $\bar{D}_J = (E_2 - E_1)/M_J(M_J$ is the actual number of resonances of spin J in the interval), the strength function $S_0 \equiv \bar{\Gamma}_n^0(J)/\bar{D}_J \neq \langle\Gamma_n^0(J)/D_J\rangle$, where $\bar{\Gamma}_n^0$ is the arithmetic mean of the individual reduced widths. The sum of the measured reduced widths is usually accurate enough for practical purposes since even though some weak levels are usually missed, their contribution to the sum is practically negligible. When $I = 0$, the measured reduced widths may be substituted directly into (11). However, when $I \neq 0$, it is usually impossible to determine the J of each resonance and one must use the approximation:

$$S_J \cong S_I \equiv \Sigma 2g\Gamma_n^0/2(E_2 - E_1) \cong$$
$$[\Sigma\Gamma_n^0(I + \tfrac{1}{2}) + \Sigma\Gamma_n^0(I - \tfrac{1}{2})]/2(E_2 - E_1) \tag{11a}$$

---

[2] Multilevel formulas both of the Bethe (Be37a,Bi61) and R-matrix (Wi47) form have been used to analyze kev resonances (Wi61,Bo62).

In practice, the numerator is obtained by summing the estimated reduced widths of unassigned resonances and then dividing by *twice* the energy interval since, as may be seen at the left of (11a), the numerator is the sum over two channels. S_I is a good approximation if S_J is not strongly dependent on J (see Section 5.G).

The experimental importance of the strength functions is made clear in our discussion of averaged cross sections while its theoretical interpretation by means of the optical model is covered in Chapter V.C. Rule 3 mentioned in the introduction was based on the assumption that all $S_l \simeq 1 \times 10^{-4}$; its actual variation with mass number and l will be discussed later. Because of the effect of spin-orbit coupling, p-wave and higher l strength functions cannot be defined so simply (see Section 5.G).

3. Experimental Techniques

A. Heterogeneous Beams

Neutron resonances were originally discovered with the highly heterogeneous sources available when fast neutrons are allowed to slow down and diffuse in a moderator. The absorption of a wide band of neutrons in the thermal region by Cd and the self-absorption effects of low energy resonances in Au, Ag, and In were recognized in early work and the energies of some of these resonances were estimated rather satisfactorily by the boron absorption method (for reference see Be37a). This method depends on the fact that epi-cadmium absorption or scattering by a nuclide is frequently due largely to a single resonance, so that, after suitable corrections, one may detect a very narrow energy component out of the $1/E$ distribution of neutron energies which arises from the slowing down of high energy neutrons in light moderators.

Resonances at energies ($\gtrsim 100$ ev) high enough so that scattering rather than capture was the dominant process were first discovered in this way (Li47). While the measurements were sometimes difficult to interpret and are largely of historical interest, it should not be forgotten that the difficulties arose mostly from the fact that there was little or no knowledge of the resonance spectra to guide the interpretation. The filtered pile beam is still useful in special cases to obtain information which cannot be found with homogeneous beams. In favorable cases the energy of the lowest resonance may be estimated

Table 1.   Resonance Energies by the Boron Method Compared with Total-Cross-Section Results

Target	$E_0(B)$, kev	$E_0(T)$, kev	Remarks
Na^{23}	1.7 (Li47)	2.9 (Ly58, Go58)	$\Gamma_n \gg \Gamma_\gamma$
Al^{27}	9.1 (Li47)	5.6 (Go58)	$\Gamma_n \gtrsim \Gamma_\gamma$
Cl^{37}	1.8 (Li47)	9.0 (Ne57)	a
V^{51}	3.4 (Li47)	4.1 (Ma57)	$\Gamma_n \gg \Gamma_\gamma$
Mn^{55}	0.26 (Li47)	0.34 (Ra47)	$\Gamma_n \gg \Gamma_\gamma$
Cu^{65}	0.57 (Li47)	0.23 (Co58)	$\Gamma_\gamma \gtrsim \Gamma_n$
Rb^{85}	1.0 (Ne54)	>0.6 (Hu58)	a
Rb^{87}	0.4 (Ne54)	>0.6 (Hu58)	a
Y^{89}	5.0 (Ne54)	2.5 (Go58)	$\Gamma_n \gtrsim \Gamma_\gamma$
Nb^{93}	0.14 (Li47)	0.035 (Sa58)	$\Gamma_\gamma \gtrsim \Gamma_n$
Cs^{133}	0.006 (Ne54)	0.0059 (La52)	$\Gamma_\gamma > \Gamma_n$
La^{139}	0.076 (Ne54)	0.073 (Hu58)	$\Gamma_\gamma \gtrsim \gamma_n$
Pr^{141}	0.38 (Ne54)	0.086 (Hu58)	$\Gamma_\gamma \gtrsim \Gamma_n$
Tl^{205}	10.00 (Ne54)	18[b] (Ro54)	$\Gamma_n \gg \Gamma_\gamma$

[a] The lowest energy resonance may capture strongly and still be undetected in a total-cross-section measurement.

[b] A resonance has been found at about 5 kev by measuring the capture cross section of Tl^{205} as a function of energy (Ro54,Ne60).

Note: Estimates of resonance energies by boron absorption $E_0(B)$ are compared to the lowest energy resonance found by total cross section measurements. The experimenter's original estimates are shown for $E_0(B)$. Both methods are likely to miss resonances under certain circumstances. Total cross section measurements in the kev region usually cannot detect a resonance if $\Gamma_\gamma \gtrsim \Gamma_n$ while the boron absorption method only fails when $\Gamma_\gamma \ll \Gamma_n$. Some of the discrepancies in the table may be due to impurities which indicate spurious resonances (usually at low energies) in a total cross section curve. Impurities (isotopic or chemical) are not detected by the boron method since the radioactive properties of the product nucleus usually identify it. The information under remarks refers to the resonance found by total cross section measurements.

from the B^{10} absorption curve when a sample is activated in a pile beam which has passed through various thicknesses of B^{10} (Li47, Ne52,Ne54). These estimates (see Table I) are only qualitative and occasionally misleading, but capture is a more sensitive method than scattering for the detection (Ro54) of weak resonances (see Fig. 2), and the boron absorption technique was able, for instance, to locate the weak resonance at 5.6 kev in aluminum which was quite difficult to detect by total cross section measurements. Conversely, if the angular momentum and energy of the first few (i.e. lowest energy)

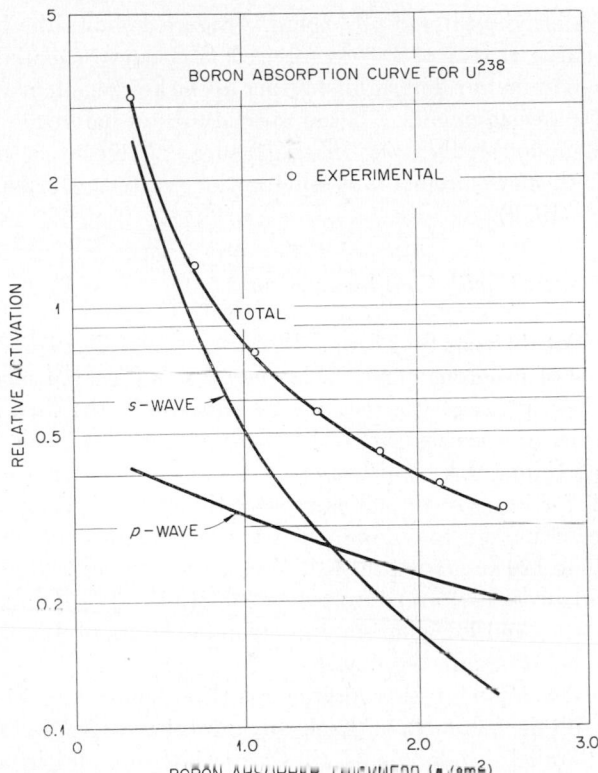

Figure 3. The activation of U²³⁸ in a pile beam ($1/E$ distribution) as a function of the thickness of a B¹⁰ absorber in the beam (Da47). The approximate s- and p-wave contributions are shown. The shape of this curve is determined by the same three parameters as the capture cross section up to about 25 kev. We are indebted to E. Merzbacher and I. Rives for this figure.

resonances are known (from total cross section data) to be in the kev region, the radiation width, Γ_γ for the lowest resonances may be determined from the activation of a sample in a filtered pile beam (Er58). Similarly, if the absorption effects of the first few resonances are eliminated either by correcting for their known properties or using very thick B¹⁰ filters, or both, the absorption will depend almost entirely on the p- and s-wave strength functions and capture functions (Fig. 3). Since these parameters determine the average capture cross section below a few kev, the latter may be measured effectively by means of a heavily filtered pile beam. Figure 3 shows the boron absorption curve (Li47) of U^{238} compared to a curve calculated from resonance parameters determined either in the kev region or from very low energy measurements. Other special uses of heterogeneous neutrons will undoubtedly arise in the future. A recent case, for example, is the measurement of differential scattering cross sections near 3 kev (Bl58).

B. Measurements with Continuous Beams

(1) **Total Cross Sections.** The use of the $Li^7(p,n)Be^7$ reaction as a source of neutrons of variable energy was initiated many years ago. A description of the reaction and its use in the forward angle for neutrons of energies greater than 120 kev has been given in Chapters I.E and V.A, respectively. Because of center-of-mass motion one is forced to go to angles greater than 90° with respect to the proton beam in order to obtain nearly monoenergetic neutrons of energies less than 120 kev (from the lithium reaction). A few limited early experiments were performed up to 1952 (Se47,Ba48) but small proton beam currents and low-efficiency neutron detectors prohibited extensive work below about 100 kev.

The development of a high-current ion source (Mo51) set the stage for full development of back-angle total cross section measurements. Parallel developments that were instrumental in achieving good resolution were the electrostatic analyzer, improved lithium target preparation techniques, better vacuum conditions in the target area, better accelerator control and proton energy resolution, and more efficient and stable neutron detectors.

(a) *Collimation, Detection, and Samples.* Problems of low neutron yields and high backgrounds were overcome by careful target design and by using a massively shielded collimator-detector with high detection efficiency (La50,Hi52,Gi53,Gi56,Bi57). Hibdon et al. (Hi52) used a 2° acceptance angle and a cylindrical collimator. Gibbons and Newson (Gi53,Gi56) used a rectangular collimator of 2 by 20° acceptance angle, thus gaining about a factor of 10 in solid angle without a significant change in resolution. Hibdon (Hi57) later also used (see Fig. 4) rectangular geometry with the critical acceptance angle variable in steps from about 0.6 to 1.8°. Bilpuch et al. (Bi57) used a circular (360°) detector where the acceptance angle

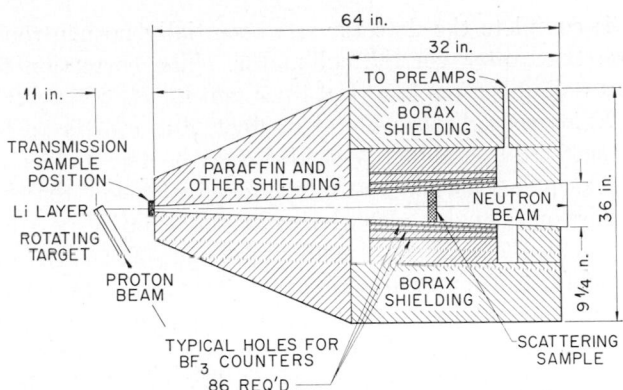

Figure 4. Schematic arrangement of neutron collimator and shield (Hi57), with neutron counter array shown inside the shield.

may be varied continuously between 0 and 2°. The reader is referred to Chapter IV.E for a full discussion of the design of collimators.

The neutron energy spread caused by a finite detector acceptance angle, $\Delta\psi$, decreases monotonically to a minimum at 180° (see Chapter I.E) with respect to the proton beam. However, the apparatus described by Hi52, Gi56, and Hi57 are operated close to 120° and that by Bi57 at 160°. These angles were chosen as a compromise between such factors as counting rate, resolution, and ease of mechanical construction.

High pressure $B^{10}F_3$ counters, embedded in a moderating matrix of paraffin, are used as the neutron detector. Spacings of counters in the matrix in one system (Gi56) were arranged for about 75 per cent *thermal utilization* at $E_n = 25$ kev; the counting efficiency, including an appreciable loss of counts in the proportional counters, is estimated to be about 20 per cent.

Samples of materials to be studied are placed between the mouth of the collimator and the target. Usually sample thicknesses are adjusted for 70 to 80 per cent transmission between resonances. Approximately 0.1 mole (g-atom) of sample (well within the range of availability of many enriched isotopes) is required.

(*b*) *Backgrounds.* Neutron backgrounds encountered in back-angle measurements may be divided into two components:

(1) *Blank Target Backgrounds.* This minor component of the background is due to all effects other than $Li^7(p,n)$ neutrons. Since

shielding is complete the detector *sees* essentially no neutrons other than those that enter via the collimator. The correction for this component (Gi56) is often less than 1 per cent for $E_n > 5$ kev.

(2) *Extraneous Neutrons.* This effect, due mostly to forward neutrons scattered by the target backing, may be detected by measuring the back-angle yield for proton energies just below threshold for neutron emission at angles >90° (back-threshold) or by measuring the transmission at the peak of a wide resonance of known σ_0. The amount and type of material used in fabricating the target backing and other components in the target area are extremely important for work in the kev range. The strong sensitivity of background intensity to target design has been shown by Gibbons (Gi56). Correction for the scattered neutrons is related to the forward angle neutron intensity and angular distribution since the effective thickness of the backing is a function of neutron emission angle. The results indicate a smooth but often surprisingly large ($\sim$10 per cent) background over the entire energy range of interest. It has been shown experimentally that these neutrons are only observable above the $\mathrm{Li}^7(p,n)$ forward threshold, that they arise at or very near the target, that the average energy as measured by their effective cross section in hydrogen is of the order of 100 kev above that of the homogeneous neutrons, and that proton scattering and possibly other side effects probably contribute slightly (Gi56,Ni58). However the effect is not yet understood well enough to eliminate background uncertainties entirely. So far, self-detection methods have been the most satisfactory in eliminating this background, but where resolution permits, true peak cross sections may be measured by the use of samples so thin that the neutrons transmitted even at the peak of a resonance are mostly homogeneous. The accuracy to which the extraneous background is known sets an upper limit on the sample thickness which may be used in a transmission experiment. For instance, if the background is (10 ± 2) per cent and the transmission ratio at the peak of a resonance is 15 per cent the true transmission ratio is about (5 ± 2) per cent, an uncertainty of almost a factor of two.[3]

(c) *Monitoring.* Since measurements of total cross sections depend on a transmission ratio, some method must be used to make certain that the same number of neutrons were incident on the sam-

---

[3] "In-scattering," a rather unimportant background in these experiments, is discussed in Chapter V.A.

ples as were measured in the open beam.   The monitoring problem would be much simpler if it were not for the roughness of thin lithium targets (see the discussion in Chapter I.E).   It was soon found (Hi52) that a McKibben-type counter placed at 0° was not a very satisfactory monitor.   The Duke group (Gi56) preferred the use of a proton current integrator for this purpose, but found that some lithium targets, which were satisfactory in other respects, failed to reproduce transmission ratios within statistical error and had to be discarded. However, the majority of the targets were quite satisfactory.   The Argonne group preferred a monitor at the same angle as the collimator and normalized their measurements to the total count in this monitor. This method is open to criticism because the statistical error of the monitor count is added to the other statistical errors.   A suggestion by Langsdorf was adopted for the 160° spectrograph at Duke (Bi57). The circular detector was broken up into a right bank and a left bank separated by sufficient polyethylene that there was no appreciable diffusion of neutrons from one bank to the other.   Measurements are made in which the same sample thickness intercepts the beam to each bank in turn.   The ratio of open to closed beam counts (taken simultaneously) is very nearly the true transmission ratio and the geometric mean of the two ratios cancels out any minor differences in the sensitivity of the two counter banks or in the geometry of the two sides of the collimator.   In this way no unnecessary statistical error is introduced into the final transmission ratio

(d) *Resolution.*   The over-all resolution figure for back or forward angle measurements is composed of three physically distinct sources.   For the puspose of predicting the neutron energy spread for a given arrangement it is sufficiently accurate to calculate the energy spreads separately, normalize rectangular or triangular spreads to an equivalent Gaussian,[4] and take the square root of the sum of the squares (of these equivalent widths at half maximum) as the effective energy spread of the beam.

(1) *Angular Acceptance Spreads,* $\delta\psi$.   The non-relativistic equation applicable to this consideration is given in Chapter I.E, namely,

[4] That is, a Gaussian distribution of the same area and standard deviation as the actual distribution curve.   The conversion factors used to change the half width of a given distribution to the equivalent Gaussian are 0.681 for a rectangle and 0.963 for a triangle.

$$\frac{\delta E_n}{\delta \psi}\bigg|_{E_p} = \frac{E_p \sin \psi (\cos \psi + Z)^2}{32Z} \qquad (12)$$

where $Z^2 = [49(E_p - E_{th})/E_p] - \sin^2 \psi$. It is easy to show from (12) that $\delta E_n/\delta \psi$ decreases monotonically from $\psi = 90°$ to $\psi = 180°$ with its most rapid fall between 90 and 120°, but that for a ring-shaped detector *of a given solid angle* (not acceptance angle) there is not much difference in energy spread between 120 and 180°. If we compare the energy spread for a given solid angle near 0 and 180° (i.e., for small values of $\sin \psi$), we find that, contrary to naive expectation, the energy spread is much greater near 0 than near 180°.

Two angular spreads must be taken into account in calculating the beam spread: (a) the angle subtended at the center of the source spot by the detector and (b) the angle subtended at the detector by the source, i.e., by the area of the beam striking the target. This second effect becomes important for high resolution work at angles near 0 or 180°.

A third energy spread is sometimes caused by using a rectangle (Gi56) rather than a ring (or arc of a ring) detector. Let $\alpha = \phi/2$ be the azimuthal half-angle subtended by the rectangle and $\delta \psi$ the effective angular spread. Then

$$\sin^2(\psi + \delta \psi) = \cos^2 \alpha [\sin^2 \psi + \tan^2 \alpha] \qquad (13)$$

The angular spread, $\delta \psi$ caused by a full ϕ acceptance angle of 20° is, for example, about 0.5° for $\psi = 120°$. This effect limits the angle ϕ which may be usefully subtended by a rectangular collimator. Angles near 90° are clearly favored by this sort of detector.

The partial energy distribution due to angle alone δE_n is very nearly rectangular (except at 0 or 180°) since $\psi \gg \delta \psi$. The width at half maximum of the equivalent Gaussian is (0.681) δE_n. There is some experimental evidence (Gi56,Ni58) for the near perfect behavior of the collimator, even though the beam spot is of finite size and a certain amount of scattering on the inner walls of the collimator is unavoidable.

(2) *Proton Beam Spread and Target Thickness.* Any energy spread in the proton beam will be reflected in the energy spread of the neutron beam according to (3) from Chapter I.E:

$$\frac{\delta E_n}{\delta E_p}\bigg|_{\psi} = \frac{(\cos \psi + Z)}{64}\left[\cos \psi + Z + \frac{49 E_{th}}{Z E_p}\right] \qquad (14)$$

It will be seen from this equation that $\delta E_n/\delta E_p$ is at a maximum at $0°$, unity at $90°$, and at a minimum at $180°$.

The lithium target will, of course, be of finite thickness and consequently there is an energy loss to the protons as they pass through the target which is equivalent to an initial spread of the proton beam. If the target were perfectly uniform, this distribution would be approximately rectangular like that due to the acceptance angle. However, a thin, uniform target, say 1 kev in thickness, is ~100 atoms thick and if the target is formed by the random process of evaporation, there will be a statistical variation in its thickness. In the same way about 30 ion pairs are formed by a single proton in traversing the target and a very considerable straggling spread will occur. A third effect, which is probably the most important, has been discussed in considerable detail in Chapter I.E.: namely, the fact that the evaporated layer tends to form in crystals which in general are thicker than the average target thickness (Ma58). Hence the surface of the target layer is apt to be extremely grainy in submicroscopic appearance possibly with bare regions between the crystals in the case of very *thin* targets. The neutron energy spread due to this cause is likely to be very complicated and probably dependent on the physical and chemical state of the surface of the backing material. If an experimental estimate of target thickness is made from the shape of the rise curve of the forward neutron yield near threshold, a *target thickness* is found which includes proton energy spread from the analyzer and the distribution may be considered Gaussian or triangular. In the case of thin targets, i.e., less than 1 kev, one often estimates the target thickness from the differential cross section and the absolute value of the neutron yield in some direction. If the average thickness measured in this manner is considered (for convenience) to be the half width of a Gaussian one will probably underestimate the overall energy spread by a roughness factor which may be estimated by comparing the calculated with the measured overall neutron energy spread.

If the proton beam has passed through an electromagnetic or electrostatic analyzer and if the slits are properly adjusted to take full advantage of the resolution of the analyzer, the energy distribution of the emergent beam will be triangular; the energy spread is usually expressed as the full width at half maximum. To reduce this to the equivalent Gaussian, one multiplies by 0.963.

Recent experiments at Duke (Pa58) justify the assumption that proton spread may be reduced to less than the uncertainty in target thickness by applying a compensating voltage to the target which cancels out the moderately fast-time fluctuations of the high voltage terminal of the Van de Graaff generator. It is unnecessary that the proton beam suffer the slit losses of a high resolution analyzer, so that beam currents of 50 μamp or more with fractional energy spreads as low as 5×10^{-5} appear to be feasible. Hence proton energy spread may be ignored in calculating the overall resolution if this *homogenizer* is employed. It should be noted that the *natural* fractional energy spreads vary widely among various accelerators, so that the *homogenizer* would vary in its improvement factor. For example, the *natural* energy spread in the Duke Van de Graaff is $\sim$1 kev at $E_p = 1$ Mev but is between 150 and 300 ev for the ORNL 3.0-Mv accelerator.

A serious limitation in ultimate resolution by steady-beam techniques is the problem of producing and maintaining sufficiently thin and uniform lithium targets ($\leq$0.2 kev). To date little success has been achieved in this direction. One proposed technique (Pa61) is to replace the lithium metal target with a tritium vapor target, where the direction of vapor is normal to that of the proton beam. Preliminary measurements indicate that this technique holds promise of producing thin, uniform targets while simultaneously eliminating spreads due to the Doppler effect.

(3) *Doppler Effect.* The target nucleus (Li) is subject to thermal motion and cannot be considered to be at rest at the time of collision. While the thermal energy (about 0.025 ev) is negligible compared to that of a 2-Mev proton, the average velocities differ by a factor of 10^{-4} which is the same order of magnitude as the best proton resolution which we will discuss. This Doppler effect on the neutron source is not completely equivalent to a spread in proton energy but may be estimated from the following simplification of an equation due to Langsdorf:

$$\Delta E_n = (2AE_pE_{th}/4)^{1/2}/(A + 1) \tag{15a}$$

where $A = 7$ for an Li target, $E_{th} = \frac{1}{40}$ ev at room temperature, and E_p is the proton energy. While a more complete treatment (Be37, La37,La54) leads to a more accurate formula, the uncertainties in estimating the true target thicknesses (in kev) are still great enough that this approximation [Eq. (15a)] is adequate. This energy spread is considered to be the width at half maximum of a Gaussian distribution.

Langsdorf's (La54) full equation follows:

$$\Delta E_n = \frac{4}{A_1 + A_2} \left(1 + \frac{\cos \psi}{y} \right) \cdot$$

$$\sqrt{A_2 E_2 [A_1 E_1 + A_3 E_3 - 2 \cos \psi (A_1 E_1 A_3 E_3)^{1/2}]} \quad (15b)$$

$$y \equiv \left[\cos^2 \psi + \frac{(A_1 + A_2)(A_2 - A_3)}{A_1 A_3} (1 - E_{BT}/E_1) \right]^{1/2}$$

where $E_{BT} = 1.9217$ Mev for Li^7 is the *back-threshold* of the reaction and the subscripts 1, 2, 3 specify the mass number A and the energy E of the proton, target nucleus (Li), and the neutron respectively. ΔE_n in Eq. (15b) is a slight overestimate of the effective energy spread.

(e) *Experimental Determination of Resolution.* Resolution may be measured from the observed transmission as a function of energy due to a narrow resonance. The resonances in aluminum near 6 kev ($\Gamma \approx 15$ ev) and in bismuth at 2.25 kev ($\Gamma = 16$ ev) are examples of narrow resonances in the kev region. The aluminum resonance, as observed by transmission and capture under various conditions of resolution is shown in Fig. 2.

In cases where the total angular momentum of the state is known the width Γ may be determined by the area method and then the instrumental resolution derived from the peak height method which relates the minimum observed transmission to the *ratio* of true width to observed (instrumental) width. This technique is especially useful when the resolution and resonance width are comparable.

Results of such measurements in the energy region from 7 to 100 kev are in good agreement with the calculated solid curve (160° back angle) in Fig. 5. For spreads greater than 1 kev the resolutions for commonly used 120° arrangements are determined almost entirely by the angular openings while the 160° measurements are limited in resolution by effective target thickness over the full energy range of the method. This is due to the fact that $\delta E_n/\delta \psi$ decreases by a factor of $\sim$4 in going from 120 to 160°.

The targets used for the 160° measurements had an average thickness of about 0.5 kev estimated from their neutron emission

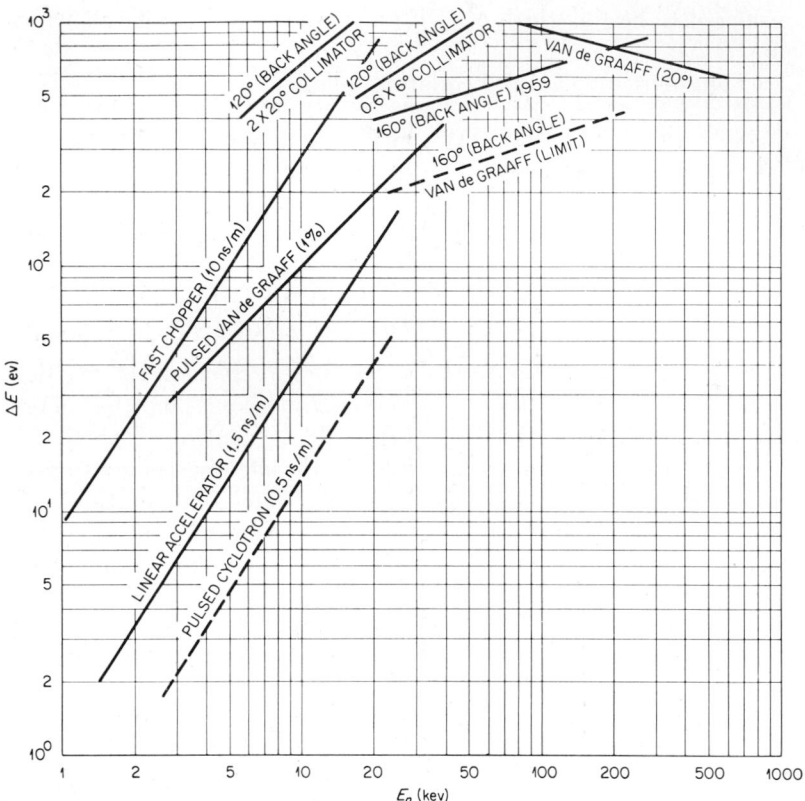

Figure 5. Energy spreads as a function of energy for various neutron spectrometers. Solid lines represent resolutions actually demonstrated while dashed lines are estimated improvements which are probably feasible. Back-angle Van de Graaff methods are limited in resolution by the acceptance angle and by the properties of Li and the Li[7] (p,n) reaction. As indicated in the lowest curve on the right, the possible improvement is only about a factor of two better than the demonstrated resolutions (Ni59). Forward-angle methods are even more sensitive to the properties of Li and the indicated curve is very optimistic. The upper curve on the right is calculated from the geometry used in the earliest back-angle work (Hi52) (Gi53) and (particularly at low energies) is considerably better than that actually attained. Similarly, the 120° $\times$ 0.6 $\times$ 6° curve is the best resolution attainable with the geometry described by Hibdon (Hi57) who evidently overlooked geometrical effects in estimating his energy spread as about 1/2 kev near 100 kev.

and their roughness factor (target non-uniformity as discussed in Chapter I.E) is therefore about $1.4/0.5 = 2.8$. Thinner targets showed no appreciable difference in neutron resolution between average thicknesses of 0.5 and 0.2 kev. Measurements on the 31-kev resonance in Ba showed roughness factors of about 7 and 2 at average thicknesses of 0.2 and 1.2 kev, respectively.

(f) *Comparison of Steady-Beam Techniques.* Assuming that a way can be found to make thin, reasonably uniform targets, it is possible to calculate an optimum practical resolution, which depends essentially only on the room temperature properties of the Li^7 (p,n) reaction (see Fig. 5), for neutron energies in forward and backward angles. A reasonable compromise between intensity and resolution is obtained by keeping the energy spreads due to acceptance angle and target thickness about equal to that of the Doppler effect. There is appreciable departure from this rule at the lowest and highest energies for 160° where intensity is at a premium. Similar calculations involving the square root of sums of squares of individual effects have also been made at 20°. The results indicate that an energy spread slightly less than 1 kev between 70 and 100 kev may be possible (see Fig. 5). For the purpose of qualitative discussion, 160 and 20° differ little from 120 and 0°, respectively. Uniform targets of thickness ~0.2 kev must be available in order to achieve these resolutions. An attempt to reduce the energy spread to the Doppler level would require a sacrifice of more than a factor of 10 in intensity for an improvement of a factor of 2 in resolution and would scarcely deliver an adequate neutron intensity with proton currents of the order of 25 μamp. If we extrapolate the 160° curve until it intersects the 20° curve (Fig. 5), the intersection point is at approximately 300 kev. However, the threshold for the lower energy group from the Li^7 $(p,n)Be^{7*}$ reaction occurs for ground state neutrons whose energy, corresponding to the excited-state back threshold, is about 200 kev at 160° and about 300 kev at 120°. While the rate of rise of the low energy yield near back threshold is not yet known, the two groups are of comparable strength at 120° a few hundred kev above threshold (Be61). The addition of a low energy neutron background to the high energy scattered neutron background already mentioned would create an even more difficult problem in correcting for background. While there appears to be an advantage in resolution in continuing the back angle measurements above back threshold of the low energy group, it is not great enough to encourage many measurements under this condition. On the other hand, the advantages of working at small forward angles may, for particular purposes, compensate for the disadvantage of poorer resolution and even for the low energy ground state group (due to C.M. motion) which accompanies forward neutrons at less than 120 kev. It is interesting to note that between 200 and 300 kev both optimum resolution and estimated intensity are about the same at the forward and backward angles.

(2) **Differential Cross Section Measurements.** If we consider the kev region to extend from 1 to 150 kev, it is not ordinarily necessary to make a detailed angular distribution measurement and phase shift analysis in order to distinguish individual s- and p-wave resonances. They may be identified usually in good resolution total cross section curves by their very different interference properties. Up to the present, only s- and p-wave resonances have been identified in this region, but eventually methods must be worked out to distinguish between p- and d-wave resonances. Largely for the purpose of verifying a few p-wave assignments already known from total-cross-section results, Block, Haeberli, and Newson (Bl58a) measured differential cross sections as a function of energy near 90° and 180°. Forward neutrons from the Li (p,n) reaction were used between about 50 and 100 kev. At lower energies, the low energy group (see Chapter I.E) becomes too large for convenient correction, and higher energies were avoided because, when there is forward emission of 120-kev neutrons, there is also backward emission which allows neutrons to enter the detectors directly from the source (in this experimental arrangement) in addition to those scattered by the sample. P-resonances such as the one in F at 100 kev (Fig. 6) may be identified by interference between s-wave potential scattering and the higher angular momentum resonance scattering. The asymmetry of the 180° differential-cross-section curve as compared to that at 90° indicates a p-resonance. A d-wave would have caused a very different behavior; also this particular resonance is so wide (approximately 11 kev) that sum rule arguments, previously mentioned, eliminate the possibility of a d-wave. For narrow resonances, p- or d-waves can often be distinguished from s-wave resonances by anisotropy near the peak, but in general a sufficient energy region should be covered with enough resolution to recognize the interference effects at the wings of the resonances. The energy spread of the neutron beam in

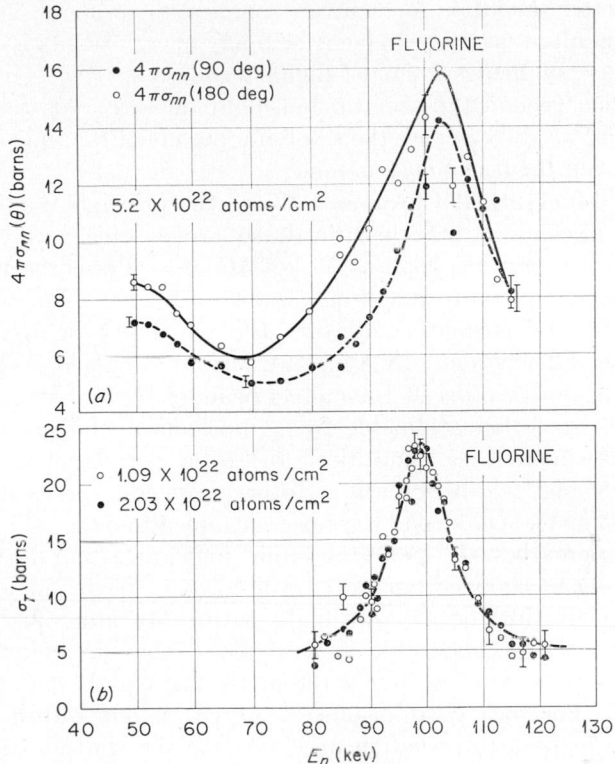

Figure 6. A resonance in fluorine near 100 kev. The lower curve (b) is the total cross section of fluorine near the 99-kev resonance (Pa62). The symmetry of the peak and lack of observable interference indicates a p-wave resonance. The peak cross section is nearly equal to $(3/4)4\pi\lambda^2$ plus potential scattering, the value to be expected for a p level. The upper curve (a) (Bl58a) shows the expected interference between s-wave potential and p-wave resonance scattering when a differential cross section is measured.

these angular distribution experiments (Bl58a) was several kev but a very similar apparatus with higher resolution should be able to distinguish the wider d-resonances from p-resonances in cases where total cross section measurements are unable to make this distinction.

C.   Time-of-Flight Techniques

The back-angle measurements described above became inconvenient at energies below about 10 kev. An approach to significantly better resolution for neutron energies up to about 50 kev as well as simultaneous measurement of many energy points is possible by the use of neutron time-of-flight techniques. We consider in this section general types of time-of-flight devices. At the end of the section we will compare the resolving powers of the time-of-flight methods and the back-angle method.

(1) **Mechanical Chopper.** While the principal studies with mechanical choppers have been in the ev range, some work has been reported at energies as high as 35 kev (Co56). Presently available (1961) resolution (width at half-maximum) is about 10 ns/meter. The most optimistic estimates entertain the possibility of attaining a resolution of 2.5 ns/meter by using two phased mechanical rotors and flight paths of the order of 100 meters or more (Eg56).

The resolution attainable by a mechanical chopper depends principally upon three quantities: (a) rotor peripheral speed, (b) slit width, and (c) flight path. Rotor peripheral speeds of up to about 500 meters per second have been attained to date. This figure closely approaches the practical limit, indicating that future improvements in chopper resolution will have to be found in either decreased slit width or increased flight path. Maximum flight paths used routinely are about 120 meters (Th57), but preliminary data have already been taken over a 180-meter flight path at Oak Ridge (Ha59a). For such great distances one encounters rather difficult problems in beam attenuation and detector size, but naturally the transmission sample size remains quite small.

Neutrons emerging from a reactor have a strong thermal peak with an $E_n{}^{-1}$ tail extending into the kev region. Thus one problem resulting from long flight paths is a *burst overlap* of fast neutrons of one pulse with slower neutrons from the preceding pulse. Further, the number of neutrons available for use decreases rapidly as one works up into the kev region. The conventional bank of bare BF_3 counters must also be replaced since their time jitter is large but, more important, they become only 1 per cent efficient at 10 kev. Bollinger (Bo57) has successfully constructed a boron-loaded liquid scintillator with 30 per cent efficiency at 10 kev.

The tremendous advantage of the stability, both in time and in spectral shape, of a reactor neutron beam over that of an accelerator-produced beam is difficult to overestimate. Thus other techniques must be significantly better in resolution to compete successfully with the nearly automatic chopper measurements. Another advantage of choppers is the extremely small sample size needed in order to perform a transmission measurement at low energies. Samples as small as 5 mg ($\sim$5 $\times$ 10^{-5} g-atoms) have been used (Co56).

Several backgrounds become increasingly important in the kev range (Bo57), principally because of the $E_n{}^{-1}$ fall-off in neutron intensity. Leakage through the rotor of fission energy neutrons and γ rays as well as slow neutrons from overlapped pulses causes the background at a resolution of 15 ns/meter and $E_n = 5$ kev to be of the order of 50 per cent. The problem of absolute counting rates is not as severe in the case or choppers as it is for accelerator work because of availability of a large number of channels and greater simplicity of apparatus. An estimate of counting rate, deduced from (Bo57) is 6 counts/min in a 10 ev interval at 1 kev. This clearly shows that in order to obtain sufficient counting statistics one is forced to make the experiment as automatic as possible.

(2) (a) **Betatron**, (b) **Synchrocyclotron**, and (c) **Linear Accelerator.** This type of experiment involves the production of extremely high intensity bursts of a broad spectrum of photo-neutrons followed by moderation at the source. Thus, in comparing this technique with the mechanical chopper, the rotor is effectively replaced by charged-particle beam pulsing and the reactor is replaced by a combination of a pulsed photo-neutron source and partial moderation. Possible advantages of this technique will become evident in the discussion that follows. We shall describe several existing methods separately below.

(a) *Betatron.* Bursts (0.1-μsec duration) of 80-Mev electrons strike a thick U^{238} target at a repetition rate of 60 pps (Ye57). The *peak* neutron intensity of 7 $\times$ 10^{15} neutrons/sec gives a *raw* neutron yield of 8 $\times$ 10^{10} neutrons/sec at an average energy of 1.5 Mev. After moderation and collimation the total integrated flux used in the energy interval 30 ev to 50 kev is about 5 per cent of the total primary flux. The neutron spectrum is $N(E)dE = dE/E^{0.75}$, where E is in ev. Fission, absorption, and total cross sections have been studied with this apparatus. A detector station at 20 meters is used for all work above 200 ev. Best observed resolution is about 25 ns/meter but the lower limit claimed is 10 ns/meter.

Factors that contribute to time resolution of this instrument are: (a) uncertainty in moderation time $\Delta t_m \approx 1/\sqrt{E(\text{ev})}$ (this is to be compared with flight times of $1400/\sqrt{E}$ for a flight path of 20 meters), (b) burst width, (c) channel width of time analyzer, and (4) jitter in detector response time ($\sim$0.2 μsec). The time spread due to source and detector dimensions is 0.1 to 0.5 per cent of the flight time.

Measurements of background indicate two components. The *blocked beam* (paraffin cone) background is about 5 per cent of the open beam count. Effects of collimator and shielding scattering, called *diffuse background* are energy dependent and of the order of 10 per cent of the open beam count.

(b) *Columbia Synchrocyclotron.* Cross section studies at Columbia using the naturally pulsed beam of the synchrocyclotron have been confined to energies less than a few kev (Ha 56). The technique is mentioned here because the time resolution ($\sim$3 ns/meter) (Ha60) and pulse repetition rate (60 pps) is comparable to that used for studies at higher neutron energies (Fig. 5). A flight path of 35 meters is normally used. Transmission studies are made with this equipment by means of self detection. Thus the system is most effective for elements where $\Gamma_\gamma \gg \Gamma_n$ but has essentially zero sensitivity for *pure* scattering resonances. Recent improvements are a 200-meter flight path, increased beam current, and shortened bursts (0.05 μsec). This should result in an ultimate resolution of 0.25 ns/meter (Ha60).

(c) *Linear Electron Accelerators.* The development of these accelerators for ev- and kev-range neutron work has centered at Harwell, England. Two accelerators have been used, but only one is now used for these purposes. However, since the first (15 Mev) "linac" was such a landmark in the development of the field a discussion of its performance is included here.

Fifteen-Mev electrons bombard a thick U^{238} target at a pulse repetition rate of 400 pps, with a pulse width of 0.15 μsec. The electron peak current is 20 milliamps, producing about 10^{13} neutrons per second *during the pulse.* Flight paths of up to 60 meters are used, giving a neutron energy resolution of about 2.5 ns/meter. At 20 meters the beam is 3 inches in diameter.

The detector, described in Chapter IV.A, is B^{10}-NaI where one observes the 478-kev γ rays from B^{10} (n,$\alpha\gamma$) with the NaI detector (Ra53). The most troublesome background is due to the intense burst of x-rays at zero time, thus limiting work in the higher kev range.

The newer linear accelerator, operating up to 30 Mev, provides more intense bursts of neutrons at pulse repetition rates of from 200 to 750 pps.   The peak electron current is 400 ma with a burst width of 0.25 μsec, producing about 10^{15} neutrons per pulse.   A "neutron booster" is a feature of this accelerator wherein the photoneutron target is surrounded by a subcritical assembly of U^{235}.   This addition gives an increase of a factor of ten in the neutron yield but adds the very bothersome problem of another time-dependent background, due to delayed neutrons from fission.

It has been pointed out (Fi60) that for work above 10 kev one can remove the moderator and probably produce neutron bursts with widths down to 0.02 μsec.   Then, operating at the 100-meter flight station a resolution of 0.2 ns/meter with a 5:1 to 10:1 signal to background for 10-kev neutrons appears quite feasible.

(3) **Pulsed Van de Graaff.**   The techniques discussed thus far in this section have dealt with *moderated* neutron sources, producing a broad energy spectrum, with flight times of many microseconds over flight paths of many meters.   For these experiments the repetition rate must be no faster than a few hundred pulses per second in order to avoid burst overlap.   Recent success in the energy range from 2 to 50 kev (Sm56,Go58,Mi59) has been achieved at a pulse repetition rate of 5×10^5 pps by using an *unmoderated* neutron source with variable energy limits.   Neutrons from the $Li^7(p,n)Be^7$ reaction are produced in a restricted energy range by using short ($\sim$5 ns) duration Van de Graaff proton pulses at energies only slightly above the reaction threshold.   Energetics of the $Li^7(p,n)Be^7$ reaction have been given in Chapter I.E.   Because of center-of-mass motion the total reaction yield for proton energies near threshold is concentrated in the forward angle.   As one increases proton energy above threshold two energy bands appear (see Fig. 2, Chapter I.E), for thin lithium targets.   The width in energy of each band is governed by the choice of lithium target thickness and the energy range covered by each band is adjusted by changing the proton energy.   One uses this *adjustable* spectrum (normally the lower energy band) as the neutron source. Neutron flight times are measured by millimicrosecond time-of-flight techniques (Fig. 7) (Ne56,Go60).   Thus this technique is a marriage between the pulsed Van de Graaff, which produces a required *band spectrum* of neutrons, and time-of-flight which in turn establishes the precise energy scale and resolution.   Data are acquired simul-

taneously for many energy points by use of flight-time to pulse-height conversion and subsequent multichannel pulse-height analysis. A more complete discussion of the electronic technique is given in Chapter IV.A.

Neutrons at 0° are detected by a B^{10}-NaI assembly, where the 478-kev γ rays from B^{10} $(n,\alpha\gamma)Li^7$ are detected by a NaI(Tl) crystal. A more complete description of this detector is also given in Chapter IV.A. Flight paths of from 1.0 to 6.0 meters are used, dependent upon the energy interval under study and desired resolution. The minimum sample for good geometry transmission measurements is

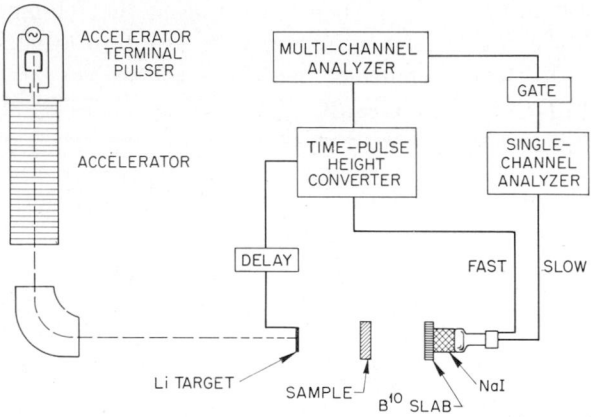

Figure 7. Block diagram of equipment used in fast (nanosecond range) time of flight studies. Typical neutron flight paths are one to four meters.

about 0.05 g-atom so that work with enriched isotopes is easily feasible. Samples as small as 0.003 g-atom can be used but inscattering corrections become appreciable under these conditions.

The overall time resolution of the system (excluding B^{10} slab thickness) is about 7 ns, measured by the time-width of γ rays from $Li^7(p,p'\gamma)$ originating in the target. It should be noted that this is the identical γ ray to the one used in neutron detection $[B^{10}(n,\alpha\gamma)Li^7]$. These same γ rays serve to calibrate the time scale in that they cause the *zero-time* pulse. Maximum neutron flight time used is about 1700 ns with pulse repetition rates of about 500 kc/sec. Thus by a suitable choice of flight path the system is capable of constant percentage energy resolution. At the present state of development the resolution (determined from total cross section measurements) is about 1.5 per cent (see Fig. 5).

Assuming a neutron pulse of 7 ns length and, 1500 ns flight time the calculated resolution is about 0.9 per cent. The difference between this and the observed figure is probably due to a combination of two effects, both of which can be improved: (a) long-time drifts in certain electronic components, (b) neutron flight time spread due to the finite thickness of the B^{10} slab (including some multiple scattering in the boron).

(4) **Modulated Van de Graaff.** Another method for measuring neutron transmission cross sections, again involving a combination of Van de Graaff and pulsing techniques, deserves some mention here. High resolution work in the hundreds of kev range becomes quite tedious when one uses the conventional neutron-producing method of a steady proton beam on a thin lithium target with data acquired on a *point-by-point* basis. Recently Cranberg (Cr57) showed that data can be obtained much less laboriously by the use of a highly efficient detector coupled with energy *modulation* at the target (Cr57a) by measuring the counting rate as a function of time as the target voltage is changed approximately linearly and the accelerator voltage is held constant.

The proton beam is first *pulsed* on a fast time scale at a high duty cycle (Cr55,Wi61) and then strikes a thin lithium target. A large, carefully shielded plastic scintillator serves as the neutron detector. Use of this detector is possible only because the fast beam pulsing allows one to separate the target γ-ray background from the neutrons by time-of-flight. Energy modulation of the proton beam allows one to gather data in 100 intervals over an energy range of up to 50 kev wide for a single accelerator voltage setting.

Resolution for this experiment is governed by the same parameters as are encountered in steady beam experiments, namely, such factors as proton energy spread, lithium target thickness, and acceptance angle of the detector. Energy calibration is also made in the usual fashion. Thus, time-of-flight for this application merely serves to reduce the background. From the point of view of *background* this method has a considerable advantage over back-angle measurements in the region from about 50–200 kev, in that *extraneous* backgrounds are eliminated. The back-angle method has the advantage of greater proton current available in a continuous beam as compared to a pulsed beam, but this advantage is at least partially off-set by the 100 per cent efficiency of the pulsed source detector. In principle, the modulated target method may be applied to a lattice of BF_3 counters if the modulation frequency is not too high (1–10 cps) so that Cranberg's method and the back-angle method should be compared on the relative merits (Fig. 5) of forward to back-angle methods in terms of resolution and intensity.

D. Comparison of Techniques

If, in selecting a developed method for measuring a given cross section curve, one had to consider only resolution (with cost, intensity, and background as secondary considerations), we have presented enough evidence (Fig. 5) to make a rather easy choice: One or more time-of-flight methods up to about 50 kev, the back-angle Li^7 (p,n) methods from 50 to 200 or 300 kev and small-angle Li^7 (p,n) methods from 150 to 700 kev (The size of the overlapping regions is important only in that it is a rough measure of the uncertainty of future developments.) However, the problem is not so simple. To consider a single example, a sample of at least 1 cm² in area is necessary for back-angle Van de Graaff measurements and very much larger areas are necessary for pulsed RF accelerators On the other hand mechanical choppers and pulsed Van de Graaffs may, at some sacrifice, reduce the necessary area down to the order of 0.1 cm². Since many cross sections may be measured quite satisfactorily without the best available resolution and there will always be interesting separated isotopes available in very small quantities, the zero-degree Van de Graff techniques will have application far beyond the ranges assigned them from consideration of resolution alone. In the same way mechanical choppers will probably continue to be useful near the lower end of the kilovolt region in spite of the improved resolution which has been attained by pulsed RF accelerators. Hence a single example is sufficient to show that all the methods we have discussed are likely to have a continuing usefulness.

4. Analysis Techniques

Techniques for the extraction of physical information from experimental data can be conveniently divided into four groups corresponding to high, intermediate, low, and poor resolution. These are

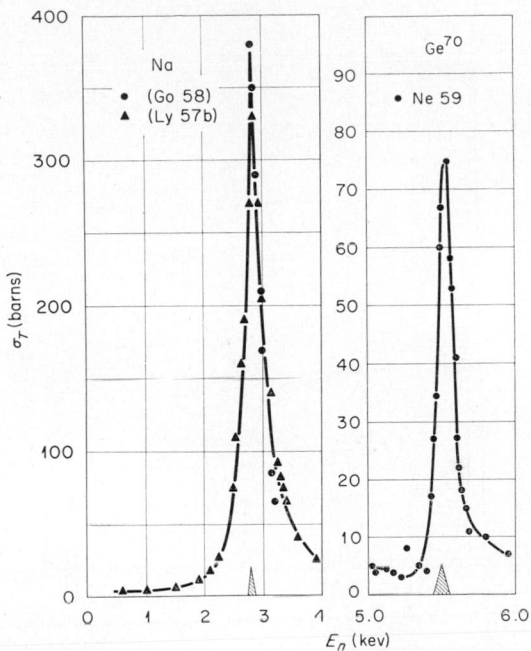

Figure 8. Resonances in Na and Ge[70].   Experimental resolution for the case of the sodium resonance was good enough to enable one to measure in detail the true resonance shape.   For the case of the germanium resonance, however, resolution was comparable with the true width so that the measured resonance shape is seriously distorted unless corrections are applied to the data.

more quantitatively defined in the following manner: Let R be the experimental energy spread (width at half maximum), D the average spacing of resonances, and Γ a resonance width.   Then *high* resolution corresponds to $R < \Gamma/5$, where Γ and σ_0 may be observed directly to within 10 per cent of their true value, *intermediate* to $R \sim \Gamma/2$, *low* to $D > R \geq 5\Gamma$ but cross section variations due to single resonances are observable and the apparent width at half-maximum is about equal to R.   Poor resolution corresponds to $R \gg D$, so that only smooth cross section variations are observed.   Illustrative examples of these regions are given in Figs. 8 and 9.   The 2.8-kev resonance in Na (Ly58,Go58), as shown in Fig. 8, corresponds to *high* resolution since the ratio of natural width to experimental resolution is 4:1, but the corresponding ratio for the 5.55-kev resonance in Ge[70] (Ne59) is 2:1,

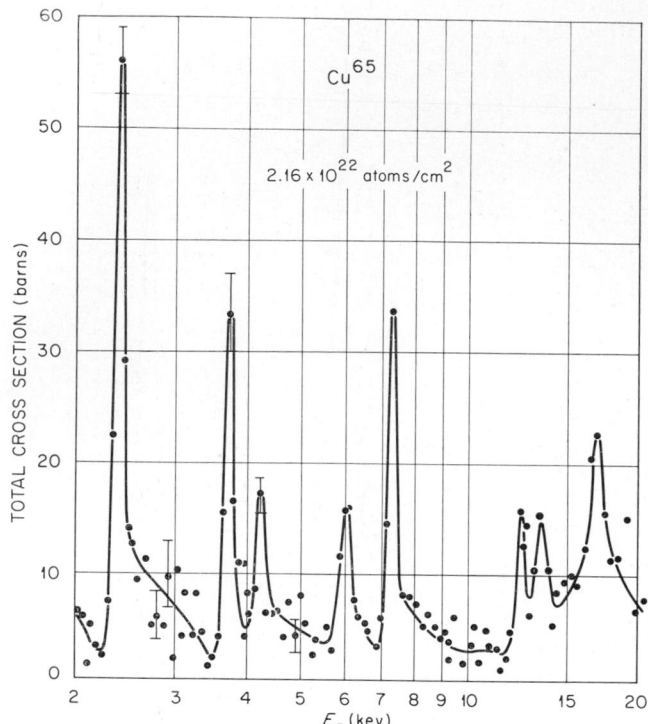

Figure 9. Total cross section of Cu⁶⁵. The observed resonance shapes are essentially all simple reflections of the resolution function. Information as to true resonance width must be obtained by area analysis in this case.

corresponding to *intermediate* resolution. The total cross section for neutrons on Cu^{65} (Ne59), shown in Fig. 9, is illustrative of *low* resolution. For instance the natural width of the 2.4-kev resonance is only 10 ev (Ne59) but the experimental (measured) width is about 75 ev which is roughly equal to R but still much less than D.

It should be recalled that in the kev region the elastic scattering width, Γ_n, accounts for essentially the entire width Γ and therefore that Γ is subject to large variations (Po56). Thus a given resolution function may range from *high* to *low* in the same energy region for a given nuclide. The question thus arises as to the best choice of analyzing techniques for any given experimental situation. Fortunately an appreciable region of overlap in the applicability of analyzing techniques exists so that in many cases a given region may be analyzed in more than one manner. We consider the techniques separately below. We assume in all cases that effects due to Doppler spreading are negligible.

If one had a spectrometer with very high resolving power such that $R \ll \Gamma$ then the observed transmission ratio,

$$T_{\text{obs}}(E) = \exp\,[-n\sigma_T(E)] \equiv T(E) \qquad (16)$$

where n is given in atoms/cm^2. For this case information about a resonance is simply obtained by observation of its peak height, width, and interference dip. However, with only rare exceptions instrumental resolution causes the observed transmission to behave differently from (16), namely,

$$T_{\text{obs}}(E) = \int_{E-E''}^{E+E''} f(E' - E)T(E')dE' \qquad (17)$$

where $f(E' - E)$ is the normalized resolution function and E'' is defined such that $f(E' - E) = 0$ outside the limits $(E - E'') < E < (E + E'')$.

For simplicity we shall assume in this section that interference effects may be neglected and that potential scattering and tails from all close resonances may be eliminated from an experimental transmission curve. Thus we write, from Eq. (2a)

$$\sigma_{\text{res}} \equiv \sigma_n - 4\pi\lambda^2 \sin^2 kr' = \frac{\sigma_0}{1+x^2} + \sigma_0 \tan\left[2kr'\left(\frac{x}{1+x^2}\right)\right]$$

$$(18a)$$

Neglecting interference terms we have

$$\sigma_{\text{res}} \approx \frac{\sigma_0}{1+x^2} \approx 4\pi\,\lambda^2 g/(1+x^2) = \frac{\sigma_{\max} - \sigma_{\min}}{1+x^2} \qquad (18b)$$

where $x = 2(E - E_0)/\Gamma$, $\sigma_0 = 4\pi\lambda^2 g \cos(2kr')$, k the neutron wave number, and r' is the effective nuclear radius. This approximation is accurate for $l \neq 0$ (i.e., $r' = 0$) and for $l = 0$ where r', sample thickness n, and energy are sufficiently small.

A.   Individual Resonances

(1) **Shape Analysis.** If a thin enough sample is used so that $n\sigma_0 < 1$, the transmission curve can be corrected for the effect of

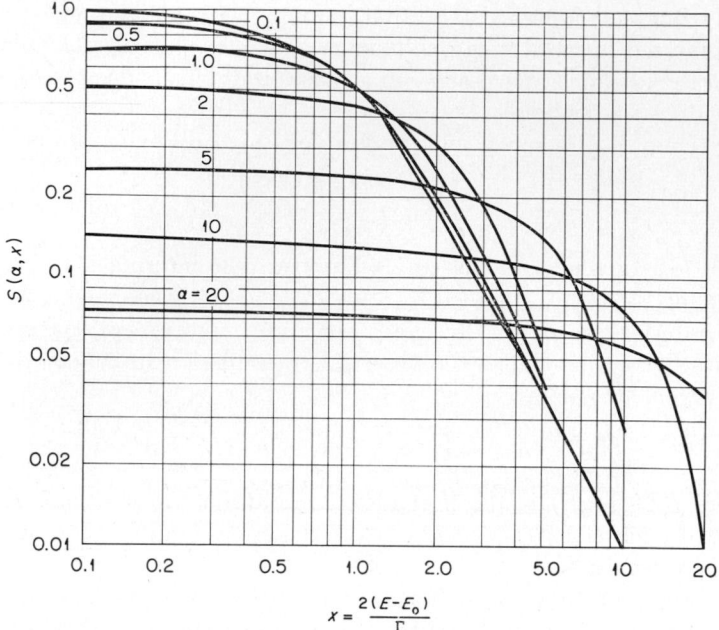

Figure 10. $S(\alpha,x)$ as a function of x and α, where α is the ratio of resolution half-width to the resonance natural width (Ly57). $S_{\max}$ for a given α is equivalent to $\sigma_0(\text{obs})/\sigma_0(\text{true})$.

resolution to give σ_0 and Γ. Assume the resolution function $f(x,x',\alpha)$ where $x' = 2(E' - E_0)/\Gamma$ and $\alpha = R/\Gamma$ with R the resolution width at half-maximum. Then the observed cross section, neglecting interference and potential terms, is given by

$$S(\alpha,x) \equiv \int_{-\infty}^{\infty} \sigma(x')f(x,x',\alpha)dx' \qquad (19)$$

Consider the case (Ly57) of a triangular resolution function with R its full width at half-maximum. Then Eq. (19) is readily integrable. Results of such an integration for various values of α are given in Fig. 10. The maximum value of S for each curve represents the ratio $\sigma_0(\text{obs})/\sigma_0(\text{true})$ while the width at half-maximum of the S function represents $\Gamma(\text{obs})/\Gamma(\text{true})$. These ratios are presented in Fig. 11. Thus the parameters σ_0 and Γ may be obtained from $\sigma_0(\text{obs})$, $\Gamma(\text{obs})$, and R. A discussion of errors associated with this technique is given by Ly57. For $\alpha = 2$, $n\sigma_0 = 1$, the error is about 10 per

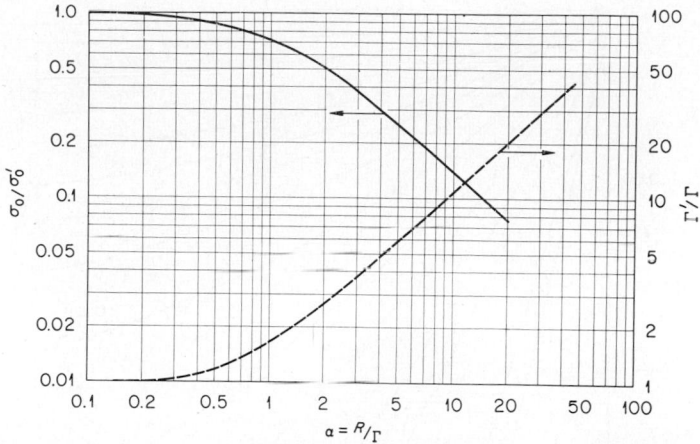

Figure 11. Ratios of observed to true peak cross section and half-width for various values of α. A triangular resolution function was assumed for the computations of these curves (Ly57).

cent at the resonance peak. Lynn *et al.* (Ly57) have also reported calculations for good resolution measurements with intermediate thickness samples ($n\sigma_0 \sim 1$).

(2) Peak Height or Minimum Transmission Analysis. The method of shape analysis described above is of limited usefulness since it is satisfactory only for thin samples and rather good resolution. In many instances one is primarily interested in the total angular momentum of a given resonance. The most important piece of information in this case is the value of the minimum transmission.

For an isolated resonance, the ratio of minimum transmission to potential transmission can be determined with fair accuracy from the experimental data and can yield valuable information provided only that instrumental resolution is known with tolerable accuracy, and that the transmission is measured for a range of sample thicknesses.

Assume the resolution to be Gaussian, defined by the normalization function

$$f_G(E) = (1/\sqrt{2\pi}\,\delta) \exp\left[-(E - E_0)^2/2\delta^2\right] \tag{20}$$

where δ is the standard (root-mean-square) deviation and E_0 the energy at resonance. Since the contributions of *potential scattering*

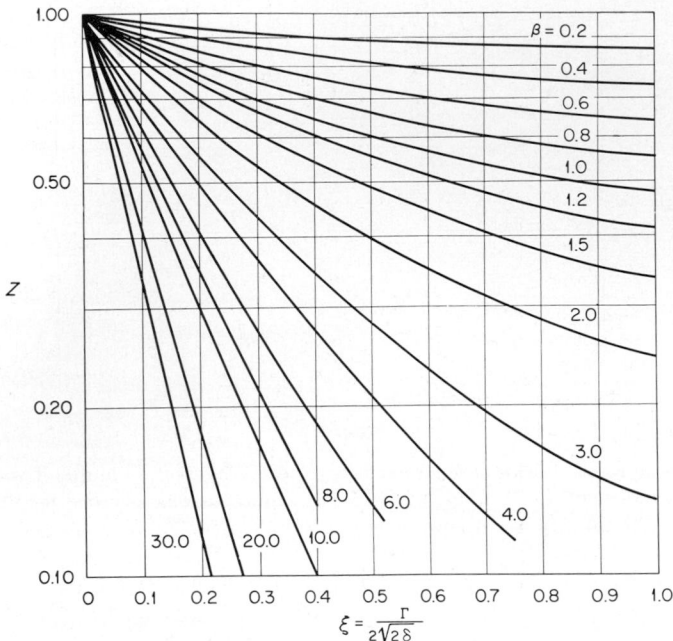

Figure 12. Z vs ξ for various values of β. From these curves one can obtain approximate values of Γ vs σ_0 if the resolution function and experimental minimum transmission are known (Me59).

and *tails* defined collectively as σ_c to σ_t are usually not sensitively dependent upon energy we can remove them from the integral in (17). Thus, neglecting interference, Eq. (17) can be written as

$$Z_{\text{exp}} \equiv T_{\text{obs}}\ (E_0)\ \exp\ (n\sigma_c)$$

$$= \frac{\Gamma}{2\sqrt{2\pi}\,\delta} \int_{-E_0}^{\infty} \exp\left[-\frac{(E-E_0)^2}{2\delta^2} - \frac{\beta}{1+x^2} \right] \frac{d(E-E_0)}{\Gamma/2} \quad (21)$$

where $\beta - n\sigma_0$ and $x = 2(E - E_0)/\Gamma$. For $E_0 \gg \Gamma$, (21) can be written as (Me59):

$$Z(\xi,\beta) = \frac{2\xi}{\sqrt{\pi}} \int_0^{\infty} \exp\left[-\xi^2 x^2 - \frac{\beta}{1+x^2} \right] dx \quad (22)$$

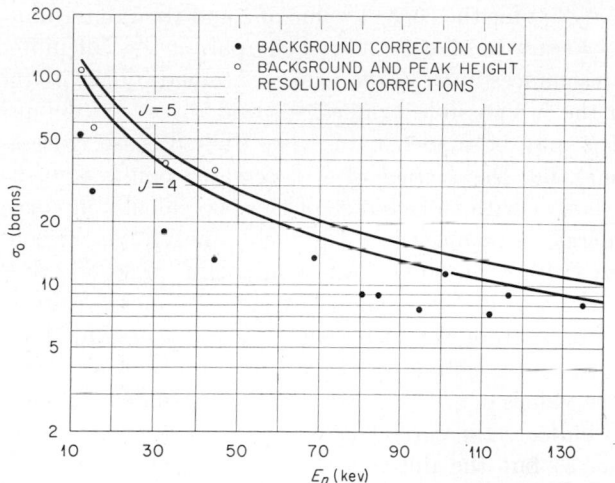

Figure 13. The maximum cross sections (above potential scattering) for the principle s-wave resonances of bismuth (solid data). The points shown as circles have been corrected for resolutions as described in the text (Ni59). The solid lines indicate the peak cross sections to be expected with perfect resolution.

where we use the abbreviation $\xi = \Gamma/(2\sqrt{2}\,\delta)$. ξ essentially determines the quality of resolution for a given resonance. The function $Z(\xi,\beta)$ is plotted in Fig. 12 for various values of ξ and β. Similar calculations may be used for rectangular resolution (Mc59). *Thus one may obtain, by means of the experimentally observed minimum transmission and a (known) resolution function, a value of Γ for an assumed value of $n\sigma_0$.* If the spin of the target nucleus and the angular momentum of the neutron are zero, one can calculate $n\sigma_0$ from the measured E_0 since $g = 1$ and thus determine Γ. Similarly for s-wave resonances if the target spin is $\geq \frac{3}{2}$ then $\frac{3}{8} \leq g \leq \frac{5}{8}$ so that Γ may be determined within about 15 per cent independent of σ_0 remembering that in this approximation $\sigma_0 = \sigma_{\max} - \sigma_{\min}$.

For s-wave neutron resonances up to about 50 kev with a proper choice of sample thicknesses the neglect of the interference term in the scattering cross section does not lead to serious errors, and the peak-height method may be used to determine $\sigma_{\max} - \sigma_{\min} = 4\pi\lambda^2 g$ if data are available for two samples differing by a factor of two or more in thickness. It is possible to perform a graphical solution of the simultaneous equations: $\beta_1/\beta_2 = n_1\sigma_0/n_2\sigma_0 = n_1/n_2$, $\beta_1 = f(Z_1,\xi)$, and $\beta_2 = f(Z_2,\xi)$ for the correct value of ξ and then determine σ_0 from Fig. 12.[5] Figure 13 shows a curve comparing the calculated values of σ_0 for resonances in Bi to the values obtained by the method given above for the two possible g values, $\frac{9}{20}$ and $\frac{11}{20}$. No definite assignments of J may be made in this very difficult case (target spin $\frac{9}{2}$ and large r), but the average of the corrected points is in reasonably good agreement with the average of the two calculated curves. The higher energy resonances in Bi are not analyzable without taking interference into account. An equivalent method of analysis (Me59,Pa61) which yields somewhat less convincing results consists in determining ξ from Fig. 12 for each thickness, assuming all possible values of σ_0, and selecting the correct one on the basis of the consistency in the values of ξ. The more consistent set of values has been shown to indicate the correct assignment for a considerable number of resonances but the differences are much less than the absolute experimental error and seem at first sight too small to be significant.

In many cases, possible assignments are eliminated when the experimental σ_0 exceeds one or more of the possible theoretical values. This is particularly true if the self-detection technique is used.

The peak-height method should not be used for thick samples since background corrections must be very accurate if serious errors are to be avoided for transmission ratios much less than ~30 per cent. The method is also useful for weak and partially overlapping resonances where the area method (see following) cannot be easily applied.

(3) **Self-Detection Peak-Height Methods.** A resonance, even though well separated from all others of comparable size, may be completely missed by total cross section measurements if its true width at half maximum is less than about 1 per cent of the energy spread R of the beam. Further, unless the true width is more than about half of the beam energy spread, a serious distortion from the true shape of the resonance will be found even when it is easily detectable. A serious distortion also results from the use of moderately thick samples in the presence of extraneous neutron backgrounds such as those discussed earlier for back angle measurements. Of

[5] Note that the value of ξ is useful in general only for the determination of σ_0 and should not be used to determine Γ for an s resonance unless interference effects are quite small.

course none of these difficulties would exist if the energy resolution were perfect and backgrounds were negligible. One can *effectively* approach this hopelessly perfect condition by first scattering (or absorbing) the nearly resonant neutrons out of the beam and then doing transmission experiments on this component alone.

Perhaps the simplest form of self-detection device is shown in Fig. 4 which was used by Hibdon (Hi57). A thin scattering sample, located at the center of the counters, transmits off-energy groups and scatters resonant neutrons into the detector with only a slight admixture of potentially scattered or background neutrons. A total cross section is then measured by finding the transmission ratio of a sample of the same material at the mouth of the collimator. If the scattering sample is so thin that only about 10 per cent of the *resonant* neutrons are removed by it the transmission ratio of the external sample (Be37a) is

$$T = \exp\,(-n\sigma_0/2)\,J_0\,(n\sigma_0/2)\,\approx\,1\,-\,n\sigma_0/2\,+\,3/8(n\sigma_0)^2 \quad (23)$$

J_0 is the zeroth-order Bessel function of imaginary argument. This function decreases much more slowly with n than an exponential and only approaches exponential behavior for extremely thin samples. The equation holds only for very poor resolution, i.e., when there is no appreciable change of neutron intensity as a function of energy over an energy range $\gg\Gamma$. Eq. (23) also applies if the detector is a rather thin foil, which is activated by the resonance neutrons at a single, well-isolated resonance. Data are available (Fig. 2) for the 7 kev resonance in Al where the attenuation of the Al^{28} induced radioactivity was measured when 1.57×20^{23} atoms/cm^2 Al were placed between the neutron source and the activated foil. From Fig. 2 it is obvious that the energy spread is much greater than the true width (obtained by area analysis) of about 15 ev (Go58). Applying (23) to the peak cross section for the 7-kev Al resonance one obtains $\sigma_0 = 88$ barns $\approx (\frac{1}{4})4\pi\lambda^2$ which is in reasonable agreement with the expected peak cross section for $J = 1$ and $l = 1$. The experimental conditions were not favorable enough to assign a definite J value, but it is clear that $\sigma_0 \approx g4\pi\lambda^2$ so that it is correct to assign the resonance to Al^{27} since if the radioactivity observed were due to an impurity of a few per cent the quantity in the transmission sample could not possibly lead to an apparent cross section as high as 88 barns.

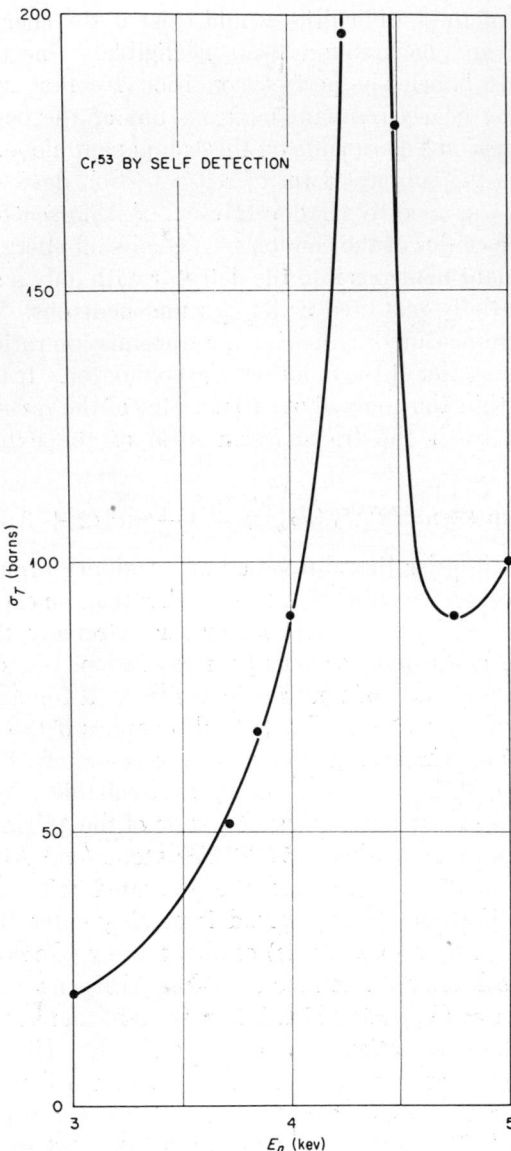

Figure 14. Total cross section of Cr^{53} near a resonance as measured by the self-detection technique (Hi57).

If Γ is equal to or greater than the average energy spread, then $T_0 \approx \exp(-n\sigma_0)$. This latter approximation is nearly enough the case for the 4-kev resonance of Cr^{53} (Fig. 14) where one finds a peak cross section of $\sigma_0 = 220$ barns by self detection as compared to calculated values 240 and 390 barns for the two possible s-wave resonances for this energy (Hi57).

Thin-sample self detection offers the possibility of detecting and interpreting resonances too narrow for detection by ordinary total cross section methods at the same neutron energy spread in the incident beam. The importance of the development of thin-target self-detection methods (now being carried out by Langsdorf and associates) is obvious.

Some of the advantages of self detection may be realized without the use of special equipment such as that shown in Fig. 4. If the scattering sample in Fig. 4 is thick enough to scatter 25 per cent of the neutron beam near an isolated resonance, a cross section may still be obtained from the transmission ratio with a sample of the same material at the mouth of the collimator. For this (thick sample) self detection it is unnecessary for the scattering sample to be within the detector as shown in Fig. 4. With any device capable of measuring total cross sections, the scattered beam may be defined simply by the difference between open beam measurement and the beam transmitted through the scattering sample. Taking this difference as a new open-beam measurement, the transmission through another sample of the same material may be measured. The *double-difference transmission ratio* (Me59), corrected for potential scattering and tails, $Z_d \equiv (Z_1 - Z_2)/(1 - Z_1) \approx (I_1 - I_2)/(I_0 - I_1)$ is the same as the transmission ratio which would be obtained with the transmission apparatus in Fig. 4 when the scattering sample and transmission sample are the same thickness. In the case of perfect resolution, i.e., if there is no appreciable change of the cross section of the sample over the full (not the average) neutron energy spread, the double-difference transmission ratio becomes

$$Z_d = (e^{-n\sigma_0} - e^{-2n\sigma_0})/(1 - e^{-n\sigma_0}) = e^{-n\sigma_0} \qquad (24)$$

In the case of a single isolated resonance narrower than the resolution spread, the double-difference ratio may be written

$$Z_d = \frac{Z_1(\xi,\beta_1) - Z_2(\xi,\beta_2)}{1 - Z_1(\xi,\beta_1)} \qquad (25)$$

If the possible values of Γ are known from area analysis and there is sufficient knowledge of the energy spread to calculate ξ, separate ratios in the above equation may be calculated for all the possible values of J and these calculated values compared to the measured value, thus determining the correct J and Γ. This application of the difference method is most useful for p-wave resonances where interference effects are small.

The use of two equal thicknesses in the difference method is a convenience and not a necessity. Any two thicknesses may be used for this measurement provided the transmission ratio is measured for each thickness and then for both samples in the beam together. This more general procedure requires measurement of three transmission ratios instead of two. In principle, one can approach more nearly the case of thin-target self detection when a thick and thin sample are used in this manner.

The subtractions necessary to determine the difference cross section, $\sigma_d = n_1^{-1} \ln Z_d$, have the advantage that background and resolution corrections are very decidedly reduced. These advantages more than offset the obvious disadvantages. The method works well for symmetric resonances or in cases where σ_d is greater than all but one possible assignment but for wide s-wave resonances like those in Bi it is less satisfactory than the multiple thickness peak height analysis already discussed.

For continuous-beam methods it is generally preferable to measure only peak heights with a variety of sample thicknesses and very good counting statistics. The peak cross section is determined from these data and the resonance width from a single sample area analysis. The latter yields the true value of Γ after σ_0 has been determined. Self-detection and other peak height techniques are less useful for time-of-flight experiments.

(4) **Area Analysis.** The use of the technique of analysis by minimum transmission assumed that the bottom of the transmission dip was the major reliable datum derived from the experiment (the usual case for very thin samples). It also presumed knowledge of the shape and width of the resolution function if Γ as well as σ_0 is to be determined. When enough data points are available over the resonance so that its shape (including resolution distortion) is determined to a fair degree of accuracy it is preferable to use an analysis that incorporates more information than merely the point of minimum

transmission. In the area method of analysis (Ha51,Me53,Se54, Hu55,Ly57,Se59a,Ly60) one can show that the area above the resonance transmission dip is related to the quantity $\sigma_0 \Gamma^p$ where p varies from 1.0 for thin samples ($\beta \ll 1$) to 2.0 for thick samples ($\beta \gg 1$). If two or more samples of *widely different thickness* are measured, the individual quantities σ_0 and Γ may sometimes be determined. *A further advantage of the area method is that little knowledge of the details of the resolution function is necessary other than that it is symmetric and reasonably well-bounded.* If these conditions are fulfilled the observed area above the transmission dip is identical to the theoretical area.

Let us again ignore the interference term in (18a). Then the observed transmission becomes, similar to Eq. (19)

$$\int_0^\infty f(E - E') \exp [-n\sigma_{res}]dE = Z_{exp}(E') \tag{24}$$

Now define the integral

$$A(\beta) = \int_0^\infty [1 - Z_{exp}(E')]dE' \tag{25}$$

Substituting Z_{exp} from (24) and recalling that $f(E - E')$ is a normalized function we obtain (for $kr \ll 1$)

$$A(\beta) = \int_0^\infty [1 - \exp (-n\sigma_{res})]dE \simeq \Gamma \int_0^\infty [1 - e^{-\beta/(1+x^2)}]dx$$

$$= (\Gamma \pi \beta/2)[J_0(\beta/2) + J_1(\beta/2)] \exp (-\beta/2) \tag{26}$$

where J_0 and J_1 are zeroth- and first-order Bessel functions of imaginary argument. Equation (26) has been evaluated by the authors mentioned above and is presented in Fig. 15. Note that $A(\beta)$ is the area of the resonance dip after the transmission curve has been *normalized to unity transmission* far from the resonance energy (where $\sigma_{res} \approx 0$). Two useful asymptotic forms of Eq. (26), corresponding to extremes in sample thickness, are (Me53)

$$A(\beta) = \left(\frac{n\pi}{2}\right) \sigma_0 \Gamma \qquad \beta = n\sigma_0 \ll 1$$

$$A(\beta) = \sqrt{n\pi} \, \sigma_0 \Gamma \qquad \beta = n\sigma_0 \gg 1 \tag{27}$$

It should be remembered that the development given above is highly simplified in that we assumed $kr' \ll 1$, $\beta \ll 1$, and neglected interference effects. This is certainly not the actual case in much of the kev range. These effects are discussed in the next section.

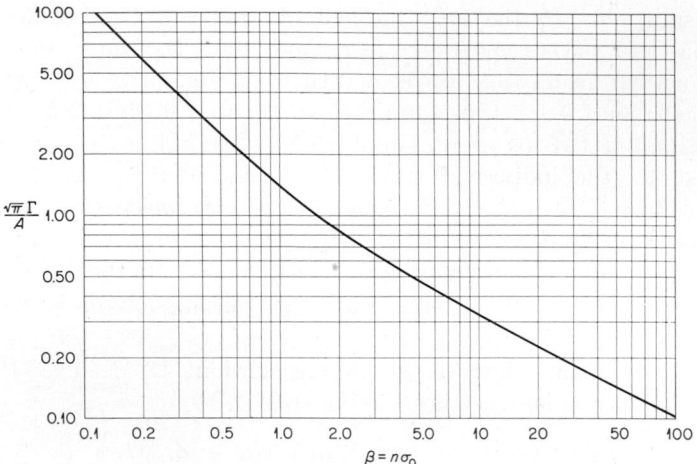

Figure 15. The ratio $\sqrt{\pi}\Gamma/A$ as a function of $n\sigma_0$. For $n\sigma_0 \ll 1$ the slope of the curve approaches unity; for $n\sigma_0 \ll 1$ the slope approaches $1/2$.

In practice one often finds it hard to determine the full wing area, due to closely neighboring resonances. It is then convenient to choose an energy region located symmetrically about E_0, i.e., perform the integration between the limits $(E_0 - \epsilon)$ and $(E_0 + \epsilon)$, with the condition $2\epsilon \gg \Gamma$ or R, whichever is larger.[6] Then we have

$$A'\epsilon(\beta) = \int_{E_0 - \epsilon}^{E_0 + \epsilon} [1 - Z_{\exp}(E')]dE' \qquad (28)$$

A', like A above, is independent of the resolution function if we can consider the resolution outside the interval of integration as *good*, so that the observed and theoretical transmissions coincide. Under these conditions we can write

$$A'_\epsilon(\beta) = \int_{E_0 - \epsilon}^{E_0 + \epsilon} [1 - e^{-n\sigma_{\mathrm{res}}}]dE_n = 2\epsilon - \frac{\Gamma}{2\epsilon} \int_0^{2\epsilon/\Gamma} e^{-\beta/(1+x^2)} dx$$

$$= 2\epsilon[1 - Z(x_0,\beta)] \qquad (29)$$

where $x_0 = 2\epsilon/\Gamma$, and $Z(x_0,\beta)$ is defined as indicated in the equation. The process of obtaining the area experimentally, if one uses (29), consists of measuring the resonance area that lies *below the transmission*

[6] Lynn and Rae (Ly57) and Seth (Se59) have computed correction terms for area analysis where the condition $2\epsilon \gg \Gamma$ does not hold.

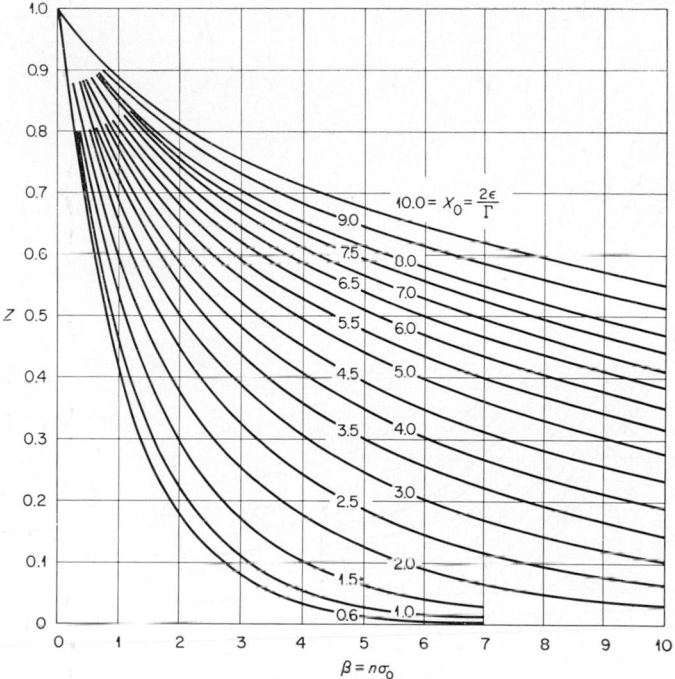

Figure 16. The function $Z(x_0,\beta)$ versus x_0 and β.

due to contributions from the tails of other resonances as well as potential scattering. It is often more convenient to measure the area from an upper limit of *unit* transmission and *compute* the correction for the extraneous cross sections. For this case we define

$$B(x_0,\beta) = \int_{E_0 - \epsilon}^{E_0 + \epsilon} [1 - T(E')]dE' \tag{30}$$

Following the same reasoning as above one obtains

$$B(x_0,\beta) = 2\epsilon[1 - Z(x_0,\beta) \exp(-n\sigma_c)] \tag{31}$$

Curves of $Z(x_0,\beta)$ as a function of x_0 and β are given in Fig. 16. The use of (31) plus these curves permits a calculation of Γ as a function of β when B is known (measured) as a function of ϵ (Me 59).

Since time-of-flight devices generally measure a whole cross section curve rather than the peak height alone it is more feasible to de-

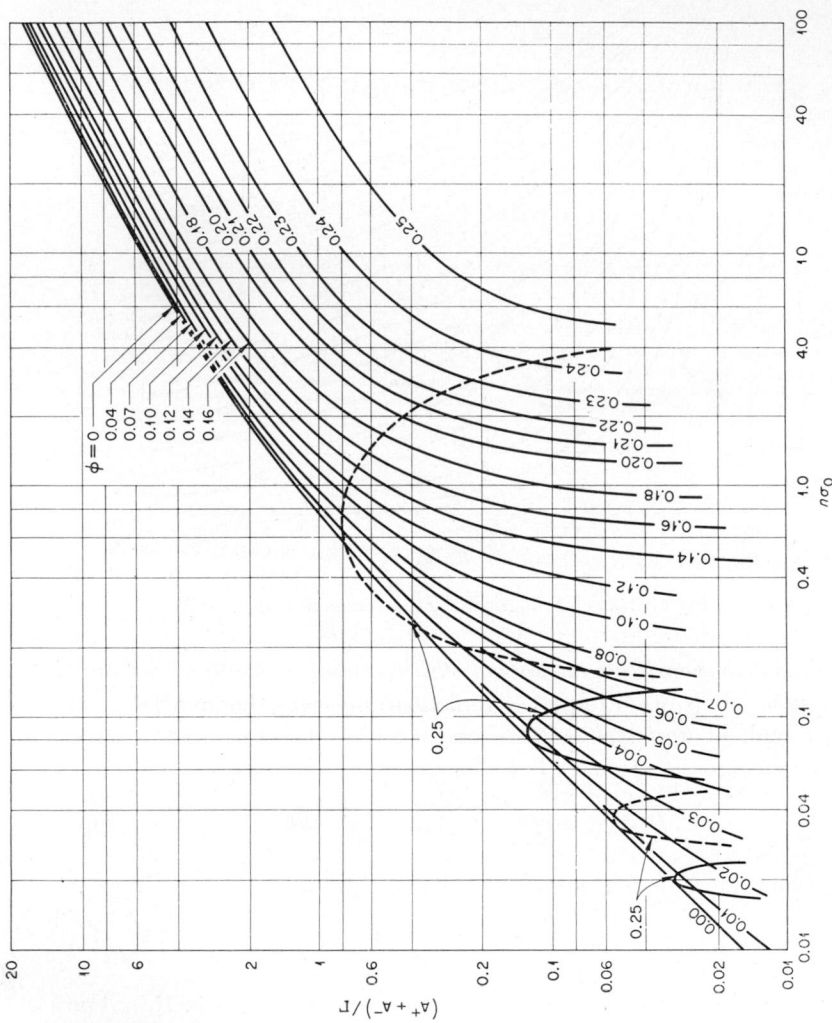

Figure 17. $(A^+ + A^-)/\Gamma$ for the different values of the parameter $\phi = [ng(r')^2\Gamma_n/\Gamma]^{1/2}$ (Se59). The dashed curves represent negative values of $(A^+ + A^-)/\Gamma$ and refer to $\phi = 0.25$. Similar loops for other values of ϕ are not shown.

termine σ_0 and Γ by means of multiple thickness area analyses, if sample thicknesses are carefully chosen.

(5) **Interference Effects.** The preceding discussion or area analysis neglected interference effects. Recently Lynn (Ly58) and Seth (Se59) have shown that interference effects on the measured area can be surprisingly large. We now proceed to reformulate the area analysis, including the interference term. The equation corresponding to (28) is

$$A'_{\text{corr}}(\beta,\epsilon) = A^+ + A^- = \int_{E_0 - \epsilon}^{E_0 + \epsilon} (1 - e^{-n\sigma_{\text{res}}})dE \qquad (32)$$

where

$$A^+(\beta) = \int_{E_0}^{E_0 + \epsilon} (1 - e^{-n\sigma_{\text{res}}})dE$$

$$A^-(\beta) = \int_{E_0 - \epsilon}^{E_0} (1 - e^{n\sigma_{\text{res}}})dE \qquad (32a)$$

and

$$n\sigma_{\text{res}} = [\beta/(1 + x^2)](1 + x \tan 2kr') \qquad (32b)$$

Here symbols have the same meaning as in (28), to which (32) reduces if $kr' = 0$ (i.e., no interference). Equation (32) has been evaluated by Seth (Se59) under the assumptions:

(a) $2\epsilon \gg \Gamma$ and $E_0 \gg \Gamma$.

(b) In the range of integration k can be assumed to be constant, equal to its value at E_0.

(c) In the range of integration, Γ and Γ_n can be assumed to be constant. The results are given in Fig. 17. It is sometimes convenient to write Eq. (32) in the form

$$A_{\text{corr}}(\beta) = A(\beta)F(\beta,r) = A(\beta)[1 - (\beta/4) \tan^2 kr' + b] \qquad (33)$$

where $A(\beta)$ is given by (26) and b is a series of higher order Bessel functions which is difficult to evaluate. However, b is negligible over a considerable range of the variables, and the approximations (Ma57,Ly57)

$$F(\beta,r) \cong 1 - (1/4)\beta \tan^2 kr$$

$$\cong 1 - \pi g n r', \ (kr' \ll 1) \qquad (34)$$

may often be used where the approximation $F = 1$, implied in Eq. (26), is no longer adequate.

Figure 17 shows a family of curves for different values of the parameter

$$\phi \equiv [ng(r')^2\Gamma_n/\Gamma]^{1/2} \approx [ng(r')^2]^{1/2}$$

These curves give the values of $(A^+ + A^-)/\Gamma$ for any value of $4\pi gn\lambda^2$ from 0.01 to 100. The regions of validity of (26) (interference neglected) and (34) are indicated in Table II. It may be noted that for large values of ϕ the areas are positive, zero, and negative in succession, as is illustrated in Fig. 17 for $\phi = 0.25$. When $A = A^+ + A^- \cong 0$ it is impossible to determine Γ by measuring the area in the usual way. However, for these cases $(A^+ - A^-)/\Gamma$ may be calculated from (32a) as a function of $4ng\pi\lambda^2$ and ϕ, and used in the same way as Fig. 17. The $(A^* = A^+ + A^-)$ method of area analysis (Se59) has been applied successfully to the resonances of Bi (Ni59). A correction (usually small) must be made for resolution and the area must always be taken over finite limits, but there is not any uncertainty in the value of Γ due to uncertainty in $(\sigma_p + \sigma_{\text{tails}}) \equiv \sigma_c$. A wing-fit method for analyzing highly unsymmetric s-wave resonances has been discussed by Levin and Hughes (Le56) and Hibdon (Hi57).

Table II.   The Validity of Approximate Treatments of Interference

$4ng\pi^2\lambda/\phi$	$(A^+ + A^-)$ Fig. 17 $A(\beta)$ Eq. (26)			$(A^+ + A^-)$ Fig. 17 $\sim(A^+ + A^-)$ Eq. (34a)		
	0.01	0.20	0.25	0.01	0.20	0.25
0.01	0.876	0.834	0.999	1.000	1.000	1.000
0.1	0.974	−0.258	0.773	1.000	1.000	1.001
1.0	0.997	−0.114	−0.582	1.001	1.027	1.007
10.0	0.999	0.257	0.060	1.000	0.933	0.393
100.0	0.999	0.448	0.091		0.909	0.455

Note: The electronic computer calculations of $(A^+ + A^-)$ (Fig. 17) are compared as ratios to the values calculated from (26) where interference is neglected and to those obtained from (33) and (34a). $\phi = r(gn\Gamma_n/\Gamma)^{1/2}$. We are indebted to K. K. Seth for the preparation of this table.

For higher angular momentum resonances interference is usually not a problem in the kev region so that (26) and the analysis methods already outlined in the previous section may be applied more easily than to s-resonances.

In conclusion it is seen that several techniques exist for the determination of the quantities Γ and g (and therefore J) for a given resonance as long as the resonance is reasonably well separated from its neighbors.   The above techniques cover the *high*, *intermediate*, and *low* resolution regions mentioned at the beginning of the section. Extraction of information in regions of *poor* resolution does not determine the parameters of individual resonances but still gives information on some valuable average properties of compound nuclei.

B.   Poor Resolution Analysis

The previous discussion of the analysis of cross section data assumed that individual resonances were not only recognizable but well enough separated to attribute a portion of a cross section curve (or at least a few points near a maximum) to a single resonance.   We will now consider the interpretation of data where this condition no longer applies.

The averaged transmission over a region from E_1 to E_2, which contains m resonances, may be written after eliminating the effect of the slowly varying cross section terms, as the sum of the effects of the individual resonances.   The averaging is often due largely to finite energy resolution $(R \gg D)$, but in some cases suitable statistical averaging of the observed transmission must be performed.   For a very thin sample $(n\sigma_0 \ll 1)$ of an even-even target nucleus, where only s-wave neutrons are important we can write

$$1 - \overline{T}e^{+n\sigma_{\text{const}}} = (E_2 - E_1)^{-1} \sum_{j=1}^{m} A_j(\beta) \tag{35a}$$

where subscript j refers to the j-th resonance.   But, for a thin sample we have from Eq. (27)

$$A_j = \pi n \sigma_{0j}\Gamma_j/2 = 2\pi^2 \lambda \lambda_1 g_J n \Gamma_{nj}^0 \tag{35b}$$

where λ_1 is the Dirac wave length of a 1-ev neutron, and $\Gamma_n^0 = \Gamma\lambda/\lambda_1$. Thus if we put $m\Gamma_n^0 = \Sigma\Gamma_{nj}^0$ and $mD = (E_2 - E_1)$ we have

$$1 - \overline{T}e^{n\sigma_{\text{const}}} = 2\pi^2 n\lambda\lambda_1(\overline{\Gamma}_n^0/D) \tag{35c}$$

If $(E_2 - E_1) \ll E_n = (E_1 + E_2)/2$ then λ in (35c) is closely approximated by the wave length at energy E_n.   We define[1] (see Section 5.G)

$$\sigma_{\text{const}} = 4\pi\lambda^2 \sin^2 kr' - \pi^3\lambda^2_1(\overline{\Gamma}_n^0/D)^2 \cos 2kr' \tag{36}$$

The second term in (36) (Se59) is included with the potential scattering ($\sim 4\pi r'^2$ at low energies) since they are both independent of E_n and sample thickness within a properly chosen interval $E_2 - E_1$. In principle, if $\bar{T}$ for a thin sample is plotted against λ or $(E_n)^{-1/2}$, the slope and intercept of the curve, respectively, yield the essential parameters $\bar{\Gamma}_n{}^0/D$, the strength function and γ', the interaction parameter of the clouded crystal ball model. The resonance interference with potential scattering is an odd function of energy and presents no complications in thin sample transmission. It is feasible (Se58) to make small corrections for the fact that when a sample (of a given n) is thin enough to satisfy (35c) at fairly high energies, it becomes somewhat too thick at lower energies. This method is satisfactory for level spacings of the order of a few hundred ev or less. When spacings approach 0.5 kev or more, individual experimental points begin to show serious statistical fluctuations since even an energy interval $(E_2 - E_1)$ of 5 kev will contain less than 10 resonances which is not a good enough sample of all the resonances to determine the strength function accurately. As spacings widen, the statistical scatter of the experimental points up to, say, 100 kev becomes so great that it is impractical to determine the slope of the best straight line through them with any accuracy, but the average of all the experimental points may still be meaningful. In this case R' and strength function may be determined with the help of measurements with more than one sample thickness. The expression analogous to (35) for thicker samples can be obtained with the help of Eq. (34). The result for a monoisotopic, $I = 0$ element is

$$1 = \bar{T}e^{n\sigma \text{const}} = (E_2 - E_1)^{-1} \sum_{j=1}^{m} A_j(\beta)F_j(\beta,\gamma')$$

$$= (\bar{\Gamma}_n{}^0/D)y(\beta)F(\beta,\gamma') \quad (37a)$$

where from Eq. (26)

$$y(\beta) \equiv [A(\beta)/\Gamma](E_n)^{1/2} = (\pi/2)\beta e^{-\beta/2}[J_0(\beta/2) + J_1(\beta/2)](E_n)^{1/2} \quad (37b)$$

and $F(\beta,r')$ is given by Eq. (34). y is dependent only on the effective sample thickness, β, the average energy $E_n = (E_2 + E_1)/2$, and r'. If the target consists of a single nuclide with $I = 0$ or of a mixture of isotopes with or without spin, a multiple sum must be used instead of Eq. (37)

$$1 - \bar{T}e^{n\sigma\text{const}} = (\bar{\Gamma}_n{}^0/D)\sum_\beta y(\beta)F(\beta,r') \tag{38a}$$

$$= (\bar{\Gamma}_n{}^0/D)\sum_\phi (A^+ + A^-)E^{1/2}/\Gamma \tag{38b}$$

The right sides of Eqs. (38a) and (38b) are proportional to the strength function averaged over the range, if any, of mass numbers in the target. There will be as many terms on the right of Eq. (38a) or (38b) as there are possible values of β or ϕ which are both dependent on J and also on the sample thickness for each isotope.

From (37) it is obvious that wherever $F(\beta,r') = 0$ (which occurs for moderately thick samples), one has regions of energy in which $T = e^{-n\sigma\text{const}}$ (see Fig. 17) when only s-waves are considered. Experiments at energies and sample thicknesses of this order of magnitude are favorable for the measurement of potential and p-wave scattering. In many cases simultaneous equations of the form of Eqs. (38a) and (38b) must be solved for two or more sample thicknesses to obtain both R' and one or more strength functions. If there are not enough resonances in an interval $(E_2 - E_1) \ll E_n$ to determine the strength function with sufficient statistical accuracy, Eqs. (38a) and (38b) must be integrated numerically over a large energy range (Ma57).

If there is an appreciable contribution from p-wave resonance scattering, the average transmission must be written (when $I = 0$):

$$1 - \bar{T}e^{n\sigma\text{const}} = (\bar{\Gamma}_n{}^0/D)_s F_s y_s + (\bar{\Gamma}_n{}^1/D)_{n+} y+$$
$$+ (\bar{\Gamma}_n{}^1/D)_{p-} y- \tag{39}$$

which may be approximated by (Ne59)

$$1 - \bar{T}e^{n\sigma\text{const}} \approx (\bar{\Gamma}_n{}^0/D)_s F_s y_s + (\bar{\Gamma}_n{}^1/D)_p (y+ + y-) \tag{40}$$

Since y is a function of the statistical weight factor g the subscripts $(+)$ and $(-)$ indicate the $(l + \tfrac{1}{2})$ and $(l - \tfrac{1}{2})$ channels for an even-even target nucleus $(I = 0)$. Note that the interference correction terms $F_\pm$ reduce to unity for the sum over p-wave resonances. It is impossible to separate the two p-wave strength functions $(\Gamma_n{}^1/D)_\pm$ which we should expect to find because of the effect of spin orbit coupling. The approximation in (40) is probably very poor (Ne59) near a p-wave giant resonance. A more complicated expression entirely analogous to either Eqs. (38a) or (38b) must be used if $I = 0$ or the sample is not isotopically pure.

5. Averaged Resonance Parameters

While the resonance energies, E_0, are measured more accurately than any other quantity by ev- and kev-region cross section experiments, no way of interpreting such detailed information has yet been conceived. A statistical point of view still prevails, as it did twenty years ago (Be37a), and it may well be that highly excited compound nuclei are too complicated to be understood in any other way. A slight indication of a more simple situation may be found in the cross sections of some nuclides, for example those shown in Fig. 18. Nearly every resonance of Ni^{58} is matched by a corresponding resonance in Ni^{60} (Ne59a). Similar cases are known for a number of other isotopic cross section measurements. It is easy to "prove" from all models known to the authors that these coincidences *must* be fortuitous, but nuclear models are notoriously narrow in their applicability (see, for example, Fe50, p. 159) and it is conceivable that the relation between the energy levels of isotopes is simpler than expected.

At present, it is certainly true that we can interpret only such numbers as the strength function and its separate components, the average resonance spacing and the average reduced width. The potential scattering parameter, R', is not, strictly speaking, an averaged parameter but it, too, is frequently determined by averaging several relatively flat regions of cross section curves. The remainder of this section will be devoted to a discussion of these quantities.

A. Distribution of Reduced Widths and Level Spacings

For low-energy resonances it has been known for some time that the distribution function for the reduced widths of s-wave resonances in the ev range falls off nearly exponentially as the reduced width increases (Ha55,Hu55a), i.e., as $\exp(-\Gamma_n^0/\bar{\Gamma}_n^0)$ where $\bar{\Gamma}_n^0$ is the average reduced width. This is also true in the kev region as may be seen in Fig. 19 where the distribution of reduced widths in bismuth is plotted. Porter and Thomas (Po56) suggested on theoretical grounds that the distribution may follow the function $(\bar{\Gamma}_n^0/\Gamma_n^0)^{1/2} \exp\left[-(\Gamma_n^0/2\bar{\Gamma}_n^0)\right]$, which would introduce a slight curvature if fitted to the experimental points shown in Fig. 19. These two distributions are nearly indistinguishable so far as the data in the kev region are concerned, and it is unlikely that small s-resonances, which are

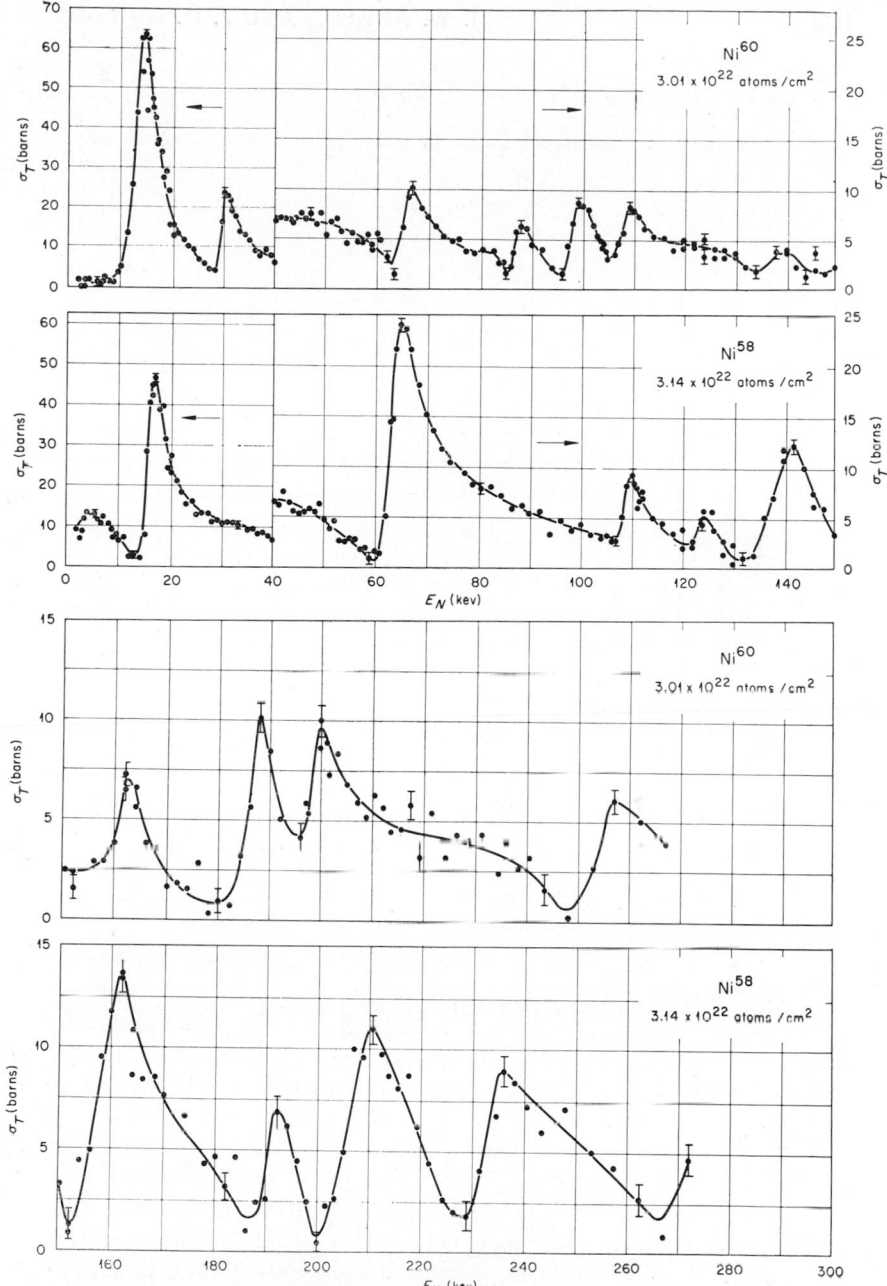

Figure 18. Total cross sections of Ni[58] and Ni[60] measured with the Duke 120° collimator. Both samples were isotopically pure within 2 per cent (Ne59a).

1655

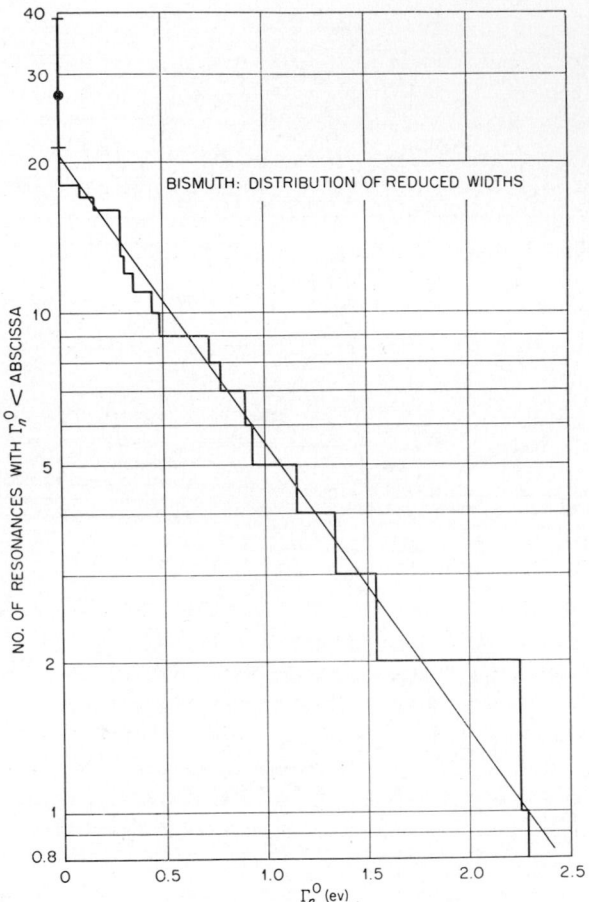

Figure 19. The number of levels stronger than a given reduced width plotted against that value of Γ_n^0 for the Bi^{209} resonances (Ni59). The point with error bars at $\Gamma_n^0 = 0$ is based on the estimated spacing per spin state, 10 ± 3 kev or $D_0 = 100 \pm 30$ kev. The reduced widths were determined by the A^* area (Se59) method [see Section 4.A(5)].

predicted to be very plentiful on the basis of the Porter-Thomas distribution, can be distinguished sufficiently well from p-resonances to allow a definite choice to be made between the two distributions in the kev region. This difficulty is present to some extent even in lower-energy neutron work. There have been strong indications recently

(Sa58) that p-wave resonances sometimes occur below 100 ev, and more care must be taken in the future to avoid counting them as s-resonances.

Most recent measurements in the ev region have been carried out in energy ranges where the resolution (i.e., the ratio of neutron energy spread, R, to E_n), is considerably less than 1 per cent. On the other hand, the best resolution attained in the kev region up to the present is only slightly better than one per cent at 200 kev and about 2 per cent at a few kev. It is evident that for investigating the distribution of spacings between individual resonances in the same channel, measurements in the ev region are much preferable to higher energy experiments.

It has recently been shown that the distribution of individual resonance spacings exhibits level repulsion (Hu58). That is, the number of adjacent resonances in one channel (J), which are separated by about 20 per cent of the average spacing is only about one-fifth the number expected by pure chance.

Knowledge of level repulsion and the unsymmetric reduced width distribution is very helpful in interpreting *averaged* level spacings deduced by counting resonances in the kev region. The s-wave resonance spacings measured in the kev range for the heavier compound nuclei vary between about 1000 kev for Pb^{208} (Ne59b) to about 1.5 kev for Cu^{65} (Fig. 9). For the former only one resonance is known, while for the latter the spacing is perilously close to available experimental resolution in the case of some of the older measurements. The existence of level repulsion allows us to draw some conclusions even in unfavorable cases. Even when the neutron energy spread is $\frac{1}{5}$ of the average spacing, the loss of one resonance should be rare so far as failure to resolve it from its nearest neighbor in the same channel is concerned. If all reduced widths were the same a useful estimate of spacing could be made even when the neutron energy spread $R = D/2$. However, the Porter-Thomas distribution of reduced widths implies that an appreciable number of resonances will be too weak for detection even under the most favorable circumstances.

The idea of level repulsion may be understood intuitively from the fact that two *resonances* in the same channel, which are much closer together in E_0 than half the width of the narrower of the two, would interfere so strongly that it would no longer be sensible to consider them separate states of the compound nucleus, nor would the cross-section curve indicate two separate resonances.[7] This effect will not be present for states of different J, so that the s-wave resonances observed in the cross section of a target nucleus with non-zero spin, should not exhibit level repulsion between the $I + \frac{1}{2}$ and the $I - \frac{1}{2}$ levels. Failure to resolve two such resonances which occur at nearly the same energy is quite likely near $A = 50$ where the giant resonance makes the width to spacing ratio, $\Gamma/D \simeq 0.1$ at 10 kev and larger at higher energies. However, this loss of resonances due to overlapping should be no more than a factor two in the worst case just mentioned and much less at lower energies or far from a giant resonance.

When a cross section curve in the kev range shows several peaks of the width of R, or a very few wider peaks which have the typical shape of an s-wave resonance, the spacing D is estimated to be roughly $(E_2 - E_1)/(j \pm \frac{1}{2}\sqrt{j})$ where j is the number of observed resonances in the energy interval $(E_2 - E_1)$.

Thus a single definite s-resonance when target spin $I \neq 0$ and one or two if $I = 0$ yield a rough lower limit to the spacing while two of the former or three of the latter (by virtue of level repulsion in the same channel) lead to estimates of spacing within a factor 6 or 4, respectively. Such rough estimates will be useful in our later discussion where even the order of magnitude of the level spacings near magic numbers is interesting.

The near coincidence of resonances in isotopes (Fig. 18) is common enough (whatever its interpretation) to discourage the use of spacings estimated from the total cross section of an isotopic mixture (with more than one major component) except again where order of magnitude estimates are of interest. Large errors are indicated near the s-wave strength function maximum ($A \simeq 50$) where overlapping of resonances in different channels is very serious and near $A = 90$ where the s-wave strength function is low and the p-wave strength function is so high that low energy p-resonances are very likely to be counted as if they were due to s-waves.

In favorable cases where about 10 or more resonances can be analyzed, the loss of levels may be estimated by plotting a reduced width distribution curve similar to that shown in Fig. 19 and extrap-

---

[7] Actually the interference patterns of two such resonances is recognizable unless the two resonances have very nearly the same E_0 (Bo62).

olating to find the total number of levels in the energy region studied.

B. Average s-Wave Resonance Spacings

The statistical theory of level densities was in such a highly developed state before the existence of much experimental data that the interpretation and planning of experimental work has been heavily influenced by theory. A short review of the latter is therefore in order; for more details the reader is referred to a lucid review by Ericson (Er60).

Continuous Approximation. Most theoretical attempts to explain resonance spacings have included the assumption that a nucleonic level spacing (for neutrons and for protons) may be expressed as a single number which varies continuously enough with energy that a saddle point integration about the Fermi level may be carried out. This assumption of the *continuous approximation* model is difficult to reconcile with the shell model which must be invoked to account for the most striking features of the experimental results in the kev region.

(1) **Gas Models.** The Fermi gas model is the most commonly used of the Continuous Approximation models; the level density is calculated statistically for a spherical box containing Z protons and N neutrons. Starting from this model Bethe (Be37a) proved that the average level spacing, D_J, of a compound nucleus of total angular momentum J is

$$D_J = D_0/(2J + 1) \qquad (41)$$

where D_0 is the spin-independent spacing parameter. Very considerable deviations (Er60,Be37a,Ha60) are to be expected for $J > 3$. We will show later that there is reason to believe that this relation is, on the average at least, a useful approximation. For the s-wave resonances corresponding to $J = I \pm \frac{1}{2}$ the two possible J values for a resonance are often not distinguishable, and only the total level density $1/D$ is observed. Thus

$$1/D = 1/D_+ + 1/D_- = [2(I + \frac{1}{2}) + 1]/D_0$$

$$+ [2(I - \frac{1}{2}) + 1]D_0$$

so that

$$D_0 = 2(2I + 1)D \qquad (42)$$

where D is the observed average level spacing of all the s-wave resonances, and *not* the *spacing per spin state* which is equal to D if the target nucleus is even-even and to $2D$ if this is not the case. It should be noted that when D_0 is calculated from (42), we have taken account of the fact that there is one s-wave channel if $I = 0$ and two channels if $I \neq 0$. Equation (41) is reasonably consistent with other models which we will find useful later on (Ne59b,Ro57a,Er60). According to the continuous approximation models D_0 is a function of the excitation energy W of the compound nucleus, the nuclear temperature t and $G = G_1 + G_2$, which is the sum of the proton and neutron level density:

$$D_0 = \pi(G_1 G_2)^{1/2}(2W + 3t)^2 \exp\left[-(2\pi^2 GW/3)^{1/2}\right] \qquad (43)$$

The symbols G_1, G_2, and t (Ne56a) may be evaluated semi-empirically by the use of the Fermi gas model; Lang and Le Couteur (La54a) show that Eq. (43) reduces to

$$D_0 = 0.11(AW)^2 \exp\left[-(4AW/11)^{1/2} + 3(11W)^{2/3}/32\right] \qquad (44a)$$

which may be simplified to the familiar form:

$$(4AW/11)^2 \exp\left[-(4AW/11)^{1/2}\right] = \text{const.} \times D_0 \qquad (44b)$$

(Be37a,Mo53) (where W is expressed in Mev) and D_0 in ev. The constants must be determined empirically (La54,Ne56). Equation (44b) is only useful in the regions where the continuous approximation is most nearly correct (i.e., far from magic numbers). Clearly, the nearly monotonic variation with mass number A is quite inconsistent with the well-known maxima in the level spacings which occur at neutron numbers 50, 82, and 126. It has been shown repeatedly (Hu51,Ne52,Hu53,Ne54,Le56; see also Chapter V.M.) that equations like (44b) and the known variations in W near the neutron magic numbers do not fully account for these maxima. We shall review the evidence in a later section.

In spite of the fact that Eqs. (44a) and (44b) do not account for all the experimental observations, their form has been used extensively to estimate the effect of excitation energy on level density. Noting that the exponent in Eqs. (44a) and (44b) will ordinarily account for most of the variation of D with energy, we may write

$$D = Ce - \sqrt{aW} \qquad (45)$$

where C and a may be assumed to be practically independent of W.[8] Equation (45) may also be derived from thermodynamic considerations; values for the coefficient a have been estimated by interpolating (B152) with the help of (45) between the spacings observed near the ground state and those observed at excitation energies B_n near those encountered at slow neutron resonances. These values of a, which are valid only to the extent that (45) is correct, are only to be considered *first guesses* (B152). Equations similar to (41) (42), (43), and (45) have been used by many authors (Hu51,Ne56a, Ca57), to reduce experimentally determined spacings to a standard excitation energy or angular momentum.

(2) **Gap Models.** It has been suggested by Bardeen (Be37a, Mo53,Ba37) that the properties of exchange forces analogous to electrons in a metallic lattice should be considered. These correlations changed A to $A/2$ in (44b) but the determination of the numerical constants in Eq. (44b) is semiempirical (La54a) so that Bardeen's suggestion cannot be tested directly.

The strong dependence of spacing on A, in (44b) enters because the nuclear volume is proportional to mass number and the individual particle level density is proportional to the volume of the box. It has been estimated (Fe50) that only about 10 particles are actually in excited nucleonic states according to the gas models. However, for the almost doubly magic compound nucleus, Pb^{207} in a $\frac{1}{2}^+$ state, at an excitation energy less than about 5 Mev only one or two nucleons may be excited according to shell model energetics (IIa51a,Kl52). Merzbacher and Newson (Ne53) carried Bardeen's analogy (Be37a) a step further by examining the consequences of a *magic* energy gap in the sequence of individual particle levels, somewhat as in a semiconductor. The presence of the gap lowers the compound nucleus level density, and a reasonable correlation can be established between the gap width required to reproduce the observed spacings and the experimental individual particle level densities near the last filled shell. For instance, if the gap width is taken as 2 Mev per nucleon the calculated ratio between the spacing of a nearly double magic compound nucleus (Bi^{210}) to that of a normal nucleus of about the same spin and mass, Ta^{182}, is of the order of the measured ratio (10^3); an identical result has been calculated by Ericson (Er58a). This approach to

---

[8] A discussion of exceptions to this statement is given by Zucker (Zu58) and Goodman and Need (Go58a).

the problem explained the large variations in spacings between *magic* and *normal* compound nuclei but so far the gap models have proved too complicated to be applied to intermediate cases. This is not surprising since there are in general gaps below and above the Fermi level for both neutrons and protons as well as a gap *at* the Fermi level because of the pairing energy.

This latter gap model (the *pairing model;* La59,Er60) raises interesting questions (to be discussed later) about the meaning of the excitation of pairs and the dependence of the pairing energy and the nuclear temperature [$11/4A$ in Eq. (44b)] on excitation energy W.

(3) **The Combinatorial Model.** A more general attack on the problem consists (B154,Ne56a,Ro57a) in assuming or calculating an energy level scheme for individual nucleons and counting the number of states of the configurations which are possible near any particular excitation energy W. It is simplest to assume that the individual nucleons occupy approximately (but not exactly) equally spaced levels in an excited nucleus. If the average separation energy between adjacent nucleonic levels is S'' [$= 1/G$ in Eq. (43)] and $W \gg S''$, the spacing is proportional to

$$(2/3) \pi^2 W \exp \left[-2\pi^2 W/3S''^{1/2}\right] \tag{46}$$

This expression is obtained by counting the number of ways in which a large integer may be made up of the sums of small integers[9] (Ha18). This combinatorial model (Mo53) is somewhat more in accord with experiment than Eq. (44b) in that there is no monotonic dependence of spacing on the mass number A.

A good fit to the resonance spacings measured in the ev region for heavy elements has been obtained by A. A. Ross (Ro57) who calculated S'' from the observed D_0's [using an expression similar to (43)] and also from a potential-well calculation. The parameters of the assumed potential (which included a spin orbit term) were such that the filling order of the nucleons (Ma50,Ma55) was predicted correctly. The parameter $S'' \cong 0.1$ Mev gives a good fit to the data between $A = 100$ and 200. Near the double magic nucleus $Z = 82$ and $N = 126$ the density of nucleonic levels is zero for about 2 Mev above the Fermi level for an approximately spherically potential but below that level the density must be about 0.1 which is the value found

---

[9] The same equation has been derived by Rosenzweig for levels which have a definite degeneracy (Ro57).

near $A = 170$ where the two shells are roughly half full. The "average" value of S'' near $_{82}Pb^{208}$ should then be 0.2 Mev. With the aid of (46) we find a peak to valley ratio of about 200 compared to a measured ratio of nearly 10^4 (see Fig. 22). However, if we remember that Eq. (46) involves the average of a roughly *uniform* spacing, it is apparent that S'' is actually meaningless near Pb^{208}, since there is a very large discontinuous change of nucleonic level spacing there.

(4) **Statistical Shell Models.** These models attempt to account for shell effects by focussing attention on relatively few isolated levels near the Fermi energy which should influence neutron resonance spacings much more strongly than higher or lower nucleonic levels.

Newton and Cameron have developed a *sub-shell* model which is able to account for maxima in spacing in the neighborhood of nucleon numbers 82 and 126 by considering that the $2j + 1$ degeneracy of each subshell is split by an unsymmetric potential so that the maximum energy spread from the lowest to the highest level in each subshell is of the order of magnitude S (Fig. 20). $G = G_1 + G_2$ in Eq. (43) then becomes proportional to $(2j_N + 2j_Z + 2)$ where the $(2j + 1)$'s are roughly equal to the degeneracies of the neutron and proton subshells nearest the Fermi level. It will be noted in Fig. 20 that $j^{\pm} = \frac{1}{2}^{\pm}$ fall just below 82 and 126 nucleons, so that according to this picture and (43) there should be maxima near $N = 82$ and 126. The Newton and Ross solutions of the problem are both most satis factory far from magic numbers (see later section).

The shell model predicts that the levels occupied by individual nucleons cannot actually be considered to be almost equally spaced as assumed in the combinatorial and simple Fermi gas models, but are clustered together in subshells of a definite degeneracy. A few (4–7) of these subshells form a major shell which is distinguished by the fact that the spacing between major shells may be as much as an order of magnitude ($\sim$2 Mev per nucleon) greater than the average spacing between the subshells within a major shell. The "gap" of 2 Mev per nucleon is so high that, for a nearly spherically symmetric compound nucleus, very few nucleons can be excited out of the major shells which they occupied in the target nucleus. This partial isolation of the major shells from each other allows us to make a specific count of the number of certain classes of configuration states. In gen-

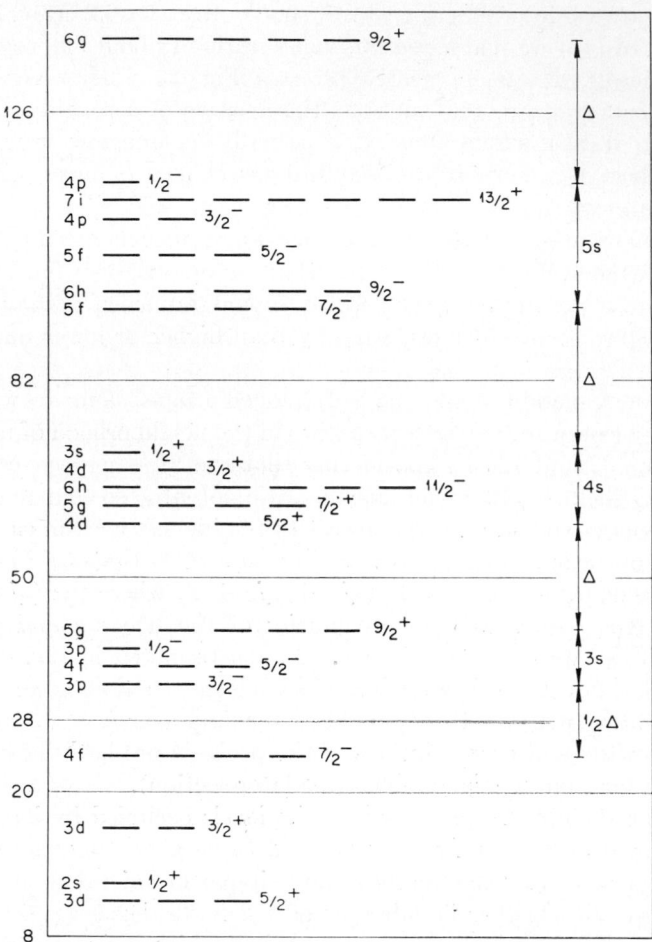

Figure 20. A shell model level scheme for neutrons similar to that of Klinkenberg (Kl52). Note that the notation used in this figure is that used in atomic
spectroscopy. Others use a slightly different notation (Ei58). For our purposes
the same diagram may be used for protons. Subshell spacings are drawn to bs
much more uniform than they actually are and are not drawn to scale. Spacinge
between major shells are drawn roughly to scale, but in our discussion they are considered to be all the same (~ 4 Mev per pair). The degeneracy of the subshell
is indicated by a number of dashes which is equal to $(2j + 1)/2$.

eral it is very difficult to count the configuration states of a compound nucleus without the help of statistical methods which involve the continuous approximation or its equivalent. To simplify the problem Newson and Duncan (Ne59b) suggested the *Super Shell Model* to explain the experimental information by considering that the density of the most stable configuration states (i.e., those most nearly analogous to the ground state) have the greatest influence on the observed variation in the spacing of neutron resonances with mass number.

If we confine ourselves, for the moment to a spherically symmetric potential and to $J^\pi = 0^+$ compound nuclei, an important class of excited configurations are analogous to the ground state in that all nucleons are paired so that the net angular momentum of each pair is zero. There are no selection rules for the excitation of such pairs; they may be excited to any empty or partially filled subshell without changing the spin and parity of the compound nucleus. When either a neutron or a proton major shell is partially filled, it is easy to count the *simple configurations*, which result from the excitation of *unbroken pairs* within the unfilled shells. These are the excited configurations which involve neither the excitation of a pair from one major shell to another, nor the excitation of *broken pairs*. In a *broken pair* configuration J^π is still 0^+, but there are two or more unpaired nucleons which are not necessarily in different subshells.[10] In addition collective modes of excitation may play a part. Any combination of these four excitations we will call *complex configurations*. If J^π is to be 0^+, a single pair can occupy a subshell in only one way even though the degeneracy of the subshell allows it to contain several pairs. It is assumed in calculating the number of simple configurations that the magnetic quantum number $\pm m_j$, which cancels for each pair, must have no effect on the total count.[10]

---

[10] According to E. Merzbacher (private communication), when $j = {}^7/_2$ for a subshell there is one and only one way for an even number of particles to occupy the subshell in a spherically symmetric potential if the total angular momentum of all the particles in the subshell is zero. These configurations can be expanded in terms of n pairs of particles each of which has zero angular momentum and even parity. When $j = {}^9/_2$ there is, in general, more than one state of a configuration, but the state of lowest energy may be described as n pairs, similar to those discussed above, if the interaction of the two particles in a pair is a short range attraction (*viz.* a Majorana exchange force). We should therefore speak of simple and complex *states* of configurations but the definitions in the text are unambiguous for the calculations which we will attempt.

Figure 20 shows the distribution of nucleonic energy levels according to the shell model. The total angular momentum and parity j^{π} is shown for each subshell as well as the usual spectroscopic designation. The degeneracy of each subshell is indicated by a number of dashes. The position of each dash may be occupied by a pair of nucleons or an unpaired nucleon. In counting the total number of simple configurations (as distinguished from complex configurations) of, say, $_{52}\text{Te}_{78}{}^{130}$, one notes that there is one pair of protons in the shell 50–82 and that there are only five different ways (corresponding to the five subshells) to place it, since the horizontal position of the pair (Fig. 20) is assumed to be unimportant; thus $n_z = 5$. There are two less pairs of neutrons than are necessary to fill the shell at $N = 82$. The two *holes* can be distributed in $5!/(2! \times 3!) + 4 = 14 = n_N$ different ways including the ground state configuration. The total number of simple configurations is, therefore, $n_z n_N = 70$ for Te^{130}.

The density of simple configurations, $r_0(W)$, may also be calculated easily. Again taking Te^{130} as an example, an excitation energy S corresponds to 2 configurations depending on whether a neutron or proton pair is excited, so that $r_0(S) = 2/S$, i.e., there are two simple configurations possible for excitation energies between $S/2$ and $3S/2$. Similarly, $r_0(2S) = 3/S$; $r_0(0) = r_0(M) = 1/S$; $r_0(M + S) = 0$; and $r_0(M - S) = r_0(S) = 2/S$. The maximum energy, M, is composed of the energy necessary $(4S)$ to move the pair of protons from the lowest to the highest subshell, and the corresponding energy $7S$ for the two *holes* in the neutron shell, so that $M = 11S$ if there is no departure from the order of the levels shown in Fig. 20. Detailed calculations in the shell 82–126 shows that $r_0(W)$ is surprisingly close to being triangular in shape and symmetric about $M/2$ even when we take account of the fact that the subshells have a different degeneracy and are by no means equally spaced in energy. A schematic plot of $r(W)$ is shown in Fig. 26. Clearly for excitation energies greater than M there are no simple configurations and $r(W > M) = 0$.

M and r_0 depend on the order of the subshells which may sometimes depart from that given in Fig. 20 but n_N and n_z may always be calculated exactly from Fig. 20. Thus the total number of simple configurations

$$\int_0^{\infty} r(W)dW = \int_0^M r(W)dW = n_N n_z \tag{47}$$

A plot of $(n_N n_Z)$ against N for even-even nuclei bears a consid-erable resemblance to a plot of experimentally measured level spac-ings determined by neutron resonances. It is tempting to assume that the change of level spacings with mass number may be attrib-uted principally to the simple configurations which we have discussed so far. However, for many heavy nuclei the excitation energy, $B \geqq M$, so that unless we consider the complex configurations, we predict a level density, $\rho(B) = r_0(B) = 0$, which is absurd.

When a pair is excited from a filled into an unfilled shell or from an unfilled shell to the empty one above, about half of the excitation energy B_n (i.e., about 4 Mev) is required to excite this pair alone. The density of this class of configurations may be approximated as $\sum_i r_0(W - \Delta_i)$ where the several values of Δ_i are due to the fact that, in general, either a proton or neutron pair may absorb the high ex-citation energy Δ_i and that a considerable variety of initial and final subshells is possible. For simplicity, we ignore the fact that the number of pairs or holes is changed so that $r_0(W)$ actually differs somewhat from $r_0(W - \Delta)$ near magic numbers, but not appre-ciably in half-filled shells.

Similarly for broken pair excitations we know that there is a pairing energy, $P(j)$ of the order of magnitude $(2j + 1)23/A$ Mev (Ne57) where j is the total angular momentum $(l + \frac{1}{2})$ of an indi-vidual nucleon. The values of P are less than the values of Δ. Furthermore, there may be a variety of ways for the not angular momenta of one or more broken pairs to combine with each other or with any unpaired particles in the compound nucleus. We may now write the total density including all sorts of complex configurations:

$$\rho_0(W) = r_0(W) + \Sigma r_0(W - \Delta_i) + \Sigma r_0(W - P_k)$$

$$= \sum_{h=0}^{\infty} r_0(W - hS') \quad (48)$$

If the density $\rho_0(W)$ may be written as the sum of a large family of curves of the shape $r_0(W)$ which are displaced at their thresholds (see Fig. 21), the displacement may be written $hS'(W)$ (where h is an integer) as in (48) without an important loss of generality. A sum arising from the effect of m_j on energy and one due to collective excitations should also be included in (48) and these effects may be considered to be included in hS'. The last sum on the right may be

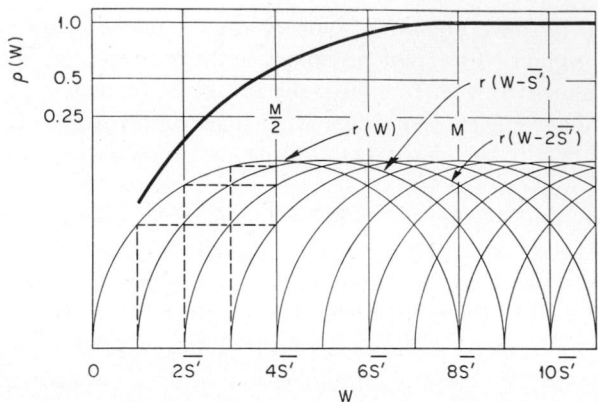

Figure 21. A schematic diagram of $\sum\limits_{h=0}^{\infty} r(W - h\bar{S}') = \rho(W)$, where W is the excitation energy in units of $\bar{S}'$, which is assumed to be independent of W. For this illustration, M is taken to be $8\bar{S}'$ rather than of the order of $100\bar{S}'$, as is more nearly the usual case. The dotted lines show clearly that the sum of the intersections of the family of $r(W - h\bar{S}')$ curves at the line $W = M/2$ is the integral of $r(W)$ (up to $M/2$) by the trapezoid method. The upper curve is $\rho(W)$, in units of $n_N n_Z/\bar{S}'$, calculated by summing the lower curves. It is clear that, for $W > M/2$, $\rho(W)$ is slowly varying for our purposes and only slightly dependent on the shape of $r(W)$ providing it is symmetric about $M/2$. The rounded distribution r (which is used in the figure) is much flatter at the maximum than curves calculated in detail as previously described. These calculations lead to a more nearly triangular distribution function, $r(W)$.

written as an infinite series since, when $hS' > W$, the higher terms make no contribution to the density at W as may be seen in the diagram in Fig. 21. Equation (48) now includes the effects of unpaired particles, and in any case we must not continue to restrict our considerations to 0^+ compound nuclei since we have practically no experimental information on them. To compare with measured spacings we must first calculate D_0 from Eq. (48) and then convert to $(J \neq 1)$ with a relation analogous to Eq. (42):

$$D_J = D_0/n_J \tag{49}$$

where $n_J \cong 2J + 1$.

For simplicity, we will solve Eq. (48) ignoring any energy dependence of $S'(W)$ (i.e., replacing it by its average value $\bar{S}'$) and assuming

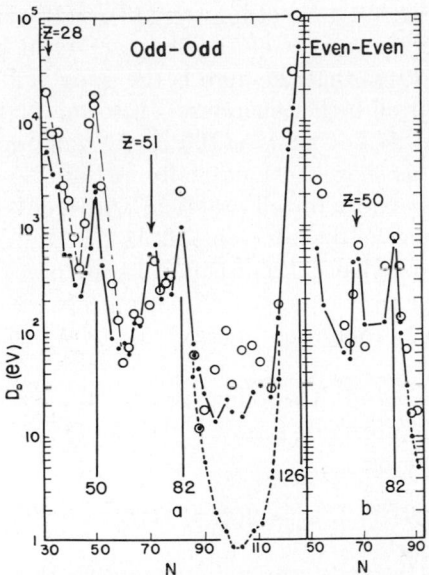

Figure 22. A comparison by Newson and Duncan (Ne60) of measured and calculated spacings [Equation (52)]. The calculated *curve* is not continuous, but the calculated points (indicated by small dots) have been connected by straight lines. The spacings are plotted against N, the number of neutrons in the *target* nucleus, but the description of the *compound* nucleus is shown on the face of the two plots. Points for odd-odd compound nuclei have been calculated for all stable and a few radioactive targets in the region shown in the figure, and the same is true of the odd-odd compound nuclei. Experimental points have been fitted by the "best" straight line only where the fit of the calculated curve is definitely unsatisfactory.

that r is symmetric about $M/2$. If $S' = \bar{S}$, the sum in Eq. (48) up to $h\bar{S}' = M$ is simply

$$\rho_0(M) = \int_0^M S^{-1}r_0(W)dW = n_N n_Z/S \qquad (50)$$

and consequently, since ρ must be inversely proportional to S', the total density

$$1/D_0 = \rho_0(M) = n_N n_Z/\bar{S}' \qquad (51)$$

At energies other than M, $\rho(W)$ will increase rapidly at low energies, be independent of energy above $W = M$ and change only a factor of 2 between $W = M$ and $W = M/2$. These properties of ρ may be seen graphically in Fig. 21. According to (48), $\rho(W)$ is the sum of the intercepts of all the curves of the shape $r(W)$ at energy W. It is obvious by inspection that this sum is the same at $W = M$, $M + \bar{S}'$, $M + 2\bar{S}'$, and at all higher energies. The sum at $W = M/2$ is less than half that at M but if $M \simeq 100 \ \bar{S}'$ (as will appear later) rather than $M = 8\bar{S}'$ (as shown schematically in Fig. 21) the ratio $\rho(M)/\rho(M/2) = 2$ is accurate for all practical purposes. The dotted lines show that the sum of the intercepts at $M/2$ is $\int_0^{M/2} r_0(W)dW$ by the trapezoid method. Hence, Eq. (51) may be compared directly with the experimental measurements (within their probable errors) when the compound nucleus excitation energy, $B_N > M$, since, in this case, $\rho_0(M) = \rho_0(B_N)$.

For convenience in the following we will restate Eqs. (49), (50), and (51) in the approximate form which is useful for even-even or odd-odd compound nuclei:

$$D_0(B) = 1/\rho_0 = 2(2I + 1)D = \alpha \bar{S}'/n_N n_Z \qquad (52)$$

and in the more general form which would result from approximate consideration of the variations of S' with W and other variables:

$$D_J = \alpha \frac{C(B,N,Z)}{n_N n n_J} \simeq D_0/(2J + 1) \qquad (53)$$

where D is the measured average spacing of *all* s-wave channels and $\alpha = 1$ when $B \gtrsim M$ but must be evaluated numerically when $B \ll M$. n_J was assumed to be equal to $2J + 1$ in the derivation of Eq. (52).

The results of calculations based on Eq. (52) (assuming $\alpha = 1$, $S' = 50$ kev for all heavy nuclei) are shown in Fig. 22 for odd-odd compound nuclei. The predicted spacings near the rare earths are much too low (dashed curve) due to the fact that $M \gg B$ for these compound nuclei so that the approximation $\alpha = 1$ breaks down very badly. The higher calculated points in this region are based on an estimate of α which assumes a triangular distribution for r_0, $B = 6$ Mev, $S' = 50$ kev and $S = 500$ kev. A value of S for the neutrons in the 82 to 126 shell has been calculated by the methods of Pryce (Pr54,Al54,Pr56) from which we estimate $S \simeq 900$ kev. A better fit between the calculated and the experimental points (in the region of the rare earths and also of the transuranics) would be obtained with this larger value of S and a smaller S'. In Fig. 22b the predictions of Eq. (52) are compared to some of the even-even compound nuclei.

It is seen that the general trend of the experimental results and their detailed behavior in some regions are correctly predicted. Although the calculated peak-to-valley ratios are too low (except in the region of the rare earths and the transuranics), the rest of the calculated curve bears a striking resemblance to the variations of the experimental points. Thus the clustering of subshells and the consequent gaps between major shells account semi-quantitatively for the high level spacings near the magic numbers.

The factor $n_N n_Z$ in (53) was originally calculated in order to illustrate possible shell effects in a simpler manner than the rather elaborate prescriptions of Cameron and Newton. The particular form of the calculation was chosen to reflect the influence both of the major shells and of the subshells. The surprisingly good agreement between the calculated relative spacings and the experimental values obviously calls for more explanation than a simple analogy to the ground state. Some light may be shed on this point by reviewing the history of independent particle models. After some early consideration of shell models (El34) it was argued most convincingly (see Be37, p. 79), that the independent particle model was not likely to be satisfactory for highly excited compound nuclei because of the short mean-free path of a nucleon in the nucleus and the consequent impossibility of maintaining stable orbits. Thus, a collective model (i.e. the liquid-drop model) seemed more likely to be a sensible description of the compound nucleus than an independent particle model. This reasoning discouraged the acceptance of the shell model until the accumulated experimental evidence became overwhelming (Ma49, Ha49). However, it was pointed out by Weisskopf that the shell model represented only an exception to the above argument in that the Pauli principle prevented collisions in the ground state because of the lack of unfilled levels below the Fermi energy. In general, for the highly excited compound nuclei which we are considering, the original argument should still be valid, and the discovery of rotational states dispelled any remaining doubts of the existence of collective states. Clearly, if there are $n_N n_Z$ highly excited nucleonic states each of which like the ground is stable enough to be the parent of a whole series of collective states, the presence of that factor in (53) is understandable. It is of course well known that a low energy nucleonic excitation may form the quasi-ground state for a series of rotational levels. We shall, therefore, identify the most stable of the highly excited nucleonic configuration states which are consequently the most likely to be the quasi-ground states of high energy collective excitations in this extension of the unified model to high excitation energies.

Consider the simple configurations of a 0^+ spherically symmetric compound nucleus. If we think of the interaction of two nucleons as a collision (We50) an effective interaction (in which energy and momentum are transferred) will leave the compound nucleus with four unpaired particles often in different subshells since a simple configuration with only one broken pair cannot be 0^+. The minimum pairing energy corresponds to one unpaired particle in a $\frac{1}{2}$ subshell, two in a $\frac{3}{2}$ subshell and one in a $\frac{5}{2}$ subshell. At $A \approx 100$ this energy is according to Ne57 $[(2 \times \frac{1}{2} + 1 + 2 \times \frac{5}{2} + 1)/2 + 2 \times \frac{3}{2} + 1]23/A = 1.8$ Mev. This energy must be supplied by two of the unpaired particles making transitions to lower subshells. The maximum available energy near $A = 100$ is $4S \approx 1.6$ Mev. Thus all the simple configuration up to $a \approx 110$ and most of them at higher A must spend some time in an energetically impossible intermediate state (the tunnel effect) to transform into another configuration of about the same energy.

The excitation of a pair from a partially filled shell into an otherwise empty major shell will not in general lead to stable orbits, since one of the highly excited nucleons may collide with a less highly excited nucleon and by dropping back into the partially filled shell increase its energy 2 Mev or more. Since this is in general sufficient energy to break one or two pairs, the pairing of two such promoted particles is unlikely to stabilize their orbits. Thus it is meaningful to speak of an excited pair only when it remains in the same major shell as its ground state and all "promoted" nucleons should be considered to be broken pair excitations.[11] The possibility that pairing becomes less important with increasing excitation energy has been discussed by Ericson (Er60) and by Lang and LeCouteur (La59).

If an unpaired particle is present, and collides with one nucleon of a pair the number of unpaired particles increases from one before collision to three afterward if total angular momentum J is to be

[11] A possible exception should be noted in the case of a pair promoted from a filled to an empty major shell.

conserved.   This is a far more energetically favorable process than
the effective collision of two paired particles in different subshells so
that the orbit of an excited unpaired particle is much less likely to
be stable than the orbits of an excited pair.

If we consider a moderately deformed nucleus, there will be
many-energy states of each simple configuration, and a pair may be excited without changing subshells.   The two particles interact strongly
and it is easy to see classically that they may collide elastically,
change the plane of their orbits and still remain paired.   Thus for a
subshell partially filled with pairs the m_j's will not be good quantum
numbers and any excitation energy absorbed by the pairs in such a subshell should be thought of as a collective excitation.   In any case,
the presence of such excitation energy by a pair will increase the
chances that one of its particles will suffer an effective collision with
a paired particle in a different subshell.   Thus, the number of states
most likely to be enough like the ground state to be parents of sets of
collective states is the same as the number of simple configurations
since the most stable states will be the lowest energy state for each
configuration.   Thus if the unified model has any validity at all at the
excitation energies considered here, some trace of a factor of the form
of $n_N n_Z$ should be found.   Ericson (Er60, p. 456) has (proposed a unified model which includes a pairing energy of the Mayer-Jensen
type like that assumed here, but he considers only rotational states.

On the other hand, Lang and LeCouteur (La59) disregard all
collective effects and must assume in addition that the importance of
pairing decreases with excitation energy in order to reconcile observed resonance spacings and ground state pairing energies.   That is,
they must either assume that a large fraction of the pairing energy
must be supplied to excite a pair of particles above the ground state
and that there is relatively little pairing between excited nucleons
or they must take collective states into account (Er60, p. 460;
La59).   Ericson also comes to similar conclusions from considering
the Ross treatment of level densities (Er60, p. 463).   The super-shell
model is reasonably consistent with these theoretical deductions;
it considers collective excitations and also pairing of excited particles
when the excitation of the latter is less than about 2 Mev per particle
but ignores pairing for more highly excited nucleons.   The super-shell
model should be comparable to that of Lang and LeCouteur for the
rare earths and the transuranics where the compound nucleus excita-

tion energy $B \ll M$ the maximum energy which can be absorbed by pair excitations within the unfilled shells *provided* pairing and collective excitations are treated consistently in both models.

The *Rosenzweig effect* is a subshell model which suggests that we should consider the possibility that a large subshell may be sufficiently isolated to have some effect on level densities (Ro57). While we have just argued that an individual particle model is not well suited to describe the excitations of the nucleons within a subshell, the effect suggested by Rosenzweig (much smaller than that at the neutron magic numbers 50 or more) may reasonably be expected. A simple calculation can be based on a combination of the super shell model and the Rosenzweig suggestion. Since the nuclear potential is not spherically symmetric, there are, for instance, 16 ways to place a pair in the 50–82 shell; when there are r pairs in that subshell there should be $16!/(16 - r)!r!$ different ways of arranging the pairs. Calculating n_N' and n_Z' in this way, replacing the corresponding unprimed quantities in (52) and normalizing, we have estimated the relative level

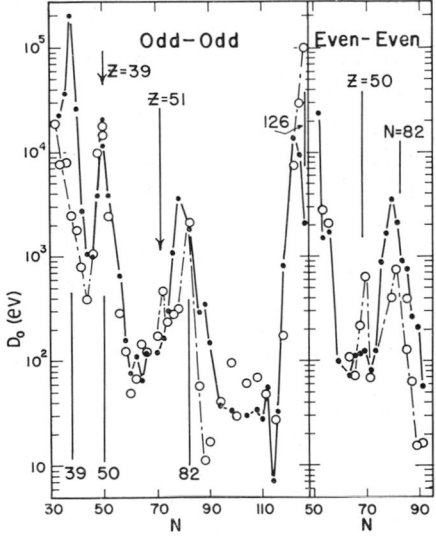

Figure 23. A plot of the same experimental data as that in Fig. 22. The theoretical points (solid dots connected by solid lines) have been calculated according to Newton's statistical shell model. The experimental points have been connected by a dashed line where they deviate appreciably from theory.

spacings in this way (curve not shown).   One still predicts maxima at $Z = 50$ and at the magic neutron numbers but the shape of the curve does not follow the experimental trends nearly as well as the calculations in Fig. 22.   The peak-to-valley ratios are too high in contrast to the low ratios in Fig. 22.   Hence our approximation fits the experimental data better if we count only the simple configurations and not the more highly excited configuration states, but the two curves are so similar that the Rosenzweig effect cannot be ruled out.

On the other hand, Rosenzweig predicted a maximum in level spacing near $N = 28$ which is not indicated in the calculations in Fig. 22.   Some experimental indications of such a maximum have been found (Bo62) although Rosenzweig and his collaborators (Ro58) were unable to confirm such a peak with measurements up to a *few tens of kev*.   Another indication of a Rosenzweig effect may be the peak in the rare earth region near $A = 164$ which corresponds to the simultaneous filling of the neutron $\frac{9}{2}^-$ subshell ($N = 100$) and the proton $\frac{7}{2}^+$ subshell ($Z = 64$).   It is not clear that any form of the super-shell model should be valid for the highly distorted nuclei in the rare earth region, but it seems possible that these excited nuclei are much more nearly spherical than their ground states.

Figure 23 shows calculated spacings according to Newton's prescription; it is evident that this calculated curve in Fig. 23 does not fit the experimental data as well as the super shell model calculations shown in Fig. 22.   Newton predicts an unobserved peak at $N = 39$ and does not predict the one at $Z = 50$.   However, the fundamental assumptions of the statistical shell models are not contradictory and a really accurate model should include all of them.   Consequently, the treatments of Newton, Rosenzweig, Cameron, and of Newson and Duncan are all oversimplifications of the problem.   In particular, the elaborate procedure of Cameron results in very useful semi-empirical predictions of level densities which have not been measured, but does not throw much light on the nature of the compound nucleus, because of the large number of free parameters which he uses.

The Liquid-Drop Model.   Calculations of level density based on this extreme form of a collective model were carried out by Bethe (Be37) and appeared to yield the correct order of magnitude for neutron resonance spacings, but when an up-to-date value for the

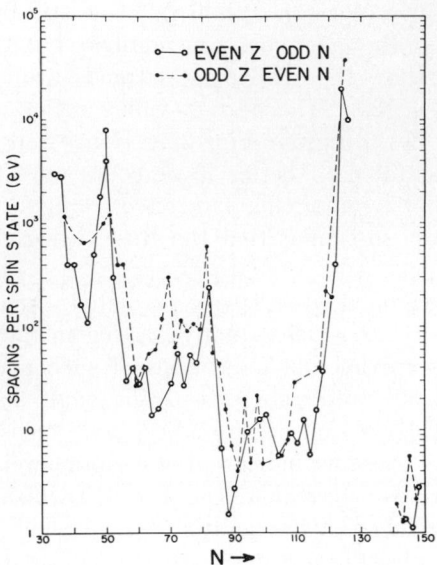

Figure 24a. Spacing per spin state plotted against neutron number N. Solid circles denote odd-odd *compound* nuclei and open circles denote even-even compound nuclei. Note that *target* nuclei are specified in the figure (Ne61a).

nuclear radius is used, the calculated spacing is much too wide. However, this model does yield the right order of magnitude for the parameter S' in (52) if we assume that it describes the collective excitations of the super shell model. Unfortunately Ericson's (Er58a) unified model includes only rotational collective states and is meant to be valid only for the rare earths and transuranics where the applicability of the super shell model is questionable.

C. Excitation Energy and Level Density

According to all the models which we have discussed, spacings should vary with energy at least roughly according to the relation

$$D_0(W) = D_0(0) \exp [-(aW)^{1/2}] \tag{45}$$

The isotopic fluctuations of level spacings in Fig. 24a (which we averaged out in order to obtain the relatively smooth curve in Fig. 24b) cast some light on the value of the coefficient a in (45). In

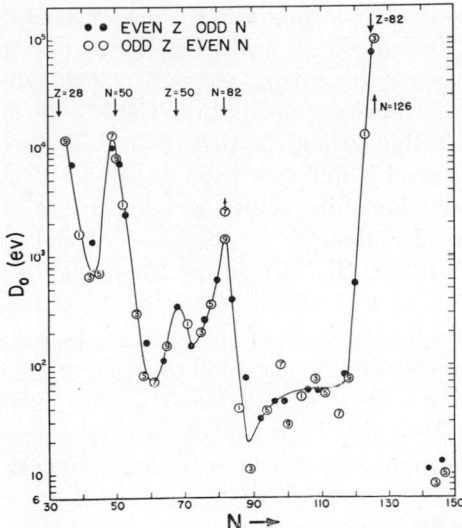

Figure 24b. D_0 plotted against neutron number N of the target nucleus. The solid dots indicate the spacing of even-even *compound* nuclei averaged over each element. The odd odd compound nuclei are plotted as open circles containing an arabic numeral which is the last digit in the Atomic number Z. Note that *target* nuclei are specified in the figure (Ne61,Ne61a).

order to make this evaluation we ignore level density information in the neighborhood of neutron magic numbers where the level spacing is very dependent on neutron number. Of the remaining isotopic pairs there are thirteen for which measured binding energies make some sensible prediction of the difference in excitation energy between the two isotopic compound nuclei. Unfortunately the actual energy difference is not known in any particular case if, as seems correct (Ne56a), we should know the excitation energy above the lowest state of the same spin and parity as the compound nucleus rather than above the ground state. However, the *average* of the differences over all thirteen pairs between the excitation energies as measured from the ground state should be statistically significant. These energy differences fluctuate between 0.1 and 1.3 Mev for pairs of isotopes in Ag, In, Sb, I, Ir, Am, Cd, Sn, Te, Hg, U, and Pu. The average energy difference is 0.5 Mev and the average ratio of the spacing of the heavier isotope relative to the lighter one is 1.8. Substituting into (45) we find

$a = 30$. A moderately strong dependence of level density on excitation energy is indicated. It will be seen later that for intermediate nuclei D_0 decreases with neutron excess T. If this effect is present in heavy nuclei, the previous calculation yields $a > 30$; however, it seems very likely that, when the neutron excess is so great that the unfilled neutron shell is different from the unfilled proton shell, any such effect should be quite small, so that $a \cong 30$. This value is decidedly smaller than $a = 58$ which would be expected by Lang and LeCouteur (La54a), $a = 37$ predicted by Blatt and Weisskopf (Bl52) or $a = 50$ as expected by Newton. However, D_0 is still sufficiently sensitive to energy that the resonance spacings of even-even targets must be corrected to a common excitation energy before attempting a theoretical fit such as that in Fig. 22, but the correction may be omitted for odd-A targets where the excitation energy of the compound nucleus is a rather smooth function of A and N. An energy correction of the indicated order of magnitude would improve the agreement between calculated and measured spacings (Fig. 22) at the neutron magic numbers.

D. Spacings Just Below Magic Numbers

A correction for neutron excitation energies should be applied to the level spacings of the compound nuclei with slightly more than a magic number of neutrons in order to compare them with the more highly excited compound nuclei with less than a magic number of neutrons. Such a correction has been applied (Hu51,Ga52,Hu53) without changing the qualitative nature of the maxima in curves like Fig. 24b and it was consequently concluded that the high resonance spacings for magic number target nuclei could not be due simply to the relatively low excitation energies of the compound nuclei. This procedure is open to some objection since the correction uses semi-empirical equations based on a thermodynamic model (Bl52) of the compound nucleus near the magic numbers where a shell model should be used. As pointed out by Newson and Rohrer (Ne54), the need for such a correction for excitation energy is largely eliminated if spacings are known for target nuclei a few neutrons lighter than the magic numbers. It has long been known experimentally (Ha51) that below the neutron magic numbers the excitation energy of the compound nucleus increases with N. As may be seen in Figs. 22 and 24, the spacings found for target nuclei a few neutrons lighter than the magic numbers are nearly as great as for those at the magic neutron numbers when no correction is made for excitation energy. Even if one were to overcorrect deliberately for the effects of excitation energy, one increases the spacings below the magic numbers, and decreases those above. The net effect is to shift the maxima without altering them significantly. Thus, the energy correction distorts Fig. 24b in such a way that the maxima must be ascribed to a direct rather than an indirect effect of the closing of the shells; *the maxima can not possibly be due only to low excitation energies of the compound nuclei near closed neutron shells.*

E. J-Dependence of Resonance Spacings

We must now justify our use of the relation

$$D_J = D_0/(2J + 1) \tag{41}$$

in reducing resonance spacing data to D_0 in Figs.22 and 23. Bilpuch et al. (Bi61) have found 14 p-wave resonances ($\frac{1}{2}^-$ and $\frac{3}{2}^-$) in the Sr^{88} cross-section curve compared to 4 s-wave levels ($\frac{1}{2}^-$). The ratio of these spacings is 3.4 ± 1.4, which is in agreement with 3.0 calculated from (41) on the assumption that D_J is independent of parity. Rae et al. (Ra58) have assigned an even smaller number of $J^\pi = 0^-$ and $J = 1^-$ s-wave resonances in silver and also report a ratio consistent with (41). This direct evidence is too meager to be very convincing. In Fig. 24, we plot resonance spacings due to odd-A targets against neutron number, N. Figure 24a is a plot of $D_J/2$ (the spacing per spin state) while Fig. 24b is a plot of D_0. The fact that the points in the latter fall on a single curve much more satisfactorily than in the former suggests very strongly that (41) is in accord with the facts. This evidence has been discussed in detail by Newson et al. (Ne61). Level densities for isotopes have been averaged in Fig. 24b in order to eliminate part of the effects of the excitation energy of the compound nuclei.

Harvey (Ha60a) has reviewed the evidence for the predicted departure from (41) at higher values of J. This deviation appears to become significant (consistent with theoretical expectations) for the largest values of J encountered in Figs. 22, 23, and 24, but the data are very sparse.

From the theoretical side, Ericson (Er60) has shown that (41) is a very general relation which is consistent with a wide variety of nuclear models. We may conclude that all available information strongly favors (41) so long as the value of J is not large.

F. Effect of Neutron Excess

In Fig. 24 we see a rather sharp drop in level spacing at proton numbers slightly greater than 28, which in Fig. 22 follows the trend of the calculated curves fairly satisfactorily. It is rather surprising that the 28-50 shell should behave as if it were as well isolated as the other shells since the gap between the $f_{7/2}$ subshell (which is filled at 28 nucleons) and the $f_{5/2}$ subshell is about 1 Mev per nucleon as compared to about 2 Mev per nucleon at the boundaries of the other shells (Ha51). However, for elements heavier than $_{28}$Ni there are an equal number of neutrons and protons in the $f_{7/2}$ and lower subshells. The theory of the *symmetry effect* has been developed by Blatt and Weisskopf (Bl52) for any independent particle model, including the shell model. Without repeating their arguments here, we can say that this core of 28 neutrons and 28 protons should have so large a symmetry binding energy that the excitation of a single nucleon or a pair of neutrons or protons should require 3 or 4 times the pairing energy and be energetically impossible at excitation energy B since the pairing energy should be 3 or 4 Mev at $A \cong 50$ and $j = \frac{7}{2}$. The excitation of both a pair of neutrons and a pair of protons into the same higher subshell should not change the symmetry energy. This four nucleon excitation would require about 4 Mev—about the same as the excitation of a pair from one major shell to another among the heavier elements. For this sort of excitation, at least, the 28-50 shell is as well isolated as the 50-82 or the 82-126 shells. We can also deduce from the theory that proton pairs and neutron pairs may be considered to be excited independently (as previously assumed) for the purpose of counting simple configurations when the neutron shell, corresponding to the partially filled proton shell, is full or nearly full. This condition is satisfied well enough above $N = 45$ that the methods already outlined for counting simple configurations are reasonably accurate.

If the above arguments are correct, however, there should be a strong dependence of spacing on the neutron excess for the lighter elements ($A < 60$) since the restrictions on independent excitation of single or pairs of nucleons apply only to the protons and an equal number of neutrons. There is actually a very decided decrease in spacing between $N = 20$ and 30, a region where the neutron excess T is (on the average) increasing rapidly. We have already argued that there is probably a decided dependence of spacing on in this region. We have therefore corrected the values of D_0 to an excitation energy of 6 Mev for all the plotted values for the isotopes of the elements lighter than copper. The values of a in (45) which have been used for this correction were derived from those deduced empirically by Ericson (Er58a). A plot of these energy-corrected D_0's shows the same general slope as Fig. 24b, i.e., a general tendency for the spacing to decrease with increasing nuclear size or neutron excess (Ne61a). We have therefore estimated $(\delta \ln D_0/\delta A)_Z$ and $(\delta \ln D_0/\delta A)_N$ by taking differences between the values of D_0 (at 6 Mev) for all pairs of isotopes (8) and isotones (13) for which data are available in the region from mass numbers 35 to 65. We find, in spite of a considerable point scatter, that while the former is nearly always negative as expected, the latter is almost invariably positive. If we average all the points and define the neutron excess $T \equiv N - Z$ we find

$$\left(\frac{\delta \ln D_0}{\delta N}\right)_Z - \left(\frac{\delta \ln D_0}{\delta A}\right)_Z = \left(\frac{\delta \ln D_0}{\delta T}\right)_Z - -0.41 \qquad (54)$$

and

$$-\left(\frac{\delta \ln D_0}{\delta Z}\right)_N = -\left(\frac{\delta \ln D_0}{\delta A}\right)_N = \left(\frac{\delta \ln D_0}{T}\right)_N = -0.48 \qquad (55)$$

We may therefore integrate the derivatives with respect to T and obtain the approximate relation

$$D_0(T) \cong D_0(0) \exp(-0.45T) \qquad (56)$$

which appears on the average to be independent of N, Z, and A for small values of $T(\leqq 6)$. The agreement between the numbers in (54) and (55) may be fortuitous, but since the experimental errors in the individual spacings arise largely from the fact that too few individual resonances are measured, the average, -0.45, of 21 values should be statistically significant. The coefficient in (56) is not dependent on the accuracy of (42) which relates the observed spacing D to the target spin I, since the same value is found if we restrict the comparison to pairs of isotones and isotopes of the same target spin. The coefficient is highly dependent on the value of a in (45) and turns out to be nearly zero if $a = 0$. We therefore have the choice of concluding that level density is dependent on both excitation energy W *and* neutron excess T or that it is independent of both. The former is by far the most likely of the two alternatives on both theoretical and experimental grounds. The experimental data have been reviewed by Newson et al. who discuss a variety of alternate interpretations all of which are consistent with the above conclusions.

A dependence of average spacing on the symmetry effect has been suggested by Bloch (Bl54). Better data are necessary to verify specific predictions, but there is already considerable evidence for a strong dependence of spacing on neutron excess.

G.   *Strength Functions and Potential Scattering*

The optical model of Feshbach, Porter, and Weisskopf (Fe54), as discussed by Emmerich in Chapter V.C, is able to predict the shape of fast ($>\frac{1}{4}$ Mev) neutron scattering, reaction, and total cross sections averaged over many resonances and summed over a number of entrance channels corresponding to several different neutron angular momenta. In the kev and ev regions observable scattering is usually due only to the effects of s- or p-waves and below about one kev only s-wave scattering and capture is usually important. The observed averaged total cross sections should therefore depend only on the s-wave strength function, the p-wave strength function, and the s-wave potential scattering length R' which differs from the nuclear radius R, but is of the same order of magnitude. The p-wave potential scattering is usually considered to contribute negligibly[12] to the total cross section in the kev region. Since the averaged cross section should depend on only three parameters, it is practical in many cases to separate s- and p-wave effects and to test the predictions of the model for a single entrance channel.

According to the average cross section theory of Feshbach, Porter, and Weisskopf (Fe54) the average s-wave total cross section is $\bar{\sigma}_T{}^0 = \pi\lambda^2(|1 - \bar{\eta}_0|^2 + 1 - |\bar{\eta}_0|^2) = 2\pi\lambda^2 \mathrm{Re}(1 - \bar{\eta}_0)$ where $\bar{\eta}_0$ is the averaged s-wave reflection coefficient and $\mathrm{Re}(1 - \bar{\eta}_0)$ is the real part of the argument. These authors expressed $\bar{\sigma}_T$ in terms of the strength

[12] For $R = 10$ fermis (a very heavy nucleus), p-wave contribution to total potential scattering is about 20 per cent at 200 kev and about 60 per cent at 400 kev (Bl52). For most nuclei below 150 kev we may therefore ignore this contribution to the *total* cross section, but not to differential scattering cross sections.

function and potential scattering cross section to an approximation (58) which is usually accurate for the ev region. For the kev region the following higher order approximation, derived from the same formalism, must be used:

$$\bar{\sigma}_{T^0} = 2\pi^2 \lambda \lambda_1 (\bar{\Gamma}_n{}^0/D) \cos 2kR' - \pi^3 \lambda_1{}^2 (\bar{\Gamma}_n{}^0/D)^2 + 4\pi \lambda^2 \sin^2 kR' \quad (57)$$

$$\bar{\sigma}_{T^0} \approx 2\pi^2 \lambda \lambda_1 (\bar{\Gamma}_n{}^0/D) + 4\pi R'^2 \quad (58)$$

Both Eq. (58) (Fe54) and Eq. (57) (Se58) were derived for single level Breit-Wigner resonances and it was shown that multilevel effects were not important for terms of the order of those in (58). It is possible that Eq. (57) might be improved by the inclusion of multilevel effects, but for our purposes it is most important to know that the sum of the second two and possibly some higher order terms in Eq. (57),

$$\sigma_{\text{const}} = 4\pi \lambda^2 \sin^2 KR' - \pi^3 \lambda_1{}^2 (\bar{\Gamma}_n{}^0/D)^2 \quad (36)$$

is not necessarily equal to the potential scattering. [λ_1 is the wavelength of a one-ev neutron and $\lambda_1/\lambda = E_n{}^{1/2}(\text{ev})^{1/2}$.] Since the terms in Eq. (36) are not sensitive to energy of sample thickness, the effect of σ_{const} can be eliminated from the average transmission ratio $\bar{T}$.

The second term in (58) is very important in the region near $A = 50$ where σ_{const} sometimes has *negative* values (Ly58a,Se59). The neglect of this term by Marshak and Newson (Ma57) was responsible, in part, for the fact that these authors were unable to obtain consistent values of the strength function from measurements with different sample thicknesses. On the other hand consistent values of the strength function and reasonable values of R' have been determined from the same data (Se58) with the help of (36). If we derive Eq. (57) from a multilevel Breit-Wigner formula (Fe54) rather than from averaged cross section theory, it can be shown that a term of the order of $\pi^3 \lambda_1{}^2 (\bar{\Gamma}_n{}^0/D)^2$ arises from the interference between neighboring resonances.

The first term in Eq. (58) is valid only for measurements with very thin samples. For measurements with thicker samples, the effect of σ_{const} is first eliminated from the measured transmission and the strength function is then determined from

$$1 - \bar{T}e^{n\sigma_{\text{const}}} = (\Gamma_n{}^0/D) \Sigma y(\beta) F(\beta,R) \quad (38a)$$

as already outlined.

The averaged p-wave total cross section for a thin sample in the kev region may be written

$$\bar{\sigma}_T{}^{(1)} = \pi^2 \lambda \lambda_1 v_1 [g_+ (\bar{\Gamma}_n{}^1/D)_+ + g_- (\bar{\Gamma}_n{}^1/D)_-] \tag{59}$$

since centrifugal barriers make the other two terms in Eq. (57) negligible.[12] The proper expression [Eq. (39) analogous to Eq. (59)] for thicker samples has already been discussed.

Analytic expressions for R' and $\Gamma_n{}^0/D$ for the spherically symmetric complex square well may be found in (Fe54). For strong interaction corresponding to the continuum theory (black nucleus) of Feshbach, Peaslee, and Weisskopf, the real and imaginary parts of the potential are about equal; consequently

$$R' = R \tag{60}$$

and

$$\bar{\Gamma}_n{}^0/D \simeq 1 \times 10^{-4} \tag{61}$$

which is independent of A, R, or neutron energy. Equation (61), which has proven to be a poor approximation, is rule 4 mentioned in the introduction.

Table III. The Square-Well Optical Model

		$\pi/2$	π	$3\pi/2$	2π	$5\pi/2$	3π	$7\pi/2$
1	s-wave KR	$\pi/2$	π	$3\pi/2$	2π	$5\pi/2$	3π	$7\pi/2$
2	A at max., $\zeta = 0$	0.45		10		50		137
3	A at max., $\zeta = 0.03$	0.5		11		55		151
4	$(\Gamma_n{}^0/D)_{max.}$, $\zeta = 0.03$	42.4		14.2		8.5		6
5	A at min., $\zeta = 0.03$		28		96		227	
6	$(\Gamma_n{}^0/D)_{min.}$, $\zeta = 0.03$		0.05		0.09		0.14	
7	p-wave Kr		π		2π		3π	
8	A at max., $\zeta = 0$		27		90		216	

Note: Locations (as a function of mass number A) and amplitudes of the giant resonances for zero energy neutrons have been calculated from the same parameters for the complex potential $V = V_0(1 + i\zeta)$ as were used in the original calculations (Fe54): $V_0 = 42$ Mev, $\zeta = 0.03$, and $R = 1.45 \, A^{1/3}$ fermis. The positions of the maxima and minima are highly dependent on $KR = (2mV_0)^{1/2}$. $A^{1/3}1.45/\hbar$. V_0 and to a lesser extent $RA^{-1/3}$ are usually adjusted to fit the experimental data. The small difference between lines 2 and 3 is proportional to the imaginary fraction ζ as are the minimum strength functions (in units of 10^{-4}) in line 6. The maximum strength functions (shown in line 4 in units of 10^{-4}) are inversely proportional to ζ.

For *weak* or *intermediate* coupling, maxima are predicted in a plot of A against strength functions. The location of the s-wave maxima and minima in the strength function are given in Table III lines 2 and 3. The locations of the peaks depend to a first approximation only on the magnitude of the real part of the potential (which we take as $V_0 = 42$ Mev) and for s-waves may be calculated from the roots of

$$KR \cot KR = kR \tag{62}$$

where the imaginary part of the potential has been set equal to zero. k and K are the neutron wave numbers outside and inside the nucleus, respectively. At a maximum when $kR \ll 1$ as it is in the ev and lower kev regions

$$KR = K \, 1.35 \, A^{1/3} \times 10^{-13} = (n + \tfrac{1}{2})\pi \tag{63}$$

and for the minima $KR = n\pi$. For p-waves when $kR \ll 1$

$$K^2R^2/(1 - KR \cot KR) - 1 = 0 \tag{64}$$

and at a maximum

$$KR = (n + 1)\pi + 1/(n + 1)\pi \tag{65}$$

where n is an integer ≥ 0. Corresponding relations for higher angular momenta may be found from the recurrence relations on p. 454 of Fc54. The values of A at the maxima are shown in line 4, Table III where they may be compared to the more exact calculation where the imaginary fraction of the potential $\zeta = 0.03$. Approximate values for A at the p-wave maxima, according to (76), are also shown in Table III, line 7. The values of the strength functions for s-waves at the maxima are, to a first approximation, determined only by the coefficient of the imaginary term,

$$\begin{aligned}
(\bar{\Gamma}_n^0/D)_{\max} &= (2k_1/\pi K)2/(n + \tfrac{1}{2})\pi\zeta \\
&= (2/(n + \tfrac{1}{2})\pi\zeta)10^{-4} \tag{66}
\end{aligned}$$

Values calculated from Eq. (66) are also shown in Table III, line 5.

These predictions of the optical model are most easily understood with the help of the giant resonance model proposed by Wigner and Eisenbud (Wi54,Ei58) and also by Scott (Sc54). Attempts to prove the two models equivalent have met with considerable, but not yet

complete, success (La55,Vo56). This model is concerned with the
single particle configuration which is formed when a neutron enters
a nucleus without any change of total energy. The neutron kinetic
energy in the nucleus is $(E + V_0)$ (for a square-well potential), but
none of this energy is lost to other nucleons so long as the compound
nucleus remains in the single particle configuration. We have already introduced the intuitive idea that a heavy compound nucleus
at resonance spends a fraction of the time, $\theta^2 = \Gamma_n/\Gamma_w$ (Γ_w is the
Wigner limit) in this single particle configuration. On the average,
at least, we should expect the fraction $\theta^2(W)$ to be at a maximum
when the energy corresponds to the resonance energy of the unmixed
single particle configuration. For s-wave neutrons this energy (for
a given radius R) may be calculated from (62) which describes the
behavior of a particle in a square well (Sc49). If one could observe
only the s-wave interactions over a wide energy range in a transmission
measurement, maxima in cross section corresponding to maxima in
θ^2 should be observed at the solutions of (62). These maxima and
those due to higher angular momentum neutrons were first observed
by Barschall and collaborators (Ba52). If, instead of varying the
neutron energy, we vary R by carrying out the measurement on a
series of neighboring nuclei with neutrons of negligibly small energy
compared to V_0, the maxima in θ^2 will be apparent as maxima in
$\bar{\Gamma}_n^0/D$ at the mass numbers predicted by (63). This variation of θ^2
is superimposed on the wide distribution of reduced widths for the
narrow resonances due to many particle excitation of the compound
nucleus, and can be observed only for the average over many individual resonances: $\bar{\Gamma}_n^l = \theta^2 \bar{\Gamma}_w^l$.

The connection between the giant resonance model and the optical
model is sometimes stated in the following manner: it is noted that
if a complex potential is introduced into the time-independent wave
equation for a single particle, the eigenvalue, $W = W_0 - i(\hbar/\tau)$,
must also be considered complex. If we introduce the complex
eigenvalue into the time-dependent wave function we find

$$e^{-iWt/\hbar} = e^{-iW_0t/\hbar}e^{-t/\tau} \tag{60}$$

The quantity $e^{-t/\tau}$ may then be interpreted as describing the simultaneous decay of the single particle state and the formation of the
compound nucleus. For a more general and much more rigorous

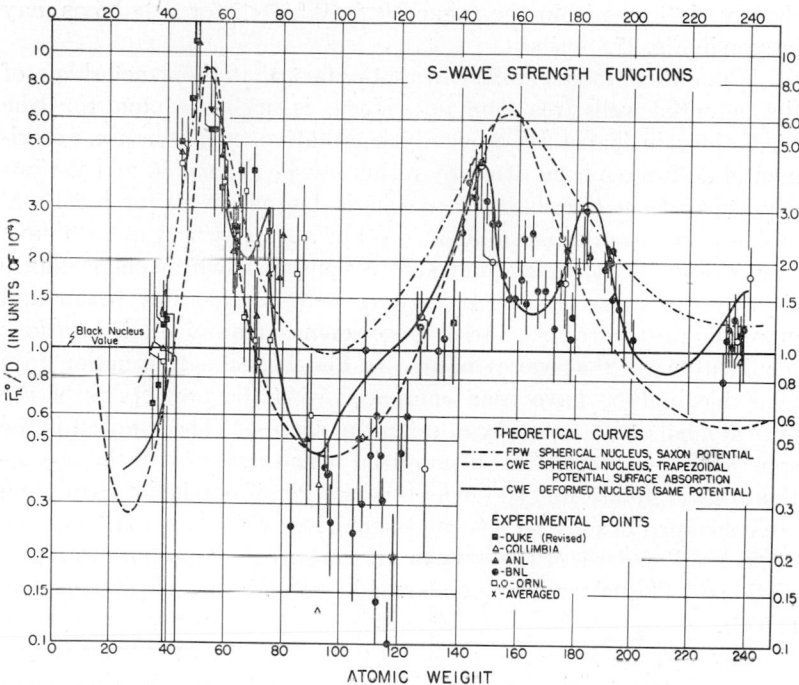

Figure 25. The s-wave strength function $\bar{\Gamma}_n{}^0/\bar{D}$ as a function of mass number A. The experimental points (see legend) are the results principally of the groups at Duke (Ma57,Se58) and Brookhaven National Laboratory (Hu58). The *black-nucleus* predictions are shown as a horizontal line. The parameters for the F.P.W. rounded-well calculations (Fe56) are $V_0 = 42$ Mev, $\zeta = 0.08$, and $dK_0 - 1.65$ where d is the roundness parameter and K_0 is the wave number of a zero (total) energy neutron in the potential well. No square-well calculations (Fe54) are shown. The parameters for both CWE curves (Ch58) are $V_0 = 44$ Mev, $\zeta = 0.05$ and the surface thickness is 2.0 fermis. We are indebted to Dr. K. K. Seth for the preparation of this figure.

discussion of the two models the reader is referred to the lucid discussion of Eisenbud and Wigner (Ei58).

The giant resonance model predicts that rule 4 of the introduction which may be written $\bar{\Gamma}_n{}^l/D \cong 1 \times 10^{-4}$ should be exact only when the average is taken over the whole giant resonance, that is over an appreciable fraction of the range in KR between $n\pi$ and $(n + 1)\pi$ for s-waves. The existing experimental measurements which extend over much smaller wave number intervals (100 ev up to 100 kev) show variations within the range $10^{-5} < \bar{\Gamma}_n^0/D < ^3$ for $A > 35$ as may be seen in Fig. 25.

The optical model suffers from the fact that the exact shape of the potential wells (real and imaginary) is not known and that the predictions in Table III are only qualitative. In practice experimental data have been fitted by adjusting V_0, $i\zeta$, and R, and various departures from the shape of a spherical square well for both real and imaginary potentials (Ch58). While a wide variety of data have been shown (Fe54) to be qualitatively consistent with a single choice of parameters for the complex square well, considerably better and more detailed agreement with experiment is obtained by various modifications of that well (Ch58). In Fig. 25, strength function data available in 1960 have been compared with the predictions of the optical model with a variety of potential shapes. The simplest is the spherically symmetric Saxon potential which agrees with the predictions of the square well so far as the location of maxima and minima are concerned as may be seen by comparison with Table III, but the peaks are broader and the valleys narrower than the square well predictions. The latter are not shown in Fig. 25 but are sketched in (Fe54).

The points above $A = 130$ do not follow the prediction of any spherically symmetric potential since there are two maxima instead of one in the neighborhood of $A = 155$. The lighter nuclei are on the whole in better agreement with the predictions of Table III. The expected peak is found slightly below $A = 55$ and for slightly lighter nuclei the agreement with spherical well predictions is fairly satisfactory. However, the right side of the maximum departs decidedly from such predictions, and there are experimental indications of a maximum near $A = 70$ (Fig. 25). The agreement between calculated and experimental strength functions is improved, near $A = 100$, if, instead of letting the imaginary portion of the potential be proportional to the real part (V_0), the imaginary portion is assumed to be small everywhere except at the nuclear surface. This is equivalent to saying that the neutron in the single particle state is *absorbed* to form the compound nucleus only at the surface where the Pauli principle inhibits nucleon-nucleon collisions less strongly than nearer the center of the nucleus. This *surface absorption* potential leads to the dashed curve in Fig. 25. The peaks in Fig. 25 near $A = 150$ may be understood if we depart from a spherically symmetric nucleus by

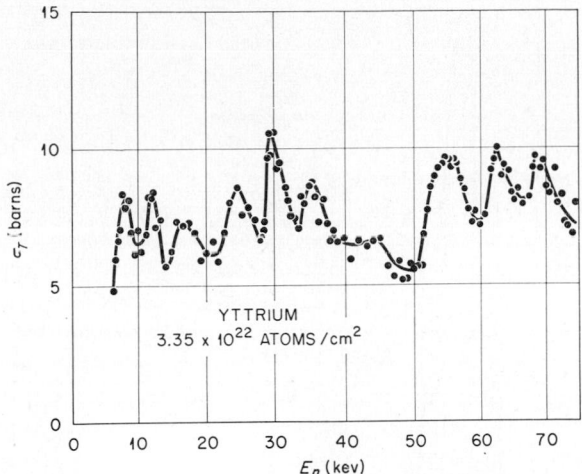

Figure 26. The total cross section of yttrium as a function of energy (Ne57). The experimental conditions are the same as Fig. 18.

an amount consistent with the measured nuclear quadrupole moments. With this sort of real potential *and* a surface imaginary potential, the model predicts the solid curve in Fig. 25. We see that the double peak near $A = 150$ and the possible small peak near $A = 70$ may be understood in terms of a nonspherical potential.

For mass numbers in the neighborhood of 10 the spacing of resonances for any given angular momentum is too great to allow the measurement of a strength function, at least in the kev region, but it is worthwhile to note that exceedingly large s-wave neutron reduced widths have been observed in the $Li^7(p,n)$, the $Li^6(n,\alpha)$, and the $B^{10}(n,\alpha)$ reactions so that there is some qualitative evidence for the s-wave giant resonance expected below $A = 11$.

From Table III p-wave strength functions should be large near $A = 27$ and $A = 90$. Strong p-wave resonances are known at rather low energy for F^{19}, Na^{23}, Mg^{24}, and Al^{27} in qualitative agreement with this prediction. For instance the p-wave strength function of fluorine is of the order of 10×10^{-4} (Ne61a).

A strong p-wave strength function near $A = 90$ is obvious from inspection of total-cross-section curves such as that of Y^{89} (Fig. 26). The average cross section of this curve (which clearly includes many resonances) increases quite definitely with energy in contrast to a

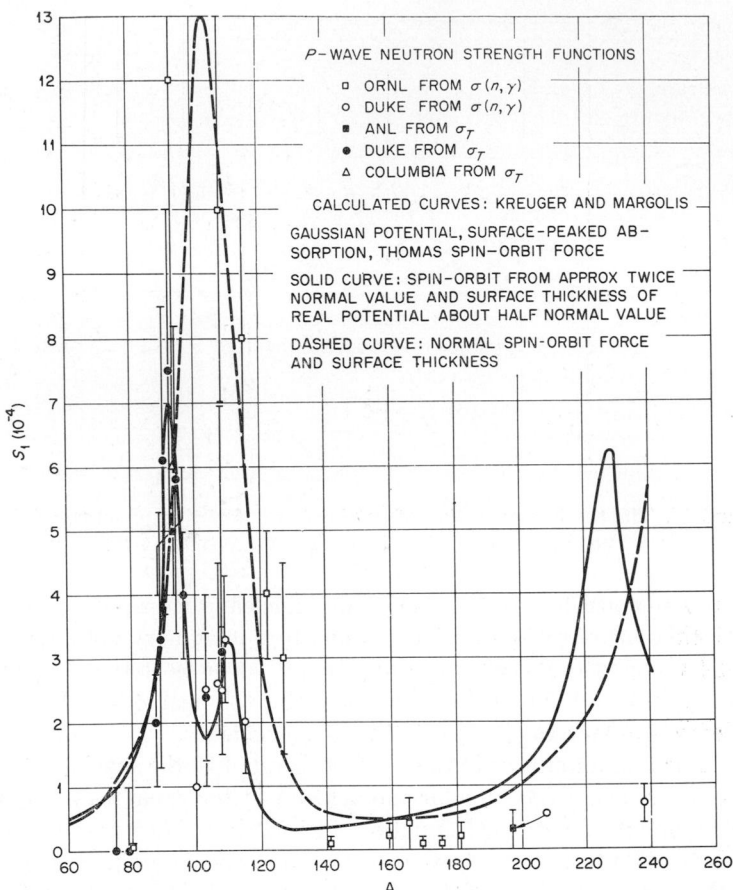

Figure 27. p-wave strength functions determined by activation cross sections (We60, Bi60), total cross sections (We60, Se61), analysis of individual resonances (Ro60), and radiative capture cross sections (Gi61). The curves are calulated from the optical model. Other calculations (Mo61) using a Woods-Saxon potential with volume absorption failed to produce a splitting even with a large spin-orbit term.

decrease which would be expected if only s-wave interactions were important. It is only in the neighborhood of A = 100 that such curves are observed in the kev region (Ne59a).

The currently available experimental and theoretical information on p-wave strength functions are given in Fig. 27. The solid curve is an optical model calculation (Kr61,Kr61a) with parameters chosen to fit the Duke data (Bi60,We60,Se61,Ne59a). The dashed curve is also an optical model calculation using the parameters which Krueger and Margolis consider normal, i.e., those which give a good fit to higher energy (greater than one Mev) neutron scattering data. This second calculation agrees better with the ORNL measurements near $A = 90$ (square points). Since only a few of the points were measured on pure nuclides, the ORNL study is coarser grained but wider ranged than Duke's. It is apparent that there are no ORNL points between $A = 93$ and $A = 108$, about where the minimum appears in the other curve. Hence, it appears possible that if an intermediate point were measured (e.g., Rh^{103}) a minimum would be found in agreement with the Duke results rather than a maximum as predicted by the upper curve. Thus the Oak Ridge results are not inconsistent with the existence of a minimum near $A = 100$. It is evident that away from the giant resonances both calculations are in rough agreement with the measured values of both Duke and ORNL. More measurements in the region between radium and plutonium should indicate the location of the next p-wave giant resonance peak.

There is a discrepancy in the absolute values of p-wave strength functions between experimental results obtained by radiative capture cross-section analysis and other techniques (near $A = 100$). The differences in the two results emphasize the difficulty in determining the p-wave strength function. For large values of S_1 the energy region of the capture cross section where p-wave effects are most easily observable is in the 1–20 kev range. This energy range, in turn, is one of the most difficult regions for accurate cross section measurements (see Chapter V.M). Actually these discrepancies, while they are disturbing, are not particularly surprising. The determination of a p-wave strength function from an experimental cross-section curve involves to some extent taking a small difference between two large numbers. Hence the absolute values of the strength functions are likely to be systematically high or low depending on the exact assumptions made in subtracting the s-wave scattering or capture from the total scattering or capture. Such a systematic error will not obscure giant resonance peaks. It is premature at the present time to explain the discrepancy in absolute values of strength functions. The high values for the strength functions determined from the Oak Ridge measurements are reinforced by the fact that they are consistent with

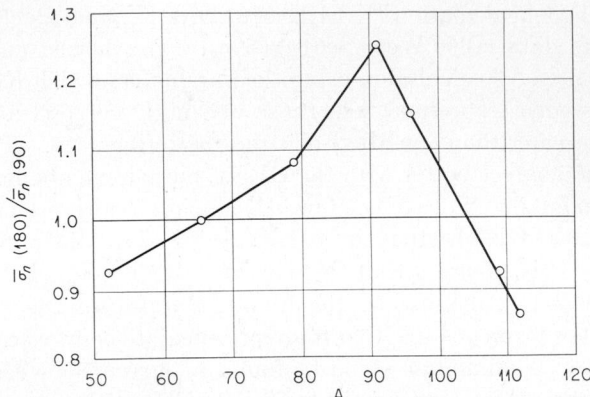

Figure 28. The average ratio of the 180 to 90° scattering cross sections of even elements (mostly even-even nuclei) are plotted for nuclei near mass number $A = 100$ (Bl58a).

the expected values for the optical model parameters. The lower values in Fig. 27 are confirmed to some extent by their rough agreement with the high resolution strength functions, which are determined by identifying and measuring the widths of individual p-wave resonances in Sr^{88} (Bi61), Nb^{93} (Ro60), and natural Ag (Ro60). It should be noted that all experiments indicate at least the "normal" amount of spin-orbit coupling.

Figure 28 is a plot of the ratio of the differential scattering at 90° to that at 180° for even Z elements in this region (Bl58a). The ratios are averaged over the energy range 50–100 kev. There are many resonances, both s- and p-wave, in this energy interval. The ratios should all be unity (corresponding to isotropic scattering) if there were no p-wave scattering. The maximum near $A = 90$, is evidently due to the $\frac{3}{2}^-$ resonance scattering ($l + \frac{1}{2}$) while the lack of a similar maximum near $A = 110$ is due to the fact that $\frac{1}{2}^-$ resonance scattering is isotropic.

In Fig. 29 the experimental measurements of R', the potential scattering length for an s-wave, are compared to the predictions of the same variants of the optical model which were considered in Fig. 25. Most of the data below $A = 80$ were obtained from average transmission ratios with the help of (57) while the data on heavier elements depend on the measured cross sections between resonances

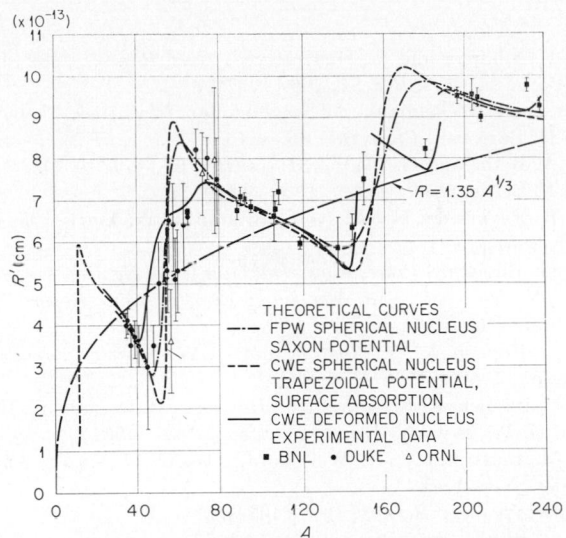

Figure 29. The *effective nuclear radius* R' (Fe54) as a function of mass number A. The legend indicates the source of the experimental points. The black-nucleus prediction is indicated by the monotonic curve marked $R = 1.35 A^{1/3}$ (fermis) which is the value assumed in all curves for the *half density* (Se58) radius of the nuclear potential. For other information see the caption of Fig. 25. We are indebted to K. K. Seth for this figure.

(Se58) as well as on averaged transmissions. The nonspherical potential appears to give a slightly better agreement with experiment than the other variations of the model (Fig. 25) and while the plotted data are insufficient to test this potential in the region $A = 150$ to 180 the data appears to favor the spheroidal potential (Ha59).

The fact that s- and p-wave strength functions as well as the s-wave potential scattering length R' appear to depend rather critically on mass number and potential-well shape offers a means of testing a much greater variety of possible average potentials than those illustrated in Fig. 25. The exploitation of presently available experimental methods for measuring strength functions (see previous section) and potential scattering cross sections is likely to yield much more detailed and accurate experimental data in the near future, and should result into a decided improvement in our knowledge of the average nuclear potential.

References

(Al54)   D. E. Alburger and M. H. L. Pryce, *Phys. Rev.* **95**, 1482 (1954).

(Ba37)   J. Bardeen, *Phys. Rev.* **51**, 799 (1937).

(Ba48)   Barschall, Bockelman, and Seagondollar, *Phys. Rev.* **73**, 659 (1948).

(Ba52)   H. H. Barschall, *Phys. Rev.* **86**, 431 (1952).

(Be37)   H. A. Bethe and G. Placzek, *Phys. Rev.* **51**, 450 (1937).

(Be37a)   H. A. Bethe, *Revs. Modern Phys.* **9** (1937).

(Be61)   P. R. Bevington, W. W. Rolland, and H. W. Lewis, *Phys. Rev.* **121**, 871 (1961).

(Bi57)   E. G. Bilpuch, *"Proceedings, Intl. Conf. on Neutron Interactions with the Nucleus,"* U. S. Atomic Energy Comm. *Report* TID 7547, Columbia Univ., unpublished (1957).

(Bi60)   E. G. Bilpuch, L. W. Weston, and H. W. Newson, *Annals of Physics* **10**, 455 (1960).

(Bi61)   E. G. Bilpuch, K. K. Seth, C. D. Bowman, R. H. Tabony, R. C. Smith, and H. W. Newson, *Ann. of Physics* **14**, 387 (1961).

(Bl52)   J. M. Blatt and V. K. Weisskopf, *Theoretical Nuclear Physics*, John Wiley, New York, 1952.

(Bl54)   C. Bloch, *Phys. Rev.* **93**, 1094 (1954).

(Bl58)   R. C. Block, *Phys. Rev.* **109**, 1217 (1958).

(Bl58a)   Block, Haeberli, and Newson, *Phys. Rev.* **109**, 1620 (1958).

(Bo36)   N. Bohr, *Nature (London)* **137**, 344 (1936).

(Bo57)   L. M. Bollinger and G. E. Thomas, *Rev. Sci. Instr.* **28**, 489 (1957).

(Bo62)   C. Bowman, *Ann. of Physics,* in press (1962).

(Br36)   G. Breit and E. P. Wigner, *Phys. Rev.* **49**, 519 (1936).

(Ca57)   A. G. W. Cameron, *Can. Jour. Phys.* **36**, 1040 (1957).

(Ch58)   Chase, Wilets, and Edmonds, *Phys. Rev.* **110**, 1080 (1958).

(Co56)   R. E. Cote, "Conf. on Neutron Physics by Time-of-Flight," *Oak Ridge National Laboratory Report* ORNL 2309, unpublished (1956).

(Cr55)   L. Cranberg and J. L. Levin, *Phys. Rev.* **100**, 434 (1955).

(Cr57)   Cranberg, Aiallo, Beauchamp, Lang, and Levin, *Rev. Sci. Instr.* **29**, 84 (1957).

(Cr57a)   Cranberg, Beauchamp, and Levin, *Rev. Sci. Instr.* **28**, 89 (1957).

(Da47)   Dancoff, Lichtenberger, Nobles, Kubitschek, and Monk, *Chicago Metallurgical Laboratory Report* CP 3781, unpublished (1947).

(Da57)   S. E. Darden, "Proceedings, Intl. Conf. on Neutron Interactions with the Nucleus," U. S. Atomic Energy Comm. *Report* TID 7547, Columbia Univ., unpublished (1957).

(Eg56)   P. A. Egelstaff, "Conf. on Neutron Physics by Time-of-Flight," *Oak Ridge National Laboratory Report* ORNL 2309, unpublished (1956).

(Ei58)   L. Eisenbud and E. P. Wigner, *Nuclear Structure*, Princeton University Press, 1958.

(El34)   J. Elsasser, *Compt. rend.* **199**, 1213 (1934).

(Er58)   W. K. Ergen, private communication (1958).

(Er58a)   T. Ericson, *Nuclear Phys.* **6**, 62 (1958).

(Er60)   T. Ericson, *Advances in Physics* **9**, 425 (1960).

(Fe47)   Feshbach, Peaslee, and Weisskopf, *Phys. Rev.* **71**, 145 (1947).
(Fe50)   Fermi, Orear, Rosenfeld, and Schluter, *Nuclear Physics*, University of Chicago Press, 1950.
(Fe54)   Feshbach, Porter, and Weisskopf, *Phys. Rev.* **96**, 448 (1954).
(Fe56)   Feshbach, Porter, and Weisskopf (reported by Weisskopf) *Physica* **18**, 952 (1956).
(Fe58)   S. Fernbach, *Revs. Modern Phys.* **30**, 414 (1958).
(Fi60)   F. W. K. Firk, private communication (1960).
(Ga52)   Garth, Hughes, and Levin, *Phys. Rev.* **87**, 222 (1952).
(Gi53)   J. H. Gibbons and H. W. Newson, *Phys. Rev.* **91**, 209A (1953).
(Gi56)   J. H. Gibbons, *Phys. Rev.* **102**, 1574 (1956).
(Gi61)   J. H. Gibbons, R. L. Macklin, P. D. Miller, and J. H. Neiler, *Phys. Rev.* **122**, 182 (1961).
(Go58)   Good, Neiler, and Gibbons, *Phys. Rev.* **109**, 926 (1958).
(Go58a)   C. D. Goodman and J. L. Need, *Phys. Rev.* **110**, 676 (1958).
(Go60)   W. M. Good, *Nuclear Inst. and Methods* **6**, 323 (1960).
(Ha18)   Hardy and Ramanujan, *Proc. Math. Soc. (London)* **42**, 75 (1918).
(Ha49)   Haxel, Jensen, and Suess, *Phys. Rev.* **75**, 1766 (1949).
(Ha51)   W. W. Havens, Jr. and L. J. Rainwater, *Phys. Rev.* **83**, 1123 (1951).
(Ha51a)   J. A. Harvey, *Phys. Rev.* **81**, 353 (1951).
(Ha55)   Harvey, Hughes, Carter, and Pilcher, *Phys. Rev.* **99**, 10 (1955).
(Ha56)   W. W. Havens, Jr., "Conf. on Neutron Physics by Time-of-Flight," *Oak Ridge National Laboratory Report* ORNL 2309, unpublished (1956).
(Ha59)   J. A. Harvey, ORNL; K. K. Seth, Duke University; and others, private communication (1959).
(Ha59a)   J. A. Harvey, ORNL, private communication (1959).
(Ha60)   W. W. Havens, Jr., Columbia University, private communication (1960).
(Ha60a)   J. A. Harvey, *Nuclear Structure*, D. A. Bromley and E. W. Vogt, Editors, University of Toronto Press, 1960, p. 659.
(Hi52)   Hibdon, Langsdorf, and Holland, *Phys. Rev.* **85**, 595 (1952).
(Hi57)   C. T. Hibdon, *Phys. Rev.* **108**, 414 (1957).
(Hu51)   Hughes, Garth, and Eggler, *Phys. Rev.* **83**, 234 (1951).
(Hu53)   Hughes, Garth, and Levin, *Phys. Rev.* **91**, 6 (1953).
(Hu55)   D. J. Hughes, *J. Nuclear Energy* **1**, 237 (1955).
(Hu55a)   D. J. Hughes and J. A. Harvey, *Phys. Rev.* **99**, 1032 (1955).
(Hu58)   D. J. Hughes and R. B. Schwartz, "Neutron Cross Sections," *Brookhaven National Laboratory Report* BNL 325, U. S. Government Printing Office, 1958, 2nd Edition.
(Kl52)   P. F. A. Klinkenberg, *Revs. Modern Phys.* **24**, 63 (1952).
(Kr61)   T. K. Krueger and B. Margolis, *Bull. Am. Phys. Soc.* **6**, 94 (1961).
(Kr61a)   T. K. Krueger and B. Margolis, *Nuclear Phys.* (to be published) 1961.
(La37)   W. E. Lamb, *Phys. Rev.* **55**, 190 (1937).
(La50)   A. Langsdorf, Jr., *Phys. Rev.* **80**, 132 (1950).
(La54)   Langsdorf, Monahan, and Reardon, "A Tabulation of Neutron Energies from Monoenergetic Protons on Lithium," *Argonne National Laboratory Report* ANL 5219, unpublished (1954).

(La54a) J. M. B. Lang and K. J. LeCouteur, *Proc. Phys. Soc. (London)* **67A,** 586 (1954).

(La55) Lane, Thomas, and Wigner, *Phys. Rev.* **98,** 693 (1955).

(La59) J. M. B. Lang and K. J. LeCouteur, *Nuclear Phys.* **13,** 32 (1959).

(La59a) J. M. B. Lang and K. J. LeCouteur, *Nuclear Phys.* **14,** 21 (1959).

(Le56) J. Levin and D. J. Hughes, *Phys. Rev.* **101,** 1328 (1956).

(Li47) Lichtenberger, Nobles, Monk, Kubitschek, and Dancoff, *Phys. Rev.* **72,** 164 (1947).

(Ly57) J. E. Lynn and E. R. Rae, *J. Nuclear Energy* **4,** 418 (1957).

(Ly58) Lynn, Firk, and Moxon, *Nuclear Phys.* **5,** 603 (1958).

(Ly58a) J. E. Lynn, *Nuclear Phys.* **7,** 599 (1958).

(Ly60) J. E. Lynn, *Atomic Energy Research Establishment Harwell Reports* AERE-R-3533-5 (unpublished) 1960.

(Ma49) M. G. Mayer, *Phys. Rev.* **75,** 1969 (1949).

(Ma50) M. G. Mayer, *Phys. Rev.* **78,** 16 and 22 (1950).

(Ma55) M. G. Mayer and J. H. D. Jensen, *Elementary Theory of Nuclear Shell Structure,* John Wiley, New York, 1955.

(Ma57) H. Marshak and H. W. Newson, *Phys. Rev.* **106,** 110 (1957).

(Ma58) R. L. Macklin and J. H. Gibbons, *Phys. Rev.* **109,** 105 (1958).

(Me53) Melkonian, Havens, and Rainwater, *Phys. Rev.* **92,** 702 (1953).

(Me59) Merzbacher, Crutchfield, and Newson, *Ann. of Physics* **8,** 194 (1959).

(Mi59) Miller, Good, Gibbons, and Neiler, *Bull. Am. Phys. Soc.* **4,** 42 (1959).

(Mi60) Miller, Gibbons, and Macklin, *Bull. Am. Phys. Soc.* **5,** 18 (1960).

(Mo51) Moak, Reese, and Good, *Nucleonics* **9,** No. 3 (Sept. 1951).

(Mo53) P. Morrison, "Nuclear Reactions," in *Experimental Nuclear Physics,* E. Segré, ed., John Wiley, New York, 1953, Vol. II, p. 1.

(Mo61) P. A. Moldauer, *Argonne National Laboratory Report* ANL-6323, unpublished (1961).

(Ne52) H. W. Newson and R. H. Rohrer, *Phys. Rev.* **87,** 177 (1952).

(Ne53) H. W. Newson and E. Merzbacher, *Phys. Rev.* **91,** 241 (1953).

(Ne54) H. W. Newson and R. H. Rohrer, *Phys. Rev.* **94,** 654 (1954).

(Ne56) Neiler, Kelley, and Bell, *Bull. Am. Phys. Soc.* **1,** 70 (1956).

(Ne56a) T. D. Newton, *Can. J. Phys.* **34,** 804 (1956).

(Ne57) Newson, Williamson, Jones, Gibbons, and Marshak, *Phys. Rev.* **108,** 1294 (1957).

(Ne59) Neiler, Gibbons, and Good, ORNL, private communication (1959).

(Ne59a) Newson, Block, Nichols, Taylor, Furr, and Merzbacher, *Ann. of Phys.* **8,** 211 (1959).

(Ne59b) H. W. Newson and M. Duncan, *Phys. Rev. Letters* **3,** 45 (1959).

(Ne60) H. W. Newson, Duke University, private communication (1960).

(Ne61) Newson, Gibbons, Marshak, Bilpuch, Rohrer, and Capp, *Ann. of Physics* **14,** 346 (1961).

(Ne61a) Newson, Bilpuch, Karriker, Weston, Patterson, and Bowman, *Ann. of Physics* **14,** 365 (1961).

(Ni58) Nichols, Bilpuch, and Newson, *Bull. Am. Phys. Soc.* **3,** 164 (1958).

(Ni59) Nichols, Bilpuch, and Newson, *Ann. of Physics* **8,** 250 (1959).

(Ok55) A. Okazaki, *Phys. Rev.* **99,** 55 (1955).

(Pa58)   Parks, Newson, and Williamson, *Bull. Am. Phys. Soc.* **3**, 164 (1958).
(Pa61)   P. B. Parks and H. W. Newson, unpublished results (1961).
(Pa62)   Patterson, Toller, Bilpuch, Seth, and Newson, to be published (1962).
(Po56)   C. E. Porter and R. G. Thomas, *Phys. Rev.* **104**, 483 (1956).
(Pr54)   M. H. L. Pryce, *Proc. Phys. Soc.* **65**, 773 (1954).
(Pr56)   M. H. L. Pryce, *Nuclear Phys.* **2**, 226 (1956).
(Ra47)   Rainwater, Havens, Dunning, and Wu, *Phys. Rev.* **71**, 65 (1947).
(Ra53)   E. R. Rae and E. M. Bowey, *Proc. Phys. Soc. (London)* **66A**, 1073 (1953).
(Ra58)   Rae, Collins, Kinsey, Lynn, and Weblin, *Nuclear Phys.* **5**, 89 (1958).
(Ro54)   Rohrer, Newson, Gibbons, and Cap, *Phys. Rev.* **95**, 302(A) (1954).
(Ro57)   N. Rosenzweig, *Phys. Rev.* **108**, 817 (1957).
(Ro57a) A. A. Ross, *Phys. Rev.* **108**, 720 (1957).
(Ro58)   N. Rosenzweig, L. M. Bollinger, L. L. Lee, and J. P. Schiffer, Geneva Paper 693 (1958).
(Ro60)   J. L. Rosen, private communication (1960).
(Sa58)   Saplakoglu, Bollinger, and Coté, *Phys. Rev.* **109**, 1258 (1958).
(Sc49)   L. Schiff, *Quantum Mechanics*, McGraw-Hill, New York, 1949.
(Sc54)   J. M. C. Scott, *Phil. Mag.* **45**, 1322 (1954).
(Se47)   L. W. Seagondollar and H. H. Barschall, *Phys. Rev.* **72**, 439 (1947).
(Se54)   Seidl, Hughes, Palevsky, Levin, Kato, and Sjostrand, *Phys. Rev.* **95**, 476 (1954).
(Se58)   Seth, Hughes, Zimmerman, and Garth, *Phys. Rev.* **110**, 692 (1958).
(Se58b) K. K. Seth, *Revs. Modern Phys.* **30**, 442 (1958).
(Se59)   K. K. Seth, *Ann. of Physics* **8**, 223 (1959).
(Se61)   K. K. Seth, R. H. Tabony, L. W. Weston, and H. W. Newson, *Bull. Am. Phys. Soc.* **6**, 252 (1961).
(Sm56)   Smith, Gibbons, Good, Neiler, and Banta, *Bull. Am. Phys. Soc.* **1**, 71 (1956).
(Te52)   T. Teichmann and E. P. Wigner, *Phys. Rev.* **87**, 123 (1952).
(Th57)   Thomas, Bollinger, Coté, and Kennett, *Bull. Am. Phys. Soc.* **2**, 338 (1957).
(Vo56)   E. Vogt, *Phys. Rev.* **101**, 1792 (1956).
(We50)   V. F. Weisskopf, *Helv. Phys. Acta* **23**, 187 (1950).
(We60)   Weston, Seth, Bilpuch, and Newson, *Ann. of Physics* **10**, 455 (1960).
(Wi47)   E. P. Wigner and L. Eisenbud, *Phys. Rev.* **72**, 29 (1947).
(Wi54)   E. P. Wigner, *Science* **120**, 1790 (1954).
(Wi61)   Wilenzick, Mitchell, Seth, and Lewis, *Phys. Rev.* **121**, 1150 (1961).
(Ye57)   Yeater, Gaerttner, and Baldwin, *Rev. Sci. Instr.* **28**, 514 (1947).
(Zu58)   A. Zucker, *Nuclear Phys.* **6**, 420 (1958).

Fast Neutron Capture Cross Sections

A. G. W. CAMERON

Institute for Space Studies, New York, New York

N. H. LAZAR and H. W. SCHMITT

Oak Ridge National Laboratory, Oak Ridge, Tennessee

1. Experimental Techniques

A. *Introduction*

The study of the neutron capture process has been of interest to physicists because of its roles in the study of nuclear structure, in reactor design, and in astrophysics. Most experimental emphasis in the past has been directed toward the capture of thermal and low-energy neutrons, readily available in moderated reactors; it has been only during the past few years that extensive fast neutron capture experiments have been done. The theory of neutron capture cross sections, described in Section 3 of this chapter, is basically understood; it has been only recently, however, that sufficient capture cross section data have existed, particularly in the kev energy range and above, to permit determination of nuclear properties important in testing various nuclear models. Recent advances in technology have made possible detailed capture cross section measurements from thermal neutron energies to Mev neutron energies; it is the purpose of this section to describe these new techniques as well as those in use over a longer period of time. In many cases well-established techniques have been applied in newer, perhaps better-understood experiments.

The measurements of fast neutron radiative capture cross-sections may be divided into three parts: the production of fast neutrons, the determination of the neutron intensity or flux, and the detection of the capture event. It is often difficult, in practice, to separate these; nevertheless we shall consider first the qualitative aspects of various methods for detecting capture events and for producing fast neutrons. Applications of these methods and the determination of neutron intensity in specific experiments will be discussed in Section 2 in connection with experimental results.

B. Experimental Detection of Neutron Capture Process

Various methods have been used for the observation of the radiative capture event. Techniques for the detection of prompt gamma rays following the capture event have been developed and used in conjunction with time-of-flight measurements of neutron energy. In special cases the delayed beta- or gamma-radiation from the radioactive product nuclei may be measured to obtain the number of capture events. Another class of experiments is based on the measurement of the reduction in the neutron intensity as a result of the capturing events; such measurements may be made either directly or with the aid of a multiplying system. Another independent approach to the problem is to measure, with a mass spectrometer, the number of nuclei of mass $(A + 1)$ produced in neutron irradiations. Let us consider each of these general methods.

(1) **Measurement of Activity from Product Nucleus.** This has been one of the most widely used methods for the detection of absorption of neutrons since it, inherently, clearly separates the product from the target nucleus (which is generally stable). The disintegration rate, R, produced in a sample after irradiation for a time t in a flux ϕ neutrons per square centimeter per second, is given by

$$R = N\phi\sigma_\gamma (1 - e^{-\lambda t}) \tag{1}$$

N is the number of nuclei in the sample, and λ is the decay constant of the daughter activity. The disintegration rate can be determined from the observed beta-ray counting rate, for example, in a scintillation counter, proportional counter, or Geiger counter, if the efficiency of the detector and solid angle subtended at the source are known. In such beta-ray measurements, the geometry and efficiency are usually determined for each sample by calibration against samples of identical composition and form which have been irradiated in a known flux and at a neutron energy where the cross section for the isotope has previously been determined. The calibration samples must have the same scattering and self-absorption properties for the emitted electrons as the unknown, particularly if low energy beta-rays constitute the major portion of the decays. In addition, for nuclei with isomeric states, care must be taken to determine that the variation in production rate of the isomer relative to the radioactive ground state at the different neutron energies does not result in a false calibration.

Since the usual calibration samples are produced by thermal neutron irradiations, and because of the large differences in thermal cross sections among the nuclides, impurities in the samples constitute a serious problem. The counting rates of the samples, however, are generally followed for sufficient time to ascertain that the excepted half-life is observed. An alternative method of avoiding the impurity problem is to select for the measurement only radiations from the expected product activity and discriminate against all others. This is most easily accomplished by detection, with a scintillation spectrometer, of selected gamma-rays following the beta decay. In the experiments of Macklin, Lazar, and Lyon (Ma57), for example, use was made of the known efficiency of 3-inch diameter, 3-inch high NaI(Tl) crystals for gamma rays with energies up to 3 Mev to determine absolutely the intensities of particular gamma rays in the various samples. This method has an added advantage; namely the self-absorption of the gamma-ray in the sample is not difficult to determine accurately. Knowledge of the branching ratio, i.e., the fraction of disintegrations for which the gamma ray of interest is emitted, is also required for a cross section determination; but this information can usually be determined by subsidiary measurements utilizing small quantities of high purity sample. In addition, as a result of the large amount of work already completed in the study of the decay of radioactive nuclei, much useful decay-scheme information is available in the literature. The activation method for measuring neutron capture cross sections has been used extensively for neutrons from photoneutron sources (Hu51, Ki53, Ma57, Bo58, Le58, Ly59, Ve59, Ko59), as well as for neutrons from charged-particle induced reactions using accelerators (Pe58, Ba59, Ga59, Ha59, Jo59, Mi59, Fe59, Bi60, We60).

(2) **Detection of Prompt Gamma Rays.** In view of the high efficiency of scintillation counters for even moderately high energy gamma rays, it is natural that they be used for detection of the prompt gamma rays following neutron capture. It has been only

during the past few years, however, that experimental techniques have been developed to a sufficient extent to carry out capture cross section measurements by this method. Background reduction, determination of (or elimination of sensitivity to) gamma-ray multiplicity following capture, and development of efficient detectors for energetic gamma rays were the principle obstacles in exploitation of this method. The product nucleus, following capture, is left in a state generally 5–8 Mev above the ground state as a result of the binding energy of the neutron in the nucleus. This energy is released, generally in times less than 10^{-14} sec, in the form of gamma rays which cascade to the ground state. Since this occurs for all capturing isotopes, the detection of prompt gamma rays provides perhaps the most generally applicable method for capture cross section measurements, at least for neutron energies below the inelastic scattering threshold. Some nuclei, upon capturing a neutron, appear to emit nearly the same characteristic spectrum of gamma rays independent of the incident neutron energy (Ra57a); thus the detector efficiency need not be calibrated for each resonance into which the neutron is absorbed. However, there are large differences in gamma-ray spectra from nucleus to nucleus (Ki55). The effect of these large differences in prompt capture gamma-ray detection may be minimized by using a sufficiently large liquid scintillation detector, i.e., one whose efficiency approaches 100 per cent event for gamma rays of relatively high energy. The solution phosphor tank constructed by Diven *et al.* (Di56, Di58) for capture-to-fission ratio measurements has, for example, an efficiency of ∼90 per cent for U^{235} capture gamma rays with a sample placed in the center of the tank; that constructed by Gibbons *et al.* (Gi61), shown schematically in Fig. 1, for neutron capture cross section measurements in the kev energy range averages well above 90 per cent for the detection of capture gamma rays. Such tanks have several advantages over large NaI(Tl) crystals in this application, not the least of which is that they do not become radioactive (and contribute to the background) when irradiated with neutrons. Using pulsed monoenergetic sources, the background may be further reduced since the counters may be gated to count gamma rays only when capture events are known to occur—thereby eliminating the background events which occur between possible capturing intervals. When a spectrum of neutrons is emitted from the pulsed source, the time-of-flight of the neutron (hence the neutron energy)

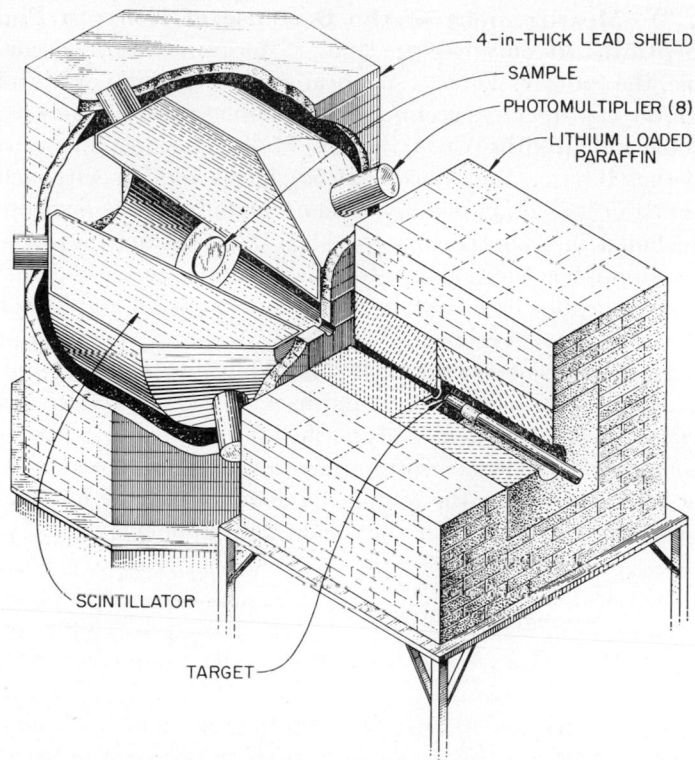

4-in-THICK LEAD SHIELD
SAMPLE
PHOTOMULTIPLIER (8)
LITHIUM LOADED PARAFFIN
SCINTILLATOR
TARGET

Figure 1. Liquid scintillation tank and experimental arrangement for neutron capture cross section measurements by time-of-flight (Gi61).

may be obtained from the time interval between the source pulse and the capture event. Further discussion of such experiments is contained in Sections 1.C and 2.

Another variation in technique for detection of prompt gamma rays consists of surrounding the sample with several gamma-ray detectors and requiring coincidences between them to establish a capture event. Since, in general, several gamma rays are emitted following capture, more than one detector may be expected to give a pulse. Background events, on the other hand, will generally be detected in only one detector. Albert and Gaerttner (Al54) have used this technique successfully in time-of-flight measurements with a betatron source, and a similar method was adopted by Rae (Ra57a).

(3) **Measurement of the Decrease of Neutron Flux by Absorption.** If only capture and scattering reactions occur in a sample, the transmission of a spherical shell of the material is a function of the capture cross section. This method, used as early as 1936 by Collie and Griffiths (Co36), has been fully developed and analyzed by Bethe, Beyster, and Carter (Be56) in connection with inelastic scattering cross section measurements. Details of this development are included in Chapter V.H by Allen, Carter, and Taylor. The shell transmission method has been applied to the measurement of neutron absorption cross sections by Belanova (Be58) and by Schmitt and Cook (Sc60). As shown schematically in Fig. 2, a neutron source is placed at the center of the shell and a detector is placed some distance away. Shell-off, shell-on, and background counts are made to determine the transmission T of the shell for the source neutrons. If the source emits neutrons isotropically and if the response of the detector is isotropic, then the source and detector may be interchanged (Be55a); in either case, then, the sphere transmission is given by

$$T = T_0 + (1 - T_0)(\sigma_n/\sigma_T) \times$$

$$\left[P_1 + (1 - P_1)P_2(\sigma_n/\sigma_T) + \frac{(1 - P_1)(1 - P_2)P_m\sigma^2_n}{\sigma_T(\sigma_X + \sigma_n P_m)} \right] \quad (2)$$

where $T_0 = \exp(-n\sigma_T t)$, σ_T and σ_n are the total and scattering cross sections, respectively, $\sigma_X = \sigma_T - \sigma_n$ is the absorption cross section, t is the shell thickness, and n the number of atoms per cm^3 in the shell, and the $P_i (i = 1, 2, \dots)$ are average probabilities for escape of a neutron after i collisions in the shell [calculated by a Monte Carlo method by Bethe et al. (Be56)]. Small corrections for finite source size, finite source-to-detector distance, and self-absorption of neutrons in the source must be included in Equation (2); however, these can be reduced to a minimum by careful design of the source and experimental arrangement.

Because the absorption cross section is obtained directly from neutron transmission measurements, into which *absolute* detection efficiencies do not enter, the absolute absorption cross sections obtained by this method are perhaps among the most accurately measured capture cross section values, at least at energies where inelastic scattering does not occur. Principal disadvantages are that large samples are required, rendering separated isotope work difficult or

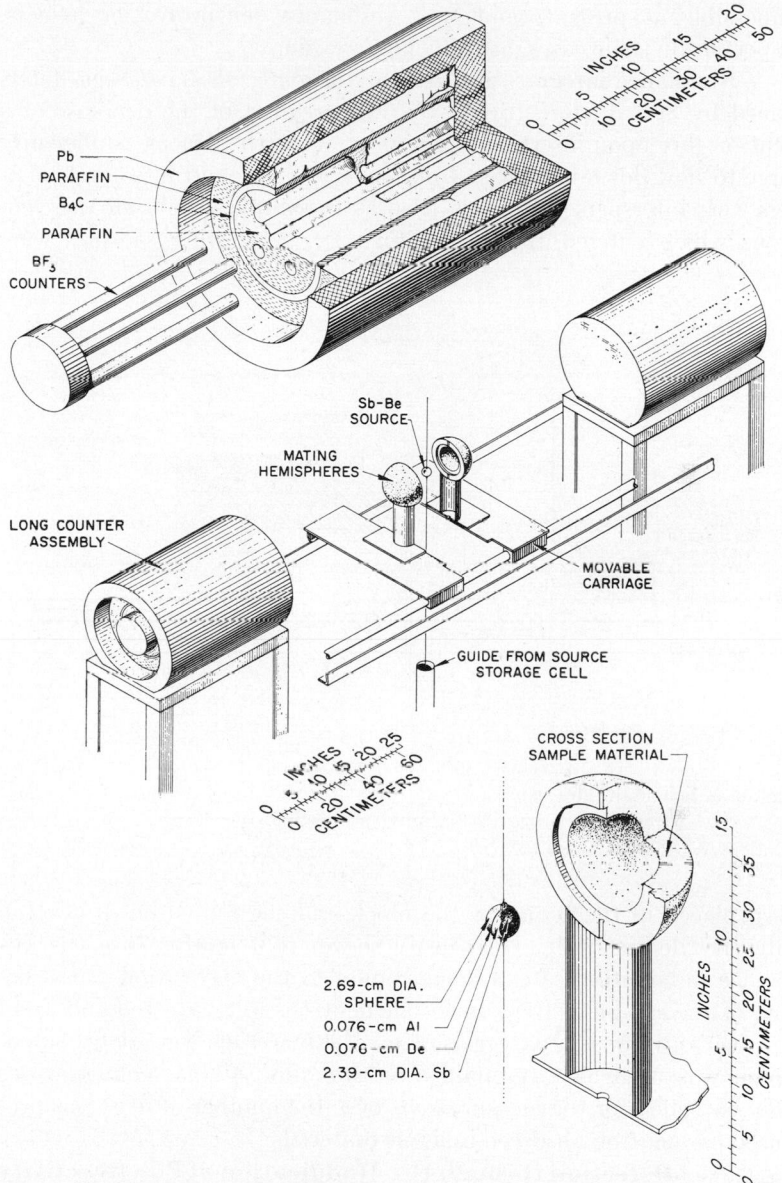

Figure 2. Experimental arrangement for the measurement of neutron absorption cross sections by the spherical shell transmission method (Sc60).

impossible at present, and that resonance self-protection effects, important in some cases, are difficult to evaluate.

Resonance integrals of a number of materials have been determined by Spivak *et al.* (Sp55) by measurement of the decrease of a neutron flux upon insertion of samples. A carbon block, sufficiently large to slow down neutrons of pile energy, was constructed and counters were interspersed through it so as to sample nearly all the neutrons which entered the block (Fig. 3). Absorbing samples were

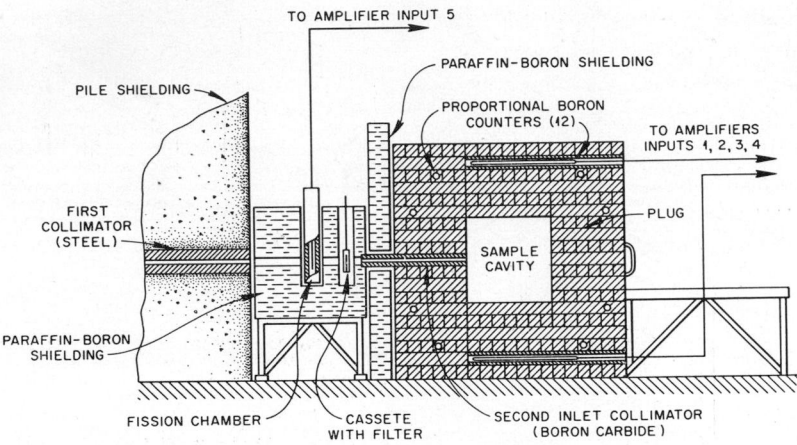

Figure 3. Schematic diagram of arrangement for the measurement of resonance integrals by Spivak *et al.* (Sp55).

then placed in the center of the block and the reduction in neutron intensity determined. It is easily shown that in this case the difference in counting rate is proportional to the absorption cross section of the sample. Resonance pile neutrons were selected and, from the results, resonance integrals of several materials were determined; boron was used as a normalization standard. This technique has been extended for the measurement of η, the number of neutrons produced per neutron absorbed in fissile materials.

(4) **Detection through the Modification of Pile Reactivity by a Sample.** The possibility of using the reactivity of a reactor as an instrument for determining nuclear properties was appreciated

quite early. Two techniques have been used for obtaining cross section information. The first method is a simple reactivity measurement, in which the perturbation of the reactor power is observed upon the insertion of an absorbing sample into the reactor center (danger coefficient method, see Hu56a). The variation in control rod position required to return the reactor to the original power level (as determined by the counting rate, say, in a BF_3 ionization chamber located at some position in the lattice) was generally calibrated with respect to results of rod-drop and multiplication studies. Calibrations thus obtained agreed well with period calibrations in which the standard relative yields of delayed neutron groups were used. If the elements were pure absorbers of neutrons, this technique could be used very effectively since its sensitivity is quite high, particularly if the reactor is run just at criticality. With the sample placed in the center of the reactor, elastic scattering will not affect the reactivity appreciably since, in general, the target mass is high, and thus the neutron energy change will be negligible. Further the angular distribution of elastically scattered neutrons will not affect the normal reactor distribution. Unfortunately, however, the sample may also scatter fast neutrons inelastically, and thereby affect the neutron energy spectrum. Since the nuclear properties of the core materials vary with energy, clearly reactivity changes due to the reduction in the neutron energy will occur as well. Thus, results of reactivity measurements are difficult to interpret in terms of neutron cross sections. Rose (Ro57) states that a change in the effectiveness of a neutron in sustaining a chain reaction of only a few per cent is sufficient to explain the discrepancies between his measurements and activation experiments. Nevertheless, qualitative information about σ_γ for medium and high Z nuclei has been obtained in the "fast" neutron region through experiments of this nature. In particular, fast neutron assemblies such as Zephyr, Godiva, SAPL PPA-5, and others have been used to obtain information of this type (Hu56a, Sn55).

A second method for observing reactivity changes involves the pile oscillator (La47, Fr54). In these experiments, the sample is periodically inserted and removed from the reactor core and the reactivity variation resulting is interpreted, again, in terms of standards with known properties. The samples are usually inserted and removed from the reactor in time intervals short compared to the periods spent in and out and thus transient effects can be made small. Typical operation is 1 second for insertion and removal and 18 seconds in and out of the reactor (La47). If the sample is left in the reactor for too long periods (more than 100 seconds, according to Fr54, in GLEEP), inaccurate results may be obtained because of pressure and temperature changes affecting reactivity in the reactor. The signal from a neutron monitor is used, essentially, with a circuit tuned to the oscillation frequency. The ratio of the power change to the operating power (essentially $\Delta I/I$, where I is the current in the neutron counter and ΔI its change due to the sample), is proportional to the absorption cross section if the delayed neutron effects are negligible. Fast neutron results may be obtained by using a cadmium absorber to remove the thermal flux in moderated reactors. This experiment has difficulties in interpretation for the same reasons as the danger coefficient experiment.

(5) **Determination of Product Nucleus by Mass Spectrometric Techniques.** In view of the relatively large amounts of material required to perform experiments of this nature, only materials involved in reactor construction have been investigated. Most experiments using this technique have been designed to determine α, the capture-to-fission ratio, for fissile materials (In55, Ka55, Ga57). In this case, the number N_{A+1} of nuclei of mass $(A + 1)$ and the fission yield are both proportional to the flux, the time irradiated, etc. It is only necessary to measure by mass spectroscopy the ratio N_{A+1}/N_A for the fissionable material since the fission yield is most easily determined by radio-chemical analysis. The ratio of these determinations yields α.

C. Sources of Fast Neutrons for Capture Cross Section Experiments

Historically, the earlier determinations of neutron capture cross sections were made with neutrons of very broad energy distributions; some were made with various (γ,n) and (α,n) sources. It has only been during the past few years that techniques have developed to the extent that relatively good resolution measurements could be made. Nuclear levels in the compound state are of the order of 5 to 8 Mev above the ground state, average spacing is generally of the order of tens to hundreds of electron volts (at least for medium and heavy nuclei). Furthermore, the average gamma ray widths in this region are only a few tenths of an electron volt. Resolutions of a few hundred ev or so for neutrons in the 10 kev range have recently been attainable, through selection of neutrons of the desired energies from a broader energy spread by millimicrosecond time-of-flight techniques (see Chapter IV.A) with pulsed accelerators (Ne59, Gi61). Energy resolutions of 20 per cent at 1 kev to 6 per cent at 100 ev neutron energy have been obtained in the energy range below about 5 kev by means of mechanical choppers (B160, B161). Generally speaking, spreads of a few kilovolts are obtained at higher energies (Ne59, Di60, Gi61) and the resulting cross sections are average results over at least several resonances; above a few hundred kev, for medium and heavy elements, the resonances themselves overlap. Neutron sources which have been used for capture cross section measurements and their energy ranges are discussed below.

(1) **Pulsed Accelerators for Time-of-Flight Measurements.** There are now several groups using Van de Graaff accelerators, cyclotrons, linear accelerators, etc., as pulsed neutron sources. The fast electronic circuitry together with the relatively high beam intensities now available permit the use of sufficiently short flight paths so that neutron intensity is no longer a severe problem. Experiments of this nature other than neutron capture measurements have involved transmission measurements and determination of total cross sections (Go58). Figure 4 illustrates in block diagram the electronic equipment used in the pulsed Van de Graaff experiments of Gibbons et al. (Gi61) to determine the neutron time-of-flight and the rate of capture in the sample. Note in particular that the time-of-flight spectrum for captured neutrons and the background time-of-flight spectrum were obtained in the same run, since background counts are taken in the interval between neutron bursts when no fast-neutron capture events could take place in the sample. Two types of experiments were done with this arrangement: In one set of measurements monoenergietic neutrons were produced either from the $T(p,n)He^3$ reaction in a thin tritium target, from the $Li^7(p,n)Be^7$ reaction in a thin lithium target, or from the $T(p,n)He^3$ or $Li^7(p,n)$-Be^7 reactions slightly above threshold. In this case the time-of-flight measurements provided only a method for background reduction. In a second set of measurements, thick lithium and tritium targets were used to produce a spectrum of neutrons, ranging in energy from 8 to 170 kev. By this method the shape of the capture cross section of a sample as a function of neutron energy over a wide

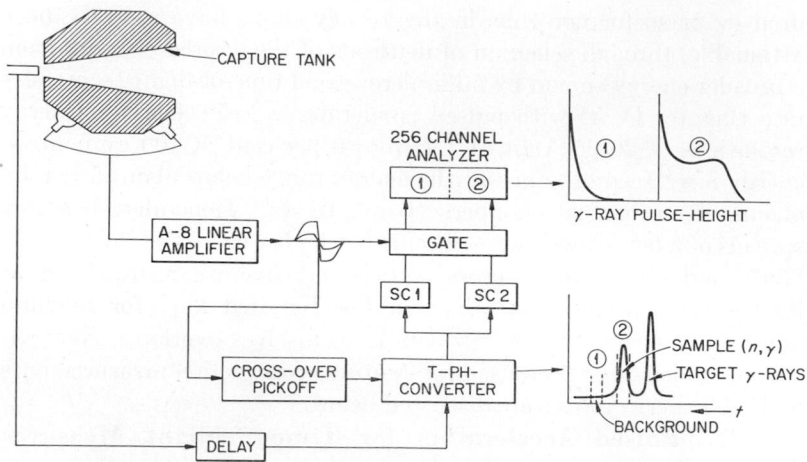

Figure 4. Block diagram of the scintillation tank and associated electronic equipment for gamma-ray spectrum measurements and capture cross section measurements by time-of-flight (Gi61). The gamma-ray spectra labeled (1) and (2) are obtained in the time intervals labeled (1) and (2) and correspond to the background spectrum and background-plus-sample spectrum, respectively.

range was obtained in a single run. As before, the background was measured in the intervals between neutron bursts when no primary capture events could occur. In these experiments typical burst duration was 10 millimicroseconds, time between bursts was 1.6 microseconds, and time-of-flight resolution was 15 to 25 millimicroseconds. In the experiments of Diven *et al.* (Di60) burst durations varied from 20 to 100 millimicroseconds, time between bursts varied from 0.75 to 100 microseconds, and timing resolution varied accordingly; capture cross section measurements were made for monoenergetic neutrons in the range 175 kev to 1 Mev, and the time-of-flight determination was used for background discrimination only.

These advances in time-of-flight and pulsed-accelerator techniques have made possible great advances in capture cross section measurements. Results suitable for theoretical analysis have now been obtained for a wide range of neutron energies and for elements throughout the periodic table. Details of some of these results will be discussed in Section 2.

Experiments in which a spectrum of neutrons was produced and time-of-flight measurements were made have been performed by Albert and Gaerttner (A154); they used a 100-Mev betatron to produce bremsstrahlung which in turn produced photoneutrons in uranium. With suitable moderation around the target, the neutron energies were in the range 1 ev to 10 kev with a distribution approximately proportional to $E^{-3/4}$. The neutron yield was greater than 10^{15} neutrons per pulse. A typical flight path was 7 meters, and a resolution of 0.08 μsec/meter at 1 kev was observed in a simple transmission experiment using Sm_2O_3 plus a scintillation counter as an (n,γ) detector.

The Harwell group (Ra57a) also has used the (γ,n) reaction on uranium for production of neutrons with a 15-Mev linear accelerator as the source of electrons. A typical flight path was 11.5 meters and a resolution of 0.17 μsec/meter was obtained. The bremsstrahlung spectrum covers the peak of the giant resonance in uranium and more than 4 x 10^{14} neutrons per pulse were obtained at a duty cycle of 400 pulses/sec.

Rainwater (Ra57b) has reported some results with the Nevis synchrocyclotron using plastic scintillation counters to detect the gamma rays from capture. Bunches of 380-Mev protons struck a tungsten target 60 times per second and 10^{17}–10^{18} neutrons were made per burst. Some of these neutrons were slowed to useful energies by moderation in a nylon box surrounding the tungsten target. A flight path of 35.22 meters was used (mostly through helium filled balloons) and the gamma-ray yield as a function of time-of-flight was measured. For an indication of the resolution, it is stated that resonances at 586, 575, 563, and 554 ev in silver are clearly resolved.

(2) **Electron Accelerators for (γ,n) Production Used with Filtration Methods.** At one time, there was considerable discussion about the possibility of developing a breeder reactor for intermediate (i.e., resonance-region) neutron energies. In an attempt to mock up the neutron distribution in such a reactor to measure poisoning effects of various fission products, a 2-Mev x-ray machine was adapted for producing neutrons by the $Be^9(\gamma,n)$ reaction (De52). The neutrons were moderated in a beryllium capsule about the target and the energy spectrum further modified by shields of boron and cadmium with "cut-offs" at 30 and 200 ev for "dE/E neutrons," i.e., 50 per cent transmission at 50 and 500 ev, respectively, for neutrons with a $1/E$ flux distribution. Samples of several elements were placed, for the irradiation, in the center of the beryllium block and subsequently analyzed by activation.

(3) "dE/E" Neutron Spectrum from Moderated Reactors. Among the most accessible high intensity neutron sources are the moderated reactors. To obtain high energy neutrons one need only filter out the thermal flux from the sample (usually with a cadmium absorber, taking advantage of the strong resonance at 0.176 ev). It is well known that in the slowing down process, for no absorption in the moderator, the flux of neutrons of energy E in the inverval dE is given by

$$(nv)_E dE = (\text{constant})(dE/E) \tag{3}$$

This neutron source has been used in conjunction with almost all the detection techniques described above. The reactor spectrum may also be modified to emphasize various neutron energy ranges for rough energy dependent cross section determinations (Ka55). For this purpose, for example, boron absorbers which gave 33 per cent transmission at 5, 30, 200, and 5000 ev were inserted in the $1/E$ beam of the Hanford reactor. Activation experiments with U and Pu were performed to obtain some indication of the variation of the capture and fission cross sections with energy.

Recent experiments giving capture cross sections as a function of energy with good resolution have been carried out at the Oak Ridge Research Reactor by Block and Slaughter (B159, B160). They used a mechanical chopper in conjunction with a large liquid scintillation tank, and hence were not dependent on the spectrum shape.

(4) Fast Neutrons from Various Reactor Types. Several reactor types with various moderator geometries have been operated as sources of intermediate or high energy neutrons in capture experiments. The neutron spectrum in such reactor assemblies bears no resemblance to the $1/E$ flux distribution usually associated with reactors and is generally different in each assembly. For example, EBR-1 was a highly enriched U^{235} fuel reactor surrounded by a natural uranium blanket. In contrast, the Harwell reactor, Zephyr, has a plutonium core and natural uranium blanket. The neutron energy distribution in Zephyr was determined at various distances from the core using a He^3 proportional counter, hydrogen recoil proportional counter and photographic plates; checks of these results were obtained through activation of threshold absorbers. In addition, photographic plates were used to determine the neutron energy

distribution in the core. The core spectrum in EBR-1 was measured by determining the energy distribution of neutrons in a beam originating at the center of the core. Both a cloud chamber and photographic plates were used in the energy spectrum determination (Li55). Experiments performed in the center of the core give information about neutrons with approximately 1.5 Mev average energy whereas some information at an average energy of about 700 kev has been obtained from experiments in the blanket of Zephyr. In both cases the neutron distribution covers a large spread in energy.

SAPL PPA-5 (Hu56a) was a mockup for an intermediate energy reactor. From theoretical considerations and threshold absorber measurements, it was determined that 50 per cent of plutonium fissions in the core of the assembly occurred for neutrons below 2700 ev in energy, and that 50 per cent occurred for neutrons of energy less than 130 ev at the edge of the core.

Experiments with the neutrons in the bare enriched uranium assemblies, Godiva and Topsy, at Los Alamos Scientific Laboratory have also been reported (Ok55). The neutron energy distributions in these assemblies have not been determined accurately, but a comparison of energy-dependent cross sections in these and the other assemblies described above gives an indication of the neutron distribution. In particular, Godiva seems to have an energy distribution somewhat enriched in high-energy neutrons, compared to Zephyr or EBR-1. By comparing these results with the fission spectrum cross sections (Hu53), it can be seen that only a slight degradation of the spectrum occurs in these assemblies (Co56).

In general, monoenergetic or pulsed sources provide more satisfactory neutron capture cross section data than do the above arrangements; the experiments described here, however, gave some of the first capture cross section results in certain energy ranges, and have had considerable value in reactor design.

(5) **Selection of Neutron Energy Distributions by Slowing-Down-Time Measurements.** A rather novel method of producing neutrons in the kilovolt region was reported at the first Geneva Conference by Bergman *et al.* (Be55). They showed that moderation of fast neutrons by high Z materials results in "bunching" of neutrons into energy groups which may be selected as a function of time after a neutron burst is fed into the system. In fact, it was shown that

the average velocity of neutrons at a time t after irradiation is given by

$$t = M\lambda(v^{-1} - v_0^{-1}) \tag{4}$$

where M is the atomic weight of the moderator, λ is the mean free path in the moderator (assumed independent of energy), and v_0 is the initial neutron velocity. It was shown by Cazarnovsky (reported in Be55) that the neutron energy distribution at any time is approximately Gaussian and the theoretical half-width is given by

$$\Delta E/E = 26 \; [1 + (1/E_{ev})] \text{ per cent} \tag{5}$$

Thus resolutions of $\sim$30 per cent may be obtained in the kilovolt region and some useful capture information has been accumulated. A schematic diagram of the experimental arrangement is shown in Fig. 5.

A series of experiments were performed using this source. A lead pile, 2 x 2 x 3 m^3, was constructed (involving $\sim$110 tons of lead).

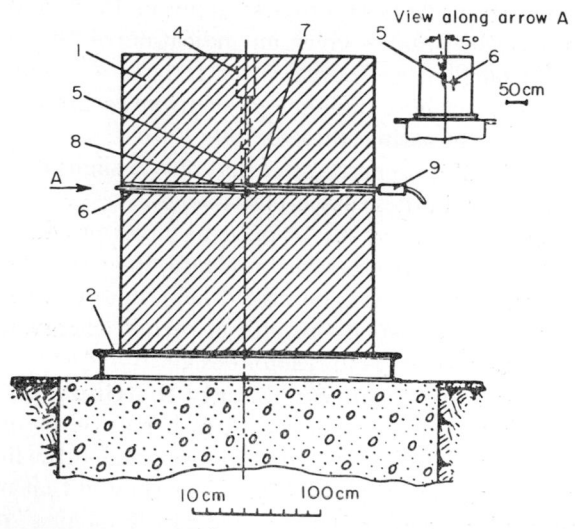

Figure 5. Schematic diagram of slowing-down-time spectrometer: (1) lead column; (2) steel frame; (3) concrete foundation; (4) channel for target tube; (5) target; (6) channel for counter and sample; (7) counter; (8) sample; (9) preamplifier (Be55).

A 300 kev accelerator was used to produce the neutrons using the T(d,n) reaction.   The ion source was pulsed at frequencies from 50–1250 cycles/sec with a 1–3 μsec duration.   Further reduction in pulse duration was attained by sweeping the beam with deflector plates across the target.   In 0.5–2 μsec pulses, $3 \cdot 10^{11}$ neutrons were obtained.   These were made directly in the center of the lead "pile."   Neutron energies up to several kilovolts were selected by observing the response of the detector in the proper time intervals after the beam struck the target.   Further discussion of this method and additional results of experiments appear in a later paper by Isakov *et al.* (Is60).

(6)   **Neutrons from Particle Reactions Using the Van de Graaff Accelerator.**   The Van de Graaff accelerator is one of the most useful sources of fast neutrons, as is clear from the many discussions in this volume based on work using this instrument as a source.   The various useful reactions and energy ranges are discussed in Chapters I.C, I.D, and I.E.   For capture cross section measurements, the $Li^7(p,n)Be^7$, $T(p,n)He^3$, and $T(d,n)He^4$ reactions have proven most useful.   The neutron energy spread is determined, mainly, by the target thickness and can be made fairly small.   Typical values may be several kilovolts at low energies, and up to $\sim$50–100 kev for neutron energies above 100 kev.   Thin sources at higher energies are seldom used since in that case nuclear properties averaged over at least several resonances are obtained.

A problem which arises when one attempts to measure capture, or indeed any cross section as a function of energy, concerns the determination of the neutron flux.   Elsewhere in these volumes, descriptions are given of energy independent detectors (see Chapter III.A); for some reactions, such as n-p scattering, the energy dependence is known accurately over the entire neutron energy range from thermal energies to 100 Mev.   In addition, some of the fission cross sections are sufficiently accurately measured for neutron energies above about 100 kev [see a review by Allen and Henkel (A158)] so that fission chambers of various designs have proven useful for flux determinations in cross sections measurements (e.g., Jo59).   There are, however, only a few reactions which may be adapted in practical counters, where the cross section is sufficiently well known in the low kilovolt energy region.   The $B^{10}(n,\alpha)Li^7$ cross section is perhaps the best investigated of this latter class and the results of Bichsel and Bonner

(Bi57), Bilpuch, Weston, and Newson (Bi60), Schmitt, Block, and Bailey (Sc60b), Safford *et al.* (Sa60), and Newson and Bilpuch (Ne59a) (see discussions in Gi61 and Sc60a) have made feasible the use (Bi60) of detectors based on this reaction.

(7) **Photoneutrons from Radioactive Sources.** The radioactive neutron source, as described in Chapter I.A, was the first neutron source developed. The earliest experiments usually involved the thermalization of neutrons produced by (α,n) reactions and measurements of activations produced in target nuclei by these neutrons. Photoneutron sources give more nearly monochromatic neutron distributions and cross sections may be determined by neutrons of particular energies through proper choice of the gamma ray energies and target thresholds. The Sb-γ-Be reaction, which yields neutrons of 24.8 ± 2.4 kev average energy (Sc60a), has been particularly useful as a neutron source for capture cross section measurements. It has been used in activation measurements by a number of investigators (Hu51, Ki53, Ma57, Bo58, Ve59) and in spherical shell transmission measurements by other investigators (Be58, Sc60). The average neutron energy for the primary neutron group from the Sb-γ-Be reaction of 24.8 ± 2.4 kev quoted above is consistent with the difference between the primary gamma-ray energy, given as 1.692 Mev by Strominger, Hollander, and Seaborg (St58), and the threshold for the $Be^9(\gamma,n)Be^8$ reaction given by Connors and Miller (Co56a) as 1.664 ± 0.004 Mev. There is a second gamma ray of 2.044 Mev energy, which gives rise to a second neutron group of 4.4 per cent intensity (Gi59) and the energy of which is $\sim$380 kev.

In addition, the average energy of neutrons from an Sb-γ-Be source depends rather critically on the source dimensions and on the thickness of the beryllium. Calculations (Sc60a) for spherical sources, assuming negligible interaction of neutrons in the antimony, have been carried out to illustrate this effect and the results are shown in Fig. 6.

Other photoneutron sources which have been used in neutron capture experiments are as follows: RdTh-γ-D_2O (Ly59), energy = 195 kev; Na-γ-D_2O (Be58), energy = 220 kev; Na-γ-Be (Be58), energy = 830 kev. These sources in general are not as convenient to use as Sb-γ-Be sources, and only a limited number of neutron capture experiments have been done with these sources; appropriate results will be described in Section 2.

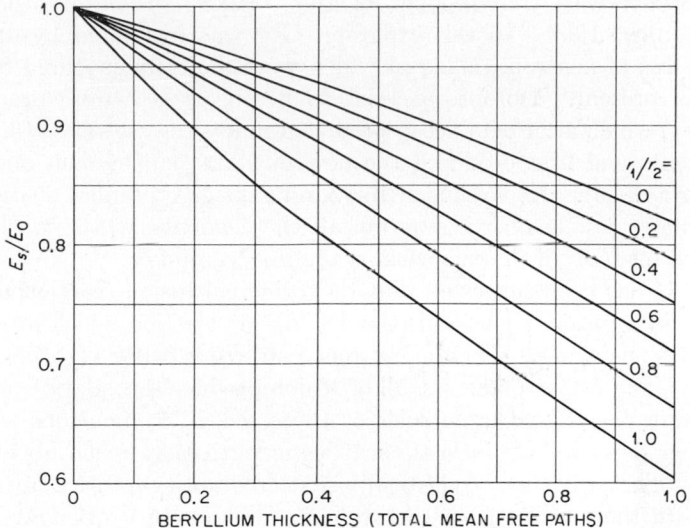

Figure 6. Calculated ratio of effective source energy to initial Sb-γ-Be photoneutron energy *vs.* beryllium thickness for various source dimensions (Sc60a). These results apply to spherical sources, r_1 = inside radius, r_2 = outside radius, and absorption of neutrons in the antimony core has been neglected.

(8) **Neutrons from Fission.** Another source which has proven useful are neutrons which result from fission of U^{235}. The median energy realized is about 2 Mev, but the effective energy is somewhat less owing to the decrease with energy of neutron capture cross sections. Hughes, Garth, and Levin (Hu53) in a most comprehensive experiment, used a U^{235} foil in a beam from the Brookhaven reactor as the source of fission neutrons for a series of experiments to measure the activation cross sections of most nuclei in the periodic table. These particular experiments, although difficult to interpret because of the very wide spread in neutron energy in the fission neutron spectrum, comprised a large part of the existing capture cross section data until about 1957. These results are still useful for certain reactor design considerations.

(9) **Neutrons from Fusion Explosions.** All the sources of neutrons described so far have very moderate neutron fluxes. Very much larger fluxes can be obtained in fusion explosions. One of the most spectacular experiments on neutron capture which has been

performed was a by-product of the "Mike" fusion explosion of November, 1952. In this explosion U^{238} was irradiated by a very high flux of neutrons, many of which were multiply captured by the nuclei present. Isotopes at least as heavy as U^{255} were produced (Fi56), which after beta decay produced many new isotopes of known elements and first produced the new elements einsteinium and fermium (Gh55). Explosions of this kind thus give promise of producing many new heavier isotopes of all the elements, which can be retained for study if the explosion occurs underground.

It has been suggested that the principal fusion reaction taking place in a fusion explosion is the $T(d,n)He^4$ reaction which produces 14-Mev neutrons. These neutrons can react with U^{238} in (n,f), $(n,2n)$, and $(n,3n)$ processes, all of which produce secondary neutrons of lower energy. The energies of these secondary neutrons will be further degraded by inelastic scattering until they reach about 100 kev. They will then be elastically scattered until capture takes place or until they escape from the system. The capture will take place mainly in the uranium isotopes and fission products present, if there is not too much absorption by light nuclei with high neutron reaction cross sections. Because of the very high neutron fluxes present, any of the individual uranium nuclei and fission products can capture several neutrons.

2. Experimental Results

A. Introduction

In Section 1 a number of methods of measurement of fast neutron capture cross sections were discussed. Many of these methods were designed to give broad-resolution results—extremely important as first indications of the magnitude of capture cross sections, and useful in reactor design considerations, but difficult to analyze in terms of basic nuclear parameters. Because of the great strides which have recently (1957 to present) been made in experimental techniques, a great wealth of capture cross section data of relatively good resolution now exists. In as much as these data are most significant in the understanding of neutron physics, we shall restrict ourselves to a discussion of these data, with reference to the earlier results as they apply in specific discussions.

B. Results of Activation Experiments—Photoneutron Sources

Activation cross sections for fast neutrons have usually been measured relative to a standard whose activation cross section is known from previous measurements. Alternatively, activation cross sections for fast neutrons are measured relative to a known reaction cross section, e.g. σ_f, $\sigma_{n,\alpha}$, etc. Detector efficiency, branching ratio in the decay scheme, and other experimental considerations enter into the cross section determination, and the previously measured thermal neutron cross section usually provides calibration for these considerations. Thus for the cases in which a standard is used, the activation cross section of isotope x for neutrons of energy E is

$$\sigma_{x,E} = \sigma_{x,th}(\sigma_{s,E}/\sigma_{s,th})(R_{x,E}/R_{x,th})(R_{s,th}/R_{s,E}) \tag{6}$$

where

$$R_{s,E} = \epsilon_s N_s \phi_s \sigma_{s,E}, \; etc. \tag{7}$$

where the subscripts x and s denote quantities associated with the unknown and standard samples, respectively, the subscript th denotes thermal neutron energies, ϵ is counting efficiency, N is the number of atoms in the sample, σ is the activation cross section, and R is the measured counting rate extrapolated to saturation activity.

One of the most precise measurements of an absolute activation cross section is that of Macklin (Ma57), in which a calibrated (National Bureau of Standards) Sb-γ-Be photoneutron source was used in conjunction with a NaI(Tl) scintillation crystal. The source strength per unit solid angle was measured as a function of orientation by rotating the source in front of a paraffin-surrounded BF$_3$ counter; the induced iodine activity in the crystal was determined by absolute beta counting. The quoted result is 0.82 ± 0.06 barns for neutrons of 25-kev energy.

This absolute determination has served as a basis for rather extensive activation cross section measurements (Ma57, Bo58) in which Sb-γ-Be photoneutron sources were employed. These results, in general superceding earlier measurements of Hummel and Hamermesh (Hu51) and Kimball and Hamermesh (Ki53), are given along with others (Ko59, Ve59) in Table I.

Also included in Table I are activation cross sections for 195-kev neutrons (RdTh-γ-D$_2$O photoneutron source)(Ly59). These meas-

Table I. Neutron Capture Cross Sections, Measured by Activation, for Sb-γ-Be and RdTh-γ-D₂O Photoneutron Sources. (1) Ko59; (2) Ve59

Z	Isotope	Half-Life	Sb-γ-Be E = 24 kev			RdTh-γ-D₂O E = 195 kev
			Ma57 *	Bo58	Others	Ly59
11	Na²³	15 hr	1.0 ± 0.2	1.10 ± 0.23	1.72 ± 0.34 (1)	0.7 ± 0.2
12	Mg²⁶	9.5 min	14		1.90 ± 0.38 (1)	
13	Al²⁷	2.3 min	1.4 ± 0.2		2.6 ± 0.22 (2)	
14	Si³⁰	2.62 hr		1.9 ± 1.5	2.09 ± 0.51 (1)	
17	Cl³⁷	37.3 min	1.1 ± 0.2		3.71 ± 0.74 (1)	
19	K⁴¹	12.5 hr	20	22 ± 5	26 (1)	
21	Sc⁴⁵	85 days		56 ± 30		
22	Ti⁵⁰	5.8 min	5 ± 3		2.3 ± 0.6 (2)	7 ± 0.7
23	V⁵¹	3.8 min	50 ± 5		32.5 ± 6.5 (1)	11 ± 1
25	Mn⁵⁵	2.58 hr	55 ± 6	52 ± 16	65 ± 13 (1)	
28	Ni⁶⁴	2.56 hr		8.7 ± 2.3	37	
29	Cu⁶³	12.8 hr	116 ± 12	114 ± 24	105 ± 21 (2)	42 ± 6
29	Cu⁶⁵	5.1 min	46 ± 5	48 ± 12	{ 38.6 ± 7.7 (1), 44 ± 10 (2) }	14 ± 3
30	Zn⁶⁸	13.8 hr		5.6 ± 2.0		
30	Zn⁶⁸	52 min		26 ± 10	24 ± 4.8 (1)	
31	Ga⁶⁹	21 min			151 ± 30 (1)	
31	Ga⁷¹	14.1 hr	140 ± 30			53 ± 3
32	Ge⁷⁴	82 min	54 ± 8			19 ± 2
33	As⁷⁵	26.7 hr	740 ± 70	650 ± 160		150 ± 15
35	Br⁸¹	35.9 hr	550 ± 55			137 ± 15
37	Rb⁸⁵	18.6 days	181 ± 35			
37	Rb⁸⁷	18 min	75 ± 15	28 ± 7	29 ± 6 (1)	
39	Y⁸⁹	64 hr				
40	Zr⁹⁴	65 days	24 ± 4			42 ± 8
40	Zr⁹⁶	17 hr	22 ± 4			7 ± 2
41	Nb⁹³	6.6 min			120 ± 24 (1)	
42	Mo⁹⁸	67 hr	209 ± 21	390 ± 120	415 ± 98 (2)	30 ± 6
42	Mo¹⁰⁰	15 min	38 ± 8		{ 148 ± 39 (2), 112 ± 22 (1) }	27 ± 6

Z	Isotope	Half-life				
44	Ru^{96}	2.9 days	321 ± 60			140 ± 28
44	Ru^{102}	40 days	386 ± 39			190 ± 25
44	Ru^{104}	4.5 hr	211 ± 21			28 ± 5
46	Pd^{108}	13.6 hr	290 ± 35	580 ± 200		77 ± 8
46	Pd^{110}	22 min	300			
47	Ag^{107}	2.3 min	930 ± 180			290 ± 60
49	In^{115}	54 min	805 ± 80	930 ± 220	{1330 ± 250 (1) / 1788 ± 208 (2)}	195 ± 10
51	Sb^{121}	2.8 days	950 ± 100	810 ± 250	590 ± 120 (1)	400 ± 40
51	Sb^{123}	60 days	456 ± 46	230 ± 100		280 ± 30
53	I^{127}	25 min	[820 ± 60]			175 ± 15
55	Cs^{133}	3.1 hr		0.6 ± 0.3		
55	Cs^{133}	2.3 yr		900 ± 300		
56	Ba^{138}	35 min	11.4 ± 1.1		8.6 ± 1.7 (1)	3.2 ± 0.3
57	La^{139}	40.2 hr	50 ± 7			10 ± 2
58	Ce^{140}	32 days	31 ± 4			
58	Ce^{142}	33 hr	425 ± 43			22 ± 5
59	Pr^{141}	19.1 hr	175 ± 15	170 ± 40		38 ± 4
62	Sm^{152}	47 hr	668 ± 100			150 ± 20
62	Sm^{154}	23 min	527 ± 70			
64	Gd^{158}	18 hr	710 ± 71			111 ± 15
66	Dy^{164}	2.32 hr	298 ± 30	330 ± 130		
68	Er^{170}	7.5 hr	441 ± 66			
72	Hf^{180}	46 days				
73	Ta^{181}	112 days		1400 ± 310		
74	W^{184}	74 days		350 ± 180		
74	W^{186}	24.1 hr	296 ± 44	270 ± 70	285 ± 60 (1)	100 ± 20
75	Re^{185}	91 hr	2650 ± 500			
75	Re^{187}	17 hr	970 ± 200			
76	Os^{190}	16 days	886 ± 130			200 ± 30
78	Pt^{196}	19 hr		210 ± 60		
78	Pt^{198}	30 min		240 ± 80		
79	Au^{197}	2.7 days	1120 ± 110	890 ± 190	960 ± 190 (1)	320 ± 20
80	Hg^{202}	48 days	57 ± 13			32 ± 5
83	Bi^{209}	5 days		1.8 ± 0.7		

urements were made relative to the Indium-115 54-minute activation cross section, which in turn was measured as follows: The absolute source intensity was determined by means of a large spherical graphite 4π neutron detector of known detection efficiency (Ma-57a). The indium sample was in the form of a thin spherical shell around the source, and the activity induced in the entire shell was measured. There are other capture cross section results at these energies obtained in other types of experiments—these will be discussed and compared below.

C. Results of Activation Experiments—Accelerator Sources

Neutron Activation experiments in which accelerator sources were used have been done as a function of energy for a number of elements by Bilpuch, Weston, et al. (Bi60, We60) and Miskel et al. (Mi59) in the kev region and by Johnsrud et al. (Jo59) and Liepunsky et al. (Le58) in the Mev region. Experiments for specific elements have been done by Cox (Co61), Weston and Lyon (We61), Bame and Cubitt (Ba59), and earlier by Martin and Taschek (Ma53) and Henkel and Barschall (He50). The experimental arrangement varies; that of Johnsrud et al. is shown, for example, in Fig. 7. Here the activation

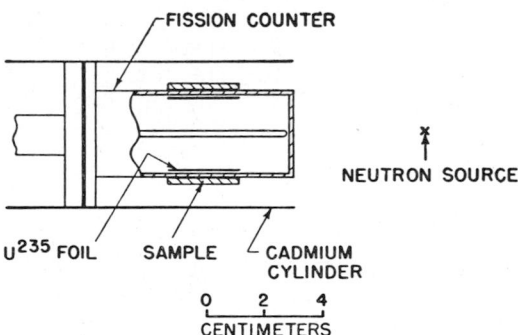

Figure 7. Experimental arrangement for the measurement of fast neutron activation cross sections as a function of neutron energy (Jo59). The neutron source was the target of an electrostatic accelerator.

cross section was measured relative to the fission cross section of U^{235}; the thermal neutron activation was done with the counter and sample assembly immersed in a water bath with a Pu-α-Be source. It is important in these experiments to have the reference material, in this case the U^{235}, in close proximity to the sample so that the spatial distribution of neutron intensity does not enter as a large correction. Similarly, in fast neutron irradiations any surrounding materials near the source or sample must be kept to a minimum so that neutrons of degraded energies are not incident on the sample.

The background may be determined by several methods; frequently a "shadow cone" is used, whereby the sample and reference material are shielded from direct neutrons from the source by a cone whose transmission is very low (say <1 per cent) for the incident neutrons. The conical geometry permits source neutrons to escape into the room (as in the primary irradiation), so that neutrons incident on the sample in such measurements are only room-scattered neutrons. Principle disadvantage of this technique is that background neutrons produced in the target assembly, e.g., where the $D(d,n)He^3$ reaction is used as a source, are also shielded from the sample. A second method, used by Johnsrud et al., involves measurement of the sample activity as a function of distance from the source. In this case the authors assumed that over some range of distances the background-induced activity was constant while the direct-neutron-induced activity varied inversely as the square of the distance. When the $D(d,n)He^3$ reaction was used to produce neutrons, the background was as high as 30 per cent or more for deuteron energies of a few Mev; when $Li^7(p,n)$ or $T(p,n)$ neutrons were used the background was less than 10 per cent for incident proton energies up to 5 Mev or so.

Representative results of the experiments of Johnsrud et al. (Jo59) are shown in Fig. 8. Capture cross sections for other elements ranging in Z and A from V^{51} to Au^{197} were also reported. Corrections were included for neutron background, difference in neutron flux at the U^{235} foil and at the sample, decay of sample activity during neutron bombardment, and variations in beam current. Corrections for attenuation and scattering of neutrons in the wall of the counter and self-protection effects were neglected; however the uncertainty in the measurements is large compared to these effects. The analysis of these results is discussed by Mossin-Kotin, Margolis, and Troubetzkoz (Mo59) in terms of competition from inelastic scattering and the effect of incident neutron partial waves with $l > 0$. Dependence of the shape of the cross section vs. energy curves

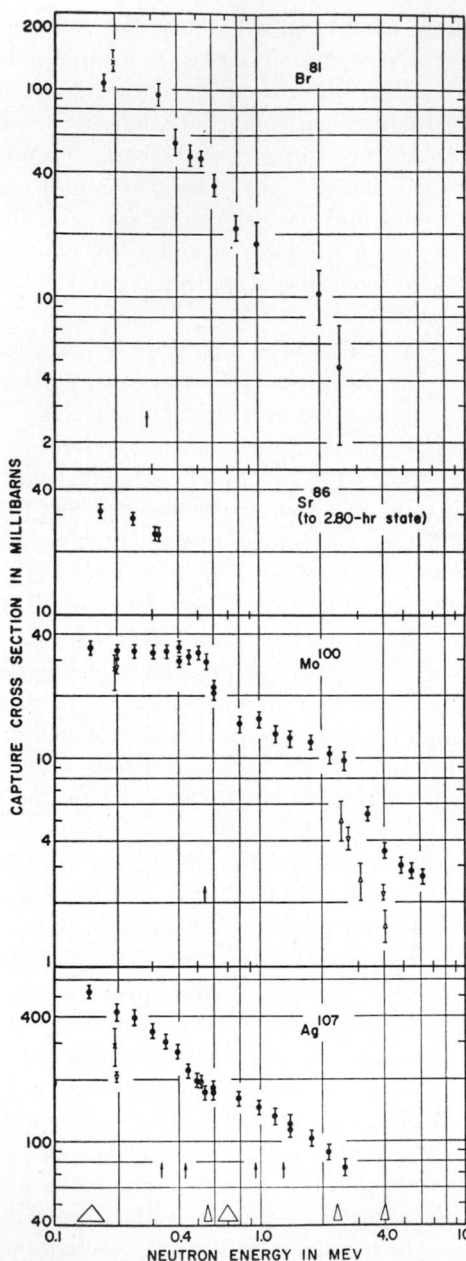

Figure 8. Activation cross sections as a function of neutron energy for the isotopes indicated in the figure, as given by Johnsrud *et al.* (Jo59). For comparison, these authors have plotted other results in the same energy range as

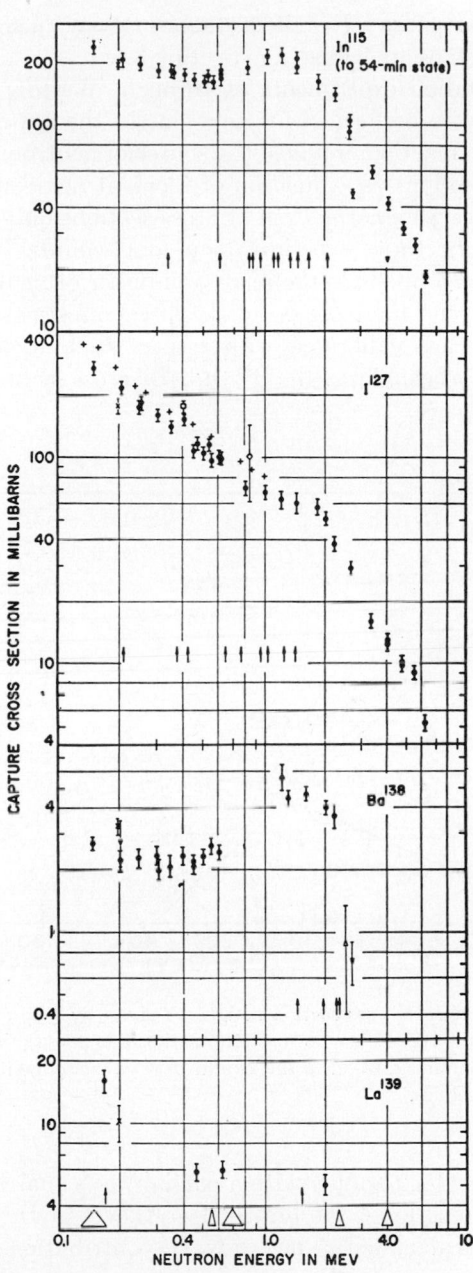

follows: Δ, Pa58; ∇, Le58; □, Diven *et al.*, preliminary report to Ref. Di60:
◊, Be58; X, Ly59; +, Ba59.

on the spin and parity of excited states in even nuclei, e.g., Mo^{100}, is discussed; details are included in Section 3.

The activation experiments of Bilpuch, Weston, and Newson (Bi60, We60) were performed for neutrons in the kev energy region. The $Li^7(p,n)Be^7$ reaction provided the source of neutrons, and relative capture cross sections as a function of incident neutron energy were obtained; values were normalized to cross sections obtained by other investigators. In these experiments a long counter (see Chapter III.A) was used to monitor the relative number of neutrons incident on the samples, and the response of the long counter as a function of neutron energy was calibrated with respect to that of a bare BF_3 counter—the $1/v$ behavior of the B^{10} $(n,\alpha)Li^7$ cross section then served as the final reference.

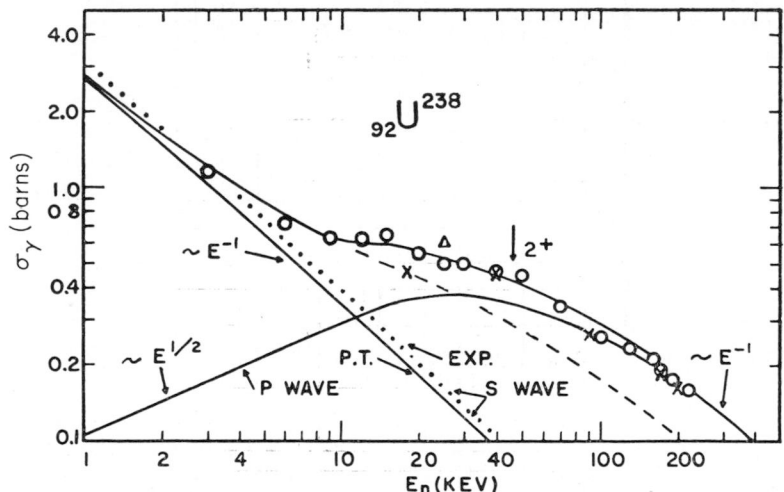

Figure 9. Capture cross section of U^{238} as given by Bilpuch *et al.* (Bi60). The upper solid line represents the best fit to the data as obtained by Bilpuch *et al.* by the incoherent addition of the *s*- and *p*-wave components illustrated by the two lower solid lines.

Typical results, together with a partial-wave analysis, are shown in Fig. 9. The energy of the first inelastic level in U^{238} is indicated along with the calculated *s*- and *p*-wave contributions. Other nuclides whose cross sections were measured by these authors (Bi60 and We60) range in atomic weight from 75 to 130 amu, and also include Au^{197} and Pt^{198}.   Details of the analysis, including spin-orbit coupling, are included in Section 3.

The fast neutron activation cross section of Au^{197} has been carefully measured by Weston and Lyon (We61), for kinematically collimated neutrons from the $Li^7(p,n)Be^7$ and $T(p,n)He^3$ reactions.   A graphite sphere neutron detector (Ma57a) served as the neutron monitor.   Average neutron energies were 30.2 kev and 63.9 kev; the measured capture cross sections were 0.767 ± 0.060 and 0.456 ± 0.040 barns, respectively.   As a check on these measurements, the Au capture cross section was also measured relative to the In^{115} activation (54-min half-life) cross section.   The absolute gold cross section was obtained from these measurements together with the average experimental value of the indium cross section (He50, Ma57, Bo58, Sc60), and agreement was well within the errors quoted above.   The same cross section was measured by Cox (Co61) as a function of neutron energy from 30 to 1500 kev.   These measurements are relative to the $B^{10}(n,\alpha)$ cross section in the range below 200 kev, and are relative to the U^{235} fission cross section in the range above 200 kev.   These results will be compared to others a little later; it is interesting to note at this point, however, that the discrepancies among experimental values of the Au^{197} capture cross section are as large as or larger than those for any other element.

Activation experiments for neutrons of about 14 Mev energy are conveniently carried out through the use of high current, low voltage machines, such as the Cockroft-Walton accelerators.   Neutrons of about 14 Mev energy are produced when deuterons accelerated to a few hundred kev are incident on a tritium target.   While most of the 14-Mev neutron activation studies have been made for the purpose of studying (n,p) and (n,α) reactions, at least two groups (Pe58, Wi60) have reported measurements of (n,γ) cross sections.   In the more comprehensive experiments of Perkin et al. (Pe58), the Al^{27} $(n,\alpha)Na^{24}$ reaction was used to monitor the neutrons.   In many cases chemical separations were made to better isolate the activity to be measured.   Results of these experiments are given in Table II. Nuclear shell effects are somewhat in evidence in these results but, as will be seen, are not as strong as in lower-energy capture cross section results.

Table II.   Neutron Capture Cross Sections for ∼14.5-Mev Neutrons

Isotope	Capture cross section, mb	Ref.	Isotope	Capture cross section, mb	Ref.
Na^{23}	0.33 ± 0.03	Pe58	La^{139}	1.1 ± 0.2	Wi60
Mg^{26}	0.20 ± 0.05	Pe58	Pr^{141}	3.33 ± 0.33	Pe58
Al^{27}	0.53 ± 0.13	Pe58	Pr^{141}	2.1 ± 1.0	Wi60
Si^{30}	0.49 ± 0.05	Pe58	Ce^{142}	$\leqslant 7.5$	Pe58
K^{41}	3.5 ± 0.7	Pe58	Gd^{160}	18.5 ± 5.5	Pe58
Ti^{50}	3.5 ± 1.0	Pe58	Gd^{160}	3.0 ± 1.0	Wi60
Mn^{55}	0.76 ± 0.08	Pe58	Dy^{164} (1.3-min.)	1.5 ± 0.5	Wi60
Cu^{63}	2.56 ± 0.38	Pe58	Dy^{164} (140-min.)	8 ± 3	Wi60
Cu^{65}	6.3 ± 1.9	Pe58	Ho^{165}	$\geqslant 9.45$	Pe58
Ga^{71}	1.9 ± 0.2	Pe58	Lu^{175}	2 ± 1	Wi60
Se^{82}	0.65 ± 0.20	Pe58	W^{186}	4.0 ± 0.8	Pe58
Br^{81}	3.5 ± 0.9	Pe58	Pt^{198}	1.7 ± 0.3	Pe58
Y^{89}	2.9 ± 0.3	Pe58	Tl^{205}	2.0 ± 0.4	Pe58
Zr^{96}	$\leqslant 4.0$	Pe58	Pb^{208}	3.05 ± 0.46	Pe58
Ru^{104}	13.6 ± 2.7	Pe58	Bi^{209}	1.45 ± 0.17	Pe58
Pd^{110}	2.0 ± 0.4	Pe58	Th^{232}	5.2 ± 0.8	Pe58
I^{127}	2.5 ± 0.5	Pe58	U^{238}	3.3 ± 0.5	Pe58
Ba^{138}	1.3 ± 0.4	Pe58			
La^{139}	1.48 ± 0.15	Pe58			

D. Results of Absorption Cross Section Measurements

The general technique and some of the limitations of sphere transmission measurements were discussed in Section 1.   Shell thicknesses are normally in the range from 0.5 to 1.5 total mean free paths; measured transmissions for Sb-γ-Be neutrons range upward from about 70 per cent.   Thus the maintenance of stability in the neutron counting apparatus and the acquisition of an adequate number of counts to minimize statistical uncertainty are extremely important in carrying out these measurements.   The resonance self-protection corrections for these rather large samples are difficult to evaluate, however certain reasonable assumptions may be applied and the problem solved on a quite reasonable basis (Dr59, Sc60).   It develops that the correction is not as large as might at first be expected, because of the Porter-Thomas distribution of widths and because of the Doppler broadening of levels.   This correction in the experiments of Schmitt and Cook (Sc60) ranged from a few per cent to approximately

35 per cent, depending on the isotope or element and the specific level parameters.

Some of the results of the sphere transmission measurements for Sb-γ-Be neutrons for a number of elements (Sc60, Be58) are tabulated in Table III, along with results of activation and time-of-flight experiments for comparison. Only a few selected elements, for which a variety of determinations have been made, are included. For comparison purposes, it should be noted that the analysis of Belanova was based on an "average path length" determination, in which the assumption was made that the distribution of path lengths of neutrons which undergo elastic scattering in the shell is an exponential distribution. Transmission values were not published by Belanova, however this analysis applied to the data of Schmitt and Cook results in cross section values 20 to 30 per cent lower than they obtain with the analysis of Bethe *et al.* (see Chapter V.H). Also, the effect of resonance self-protection was not mentioned by Belanova, nor were uncertainties other than statistical uncertainties evaluated. The results of time-of-flight experiments with direct gamma ray detection will be presented and discussed below; however the selected results which appear in the table are included for direct comparison.

It is interesting that there is general agreement in σ_γ for only a few elements listed in the table. In the case of Cu and Au there seems to be agreement among the activation results and agreement among the others, but the values differ by about a factor of two. For most of the other elements (Al and V excepted) cross section values agree within about 20 per cent—a situation not as desirable as might be hoped for, but indicative of the formidable difficulties present in the measurements of capture cross sections, particularly in an absolute fashion.

E. Results of Direct Gamma Ray Detection, with Time-of-Flight

The development of fast time-of-flight techniques (see Chapter IV.A) and of large liquid scintillation gamma ray detectors has brought about a most striking advance in the measurement of capture cross sections. It was pointed out in Section 1 that the principal difficulty in these measurements is the normalization required to yield absolute values; in spite of this difficulty, however, the results of these measurements over a wide range of energies and over a wide

Table III. Comparison of Measured Neutron Capture Cross Sections for Selected Elements at ~24 kev. Elements Included are Those Whose 24-kev Capture Cross Sections Have Been Most Often Measured

Z	Element	Direct γ-ray detection	Spherical shell transmission		Ma57	Activation Bo58	Others
			Sc60	Be58			
13	Al	2.8 ± 0.7*		17	1.4 ± 0.2		$\{$ 1.9 ± 0.4 (1) / 2.6 ± 0.2 (2)
23	V	30 ± 5*			50 ± 5		
29	Cu	39 ± 5*	42 ± 15	32	94 ± 9	94 ± 17	32.5 ± 6.5 (1)
47	Ag	1160 ± 120	1185 ± 80	984			86 ± 15 (2)
49	In	910 ± 95	823 ± 60		805 ± 80	980 ± 220	590 ± 120 (1)
51	Sb	540 ± 55	565 ± 45	444	739 ± 65	562 ± 150	
53	I	820 ± 85	885 ± 90	990	820 ± 60		
59	Pr	140 ± 15			155 ± 15	170 ± 40	
79	Au	635 ± 65	585 ± 60	605	1120 ± 110	890 ± 190	$\{$ 960 ± 190 (1) / >1100 (3) / 767 ± 60* (4)

* These results for 30-kev neutrons.

(1) Ko59.
(2) Ve59.
(3) Co61.
(4) We61.

range of elements have contributed immensely to the understanding of neutron capture. They have demonstrated conclusively the contribution of higher l-waves at relatively low incident neutron energies (a few kev in some cases); they have been susceptible to analyses in which the average over many resonances is considered (see Section 3, also La57) and have yielded quantitative p-wave strength function determinations; at higher incident energies they have clearly and quantitatively demonstrated competition from inelastic channels.

Since the space required for the presentation of all of the recent capture cross section results as a function of neutron energy would be too great, we shall select a few representative cases for discussion.

The capture cross section for silver is shown as a function of neutron energy in Fig. 10. Characteristic of these data is the large fluctuation in cross section for the lower incident energies, showing the effects of individual resonances or groups of resonances. As the energy increases, the cross section becomes a smoothly varying function, indicating here that averages over many resonances are being observed. Shown in the figure are: the low energy neutron chopper results of Block and Slaughter (Bl60), the results from about 1 to 20 kev of Isakov et al. (Is60) obtained by means of a slowing-down time spectrometer, the results of spherical shell transmission measurements (Sc60) at 24 kev, and the results of the direct capture gamma-ray measurements, with neutron time-of-flight, of Gibbons et al. (Gi61) from about 10 to 170 kev and Diven et al. (Di60) from about 175 to 1000 kev. The solid curve was obtained using low-energy parameters modified to take into account the occurrence of p-wave resonances in the ev range; the value of S_1 given in the figure yielded the curve best fitting the data (Gi61).

The difference in the two sets of experimental results at $\sim$170 kev may be demonstrative of the difficulty in determining absolute capture cross section values. The results of Gibbons et al. were normalized at 30 kev as follows: The capture tank measurements of the shapes of $\sigma_\gamma(E)$ for five elements, chosen to correspond to the best five absolute determinations of Schmitt and Cook (Sc60), were used to extend the spherical shell cross sections to 30 kev. The five elements were compared at 30 kev, and the five ratios $\sigma_{shell}/\sigma_{\text{"tank"}}$ were formed; a weighted mean capture cross section for indium was then determined to be 760 $\pm$ 50 mb at 30 kev, and this

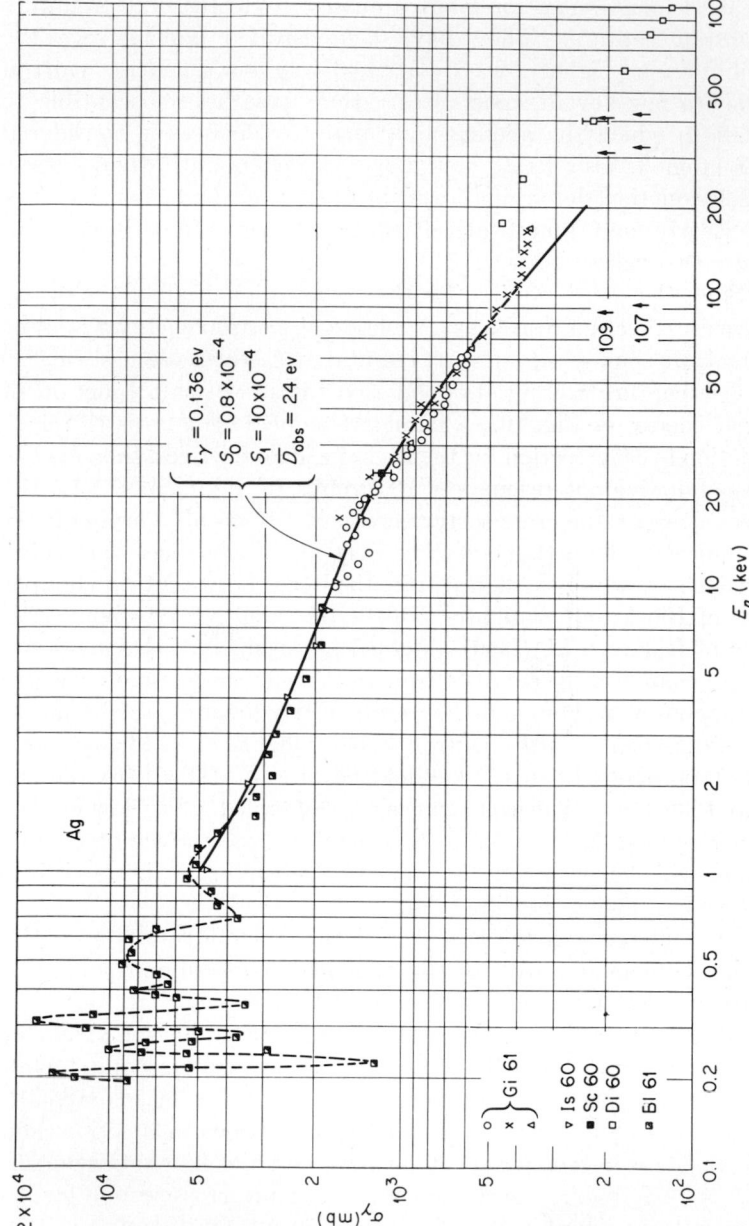

Figure 10. Compilation of neutron capture cross section measurements for silver. The solid line and level parameters represent the best fit obtained by Gibbons *et al.* (Gi61) for their data.

was used as the "standard" for the entire series of measurements. The capture cross sections of Diven *et al.* were determined relative to the capture-plus-fission cross section of U^{235} (Di58).

Related to the problem of absolute normalization in these measurements is the problem of determining the so-called "spectrum fraction." In the large liquid scintillation tanks a high background of gamma rays is usually found in the region of 2.2 Mev from hydrogen capture and below about 1 Mev; as a result the gamma-ray detector must be biased at about 1 Mev or higher, and an assumption must be made about the fraction of pulses ("spectrum fraction") occurring below the bias level. Relevant assumptions involve the behavior of the spectrum fraction as a function of incident neutron energy and as a function of target nucleus. Figure 11 shows, for example, the pulse-height distributions for capture gamma ray pulses in the one-meter diameter cylindrical tank of Diven *et al.* Note the relatively great abundance of high energy gamma-ray pulses in the case of U^{235} capture-plus-fission and the relatively large differences in spectra among the various elements. Figure 12 shows the calculated detection efficiency for single gamma rays in the one-meter diameter spherical tank of Gibbons *et al.* All three groups who have used "capture tanks" up to the present (B161, Di60, and Gi61) have made careful studies of these effects for the particular tanks employed.

Capture cross section results for indium are shown in Fig. 13. Features observed are quite similar to those observed in the case of silver. Activation results are included for comparison; those plotted are 15 per cent (Gi61) higher than the measured 54-minute activation cross sections to account for capture into the 13-second state of In^{116}. In this case essentially all of the measurements except those of Diven *et al.* are in agreement within experimental error.

In contrast, the cross section of gold as a function of neutron energy is shown in Fig. 14. We show these cross section data for two reasons, namely, the *p*-wave strength function is small relative to that for silver and indium where it is near maximum, and the lack of agreement among experimentally-measured values is striking. Gold has been perhaps the most often measured nucleus, yet it presents at present one of the most inconsistent group of measurements among all the elements. At some energies the largest discrepancies are larger than a factor of two. Careful analysis in the middle kev range will show that the measurements may be divided into three

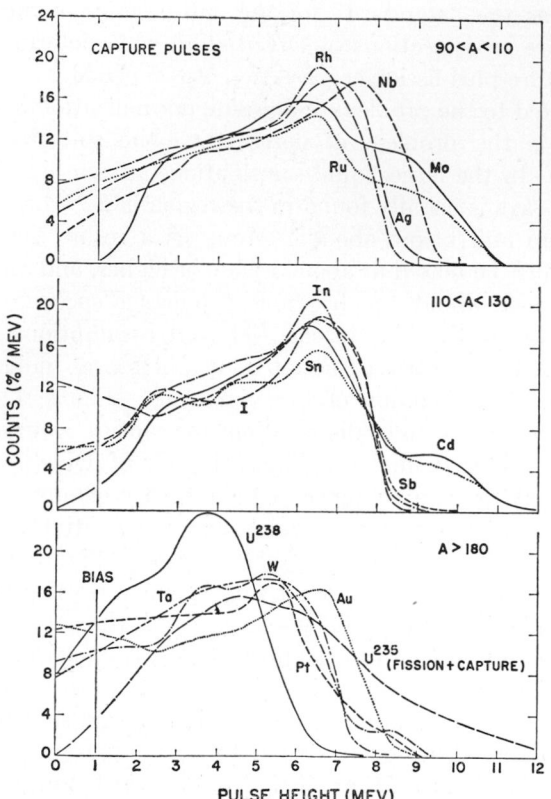

Figure 11. Gamma-ray pulse height distributions for capture events in various elements for a 1-meter-diameter cylindrical liquid scintillation tank (Di60). Background was subtracted, and below 1 Mev the curves represent extrapolations, not data.

groups; the highest values, which were all obtained by activation techniques; the lowest values, which were obtained in capture tank and shell-transmission measurements; and a group of activation measurements approximately centered between the lowest and highest values. The situation is disturbing, and continuing study is in progress to determine the origin of these discrepancies.

Capture cross section results for iodine are shown in Fig. 15. The p-wave strength function is relatively high in this case, and the agreement among various measurements is relatively good, except at the higher energies.

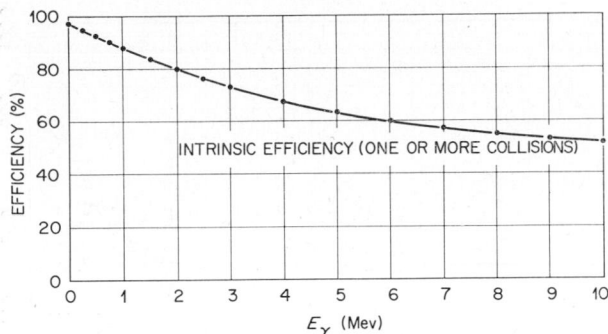

Figure 12. Intrinsic efficiency of a $\sim$1 meter diameter, nearly spherical, scintillation tank (Gi61) for producing at least one light pulse. The value, 97 per cent, for zero γ-ray energy represents the solid angle for escape through the collimator hole.

For an index, by element, of capture cross section measurements as a function of incident neutron energy, see Table IV.

F. Capture Cross Section Results from Thermonuclear Explosion

The yields of heavy nuclides from fusion explosions can also give information about neutron capture cross sections averaged over a rather wide range of neutron energies. 100 kev is perhaps a characteristic energy for this process. Some of the yields of heavy uranium nuclei produced in the Mike fusion explosion of November, 1952, have been discussed in the literature (Hu57, Ca59, Di60a). These yields are plotted in Fig. 16. The yields of isotopes with even mass numbers appear to decrease exponentially in a very regular way. The yields of the odd mass numbers have about half of the yields one would interpolate between the even mass numbers. Neglecting this odd-even effect, the yields decrease from one mass number to the next by a factor of 5.8.

An approximate analysis of these yields has been given by Cameron (Ca59). The ratio of abundances of two successive members of a multiple neutron capture chain may be written as $N_n/N_{n-1} = \sigma_{n-1}f(\phi t,n)$, where σ_{n-1} is the capture cross section of the $n-1$ member of the chain, and ϕt is the integrated neutron flux. $f(\phi t,n)$ is a function of the distribution of integrated neutron flux throughout the mass of irradiated uranium and of the depletion of the source

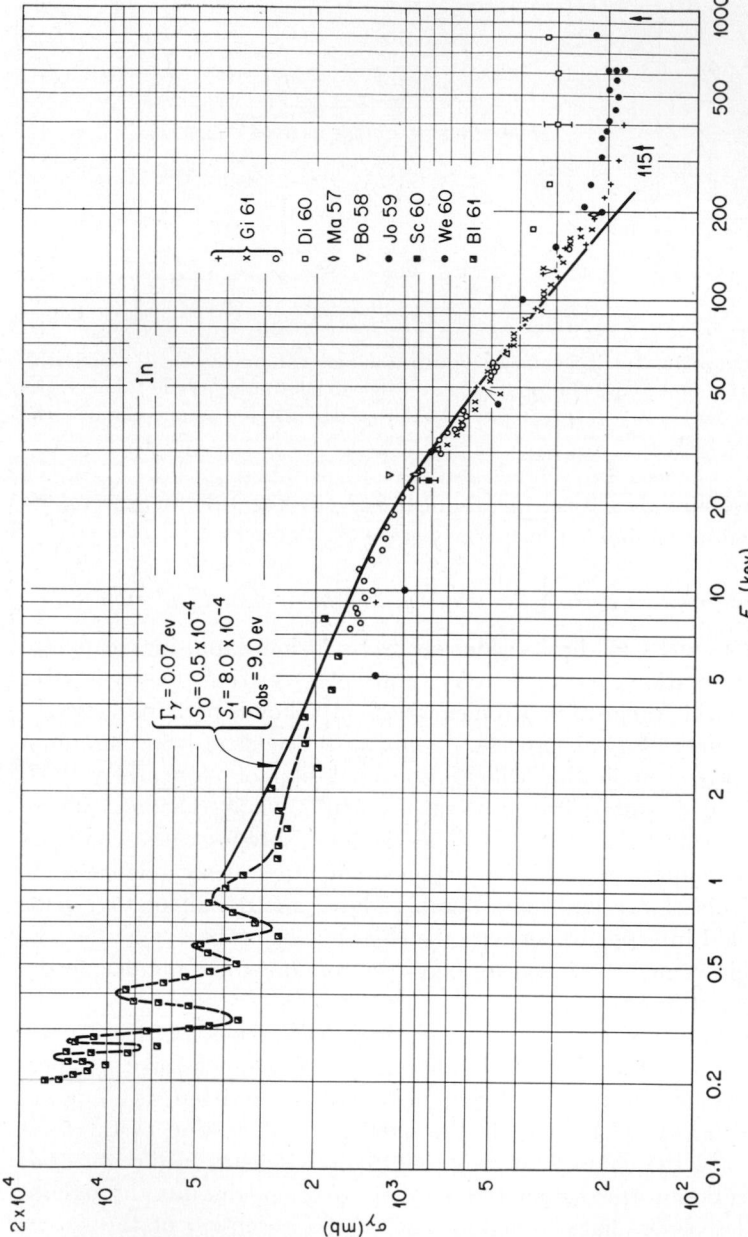

Figure 13. Compilation of neutron capture cross section results for indium.   The solid line and level parameters represent the best fit obtained in Gi61 for their data.

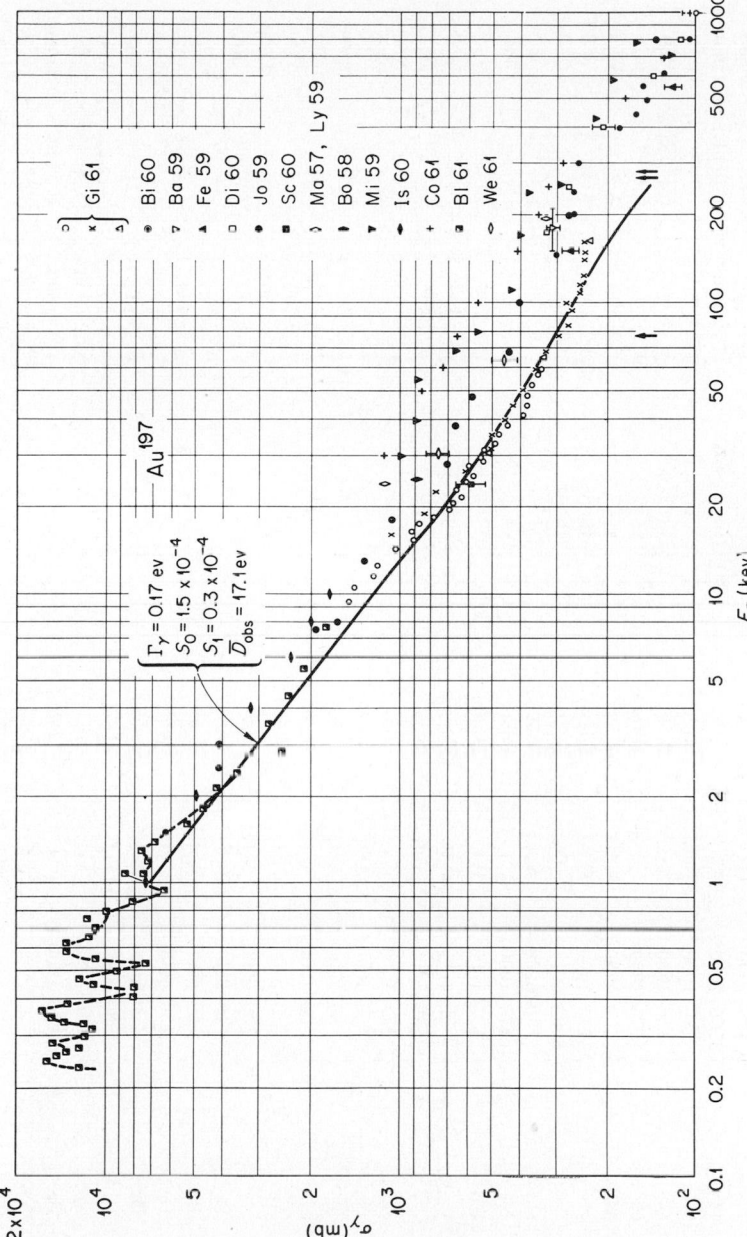

Figure 14. Compilation of neutron capture cross section results for gold. The solid line and level parameters represent the best fit obtained in Gi61 for their data.

Table IV. Index, by element, of published neutron capture cross section measurements as a function of neutron energy

Element	Energy range[+]	Method	Ref.	Element	Energy range[+]	Method	Ref.
Na	20–1000	Act.	Ba59	Mo[100]	3–200	Act.	We60
Al	10–550	Act.	He50		150–6200	Act.	Jo59
Ti	175–1000	CT-TF	Di60	Ru	2500–4000	Act.	Pa58
Ti[50]	2500–4000	Act.	Pa58		175–1000	CT-TF	Di60
V	30–1000	Act.	St60		0.2–10	CT-FC	Bl61
	150–3000	Act.	Jo59	Rh	175–1000	CT-TF	Di60
Cr	175–1000	CT-TF	Di60		0.2–10	CT-FC	Bl61
	150–6200	Act.	Jo59		3–300	Act.	We60
Mn	175–1000	CT-TF	Di60	Rh[103]*	2500–4000	Act.	Pa58
Fe	0.0002–50	SDTS	Is60	Rh[103]*	2500–4000	Act.	Pa58
Co[59]*	150–6200	Act.	Jo59	Pd	10–200	CT-TF	Gi61
Ni	175–1000	CT-TF	Di60		0.2–10	CT-FC	Bl61
Cu	175–1000	CT-TF	Di60	Pd[108]	3–700	Act.	We60
Cu[65]	2500–4000	Act.	Pa58	Pd[110]	2500–4000	Act.	Pa58
	150–6200	Act.	Jo59	Ag	10–200	CT-TF	Gi61
Zn	175–1000	CT-TF	Di60		175–1000	CT-TF	Di60
Ga[69]	2500–4000	Act.	Pa58		0.2–10	CT-FC	Bl61
Ga[71]	150–3000	Act.	Jo59		0.04–20	SDTS	Is60
Ge[74]	2500–4000	Act.	Pa58	Ag[107]	150–3000	Act.	Jo59
As	3–200	Act.	We60		3–200	Act.	We60
	150–6200	Act.	Jo59		3–200	Act.	We60
Br	10–200	CT-TF	Gi61	Ag[109]	10–200	CT-TF	Gi61
Br[79]*	150–4000	Act.	Jo59	Cd	0.2–10	CT-FC	Bl61
Br[79]*	150–4000	Act.	Jo59	In	7–400	CT-TF	Gi61
Br[81]	150–2000	Act.	Jo59		1.75–1000	CT-TF	Di60
Rb[87]	2500–4000	Act.	Pa58		0.2–10	CT-FC	Bl61
Sr[86]*	150–6200	Act.	Jo59	In[115]*	5–200	Act.	We60
Zr	175–1000	CT-TF	Di60	Sn	150–6200	Act.	Jo59
Nb	7–200	CT-TF	Gi61		175–1000	CT-TF	Di60
	175–1000	CT-TF	Di60	Sn[112]	2500–4000	Act.	Pa58
	30–1000	Act.	St60	Sb	7–200	CT-TF	Gi61
Mo	175–1000	CT-TF	Di60		175–1000	CT-TF	Di60
					0.2–10	CT-FC	Bl61

Element	Energy+	Method	Reference
I	9–200	CT-TF	Gi61
	0.2–10	CT-FC	Bl61
	5–200	Act.	We60
Ba138	150–6200	Act.	Jo59
	20–1000	Act.	Ba59
La139	150–2000	Act.	Jo59
	2500–4000	Act.	Pa58
Pr	150–2000	Act.	Jo59
	2500–4000	Act.	Pa58
	10–200	CT-TF	Gi61
Nd148	150–2000	Act.	Jo59
Nd150	150–2000	Act.	Jo59
Sm	10–200	CT-TF	Gi61
	0.2–10	CT-FC	Bl61
Sm154	150–6200	Act.	Jo59
Eu	0.2–10	CT-FC	Bl61
Eu151*	150–2000	Act.	Jo59
Gd	10–200	CT-TF	Gi61
	0.2–10	CT-FC	Bl61
Tb	10–200	CT-TF	Gi61
	0.2–10	CT-FC	Bl61
Dy	10–200	CT-TF	Gi61
	0.2–10	CT-FC	Bl61
Dy164*	150–6200	Act.	Jo59
Ho	10–200	CT-TF	Gi61
	0.2–10	CT-FC	Bl61
Ho165*	150–6200	Act.	Jo59
Er	10–200	CT-TF	Gi61
	0.2–10	CT-FC	Bl61
Tm	10–200	CT-TF	Gi61
	0.2–10	CT-FC	Bl61
	0.2–10	CT-FC	Bl61
	10–200	CT-TF	Gi61
Lu	0.2–10	CT-FC	Bl61
	0.2–10	CT-FC	Bl61
Hf	7–200	CT-TF	Gi61
Ta	175–1000	CT-TF	Di60
	0.2–10	CT-FC	Bl61
W	10–200	CT-TF	Gi61
	175–1000	CT-TF	Di60
	0.2–10	CT-FC	Bl61
W186	30–1000	Act.	St60
	150–3000	Act.	Jo59
	2500–4000	Act.	Pa58
Re	0.2–10	CT-FC	Bl61
Os	0.2–10	CT-FC	Bl61
Ir	0.2–10	CT-FC	Bl61
Pt	10–200	CT-TF	Gi61
	175–1000	CT-TF	Di60
	0.2–10	CT-FC	Bl61
Pt198	2–300	Act.	Bi60
Au	9–200	CT-TF	Gi61
	175–1000	CT-TF	Di60
	0.2–10	CT-FC	Bl61
	0.04–20	SDTS	Is60
	2–200	Act.	Bi60
	150–6000	Act.	Jo59
	150–1000	Act.	He50
	30–1500	Act.	Co61
Tl205	30–2000	Act.	St60
	2500–4000	Act.	Pa58
Pb	175–1000	CT-TF	Di60
U238	175–1000	CT-TF	Di60
	25–200	Act.	Bi60

Act. = Activation. CT-TF = Capture Tank—Time-of-Flight. CT-FC = Capture Tank—Fast Chopper. SDTS = Slowing-Down-Time Spectrometer. * To one of two possible states. + Energy in kilovolts.

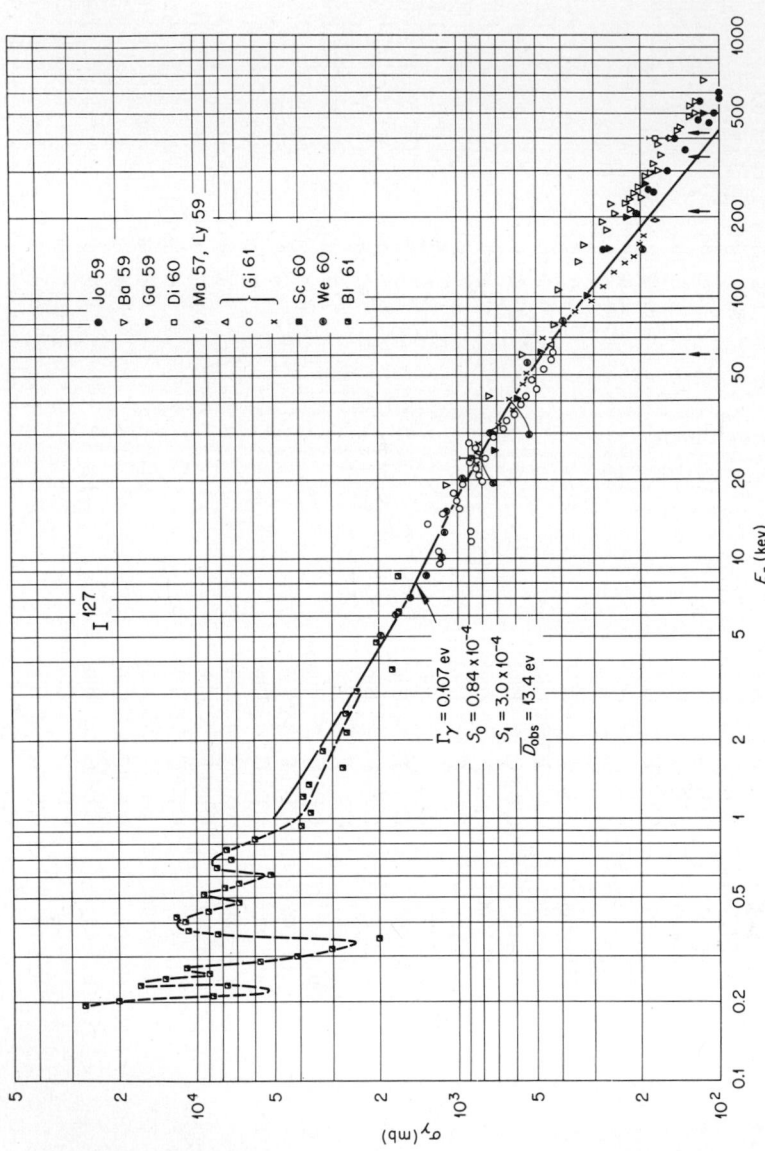

Figure 15. Compilation of neutron capture cross section results for iodine. The solid line and level parameters represent the best fit obtained in Gi61 for their data.

nuclei at the beginning of the chain.   It can vary rapidly only for small values of n.   It follows that the constancy of the abundance ratios shown in Fig. 16 implies the approximate constancy of the capture cross sections near 100 kev among the heavier uranium nuclei, from U^{238} to U^{254}.   The implications of this result will be discussed later.

G. Summary of Results

We have included in Table I the results of activation experiments for neutrons of $\sim$24 kev and $\sim$195 kev.   Results of activation experiments for 14-Mev neutrons are tabulated in Table II. Results of spherical shell transmission and other experiments at $\sim$24 kev neutron energy are given for some elements in Table III.   Elements whose capture cross sections have been measured in shell transmission experiments follow.   Sc60: Cu, Zn, Ag, Cd, In, Sb, I, Au, Hg, Pb; Be58: Mg, Al, Si, S, Ca, Ti, Cr, Fe, Ni, Cu, Zn, Se, Sr, Mo, Ag, Cd, Sn, Sb, Te, I, Ba, W, Au, Hg, Pb, Th, U.   The latter measurements (Be58) were carried out for neutron energies of 220 kev (Na-γ-D$_2$O source) and 830 kev (Na-γ-Be source) in addition to 24 kev (Sb-γ-Be source).   All of the above results have been discussed in Section 2.

In an attempt to indicate the measurements to date of neutron capture cross sections as a function of energy, we have included the representative compilations shown in Figs. 10, 13, 14, and 15.   Table IV provides an index by element of capture cross section measurements as a function of energy to date.

An interesting result of the capture cross section measurements near 65 kev [T(p,n) threshold neutron energy] of Gibbons et al. (Gi61) is shown in Fig. 17.   Note that nuclear shell effects are strikingly apparent in these results, as are the odd-even effects, which appear to be independent of Z in this plot.

3. Theoretical Treatment of Capture Cross Sections

A. Average Cross Sections

The first detailed theory of neutron capture cross sections was given by Margolis (Ma52) who gave explicit expressions for the contributions to the capture from the various partial neutron waves.

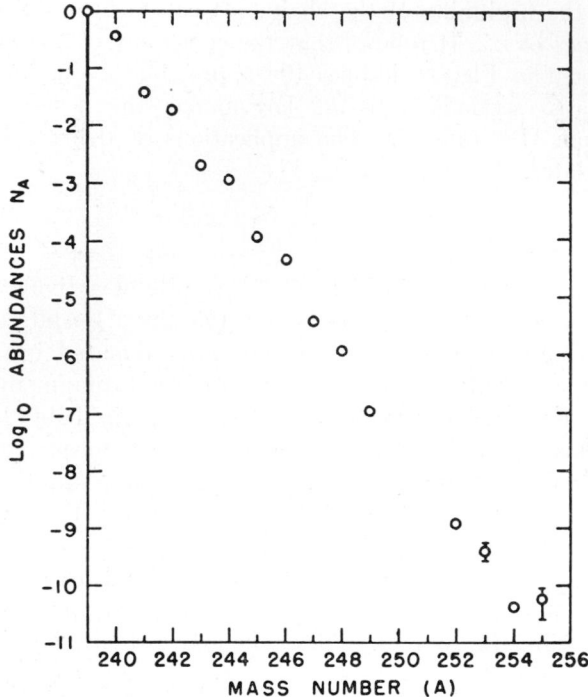

Figure 16. The $\log_{10}$ of the abundance of the various nuclides *vs* mass number at the time of detonation of the thermonuclear explosion "Mike," as given by Diamond *et al.* (Di60a).

Dresner (Dr56) compared this expression to an older one in which a crude allowance had been made for the higher partial waves, and he concluded that calculated capture cross sections are likely to be considerably in error unless the detailed formula is used. The treatment of Margolis used the statistical nuclear theory of Feshbach, Peaslee, and Weisskopf (Fe47). It now appears to be more useful to use the formulation given by Wigner and Eisenbud (Wi47). The capture theory in this revised form has been given by Cameron (Ca57a) and more elegantly by Lane and Lynn (La57). The following treatment is a modified version of that given by Lane and Lynn.

If we are near an isolated resonance λ of spin J, the capture cross section due to the partial wave of angular momentum l is given by the Breit-Wigner formula:

$$\sigma_\gamma(Jl) = \frac{(2J+1)}{2(2I+1)} \frac{\pi}{k^2} \frac{\sum_j \Gamma_n(\lambda Jlj)\Gamma_\gamma(\lambda J)}{(E_\lambda - E)^2 + [\Gamma_T(\lambda J)/2]^2} \qquad (8)$$

where k is 2π times the wave number of the incident neutron, E_λ is the resonance energy, I is the spin of the ground state of the target nucleus, $\Gamma_\gamma(\lambda J)$ is the radiation width of the resonance, $\Gamma_n(\lambda Jlj)$ is the entrance channel neutron width for channel spin j (which may take the values $j = I \pm 1/2$ except for the case $I = 0$ when $j = 1/2$), and $\Gamma_T(j\lambda)$ is the total width of the resonance. It is the sum of all the partial widths:

$$\Gamma_T(\lambda j) = \sum_{l,j} \Gamma_n(\lambda Jlj) + \sum_{n',l',j'} \Gamma_{n'}(\lambda Jl'j') + \Gamma_\gamma(\lambda J) \qquad (9)$$

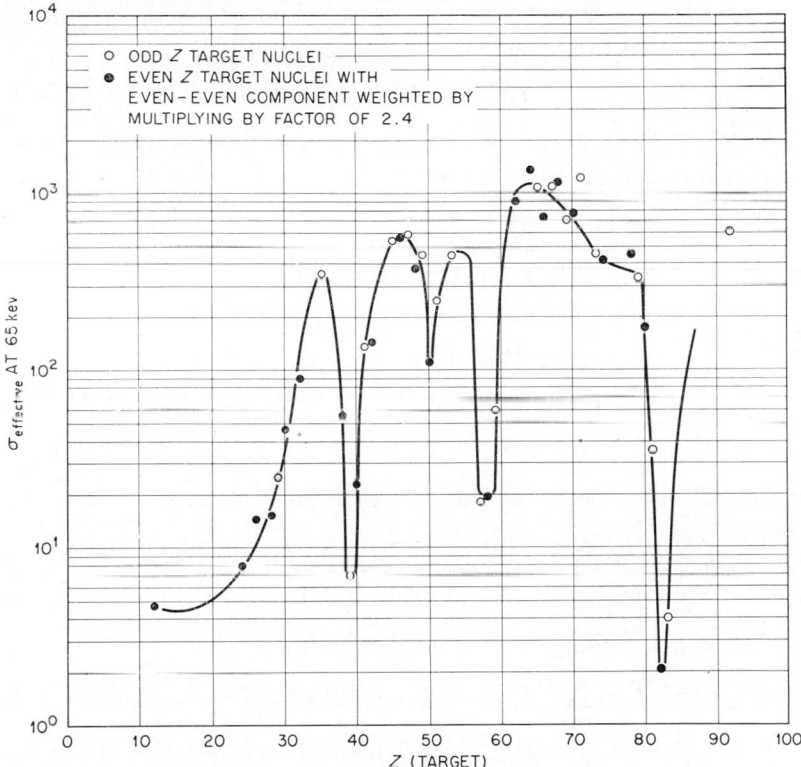

Figure 17. Average capture cross sections measured near 65 kev as a function of atomic number (Gi61). An empirical factor of 2.4 was determined for correlating cross sections of even-even vs. odd target nuclei. Effects of the 50-, 82-, and 126-neutron shells and of the 50-proton shell are evident.

where $\Gamma_{n'}(\lambda J l' j')$ is the width for an inelastic scattering process which leaves the residual nucleus in a given excited state, the emitted neutron having orbital angular momentum l' consistent with conservation of parity and with an exit channel spin j'.

We obtain the average cross section for this partial wave and for resonances of spin J by taking the average value of Eq. (8). This gives

$$\langle \sigma_\gamma(Jl) \rangle = \frac{(2J+1)}{(2I+1)} \frac{\pi^2}{k^2} \frac{1}{\langle D(\lambda J) \rangle} \sum_j \left\langle \frac{\Gamma_n(\lambda J l j)\Gamma_\gamma(\lambda J)}{\Gamma_T(\lambda J)} \right\rangle \quad (10)$$

where $\langle D(\lambda J) \rangle$ is the average spacing between resonances of spin J and given parity at the excitation energy at which the capture is occurring. The total capture cross section is

$$\langle \sigma_\gamma \rangle = \sum_l \sum_J \langle \sigma_\gamma(Jl) \rangle \quad (11)$$

It is inconvenient to work with the average ratio of the various widths on the right hand side of Eq. (10). However, if we use the average values of the widths themselves, we commit an error which must be corrected by multiplying the resulting equation by a correction factor. The equation then becomes:

$$\langle \sigma_\gamma(Jl) \rangle = \frac{(2J+1)}{(2I+1)} \frac{\pi^2}{k^2} \frac{1}{\langle D(\lambda J) \rangle} \sum_j \frac{\langle \Gamma_n(\lambda J l j) \rangle \langle \Gamma_\gamma(\lambda J) \rangle}{\langle \Gamma_T(\lambda J) \rangle}$$

$$\times S \left(\frac{\langle \Gamma_n(\lambda J l j) \rangle}{\langle \Gamma_\gamma(\lambda J) \rangle} \right) \quad (12)$$

where S denotes the correction factor. It is defined as

$$S \left(\frac{\langle \Gamma_n(\lambda J l j) \rangle}{\langle \Gamma_\gamma(\lambda J) \rangle} \right) = \left\langle \frac{\Gamma_n(\lambda J l j)\Gamma_\gamma(\lambda J)}{\Gamma_T(\lambda J)} \right\rangle \Big/ \frac{\langle \Gamma_n(\lambda J l j) \rangle \langle \Gamma_\gamma(\lambda J) \rangle}{\langle \Gamma_T(\lambda J) \rangle} \quad (13)$$

The average total width can be written in the form

$$\langle _T(\lambda J) \rangle = \sum_{l,j} \langle \Gamma_n(\lambda J l j) \rangle + \sum_{n',l',j'} \langle \Gamma_{n'}(\lambda J l' j') \rangle + \langle \Gamma_\gamma(\lambda J) \rangle \quad (14)$$

Lane and Lynn (La57) have pointed out that the above expressions are modified by interference effects at higher excitation energies where resonance widths are no longer very much smaller than level spacings. However, they show that these modifications are probably very small.

B. *Corrections for Variations of Neutron Widths*

Measurements show that there is very little variation in radiation widths between levels that can be formed by s-wave neutrons. Therefore, the properties of the correction factor S, defined in Eq. (13), are essentially determined by the variations in the neutron widths. These widths are subject to very large variations. If we are dealing with fissionable nuclei it would also be necessary to take into account the considerable variation in fission widths which occurs from level to level.

Several expressions for the probability distribution of neutron widths have been suggested, but Porter and Thomas (Po56) have shown that both theoretical considerations and experimental measurements favor a chi-squared distribution of the widths with one degree of freedom. The general expression for the chi-squared distribution is

$$p_\nu(x)dx = (\nu/2)\Gamma^{-1}(\nu/2) \ (\nu x/2)^{(\nu-2)/2} \exp(-\nu x/2)dx \tag{15}$$

the distribution is normalized so that

$$\langle x \rangle = 1 \tag{16}$$

$$\int_0^\infty p_\nu(x)dx = 1 \tag{17}$$

Here ν is the number of degrees of freedom of the distribution. For $\nu = 1$ we have

$$p_1(x)dx = (2\pi x)^{-1/2} \exp(-x/2)dx \tag{18}$$

If the radiation width is factored out of Eq. (13), we have

$$S\left(\frac{\langle \Gamma_n(\lambda Jlj)\rangle}{\langle \Gamma_\gamma(\lambda J)\rangle}\right) = \left\langle \frac{y_1}{y_1 + y_2 + 1} \right\rangle \bigg/ \frac{\langle y_1 \rangle}{\langle y_1 \rangle + \langle y_2 \rangle + 1} \tag{19}$$

where

$$y_1 = \frac{\Gamma_n(\lambda Jlj)}{\langle \Gamma_\gamma(\lambda J)\rangle} \tag{20}$$

and

$$y_2 = \frac{\Gamma_n(\lambda Jlj'') + \sum_{n',l',j'} \Gamma_{n'}(\lambda Jl'j')}{\langle \Gamma_\gamma(\lambda J)\rangle} \tag{21}$$

j'' referring to elastic scattering in which the neutron emerges with channel spin other than that of the entrance channel.

In the general case y_2 will have a complicated distribution probability. If there is only one channel included in y_2, then the distribution function is that of Eq. (15). As other channels are included the width of distribution becomes smaller, until when there are very many channels the y_2 probability becomes strongly peaked in the vicinity of the average value. It is perhaps useful to introduce the concept of fractional degrees of freedom, and to assume that the probability distribution of y_2 is given by Eq. (15) with ν degrees of freedom, where

$$\nu = \frac{\langle \Gamma_n(\lambda Jlj'') \rangle + \sum_{n',l',j'} \langle \Gamma_{n'}(\lambda Jl'j') \rangle}{\langle \Gamma_{n'}(\lambda Jl'j) \rangle_{\max}} \tag{22}$$

where $\langle \Gamma_{n'}(\lambda Jl'j) \rangle_{\max}$ is the largest of the average widths in the numerator of (22). In this case the correction factor can be written as $S(\alpha,\beta,\nu)$, where

$$\alpha = \langle y_1 \rangle \tag{23}$$

and

$$\beta = \langle y_2 \rangle \tag{24}$$

If there is only one neutron channel ($\beta = 0$), then the correction factor is

$$S(\alpha,0,0) = (\alpha + 1/\alpha) \, [1 - \psi(0,\alpha/2)] \tag{25}$$

where

$$\psi(u,t) = \frac{1}{2(\pi t)^{1/2}} \int_{-\infty}^{\infty} \frac{\exp{-(u-v)^2/4t}}{1+v^2} \, dv \tag{26}$$

The integral in Eq. (26) has been tabulated by Rose, Miranker, Leak, and Rabinowitz (Ro53), and more extensively by Rose, Miranker, Leak, Rosenthal, and Hendrickson (Ro54). The integral in Eq. (25) may also be calculated from the following series (J. M. Kennedy, private communication):

$$\psi(0,t) = h/\pi^{1/2} \left[1 + 2 \sum_{1}^{\infty} \frac{\exp(-n^2 h^2)}{1 + 4n^2 h^2 t} \right] - f(t) \tag{27}$$

where

$$f(t) = 0 \qquad t^{1/2} < h/2\pi$$

$$= (\pi/t)^{1/2} \frac{\exp(1/4t)}{\exp(\pi/ht^{1/2})\text{-}1} \qquad t^{1/2} > h/2\pi \tag{28}$$

The relative error in this expansion is of the order $(\pi/h)\exp(-\pi^2/h^2)$, except for very large values of t. The quantity h may be chosen of suitable size to give any required accuracy; $h - 1$ gives four significant figures.

$S(\alpha,0,0)$ is plotted in Fig. 18. It may be seen that the cor-

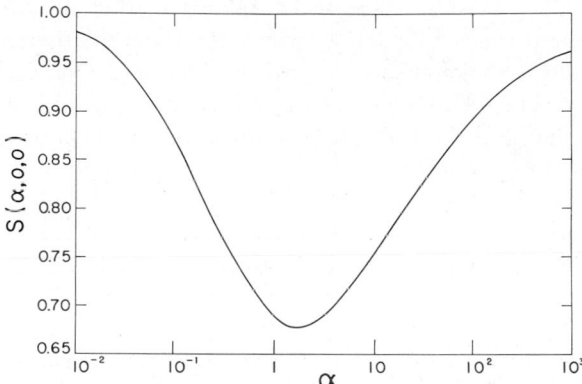

Figure 18. The correction factor $S(\alpha,0,0)$.

rection factor is unity for very small and very large values of α, but it drops to about 0.7 where α is of order unity.

The general case must be evaluated numerically. It may be shown that

$$S(\alpha,\beta,\nu) = (\nu/2\beta)^{\nu/2}\Gamma^{-1}(\nu/2)\left(\frac{\alpha+\beta+1}{\alpha}\right)\int_0^\infty y_2^{(\nu-2)/2}\exp\left(\frac{-\nu y_2}{2\beta}\right)$$

$$\times \left\{1-\psi\left[0, \frac{\alpha}{2(1+y_2)}\right]dy_2\right\} \tag{29}$$

There are very few values of $S(\alpha,\beta,\nu)$ reported in the literature. Lane and Lynn (La57) tabulate a few values of $S(\alpha,\beta,1)$. Some of these considerations have also been published by Kuhn and Dresner (Ku58).

Dresner (Dr57) has taken a more direct approach to this problem and has programmed the calculation of the correction factor S on a computer by a Monte Carlo method.

In the case of a fissionable nucleus the width y_2 must include a contribution from the fission process. This may be done within the framework of the above considerations if Eq. (22) is rewritten as

$$\nu = \frac{\langle \Gamma_n(\lambda J l j'') \rangle + \sum_{n',\nu,j'} \langle \Gamma_{n'}(\lambda J l' j') \rangle + \langle \Gamma_f(\lambda J) \rangle}{\langle \Gamma_i(\lambda J) \rangle_{\max}} \tag{30}$$

where $\langle \Gamma_i(\lambda J) \rangle_{\max}$ is the largest of the individual neutron widths in the numerator or of $\Gamma_f(\lambda J)/\nu_e$, where $\Gamma_f(\lambda J)$ is the fission width of the level and ν_e is the effective number of fission channels, generally about 2.5 for low neutron energies and fissionable nuclei like U^{235}.

This method of an effective number of channels or degrees of freedom is most accurate when the number of channels is small and the average widths are comparable in size. If there is a large number of channels with very different widths, the generalized chi-squared distribution fails to give a good representation of the distribution of the total width. It may be seen, for example, that in the case of one channel with unit width being combined with N channels of width N^{-1}, where N is a large integer, the resulting distribution differs very much from a chi-squared distribution with two degrees of freedom. However, if there are many channels the correction factor S does not differ much from unity over the important range where contributions to the capture cross section are large.

Lane and Lynn (La57) have also given expressions and tables for some cases in which the assumption is made that there are two degrees of freedom for each neutron channel.

C. Neutron Widths

Following the procedure of Wigner and Eisenbud (Wi47), we write the neutron width for a single channel in the form

$$\Gamma_n(\lambda J l j) = 2k P_l \gamma_n^2(\lambda J l j) \tag{31}$$

where

$$P_l = \frac{1}{|F_l^2 + G_l^2|} = \frac{1}{|x[j_l(x) + in_l(x)]|^2} \tag{32}$$

$$x = kR,$$

R is the nuclear radius, and $j_l(x)$ and $n_l(x)$ are the spherical Bessel and Neumann functions. $\gamma_n^2(\lambda Jlj)$ is the reduced width of the level for the neutron channel under consideration.

The first four barrier penetrabilities P_l are as follows:

$$P_0 = 1$$

$$P_1 = x^2/(1 + x^2)$$

$$P_2 = x^4/(9 + 3x^2 + x^4) \tag{33}$$

$$P_3 = x^6/(225 + 45x^2 + 6x^4 + x^6)$$

For purposes of orientation, these barrier penetrabilities have been plotted in Fig. 19 for three typical nuclei of mass numbers $A = 50$, 100, and 200, using as the nuclear radius

$$R = 1.45(A^{1/3}+1) \cdot 10^{-13} \text{ cm} \tag{34}$$

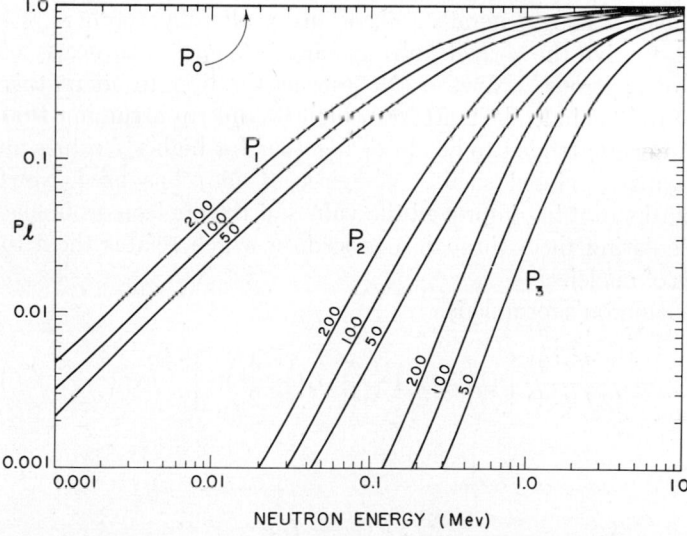

Figure 19. Neutron penetration factors P_l computed for $0 \leq l \leq 3$ and for nuclei of mass numbers 50, 100, and 200, using Eq. (34) for nuclear radius.

The reduced neutron widths are subject to large variations, as described above. However, with the use of the correction factor S we need only use the average values $\langle \gamma^2_n(\lambda Jlj) \rangle$. These average values can be obtained if the neutron strength function is known. For a black nucleus,

$$\frac{\langle \gamma_n^2(\lambda Jlj) \rangle}{\langle D(\lambda J) \rangle} \approx 2.3 \cdot 10^{-14} \text{ cm} \tag{35}$$

D. Nuclear Level Spacings

As we shall see, the neutron capture cross sections vary among themselves more due to variations in the nuclear level spacings than to any other factor. It is therefore important to use level spacings which are as realistic as possible. If for any given nucleus there are experimental measurements of the level spacing, these should be used. Otherwise it is necessary to appeal to a level spacing formula.

It has been usual to calculate level spacings by counting the number of ways in which the particles in a nuclear Fermi gas can recombine to give different states in a unit interval of excitation energy. Such formulas have been adjusted to fit observed level spacings in a few nuclei. They generally fail, often by about two orders of magnitude, to give the correct level spacing in nuclei with nearly closed shells of neutrons. Newton (Ne56) was the first to adapt this calculation to include shell effects, which he did by assuming that the nucleon orbits tended to lie closer together for higher j values and to have gaps at closed shells. Cameron (Ca58) has used Newton's formulation but has improved the values of the nucleon orbit spacings by calculating them through a procedure which relates them to the masses of nuclei.

Cameron's formula is

$$\langle D(\lambda J) \rangle = \frac{3.26 \cdot 10^5}{(2J+1)} \left[G_Z G_N G^3 A^2 \left(\frac{\pi^2}{3} Gt - \frac{3}{2} \right) t^7 \right]^{1/2} \exp\left(\frac{-\pi^2}{3} Gt \right) \tag{36}$$

where

$$G = G_Z + G_N \tag{37}$$

and

$$t = \frac{3}{\pi^2 G} \left[\frac{3}{2} + \left(\frac{9}{4} + \frac{2\pi^2 GU}{3} \right)^{1/2} \right] \tag{38}$$

Here G_Z and G_N are the average spacings of the proton and neutron orbits at the Fermi level of the nucleon gas, U is the effective excitation energy in Mev (defined as the actual excitation energy minus the pairing energy of the paired nucleons), t is the nuclear temperature, and $\langle D(\lambda J) \rangle$ is in electron volts. Cameron has given formulas and coefficients by which G_Z and G_N may be calculated for a given nucleus at a given excitation energy; G_Z and G_N depend on this excitation energy to some extent. This formula has fitted 82 observed level spacings with a root mean square error factor of 1.74, and it is therefore a realistic formula, although a complicated one. However, recent comparisons between the predictions of this formula and measurements of level spacings in light nuclei by charged particle methods have revealed systematic discrepancies. For nuclei with mass numbers below 60, Eq. (36) predicts level spacings an order of magnitude too small. It is believed that these discrepancies arise from the short-cut methods recommended by Cameron for the calculation of G_Z and G_N.

Because of the great sensitivity of level spacings to the excitation energy, it is important to use values for neutron binding energies which are as accurate as possible. Good compilations of experimental masses have been given by Mattauch, Waldmann, Bieri, and Everling (Ma56), by Wapstra (Wa56a, Wa56b) and by Huizenga (Hu56). A recent revision of these masses has been published by Everling, Konig, Mattauch, and Wapstra (Ev60). Weizsacker's semi-empirical mass formula has been revised and corrected for shell effects by Cameron (Ca57b), who has also tabulated the resulting neutron binding energies (Ca57c).

E. Radiation Widths

The radiation process is rather complex, since there are usually a very large number of levels which are energetically accessible for radiative transitions from the capturing state. It has been shown that electric dipole transitions predominate in the capture process (Ba57). In such transitions the angular momentum spin vector must change by one unit and the parity must change. Hence in general any given spin state radiates to states of opposite parity and three values of spin. In calculating total radiation widths it is necessary to sum over all these transitions.

Blatt and Weisskopf (B152) have argued that in general the matrix elements for the transitions to lower states will be reduced as the level spacing in the vicinity of the radiating state decreases. In the radiation process all but one of the nucleons form a core which remains unchanged; coupled to this core is the remaining nucleon which changes its angular momentum. The total radiation probability for the transition between two given states is composed of all the ways in which A-1 nucleons can form a common parent in the initial and final states while the last nucleon changes its state. The probabilities of admixture of these single particle wave functions into the initial and final states decrease as the number of states into which admixture can occur increases. Therefore the total radiation width may be expected to be proportional to the spacing of levels $D(\lambda J)$ near the radiating state multiplied by the sum of all the individual transition probabilities.

Summations of this kind have been carried out by Cameron (Ca57d) who found that total radiation widths (in milli-electron volts) could be approximately fitted by

$$\Gamma_\gamma(\lambda J) = A^{2/3} \langle D(\lambda,0,U) \rangle \int_0^U \frac{E^3 dE}{\langle D(\lambda,0,U\text{-}E) \rangle} \qquad (39)$$

where level spacings calculated from Eq. (36) were used. Here U is the effective excitation energy, and in the level spacing formula it has been assumed for convenience that $J = 0$. This assumption is not in fact necessary, since it may be seen that the final states combine to give a total statistical weight proportional to $(2J + 1)$ which cancels a $(2J + 1)$ factor in the level spacing for the initial state. The radiation width is therefore expected to be independent of J.

If Eq. (39) gives a good determination of the total radiation width, the integrand should give the shape of the primary photon spectrum. Unfortunately it is necessary to measure the total photon spectrum. Figure 20 shows the result of a calculation of the spectrum to be expected from neutron capture in the silver isotopes, compared with the experimental results (Ba57). In the figure P denotes the primary spectrum and T the total spectrum calculated by a simple cascade procedure. It may be seen that there is a good fit to the spectrum shape. This is one of the better fits that can be obtained;

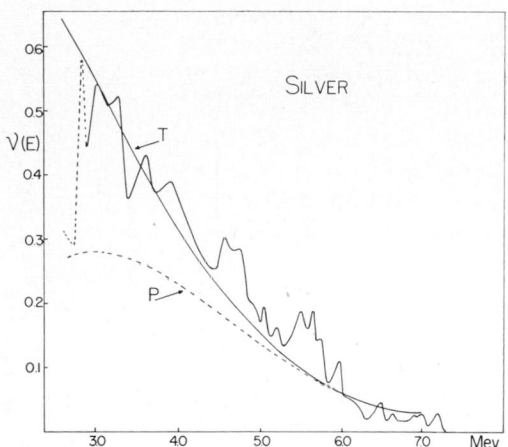

Figure 20. Theoretical and experimental photon spectra for neutron capture in silver. P denotes the primary spectrum, T the total spectrum including cascades to lower levels from those formed by the primary radiations.

often the experimental results are distorted relative to the calculated prediction by having too many photons at high or medium energies. These distortions can sometimes be understood as resulting from a favoring of certain of the matrix elements in cases where nuclear structure considerations lead to an expectation of large overlaps between the initial and final wave functions (Ba57).

Actually we must also regard the calculated spectrum of Fig. 20 as having too many high energy photons. The number of individual transitions seen near the upper limit of the spectrum is considerably smaller than the number predicted from the use of Eq. (39). This appears to be due to the failure of the Fermi gas model used in calculating level densities near the nuclear ground state. Thus even in this case of silver there is a relative strengthening of high energy transitions.

In Fig. 21 are plotted a number of ratios of observed radiation widths to widths calculated from Eq. (39). The resulting points appear to define a structure, the trend of which is suggested by the curve which has been drawn in the figure. Cameron (Ca57d) has suggested the following interpretation of this structure.

The admixture of single particle wave functions into the actual wave functions at the region of excitation corresponding to the neu-

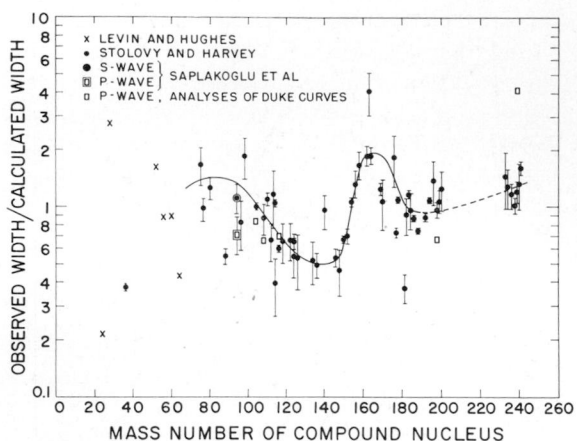

Figure 21. Ratios of observed radiation widths to those calculated from Eq. (39). The solid line is intended as a guide to the eye to denote the trend of the points with mass number.

tron binding energy is largest in the vicinity of the appropriate maxima of the neutron strength functions. According to simple optical models of the nucleus the even partial neutron waves have strength function maxima in the same regions of mass number and the odd partial waves have maxima at intermediate regions of mass number. If a nucleus absorbs an s-wave neutron, the wave function of the compound state may be thought of as a combination of a large subset of the excited states of the target nucleus which combine with the s-wave neutron to preserve the total angular momentum of the state. Certain other excited states of the target nucleus couple d-, g-, . . . wave neutrons in such a way as also to preserve the total angular momentum and parity of the compound state. Still further representations of the compound state may be obtained by coupling the excited states of that nucleus, with one more neutron and one less proton than the target nucleus, to s-, d-, g-, . . . wave protons. In general the fractional admixtures of these wave functions into that of the compound state probably diminish as the amount of recoupling of the nucleons increases, since extensive recouplings usually represent highly excited states.

The electric dipole transition matrix elements are proportional to the amount of overlap of these parent cores between the initial and final states. The overlap integrals will be larger when the admixtures of single particle wave functions into the initial states are larger, such as will occur in the regions of the s-wave neutron strength function peaks ($A \sim 55$ and 160), the d-wave neutron peaks ($A \sim 50$ and 200), and the s- and d-wave proton peaks ($A \sim 75$ and 50 respectively). It may be seen that the curve shown in Fig. 21 is generally in accord with these expectations.

It is also necessary to consider the strengthening of the transition matrix elements owing to increased admixtures of single particle wave functions into the final states. Most of the transitions go to states with excitation energies of roughly half the neutron binding energy. Since the single nucleon changes its orbital angular momentum in the radiative transition, s-wave neutron capture should be enhanced when the middle range of excited states has large admixtures of p-, f-, h-, ... wave nucleons. Again the lower partial waves should be more important than the higher ones owing to the fact that more extensive recouplings correspond in general to higher excitation energies. This enhancement occurs in between the strength function peaks for the odd partial wave nucleons, in the same general region as the strength function peaks for the even partial wave nucleons.

These considerations lead to the prediction that the radiation widths associated with p-wave neutron capture may be somewhat different from those associated with s-wave capture. The broad structure peaks should occur in different regions of mass number. There is as yet insufficient experimental data to test this prediction. The meager information available about radiation widths associated with p-wave capture is also plotted in Fig. 21. Only one of these points is a direct experimental measurement (Sa58); the others have been deduced by Cameron from the capture cross section curves measured in the kev region at Duke University (Bi60). These latter points are subject to considerable uncertainty.

These general ideas have been quantitatively investigated by Lane and Lynn (La60b). They found that transitions to low-lying p-states could enhance the radiation widths above the ordinary statistical values by a significant but very uncertain amount. This enhancement should be larger when there is a particularly strong s-wave interaction between the neutron and the nucleus. From numerical calculations involving a complex potential well, they have found it possible to reproduce the enhancement peak near mass number 160.

The absolute values of the radiation widths are slowly-varying quantities. They have a general decreasing trend with increasing mass number, with superposed increases just below closed neutron shells. The measured values collected by Levin and Hughes (Le56) and by Stolovy and Harvey (St57) are plotted in Fig. 22.

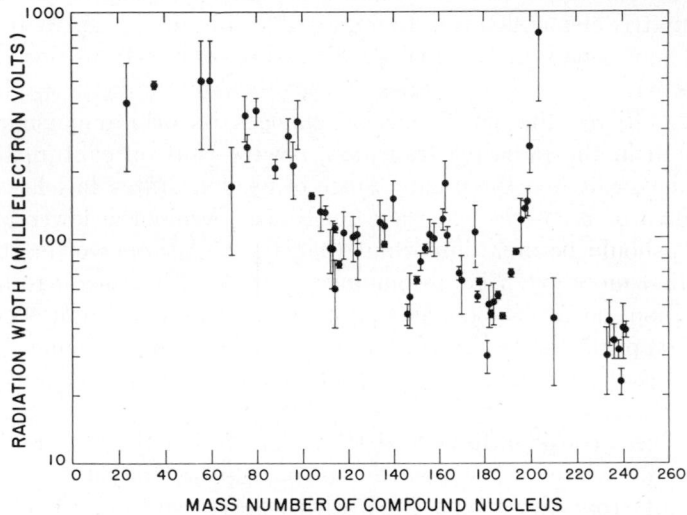

Figure 22. Total radiation widths as compiled by Stolovy and Harvey (St57) and Levin and Hughes (Le56).

In connection with the analysis of capture cross section curves which cover an extended range of excitation energy, it is of interest to consider the rapidity with which total radiation widths change with excitation energy. The empirical analysis of Stolovy and Harvey (St57) suggests that the radiation widths increase rapidly with excitation energy. This is contradicted by the calculations of Lane and Lynn (La57) and by Cameron in which it is found that in general the radiation widths should increase by much less than a factor two over a one-Mev range of excitation energy. The conclusion of Stolovy and Harvey (St57) appears to be in error because the measurements which correspond to higher excitation energies are usually for nuclei of low mass number; those corresponding to lower excitation energies are usually for very heavy nuclei. As may be seen from Fig. 22, the large variation with excitation energy is thus associated with a correlated variation in mass number.

F. Analysis of Cross Section Curves

It may be seen from Eqs. (10) and (11) that the average capture cross section is the sum of many contributions from different level spins J, channel spins j, and neutron partial waves l. We can most easily obtain an insight into the relative importance of these various contributions by constructing synthetic cross-section curves corresponding to very simplified assumptions.

In Fig. 23 is plotted a synthetic average cross-section curve for a hypothetical even-even nucleus with the parameters $A = 100$, $\langle D(\lambda,0)\rangle = 200$ ev, $\Gamma_\gamma(\lambda J) = 0.1$ ev, and with $\langle \gamma_n^2(\lambda Jlj)\rangle / \langle D(\lambda J)\rangle = 2.3 \cdot 10^{-14}$ cm. It has been assumed that there is no

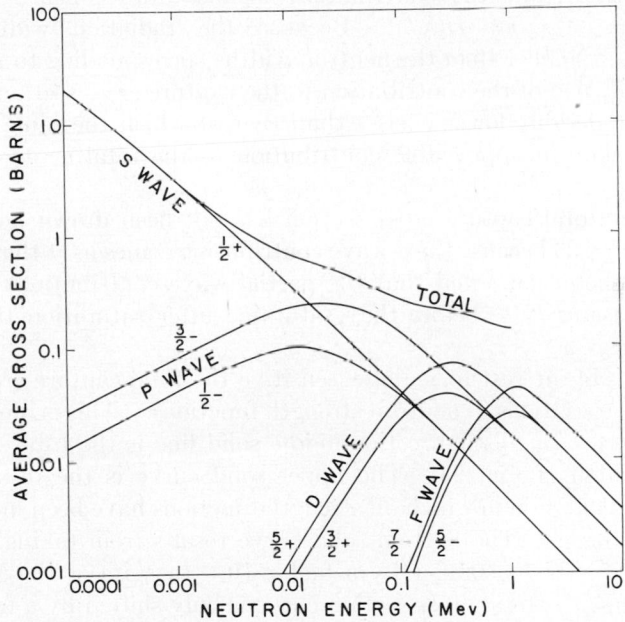

Figure 23. Synthetic capture cross section curve, showing also the contributions from the various partial neutron waves. The partial contributions labeled with the spins and parities of the compound states which are formed.

inelastic scattering, that there is no energy dependence of the radiation widths or level spacings, and that the correction factor S is always unity. The partial cross section contributions are also shown in Fig. 23.

It may be seen in this figure that the higher partial waves give full contributions to the capture cross section at considerably lower energies than they do to the total neutron interaction cross section. The reason for this is that the partial contributions are proportional to a term

$$\frac{\langle\Gamma_n(\lambda Jlj)\rangle\langle\Gamma_\gamma(\lambda J)\rangle}{(\langle\Gamma_n(\lambda Jlj)\rangle + \langle\Gamma_\gamma(\lambda J)\rangle)\langle D(\lambda J)\rangle}$$

If $\langle\Gamma_\gamma(\lambda J)\rangle \gg \langle\Gamma_n(\lambda Jlj)\rangle$, then this term is essentially equal to $\langle\Gamma_n(\lambda Jlj)\rangle/\langle D(\lambda J)\rangle$, which is the neutron strength function for the particular partial wave involved. This proportionality occurs at low neutron energies. At higher neutron energies, $\langle\Gamma_\gamma(\lambda J)\rangle \ll \langle\Gamma_n(\lambda Jlj)\rangle$, and the contribution then saturates, being proportional to $\langle\Gamma_\gamma(\lambda J)\rangle/\langle D(\lambda J)\rangle$. Because the radiation widths are very much smaller than the neutron widths corresponding to $P_l \sim 1$, this saturation of the contribution to the capture cross section occurs at a considerably lower energy than that at which the same partial wave makes an appreciable contribution to the total neutron cross section.

The total capture cross section has not been drawn beyond 1 Mev in Fig. 23 because the g-wave contribution comes in at that point.

It should be noted that the partial wave contributions in Fig. 23 increase as $E^{-1/2}$ before they saturate; after saturation the contributions vary as E^{-1}.

It is of interest to see how sensitive the total capture cross section is to variations in neutron strength functions. This is illustrated by Fig. 24. In this figure the middle solid line is the total capture cross section of Fig. 23. The upper solid curve is the result of a similar calculation in which all strength functions have been increased by a factor 10. The bottom solid curve results from taking all the strength functions smaller by a factor 10. In spite of these major alterations, the total cross-section curve is only shifted by a factor of not much more than two, except at very low energies where only s-waves make an appreciable (and unsaturated) contribution. This result shows the importance of the saturation of the cross section con-

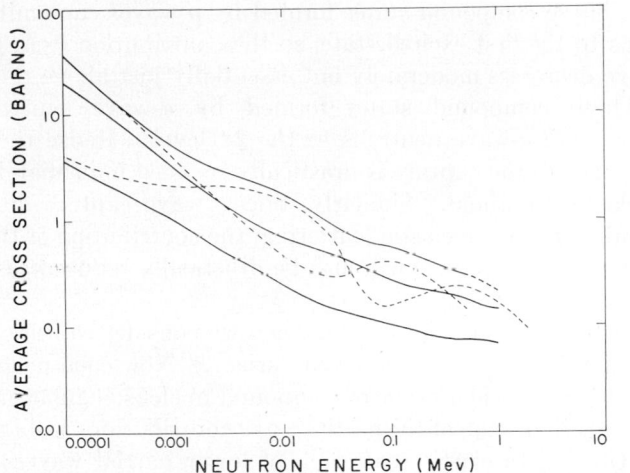

Figure 24. The effects of strength function variations on the synthetic cross section curve of Fig. 24, which is the middle solid line. The upper and lower solid lines represent cases in which the strength functions are all taken to be 10 and 0.1 times the black nucleus value, respectively. The dashed curves represent cases in which the strength functions are alternately 10 and 0.1 times the black nucleus value.

tributions. Finally, the dashed curves in Fig. 24 show the more realistic cases in which the neutron strength functions are alternately 10 and 0.1 times the black nucleus values. While these extreme variations exaggerate the effects, it may be seen that small s-wave and strong p-wave strength functions cause the curve to have a very small slope in the region 1–10 kev. Similarly, particularly strong d-, f-, g-, . . . strength functions can cause bumps in the curve in the vicinity of 0.1, 0.5, 1, . . . Mev. These bumps tend to become sharper as the higher partial wave contributions rise more steeply with energy.

These considerations have so far neglected the effects of inelastic scattering. When the neutron energy exceeds the threshold for inelastic scattering, the contributions of many of the partial neutron waves to the capture fall sharply, owing to the increased competition. For example, most even-even nuceli have a 2^+ first excited state. When the neutron energy exceeds the excitation energy of this state, the following effects will occur: the s-wave contribution is decreased only negligibly for the first Mev above threshold because the inelastic scattering in this case requires the emission of d-wave neutrons.   Those compound states formed by p-waves can emit p-wave neutrons to the first excited state, so the contribution from this partial wave decreases moderately but essentially just above the threshold.   Those compound states formed by d-wave neutrons can, however, emit s-wave neutrons to the 2^+ level.   Hence the d-wave contribution to the capture is drastically reduced immediately above the inelastic threshold.   Similarly, since f-wave capture must compete against p-wave inelastic scattering, the contribution of these partial waves to the capture will also be drastically reduced just above the inelastic threshold.

Further complications set in when we consider capture in a nucleus which is not of the even-even variety.   Now each partial wave can form a much wider range of compound nucleus angular momenta. This means that some of the partial wave contributions will be greatly reduced owing to elastic scattering of lower partial waves; for example, the capture contribution will be small when d-wave absorption can be followed by s-wave re-emission of the neutron.   However, inelastic scattering does not in general result in the reduction of all partial contributions owing to the emission of lower partial waves. For example, consider a nucleus with a $9/2^-$ ground state and a $5/2^-$ first excited state.   The capture of an f-wave neutron will excite compound states with $1 < J < 8$.   Only those with $1 < J < 4$ can emit p-wave neutrons leaving the nucleus in its first excited state.   The compound states with $5 < J < 6$ can inelastically scatter f-waves, but their contributions to the capture are not materially reduced until several hundred kev above the inelastic threshold.   Inelastic scattering effects of this kind may serve to accentuate bumps in the cross-section curve associated with f- and g-wave capture.   In all of these considerations care must be taken to include properly the effects resulting from formation of compound states of given J by more than one channel spin, and inelastic scattering from such states of more than one channel spin.   The number of contributing channel spins is convenietly given by a symbol ϵ'_{jl} introduced by Hauser and Feshbach (Ha52):

$$\epsilon'_{jl} = 2 \qquad |J-l| \leqslant I \pm {}^1\!/_2 \leqslant J + l$$

$$= 1 \qquad |J-l| \leqslant \text{ only one of } I \pm {}^1\!/_2 \leqslant J + l \qquad (40)$$

$$= 0 \qquad \text{otherwise.}$$

Very few capture cross section curves that have so far been measured over a large energy range and with considerable accuracy have been subjected to full analyses in which attempts are made to include effects due to energy variations of radiation widths and level spacings and the correction factor S. However, the experimental measurements at Duke University (Bi60) satisfy these requirements, and Cameron has attempted an analysis of them in which the energy variation of the level spacings is included, the radiation width is assumed to be independent of energy but not of the neutron partial wave, the correction factor S is taken to be $S(\alpha,0,0)$, and only s- and p-wave contributions have been included.

Two of the more interesting analyses are shown in Figs. 25 and 26. The $Au^{197}(n,\gamma)Au^{198}$ cross section, shown in Fig. 25, was fitted taking into account inelastic scattering to the first excited state at 77 kev and assuming the experimental low energy values of the s-wave neutron strength function and the level spacings to be correct. Three parameters were adjusted to obtain the fit: a normalization factor (of order unity) needed to reconcile the cross section curve calculated from low energy parameters with the measurements at neutron ener-

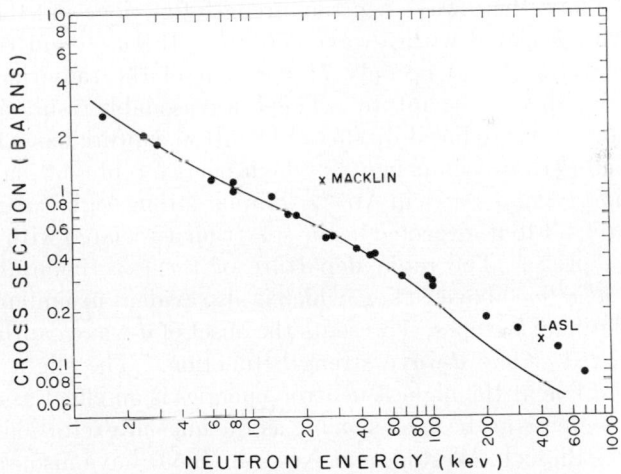

Figure 25. The cross section for the $Au^{197}(n,\gamma)Au^{198}$ reaction, as measured at Duke University (Bi58) and analyzed for s- and p-wave contributions by Cameron. The point marked *Macklin* is a 25-kev measurement (Ma57). The Duke points have been normalized to a Los Alamos point (unpublished).

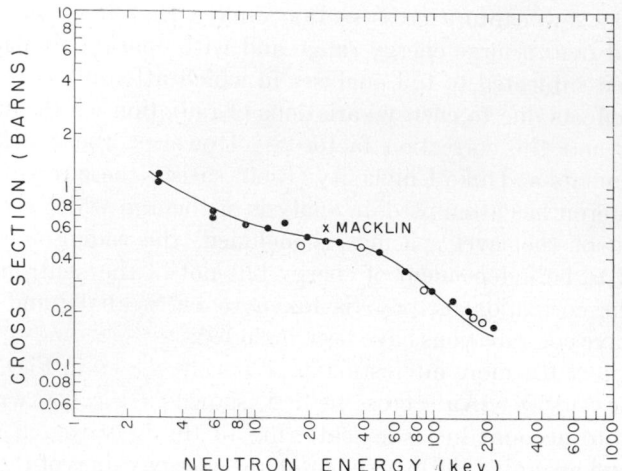

Figure 26. The cross section for the $U^{238}(n,\gamma)U^{239}$ reaction, as measured at Duke University (Bi60) and analyzed for s- and p-wave contributions by Cameron. The point marked *Macklin* is a 25-kev measurement (Ma57). The Los Alamos points are unpublished results.

gies near 1 kev, the p-wave neutron strength function, and the radiation width associated with p-wave capture. It was found that this radiation width should be only 71 per cent of the radiation width associated with s-wave capture. This is a reasonable result since the photon spectrum produced by thermal neutron capture has a number of unusually strong components at high energy representing transitions to low lying p-states in Au^{198}. Similar strong high energy components are not to be expected in the spectrum associated with p-wave neutron capture. The rapid departure of the experimental points from the solid line above 70 kev, which is also evident in similar curves for the platinum isotopes, represents the onset of d-wave capture with an associated strong d-wave strength function. The slight turnup of the solid line at the highest neutron energies is an effect associated with the decrease in the level spacing as the nuclear excitation energy increases. Bilpuch, Weston, and Newson (Bi60) have also analyzed this curve with some simplifying assumptions, including neglect of the energy variation of level spacings and of inelastic scattering to the 77 kev level. They do not find it necessary to use different values for the radiation width associated with s-wave and p-wave capture.

The $U^{238}(n,\gamma)U^{239}$ cross-section curve, shown in Fig. 26, was fitted taking into account inelastic scattering to the 45 kev first excited state.   It was found necessary to use a radiation width associated with p-wave capture larger than that associated with s-wave capture by a factor 3.5.   This result is perhaps reasonable if the single particle d-states responsible for the strong d-wave strength function near $A = 200$ have become bound at $A = 239$ and enhance the p-wave capture probability relative to that for s-waves.   However, L. Dresner (private communication) finds that this large radiation width leads to trouble in fitting the cross-section curve at higher neutron energies.   The analysis of Bilpuch, Weston, and Newson (Bi60) leads to the conclusion that the value of $\Gamma_\gamma/\langle D(\lambda,0)\rangle$ must be higher for p-wave capture than for s-wave capture.   However, they interpret this as meaning that level spacings are parity-dependent rather than that the radiation widths are parity-dependent.   The difficulty pointed out by Dresner would also apply to this interpretation.

The $U^{238}(n,\gamma)U^{239}$ capture cross section and also that for the $Th^{232}(n,\gamma)Th^{233}$ reaction have been analyzed at higher energies by Lane and Lynn (La57).   Their results are shown in Figs. 27 and 28.

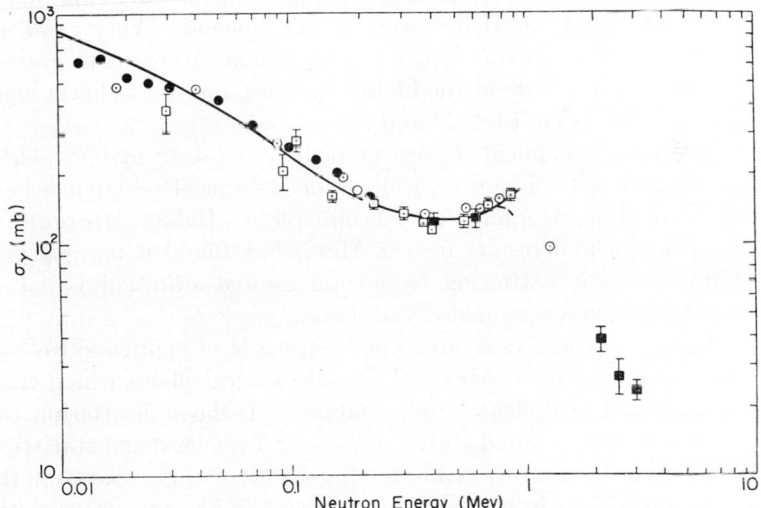

Figure 27. The cross section for the $U^{238}(n,\gamma)U^{239}$ reaction as analyzed By Lane and Lynn (La57).

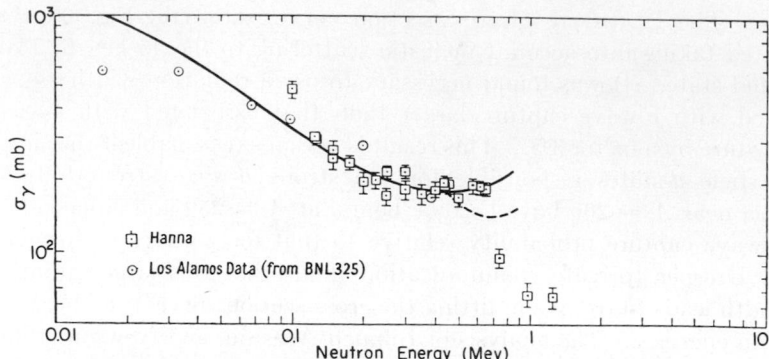

Figure 28. The cross section for the Th²³²(n,γ)Th²³³ reaction as analyzed by Lane and Lynn (La57).

They have assumed that all neutron strength functions and radiation widths are independent of angular momentum and that the correction factor S is $S(\alpha,0,0)$ below 150 kev and unity above 150 kev. The solid curves show the results of including inelastic scattering to the 2^+ and 4^+ levels forming the ground state rotational bands. The broken curve shows the effect of including inelastic scattering due to expected 1^- and 3^- excited states in each nucleus. Very good absolute fits to the experimental cross section measurements are obtained by this procedure at the higher energies, but not as lower energies, as may be seen in Figs. 27 and 28.

The more complicated case of neutron capture in U²³⁵, which must compete with fission as well as inelastic scattering, has been analyzed by Rae, Margolis, and Troubetzkoy (Ra58). In order to fit the experimental results near 1 Mev, they found it necessary to postulate inelastic scattering to several excited states of U²³⁵ that have not yet been experimentally observed.

No detailed analyses have yet been made of capture cross sections at energies above 1 Mev. There are several effects which enter the picture and complicate such analyses. Inelastic scattering can take place to many excited states of the target nucleus, and statistical methods must be used to evaluate the effects of this. Some of the radiative transitions in the capture process take place to states of the compound nucleus which lie above the neutron binding energy, which will usually emit a neutron unless discouraged from doing so by angular momentum considerations. This leads to $(n,\gamma n')$ reactions which could be experimentally distinguished from $(n,n'\gamma)$ reactions (inelastic scattering) only by a very rigorous statistical analysis. At higher energies some of the radiative transitions may be enhanced by collective effects associated with the giant resonance in the electric dipole transition probabilities.

It is appropriate here to comment on the approximate constancy of the average capture cross sections near 100 kev in the heavy uranium nuclei, which were deduced from the yields of the Mike fusion explosion (Section 2.F). From Eqs. (11), (10), (12), and (39) it follows that for these nuclei:

$$\langle\sigma_\gamma\rangle \approx \text{constant} \times \Gamma_\gamma/\langle D(\lambda,0)\rangle \approx \text{constant} \times \int_0^U E^3 dE/$$
$$\langle D(\lambda,0,U\text{-}E)\rangle$$
$$\approx \text{constant}$$

From these relations it appears that as the neutron binding energy decreases the capture cross section can stay constant only if the total number of levels below the neutron binding energy increases slightly. This effect is not to be expected in the case at hand (Ca59). Hence Cameron has concluded (Ca59) that neutron binding energies probably do not decrease appreciably between U^{238} and U^{254}, contrary to the predictions of the usual mass formulas.

G. Capture Cross Sections Between Resonances

Most capture cross sections measured with thermal neutrons represent cases in which the neutron energy lies between resonances in the compound nucleus. The thermal cross section then results from contributions from the Breit-Wigner tails of nearby resonances. In light nuclei, where one or two radiative transitions comprise nearly the entire radiation width, there may be interference in the capture cross section between adjacent resonances of the same angular momentum, and a multi-level formula would have to be used in the analysis. However, in heavier nuclei, where there are very many radiative transitions, such interference effects should be negligible.

In nuclei with smaller level spacings there is in general a greater chance that the main contributing levels lie closer to the thermal energy region, and the thermal capture cross section will tend to be larger. For this reason the odd mass number isotopes of even-Z

elements tend to have larger thermal capture cross sections than the even mass number isotopes. The odd mass number isotopes usually have a ground state spin considerably greater than zero and hence there is a considerably smaller level spacing in the compound nucleus.

There is considerable practical interest in resonance integrals, defined as

$$\text{Resonance Integral} \equiv \int (\sigma_\gamma/E)dE$$

where the integral usually has the cadmium cut-off energy as its lower limit. This integral is strongly weighted by the cross section at low neutron energies. Dresner (Dr55) has analyzed these integrals and finds that the $E^{-1/2}$ extension of the thermal cross section gives the major contribution to the resonance integral for light nuclei ($A < 50$) and for nuclei near closed neutron shells. For heavier nuclei the major contribution comes from the resonances. Because of the large variation in neutron widths, sometimes a single one of these resonances will make the major contribution to the integral. Goldstein and Kalos (Go57) have shown that in the case of Fe^{56} and similar nuclei the p-wave resonances may make the major contribution to the resonance integral.

However, in the case of certain nuclei with very large level spacings there is an additional process which may give a larger contribution to the capture process than any so far considered. This is the direct capture of an incoming neutron into a single particle state which is made up of the target nucleus plus a neutron with partial wave differing by unity from that of the incoming neutron. This is of greatest interest in the case of thermal neutron capture into low-lying p-states. The basic theory of the direct capture process is contained in papers by Thomas (Th52), Courant (Co51), Breit and Yost (Br35), Wilkinson (Wi54), Lane (La59a), and Lane and Lynn (La60a).

In the direct capture process the matrix element for the transition connects the wave function for the incoming neutron with the single particle part of the wave function of the final state; the transition probability is therefore proportional to the reduced neutron width of the final state. An important feature of this matrix element is that the contribution to it from outside the usual nuclear radius is often much larger than the contribution from inside the nuclear radius.

Thomas (Th52) has shown that the thermal cross section for the $C^{12}(n,\gamma)C^{13}$ reaction is much smaller than one would expect from resonance parameters because there is a large cancellation between the internal and external contributions to the capture.

Peker (Pe55) and Shut'ko and Zaretskii (Sh55) have pointed out that direct capture probably accounts for most of the thermal cross section in Pb^{206} and Pb^{207}. For example, Pb^{207} has low-lying $p_{1/2}$ and $p_{3/2}$ levels. The $p_{1/2}$ level is a single-particle state, while the $p_{3/2}$ level is a hole state. Only the $p_{1/2}$ level can therefore participate in direct neutron capture, but both states should participate in capture which proceeds through compound nucleus formation. In fact, only capture to the $p_{1/2}$ state is observed. Shut'ko and Zaretskii find that the thermal cross section is consistent with that expected for the direct capture process. A more extensive analysis of this situation is given by Lane and Lynn (La60b).

Lane and Lynn (La58) have recently pointed out that the capture cross sections observed at higher neutron energies ($\gtrsim 5$ Mev) must be almost entirely due to a direct process. As the neutron energy increases into the several Mev region, the number of levels available for inelastic scattering increases rapidly, and hence the neutron width also increases rapidly. On the other hand, Eq. (39) for the radiation width must be modified by replacing the lower limit of the integral by the difference between the excitation energy and the neutron binding energy. This equation then gives not the total radiation width but the width for that radiation which cannot be followed by neutron emission. This modified effective radiation width decreases rapidly as the neutron energy increases. The net result is that this compound nucleus theory predicts that the capture cross sections will decrease by 3 to 6 orders of magnitude as the neutron energy goes from 1 to 14 Mev. However, the experimental fact is that the capture cross sections decrease by only about a factor 20 in this energy range (Pe58).

The direct capture process must involve a transition between the system formed by the target nucleus and the incoming nucleon and a final single-particle state which is bound in the compound nucleus. Since there are several orbital angular momentum states available for the incoming neutron of several Mev energy, there is always at least one such bound single-particle state available in the compound nucleus. Lane and Lynn (La58) roughly estimate that the cross section for this direct process is

$$\sigma_\gamma \approx 6\left(\frac{Z}{A}\right)^2 \frac{R^4\sqrt{\overline{E}_n}E_\gamma{}^3 \cdot 10^{-10}}{2 + 0.5E_n + 16.8\sqrt{\overline{E}_n}/R} \text{ barns} \qquad (41)$$

where Z and A are the charge and mass numbers of the compound nucleus, R is its radius in units of 10^{-13} cm., and E_n and E_γ are the neutron and radiated photon energies in Mev.

The cross sections calculated from Eq. (41) for 14.5 Mev neutrons incident on various nuclei are plotted in Fig. 29, where they are compared with the experimental results of Perkins et al. (Pe58). Also shown in the figure are estimates of the compound nucleus cross section made by Lane and Lynn. It may be seen that the calculated

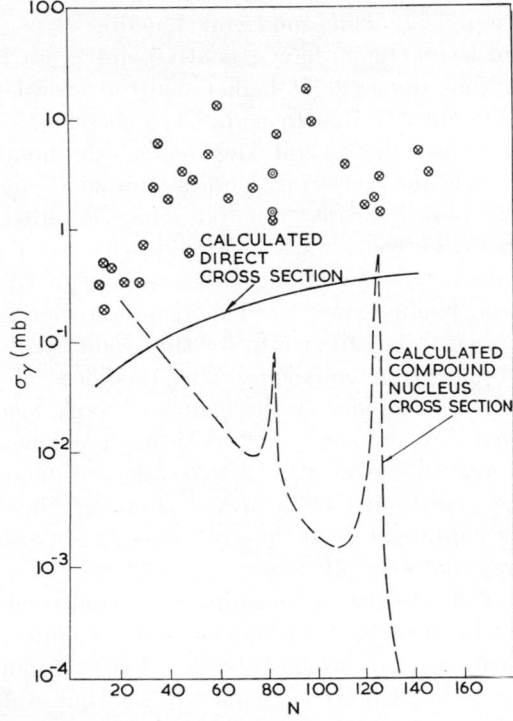

Figure 29. The capture cross sections for 14-Mev neutrons measured by Perkins, O'Connor, and Coleman, compared with the calculations of Lane and Lynn for the direct and compound nucleus processes.

direct capture cross section falls below the experimental points by slightly more than an order of magnitude.

When Lane and Lynn derived Eq. (41) they included estimates of the relevant electric dipole transition matrix elements which contained only contributions from distances less than the nuclear radius. However, they have recently found (La58a) that the contribution from larger distances is an order of magnitude or so larger than that from inside the nuclear radius, even for 14-Mev neutrons. If Eq. (41) is amended accordingly, quite good agreement between calculation and experiment would be obtained in Fig. 29. They have recently published a fuller description of these external contributions to the matrix element (La59b), but have given only one illustrative quantitative estimate of them.

Lane and Lynn (La60a) have also recently published an extensive analysis of the theory of radiative capture in the resonance region for low energy neutrons. They have shown how ordinary resonance capture can interfere with the direct capture process. They have also shown that ordinary resonance capture can be enhanced if there are transitions to relatively pure final single-particle states. In such cases the external part of the neutron wave function in the entrance channel usually gives the greatest contribution to the transition matrix element, as in direct capture. Such effects are therefore enhanced for those resonances with a large reduced neutron width. Since most resonances have small reduced neutron widths, it follows that spectrum anomalies will become more important as the neutron energy is moved off resonance and contributions from nearby levels of large width become more important. The spectrum anomalies due to direct capture (which can be thought of as due to the combined effect of all distant levels) also are more important between resonances.

References

(A154)   R. D. Albert and E. R. Gaerttner, *Knolls Atomic Power Laboratory Report KAPL* 1083, unpublished (1954).

(A158)   W. D. Allen and R. L. Henkel, *Progress in Nuclear Energy*, Ser. I, Vol. II, Pergamon Press, New York, 1958.

(Ba57)   Bartholomew, Campion, Knowles, and Manning, "Proc. Internat. Conf. on Neutron Interactions with Nuclei," Columbia University, *U. S. Atomic Energy Comm. Report* TID-7547, unpublished (1957).

(Ba59)   S. J. Bame and R. L. Cubitt, *Phys. Rev.* 113, 256 (1959).

(Be55)   Bergmann, Isacoff, Murin Shapiro, Shtranikh, and Cazarnovsky, International Conf. on Peaceful Uses of Atomic Energy; Paper P/642, 4, 135 (1955).

(Be55a)   H. A. Bethe, *Los Alamos Sci. Lab. Report* 1428, unpublished (1955).

(Be56)   Bethe, Beyster, and Carter, *J. Nucl. Energy* 3, 207, 273 (1956); 4, 3, 147 (1957).

(Be58)   T. S. Belanova, *J. Exp. and Theor. Phys. (USSR)* 34, 574 (1958); translation, *Soviet Phys. JETP* 7, 397 (1958); see also *Atomnaya Energiya* 8, 549 (1960).

(Bi57)   H. Bichsel and T. W. Bonner, *Phys. Rev.* 108, 1025 (1957).

(Bi60)   Bilpuch, Weston, and Newson, *Ann. Phys.* 10, 455 (1960).

(B152)   J. M. Blatt and V. F. Weisskopf, *Theoretical Nuclear Physics*, John Wiley and Sons, New York, 1952.

(Bl59)   R. C. Block, *Bull. Am. Phys. Soc.* 4, 474 (1959).

(B160)   R. C. Block and G. G. Slaughter, *Oak Ridge Nat. Lab. Report ORNL* 2910, p. 35, unpublished (1960).

(B161)   Block, VonderLage, and Weston, *Oak Ridge Nat. Lab. Report ORNL* 3085, p. 48, unpublished (1961).

(Bo58)   Booth, Ball, and MacGregor, *Phys. Rev.* 112, 226 (1958).

(Br35)   G. Breit and F. L. Yost, *Phys. Rev.* 48, 203 (1935).

(Ca57a)   A. G. W. Cameron, *Chalk River Lab. Report* CRL-41, unpublished (1957).

(Ca57b)   A. G. W. Cameron, *Can. J. Phys.* 35, 1021 (1957).

(Ca57c)   A. G. W. Cameron, *Chalk River Lab. Report* CRP-690, unpublished (1957).

(Ca57d)   A. G. W. Cameron, "Proc. Internat. Conf. on Neutron Interactions with Nuclei," Columbia University, *U. S. Atomic Energy Comm.* Report TID-7547, unpublished (1957).

(Ca58)   A. G. W. Cameron, *Can. J. Phys.* 36, 1040 (1958).

(Ca59)   A. G. W. Cameron, *Can. J. Phys.* 37, 322 (1959).

(Co36)   C. H. Collie and J. H. E. Griffiths, *Proc. Roy. Soc. (London)* 155A, 434 (1936).

(Co51)   E. D. Courant, *Phys. Rev.* 82, 703 (1951).

(Co56)   Codd, Shepherd, and Tait, *Progress in Nuclear Energy*, Ser. I, Vol. II, Pergamon Press, London, and McGraw-Hill, New York, 1956.

(Co56a)   D. R. Connors and W. C. Miller, *Bull. Am. Phys. Soc.* 1, 340 (1956).

(Co61)   S. A. Cox, *Phys. Rev.* 122, 1280 (1961).

(De52)   Dearnley, Soisson, and Junker, *Knolls Atomic Power Lab. Report* KAPL-813, unpublished (1952).

(Di56)   Diven, Martin, Taschek, and Terrell, *Phys. Rev.* 101, 1012 (1956).

(Di58)   Diven, Terrell, and Hemmendinger, *Phys. Rev.* 109, 144 (1958).

(Di60)   Diven, Terrell, and Hemmendinger, *Phys. Rev.* 120, 556 (1960).

(Di60a)   Diamond, Fields, Stevens, Studier, Fried, Inghram, Hess, Pyle, Mech, Manning, Ghiorso, Thompson, Higgins, Seaborg, Browne, Smith, and Spence, *Phys. Rev.* 119, 2000 (1960).

(Dr55)   L. Dresner, *J. Nuclear Energy* 2, 118 (1955).

(Dr56)   L. Dresner, *Nucl. Sci. and Eng.* 1, 103 (1956).

(Dr57)   L. Dresner, "Proc. Internat. Conf. on Neutron Interactions with Nuclei," Columbia University *U. S. Atomic Energy Comm. Report* TID-7547, unpublished (1957).

(Dr59)   L. Dresner, *Oak Ridge Nat. Lab.* Report 2659, unpublished (1959).

(Ev60)   F. Everling, L. A. Konig, J. H. E. Mattauch, and A. H. Wapstra, *Nuclear Phys.* **18**, 529 (1960).

(Fe47)   Feshbach, Peaslee, and Weisskopf, *Phys. Rev.* **71**, 145 (1947).

(Fe59)   A. T. G. Ferguson and E. B. Paul, *J. Nuclear Energy* **A10**, 19 (1959).

(Fi56)   Fields, Studier, Diamond, Mech, Inghram, Pyle, Stevens, Fried, Manning, Ghiorso, Thompson, Higgins, and Seaborg, *Phys. Rev.* **102**, 180 (1956).

(Fi61)   F. W. K. Firk and J. H. Gibbons, *Bull. Am. Phys. Soc.* **6**, 252 (1961).

(Fr54)   O. R. Frisch and D. S. Littler, *Phil. Mag.* **45**, 126 (1954).

(Fu58)   Fuller, Petree, and Weiss, to be published.

(Ga57)   E. R. Gaerttner, "Proc. Tripartite Conf. on Cross Sections of Fissile Nuclei," *Atomic Energy Res. Establ. (Harwell) Report* AERE NP/R 2076, unpublished (1957).

(Ga59)   Gabbard, Davis, and Bonner, *Phys. Rev.* **114**, 201 (1959).

(Gh55)   Ghiorso, Thompson, Higgins, Seaborg, Studier, Fields, Fried, Diamond, Mech, Pyle, Huizenga, Hirsch, Manning, Browne, Smith, and Spence, *Phys. Rev.* **99**, 1048 (1955).

(Gi59)   Gibbons, Macklin, Marion, and Schmitt, *Phys. Rev.* **114**, 1319 (1959).

(Gi61)   Gibbons, Macklin, Miller, and Neiler, *Phys. Rev.* **122**, 182 (1961).

(Go57)   H. Goldstein and M. H. Kalos, *Nuclear Development Corporation of America Report* NDA 2-62, unpublished (1957).

(Go58)   Good, Neiler, and Gibbons, *Phys. Rev.* **109**, 926 (1958).

(Ha52)   W. Hauser and H. Feschbach, *Phys. Rev.* **87**, 366 (1952).

(Ha59)   R. C. Hanna and B. Rose, *J. Nuclear Energy* **8**, 197 (1959).

(He50)   R. L. Henkel and H. H. Barschall, *Phys. Rev.* **80**, 145 (1950).

(Hu51)   V. Hummel and B. Hamermesh, *Phys. Rev.* **82**, 67 (1951).

(Hu53)   Hughes, Garth, and Levin, *Phys. Rev.* **91**, 1423 (1953).

(Hu56)   J. R. Huizenga, *Physica* **21**, 410 (1956).

(Hu56a)   H. Hurewitz and R. Ehrlich, *Progress in Nuclear Energy*, Ser. I, Vol. II, Pergamon Press, London, and McGraw-Hill, New York, 1956.

(Hu57)   J. R. Huizenga and H. Diamond, *Phys. Rev.* **107**, 1087 (1957).

(In55)   Inghram, Hess, Hayden, and Stevens, International Conference on Peaceful Uses of Atomic Energy, Paper P/596, **4**, 105 (1955).

(Is60)   Isakov, Popov, and Shapiro, *J. Exptl. and Theor. Phys. (USSR)* **38**, 989 (1960); translation, *Soviet Phys. JETP* **11**, 712 (1960).

(Jo59)   Johnsrud, Silbert, and Barschall, *Phys. Rev.* **116**, 927 (1959).

(Ka55)   Kanne, Stewart, and White, International Conference on Peaceful Uses of Atomic Energy, Paper P/595 **4**, 315 (1955).

(Ki53)   C. Kimball and B. Hamermesh, *Phys. Rev.* **89**, 1306 (1953).

(Ki55)   B. B. Kinsey, *Beta and Gamma Ray Spectroscopy*, K. Siegbahn, ed., Interscience Publishers, Inc., New York, 1955, p. 795.

(Ko59)   Kononov, Staviskii, and Tolstikov, *J. Nuclear Energy* **A11**, 46 (1959).

(Ku58)   E. Kuhn and L. Dresner, *J. Nuclear Energy* **7**, 69 (1958).

(La47)   A. Langsdorf, *Argonne Nat. Lab. Report* ANL 4342, unpublished (1947).

(La57)   A. M. Lane and J. E. Lynn, *Proc. Phys. Soc.* (*London*) **70A,** 557 (1957).

(La58)   A. M. Lane and J. E. Lynn, Second United Nations Conference Peaceful Uses of Atomic Energy, Geneva, Paper P/4 **15,** 38 (1958).

(La58a) A. M. Lane, remarks at informal session, Second United Nations Conference Peaceful Uses of Atomic Energy, Geneva, and private communication (1958).

(La59a) A. M. Lane, *Nuclear Phys.* **11,** 625 (1959).

(La59b) A. M. Lane and J. E. Lynn, *Nuclear Phys.* **11,** 646 (1959).

(La60a) A. M. Lane and J. E. Lynn, *Nuclear Phys.* **17,** 563 (1960).

(La60b) A. M. Lane and J. E. Lynn, *Nuclear Phys.* **17,** 586 (1960).

(Le56)   J. S. Levin and D. J. Hughes, *Phys. Rev.* **101,** 1328 (1956).

(Le58)   A. I. Leipunsky, *et al.*, Second United Nations International Conference on the Peaceful Uses of Atomic Energy, Paper P/2219 **15,** 50 (1958).

(Li55)   Lichtenberger, Thalgott, Kato, and Novick, International Conference on Peaceful Uses of Atomic Energy, Paper P/813 **3,** 345 (1955).

(Ly59)   W. S. Lyon and R. L. Macklin, *Phys. Rev.* **114,** 1619 (1959).

(Ma52)   B. Margolis, *Phys. Rev.* **88,** 327 (1952).

(Ma53)   H. C. Martin and R. F. Taschek, *Phys. Rev.* **89,** 1302 (1953).

(Ma56)   Mattauch, Waldmann, Bieri, and Everling, *Ann. Rev. Nuclear Sci.* **6,** 179 (1956).

(Ma57)   Macklin, Lazar, and Lyon, *Phys. Rev.* **107,** 504 (1957).

(Ma57a) R. L. Macklin, *Nuclear Instruments*, **1,** 335 (1957).

(Mi59)   Miskel, Marsh, Lindner, and Nagle, *Bull. Am. Phys. Soc.* **4,** 475 (1959).

(Mo59)   Mossin-Kotin, Margolis, and Troubetzkoy, *Phys. Rev.* **116,** 937 (1959).

(Ne56)   T. D. Newton, *Can. J. Phys.* **34,** 804 (1956).

(Ne59)   Neiler, Gibbons, Macklin, and Miller, *Bull. Am. Phys. Soc.* **4,** 474 (1959).

(Ne59a) H. W. Newson and E. G. Bilpuch, private communication (1959).

(Ok55)   Okrent Avery, and Hummel, International Conference on Peaceful Uses of Atomic Energy, Paper P/609 **5,** 347 (1955).

(Pa58)   Pasechnik, Barchuk, Totsky, Strizhak, Korolev, Gofman and Lovchikova, International Conference on Peaceful Uses of Atomic Energy, Paper P/2030 **15,** 18 (1958).

(Pe55)   L. K. Peker, *J. Exp. and Theoret. Phys.* (*USSR*) **29,** 855 (1955).

(Pe58)   Perkin, O'Conner, and Coleman, *Proc. Phys. Soc.* (*London*) **72A,** 505 (1958).

(Po56)   C. E. Porter and R. G. Thomas, *Phys. Rev.* **104,** 483 (1956).

(Ra57a) E. R. Rae and E. M. Bowey, *J. Nucl. Energy* **4,** 179 (1957).

(Ra57b) L. J. Rainwater, "Proc. Tripartite Conf. on Cross Sections of Fissile Nuclei," *Atomic Energy Res. Establ.* (*Harwell*) *Report* AERE NP/R 2076, unpublished (1957).

(Ra58)   E. R. Rae, B. Margolis, and E. S. Troubetzkoy, *Phys. Rev.* **112,** 492 (1958).

(Ro53) Rose, Miranker, Leak, and Rabinowitz, *U. S. Atomic Energy Comm.* Report BNL-257, unpublished (1953).
(Ro54) Rose, Miranker, Leak, Rosenthal, and Hendrickson, *U. S. Atomic Energy Comm. Report* WAPD-SR-506 (2 vols.), unpublished (1954).
(Ro57) H. Rose, *J. Nuclear Energy* **5**, 4 (1957).
(Sa58) Saplakoglu, Bollinger, and Cote, *Phys. Rev.* **109**, 1258 (1958).
(Sa60) Safford, Taylor, Rustad, and Havens, *Phys. Rev.* **119**, 1291 (1960).
(Sc60) H. W. Schmitt and C. W. Cook, *Nuclear Phys.* **20**, 202 (1960).
(Sc60a) H. W. Schmitt, *Nuclear Phys.* **20**, 220 (1960).
(Sc60b) Schmitt, Block, and Bailey, *Nuclear Phys.* **17**, 109 (1960).
(Sh55) A. V. Shut'ko and D. F. Zaretskii, *J. Exp. and Theoret. Phys. (USSR)* **29**, 866 (1955).
(Sn55) T. M. Snyder, International Conference on Peaceful Uses of Atomic Energy Paper, P/602 **5**, 162 (1955).
(Sp55) Spivak, Erozoliminsky, Lavrenchik, and Dorofew, International Conference on Peaceful Uses of Atomic Energy, Paper P/659 **5**, 91 (1955).
(St57) A. Stolovy and J. A. Harvey, *Phys. Rev.* **108**, 353 (1957).
(St58) Strominger, Hollander, and Seaborg, *Revs. Modern Phys.* **30**, 585 (1958).
(St60) I. I. Staviskii and V. A. Tolstikov, *Atomnaya Energ.* **9**, 401 (1960).
(Th52) R. G. Thomas, *Phys. Rev.* **88**, 1109 (1952).
(Ve59) J. F. Vervier, *Nuclear Phys.* **9**, 569 (1959).
(Wa56a) A. H. Wapstra, *Physica* **21**, 367 (1956).
(Wa56b) A. H. Wapstra, *Physica* **21**, 385 (1956).
(We60) Weston, Seth, Bilpuch, and Newson, *Ann. Phys.* **10**, 477 (1960).
(We61) L. W. Weston and W. S. Lyon, *Phys. Rev.* **123**, 948 (1961).
(Wi47) E. P. Wigner and L. Eisenbud, *Phys. Rev.* **72**, 29 (1947).
(Wi54) D. H. Wilkinson, *Phil. Mag.* **45**, 259 (1954).
(Wi60) R. G. Wille and R. W. Fink, *Phys. Rev.* **118**, 242 (1960).

Neutron-Induced Reactions

F. L. RIBE

Los Alamos Scientific Laboratory, Los Alamos, New Mexico

1. Introduction

In contrast to its prewar state, experimental neutron physics has become a relatively more exact art, largely as a result of the use of precise monoenergetic neutron sources and the many new detecting and measuring techniques which have been discussed in the preceding chapters of this volume. In the present article we shall summarize experimental results in which neutron-induced reactions have provided the framework for clarifying various aspects of our conception of nuclear interactions.

We shall not deal here with the measurements of total cross sections, nonelastic and elastic scattering, nuclear fission, and capture processes, which are dealt with elsewhere in the present chapter. The main emphasis of this article will be on those reactions in which charged particles are emitted as a result of bombarding target nuclei with fast neutrons. However, we shall consider also $(n, 2n)$ measurements and some inelastic scattering measurements for which the analogy to certain (n, p) reaction measurements is quite close. We further limit the scope of the discussion primarily to those measurements which have been made with monoenergetic bombarding neutrons and which have yielded absolute cross section values.

The first topic to be discussed will be that of reactions induced by 14-Mev neutrons in some light, but mainly medium-weight and heavy nuclei. Following this, we shall review the $(n, 2n)$ work, both at 14 Mev and at lower neutron bombarding energies. Finally, the $(n, charged particle)$ reactions on light nuclei at various neutron energies will be discussed.

2. Reactions Induced by 14-Mev Neutrons, Primarily in Medium-Weight and Heavy Nuclei

A. Introduction

Because of the widespread availability of intense, inexpensive sources of monoenergetic neutrons made possible by utilization of the $T(d, n)He^4$ reaction, work performed at a neutron energy of 14 Mev occupies a unique place in fast neutron physics. The neutron flux produced by the D-T reaction is easily measured in an absolute manner by counting the α particles associated with the neutrons (cf. Chapter IV.B). As a result, many accurate absolute measurements of 14-Mev, neutron-induced reactions exist. We shall consider these measurements against the background of the question which has arisen in recent years of the degree to which the classical *compound nucleus* theory of nuclear reactions must be modified to include *direct interaction* processes. The discussion will be divided into the following categories: (a) energy spectra and angular distributions of the neutrons from inelastic scattering; (b) total (n, p) cross sections and the energy spectra and angular distributions of the emitted protons; (c) similar considerations regarding the (n, α) interactions.

B. The Statistical, Compound Nucleus Theory

In considering nuclear reactions in the region of the medium-weight and heavy nuclei, at bombarding energies in excess of several Mev, it is reasonable to take as a theoretical frame of reference the statistical theory of nuclear reactions which was developed primarily by Weisskopf and his collaborators (We37, We40, Bl52, Fe55). This theory is based upon Bohr's postulate (Bo36) that nuclear reactions proceed in two stages: (a) the formation of a compound nucleus, followed by (b) its decay into the reaction products in a manner independent of the method of compound nucleus formation. The independence of the decay in the second stage of the process is assured by assuming that many levels of the compound nucleus are excited, i.e., that the energy spread of the incident beam is much greater than the level spacing. In addition, the decay of the various levels must be incoherent. This will be the case if the phases of the states corresponding to these levels are random, i.e., uncorrelated.

The transition probability for decay of the compound nucleus is proportional to the square of a sum of matrix elements involving the compound nuclear states. Since the signs of these matrix elements are random, all of the cross product, interference terms in the squared sum drop out on the average, and only functions which are even in the scattering angle (such as sin 2θ) remain. Thus it is a consequence of the statistical theory that the differential cross sections of nuclear reactions are symmetric about an angle of emission of the reaction products of 90° with respect to the incident beam. If the statistical assumption outlined above applies also to the levels of the residual nucleus, and their density, as a function of their spins j, is proportional to $2j + 1$, then the differential cross sections are isotropic (Wo51, Ha52).

In the statistical theory, a thermodynamic treatment of the nucleus is used to obtain estimates of emission probabilities and energy spectra of reaction products. It is assumed that the nucleons of a heavy nucleus may be treated as a system in thermodynamic equilibrium. If the nucleons are assumed to constitute a degenerate Fermi gas, then the temperature T of the nucleus is related to its energy E, above the ground state, by

$$T = (aE)^{\frac{1}{2}} \tag{1}$$

where a is a constant equal roughly to the spacing of the low-lying nuclear levels. From this function an expression for the entropy of the nucleus follows, and hence that for the nuclear level density $\omega(E)$, which is given by

$$\omega(E) = \text{const. exp } [2(E/a)^{\frac{1}{2}}] \tag{2}$$

Let us consider the residual nucleus in a reaction in which particles (e.g., protons) of center-of-mass energy ϵ are emitted from the compound nucleus with a maximum possible energy $\epsilon_{\max} = \epsilon + E$. Then if ϵ is much smaller than $\epsilon_{\max}$, Eqs. (1) and (2) give the following expression for the level density of the residual nucleus:

$$\omega_r(\epsilon) = \text{const. exp } (-\epsilon/T) \tag{3}$$

Weisskopf considered detailed balancing between the process of emission (evaporation) of particles from the compound nucleus and the inverse process in which particles are captured by the residual nucleus with a cross section $\sigma_c(\epsilon)$. For neutrons, $\sigma_c(\epsilon)$ would be the measured total nonelastic cross section.   As a result he arrived at the following expression for the energy spectrum or number of particles emitted by the compound nucleus with energy ϵ:

$$W(\epsilon) \approx d\sigma/d\epsilon = \text{const. } \sigma_c(\epsilon)\epsilon \exp(-\epsilon/T) \tag{4}$$

Thus the level density of the residual nucleus can be obtained from the observed energy spectrum of the emitted particles by dividing the ordinates of the energy spectrum $W(\epsilon)$, for each particle energy ϵ, by the quantity $\epsilon\sigma(\epsilon)$.   In the summary of experimental work to follow, we shall therefore call such graphs of $W(\epsilon)/[\epsilon\sigma(\epsilon)]$ *level density* graphs.

According to the Bohr assumption, one can express the cross section for the reaction $A(a,b)B$ as

$$\sigma(a,b) = \sigma_c(a)f_b/\Sigma f_{b'} \tag{5}$$

where f_b is proportional to the total width for emission of particle b by the compound nucleus, summed over the states of the residual nucleus, and the $f_{b'}$ represent competing processes in which different particles are emitted. $\sigma_c(a)$ is the total (nonelastic) cross section for formation of the compound nucleus.   If ϵ represents the center-of-mass energy of the emitted particle b, then the function f_b is given by

$$f_b = \int_0^{\epsilon_{\max}} \sigma_c(\epsilon)\omega_B(\epsilon_{\max} - \epsilon)d\epsilon \tag{6}$$

Thus f_b, and hence the reaction cross section, depends directly upon the magnitude of the level density of the residual nucleus.

In the experimental survey we shall quote calculations of absolute reaction cross sections in which, essentially, use is made of Eqs. (5) and (6).   In the case of charged particle emission, the function $\sigma_c(\epsilon)$ in Eq. (6) accounts for the effects of the Coulomb barrier.   For neutron emission $\sigma_c(\epsilon)$ is just the nonelastic cross section for bombarding neutrons of energy ϵ on the residual nucleus.   For details of the expressions used for the function σ_c and the level density ω, the reader is referred to the quoted papers.

A complete account of the statistical theory is given in Chapter V.J.

C. Direct Interactions

Recently considerable evidence has accumulated which indicates that the classical compound nucleus theory may represent an over-simplification of the facts. One must also consider the possibility of nuclear reactions which proceed by direct interaction processes in which no compound nucleus is formed. An example of such a direct interaction is an (n, p) exchange reaction in which the incident neutron might cause the ejection of a proton from the surface of the target nucleus. Following some initial work by McManus and Sharp (Mc52, Mc55), Austern, Butler, and McManus (Au53) provided a theoretical model for such *surface-direct* interactions. The incident nucleon was assumed to interact with individual nucleons of the target nucleus through the *tails* of their wave functions extending outside the nuclear boundary. Their model is somewhat analogous to that of Butler (Bu51), which provides a model for direct stripping [e.g., (d, n) reactions]. Theories of *volume-direct* interactions between an incident nucleon and those inside the target nucleus have been provided by Hayakawa *et al.* (Ha55), Lamarsh and Feshback (La56), and more recently by Brown and Muirhead (Br57). We shall later compare experimental results with the direct interaction calculations of Brown and Muirhead. In their theory the target nucleus is represented as a Fermi gas of nucleons with which the incident nucleon interacts with a cross section which differs from that for free nucleons only through the restrictions of the Pauli principle on the states of excitation available in the nucleus. They assume that ejection of particles can occur either through direct interaction or during the de-excitation of the nucleus following direct interaction.

As a replacement for the compound nucleus model, Weisskopf (We55, We56, We57) has proposed a model in which nuclear reactions proceed in three stages: (a) an *independent-particle* stage in which the bombarding particle retains its identity and interacts with the target nucleus as a whole; (b) a *compound-system* stage which includes both compound nucleus formation and direct interactions; and (c) a final stage in which the reaction products separate from each other.

A complete account of the direct interaction theories of nuclear reactions is given in Chapter V.D.

D. Inelastic Scattering Experiments

Experiments on the inelastic scattering of neutrons provide one of the oldest methods of assessing the statistical theory. Ideally one would desire measurements of the absolute energy spectra of the inelastically scattered neutrons at enough scattering angles to provide the differential cross section $\sigma_{n'}$ (14; ϵ, θ) with respect to both center-of-mass energy ϵ and solid angle $\Omega(\theta)$ of emitted neutrons.

Experiments with threshold detectors (Ba47, Ba47a, Gi49, Ph52) provided qualitative information on the degradation of the incident energies of neutrons in inelastic scattering. However, the first quantitative results on the energy distribution of the inelastically scattered neutrons were provided by Stelson and Goodman (St51), who carried out measurements on Al, Pb, and Fe, and by Whitmore and Dennis (Wh51), who measured Pb and Bi. These experiments were followed by those of Graves and Rosen (Gr53), who also used nuclear emulsions to detect and measure the scattered neutrons from targets of 11 elements, varying from carbon through bismuth. In these experiments the absolute energy spectra $d\sigma(\epsilon)/d\epsilon$ were obtained by using spherical scatterers surrounding the approximately isotropic 14-Mev, D-T neutron source. The effect of the spherical scatterer was to integrate the yield of inelastically scattered neutrons over all scattering angles.

As we have seen in connection with Eq. (4), a plot of the quantity $\epsilon^{-1}d\sigma/d\epsilon$ should be proportional to $\exp(-\epsilon/T)$, since σ_c may be taken to be constant in the case of neutron scattering. One can therefore obtain the nuclear temperature T of the residual (also target) nucleus by observing the slope of a semilog graph of $\epsilon^{-1}d\sigma/d\epsilon$ *versus* ϵ. In the three experiments discussed above these graphs were remarkably straight lines, corresponding to constant T. However, T was in the neighborhood of 1 Mev for all the elements studied. No appreciable decrease in T with atomic weight A was observed such as one might expect as a result of the sharing of the incident neutron's energy with progressively greater numbers of nucleons in the heavier nuclei. Values of the constant a of the level density formula [Eq. (1)] were in the neighborhood of 0.05. It should be pointed out that these experiments suffered from two defects: (a) no account was taken of the successive emission of two neutrons in $(n, 2n)$ reactions, and (b) no corrections were made for the non-negligible multiple scattering of the neutrons in the scattering samples. Such corrections are discussed in Chapter V.B.

The earliest attempt to measure both angular and energy distributions was that of O'Neill (On54), who bombarded cylindrical samples of the scattering elements C, Al, Cu, Sn, and Pb with 14.8-Mev neutrons and measured the energies of the inelastically scattered

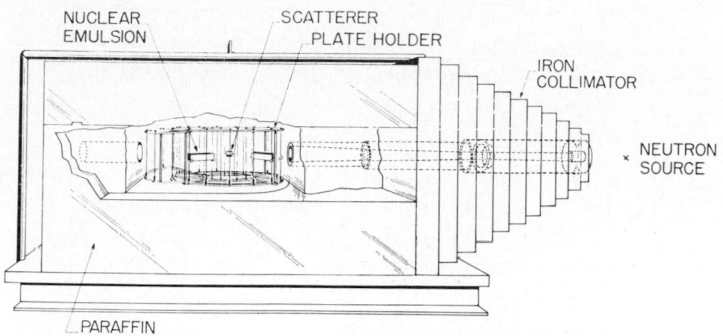

Figure 1. Nuclear multiplate camera of Ro55 for measuring angular distributions and energy spectra of inelastically scattered neutrons.

neutrons at various scattering angles by means of their time of flight from scatterer to detector.   Measurements were limited to those scattered neutrons in the energy range from 0.5 to 4 Mev.   Again, nuclear temperatures of approximately one Mev were deduced for all the elements studied.   In this experiment, as well as in that of Graves and Rosen, the value of T for Sn was about 0.6 Mev, significantly lower than the average value found for all the other elements measured.   O'Neill found that the angular distribution of the inelastically scattered neutrons in the energy range 0.5 to 4 Mev was isotropic to within ±15 per cent.

The first evidence from the inelastic scattering of neutrons in conflict with the statistical theory was provided by the experiment of Rosen and Stewart on the energy spectra and angular distributions of the neutrons scattered by Ta and Bi (Ro55, Ro57).   This was a good-geometry experiment in which the scattered neutrons were detected by means of the proton recoils which they produced in the hydrogenous material of nuclear emulsions (cf. Chapter II.D).   The apparatus is shown in Fig. 1.   A beam of 14-Mev neutrons produced by the D-T source and collimated by the massive iron shield impinged on cylindrical scattering samples suspended at the center of a *squirrel-cage* containing many nuclear emulsions capable of detecting neutrons at various scattering angles.   The nuclear emulsions were placed well outside the incident neutron beam.   By scanning the nuclear emulsion from each angular position and analyzing the proton recoils from the scattered neutrons, it was possible to obtain the energy spectrum

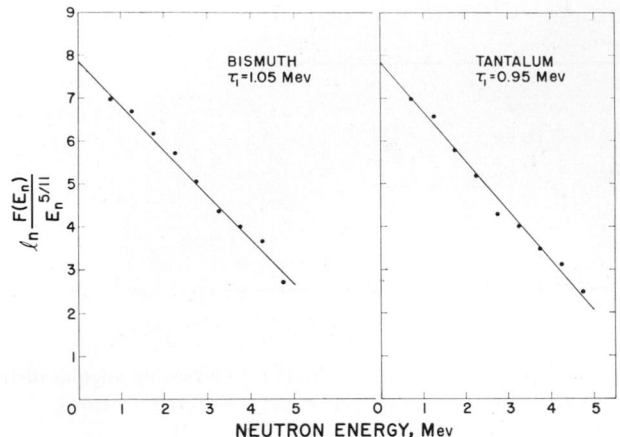

Figure 2. Nuclear level density plots for bismuth and tantalum (Ro55). τ_1 represents the nuclear temperature following emission of the first neutron after inelastic scattering.

of the neutrons at each scattering angle. It was then possible to obtain the over-all differential cross section $\sigma_{n'}(14; \epsilon, \theta)$ between the energy limits of 0.5 and 14 Mev and in the angular region between 20° and 150°.

In analyzing the space-integrated energy spectra of the neutrons, Rosen and Stewart took account of the successive emission of two neutrons in $(n, 2n)$ processes according to a method developed by Lang and LeCouteur (La54, Le52). Instead of being given by Eq. (4), the energy spectrum in this case is given by

$$d\sigma/d\epsilon = \text{const. } \epsilon^{5/11} \exp\left(-12 \, \epsilon/11 T_1\right), \tag{7}$$

where T_1 is the average temperature of the residual nucleus after removal of the first neutron. Figure 2 presents the energy spectra of Rosen and Stewart in the form of a graph of $\log\left(\epsilon^{-5/11} d\sigma/d\epsilon\right)$ versus ϵ for Bi and Ta. The respective values of T_1 are 1.05 Mev and 0.95 Mev—about 10 per cent higher than would have been obtained with no correction for second-neutron emission. By subtracting the contribution of the first neutrons, corresponding to temperature T_1, from the energy spectra, Rosen and Stewart obtained the energy distribution of the second neutrons. Analysis of these spectra by means of Eq. (4) yielded values of T_2, the temperature of the nucleus after

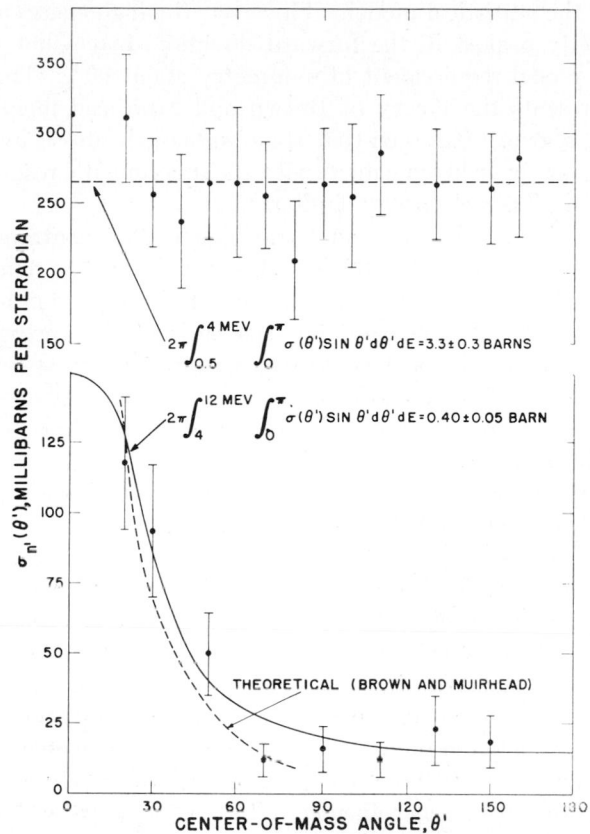

Figure 3. Differential cross sections of the inelastically scattered neutrons from bismuth at 14.1 Mev (Ro55). The upper graph represents the low energy emitted neutrons and the lower graph those of higher energy. The dashed theoretical curve is that of Br57.

emission of two neutrons. In the cases of both Bi and Ta this temperature was about 0.5 Mev.

In presenting their data on the energy-integrated angular distributions, these authors chose to present separately the angular distributions of the low energy neutrons in the region from 0.5 to 4 Mev and the high energy neutrons in the region from 4 to 12 Mev. The results for Bi are shown in Fig. 3. One sees that the low energy, evaporated neutrons have an isotropic angular distribution, in accord with the statistical model. However, the high energy neutrons are distinctly peaked in the forward direction, in conflict with the statistical model requirement of symmetry about 90°. The dashed curve represents the theory of Brown and Muirhead mentioned in Section C, above. It is seen that the results of the direct interaction calculation are in good agreement with the experimental results. The results for the Ta nucleus were similar.

Even though the data on these high energy neutrons offer a striking contradiction to the statistical theory, it must be remembered that they represent only a small portion of the total number of inelastically scattered neutrons. On the basis of these experimental results, the statistical model would still appear to apply to roughly 90 per cent of the inelastic collisions. Similar experimental data for the case of a Zr scatterer were analyzed by Ahn and Roberts (Ah57). The conclusions were similar to those of the Bi-Ta experiment. In this case the temperatures after the emission of the first and second neutrons were 0.99 and 0.57 Mev, respectively.

Corroboration of the observation of forward peaking of the high energy neutrons inelastically scattered in heavy and medium-weight elements has been obtained with an entirely different technique by Coon and collaborators (Co58). Their experiment was also a good geometry experiment in which thin ring scatterers were used to deflect the 14-Mev source neutrons into a small plastic scintillation detector. A shadow bar between the neutron source and the detector prevented the detection of unscattered neutrons directly from the source. The axes of the ring scatterers coincided with the line between the neutron source and the detector. When the diameters and positions of the ring scatterers were varied, different scattering angles could be obtained. In addition, the energy (pulse-height) spectrum of proton recoils produced in the scintillator by the inelastic neutrons was observed for each mean scattering angle. As a result of careful energy calibrations, it was possible to determine the limits of the energies of the inelastically scattered neutrons detected at given bias settings of the scintillation detector.

The experimental angular distributions of the inelastically scattered neutrons in the energy range from 9 to 14 Mev for the target elements Fe, Cu, Sn, and Pb are shown in Fig. 4. For the lightest scattering element (Fe), the angular distribution of scattered neutrons is nearly symmetric about 90°, and the angular distribution becomes

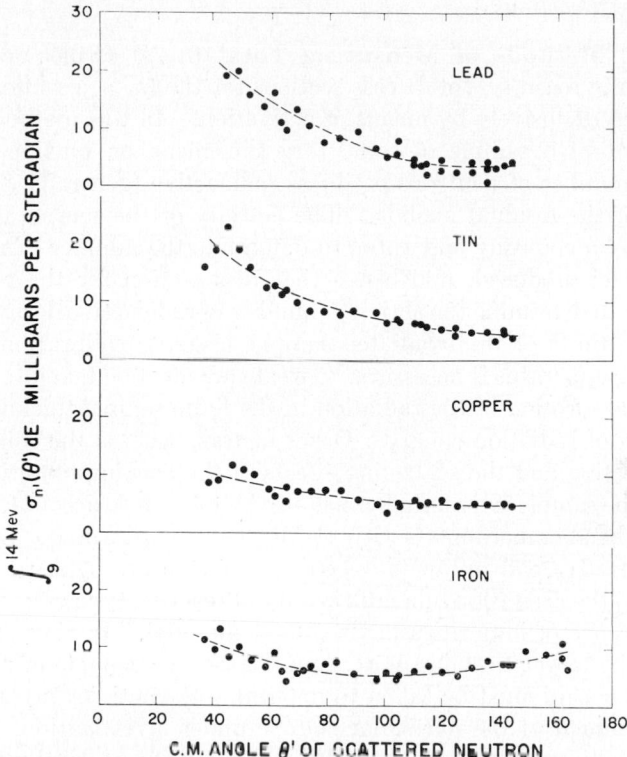

Figure 4. Differential cross sections of inelastically scattered neutrons from various target elements at 14 Mev (Co58). The differential cross sections include contributions only from emitted neutrons having energies greater than 9 Mev.

progressively more peaked in the forward direction as the atomic weight of the scatterer increases. The cross section for inelastic scattering into this range of energies is about the same for all the elements illustrated. Coon *et al.* give the following values for Fe, Cu, Sn, and Pb, respectively: 76, 72, 91, and 88 millibarns, all with an error of ± 30 millibarns. The fractions of nonelastic scattering represented by these high energy neutrons are, respectively, 6, 5, 5, and 4 per cent. Thus there is an indication that direct interaction scattering asymmetries increase with the atomic weight of the scattering nucleus, although the fraction of neutrons in the direct interaction *tail* of the spectrum remains small.

E. (n, p) Reactions

(1) **Methods of Measuring Total (n, p) Cross Sections.**
Until quite recently, total cross sections for the (n, p) reactions were measured exclusively by means of activation. In this method, bombardment of a sample of some target element or nuclide with a known number of neutrons produces radioactive (generally β-active) nuclei of the residual nuclide. The activity of the sample is determined by a counting apparatus to determine the number of radioactive nuclei produced, and hence the cross section for the reaction. In order to determine the activity (number of radioactive decay events per unit time) of the irradiated sample, absolute calibration of the counting apparatus is necessary. Great care must be taken to correct for the absorption of the radiation in the finite sample thickness as a function of radiation energy. Other factors, such as the solid angle for detection and the scattering effects of the backing material upon which the sample is mounted, must also be taken into account.

When bombardments with 14-Mev neutrons are made, a number of radioactive end products may result from a given target nuclide owing to the excitation of a multiplicity of reaction types, as well as to the presence of impurities in the target material. In those cases in which the target contains more than one isotope capable of reaction, particular care must be taken to determine the activity arising from bombardment of the particular isotope under investigation. In the earliest activation measurements identification of a particular reaction end product was made exclusively by identifying its decay scheme. In the simplest cases this amounted simply to measuring and identifying the half-life of the reaction product. In addition, the maximum energy (end point) of the β radiation was sometimes measured, as well as possible β-γ coincidences. Modern practice makes increasing use of chemical separation of the desired end product element as a preliminary to reaction product identification by means of counting techniques. This not only strips the counting sample of unwanted competing activities but also increases the concentration of the activity in the final sample over that which is present before chemical separation. The final counting sample after chemical separation is generally quite thin, requiring little correction for absorption and scattering.

Recent improvements in the means for detecting charged particles in the presence of intense neutron fluxes have led to an alternative method for measuring (n, p) cross sections. The energetic protons arising from the reaction are counted directly upon their emission from the irradiated target. Identification of the protons is made primarily by their energy spectrum and rate of ionization in the detector. Such detection methods have used nuclear plates, as well as combinations of scintillating crystals and gas-filled proportional counters. In the experiments to be described, it is usual to refer to the total (n, p) emission cross section not limited to those events which merely exchange a target proton for a bombarding neutron but including also such processes as the (n, np) and (n, pp) reactions. It is therefore conventional to describe the most elementary (process, whose inverse is β^- decay) by the symbol $(n, p\gamma)$.

(2) **Survey of the Measurements of Total** $(n, p\gamma)$ **Cross Sections at 14 Mev.** Comparisons of experimental results with the predictions of the statistical and direct interaction theories are most easily made when only one neutron bombarding energy need be considered. We shall present data at 14 Mev which were obtained in nearly all cases through the use of neutrons from the $T(d, n)He^4$ reaction. However, the earliest extensive activation survey, involving nine elements with atomic weights between 56 and 139, was that of Wäffler (Wa50), who made use of bombarding neutrons from the reactions $Li(d, n)Be$ and $B(d, n)C$. These reactions provide complex spectra of neutrons, extending from low energies to approximately 15 Mev, thus making comparison with the theory somewhat complicated. Such a comparison was, however, made by Wäffler, and the experimental cross sections were found to be larger than those of the Weisskopf-Ewing statistical theory by a factor of approximately five for elements with $A < 110$ and by a factor of approximately 10 for Sm^{117}, I^{127}, and La^{139}.

Forbes (Fo52) provided an activation survey at 14.1 Mev which included $(n, p\gamma)$ cross section determinations for Al^{27}, P^{31}, Fe^{56}, and Cu^{65}. Absolute β counting and identifications by radioactive half-lives were employed. The most extensive activation survey which has been made is that of Paul and Clarke (Pa53) at 14.5 Mev. They provided measurements of $(n, p\gamma)$, $(n, \alpha\gamma)$, and $(n, 2n)$ cross sections for 57 elements. Among these measurements were those of 38 $(n, p\gamma)$ reactions with target nuclides ranging from O^{16} to Pb^{208}. Their technique involved the use of rather thick targets and counting samples in most cases, absolute β and γ-ray counting that was only approximate, and identification of the reaction products by means of their half-lives. The aim of the experiment was to provide an extensive survey without stressing great accuracy.

The comparison which Paul and Clarke provided between their measured cross sections and those calculated from the Weisskopf-Ewing statistical theory showed striking divergences between theory and experiment. For atomic weights lower than 77 the experimental cross sections agreed to within a factor of approximately eight with those calculated from the theory. However, for the higher mass numbers much larger discrepancies were found, generally by factors of the order of 100, with a factor of 16,000 occurring in the case of Pb^{208}.

Another activation survey has been made by Yasumi (Ya57), who used 4π absolute β counting and half-life identification of the reaction products. He measured $(n, p\gamma)$ cross sections for Al^{27}, Fe^{56}, and Zn^{66}.

In the case of the following measurements, chemical separations of the end products were made before the usual half-life identifications. Blosser (Bl57a) measured eight target nuclides with mass numbers ranging from 56 to 73. Bayhurst and Prestwood (Ba58) have provided measurements for Ti^{46}, Ti^{47}, Ti^{48}, and As^{75} in the form of absolute excitation functions of the $(n, p\gamma)$ reactions between 13.5 and 15.0 Mev. In addition, they give preliminary $(n, p\gamma)$ cross sections for W^{183} and W^{184}. The latter values depend, through the absolute beta counting efficiency, upon assumed decay schemes which are at present somewhat uncertain. The $S^{32}(n, p)P^{32}$ cross section has been measured by Allen et al. (Al57b) at 14.1 Mev as part of an absolute excitation function for this reaction. Additional measurements in a region of the heavy elements not previously covered have been provided by Levkovskiĭ and collaborators (Le57, Dz57), who measured $(n, p\gamma)$ cross sections for Cd^{106}, Cd^{111}, Cd^{112}, Cd^{113}, and Ag^{109}. The residual nuclides were identified by means of their half-lives, as well as by the absorption characteristics of their radiation. In the case of the target nuclide Ag^{109}, the absolute cross section was obtained by comparing the $(n, p\gamma)$ activity with that produced in a parallel irradiation of Cu^{63}, for which the $(n, 2n)$ cross section is known (Fo52, Br52). In the cases of the Cd isotopes, absolute determinations were made by normalizing to the Cd^{112} (n, α) cross section, which in turn was obtained by normalization to the $Cu^{63}(n, 2n)$ cross section. In addition, Levkovskiĭ (Le56) provided measurements of the relative $(n, p\gamma)$ cross sections of the isotopes in the elements Ca, Ti, Sr, Zr, and Cd, demonstrating a systematic decrease of the $(n, p\gamma)$ cross section with increasing atomic weight of isotope for each element.

In addition to the activation data, we include $(n, p\gamma)$ cross section values and upper limits obtained from the nuclear plate experiments of Brown and collaborators (Br57a) and Haling, Peck, and Eubank (Ha57) for the target nuclides Al^{27}, Fe^{56}, Zr^{90}, and Pd^{105}.

Table I gives a digest of the experimental $(n, p\gamma)$ cross sections for all the target nuclides between O^{16} and Pb^{208} known to the author to have been measured at the present writing. For reference, in the sixth column are listed also the cross section values computed by Brown and Muirhead (Br57) on the basis of the compound nucleus theory, using formulas for the f functions [cf. Eq. (5)] and level densities given by LeCouteur (Le52). In the cases of Ba^{138}, La^{139}, Tl^{205}, and Pb^{208}, however, we list the Weisskopf-Ewing values as given by Paul and Clarke. In the seventh column are listed the direct interaction cross sections computed by Brown and Muirhead, and in the eighth column are listed the cross sections given by the sums of the two theoretical contributions. In the cases of the Cd isotopes and Ag^{109} we have listed values interpolated in both the atomic number and reaction Q-value from the calculations of Brown and Muirhead. In these interpolations account was taken of the variation of level density between odd-odd and even-odd (odd-even) residual nuclei as given in the paper of Brown and Muirhead.

From the point of view of number and consistency of the various determinations, only the nuclides Al^{27}, Fe^{56}, and possibly Zn^{66} may be considered as accurately known. Discrepancies in order of magnitude between different measurements exist for Ge^{73} and Pd^{105}.

In comparing the data of Paul and Clarke with the theoretical compound nucleus values, it is seen that there is a demarcation in the region of heavy nuclei at $A \approx 70$ below which the ratio of experimental and theoretical values is generally within a factor of nine greater or smaller than unity. Above this demarcation the ratio varies by factors which are between approximately 10 and something in excess of 100 greater than unity. The results of Levkovskiĭ et al. in the region $106 \leq A \leq 113$ are in contradiction to this trend, as is the determination of Blosser for Ge^{73}. Both of these investigations made use of radiochemical techniques. The upper limit of Rosen and

Table I. Experimental Values of $(n, p\gamma)$ Cross Sections for Various Target Nuclides at 14-Mev Bombarding Energy

| Target nuclide | Q-value (Mev) | Experimental $(n, p\gamma)$ cross section (millibarns) | | | Calculated $(n, p\gamma)$ cross section (millibarns) | | |
		Paul and Clarke	Other	Ref.	Compound nucleus[a]	Direct inter-action[b]	Sum
O^{16}	−9.4	49 ± 25	89 ± 30	Ma54	15	5	20
F^{19}	−3.7	135 ± 47			15	25	40
Na^{23}	−3.4	34 ± 15			15	30	45
Mg^{24}	−4.7	191 ± 34			160	45	205
Mg^{25}	−2.9	45 ± 18			60	60	120
Al^{27}	−1.9	52 ± 9	79 ± 6	Fo52	25	40	65
			87 ± 7	Ya57			
			55 ± 10	Br57a			
			79 ± 15	Ha57			
Si^{28}	−3.8	220 ± 51	292 ± 45	Th58	215	45	260
Si^{29}	−3.0	101 ± 30			45	55	100
P^{31}	−0.7	64 ± 8	91 ± 9	Fo52	30	35	65
			86 ± 7	Gr58			
S^{32}	−0.9	369 ± 44	254 ± 10	Al57b	170	50	220
S^{34}	−4.3	85 ± 38			70	30	100
Cl^{37}	−3.5	33 ± 7			10	30	40
K^{41}	−1.8	81 ± 32			10	35	45
Ti^{46}	−1.6		240 ± 40	Pr58			
Ti^{47}	+0.3		170 ± 15	Pr58			
Ti^{48}	−3.2	93 ± 32	61 ± 3	Pr58	100	30	130
V^{51}	−1.4	27 ± 4			10	30	40
Cr^{52}	−3.0	78 ± 11	87 ± 13	Th58	75	30	105
Fe^{56}	−2.9	97 ± 12	124 ± 12	Fo52	60	30	90
			125	B157			
			144 ± 19	Ya57			
			120 ± 30	Br57a			
Ni^{61}	−0.5	181 ± 25	91	B157	30	45	75

Nuclide	Q	σ	σ	Ref.			
Zn^{64}	+0.2	386 ± 58	216	Bl57	110	45	155
Cu^{65}	−1.3	101 ± 17	200 ± 30	Ar56	5	30	35
Zn^{66}	−1.9	24 ± 19c	19 ± 4	Fo52	45	30	75
Ga^{69}	−0.1	129 ± 65	20	Bl57	5	25	30
Ge^{70}	−1.0	65 ± 26	80 ± 7	Bl57	60	30	90
Ge^{72}	−3.2	137 ± 68	60	Ya57	10	20	30
Ge^{73}	−0.6	12 ± 2	93	Bl57	6	30	36
As^{75}	−0.4	45 ± 23	32	Bl57	3	30	33
Se^{77}	0.0	18 ± 3	20	Bl57	5	20	25
Sr^{88}	−4.4	247 ± 99	—		2	9	11
Zr^{90}	−1.4	11 ± 4	—		20	20	40
Zr^{94}	−4.6	108 ± 54	—		0.3	6	6
Mo^{97}	−1.3	199 ± 139	—		2	20	22
Ru^{101}	−0.7	132 ± 66	—		3	22	25
Rh^{103}	0.0	743 ± 52	19 ± 1	Pr58	5	19	24
Pd^{104}	−1.5	—	11 ± 3	Br57	6	17	23
Pd^{105}	+0.2	—	≤ 10	Ar56	4	25	29
Ag^{109}	+0.5	—	11 ± 2	Dz57	3	21	24
Cd^{106}	−0.3	—	76 ± 24	Le57	10	33	43
Cd^{111}	−3.2	—	15 ± 4	Le57	3	21	24
Cd^{112}	−1.3	—	10 ± 3	Le57	1	10	11
Cd^{113}	0.0	—	7.2 ± 2.2	Le57	2	18	20
I^{127}	−4.1	231 ± 139c	—		1	16	17
Ba^{138}	−1.5	6.3 ± 2.2	—		0.24d	3	3
La^{139}	−1.0	5.7 ± 2.4	—		0.33d	9	9
W^{182}	−0.3	—	6.0 ± 1.0	Ba58			
W^{183}	−0.5	—	8.0 ± 0.8	Ba58			
W^{184}	−1.0	—	4.5 ± 0.5	Ba58			
Tl^{205}	−1.0	3.0 ± 1.5	—		0.016d	3	3
Pb^{208}	−4.2	0.96 ± 0.96	—		0.00006d	0.3	0.3

ᵃ Computed by Brown and Muirhead unless otherwise indicated. ᵇ Computed by Brown and Muirhead. ᶜ Isomeric state only. ᵈ Weisskopf-Ewing values as given by Paul and Clarke.

Armstrong for Pd[105] also casts doubt upon the existence of discrepancies between experiment and theory that are as large as factors of 100 for this region of the heavy nuclei.

As a measure of the adequacy of the direct interaction model of Brown and Muirhead in predicting the magnitudes of $(n, p\gamma)$ cross sections, one may compare the sums of their theoretically computed values for direct interaction and compound nucleus processes with the corresponding experimental values of the $(n, p\gamma)$ cross sections. In this case, all the measured cross sections except those of Paul and Clarke have magnitudes within a factor of approximately three of the calculated value. The data of Paul and Clarke are also generally more nearly reconciled with the theory when direct interactions are taken into account but continue to indicate discrepancies by larger factors (up to 25 greater than unity) in the region of atomic weights between 90 and 139. Again, this trend is not in agreement with that demonstrated by the measurements of Levkovskiĭ *et al.* and Rosen and Armstrong. However, the experimental cross sections for Tl[205] and Pb[208], which differ so widely from the compound nucleus predictions, are now reconciled with the theory.

As is indicated by the preceding discussion, much work remains to be done in the region of heavy elements $(A > 90)$ before a dependable correlation can be made between theory and experiment. It is likely that dependable results will best be obtained by the use of radiochemical techniques as a preliminary to counter measurements. Even if one takes account of the discrepancies between different experimental results, however, the present digest of data indicates that the $(n, p\gamma)$ cross sections contain appreciable direct interaction components, which become quite predominant for mass numbers in excess of approximately 70.

(3) **Energy Spectra and Angular Distributions of the Protons from (n, p) and (n, np) Reactions.** In connection with (n, p) reactions, the definitive demonstrations of the presence of direct interaction mechanisms have been those of the experimental observations of the energy spectra and angular distributions of the emitted protons. A considerable clarification of the (n, np) process has also resulted from these experiments. The pre-eminent workers in this field have been D. L. Allan (Al55, Al57, Al57a) and Brown and collaborators (Br57a, Ma57), using nuclear emulsions, and Colli, Facchini, and collaborators (Ba56, Co56, Co57, Co57a, Co57b,

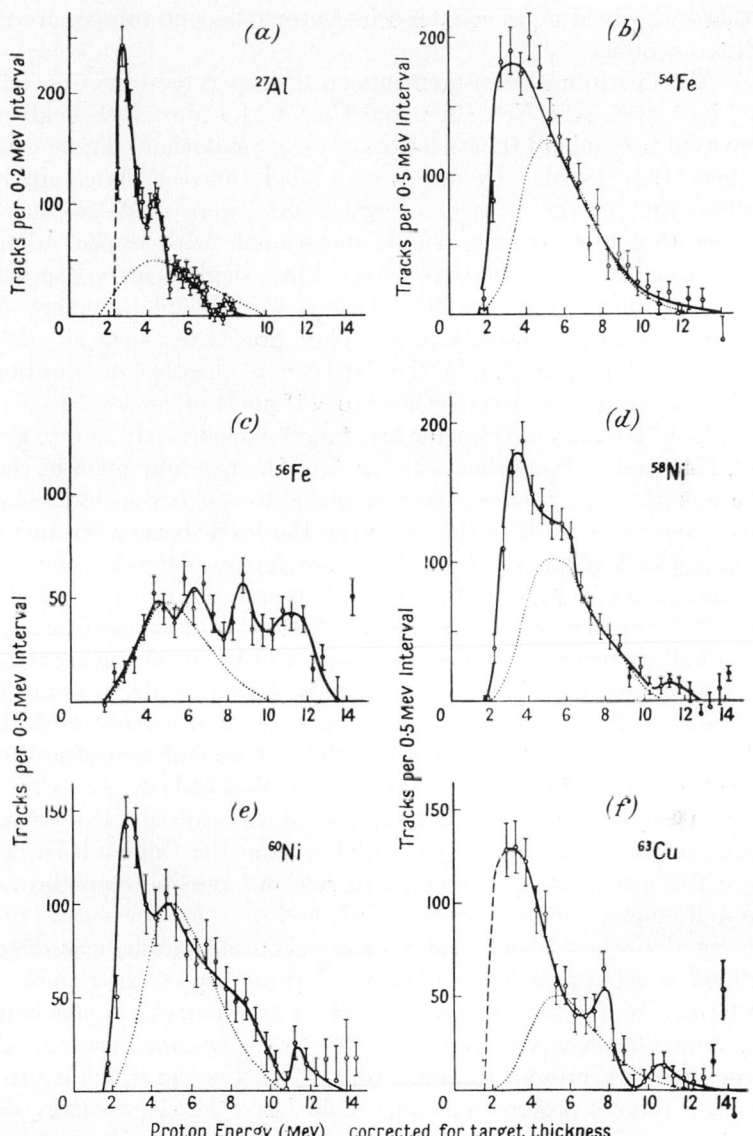

Figure 5. Energy spectra of emitted protons from the (n, p) reactions of 14-Mev neutrons with various target nuclides (Al57).

Co58a), who used a gas counter-scintillator telescope to measure the emitted protons.

Allan performed measurements on the separated target nuclides Al^{27}, Fe^{54}, Fe^{56}, Ni^{58}, Ni^{60}, Cu^{63}, and Cu^{65}. 14.5-Mev D-T neutrons were used to bombard thin radiators of target material. The emitted protons were detected by means of a single nuclear plate. In his earlier work, observations of energy spectra were made in such a manner that protons at a definite mean angle with respect to the incident neutron direction were detected in a single neutron exposure with an angular spread of $\pm 20°$. In later work the plate camera was such as to record on a single nuclear plate proton tracks at all angles between $15°$ and $165°$. In the latter case angular distributions could be measured between the limits of $20°$ and $150°$.

Allan's energy spectra for the target nuclides Al^{27}, Fe^{54}, Fe^{56}, Ni^{58}, Ni^{60}, and Cu^{63} are shown in Fig. 5. The reaction angle in each case was 34 ± 20 degrees. For reference, the energy spectra calculated from the statistical theory, using the level density formula of Lang and LeCouteur (La54), is given in each case as the dotted curve, normalized to the experimental data at some proton energy between 5 and 7 Mev. The low energy ends of these theoretical spectra show the cutoff produced by the Coulomb barrier of the proton evaporating compound nucleus, while the upper ends show the effects primarily of the level density of the residual nucleus. A discovery made by Allan by means of these spectra was the intense emission of protons *below the Coulomb barrier* in all cases except that of Fe^{56}.

In the case of Fe^{56} the lower end of the experimental energy spectrum coincided with that calculated from the Coulomb barrier. Since this particular case seemed to rule out possible violations of the well known Coulomb barrier effect, and since the low energy protons in the other cases had approximately isotropic angular distributions which precluded confusion of their tracks with those of deuterons from a forward-peaked pickup reaction, Allen concluded that these low energy protons were due to the (n, np) reaction. As he pointed out, protons from the (n, pn) reaction, in which neutron emission follows proton emission, would have the same energy distribution as those from the $(n, p\gamma)$ reaction, since their manner of emission is unaffected by subsequent emission of a neutron. In the (n, np) case, however, the emission of a proton following neutron emission from the compound nucleus would have to be in favorable competition with emission of a second neutron through the $(n, 2n)$ reaction. As expected, a consideration of the Q-values of the $(n, 2n)$ and (n, np) reactions for each of the target nuclides of Fig. 5 showed that in all cases except that of Fe^{56} the (n, np) protons would have to compete only with (negligible) γ-ray emission for emitted proton energies up to several Mev because the Q-value for the (n, np) reaction was sufficiently greater (less negative) than that for the $(n, 2n)$ reactions. Thus the low energy tails in the proton spectra in all cases except that of Fe^{56} were easily explained, as was the lack of a low energy tail in this exceptional case in which second neutron emission was energetically possible for all emitted proton energies observed in the proton spectrum.

Particularly large excesses of high energy protons (above the statistical high energy tail) were seen in the cases of Fe^{56} and Ni^{60}. These were attributed to direct interactions, which would be expected preferentially to produce high energy protons at predominantly forward angles of emission.

Allan carried out detailed measurements of the angular and energy distributions of the Cu (n, p) reaction for energy intervals between 2 and 14.5 Mev and at six angles between 20° and 150°. Only in the energy interval of 2 to 3 Mev was the angular distribution symmetric about 90°. As the mean energy of observation increased, the asymmetry about 90° became progressively more pronounced, resulting in very large *front to back* ratios for proton energies greater than approximately 7 Mev. Allen estimated the ratio of the asymmetric portion of the angular distribution to be 24 per cent over the total energy range of emitted protons, providing a rough measure of non-compound nucleus effect. [The corresponding figure calculated by Brown and Muirhead (see below) on the basis of their direct interaction model for Fe^{56} was 21 per cent.] For the energy interval 9 to 14.5 Mev the asymmetric component is approximately 90 per cent of the total. However, the total cross section contributed by the protons above 9 Mev is only 3 per cent of the total proton emission cross section. This is approximately the same proportion found by Coon and collaborators in the asymmetric (n, n') contributions for inelastic neutrons with energies greater than 9 Mev (cf. Section 2.D above).

In the energy spectra of Fig. 5, particularly those for Al^{27}, Fe^{56}, and Cu^{63}, may be seen peaks or humps having spacings many times the level spacings of the residual nuclei. These will be discussed later in connection with the work of Colli, Facchini, and collaborators.

Brown *et al.* have provided nuclear emulsion measurements of the energy spectra and angular distributions of emitted protons for the target elements Al, Fe, and Rh, as well as the separated nuclides Fe^{54} and Fe^{56}. Their method of exposure is illustrated in Fig. 6.

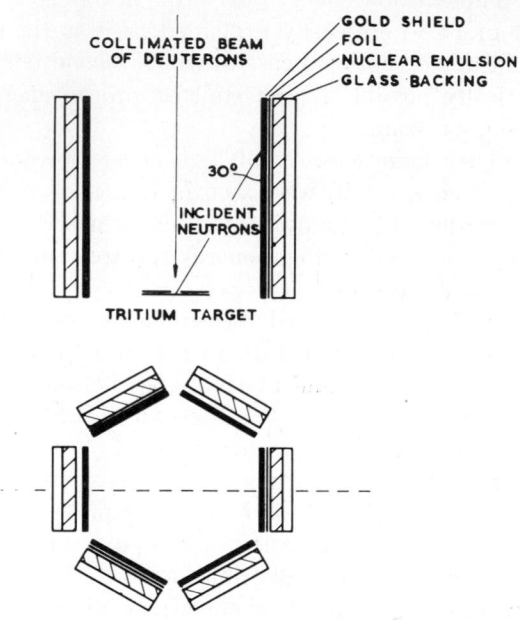

Figure 6. Experimental arrangement of Br57a for measuring the angular distributions and energy spectra of protons from the (n, p) reactions of 13.2-Mev neutrons with various target elements and nuclides.

The target foils were placed next to the nuclear emulsion with a thin gold covering to shield the emulsions from external protons. The bombarding D-T neutrons were produced at a mean angle of 150° with respect to the deuteron beam which bombarded the tritium target, and their mean energy was 13.2 Mev. By a choice of scanning area, the angle between the emitted neutrons and the deuteron beam was limited to 150 ± 2 degrees, and (n, p) reaction angles ranging from 0° to 140° were observed.

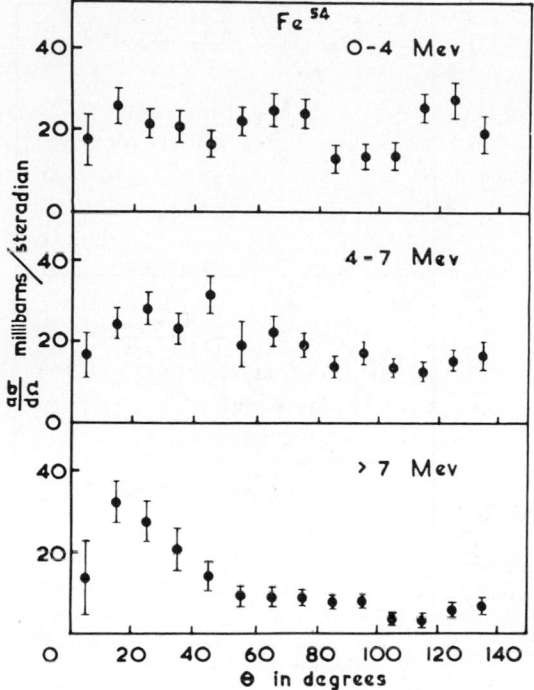

Figure 7. Differential cross sections of the (n, p) reactions on Fe⁵⁴ at 13.2 Mev (Br57a). The three graphs represent the results for emitted neutrons in three energy intervals.

The energy spectra observed by Brown *et al.* for the angular interval 0° to 140° for the target elements Al and Fe were quite similar to those of Allan, being distinguished also by appreciable low energy (n, np) tails. In the cases of Fe and Rh quantitative comparisons with the statistical theory spectra showed large excesses of emitted protons, extending from high energies down to approximately 5 Mev. When the direct interaction theory of Brown and Muirhead was used to calculate the energy spectra, the agreement with experiment, except for the (n, np) tails, was found to be much better.

Angular distributions were measured in each case for three proton energy groups: <4 Mev, 4 to 7 Mev, and >7 Mev. There was in general distinct asymmetry about 90°, which became pro-

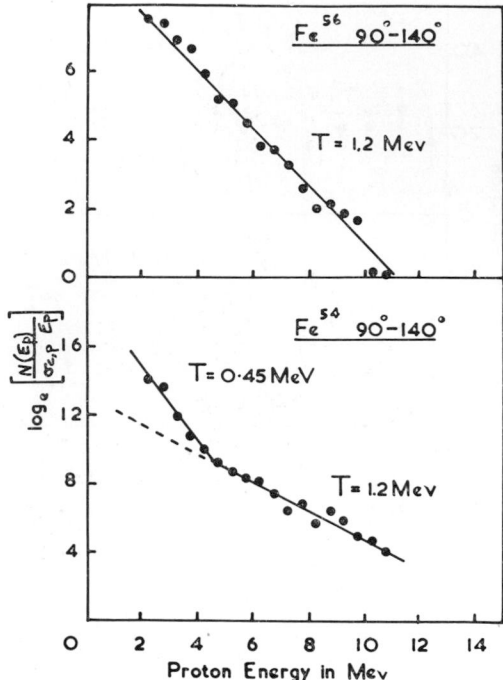

Figure 8. Level density plots for the emitted protons from the (n, p) and (n, np) reactions on Fe^{54} and Fe^{56} at 13.2 Mev (Br57a).

gressively more pronounced as the proton energy increased. The effect in Rh was more pronounced than that for the lighter elements Al and Fe and was quantitatively accounted for by the theory of Brown and Muirhead. In Fig. 7 are shown the data for the angular distributions from Fe^{54}. The 0 to 4 Mev group [mostly (n, np) protons] has an isotropic angular distribution. The energy groups extending from 4 to 7 Mev and from 7 Mev upwards are seen to exhibit forward peaking.

In Fig. 8 are shown the level density graphs of Brown *et al.* for Fe^{54} and Fe^{56}. It is seen that the data for Fe^{56} at back angles (little direct interaction) are reproduced quite well by a line of constant nuclear temperature, corresponding to a temperature of 1.2 Mev. In the case of Fe^{54} there is a distinct break in the level density graph, allowing a representation corresponding to two component temperatures of 1.2 Mev and 0.45 Mev. The latter characterizes

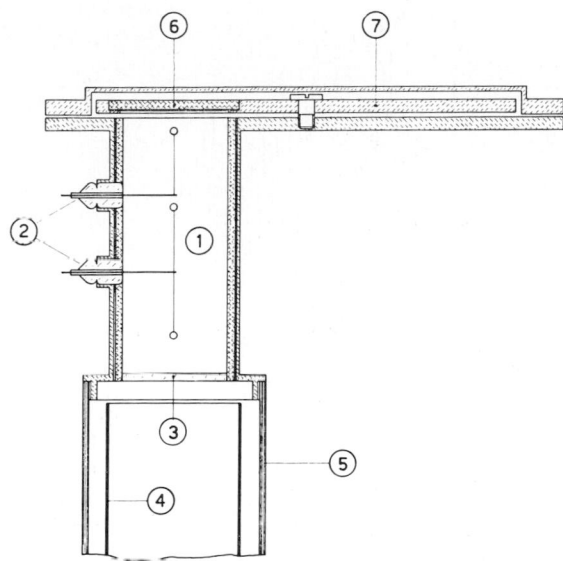

Figure 9. Counter telescope (Co57b) used in obtaining differential cross sections and proton energy spectra of (n, p) reactions for various target elements at 14 Mev.

the (n, np) energy distribution and measures the nuclear cooling brought about by emission of a neutron preceding the proton emission. Note the similarity of those temperatures to the two corresponding temperatures (1 and 0.5 Mev) observed by Rosen and Stewart and by Ahn and Roberts in the cases of neutron inelastic scattering and the $(n, 2n)$ reactions (cf. Section 2.D above).

Results similar to those of Brown *et al.* have been obtained by Armstrong and Rosen (Ar56) in the case of Zn^{64}. They used essentially the multiplate nuclear emulsion camera illustrated in Fig. 1 with a thin Zn^{64} radiator at its center in place of a neutron scattering sample.

Colli, Facchini, and collaborators have performed measurements of the proton emission energy spectra of (n, p) reactions for the target elements S, Al, Mg, Si, Ca, Ti, Fe, Ni, Cu, Zn, Zr, Rh, Sn, Ta, and Au, thus providing the most extensive survey to date and including heavy elements. Their technique involved electronic means for detecting the protons, and one of their spectrometers is illustrated in Fig. 9. 14-Mev neutrons impinged on radiators of target material (6) from

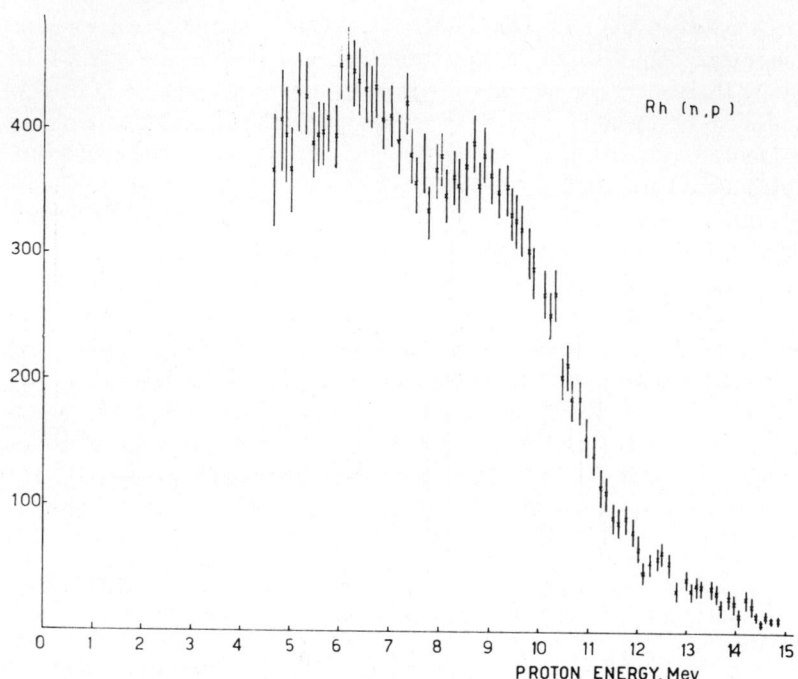

Figure 10. Energy spectrum of emitted protons from the (n, p) reactions on rhodium at 14 Mev (Co58a).

which the emitted protons passed through a double proportional counter (1) and expended their energy in a CsI scintillation crystal (3). The double proportional counter was provided with two separate center wires (2). By measuring the pulse-height spectrum of the scintillations from the CsI crystal, in coincidence with the pulses from the proportional counters, the energy spectrum of protons emitted from the radiator was obtained and most of the background pulses produced by the neutrons in the crystal were eliminated. In order to be sure of recording all protons, the lower limit bias for detection of the proportional counter pulses was set at a level corresponding to the pulse height obtained from 14-Mev protons. The use of such coincidence telescopes is discussed in detail in Chapter II.C.

In those cases for which the measurements of Colli, Facchini *et al.* duplicated those of Allan, namely Al, Fe, Cu, and Ni, the agreement between the two sets of energy spectra was quite good, even to the extent that small humps were often reproduced. Figure 10 shows their energy spectrum for Rh, corresponding to angles of proton emission between $0°$ and $40°$. A broad hump in the spectrum is evidenced at a proton energy of about 8.5 Mev. This spectrum is in agreement with that found by Brown *et al.* for the same element. A similar hump was observed by Colli, Facchini *et al.* in the spectrum of Mg at a proton energy of approximately 7 Mev.

In the cases of the target elements Cu and Ni, these investigators obtained spectra at mean proton emission angles of $0°$, $45°$, $90°$, and $135°$, demonstrating the (by now usual) forward-peaking asymmetry about $90°$ for proton emission energies as low as approximately 4 Mev. The cross sections for Ta and Au for the emission of protons in the forward direction ($0°$ to $40°$) were found to be roughly five per cent of those which were measured for Fe and Ni. This is roughly two orders of magnitude greater than would be predicted by the statistical model.

In connection with the broad humps observed in the proton energy spectra by Colli, Facchini *et al.* and by Allan, it has been proposed (Bl57, Co57c) that they may correspond to giant resonances among the levels of the residual nuclei. These giant resonances are supposed to contain many single levels and to correspond to a modulation of the intensity of excitation of the levels of the residual nucleus. Similar broad peaks have been observed in the energy spectra of protons from (p, p') inelastic scattering (Gu54, Co57d) and from low-energy (d, p) reactions (Pe59, Sc59). Blok and Jonker (Bl57) have correlated the proton energy spectrum observed by Colli, Facchini *et al.* for the reaction $Mg^{24}(n, p)Na^{24}$ under poor energy resolution with the levels observed under good resolution for the reaction $Na^{23}(d, p)Na^{24}$, which yields the same residual nucleus. By averaging the isolated resonances over energy intervals of 0.5 Mev in the latter case, they obtained a satisfactory correspondence to the humps in the proton energy spectrum from the (n, p) reaction. A similar comparison was made in the case of the residual nucleus Al^{28} corresponding to the $Si^{28}(n, p)Al^{28}$ reaction.

A recent experiment by Verbinski *et al.* (Ve57), utilizing electronic techniques, has provided additional data on the energy spectra and angular distributions from the (n, p) reactions produced by 14-Mev neutrons on the target elements Mg, Ni, Cu, Rh, and Pd.

They compared the energy spectra of protons emitted within the forward and backward reaction hemispheres. In the cases of Mg, Ni, and Cu this comparison demonstrated a difference in absolute magnitudes of the spectra of the order of 20 per cent, similar to that found by Colli, Facchini *et al.* In the cases of the heavy elements Rh and Pd the difference was much more pronounced. In these cases the front to back ratio of numbers of emitted protons was roughly three.

Haling, Peck, and Eubank (Ha57, Pe57) provided additional nuclear emulsion measurements of the reactions $Al^{27}(n, p)Mg^{27}$ and $Au^{197}(n, p)Pt^{197}$ for 14-Mev bombarding neutrons. In the case of Al^{27} the level density graph yields a nuclear temperature of 1.16 Mev. In the case of Au^{197} their angular distribution results again demonstrate a forward peaking of the high energy protons.

(4) **Summary of** (n, np) **Cross Section Measurements.** A summary of the presently known values of total (n, np) cross sections is given in Table II. The values in the third and fourth columns are those of Allan and of Brown *et al.*, discussed above.

Cohen, Hyder, and White (Co56a) have searched for the radioactivity which would be produced by the (n, np) [or (n, pn)] reaction in the target nuclides Se^{80}, Pd^{108}, Ce^{142}, and W^{186}. They used 14.5-Mev neutrons in the bombardments and were able to observe none of the looked-for activities. The values given in the fifth column of Table II represent their upper limits at the 1 per cent statistical level of confidence. Allan (Al57) has conjectured that the reason for the relatively low values of the (n, np) cross section of these nuclides, aside from the large Coulomb barriers, may be that they all have high neutron numbers for the group of isotopes to which they belong. Under these circumstances it is unlikely that proton emission would compete favorably with neutron emission. Therefore $(n, 2n)$ reactions would be preferred.

(5) **The Excitation Functions for** $(n, p\gamma)$ **Reactions.** We depart briefly from the discussion of cross section measurements at a single neutron bombarding energy in the neighborhood of 14 Mev to consider measurements of total $(n, p\gamma)$ cross sections as functions of neutron energy. Aside from measurements performed for very light elements, which will be discussed in a later section, the only absolute yield curves for these reactions which have been measured at this writing are those for the following target nuclides: Al^{27} (Sm52);

Table II. Experimental Values and Upper Limits of the (n, np) Cross Sections for Various Target Nuclides at 14-Mev Bombarding Energy

Target nuclide	Q-value (Mev)	Measured cross section (millibarns)		
		Allan	Brown *et al.*	Cohen *et al.* (n, np) + (n, pn)
Al^{27}	-8.3	70	85 ± 35	
Fe^{54}	-9.2	220		
Fe^{56}	-10.2	0	0	
Ni^{58}	-7.7	220		
Ni^{60}	-9.6	60		
Cu^{63}	-6.2	130		
Cu^{65}	-7.6	<40		
Se^{80}	-11.5			<0.8
Rh^{103}	-6.5		14 ± 6	
Pd^{108}	-9.7			<65
Ce^{142}	-8.8			<18
W^{186}	-8.0			<1.6

S^{32} (Al57b); P^{31} (Gr58); Mg^{24}, Si^{28}, Cl^{37}, and Sr^{88} (Co56b); Ti^{47}, Ti^{48}, and As^{75} (Ba58); and Fe^{56} (Te58). In addition Yasumi (Ya57) has measured the gradients of the excitation curves for the $(n, p\gamma)$ reaction on Al^{27} and Cl^{37} at 14 Mev. In these measurements the activation technique was used.

Cohen and White (Co56b), in their measurements of the excitation functions for Mg^{24}, Si^{28}, Cl^{37}, and Sr^{88}, found cross sections which decreased with increasing neutron energy in the first two cases and which rose in the last two cases. In the latter cases the trend of the data can not be accounted for by the Weisskopf-Ewing statistical theory. Brown and Muirhead (Br57) have since calculated these excitation functions on the basis of their theory of direct interactions, as well as on the basis of the compound nucleus theory, and have been able to account quantitatively for the yield curves in the cases of Mg^{24} and Si^{28}. They account for the rising trend of the Sr^{88} curve only by invoking direct interactions. However, the Cl^{35} excitation function remains an anomaly. Even under the assumption of predominant direct interaction, its rising trend is not duplicated by the theory. This trend is confirmed by the measurement of Yasumi, who found the gradient of the Cl^{37} (n, p) excitation function to be $+6$ per cent per Mev.

Terrell and Holm (Te58) found good agreement between their measured Fe^{56} (n, p) excitation function and the statistical theory for neutron energies between 12 and 18 Mev. In the 5 to 8-Mev region the experimental cross section exceeded that of the theory, indicating the presence of direct interactions, relatively less inhibited by the Coulomb barrier.

F. (n, α) Reactions

(1) **Methods of Measurement.** The techniques for measuring (n, α) cross sections are quite similar to those which were just reviewed for (n, p) reactions, namely the use of the activation method and more direct methods involving direct detection of the emitted α particles. Owing to the weakness of the (n, α) reactions, which becomes more pronounced as the atomic weight of the target nuclide increases, direct detection has until recently been little used. Background effects make the detection of the small α-particle yields difficult. Particularly in the case of targets of heavy elements, the problem of target thickness is an acute one, and rather elaborate corrections for energy loss by the α particles are required in order that energy spectra may be correctly determined. We shall discuss direct detection experiments in which both nuclear emulsions and a counter telescope were used.

In connection with the activation technique, the weakness of the activities resulting from the small $(n, \alpha\gamma)$ reactions makes their proper identification difficult in the presence of competing activities from other, inevitably excited reactions. This fact makes the use of radiochemical separations before counting even more important here than in the case of $(n, p\gamma)$ determinations.

(2) **Survey of Total $(n, \alpha\gamma)$ Reactions at 14 Mev.** The earliest extensive activation survey was that of Paul and Clarke (Pa53), whose method has already been described in connection with their $(n, p\gamma)$ measurements. They measured the $(n, \alpha\gamma)$ cross sections for 25 target nuclides at 14.5 Mev and compared the resulting values with those calculated from the statistical theory. As in the case of their $(n, p\gamma)$ measurements, they found that the measured $(n, \alpha\gamma)$ cross sections far exceeded the predictions of the theory, with a progressively larger discrepancy for target nuclides of high mass number. In the region $80 \leq A \leq 110$ their measured cross sections

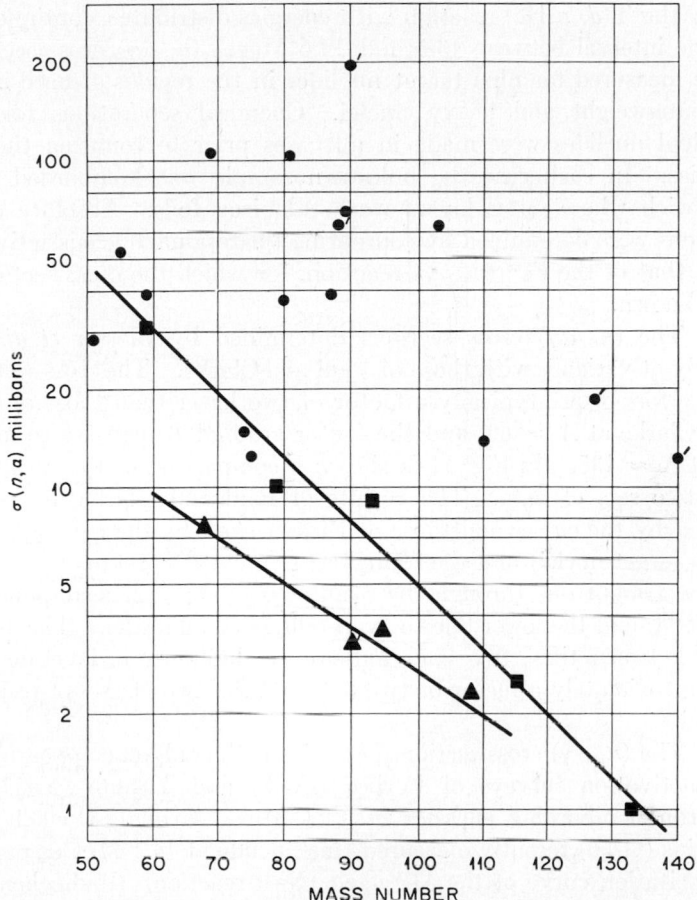

Figure 11. Graph of the (n, α) cross sections of various target nuclides *versus* mass number for 14-Mev bombarding neutrons (B158). The circles represent the data of Pa53 and the squares (odd-mass target nuclei) and triangles (even-mass target nuclei) the data of B158. In the case of the primed data points only an isomer of the reaction product was observed.

were generally larger by factors of hundreds. For the four nuclides I^{127}, Ce^{140}, Sm^{152}, and Bi^{209} the factors of discrepancy were thousands.

Another extensive activation survey has been made by Blosser, Goodman, and Handley (B155, B158), who used bombarding neutrons from the $T(d, n)He^4$ reaction with energies distributed continuously in the interval between 13.5 and 14.6 Mev. $(n, \alpha\gamma)$ cross sections were measured for nine target nuclides in the regions of both intermediate-weight and heavy nuclei. Chemical separations for the residual nuclides were made in all cases prior to counting the activities. In each case the unknown sample was bombarded in a sandwich whose outer layers were thin iron foils. Absolute cross sections were determined by comparing the residual nucleus activities with that of the Fe^{56} $(n, p\gamma)$ reaction, for which the cross section is well known.

The $(n, \alpha\gamma)$ cross sections determined by Blosser et al. are widely at variance with those of Paul and Clarke. The cross sections of the former are typically a factor of two lower than those of Paul and Clarke at $A \approx 60$, and the factor gradually increases to about 20 at $A \approx 135$. In Fig. 11 is shown a comparison of the results of the two sets of data. The results of Paul and Clarke are represented by the circles and those of Blosser et al. by the squares (odd-mass target nuclei) and the triangles (even-even target nuclei). The upper straight line through the squares on the graph corresponds to odd-odd, and the lower line to even-odd, residual nuclei. The difference between these two lines indicates a difference in level density of approximately a factor of two between the two classes of residual nuclei.

The $(n, \alpha\gamma)$ cross section for Al^{27} was the only one appearing in the activation surveys of Forbes (Fo52) and Yasumi (Ya57) at neutron bombarding energies of 14.1 Mev. Grundl, Henkel, and Perkins (Gr58) recently measured this nuclide at 14.1 Mev as part of an excitation curve of the $Al^{27}(n, \alpha\gamma)Na^{24}$ reaction. Radiochemical techniques were used. Similarly, Allen et al. (Al57b) measured the $S^{34}(n, \alpha\gamma)Si^{31}$ cross section at 14.1 Mev as part of an excitation function. In the case of F^{19} only the ratio of the (n, α) and (n, p) cross sections has been measured at 14.5 Mev, by Kondaiah et al. (Ko58). A radiochemical activation measurement of the As^{75} $(n, \alpha\gamma)$ reaction has been provided by Bayhurst and Prestwood (Ba58).

Brolley et al. (Br55) measured the $(n, \alpha\gamma)$ cross sections for Zr^{90} and Zr^{94} at 14.1 and 14.9 Mev. They used chemical separations, followed by absolute γ-ray counting of the residual activities. In the case of Zr^{90} only the 2.8-hour isomer of Sr^{87} was counted.

In the region of heavier nuclides Dzantiev *et al.* measured the $(n, \alpha\gamma)$ activation cross sections for Cd^{112} and Cd^{114}, also utilizing chemical separations. In the case of Cd^{114} the activities corresponding to both the 5.5-hour isomer and the 22-minute β-active state of Pd^{111} were measured.

Recent nuclear emulsion work at 14.8 Mev by Kumabe *et al.* (Ku57, Ku58, Ku58a), to be described in the next section, has yielded total $(n, \alpha\gamma)$ cross sections for five light and intermediate-weight nuclides. These investigators eliminated the α particles arising from $(n, n\alpha)$ reactions from their (n, α) measurements by subtracting those portions from the α-particle energy spectra which could be attributed to the former reaction. In another nuclear emulsion experiment at 14.1 Mev Armstrong and Brolley (Ar55) were able to estimate the Zr^{90} (n, α) cross section as 10 ± 10 millibarns, again in agreement with Blosser *et al.* Using a counter telescope and neutrons at 14.1 Mev, Ribe and Davis (Ri55) measured the total yield of α particles from the Zr (n, α) reaction for the forward hemisphere of reaction angles. The corresponding cross section was $7 + 2$ millibarns.

In Table III is presented a summary of all the measured total $(n, \alpha\gamma)$ cross sections known to the author at the present writing. There is fairly good agreement among the various determinations in the region of light and intermediate-weight nuclides, extending to nuclides as heavy as As^{75}. In the case of Al^{27} the three activation measurements by Forbes, Yasumi, and Grundl *et al.* are satisfactorily consistent, although they are inconsistent with the determinations of Paul and Clarke and of Kumabe *et al.*

In the region of heavy nuclei the discrepancy between the results of Paul and Clarke and of Blosser *et al.* has been pointed out. The lower trend of the $(n, \alpha\gamma)$ cross sections found by the latter is confirmed by other measurements in the cases of Zr^{90}, Zr^{94}, Cd^{112}, and Cd^{114}. The Cd^{114} cross section value of Dzantiev *et al.* lies on the lower line of the graph of Fig. 11, while the value for Cd^{112} falls somewhat below it.

In regard to the degree of agreement between the experimental results and the cross sections calculated from the statistical theory, it can be seen that in the region of atomic weights up to $A = 75$ there is agreement within an order of magnitude. If one considers the cross section determinations in the third and fourth columns of Table III, this degree of consistency between theory and experiment

Table III. Experimental Values of $(n, \alpha\gamma)$ Cross Sections for Various Target Nuclides at 14-Mev Bombarding Energy

Target Nuclide	Paul and Clarke	Blosser et al.	Other			Ref.	Calculated[a]
Al^{27}	79 ± 16		135	±	10	Fo52	273
			120	±	14	Ya57	
			116	±	8	Gr58	
			82	±	17	Ku58	
Si^{30}	46 ± 25						13
P^{31}	146 ± 29						70
S^{32}			38	±	8	Ku58	
S^{34}	138 ± 35		126	±	7	Al57b	253
Cl^{35}	191 ± 31						267
Cl^{37}	52 ± 26						19
K^{41}	31 ± 11						15
V^{51}	29 ± 12		43	±	9	Ku58	4.6
Mn^{55}	53 ± 8		39	±	8	Ku58	4.5
Co^{59}	39 ± 8	31 ± 3	25	±	5	Ku58	3.7
Zn^{68}		7.6 ± 0.8					
Ga^{69}	105 ± 57						12.3
Ge^{74}	15 ± 6						1.5
As^{75}	12 ± 2		10.0	±	0.5	Ba58	2.0
Br^{79}		10.0 ± 1.8					
Se^{80}	38 ± 16						0.17
Br^{81}	103 ± 21						0.18
Rb^{87}	39 ± 16						0.14
Sr^{88}	64 ± 19[b]						0.14
Y^{89}	70 ± 42						1.2
Zr^{90}	194 ± 107[b]	3.3 ± 0.6[b]	3.1	±	0.2[b]	Br55	2.15
			10	±	10	Ar55	
			3.3	±	0.2	Re58	
Nb^{93}		9.0 ± 2.2					
Zr^{94}		3.6 ± 0.5	4.9	±	0.6	Br55	
		4.0 ± 0.2				Re58	0.8
Rh^{103}	63 ± 25[c]						
Pd^{108}		2.3 ± 0.4					
Pd^{110}	14 ± 6						0.29
Cd^{112}			0.51	±	0.13	Dz57	
Cd^{114}			1.35	±	0.27	Dz57	
Cd^{114}			0.13	±	0.04[b]	Dz57	
In^{115}		2.5 ± 0.4					
I^{127}	18 ± 2						0.02
Cs^{133}		1.0 ± 0.3					
Ce^{140}	12 ± 6[b]						0.0015
Sm^{152}	9 ± 5						0.0064
Bi^{209}	1 ± 1						0.00005

[a] Values calculated by Paul and Clarke (Pa53) on the basis of the Weisskopf-Ewing statistical theory.   [b] Isomeric state only.   [c] Assignment in doubt.

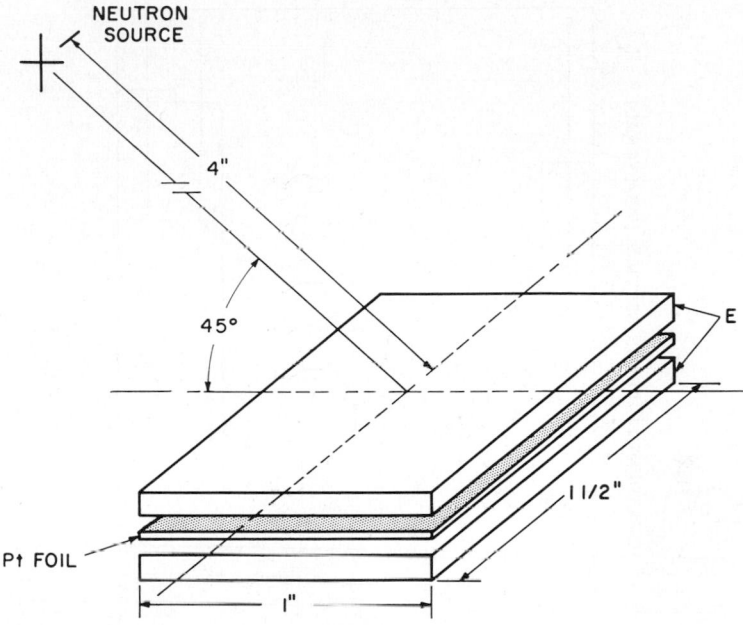

Figure 12. Experimental arrangement of Ku58 for measuring the differential cross sections and energy spectra of emitted α particles from (n, α) reactions a 14 Mev.

persists through Cd^{114}.   For higher atomic weights the extrapolated trend of the data of Blosser *et al.* would indicate discrepancies by factors of perhaps hundreds, as opposed to the many thousands indicated by the data of Paul and Clarke.   However, the experimental data in the region of the heavy nuclei are still very sparse, and it would be premature to conclude that any significant order-of-magnitude discrepancy exists between the statistical theory and the experiments in the case of total $(n, \alpha\gamma)$ cross sections.   Further measurements are needed in the region of the heavy nuclei, as well as calculations which make use of level density formulas which are improvements over the simple Weisskopf formula given by Eq. (2).

   (3) **Energy Spectra and Angular Distributions of (n, α) and $(n, n\alpha)$ Reactions.**   The only extensive work concerned with directly detecting and measuring the α particles from (n, α) reactions, except for the very light nuclei, has been that of Kumabe *et al.*

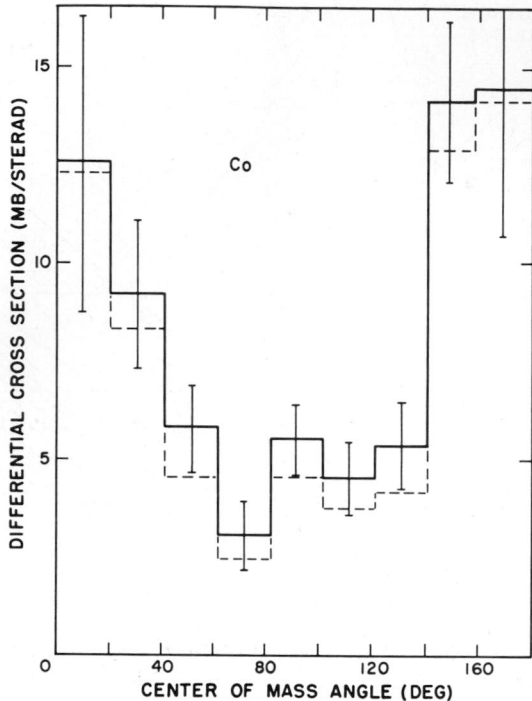

Figure 13. Differential cross section of the (n, α) reaction on cobalt at 14 Mev (Ku58).

(Ku57, Ku58, Ku58a). These investigators measured the energy spectra and angular distributions of the α particles from thin targets of Al, S, V, Mn, and Co, bombarded by 14.8-Mev neutrons. Their experimental arrangement is shown schematically in Fig. 12. In each case the target element formed a thin layer on either side of a thick platinum foil, sandwiched between two 200-micron nuclear emulsions E. The sandwich was bombarded by D-T neutrons from a tritium target in such a manner that the mean angle of incidence between the neutrons and the layer of target material was 45°. Special photographic processing was applied in order to discriminate α-particle tracks from those of protons in the emulsions. After scanning, complete energy distributions, as well as angular distributions over the entire 180° of α-particle reaction angles, were obtained.

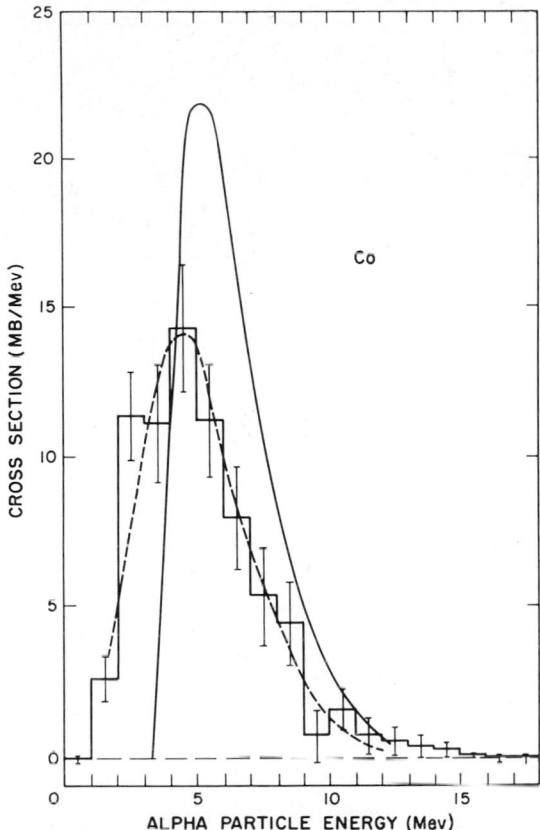

Figure 14. Energy spectrum of the alpha particles from the (n, α) reaction on cobalt at 14 Mev (Ku58).

In marked contrast to the results for the (n, p) case, Kumabe et al. found in all cases, with the possible exception of the target element Mn, that the angular distributions of the α particles were symmetric about a reaction angle of $90°$. A typical graph, their differential cross section for the target element Co, is shown in Fig. 13. The histogram composed of solid line segments has been corrected for the effects of target thickness. The corresponding energy distribution of the α particles from Co is shown in Fig. 14. The histogram and dashed curve represent the observed, uncorrected energy distribution and the solid curve the energy distribution cor-

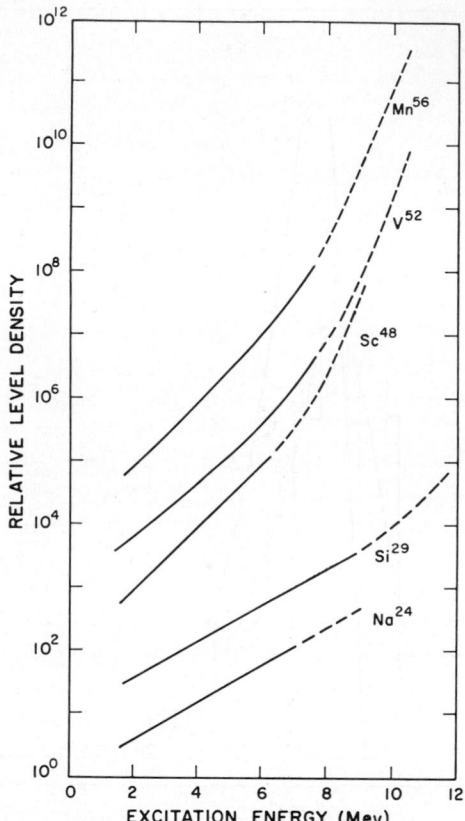

Figure 15. Graph of nuclear level density of various nuclides *versus* excitation energy as derived from the energy spectra of emitted α particles from (n, α) reactions on various target nuclides at 14 Mev (Ku58a).

rected for the effects of cobalt target thickness. It was found that if the angular distributions were plotted separately for the α particles in the two (uncorrected) energy regions < 6 Mev and > 6 Mev, then for all target elements studied the angular distributions were nearly the same. Thus, again in contrast to the (n, p) case, there is no asymmetry giving preference to forward reaction angles at the higher α particle energies.

The energy spectrum data of Kumabe *et al.* are summarized in Fig. 15. Here the logarithm of the level density $(1/\epsilon\sigma_c)d\sigma/d\epsilon$ [cf. Eq. (4) and succeeding discussion] is plotted against the excitation energy ($\epsilon_{max} - \epsilon$) for each of the five residual nuclei investigated. The straight portions of these curves correspond to the following temperatures for Na^{24}, Si^{29}, Sc^{48}, V^{52}, and Mn^{52}, respectively: 1.45, 1.5, 0.9, 0.85, and 0.7 Mev. The dashed portions of the curves correspond to regions in which $(n, n'\alpha)$ processes are energetically possible. In the cases of the three upper curves, however, there is competition from proton emission following neutron emission from the compound nucleus. Under these circumstances Kumabe et al. believe that α-particle emission would not be favored and that the upward concavity of these curves may be indicative of a diffuse nuclear boundary, leading to emission of more low energy α particles than would obtain for a sharp nuclear boundary of radius $1.5 \times 10^{-13} A^{1/3}$ cm, for which the curves of Fig. 15 were drawn.

The (n, α) results of Kumabe et al. show no contradiction to the theory of a statistical compound nucleus. The fact that their symmetric angular distributions are far from isotropic indicates a deviation from a statistical distribution of residual nucleus levels, possibly, as these authors point out, due to the interposition of parity selection rules.

It is unfortunate that these results do not yet include measurements for heavy nuclei, for which possible asymmetries of the angular distributions about 90° might be expected. The only heavy element for which the (n, α) angular distribution has been investigated is zirconium. Using a counter telescope similar to that illustrated in Fig. 9, Ribe and Davis (Ri55) determined the angular distribution of the emitted α particles over the complete range of emission energies for 14.1-Mev bombarding neutrons. Their results extend only to angles as large as 115° and do not conclusively indicate any asymmetry about 90° although nonisotropy is clearly shown.

3. $(n, 2n)$ Reactions

A. Methods of Measurement

There are four general methods by means of which $(n, 2n)$ cross sections are measured. (a) In the sphere multiplication method use is made of the fact that the number of neutrons emerging from a sample of some target element tends to be increased by the $(n, 2n)$ reaction over the number of bombarding neutrons striking the sample. (b) In a second method the neutrons emitted from the

(n, $2n$) reaction are all *caught* in some sort of 4π detector.   (c)   One may identify the neutrons from the (n, $2n$) reaction by some means of neutron spectroscopy and add together the contributions from all neutron energies and angles to give the total emission cross section. (d)   For those (n, $2n$) reactions which lead to radioactive residual nuclei one may apply the activation method just as in the cases of the (n, p) and (n, α) reactions discussed previously in Sections 2.E and 2.F of this article.

In the following we shall discuss some experiments which illustrate each of these methods.   Particular reference will be made to measurements of the $Be^9(n, 2n)$ cross section in which case no residual radioactivity results.   The (n, $2n$) reaction on the Be^9 is important in the design of fast reactors, and the history of its measurements has been particularly confusing [see the summary in (Ag52)].   In connection with the activation measurements we shall briefly summarize the measured excitation functions of cross section *versus* neutron energy as well as the measurements for various target nuclides at 14 Mev.   We shall consider only those measurements made with mono-energetic neutron sources.

(1) **The Sphere Multiplication Method.**   In so called good geometry experiments an attempt is made to limit the observation of bombarding and reaction-product particles within narrow angular limits.   Poor geometry, on the other hand, is used when it is desired to observe the effects of reactions without regard to reaction angles. The *poorest* geometry is provided by spherical shells of target material surrounding isotropic neutron sources or detectors.   Depending both upon the type of geometry and the nature of the detector, one may measure the total cross section σ_T for all types of neutron interactions or various of its component cross sections.   The various cross sections are classified as follows: (a) the *nonelastic* cross section σ_X measures all reactions other than that of (b) *elastic scattering* σ_n, where in the latter case no energy is lost by the incident neutrons; (c) the *inelastic scattering* cross section $\sigma_{n'}$ measures those reactions in which the neutron energy is lessened, but in which one neutron nevertheless appears after the reaction; (d) the disappearance cross section σ_D measures those reactions in which a neutron disappears in favor of a γ ray or a charged particle; (e) the (n, $2n$) reaction leads to energy degradation as well as neutron multiplication.   We do not consider the possibility of fission.

In a good geometry experiment a small target sample placed between a neutron source and a detector scatters or absorbs all but a fraction T of the flux within the solid angle subtended by the detector. The transmission T in this case is related to the total cross section by the equation (cf. Chapter V.A)

$$T_g = \exp\left(-n\sigma_T x\right), \quad \text{(good geometry)} \tag{8}$$

where x is the thickness of the scatterer and n the density of scattering nuclei. If instead one uses a spherical shell of target material the scattering away from the detector by that portion of the scatterer covering its solid angle is made up by scattering into the detector from all other portions of the sphere. Under these conditions a detector capable of detecting only neutrons of undegraded energy will not detect the presence of elastic scattering (Ba52), and the transmission will provide a measure of the nonelastic scattering cross section according to the relation

$$T_p = \exp\left(-n\sigma_x x\right), \quad \text{(poor geometry)} \tag{9}$$

If in addition to a spherical scatterer around the (isotropic) neutron source one uses a detector (long counter) whose response is independent of energy then the only contribution to the attenuation of the neutron flux into the solid angle of the detector is that from the disappearance cross section σ_D. In the case of the $(n, 2n)$ reaction source neutrons are removed owing to scattering by that portion of the spherical shell intercepted by the detector solid angle and returned twofold by reactions from other portions of the shell. One defines the multiplication M as the ratio of the fluxes at the energy insensitive detector with and without the spherical scatterer. It is given by

$$M = \exp\left[n(\sigma_{2n} - \sigma_D)\,x\right] \tag{10}$$

This is the basis of the sphere multiplication method. One can determine from M the quantity

$$\sigma_{2n} - \sigma_D \equiv \sigma_M \tag{11}$$

and hence also σ_{2n} in case σ_D is known independently. In any case the quantity σ_M provides a lower limit for σ_{2n}. The upper limit can be determined as follows. By definition

$$\sigma_X \equiv \sigma_{n'} + \sigma_{2n} + \sigma_D = \sigma_{n'} + \sigma_M + 2\sigma_D \tag{12}$$

$\sigma_{n'}$ is at least zero, so the corresponding upper limit of σ_D is $(\sigma_X - \sigma_M)/2$. From Eq. (11) the corresponding upper limit for σ_{2n} is given by

$$\sigma_{2n} \leqq [\sigma_M + (\sigma_X - \sigma_M)/2] = (\sigma_M + \sigma_X)/2 \qquad (13)$$

The sphere multiplication method has been extensively applied by Graves and Davis (Gr55) who used a long counter and a threshold detector to measure both T_p and M, providing measurements of both σ_X and σ_M for eleven target elements from carbon through bismuth. In these experiments 14-Mev source neutrons were produced isotropically by means of the D-T reaction. Low energy (110 kev) deuterons were used to bombard thick Zr-T targets placed at the center of the spherical scatterers. The upper and lower limits of the $(n, 2n)$ cross sections are tabulated in the sixth and seventh columns of Table IV, except for those target elements where σ_D is independently known, for which the corresponding values of σ_{2n} are given.

(2) **4π Detection Methods.** The first experiment to be described was that of Fischer (Fi57) who measured the $Be^9(n, 2n)$ cross section for the neutron bombarding energies 2.57, 2.69, 2.93, and 3.19 Mev. The bombarding neutrons were obtained at various angles of emission with respect to a 350-kev deuteron beam impinging on a thick deuterium target. The detector was a large activation tank almost completely surrounding the beryllium target sample. This tank was filled with an aqueous solution of potassium permanganate (manganese bath) in which the emitted neutrons were moderated and captured by the manganese nuclei to form 2.59-hour Mn^{56} whose β activity provided a measure of the numbers of neutrons emitted by the target sample. Details of the method by which the Szilard-Chalmers reaction was utilized to provide a quantitatively isolated sample of Mn^{56} were essentially the same as described in Chapter IV.C. In the $(n, 2n)$ experiment the manganese bath provided a detector insensitive both to emitted neutron angle and energy.

Fischer used a multiplication technique in which cylindrical samples of carbon and beryllium were alternately bombarded inside the manganese bath. Care was taken that the collimated bombarding neutrons passed through a hole along the axis of the detector without directly activating the manganese. The interaction of the neutrons with carbon at the neutron energies used in the experiment was entirely elastic ($\sigma_T = \sigma_n$). As a result, the activation produced in the manganese bath by the neutrons from the opaque ($T_g \approx 1$) carbon sample was the same as that which would have been produced by the neutrons produced in a fictitious opaque beryllium sample from which each (n, $2n$) neutron was counted only once. Under these conditions the multiplication M', or ratio of Mn^{56} activities produced by identical bombardments of beryllium and carbon samples, was given by

$$M'\sigma_T = \sigma_n + 2\sigma_{2n} + \sigma_{n'} \tag{14}$$

Since

$$\sigma_T = \sigma_n + \sigma_{2n} + \sigma_{n'} + \sigma_D \tag{15}$$

the (n, $2n$) cross section was given by

$$\sigma_{2n} = (M' - 1)\,\sigma_T + \sigma_\alpha \tag{16}$$

since essentially all of the absorption in beryllium was due to the (n, α) reaction for the neutron energies employed in the experiment. Fischer obtained the following (n, $2n$) cross sections at 2.57, 2.69, 2.93, and 3.19 Mev: 0.016, 0.030, 0.372, and 0.068 barns. It is seen that below 2.70 Mev the measured cross section was quite small. This led Fischer to conclude that the (n, $2n$) reaction in beryllium proceeds primarily by the process Be^9 (n, n')$Be^{9*}(n)Be^8$ (or $2He^4$) in which the 2.43-Mev level of Be^9 is excited and subsequently decays, emitting the second neutron. This process has a threshold of 2.70 Mev as opposed to the *direct* process Be^9 (n, $2n$)Be^8 (or $2He^4$) which becomes possible at a lower neutron energy of 1.85 (or 1.74) Mev.

Another interesting 4π detector experiment was that of Taylor, Ashby, Catron, and Newkirk (Ta57, As58) who used a 240-gallon cadmium loaded liquid scintillation counter to catch the neutrons emitted by various target elements bombarded by 14-Mev neutrons. The scintillation counter was an adaptation of that developed by Reines, Cowan, Harrison, and Carter (Re54a) in connection with the free-neutrino detection experiment (Co56c).

In the (n, $2n$) experiment targets were placed at the center of a cylindrical hole along the axis of the scintillation detector and bombarded by 14.1-Mev neutrons produced in short bursts and collimated so as to impinge only upon the targets. The neutrons emitted by the targets were slowed down by collisions in the liquid of the scin-

tillator and captured in the cadmium. The resulting prompt capture
γ rays were detected by the scintillator. (n, 2n) events were identified by observing two γ-ray pulses occurring in close time sequence
within 25 microseconds of the corresponding bombarding neutron
burst.

The measured (n, 2n) cross sections of Taylor *et al.* for 14
target elements from deuterium through bismuth are given in the
third column of Table IV. In all except the five cases of N, F, B, Fe,
and Cu the (n, 2n) cross section was found to be approximately equal
to the total nonelastic cross section.

(3) **Neutron Spectroscopic Methods.** Rosen and Stewart
(Ro57) have performed an experiment in which they measured both
the spatial and energy distributions of all the neutrons emitted by
tantalum and bismuth when bombarded by 14-Mev neutrons. This
nuclear emulsion experiment has already been discussed in Section
2.D in connection with their 14-Mev inelastic scattering measurements. The nuclear plate camera and neutron collimator are illustrated in Fig. 1. By integrating their differential cross sections over
both angle and energy Rosen and Stewart were able to obtain the
total cross section for emission of nonelastic neutrons:

$$\sigma_e = \sigma_{n,n'} + 2\sigma_{(n,2n)} \tag{17}$$

In addition, by observing the energy spectra and assuming that an
(n, 2n) reaction was realized whenever the energy of the first neutron
was low enough to make the emission of a second neutron energetically
possible, they were able to evaluate separately the (n, 2n) and inelastic scattering cross sections. Measurements were also made for a
beryllium target. In this case however the energy spectrum of
emitted neutrons was spatially integrated by using a thin spherical
shell of beryllium around the isotropic 14-Mev neutron source. The
nuclear emulsions were placed at some distance from the neutron
source, outside the spherical shell, and the integrated neutron energy
spectrum was obtained from that of the proton recoils in the nuclear
emulsions. For the three target elements Be, Ta, and Bi, the (n, 2n)
cross sections obtained in this experiment were 0.42 ± 0.07, 1.8 ±
0.3, and 2.3 ± 0.3 barns. As can be seen from Table IV the results
for Be and Bi are in good agreement with those of Taylor *et al.*, while
that for Ta is somewhat lower.

In a similar experiment already discussed in Section 2.D Ahn and Roberts (Ah57) obtained a value of 0.61 ± 0.10 barns for the 14.1-Mev $(n, 2n)$ cross section of zirconium.

A second neutron spectroscopic method which has been used in order to measure the Be^9 $(n, 2n)$ cross section is the time-of-flight method, discussed in Chapter IV.A. In a good-geometry experiment Marion, Levin, and Cranberg (Ma59) used short bursts of p-T neutrons at 2.6, 3.5, and 4.1 Mev to bombard a beryllium sample. Additional measurements were made at 5.0 and 6.0 Mev using D-D neutrons. Neutrons from scattering and reaction processes were detected at various emission angles with respect to the incident neutron direction by means of a fast scintillator. The times of flight of the neutrons emitted by the sample, and hence their velocity and energy spectra at each reaction angle, were measured by observing the time delays of the detector pulses with respect to the initiating bursts of bombarding neutrons. By measuring the neutron group with the shortest flight time, the differential elastic scattering cross section was obtained at each energy. In addition a continuous spectrum of neutrons was observed, as well as a group at a flight time corresponding to inelastically scattered neutrons leaving Be^9 in its 2.43-Mev excited state. By subtracting the integrated elastic scattering cross sections from the independently measured total cross sections at each energy, Marion *et al.* obtained the total nonelastic cross sections. In addition by subtracting the integrated inelastic $(Q - 2.43$ Mev$)$ and (n, α) cross sections, values of the direct $(n, 2n)$ cross sections which proceeds without excitation of the 2.43-Mev excited level in Be^9 were obtained. At 2.6, 3.5, and 4.1 Mev the direct $(n, 2n)$ cross sections were found to be 0.19 ± 0.10, 0.11 ± 0.09, and 0.19 ± 0.08 barns, respectively. At 6.0 Mev the continuous time delay spectrum was observed to have an end point corresponding to the energy appropriate to the direct $(n, 2n)$ reaction. This observation and that of an appreciable $(n, 2n)$ cross section below 2.70 Mev are in contradiction to Fischer's conclusion that the reaction proceeds mainly through the 2.43-Mev level of Be^9.

In a third neutron spectroscopic experiment Fowler, Owen, and Hanna (Fo54, Fo55) used the proton recoils produced in *trans*-stilbene scintillation crystals to detect the neutrons emitted by Be^9 when bombarded with 3.7-Mev, D-D neutrons. They bombarded a cylindrical sample of beryllium and observed the proton-recoil scintillations from two large crystals whose outputs in coincidence identified $(n, 2n)$ events. Corresponding to the coincidences, the pulses from one crystal were recorded on a pulse-height analyzer and the corresponding proton energy spectra determined for six pairs of coplanar neutron emission angles with respect to the incident neutron beam. In order to determine background a carbon scatterer was used, according to the principle discussed above in connection with Fischer's experiment. The proton recoil spectrum in each case had a fairly sharp cutoff at its high neutron energy end, corresponding to the $Be^9 (n, n')Be^9*(n,)Be^8$ process, rather than to the direct $(n, 2n)$ process.

In analyzing their data, Fowler et al. assumed that the emission of $(n, 2n)$ neutrons was isotropic and uncorrelated. The consistency of the total $(n, 2n)$ cross section determinations for the six different pairs of neutron emission angles seemed to bear out this assumption. The resulting cross section of 0.34 ± 0.10 barns at 3.7 Mev is in disagreement with the trend of Fischer's results; although the conclusion that the $(n, 2n)$ reaction proceeds through the first excited state of Be^9 is the same in the two cases. The $Be^9 (n, 2n)$ cross section value of Fowler et al. is in good agreement with the value obtained by subtracting the $Be^9 (n, \alpha)$ cross section (St57, Wa58) from the total nonelastic cross section of Marion et al. (Ma59), while the $(n, 2n)$ cross sections determined by Fischer (Fi57) are not. Since the first excited level of Be^9 is known to decay by neutron emission, the nonelastic cross section is comprised of only the $(n, 2n)$ and (n, α) cross sections for incident neutron energies as high as 11.5 Mev, which is the threshold of the $Be^9 (n, t)$ reaction.

In a recent nuclear emulsion experiment also at 3.7 Mev Wagner and Huber (Wa58) measured the energy spectrum and differential cross section of the neutrons emitted at 90° with respect to the neutron beam on a beryllium sample. The presence of the two stage process $Be^9(n, n')Be^9*(n)Be^8$ was established by the observation of neutron energy groups corresponding to excited levels at 2.43 and 3.1 Mev in Be^9. Their differential cross section of 0.039 ± 0.008 barns agrees within experimental error with the result of Fowler et al., quoted above, if isotropy is assumed.

(4) **The Activation Method.** Since the activation method (cf. Section 2.E) as applied to $(n, 2n)$ measurements generally has few unique features, it need not be discussed at length. It is of course not

possible to perform chemical separations of the residual radioactive nuclides from the bulk of the target elements; although radiochemistry may be desirable in order to strip away competing activities arising from (*n, charged particle*) reactions. A particular example of a difficult (*n, 2n*) activation measurement is that of Prestwood (Pr55) who measured the weak 26-year β^+ activity of Na^{22} produced by the Na^{23} (*n, 2n*) reaction at 14.1 Mev. Radiochemistry was used in this experiment in order to provide clean separated Na^{22} Cl samples which were counted in a standard, low background geometry which was calibrated with respect to a 4π counter, in which were placed "weightless" samples from an Na^{22} solution of known activity.

B. Excitation Functions

A knowledge of the excitation functions of (*n, 2n*) cross sections *versus* bombarding neutron energy is of interest primarily in connection with the use of certain target nuclides as threshold detectors and their cross sections as secondary flux standards (cf. Sections 3.C and 3.D). The reactions generally have large threshold energies, given by the binding energy of a neutron in the target nuclide, and the (*n, 2n*) measurements serve to determine these binding energies in a manner independent of the corresponding (*γ, n*) threshold measurements. In addition they provide a test of the statistical theory (Bl52) according to which the (*n, 2n*) cross section is given by

$$\sigma_{2n} = \sigma_X(\epsilon) \, [1 - (1 + \Delta\epsilon/T) \exp (-\Delta\epsilon/T)] \qquad (18)$$

where $\Delta\epsilon$ is the excess bombarding energy in the center-of-mass system above the threshold of the reaction, and T is the nuclear temperature given by Eq. (1).

We shall briefly review the excitation function measurements. Graphs of these functions are given in the cross section compilation of Hughes *et al.* (Hu55, Hu57). In all cases unless otherwise noted the bombarding neutrons were produced by the D-T reaction at various emission angles with respect to deuteron (or triton) beams from either cyclotrons or electrostatic accelerators. In these cases an independent knowledge of the neutron angular distribution of the D-T reaction at each deuteron bombarding energy was necessary for the flux determinations at the various neutron emission angles. In all the measurements use was made of the activation method.

(1) $C^{12}(n, 2n)C^{11}$, $E_{th} = 20.2$ **Mev**. Cyclotron-produced neutrons were used by Brolley, Fowler, and Schlacks (Br52) to activate polyethylene foils whose positron activities were counted in a standard geometry calibrated with a RaD + E standard.

(2) $Ni^{58}(n, 2n)Ni^{57}$, $E_{th} = 11.7$ **Mev**. Martin and Diven (Ma52) measured this reaction, using D-T neutrons produced by a 1.80-Mev beam of tritons on a thin deuterium gas target. Only a relative excitation function was obtained. The data given in BNL-325S (Hu57) are normalized to the 14.5-Mev value of Paul and Clarke (Pa53). More recent measurements have been made by Bayhurst and Prestwood (Ba58).

(3) $Cu^{63}(n, 2n)Cu^{62}$, $E_{th} = 11.1$ **Mev**. In an experiment similar to that on the $C^{12}(n, 2n)$ excitation function Brolley *et al.* (Br52) counted the Cu^{62} positron activity in a standard geometry calibrated by means of Cu^{66} β activity produced in a pile irradiation of normal copper. The agreement of these measurements with earlier data of Fowler and Slye (Fo50) was satisfactory. More recently the relative excitation function has been measured by Martin and Diven (Ma52) and by Cohen and White (Co56b).

(4) $Zn^{64}(n, 2n)Zn^{63}$, $E_{th} = 12.0$ **Mev**. The relative excitation function of this reaction was measured by Cohen and White (Co56b) who normalized their results to the cross section measurement of Paul and Clarke (Pa53) at 14.5 Mev.

(5) $Mo^{92}(n, 2n)Mo^{91}$, $E_{th} = 13.2$ **Mev**. In the experiment referred to above in connection with C^{12} and Cu^{63}, Brolley *et al.* (Br52) measured the cross section for the 15.5-minute Mo^{91} positron activity from threshold to 27 Mev. The cross section was measured relative to that of Cu^{63} by means of simultaneous ir-radiations of molybdenum and copper foils. In a later experiment Brolley (Br53) was able to observe a weak 65.5-second positron activity at a neutron bombarding energy from 18 Mev due to the other isomer of Mo^{91}. An additional measure-ment of the absolute excitation function was made by Yasumi (Ya57) who used ab-solute β counting to determine the 15.5-minute Mo^{91} activities for bombarding neutron energies between 13.51 and 14.80 Mev. The resulting cross sections were lower by approximately a factor of 2 than those found by Brolley *et al.*

(6) $I^{127}(n, 2n)I^{126}$, $E_{th} = 9.5$ **Mev**. The excitation function was measured by Martin and Taschek (Ma53) who bombarded NaI(Tl) crystals with D-T neutrons and counted the scintillations produced by the 13.1-day I^{126} activity. A long counter was used to monitor the flux of D-T neutrons emitted at various angles with respect to a 2.00-Mev deuteron beam. In order to normalize the relative excitation function thus obtained, the absolute cross section was measured at 14.1 Mev, using D-T neutrons from a Cockcroft-Walton accelerator whose flux was determined absolutely by means of an associated α-particle monitor.

(7) $Tl^{203}(n, 2n)Tl^{202}$, $E_{th} = 8.2$ **Mev**. The relative excitation function was measured by Martin and Diven (Ma52) whose technique is described above in connection with the $Ni^{58}(n, 2n)$ reaction. The excitation function may be nor-malized at 14.1 Mev by means of the cross section recently measured by Bayhurst and Prestwood (Ba58) given in Table IV.

(8) **Various Other Excitation Functions.** Bayhurst and Prestwood (Ba58) have measured the $(n, 2n)$ excitation functions of the following nuclei for

neutron bombarding energies between 13.5 and 15.0 Mev: Sc^{45} (E_{th} = 11.6 Mev), Ti^{46} (13.3 Mev), Ni^{58} (11.9 Mev), As^{75} (10.3 Mev), Zr^{90} (11.8 Mev), Ta^{181} (7.7 Mev), and Tl^{203} (8.2 Mev). They used D-T neutrons at various emission angles for which the neutron flux had been mapped by means of a separate measurement.

At 14.1 Mev Yasumi (Ya57) measured the gradients of the excitation functions of the $Zn^{64}(n, 2n)$ and $Ag^{109}(n, 2n)$ reactions for which the values were respectively $+52$ and -10.2 per cent Mev^{-1}.

C. Survey of the 14-Mev Measurements

The most extensive activation measurements are those of Paul and Clarke (Pa53) at 14.5 Mev, Forbes (Fo52) at 14.1 Mev, and Yasami (Ya57) at 14.1 Mev. The techniques used by these investigators have already been discussed in connection with the $(n, p\gamma)$ survey of Section 2.E. In addition the recent excitation function work of Bayhurst and Prestwood (Ba58) discussed in the last section provided absolute measurements of a number of $(n, 2n)$ cross section at 14.1 Mev.

Table IV presents a summary of the 14-Mev $(n, 2n)$ cross section measurements known to the author at this writing. The second column lists the measurements of Paul and Clarke and the third column various other measurements for all of which use was made of the activation technique except in the cases of the target elements D, Be, Zr, Ta, and Bi. For these measurements as well as those of Taylor et al. (Ta57, As58) (second column) and Graves and Davis (Gr55) (sixth and seventh columns) some method of detecting the emitted neutrons was used. In the case of deuterium Seagrave (Se55) measured the differential cross section of the elastically scattered neutrons by means of a counter telescope. The $(n, 2n)$ cross section was obtained by subtracting the total elastic cross section from the total cross section. The spectroscopic measurements of Be, Ta, and Bi (Ro57) and Zr (Ah57) have already been discussed in connection with neutron spectroscopic methods of measuring $(n, 2n)$ cross sections.

There are no order-of-magnitude discrepancies between the results listed in Table IV and the predictions of the Weisskopf-Ewing statistical theory discussed in Section 2.B. The most striking feature of these cross sections is their approximate equality to the corresponding total nonelastic cross sections in most cases as pointed out by Taylor et al. (Ta57).

Table IV. Experimental Values of $(n, 2n)$ Cross Sections for Various Target Elements and Nuclides at 14-Mev Bombarding Energy

Target element or nuclide	Paul and Clarke	Taylor et al.	Experimental $(n, 2n)$ Cross Section (barns)		Graves and Davis	
			Other	Ref.	Lower Limit	Upper Limit
D		0.20 ± 0.02	0.193 ± 0.030	Se55		
Be[9]		0.54 ± 0.04	0.42 ± 0.07	Ro57		0.00
C		0.006 ± 0.006				
N[14]	0.0057 ± 0.0008	0.019 ± 0.010	0.0034 ± 0.0001	Du54		
F[19]	0.061 ± 0.018	0.062 ± 0.009				
Na[23]			0.014 ± 0.002	Pr55		
Al[27]					0.00 ± 0.02	
Cl[35]	0.0035 ± 0.0016					
K[39]	0.010 ± 0.005					
Sc[45b]			0.105 ± 0.005[a]	Ba58		
Ti[46]			0.013 ± 0.001[a]	Ba58		
V		0.66 ± 0.05				
Fe[56]		0.50 ± 0.04			0.18 ± 0.03	0.67 ± 0.04
Ni[58]	0.041 ± 0.012		0.021 ± 0.002[a]	Ba58		
Cu[63]	0.480 ± 0.070		0.510 ± 0.036	Fo52		
			0.556 ± 0.028	Ya57		
Cu[65]	1.09 ± 0.17		0.970 ± 0.078	Fo52		
Cu		0.76 ± 0.06				
Zn					0.33 ± 0.06	0.79 ± 0.05
Zn[64]	0.224 ± 0.045		0.119 ± 0.014	Ya57		
Ga[69]	0.550 ± 0.017					
Ga[71]	0.700 ± 0.100					
Ge[70]	0.670 ± 0.230					
As[75]	0.540 ± 0.160		1.02 ± 0.05[a]	Ba58		
Ge[76]	1.82 ± 0.55					

Br79	1.14 ± 0.29				
Br81	0.83 ± 0.17b				
Se82	1.50 ± 0.50b				
Zr90	0.080 ± 0.040b				
Zr			0.54 ± 0.05	Re58	
Mo92	0.190 ± 0.028		0.074 ± 0.003b	Re58	
Ru96	0.480 ± 0.090		0.63 ± 0.03a	Ba58	
Mo100	3.79 ± 1.90		0.61 ± 0.10	Ah57	
Pd105	0.560 ± 0.056		0.132 ± 0.020	Ya57	
Ag107	0.52 ± 0.26c		0.230 ± 0.085	Br52	1.42 ± 0.04
Ag109	0.31 ± 0.15		0.458 ± 0.050b	Ya57	1.50 ± 0.04
Ag	1.73 ± 0.03		1.00 ± 0.10	Fo52	0.89 ± 0.02
Pd110	1.95 ± 0.97		0.504 ± 0.066	Ya57	1.04 ± 0.02
Cd		1.92 ± 0.14			
Sn					
Sb121	0.75 ± 0.19b				
Sb123	1.25 ± 0.31				
I127	1.12 ± 0.39		1.25 ± 0.07	Ma53	
Pr141	2.06 ± 0.72				
Sm154	0.22 ± 0.09				
Gd160	1.47 ± 0.81		1.15 ± 0.11b	Ba58	
Ta181	0.87 ± 0.22				
Ta	1.72 ± 0.46	2.64 ± 0.20	1.8 ± 0.3	Ro57	
Au197	2.8 ± 1.5	2.60 ± 0.20			1.22 ± 0.02
Pt198					1.83 ± 0.03
Tl203			1.30 ± 0.06	Ba58	
Pb		2.74 ± 0.20			1.76 ± 0.04
Bi		2.60 ± 0.19	2.3 ± 0.3	Ro57	1.86 ± 0.02

a Based on decay scheme given in Wa55.   b Isomeric state only.   c Based on decay scheme given in Br51.

4. Neutron-Induced Reactions in Light Nuclei that Yield Charged Reaction Products

A. Introduction

Before the widespread utilization of variable energy mono-energetic neutron sources, the spectroscopy of light nuclei was almost solely the province of experimenters who made use of the charged particle beams from electrostatic and Cockcroft-Walton accelerators. However, in recent years neutron experiments have provided progressively more data in this field. In contrast to the situation in charged beam work the determination of beam intensity (flux) has presented a major problem to the neutron experimenter, while the determination of the number of target atoms exposed in a given reaction solid angle has been relatively simple.

We shall discuss neutron-induced reactions in light nuclei which yield charged reaction products, beginning with a discussion of the excitation functions of total (n, charged particle) cross sections versus neutron energy. The second topic to be discussed will be the differential cross section measurements of the surface interactions, of which the pickup reactions are predominant examples. This will be followed by a discussion of some of the nuclear-emulsion studies of reactions yielding three, or more reaction products.

B. Monoenergetic Neutron Sources

In all the measurements to be described, use was made of one or more of the following reactions as a source of monoenergetic neutrons:

(a) $T(p, n)He^3$. The p-T neutrons which are produced in the forward direction with respect to the proton beam of an electrostatic accelerator are usually utilized. The neutron energy is varied by varying the proton energy of the beam striking a thin tritium target. By using neutrons emitted at larger angles, it is possible, of course, to obtain lower energy neutrons.

(b) $Li^7(p, n)Be^7$. This reaction was much used in the early work and again in recent work in the kev region of neutron energies. Details of the use of this reaction as a neutron source are given in Chapter I.E. Some experimental results in the kev region are reviewed in Chapter V.L.

(c) D(d, n)He³. The D-D reaction has been used extensively in cases in which low energy Cockcroft-Walton deuteron beams of essentially fixed energy were available. The large positive Q-value of the reaction provides neutrons in the region near 2 Mev. The energy can be varied conveniently by choosing various neutron emission angles with respect to the deuteron beam. The use of this reaction with variable energy electrostatic-accelerator beams on thin deuterium targets to provide neutrons with energies in excess of 5 Mev is somewhat limited. This is because extraneous neutrons are produced from the deuterium atoms adsorbed on the walls of the accelerating tube.

(d) T(d, n)He⁴. The D-T reaction is used extensively with low energy Cockcroft-Walton accelerators to provide monoenergetic 14-Mev neutrons from a thick tritium target. In addition one may obtain variable energy neutrons in this high energy region by bombarding thin targets with beams from variable energy electrostatic accelerators or cyclotrons. The variable energy obtained by changing the neutron angle with respect to the deuteron beam is often used to obtain small variations of neutron energy about 14 Mev.

Complete details of the neutron-producing reactions are given in Chapters I.B, I.C, and I.D. Other possible monoenergetic neutron sources are discussed in Chapter I.D.

C. Flux Determinations

For measurements of (n, charged particle) cross sections it is always necessary to compare the unknown bombarding neutron flux with that of a primary standard, either directly or indirectly. One of the widely applied methods of comparison makes use of a long counter (Chapter III.A) whose response to neutrons is approximately independent of neutron energy which is calibrated by means of a radioactive neutron source (e.g., Ra-α-Be).

Another type of primary flux standard is provided by *associated particle* counting. A common example is that of α-particle counting from the D-T reaction. By counting α particles at a known reaction angle over a known solid angle, one can deduce from the angular distribution and mechanics of the reaction the flux of the associated neutrons in a given direction. This method also applies to the D-D reaction but with somewhat more difficulty owing to the lower Q-value.

It is often convenient to make use of secondary flux standards. These are provided by accurately known cross sections of neutron-induced reactions. A notable case is that of the n-p elastic scattering reaction, for which the absolute differential cross section is known. If a known (thin) hydrogeneous sample is bombarded by neutrons, then counting the recoil protons provides the neutron flux measurement. Other examples of secondary flux standards are the fission cross sections of the isotopes of uranium and the $Li^6(n, \alpha)T$ and $B^{10}(n, \alpha)Li^7$ reactions. Use may also be made of the radioactivity produced by reactions whose cross sections are accurately known. Examples are the Fe^{56} (n, p) and Cu^{63} $(n, 2n)$ reactions. Methods of flux measurement are treated in detail in Chapters IV.B and IV.C.

D. Absolute Excitation Functions of $(n,$ charged particle$)$ Reactions

In comparison with the large body of work on the excitation functions of nuclear reactions induced by charged particles in light nuclei, there are as yet relatively few such determinations for neutron-induced reactions. At the present writing absolute excitation functions have been obtained for the (n, p) reactions on N^{14}, O^{16}, F^{19}, Na^{23}, Mg^{24}, Al^{27}, Si^{28}, P^{31}, S^{32}, and Cl^{37} and for the (n, α) reactions on Li^6, Be^9, B^{10}, B^{11}, N^{14}, O^{16}, F^{19}, Ne^{20}, Al^{27}, S^{32}, S^{34}, Cl^{35}, and A^{36}. These reactions will be reviewed in this section. The discussion will be limited to those excitation curves for which absolute cross sections have been obtained, using monoenergetic neutron sources. We shall not include the (n, p) reaction on He^3 since this special subject is discussed in connection with He^3 neutron spectrometers in Chapter III.C and in connection with the inverse reaction $T(p, n)He^3$ in Chapter I.C. It will not be necessary to present graphs of all the excitation functions to be discussed, since in many cases these are given in the cross section compilations of Hughes et al. (Hu55, Hu57).

Of considerable interest is the information which the excitation functions provide concerning the energies and spectroscopic properties of the levels of the intermediate nuclei of the reactions involved. We shall not deal extensively with the properties of the resonances of excitation functions here, since they are dealt with in detail in Chapter V.E.

Two methods have been used to detect the products of the nuclear reactions to be discussed. In the first method the charged reaction products are detected directly by means of their ionization in counters. In this case, in order to obtain total reaction cross sections, it is necessary to be sure that all energies and reaction angles of the charged particles are detected. In the second method, the activation method, one observes the total number of radioactive residual nuclei which are produced in a known target sample by a known neutron irradiation.

Excitation functions which yield radioactive residual nuclei from target elements which are chemically stable and readily available provide the basis for the use of these elements as *threshold detectors*. An example of such a threshold reaction is $S^{32}(n,p)P^{32}$. The residual nucleus provides a conveniently detectable β activity which measures that portion of a continuous neutron spectrum which lies above the threshold of the reaction at about 3 Mev and hence serves as a crude sort of neutron spectrometer.

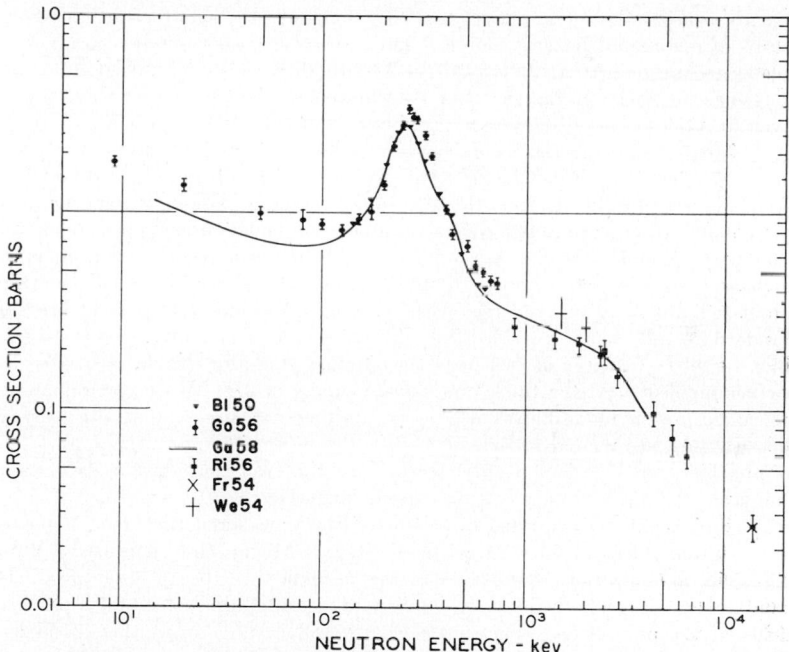

Figure 16. Excitation function of the total Li⁶ (n, α) cross section *versus* neutron energy, including the measurements of various investigators. The results of Ri56 have been recorrected in this graph to take account of the response of the long counter as given in A158.

(1) Li⁶(n, α)T $(Q = 4.780$ Mev). Nearly all of the absorption of low energy neutrons in lithium takes place by means of the (n, α) reaction in the Li⁶ isotope which has an abundance of 7.5 per cent. From its thermal value of 945 barns this cross section decreases with increasing neutron energy according to the $1/v$ law until it first exhibits a resonance in the region of 260 kev. The cross section in the resonance region was first measured by Blair and Holland (Bl50), who compared the yield of charged particles from natural lithium targets with that of the fission fragments from U²³⁵. These data were taken with a statistical accuracy of about two per cent and an energy resolution of 25 kev and are regarded as preliminary by their authors. The values of Blair and Holland are plotted as the triangles in Fig. 16. The values given here differ from those of Hu55 because of a correction, made by Devaney (De56), for more recently measured values of the U²³⁵ fission cross section.

Another measurement in the resonance region is that of Gorlov, Gokhberg, Morozov, and Otroschenko (Go56) between 9 and 700 kev. These authors used p-T neutrons. In the energy region from 9 to 350 kev they used a single bombarding energy of 1214 kev, obtaining different neutron energies by varying the angle of emission. They used 92 per cent enriched Li⁶F foils in ionization chambers to measure the cross section against a long-counter monitor calibrated by means of a standard natural source. Their cross section value at 9 kev extrapolates by means of the $1/v$ law to the known thermal value. Their data are plotted as the circles in Fig. 16. In Ri56 the connection for long counter response given in A158 was applied inversely. The data of Fig. 16 have been recorrected.

Measurements in the region between 0.88 and 14.1 Mev, above the resonance, were made by Ribe (Ri56). Thin foils of enriched lithium metal and LiF were bombarded inside a proportional counter in whose pulse-height spectrum it was possible to observe pulses corresponding to all emission energies (angles) of the α particles and tritons (as in a conventional fission experiment). A number of flux standards were used in order to obtain absolute cross sections. For the thin target p-T and D-D neutron regions of 0.88 and 2.90 and 4.44 to 6.52 Mev, a standard Po-α-Be source provided the calibration of a long counter. At the single thick target D-T energy of 14.1 Mev the primary standard was an associated α-particle monitor. At the thick target D-D energy of 2.50 Mev a corresponding associated-proton monitor was used. In another measurement at this energy the D-D flux was related to that at 14 Mev by using the known ratio of values for the U²³⁵ and U²³⁸ fission cross sections at the two energies as a secondary standard. Ribe's data are plotted as the rectangles in Fig. 16.

Elpidinskiĭ, Shapiro, and Shmranich (El57) measured the Li⁶(n, α) cross section using thick target D-D neutrons at 2.50 Mev. They bombarded thin Li⁶F foils in ionization chambers capable of detecting the reaction products simultaneously from both sides of the foils and measured the triton and α-particle yields in the pulse-height spectrum. Flux was measured by means of an associated proton monitor. Their cross section value of 170 ± 20 millibarns and those determined by Ribe are in agreement.

A single measurement at 14.1 Mev has been provided by Frye (Fr54), who measured the differential cross section by detecting in nuclear emulsions the tritons from a thin, enriched, lithium metal target and integrating the yield over all reaction angles. Frye's cross section is given by the $\times$ in Fig. 16. Two measurements by Weddell and Roberts (We54) at 1.5 and 2.0 Mev are given by the crosses in Fig. 16. These authors used Li⁶-loaded nuclear emulsions and identified the (n, α) events by the characteristic appearance of the corresponding tracks and the known energy released to the α particle and triton in each case. They integrated the yields over all triton-emission angles in order to obtain total relative cross sections. By means of a neutron exposure at 0.60 Mev they normalized their cross sections to that of Blair and Holland. In Fig. 16, we have renormalized their values to the corrected Blair and Holland value at 0.60 Mev.

A recent measurement in the energy region from 15 kev to 4.07 Mev is that of Gabbard, Bonner, and Davis (Ga58). They used Li(p, n)($E_n < 600$ kev) and p-T neutrons to bombard a 4×4 mm LiI(Eu) scintillation crystal, obtaining a pulse-height spectrum which included the contributions of α particles and tritons at all reaction angles and energies. Flux was determined by means of a long counter and standard natural neutron source. The data of Gabbard et al. are represented by the continuous line of Fig. 16. Their data points over most of the energy region investigated overlapped in energy resolution (approximately 10 kev) making a representation by means of separate points impractical.

Recently Kern and Kreger (Ke58) have extended the measurement of the Li⁶(n, α) excitation function to energies in excess of 14 Mev. They bombarded a Li⁶I(Eu) scintillation crystal with D-T neutrons with energies between 12.5 and 18.3 Mev, and measured the (n, α) relative cross section with an accuracy of ± 10 per cent. Their cross section values, normalized to the value given by Frye and Ribe, at the bombarding energies 12.5, 13, 15, 16, 17, 17.9, and 18.3 Mev were respectively: 30.7 ± 5.5, 29.1 ± 5.2, 23.4 ± 4.2, 20.0 ± 3.6, 17.4 ± 3.1, 16.9 ± 3.0, and 16.6 ± 3.0 millibarns.

In assessing the cross section data as it now stands, we see that there is an unresolved discrepancy of about 25 per cent in the values below the resonance. The measurements of Gorlov et al. place both the energy and cross section of the resonance peak somewhat higher than do the others. It can be seen that the asymmetry on the upper energy edge of the resonance in the data of Gabbard et al. is exactly reproduced, as are the rest of their resonance data, in the Blair-Holland measurement. The hump in the cross section at about 2.5 Mev in the data of Gabbard et al. is also reproduced by Ribe's results. This hump is thought to be due to the onset of competition to the (n, α) reaction by the (n, n'), $(n, n'd)$, and (n, d) reactions in Li⁶.

The Li⁶ total (transmission) cross section at the peak of the resonance as measured by Johnson, Willard, and Bair (Jo54) and by Gorlov et al. (Go56a) requires that the spin of the corresponding 7.46-Mev level of Li⁷ be 5/2. This in turn rules out the participation of s-wave neutrons in the resonance, since Li⁶ has a spin of 1. Results by Darlington et al. (Da53) on the angular distribution of the Li⁶(n, α) reaction in the resonance region also showed the effects of p-wave and possibly higher orbital neutrons, although an analysis of these data by Peshkin and Siegert (Pe52) gave a most probable spin of the Li⁷ state of 3/2, an error largely due to the sensitivity of their calculations to errors in the angular distribution measurements. On the basis of a Breit-Wigner one-level fit to their excitation function for total cross section and the uncorrected (n, α) cross section of

Blair and Holland, Johnson *et al.* arrive at total neutron and α-particle widths of 114 and 60 kev, respectively, for the 7.46-Mev level in Li^7. Gorlov *et al.*, on the basis of both of their measurements, obtain $\Gamma_n/\Gamma_\alpha = 1.87$. A similar analysis, yielding only slightly different results, has been made by Marion *et al.* (Ma56a). All of these analyses are based upon the assumption of a p-wave resonance neutron interaction in the presence of s-wave potential scattering.

A direct interaction calculation of the $Li^6(n, \alpha)T$ total cross section has been carried out by Kopaleishvili (Ko57). Following proposals by Vashakidze and Chilashvili (Va54) and Dabrowski and Sawicki (Da55), he assumed the Li^6 nucleus to be composed of an α particle and a deuteron with the $(n, \alpha)T$ reaction proceeding by direct pickup of the deuteron by the incident neutron. The resulting computed cross section reproduces the experimental results quite well in the neutron energy region between 1 and 14 Mev with a slight upward concavity on a plot like that of Fig. 16, suggestive of the hump observed in the experimental cross section at about 2.5 Mev.

(2) $Be^9(n, \alpha)He^6$ ($Q = -0.64$ Mev). The measurement of this cross section has been carried out by means of the activation method involving β counting of the radioactive He^6 nucleus. Since the half-life of the He^6 activity is only 0.83 second, special neutron beam pulsing techniques were required in order that the activity might be counted in the absence of neutrons without, however, requiring a change in the location of the irradiated sample in order to count the He^6 activity.

The earliest quantitative measurement of the excitation function of the $Be^9(n, \alpha)$ cross section was that of Allen *et al.* (Al47) in the D-D neutron energy region from 1.8 to 4.0 Mev. These results are quoted in Hu55. A measurement by Sattar, Morgan, and Hudspeth (Sa55), using thin target D-D neutrons in the energy region from 3.3 to 6.1 Mev, has as yet not been normalized absolutely. A definitive measurement is that of Stelson and Campbell (St57), who covered the neutron energy region from threshold (0.7 Mev) to 4.4 Mev. They used thin target $Li(p,n)$ and p-T-neutrons, obtaining variable energy protons from an electrostatic accelerator. Absolute, $2\pi \beta$ counting was used to determine the He^6 activity, and flux was determined both by the long counter, standard source method and through the use of the U^{238} fission cross section as a secondary standard.

Stelson and Campbell found the threshold of the reaction to be 0.70 Mev, the identical value computed from the 3.50 ± 0.05 Mev end point of the decay of He^6 (Wu52). No resonances in the $Be^9(n, \alpha)$ excitation function were observed; although the corresponding total cross section of Be^9 exhibits two resonances above the (n, α) threshold at 0.81 and 2.73 Mev. Instead, the (n, α) cross section rises from its threshold to a broad maximum of 104 ± 7 millibarns at 3.0 Mev, followed by a gradual decrease to 70 millibarns at 4.4 Mev.

In another measurement of the absolute excitation function Vasilev, Komarov, and Popova (Va57) bombarded nuclear emulsions loaded with beryllium powder with $Li(d, n)$ neutrons in the energy range from 1 to 7 Mev. (n, α) events were identified and the bombarding neutron energy determined in each case from the characteristic two-pronged stars originating at the grains of beryllium. Neutron flux was determined by counting proton recoils from the hydrogenous emulsion material. For the neutron bombarding energies, 1, 2, 3, 4, 5, 6, and 7 Mev the (n, α) cross sections were found to be respectively: $12 \pm 5, 55 \pm 15, 95 \pm 25$, $86 \pm 30, 50 \pm 20, 16 \pm 10$, and 19 ± 15 millibarns. The neutron energy spread associated with each determination was ± 0.5 Mev. These results and those of Stelson and Campbell are in good agreement.

An additional absolute measurement at 14.1 Mev (thick target D-T neutrons) was made by Battat and Ribe (Ba53) who obtained the value 10 ± 1 mb for the $Be^9(n, \alpha)$ cross section. This result, as well as those of Stelson and Campbell, is quoted in Hu57.

(3) $Be^9(n, t)Li^7$ $(Q = -10.34$ Mev$)$ and $B^{10}(n, t)2He^4$ $(Q = +0.33$ Mev$)$. These cross sections have been measured by means of a tritium activation technique by Wyman (Wy58). After bombardment of B^{10} and Be^9 samples by monoenergetic neutrons the tritium gas produced by the (n, t) reaction was expelled and quantitatively collected for absolute β counting. At 14.1 Mev the $Be^9(n, t)$ cross section was found to be 17.8 ± 1.3 millibarns. At 4.0, 5.6, 9.6, and 14.1 Mev the $B^{10}(n, t)$ cross sections were respectively: $95 \pm 10, 242 \pm 12, 123 \pm 15$, and 85 ± 6 millibarns.

In a nuclear emulsion experiment discussed in Section 3.F of this article Frye and Gammel (Fr56) measured the excitation function of the $B^{10}(n, t)$ reaction between 5.6 and 19.5 Mev. The results of the two measurements are in agreement.

(4) $B^{10}(n, \alpha)Li^7$ $(Q = +2.792$ Mev$)$. This reaction has long been utilized as the basis for the shielding provided by boron and its compounds to slow neutrons. It is hoped that the cross section for this reaction, along with that of the reaction $Li^6(n, \alpha)T$, will provide an accurate secondary flux standard.

The thermal cross section of the B^{10} isotope is 3390 barns and the corresponding value per natural boron atom (18.8 per cent B^{10}) is 750 barns. The cross section decreases according to the $1/v$ relationship with increasing energy up to 100 kev. Past this limit the measured cross section falls below the $1/v$ extrapolation (Pe51, Bi57, Hu57).

The earliest work on the $B^{10}(n, \alpha)$ reaction utilizing fast neutrons was that of Bailey et al. quoted in the 1950 review article by Adair (Ad50). There have since been two measurements of the total (n, α) cross section in the fast neutron region, both with an absolute accuracy of 25 per cent. Measurements have been made by Petree, Johnson, and Miller (Pe51) in the neutron energy region from 0.35 to 2.6 Mev, and by Bichsel and Bonner (Bi57), from 20 kev to 4.8 Mev. Both groups bombarded BF_3-filled proportional counters in whose pulse-height spectra the group(s) corresponding to the disintegration α particles and Li^7 ions could be distinguished. Both used thin target $Li(p, n)$ neutrons from electrostatic accelerators at their lower energies and thin target p-T at their higher energies. Petree et al. obtained their flux values from a long-counter monitor, calibrated by means of a standard Ra-α-Be source; Bichsel and Bonner also used a long-counter monitor but normalized their data at 20 kev to the cross section value extrapolated by means of the $1/v$ law from the thermal value.

In Fig. 17 are plotted some of the results of Bichsel and Bonner. The ordinate represents the total isotopic $B^{10}(n, \alpha)$ cross section multiplied by $E_n^{1/2}$, where E_n is in ev. The constancy of this quantity for neutron energies as high as 100 kev indicates the degree to which the $1/v$ law holds for the $B^{10}(n, \alpha)$ cross section.   The measurements of Petree *et al.* of the total $B^{10}(n, \alpha)$ cross section (per atom of normal boron) are given in the upper graph of Fig. 18.   The broad resonance observed by these authors at 1.9 Mev was also observed by Bichsel and Bonner, who found in addition three other resonances at 0.53, 2.8, and 4.1 Mev. The (n, α) resonances correspond to broad resonances at 0.45, 1.8, 2.75, and 4.3 Mev observed by Bockelman *et al.* (Bo51) in the B^{10} total cross section.

There is agreement between the two sets of $B^{10}(n, \alpha)$ cross section measurements in the energy region between 0.5 and 1.0 Mev to within approximately 10 per cent.   However, for higher energies the agreement between the absolute cross sections becomes considerably less satisfactory.   In addition the ratio of the cross sections varies from constancy by approximately 30 per cent.   If the $B^{10}(n, \alpha)$ cross section is to be used as a secondary flux standard above 1 Mev, further absolute measurements are desirable.

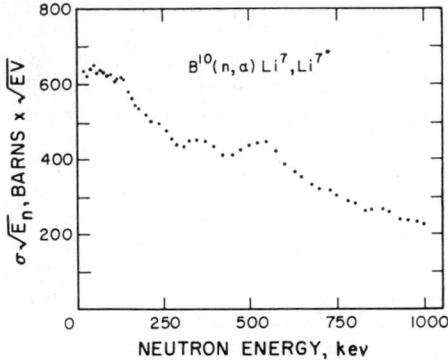

Figure 17.   Excitation function showing the degree of validity of the inverse velocity law for the $B^{10}(n, \alpha)Li^7$ reaction (Bi57).

The $B^{10}(n, \alpha)Li^7$ reaction proceeds both to the ground and first excited (0.478-Mev) state of Li^7.   Numerous measurements (cf. Aj52) have shown that at thermal neutron energies only six per cent of the reactions lead to the ground state.   In the lower graph of Fig. 18 is shown the variation of the branching ratio $\sigma(Li)/\sigma(Li^*)$ with neutron energy as measured by Petree *et al.*   This branching ratio has also been measured by Bichsel, Hälg, Huber, and Stebler (Bi51, Bi52). They used zero degree, thick target D-D neutrons at 1.80, 2.10, 2.55, 2.95, 3.5, and 3.9 Mev.   In addition, they made a measurement at 0.5 Mev, using neutrons from the $C^{12}(d, n)N^{13}$ reaction.   The branching ratios which they observed at these energies were respectively 1.7 ± 0.3, 1.5 ± 0.4, 1.5 ± 0.4, 1.8 ± 0.3, 1.4 ± 0.3, 0.9 ± 0.2, and 0.31 ± 0.04.   Bichsel *et al.* point out that their values at 2.10 and 2.55 Mev take on large uncertainties owing to the production of spurious peaks in the α-particle pulse-height spectrum from interactions of neutrons in the low-energy tails of their thick target energy distributions with the 1.9-Mev resonance.   These degraded neutrons should not have been present in the thin target experiments of Petree *et al.*

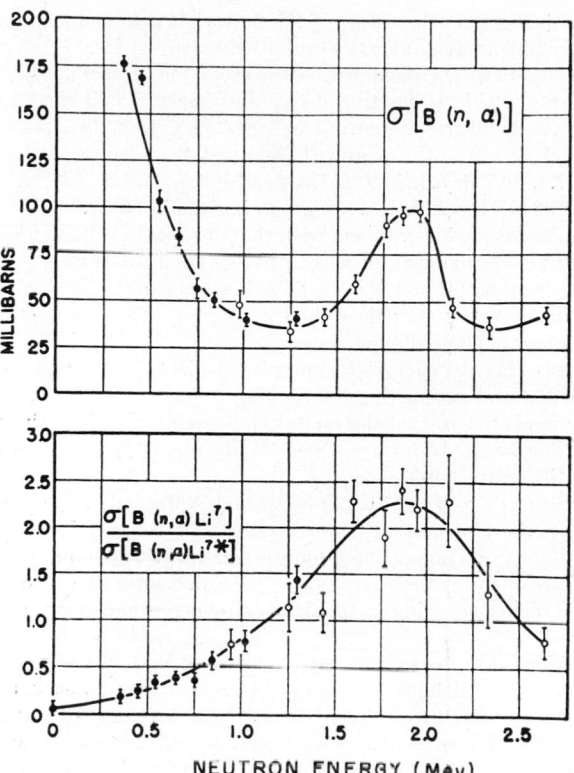

Figure 18. Measurements of Pe51. Upper graph: (n, α) disintegration cross section of ordinary boron *versus* neutron energy. Lower graph: ratio of the number of disintegrations leading to the ground state of Li^7 to the number leading to the 478-kev excited state *versus* neutron energy.

In regard to the 1.9-Mev resonance, Petree *et al.* point out that reasonably small J values of states at the corresponding (13.2-Mev) excitation of B^{11} can be made plausible only if it is assumed that the resonance corresponds to two levels in the B^{11} intermediate nucleus.

(5) $B^{11}(n, \alpha)Li^8(\beta-)Be^8*(2\alpha)$ $(Q = -6.63$ Mev). Armstrong and Frye (Ar56a) measured the cross section of this reaction for D-T neutron energies between 12.6 and 20.0 Mev by means of B^{11}-loaded nuclear emulsions. Events were identified by observing the *hammer* tracks produced when Li^8 nuclei came to rest, producing Be^8 which decayed into two oppositely directed α particles. The electron from the β decay of Li^8 left no visible trace in the Ilford C-2 emulsions used in this experiment. Neutron fluxes were determined by counting proton recoils in the nuclear emulsions.

By analyzing only the tracks of the first α particle and Li^8 nucleus in each case it was possible to determine the excitation energy of Li^8. All events were observed to go either to the ground or 1.0-Mev excited levels of Li^8. Levels of higher excitation are unstable to neutron decay and hence would not have been observed. At the bombarding neutron energies 12.6, 13.0, 14.7, 15.4, 16.9, 17.6, 18.9, 19.8, and 20.0 Mev the measured cross sections were respectively: 27.0 ± 6.5, 38.4 ± 7.4, 30.9 ± 6.3, 36.9 ± 7.0, 21.9 ± 3.6, 23.7 ± 4.8, 19.7 ± 3.7, 16.3 ± 3.1, and 15.8 ± 3.1 millibarns. A graph is given in Hu57.

These results are in agreement with that of Heiberg (He54) who bombarded a BF_3-filled proportional counter with a pulsed beam of 14-Mev D-T neutrons. Following each neutron burst α-particle pulses appeared and decayed with the 0.88-second half life characteristic of the Li^8 β decay. The cross section was found to be of the order of 30 millibarns.

By measuring the sum of the energies of the two α particles produced by the decay of Be^8 and subtracting the binding energy of the ground state of Be^8, Frye and Gammel determined the excitation energy of Be^8 in each nuclear disintegration. The broad 3-Mev level was clearly observed, and there was also a slight indication of the 4.0-Mev level.

(6) $N^{14}(n, p)C^{14}$ ($Q = +0.627$ Mev) and $N^{14}(n, \alpha)B^{11}$ ($Q = -0.154$ kev). These two reactions have usually been studied at the same time by bombarding the nitrogen filling of a proportional counter or ionization chamber with neutrons. Those portions of the pulse height spectrum which were due to α particles and protons were separable owing to the different energies and specific ionizations of these particles.

Following early measurements by Barschall and Battat (Ba46) and Sikkema (Si48), the first definitive measurement was that of Johnson and Barschall (Jo50), who used thin target $Li(p, n)$ neutrons between 0.19 and 1.68 Mev. Flux was measured by means of a long counter and a Ra-α-Be source. (n, p) resonances were observed at 0.499, 0.640, 0.993, and 1.415 Mev and (n, α) resonances at 1.415 and 1.800 Mev. These data are compiled in Hu55. The resonances at 0.640, 0.993, and 1.415 Mev were also observed in the N^{14} total cross section by Johnson, Petree, and Adair (Jo51a). The absence of the 0.499-Mev resonance is attributed to a very small neutron width. Bollman and Zünti (Bo51a) used 560-kev deuterons on a thick ($^1/_4$ saturation thickness) heavy ice target, obtaining bombarding neutrons, ranging in energy from 1.9 to 3.7 Mev, at various emission angles. Fluxes were calculated from the measured differential cross section of the D-D reaction. (n, p) resonances were observed at 2.26 and 2.80 Mev and (n, α) resonances at 2.26, 2.56, and 2.75 Mev. Sikkema also observed the lowest (2.23 Mev) resonance in his D-D work on the combined (n, α) and (n, p) yield. An exhaustive compilation of N^{15} resonances observed by means of these reactions has been given by von Gierke (Gi54).

The data of Bollmann and Zünti at their lower energies just overlap those of Johnson and Barschall at the upper end of the latters' energy region. The (n, α) cross sections of the former are however higher by a factor of two in the overlap region. In the case of the (n, p) cross section, the two sets of measurements agree to within about 20 per cent in the region of overlap.

A single early measurement of the $N^{14}(n, p)$ and $N^{14}(n, \alpha)$ cross sections at the D-D neutron energy 2.8 Mev was reported by Baldinger and Huber (Ba39). Both cross section values are considerably higher than those of Bollmann and Zünti. As a result of irradiating a nitrogen-filled cloud chamber with 14.1-Mev d-T neutrons and identifying the tracks from nuclear reactions, Lillie (Li52) found the $N^{14}(n, \alpha)$ cross section to be 100 millibarns (cf. Hu55).

(7) $O^{16}(n, p)N^{16}$ ($Q = -9.62$ Mev). This cross section has been measured by activation of the 7.35-second, β-emitting N^{16}. One measurement of the excitation function was made by Martin (Ma54), who used thin target D-T neutrons in order to exceed the threshold of the reaction. Neutron energies between 12.4 and 18.0 Mev were obtained for neutron emission angles between 0° and 150°. A relative yield curve was measured for a thick (5-gram) water sample, and the cross section was normalized at 14.1 Mev by comparing the N^{16} activity with that from the known $Cu^{63}(n, 2n)Cu^{62}$ reaction. The cross section was observed to rise smoothly from threshold to a peak of 90 millibarns at 13.5 Mev, thereafter falling smoothly to 41 millibarns at 18 Mev. In the cloud chamber measurement referred to in the last paragraph, Lillie observed with oxygen fillings a total (n, p) cross section of 35 millibarns at 14.1 Mev.

(8) $O^{16}(n, \alpha)C^{13}$ ($Q = -2.201$ Mev). This reaction is of practical interest in connection with applications in which water or other oxygen-containing media serve as moderators of fast neutrons. The cross section has been measured by observing the pulses of the disintegration α particles from gas filling in ionization chambers and proportional counters irradiated with fast neutrons. The techniques are similar to those already described in connection with the $N^{14}(n, \alpha)$ and $N^{14}(n, p)$ experiments.

Two measurements of the excitation function exist. In the first Seitz and Huber (Se55a) used D-D neutrons at various emission angles in order to cover the energy region from 3.65 to 4.2 Mev. Flux was monitored by a Hornyak button consisting of a ZnS-Lucite scintillator (cf. Chapter III.B) calibrated absolutely by comparison with proton recoils. An oxygen-filled ionization chamber was used. Seitz and Huber observed the cross section to rise from zero at 3.65 Mev to a value of 137 millibarns at 4.21 Mev in a manner consistent with the increasingly probable penetration by the α particles of the Coulomb barrier of the C^{13} residual nucleus. On this smooth rise they observed two anomalies at the neutron energies 3.90 and 4.05 Mev, corresponding to excitations in the O^{17} intermediate nucleus of 7.81 and 7.95 Mev.

The other measurement of the $O^{16}(n, \alpha)C^{13}$ excitation function was performed by Walton, Clement, and Boreli (Wa57), who used thin target D-D neutrons between 3.98 and 5.21 Mev to bombard the CO_2 filling of a proportional counter. At the same time they also measured the total cross section of the inverse reaction $C^{13}(\alpha, n)O^{16}$ in the same equivalent neutron energy region and also the O^{16} total cross section between 3.45 and 4.46 Mev. Their (n, α) excitation function agrees fairly well with that of Seitz and Huber in the region of overlapping neutron energies. Both sets of data are plotted in Hu57.

Since $C^{13}(\alpha, n)O^{16}$ is the inverse reaction to $O^{16}(n, \alpha)C^{13}$, the excitation function of one should be derivable from that of the other by means of the reciprocity theorem of nuclear reactions (Bl52) based upon the principle of detailed balancing

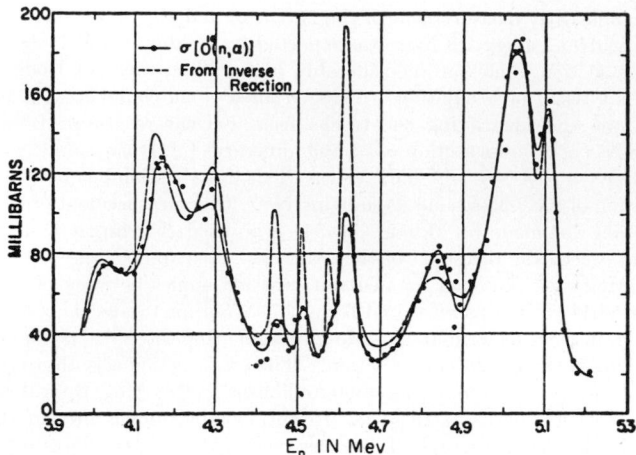

Figure 19. Cross section for the $O^{16}(n, \alpha)C^{13}$ reaction (Wa57). The dashed curve represents the $O^{16}(n, \alpha)C^{13}$ cross section calculated from that of the inverse $C^{13}(\alpha, n)O^{16}$ reaction, using the principle of detailed balancing.

which relates the cross sections of inverse reactions. Such a comparison was made by Walton *et al.*, whose results are shown in Fig. 19. The solid curve is the measured excitation function of the $O^{16}(n, \alpha)C^{13}$ reaction, and the dashed curve represents the same cross section derived by the reciprocity relation from their measured $C^{13}(\alpha, n)O^{16}$ cross section. It is seen that all of the resonances observed occur in both cases. These resonances were also seen in the O^{16} total cross section (Be56), indicating that in each case the neutron width of the O^{17} level is appreciable compared to the α particle width. The resonance of lowest energy in Fig. 19 corresponds to that observed by Seitz and Huber at the neutron energy 4.05 Mev. However, no indication of the anomaly at a neutron energy of 3.90 Mev in the O^{16} (n, α) excitation function was seen by these authors in the inverse C^{13}-(α, n) experiment. Using the cloud chamber technique discussed earlier in connection with the $N^{14}(n, \alpha)$ reaction, Lillie (Li52) found the $O^{16}(n, \alpha)$ cross section to be 310 millibarns at 14.1 Mev.

An extensive survey of the properties of the O^{17} levels, corresponding to the resonances of Fig. 19 is given by Walton *et al.* Another survey by von Gierke (Gi54) correlates the O^{17} level observations of various neutron spectrometer and excitation function experiments.

(9) $F^{19}(n, p)O^{19}$ ($Q = -4.00$ Mev) and $F^{19}(n, \alpha)N^{16}$ ($Q = -1.49$ Mev). In both cases these reactions can be detected by means of the induced β activity of the residual nuclei O^{19} (20 seconds) and N^{16} (7 seconds). Preliminary measurements of the (n, α) excitation function were reported by Bostrom, Hudspeth, and Morgan (Bo55), who used thin target D-D neutrons between 3.5 and 6.2 Mev.

Marion and Brugger (Ma55) used thin target p-T and D-D neutrons (4.6 to 8.0 Mev) from an electrostatic accelerator to measure both the (n, p) and (n, α)

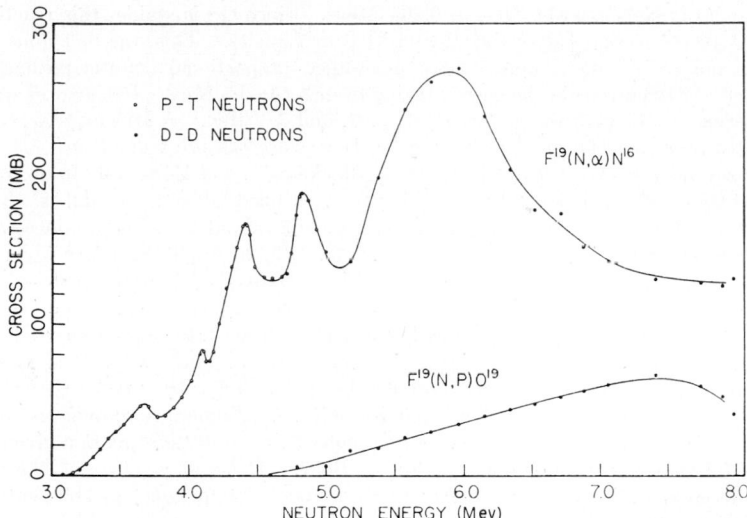

Figure 20. Excitation functions for the reactions $F^{19}(n,\ \alpha)N^{16}$ and $F^{19}(n,\ p)O^{19}$ (Ma55).

reactions in F^{19}. CaF_2 scintillation crystals were used both as targets and $4\pi\ \beta$ counters. The relative $(n,\ \alpha)$ yield curve was also measured in the p-T neutron region by irradiating a Teflon (CF_2) cylinder and observing the N^{16} activity with an anthracene scintillation counter. The flux of p-T neutrons was determined by using the measured yield curve and that of the D-D neutrons by the long counter-standard source method. In Fig. 20 are shown the excitation functions obtained by Marion and Brugger for both the $(n,\ p)$ and $(n,\ \alpha)$ reactions in F^{19} above the effective thresholds of 3.1 and 4.7 Mev. The relative accuracy of the cross sections is 10 to 15 per cent, and the accuracy of the absolute cross section measurement is about 40 per cent. Resonances are indicated at 3.4, 3.70, 4.11, 4.22, and 4.86 Mev.

The p-T neutrons used in obtaining these data had an energy spread of 60 kev. With 30-kev resolution the 3.70-Mev resonance was observed to consist of three resonances at 3.61, 3.69, and 3.77 Mev. The large resonance at 5.9 Mev was observed with a D-D neutron energy spread of 100 kev. Bostrom *et al.* reported resonances at 4.17, 4.68, 5.04, 5.40, 5.59, 5.90, and 6.08 Mev with 25-kev energy resolution. It is likely that those resonances near 6 Mev are included in the large 5.9-Mev resonance observed by Marion and Brugger.

In Fig. 20 it is seen that the observed threshold of the $(n,\ \alpha)$ reaction at 3.1 Mev is much larger than the value 1.57 Mev calculated from the known Q-value of the reaction. This is due to the effect of the N^{16} Coulomb barrier to the α particles. No resonances were observed in the $F^{19}(n,\ p)$ cross section corresponding to those seen in the $(n,\ \alpha)$ cross section.

(10) $Ne^{20}(n, \alpha)O^{17}$ ($Q = -0.603$ Mev). Since O^{17} is stable, this reaction must be observed by detecting the emitted α particles. This was first done by Sikkema (Si50), who bombarded a neon-filled proportional counter with thin target D-D neutrons in the energy region from 2.2 to 3.4 Mev. Resonances were observed at the neutron energies 2.47, 2.93, and 3.3 Mev. A BF_3 counter, calibrated by means of a natural neutron source was used as a flux monitor. A later measurement was performed by Johnson, Bockelman, and Barschall (Jo51), who used thin target p-T neutrons to bombard a neon-filled ionization chamber. The $Ne^{20}(n, \alpha)$ reaction had its first observable yield at about 1.8 Mev and increased thereafter, exhibiting resonances at 2.12, 2.45, 2.62, 2.72, 2.87, and 3.26 Mev.

(11) $Na^{23}(n, p)Ne^{23}$ ($Q = -3.603$ Mev). This reaction was observed by means of the induced activity of the 37.5-second Ne^{23} by Williamson *et al.* (Wi58, Bo57), who used thin target D-D and $N^{14}(d, n)$ neutrons in the energy region from 3.3 to 8.2 Mev. A NaI(Tl) scintillation crystal served both as target and $4\pi \beta$ counter. The cross section first became observable at 4.1 Mev, rising thereafter in accordance with the Coulomb barrier of Ne^{23}. Numerous resonances were seen between 5.21 and 7.76 Mev. The graph of the excitation function given in Hu57 represents the preliminary data of Bo57. The quoted error of the absolute cross-section determinations was $\pm$ 20 per cent for most of the neutron energies.

(12) $Mg^{24}(n, p)Na^{24}$ ($Q = -4.731$ Mev). The excitation function has been measured between 12.5 and 17.5 Mev by Cohen and White (Co56b), who used thin target D-T neutrons at various emission angles to activate the 14.9-hour Na^{24}. The measured angular distribution of the D-T reaction was used in order to obtain the relative fluxes of the different bombardments. The relative excitation function was normalized at 14.5 Mev to the cross section measured by Paul and Clarke (Pa53). A graph is given in Hu57.

(13) $Al^{27}(n, p)Mg^{27}$ ($Q = -1.811$ Mev). Because of this reaction Al^{27} is a useful threshold detector. The first activation measurement of the 9.45-minute Mg^{27} activity was made by Bretscher and Wilkinson (Br49), who observed a threshold of 2.3 Mev. A more exact measurement was that of Smith and Henkel (Sm52), quoted in Hu55. They measured the relative activation cross section from threshold to 7.7 Mev, using thin target p-T and D-D neutrons from an electrostatic accelerator. Flux was monitored by means of a U^{238} fission chamber, and the data were normalized at 14.1 Mev to the cross section measured by Forbes (Fo52). The U^{238} cross section which they used was measured with respect to a long counter whose sensitivity function has since undergone a correction. The authors estimate that the cross section in Hu55 should be revised upward for neutron energies above 5 Mev with a maximum correction of 10 per cent at 7 Mev.

(14) $Al^{27}(n, \alpha)Na^{24}$ ($Q = -3.136$ Mev). The excitation function of this cross section was measured by Grundl, Henkel, and Perkins (Gr58) between 6.73 and 9.01 Mev. Thin target, zero degree, D-D neutrons from an electrostatic accelerator were used. Flux was measured absolutely by means of a U^{238} fission chamber. In addition Grundl *et al.* measured the cross section at 14.1 Mev, using an associated α-particle counter to measure the flux of thick target D-T neutrons produced by a Cockcroft-Walton accelerator. The 15.0-hour Na^{24} activity of the irradiated samples was counted by means of calibrated (Ba58) absolute β counters.

The measured cross sections at the neutron energies 6.73, 7.45, 8.09, 8.58, 8.90, 9.01, and 14.1 Mev were 11.3, 25.5, 37.6, 39.7, 48.1, 51.3, and 116 millibarns, all with absolute errors in the neighborhood of ± 12 per cent. A summary of the measured cross section values of the $Al^{27}(n, \alpha)$ reaction at 14 Mev is given in Table III.

(15) $Si^{28}(n, p)Al^{28}$ ($Q = -3.87$ Mev). Marion, Brugger, and Chapman (Ma56) measured this excitation function, using thin target D-D neutrons between 4.4 and 8.0 Mev. The method of flux determination has been described in connection with their $F^{19}(n, p)$ and $F^{19}(n, \alpha)$ measurements. A relative excitation function was taken with thick glass samples in which the 2.30-minute Al^{28} was activated and counted. The results were normalized to an absolute measurement at 7 Mev made by means of approximate absolute β counting. Marion et al. quote an absolute cross section accuracy of ± 50 per cent. The lowest energy at which Al^{28} activity was observed ($\sigma \leq 2$ millibarns) was 4.5 Mev. With 100-kev energy resolution, resonances were observed at the neutron energies 5.14, 5.62, 6.51, 6.81, and 7.45 Mev. Broad resonances at 4.8 and 6.0 Mev, observed in the total cross section of silicon (Ne52), were not seen.

The excitation function between the neutron energy limits 12.5 and 17.5 Mev has been measured by Cohen and White (Co56b), using the method already described in connection with the $Mg^{24}(n, p)$ excitation function. A graph of their results, as well as those of Marion et al., is given in Hu57.

More recently Thompson, Ferguson, and Kern (Th58), in an experiment similar to that of Cohen and White, measured the excitation function between the neutron energy limits 12.3 and 17 Mev. The absolute cross section was determined at 14.5 Mev, using the 14-Mev value of the $Li^6(n, \alpha)$ cross section (Fr54, Ri56) as a flux standard. For the neutron energies 12.3, 13, 13.7, 14.5, 15, 16, and 17 Mev they found the $Si^{28}(n, p)$ cross section to be 371 $\pm$ 57, 342 $\pm$ 53, 368 $\pm$ 57, 292 $\pm$ 45, 281 $\pm$ 43, 242 $\pm$ 37, and 201 $\pm$ 31 millibarns, respectively. The 14-Mev cross sections are given in Table I.

(16) $P^{31}(n, p)Si^{31}$ ($Q = -0.698$ Mev). This reaction and the conveniently long (157-minute) half-life of Si^{31} make phosphorous a useful 2-Mev threshold detector. Following preliminary work by Lüscher, Ricamo, Scherrer, and Zünti (Lu50), the $P^{31}(n, p)$ excitation function was measured by Ricamo (Ri51), who used thin target D-D neutrons at various emission angles with energies ranging from 1.90 to 3.66 Mev. Absolute fluxes were calculated from the measured differential cross section of the D-D reaction. Numerous resonances were observed, and those below 2.5 Mev were reproduced in detail in a separate measurement of the P^{31} total cross section, while at higher energies the correspondence was not as complete. Ricamo's excitation function is shown by the solid line in Fig. 21.

Grundl, Henkel, and Perkins (Gr58) measured the excitation function between 1.6 and 9.5 Mev, using thin target p-T and D-D neutrons. Fluxes were determined by means of an absolute U^{238} fission chamber. Calibrated β counting, based upon 4π counting of chemically separated Si^{31} samples, was used in the activity determinations. The excitation function measured by Grundl et al. is shown in Fig. 21. The various 14-Mev cross section determinations are summarized in Table I.

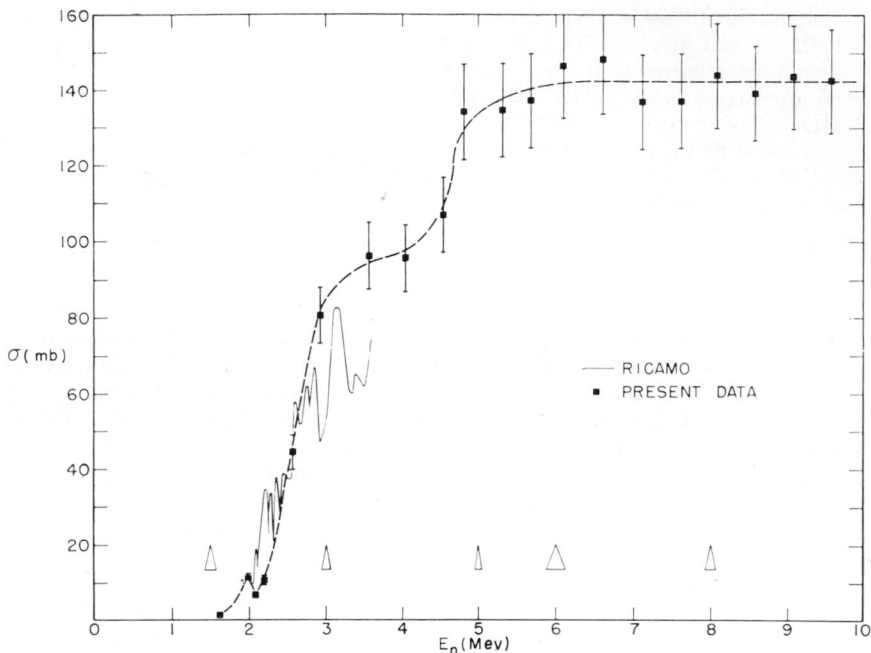

Figure 21. Excitation function for the $P^{31}(n, p)Si^{31}$ reaction. The solid curve represents the measurements of Ri51, and the squares those of Gr58.

(17) $S^{32}(n, p)P^{32}$ ($Q = -0.921$ Mev). S^{32} provides a 3-Mev threshold detector from which the 14.3-day P^{32} β activity is conveniently counted. The earliest measurement of the excitation function was that of Klema and Hanson (Kl48), using thin target Li(p, n) (1.62 to 1.83 Mev) and D-D (2.5 to 2.9 Mev) neutrons. They observed that the rise of the cross section from its threshold was of the form dictated by the penetrability of the P^{32} Coulomb barrier. Their data are plotted on the graph of Fig. 22 by means of the squares.

The excitation function was next measured by Ricamo *et al.* (Lu50, Ri51). Their technique has been described above in connection with the $P^{31}(n, p)$ excitation function. Ricamo presented a comparison between the resonances observed in the (n, p) cross section and those found by him in the S^{32} total cross section.

In contrast to the above measurements which made use of the induced radioactivity of P^{32}, Hürlimann aud Huber (Hu55a) measured the $S^{32}(n, p)$ [as well as the $S^{32}(n, \alpha)$] excitation function by observing the protons (and α particles) from the reaction in the neutron energy region from 2 to 4 Mev. A SO_2-filled ionization chamber was bombarded with D-D neutrons, and the proton (α-particle) pulses counted in the pulse-height spectrum. The techniques for neutron production and absolute flux monitoring were the same as those described above in connection with the $O^{16}(n, \alpha)$ measurements of Seitz and Huber (Se55a). Hürlimann

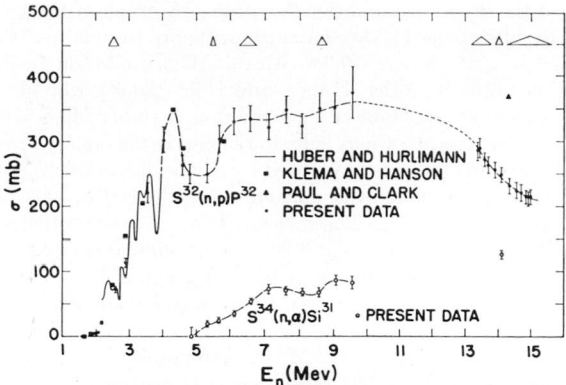

Figure 22. Cross sections for the reactions $S^{32}(n, p)P^{32}$ and $S^{34}(n, \alpha)Si^{31}$ *versus* neutron energy (Al57b). The open and closed circles represent the measurements of Al57b. The other measurements are identified in the text.

and Huber's results for the $S^{32}(n, p)P^{32}$ excitation function are shown as the solid curve on the graph of Fig. 22 and are in good agreement with those of Klema and Hanson, whose isolated measurements would not be expected to show the resonances.

A more recent measurement of the $S^{32}(n, p)$ excitation function is that of Allen, Biggers, Prestwood, and Smith (Al57b), who made activation measurements in the neutron energy regions from threshold to 9.56 Mev (thin target p-T and D-D neutrons) and also between 13.3 and 14.9 Mev (D-T neutrons). The flux monitoring and β counting techniques were generally the same as those described in Gr58. The results, plotted in Fig. 22, are in good agreement with the other measurements. The results of the 14-Mev measurements are summarized in Table I.

(18) $S^{32}(n, \alpha)Si^{29}$ ($Q = +1.553$ Mev). Since Si^{29} is stable, the activation method cannot be used. In addition to the measurement of Hürlimann and Huber (Hu55a) described immediately above, the cross section of this reaction was determined at the single D-D neutron energy 2.76 Mev to be 65 millibarns by Huber (Hu41). In both experiments use was made of SO_2-filled ionization chambers whose fillings served both as targets and means of detection of the α particles from the reaction. Hürlimann and Huber observed α-particle groups corresponding both to the ground and 1.28-Mev excited levels of the Si^{29} residual nucleus and obtained complex absolute excitation functions for each branch of the (n, α) reaction. In general the resonances were at different energies for the two branches, which in turn did not follow the resonance structure of the $S^{32*}(n, p)$ reaction.

(19) $S^{34}(n, \alpha)Si^{31}$ ($Q = -1.309$ Mev). The excitation function was measured by means of the induced activity of the 157-minute Si^{31} by Allen, Biggers, Prestwood, and Smith (Al57b) in the same experiment, described above, in which

they measured the $S^{32}(n, p)$ excitation function. A graph of the results is given in Fig. 22. Results of the 14-Mev measurements are summarized in Table III.

(20) $Cl^{35}(n, \alpha)P^{32}$ $(Q = +0.936$ Mev). The excitation function of this reaction was measured by Adler, Huber, and Hälg (Ad53), who observed the α-particle pulses from the reaction in an ionization chamber filled with argon and chlorine. D-D neutrons at various emission angles in the energy region from 3 to 4.1 Mev were used, and flux was monitored by means of a uranium fission counter. The relative excitation function was normalized to the $N^{14}(n, \alpha)$ cross sections of Johnson and Barschall (Jo50). The measured (n, α) cross section was observed to rise smoothly from 11 millibarns at 3 Mev to 68 millibarns at 4.06 Mev, following the Coulomb-barrier penetrability of P^{32}. A graph of the excitation function is given in Hu57. The cross section at 14 Mev was measured by Paul and Clarke (Pa53).

(21) $A^{36}(n, \alpha)S^{33}$ $(Q = +1.922$ Mev). The excitation function was measured by Toppel and Bloom (To53), who used D-D neutrons to bombard an ionization chamber filled with separated A^{36}. Flux was calculated from the published D-D cross sections. Alpha-particle groups corresponding to the ground state of S^{33} and the first excited state at 0.87 Mev were measured at the neutron energies 2.15, 2.76, 3.23, 3.76, and 4.40 Mev. The cross sections for the ground state reaction were 40 ± 12, 58 ± 17, 98 ± 30, 113 ± 34, and 208 ± 63 millibarns, respectively. For the excited state reaction the corresponding cross sections were <5, <5, 3 ± 3, 22 ± 13, and 41 ± 25 millibarns.

(22) $Cl^{37}(n, p)S^{37}$ $(Q = -3.9$ Mev). The excitation function was measured for neutron bombarding energies between 12.5 and 17.5 Mev by Cohen and White (Co56b), whose technique has been discussed above in connection with the Mg^{24}-(n, p) reaction. The anomalous positive gradient of the excitation function has already been discussed in Section 2.E of this article. A graph is given in Hu57 and the 14-Mev cross section in Table I.

E. (n, d) and (n, p) Surface Interactions

(1) **Introduction.** In Section 2 of this article we discussed neutron-induced reactions in the medium-weight and heavy nuclei proceeding (a) through the intermediate stage of the compound nucleus and (b) by direct interaction. In regard to the latter reactions, the theory of those which proceed by single particle interaction at the surface of the nucleus has reached an advanced stage of development. It has been quite successful in explaining the results of experiments on the (d, p) and (d, n) stripping reactions, concerning which there is now an extensive body of literature. In this section we shall consider experiments on (n, d) pickup reactions of the inverse type, as well as somewhat similar (n, p) experiments. In all of the experiments to be discussed use was made of 14-Mev bombarding neutrons produced by the D-T reaction. In all the primary concern

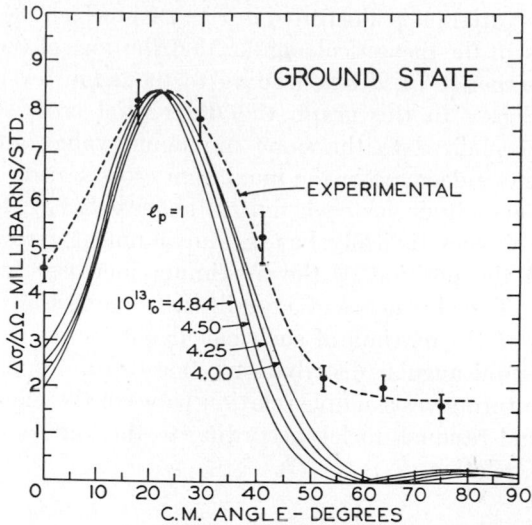

Figure 23. Measured and calculated differential cross sections for the B^{10} $(n, d)Be^9$ pickup reaction leading to the 2.43-Mev excited state of Be^9 (Ri54). The three solid curves correspond to the values 0, 1, and 2 for the orbital angular momentum of the picked up proton.

was the measurement and interpretation of the differential cross sections of the surface reactions.

(2) **Theory of Stripping and Pickup Reactions.** In the theory of Butler and others (Bu51, Bh52, Ho53) the (d, n) reaction is considered to proceed by a process in which the incident deuteron approaches the surface of the target nucleus closely enough to permit its loosely bound proton to be stripped from it and captured into one of the levels of the residual nucleus. From the reciprocity theorem of nuclear reactions (Bl52), based upon the principle of detailed balancing, it is clear that the results of the theory apply equally well to inverse pickup reactions in which an incident neutron captures a proton from a level of a target nucleus to form a deuteron. We shall present the discussion in these terms.

The most striking result of the theory is its prediction that there is a maximum of the angular distribution in the forward hemisphere of reaction angles and that the angular position of the maximum varies in a well defined manner with different values l_p of the orbital angular momentum of the captured proton. A typical example of this variation is illustrated in Fig. 23, in which the three solid curves represent the theoretical angular distributions of the deuterons from the reaction $B^{10}(n, d)Be^9$, leading to the 2.43-Mev level of the residual nucleus. In this graph the differential cross sections are arbitrarily normalized to the same maximum value, although the theory predicts a decrease in the maximum cross section by roughly an order of magnitude for each unit of increase in l_p. The angular distribution characteristically has its maximum at zero degrees for $l_p = 0$, and the position of the maximum increases markedly as l_p increases. Thus by means of a qualitative comparison of the angular positions of the maxima of such calculated curves with those of the experimental angular distributions, one can determine l_p. The value of l_p in turn gives a simple relation between the spins J and j of the target and residual nuclei, according to the angular-momentum conservation relation

$$l_p + s_p + j = J \tag{19}$$

where s_p is the spin angular momentum of the captured proton. An additional conservation relation for pickup reactions states that the parities of the target and residual nuclei are the same or opposite according as l_p is even or odd. Thus in case the spin and parity of either the target or residual nucleus is known, those of the other can be determined within the limits defined by Eq. (19).

The magnitudes of the maxima of the differential cross sections of pickup reactions, as well as their angular positions, may be used to provide information on nuclear levels. It has been shown (Th55) that the normalizing factor of the angular distribution of a reaction

$$(A, Z) + n \rightarrow (A - 1, Z - 1) + d \tag{20}$$

which provides the absolute differential cross section is just the reduced width γ_p^2 for the transition

$$(A, Z) \rightarrow (A - 1, Z - 1) + p \tag{21}$$

in which the target nucleus might decay by proton emission into the final level of the residual nucleus. The reduced widths are determined primarily by the *overlap* of the wave functions of the initial and final nuclei and may be calculated if these wave functions are known. Usually the wave functions of the target and residual nuclei are predicted theoretically on the basis of the nuclear shell model, and the reduced widths (or their equivalent) are calculated for comparison with the experimental results. However, it is necessary to use care in making the comparison. It has been found that the absolute values of the $\gamma_p{}^2$ derived from stripping reactions may differ from known values, determined by other experiments, by factors as large as 4, owing to various simplifying assumptions made in the theory. This difficulty can be largely avoided in those cases where the differential cross sections are observed for two or more levels of a single residual nucleus. In this case the ratios of reduced widths deduced from the ratios of the peak differential cross sections for the various levels are dependable. This is particularly true if the levels all correspond to a single value of l_p. For different values of l_p the effects of the different centrifugal force barriers cause an appreciable difference in the peak differential cross sections, quite aside from differences in $\gamma_p{}^2$. A correction of limited accuracy for this *kinematic* effect can be made on the basis of the theory.

The preceding was necessarily but a brief sketch of the uses of the pickup theory. For a more complete account the reader is referred to Chapter V.D. and the bibliography given there.

(3) Differential Cross Sections of (n, d) Reactions at 14 Mev.

(a) $Li^6(n, d)He^5$ $(Q = -2.35$ Mev). The first measurement of the absolute differential cross section of an (n, d) reaction was that of Frye (Fr54), who determined the charged particle yields from the interaction of 14-Mev neutrons with Li^6 and Li^7 by means of nuclear emulsions. The apparatus was essentially the same as that shown in Fig. 1, with the exception that thin metallic targets of separated Li^6 and Li^7 metal were placed at the center of the array of nuclear emulsions. By means of a range and grain-density analysis of the tracks produced in the emulsions at various reaction angles by charged particles from the thin targets, Frye was able to separate the various species of charged reaction particles and to measure the differential cross sections for their emission. In the case of Li^6 the (n, d) reaction was predominant, leading to a discrete group of deuterons corresponding to the ground state of He^5, as well as to a lower energy continuum corresponding to both an excited level of He^5 and the three body reaction $Li^6(n, dn)He^4$. The differential cross section for the ground state reaction exhibited a maximum at $12°$, in good agreement with the shape of the Butler curve for $l_p = 1$. This value of orbital angular momentum is to be expected, since the spins of Li^6 and He^5 are known to be 1^+ and $3/2^-$, respectively. The total (n, d) cross section for the ground state reaction was found to be 89 ± 10 millibarns. The cross section for the (n, d) reaction producing the continuous energy spectrum of deuterons $(-6.7$ Mev $\leqq Q \leqq 4.3$ Mev) was found to be 77 ± 9 millibarns.

(b) $B^{10}(n,d)Be^9$ $(Q = -4.36$ Mev). Ribe and Seagrave (Ri54) measured the differential cross sections for the $B^{10}(n, d)$ reactions leading to the ground and

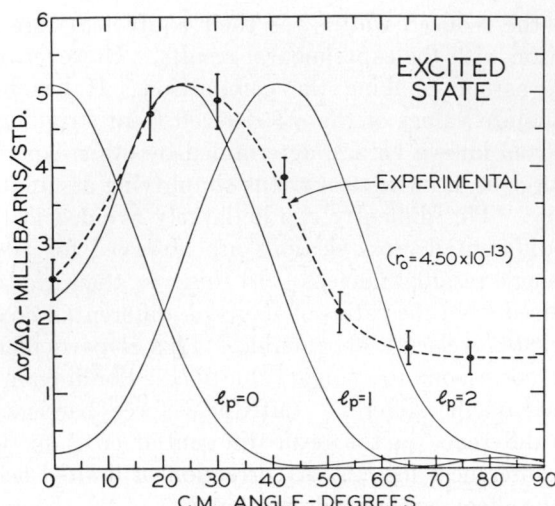

Figure 24. Measured and calculated differential cross sections for the B^{10} $(n, d)Be^9$ pickup reaction leading to the ground state of Be^9 (Ri54). The four solid curves correspond to $l_p = 1$ for the orbital angular momentum of the picked up proton and four different values of r_0, the nuclear radius.

2.43-Mev excited state of Be^9. They used a counter telescope consisting of two proportional counters and a NaI(Tl) scintillator to detect the deuterons produced by 14-Mev neutrons in a thin target of separated B^{10}. The counter telescope was similar to that shown in Fig. 9. Charged particles emerging from the target (6) passed through the two gas-filled counters (1) before impinging on the sodium iodide crystal (3) and were identified by a threefold coincidence of the ionization pulses from the three counters. Corresponding to each coincidence, an electronic gate allowed the scintillation pulse to be recorded in one of the channels of a pulse height analyzer. A bias adjustment of the proportional counter channels provided separation of deuteron and proton events. Such a coincidence telescope was necessary in order to separate the desired (n, d) scintillator pulses from the background pulses occurring as a result of its bombardment by neutrons from the D-T source.

The ground state differential cross section is shown in Fig. 24 as the dashed curve. For comparison the solid curves, which give the results of the Butler theory, are shown for $l_p = 1$ and various values of the adjustable parameter r_o of the theory, representing the nuclear radius. The experimental differential cross section exhibits a finite, nearly isotropic "background" at angles in excess of 50°. Such backgrounds have also been observed in (d, p) stripping reactions (Ho53) and are believed to be due to nonstripping (nonpickup) processes involving compound nucleus formation. Thomas (Th55) has shown that under conditions like those in the experiment under discussion, where the assumptions of the statistical theory regarding the signs of the compound nuclear wave functions (cf. Section 2.B) are valid, the pickup and compound nuclear contributions to (n, d) reactions are incoherent. The isotropic background can then be subtracted from the composite differential cross section.

Returning to Fig. 24, the assignment $l_p = 1$ for the orbital angular momentum of the captured proton is seen to be appropriate, as would be expected from Eq. (19), since B^{10} and Be^9 have ground state spins 3^+ and $3/2^-$, respectively. In Fig. 23 the dashed curve represents the differential cross section for the (n, d) reaction leading to the 2.43-Mev level of Be^9. Again the assignment $l_p = 1$ is applicable, leading to the assignment of any of the spins $3/2^-$, $5/2^-$, $7/2^-$, or $9/2^-$ to the excited level of Be^9.

On the basis of calculations taking into account the nucleon-nucleon coupling of the p-wave nucleons in B^{10} and Be^9, French, Halbert, and Pandya (Fr55) computed the theoretical ratio of the peak differential cross sections shown in Figs. 23 and 24. The analysis was consistent with the spin $5/2^-$ for the 2.43-Mev level of Be^9 with intermediate coupling close to the L-S limit. The same result was derived from an analysis of a similar experiment by Reynolds and Standing (Re54, St56), who measured the conjugate B^{10} (p, d) differential cross sections for the ground and 2.37-Mev states in B^9.

(c) $N^{14}(n,d)C^{13}$ $(Q = -5.32$ Mev). In an experiment similar to that just described, Carlson (Ca57) measured the differential cross sections for the (n, d) reactions leading to the ground and 3.68-Mev excited states of C^{13}. The ground state differential cross section exhibited a peak at a deuteron reaction angle of $18°$, corresponding to the assignment $l_p = 1$, which would be expected from Eq. (19), since the ground state spins of N^{14} and C^{13} are known to be 1^+ and $1/2^-$. The orbital angular momentum of the captured proton in the excited state reaction was also found to be 1, eliminating the possibility that the observed differential cross section was due to the two even-parity neighboring levels at 3.09 and 3.86 Mev. These levels would have required s-wave and d-wave pickup, respectively.

Carlson found the ratio of reduced widths to the ground and excited levels of C^{13} to be 0.47, in good agreement with the calculated value based upon a small amount of intermediate coupling in C^{13}, close to the L-S limit. In addition this ratio of reduced widths rules out an assignment of a pure $^3D_1$ configuration for the ground state of N^{14}, such as had been adduced (Me52) in an attempt to explain the puzzlingly long-lived C^{14} β decay. The absolute reduced width of the (n, d) reaction leading to the ground state of C^{13} agreed to within 25 per cent with that found by Standing (St56) for the ground state pickup reaction $N^{14}(p, d)N^{13}$. Since C^{13} and N^{13} are mirror nuclei, such agreement provides additional evidence of the validity of the hypothesis of the charge independence of nuclear forces.

(d) $F^{19}(n, d)O^{18}$ $(Q = -5.73$ Mev). In another counter-telescope experiment similar to those just described, Ribe (Ri57) measured the differential cross sections for the F^{19} (n, d) reactions leading to the ground and 1.99-Mev excited levels of O^{18}. The measured differential cross section for the ground state reaction is indicated by means of the data points in Fig. 25. The dashed curve represents the calculated differential cross section for $l_p = 0$ and the solid curve the same theoretical result "smeared" to take account of the finite angular aperture of the

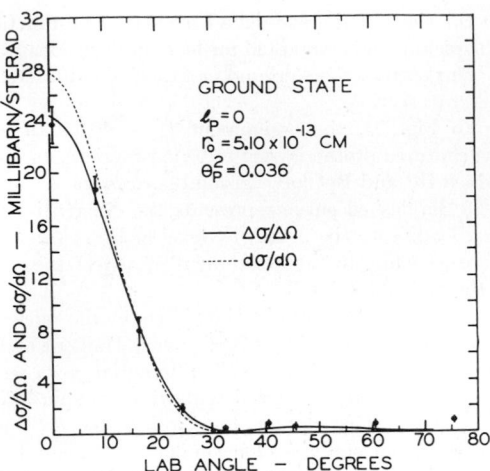

Figure 25. Measured and calculated differential cross sections for the F^{19} $(n, d)O^{18}$ pickup reaction leading to the ground state of O^{18} (Ri57). The solid curve is the theoretical cross section (Bu51), and the dashed curve contains a correction for the finite angular aperture of the apparatus.

counter telescope. The parameter $\theta_p{}^2 = 0.036$ represents the reduced width $\gamma_p{}^2$ in units of the Wigner limit $\hbar^2/2\mu r_0$ (μ is the reduced mass) which provides the best fit of the theoretical curve to the experimental data. It is worth remarking that the 8.3-Mev deuterons which are produced copiously in the forward direction by bombarding a thin Teflon (CF_2) foil with 14-Mev neutrons provide a good experimental energy reference.

The differential cross section leading to the 1.99-Mev level of O^{18} was observed to be quite small, corresponding to d-wave pickup much inhibited by the centrifugal barrier. The ratio of the reduced widths of the transitions leading to this state and to the ground state was found to be at most 0.87. This upper limit is in agreement with the value of the reduced-width ratio computed by Elliott and Flowers (El55) on the basis of their intermediate coupling wave functions which placed the first excited level of O^{18} at 2 Mev and assigned it the spin value 2^+. This assignment has been made with greater experimental precision by Bilaniuk and Hough (Bi57a) who measured $O^{17}(d, p)$ stripping reactions to the ground state of O^{18}, as well as to the levels at 1.99 and 3.56 Mev. They assigned the last mentioned level the spin value 4^+.

(4) **Theory of (n, p) Exchange Reactions.** Austern, Butler, and McManus (Au53) sought to extend the theoretical point of view which accounted for the success of the pickup (stripping) calculations to a similar calculation of (n, p) surface interactions. It was assumed that an incident neutron could interact with a loosely bound proton

through its wave function "tail" at the surface of the target nucleus. The (n, p) reaction would then proceed by ejection of the loosely bound proton from its level and subsequent capture of the neutron into a similar level of the residual nucleus.

In the simplest case, in which the ejected proton and captured neutron had associated levels with single values l_p and l_n of orbital angular momentum, Austern et al. predicted that the angular distribution of the (n, p) reaction should be characterized by a set of spherical Bessel functions $j_l(kr_0)$, having l values given by the inequality

$$l_n + l_p \geq l \geq \left| l_n - l_p \right| \tag{22}$$

Here $k = \left| k_p - k_n \right|$, where k_p and k_n are the proton and neutron wave-number vectors, and r_0 is the nuclear radius. The value $l = 0$ leads to an angular distribution peaked at zero degrees, and higher l values give peaks at larger angles, much as in the case of the pickup theory.

In case there was no particular reason for picking out special orbitals for protons and neutrons, Austern et al. predicted that the dominant l values would be given in terms of the spins J and j of the target and residual nuclei by the relationship

$$j + J + 1 \geq l \geq \left| \mathbf{J} + \mathbf{j} - \mathbf{1} \right|_{\min} \tag{23}$$

where $\mathbf{1}$ is an "angular momentum" vector of unit magnitude. Conservation of parity would lead to odd and even values of l according as there was or was not a change of nuclear parity.

(5) **Differential Cross Sections of the** $\text{Al}^{27}(n, p)\text{Mg}^{27}$ $(Q = -1.83$ **Mev) and** $\text{Al}^{27}(n, n')\text{Al}^{27}$ **Reactions.** Oshima (Os56) bombarded thin aluminum targets by means of collimated D-T neutrons in an experimental arrangement similar in principle to that shown in Fig. 1. Nuclear emulsions were placed at angular intervals of $10°$ around the target in such a way as to detect both protons from the the Al^{27} (n, p) reaction and proton recoils produced by inelastically scattered neutrons. An analysis of the proton tracks showed energy groups corresponding to the ground state (n, p) reaction, as well as the (n, n') reactions leading to the excited levels of Al^{27} at 0.84, 1.01, and 2.23 Mev.

The (n, p) differential cross section was peaked at a reaction angle of zero degrees and closely followed a curve given by $[j_0(kr_0)]^2$

($l = 0$), where the nuclear radius was taken to be 5.5×10^{13} cm. The spins of Al^{27} and Mg^{27} are known to be $5/2^+$ and $1/2^+$, and the shell-model orbital assignments for the odd proton and odd neutron in the respective cases are $d_{5/2}$ and $s_{1/2}$. Hence, according to Eq. (22) a value of 2 for l would be expected, while in the case of Eq. (23) possible values would be either 2 or 4. It was concluded that there was disagreement with the theory in this case but that the (n, p) reaction does proceed by direct interaction. The angular distributions of the inelastic scattering reactions leading to the first three excited levels of Al^{27} were also observed to follow the function $[j_0(kr_0)]^2$.

In a somewhat similar nuclear emulsion experiment at 14.1 Mev, Overseth and Peck (Ov59) measured angular distributions of the (n, p) reactions leading to discrete levels of Mg^{27} with excitations less than 5 Mev. They reported peaks in the angular distributions of the ground-state and 1-Mev excited state reactions at 30° and 40°, respectively, in disagreement with Oshima's result for the ground state reaction.

F. Neutron-Induced Reactions in Light Nuclei That Yield Three or Four Reaction Products

(1) **Introduction.** Those nuclear reactions which lead to more than two disintegration products have been little studied because of their complexity. Since it is necessary simultaneously to detect and measure at least two of the disintegration particles, electronic counting techniques are not well adapted to the measurement of such reactions. In all the experiments to be discussed use was made of nuclear emulsions or cloud chambers in which the charged reaction products were made visible by means of ionization tracks from which their momenta, energies, and reaction angles could be measured.

As will be seen, when two or more reaction particles are observed, there is often a possibility of measuring various alternative transition modes by means of which the reaction might proceed. The most obvious possibility is a *direct* process such as

$$C^{12}(n, n')3\alpha \tag{24}$$

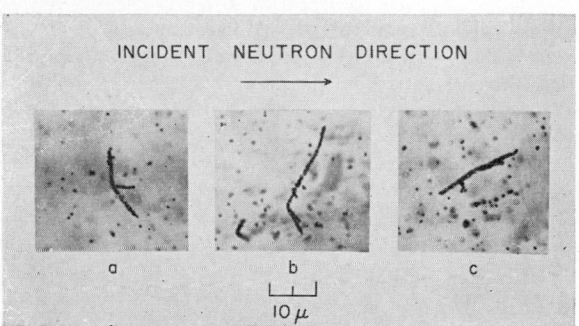

Figure 26. Typical carbon stars observed in a nuclear emulsion measurement of the C^{12} $(n, n')3\alpha$ cross section (Fr55a). In (b) and (c) the two prongs close together arise from Be^8 being left in its ground state. (c) illustrates the difficulty that often arises in resolving these two prongs. Only the thickness of the track and the scattering of the last grain of the shorter track indicate that these are actually two tracks.

However there may be competition from an indirect chain of two- or three-body reactions, for example, an (n, α) reaction followed by neutron emission:

$$C^{12}(n,\ \alpha)Be^{9*}(n')Be^{8*}(2\alpha). \tag{25}$$

Such reaction chains are possible because the light nuclei involved are unstable against charged particle emission when excited to energies in excess of a few Mev.

In the following we shall discuss many-particle reactions induced by fast neutrons in the target nuclides C^{12}, B^{10}, and Li^7. In order to facilitate the discussion the reactions will be considered in the reverse order of atomic weights.

(2) $C^{12}(n, n')3\alpha$ $(Q = -7.28$ Mev). Events corresponding to this reaction can be identified by the typical three-pronged stars which are observed when the carbon in nuclear emulsions is bombarded by neutrons with energies in excess of 8 Mev. Three such stars composed in each case of three α-particle tracks are shown in Fig. 26.

The first quantitative experiment was that of Green and Gibson (Gr49) who bombarded nuclear emulsions with $Li(d, n)$ neutrons. The energy spectrum of the neutrons from this reaction consists mainly of two groups in energy regions near 11 and 14 Mev. Green and Gibson analyzed each star to obtain the energies and momenta of all three α particles. They were then able to calculate for each event the momentum (magnitude and direction) of the unseen inelastically scattered neutron as well as the energy of the incident neutron which caused the reac-

tion.   From these data they showed that as many neutrons were scattered into
the backward as into the forward hemisphere with respect to the incident neutron
beam.   At the neutron bombarding energies 10.8, 12.0, 13.2, and 14.5 Mev they
obtained the following cross sections for the $C^{12}(n, n')3\alpha$ reaction: 23, 31, 90, and
157 millibarns.

In their calculations Green and Gibson added together the energies E_1, E_2,
and E_3 of the three α particles and their binding energy in the C^{12} nucleus (7.28
Mev) to obtain the energy ΔE_n lost by the incident neutron in being scattered.
Since the initial energy of the incident neutron could also be calculated, it was
possible to determine, at least formally, the energy of excitation of the C^{12} nucleus if the reaction proceeded by either of the two-stage processes,

$$C^{12}(n, n')C^{12}*(\alpha)Be^8*(2\alpha) \tag{26}$$

or

$$C^{12}(n, n')C^{12}*(3\alpha) \tag{27}$$

This was done by Livesey and Smith (Li53) who determined the numbers of
$(n, n'3\alpha)$ events corresponding to each excitation energy of C^{12}.   If neither of the
modes (26) or (27) existed they should have obtained for all the events so analyzed
a random probability distribution in C^{12} excitation energy.   In fact two peaks
were observed at C^{12} excitation energies near (a) 9.6 Mev and (b) 11.8 Mev.
Group (a) corresponds to a known level of C^{12} which decays into an α particle
and Be^8 in its ground state.

In order to distinguish between the reaction modes (26) and (27) it was
necessary to take the α-particle tracks in pairs, assumed to arise from the Be^8*
decay of mode (26), and calculate the Be^8 excitation energies in a manner similar
to that just outlined for the C^{12} excitation energies.   When this was done Livesey
and Smith found that of those events in group (a) which corresponded to the 9.6-
Mev level in C^{12} there was a large fraction leading to the ground state of Be^8.   In
addition there were uncorrelated events at other equivalent excitations, corresponding to mode (27).

Jackson and Wanklyn (Ja53) reached a similar conclusion regarding the
formation of the 9.6-Mev level of C^{12} and its decay into the Be^8 ground state for
neutron bombarding energies less than 20 Mev.   They bombarded a cloud chamber with $Be(p, n)$ neutrons, predominantly in the neutron energy range from 8 to
25 Mev.   Above 20 Mev, however, the 2.91-Mev level of Be^8 was favored.

Frye, Rosen, and Stewart (Fr55a) used monoenergetic D-T neutrons between 12.3 and 20.1 Mev to investigate the reaction by means of nuclear emulsions.   There data were shown to exclude the possible reaction modes,

$$C^{12}(n, \alpha)Be^9*(n')Be^8*(2\alpha) \tag{25}$$

and

$$C^{12}(n, \alpha)Be^9*(\alpha)He^5(n')\alpha \tag{28}$$

and to confirm the presence of reactions (26) and (27).   Again it was found that
the 9.6-Mev level of C^{12} was excited and decayed to the ground state of Be^8.

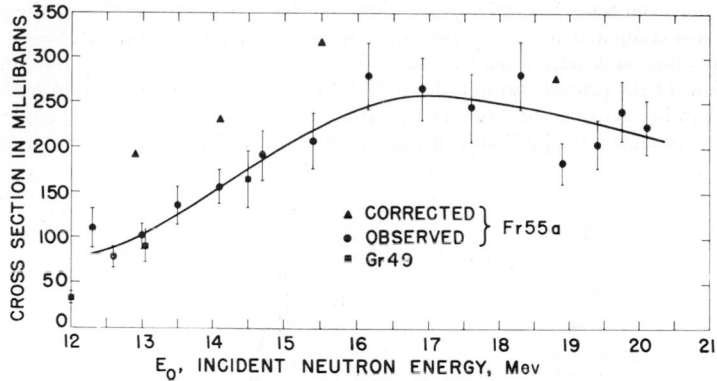

Figure 27. Excitation function of the $C^{12}(n, n')3\alpha$ cross section *versus* neutron energy (Fr55a). The squares represent the values of Gr49. The triangles represent the cross section corrected for unobserved events.

Events corresponding to C^{12} excitation energies greater than 10.5 Mev were found partially to excite the 2.91-Mev level in Be^8. There was some evidence for the formation of the 7.68-Mev level in C^{12}. Aside from the reaction modes involving C^{12} as an intermediate nucleus, it was observed that a considerable fraction of the inelastic scattering events were followed by direct 3α decay. In these events the sums of α-particle energies for the various events were statistically correlated only by the energy limitations on the regions of phase space available to each of the α particles.

Frye *et al.* evaluated the total $C^{12}(n, n')3\alpha$ cross section at each bombarding energy and found good agreement with the results of Green and Gibson. Both sets of results are plotted in Fig. 27. However, Frye *et al.* found that when a reaction proceeded via the 9.6-Mev level of C^{12}, its event was likely to appear as a two-pronged star and hence to be disregarded. The data were grouped according to four intervals of neutron bombarding energy, and a correction was made for this effect. The corrected cross sections are shown by means of the triangles in Fig. 27.

The inelastic neutrons were observed to be scattered isotropically. Their energy distribution was indistinguishable from that which would arise from a direct 4-body disintegration in which each particle could occupy all those portions of phase space allowed it by the energetics of the reaction.

(3) $B^{10}(n, t)2\alpha$ ($Q = 0.93$ Mev) and $B^{10}(n, dn')2\alpha$ ($Q = -5.93$ Mev). Both of these reactions were examined by Frye and Gammel (Fr56) who bombarded B^{10}-loaded nuclear emulsions with monoenergetic D-D and D-T neutrons with energies ranging from 5.6 to 20.0 Mev. Events from both reactions gave rise to 3-pronged stars which were assigned to one or the other of the reactions by means of momentum and energy balance calculations. Three computations were made in which each prong was assumed to be a triton track. Then three computations were made assuming each in turn to be a deuteron track. In the first set of com-

putations the sum of energies of the three tracks, minus the Q-value of the reaction was compared with the known neutron bombarding energy.   In the second set the unseen scattered neutron made it necessary to take into account the directions of the prongs also in order to obtain a quantity for comparison with the bombarding neutron energy.   Those events for which none of the six computations reproduced the incident neutron energy were $C^{12}(n, n')3\alpha$ events, caused by

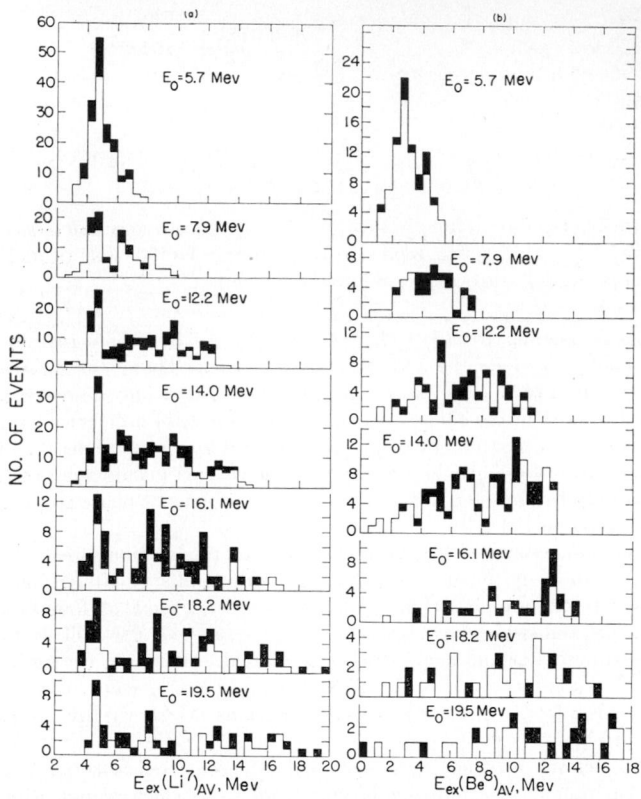

Figure 28. Excitation energies of (a) Li^7 and (b) Be^8 when these nuclei occur as intermediate nuclei in the $B^{10}(n, t2\alpha)$ reaction.   The results are those of a nuclear emulsion experiment (Fr56).

bombardment of the carbon nuclei in the emulsion.   Since in all 1541 stars were analyzed, a digital computer was used as an adjunct to the experiment capable of discriminating between the various types of reactions.

Having identified the events, it was known in the case of the triton reactions which tracks were to be associated with the tritons.   It was then possible to determine which of the three decay modes:

$$B^{10}(n, \alpha_1)Li^7{}^*(\alpha_2 t) \tag{29}$$

$$B^{10}(n, t)Be^8{}^*(\alpha_1\alpha_2) \tag{30}$$

or the direct 3-body reaction,

$$B^{10}(n, t)2\alpha \tag{31}$$

was followed. In order to do this in the case of mode (29) the excitation of the assumed Li^7 was calculated from the bombarding neutron energy and the energy and direction of α_1 and also from the energies and directions of t and α_2. Since it was not known which was α_1 and which α_2, it was necessary to perform the calculation twice. In the case of mode (30) the bombarding neutron energy and the data for t, α_1, and α_2 were used with no ambiguity to calculate the excitation energy of the assumed Be^8.

If modes (29) or (30) were followed probability distributions of the number of events *versus* the computed excitation energies of Li^7 and Be^8 should have shown correlations in the form of peaks corresponding to known levels of these nuclei. Histograms of these distributions are shown in Fig. 28. For all the neutron bombarding energies a correlation peak corresponding to the 4.61-Mev level of Li^7 is shown, indicating the presence of mode (29). No such consistent correlations are seen in the case of the $Be^8{}^*$ mode. Frye and Gammel concluded that the ground state of Be^8 was formed at most in only about one per cent of the events.

After removal of those events corresponding to the 4.61-Mev level of Li^7, the remaining events showed the smooth, essentially uncorrelated probability distribution *versus* equivalent Be^8 excitation energy which is shown in the upper graph of Fig. 29. The solid curve is the probability distribution to be expected if each of the three particles were allowed to occupy any portion of phase space at random, subject only to the limitation provided by the energetics of the reaction. In particular the angular distribution of any of the particles in geometrical space would be isotropic. In the lower graph of Fig. 29 is plotted the angular distribution of the tritons, which is seen to be isotropic. Both of these uncorrelated probability distributions establish the presence of the direct 3-body mode (31).

The total $B^{10}(n, t)$ cross sections at the neutron bombarding energies 5.6, 7.7, 12.2, 14.1, 16.1, 18.2, and 19.5 Mev were found to be 239 ± 40, 131 ± 23, 96 ± 21, 102 ± 17, 84 ± 16, 81 ± 16, and 60 ± 12 millibarns, respectively.

In a similar experiment on the $B^{10}(n, t)Be^8(2\alpha)$ reaction at 14.1 Mev Titterton and Brinkley (Ti57) found correlations indicating the formation of Be^8 in its ground state for 3 per cent of the reactions.

By means of correlation calculations similar to those described above for the (n, t) reactions, Frye and Gammel established the following two reaction modes for the deuteron reactions:

$$B^{10}(n, d)Be^9{}^*(n')Be^8{}^*(2\alpha) \tag{32}$$

and

$$B^{10}(n, \alpha_1)Li^7{}^*(n')Li^6{}^*(d\alpha_2) \tag{33}$$

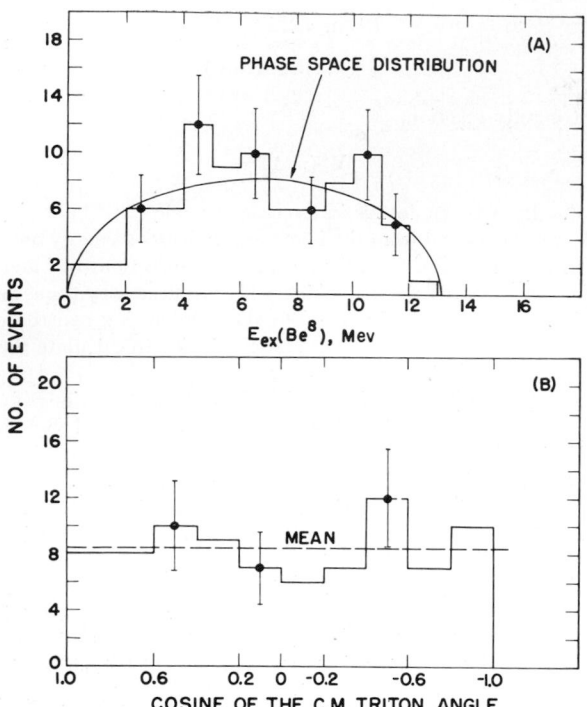

Figure 29. (A) Probability distribution of $B^{10}(n, t2\alpha)$ events as a function of the excitation energy of Be^8, considered as an intermediate nucleus in the reaction (Fr56). In this graph all events corresponding to possible excitation of 4.61-Mev level of Li^7 have been excluded. (B) Angular distribution of the triton in the B^{11} center-of-mass system for the same events.

In the first mode the 2.43-Mev level of Be^9 was observed, as were the ground and possibly the 2.9-Mev levels in Be^8. Events corresponding to deuteron emission at small reaction angles would not have been identified, owing to the short ranges of the succeeding α particles. However the cross section for such events was measured independently by Ribe and Seagrave (Ri54) in the experiment described in Section 4.E of this article. A combination of the results of both experiments gives the value 28 ± 4 for the total cross section of the $B^{10}(n, d)$ reaction proceeding through the 2.43-Mev level of Be^9.

(4) $Li^7(n, nt)He^4$ ($Q = -2.465$ Mev). This reaction was studied by Allan (Al54) for the purpose of separating the decay modes

$$Li^7(n, n')Li^{7*}(t)He^4 \tag{34}$$

and

$$Li^7(n, t)He^5(n')He^4 \tag{35}$$

and observing the formation of excited levels of Li⁷ in the former case. Lithium-loaded nuclear emulsions were bombarded 14.1-Mev neutrons and scanned for two-pronged stars. The data on the energies (ranges) of the triton and α-particle tracks and their emission angles were sufficient to calculate the excitations of Li⁷ in the case of mode (34). Previously observed levels at 4.61, 7.46, and 6.56 Mev were identified. In the case of mode (35) there were indications of the ground state of He⁵ as well as a level at 2.4 ± 0.6 Mev.

References

(Ad50)   R. K. Adair, *Revs. Modern Phys.* **22**, 249 (1950).

(Ad53)   Adler, Huber, and Hälg, *Helv. Phys. Acta* **26**, 349 (1953).

(Ag52)   H. M. Agnew, *Los Alamos Sci. Lab. Report* LA-1371 (1952).

(Ah57)   S. H. Ahn and J. H. Roberts, *Phys. Rev.* **108**, 110 (1957).

(Aj52)   F. Ajzenberg and T. Lauritsen, *Revs. Modern Phys.* **24**, 321 (1952).

(Al47)   Allen, Burcham, and Wilkinson, *Proc. Roy. Soc.* (*London*) **192A**, 114 (1947).

(Al54)   D. L. Allan, *Nature* (*London*) **174**, 267 (1954).

(Al55)   D. L. Allan, *Proc. Phys. Soc.* (*London*) **68A**, 925 (1955).

(Al57)   D. L. Allan, *Proc. Phys. Soc.* (*London*) **70A**, 195 (1957).

(Al57a)   D. L. Allan, Columbia International Conference on the Neutron Interactions with the Nucleus, New York, 1957.

(Al57b)   Allen, Biggers, Prestwood, and Smith, *Phys. Rev.* **107**, 1363 (1957).

(Al58)   W. D. Allen and R. L. Henkel, *Progress in Nuclear Energy, Series I—Physics and Mathematics*, Pergamon Press, London, 1958; Vol. 2,.p. 1.

(Ar55)   A. H. Armstrong and J. E. Brolley, Jr., *Phys. Rev.* **99**, 330 (1955)

(Ar56)   A. H. Armstrong and L. Rosen, *Bull. Am. Phys. Soc.* **1**, 224 (1956), and private communication.

(Ar56a)   A. H. Armstrong and G. M. Frye, Jr., *Phys. Rev.* **103**, 335 (1956).

(As58)   Ashby, Catron, Newkirk, and Taylor, *Univ. Calif. Radiation Lab. Report* UCRL-5054 (1958).

(Au53)   Austern, Butler, and McManus, *Phys. Rev.* **92**, 350 (1953).

(Ba39)   E. Baldinger and P. Huber, *Helv. Phys. Acta* **12**, 330 (1939).

(Ba46)   H. H. Barschall and M. E. Battat, *Phys. Rev.* **70**, 245 (1946).

(Ba47)   Barschall, Battat, Bright, Graves, Jorgensen, and Manley, *Phys. Rev.* **72**, 881 (1947).

(Ba47a)   Barschall, Manley, and Weisskopf, *Phys. Rev.* **72**, 875 (1947).

(Ba52)   H. H. Barschall, *Revs. Modern Phys.* **24**, 120 (1952).

(Ba53)   M. E. Battat and F. L. Ribe, *Phys. Rev.* **89**, 80 (1953).

(Ba56)   Badoni, Colli, and Facchini, *Nuovo cimento* **4**, 1618 (1956).

(Ba58)   B. P. Bayhurst and R. J. Prestwood, Los Alamos Sci. Lab., private communication (1958).

(Bc56)   R. L. Becker and H. H. Barschall, *Phys. Rev.* **102**, 1384 (1956).

(Bh52)   Bhatia, Huang, Huby, and Newns, *Phil. Mag.* **43**, 485 (1952).

(Bi51)   Bichsel, Hälg, Huber, and Stebler, *Phys. Rev.* **81**, 456 (1951).

(Bi52)   Bichsel, Hälg, Huber, and Stebler, *Helv. Phys. Acta* **25**, 119 (1952).

(Bi57)   H. Bichsel and T. W. Bonner, *Phys. Rev.* **108**, 1025 (1957).

(Bi57a)   O. M. Bilaniuk, and P. V. C. Hough, *Phys. Rev.* **108**, 305 (1957).
(Bl50)   J. M. Blair and R. E. Holland, private communication to F. C. Hoyt, (1950). See also Hu55.
(Bl52)   J. M. Blatt and V. F. Weisskopf, *Theoretical Nuclear Physics*, Wiley, New York, 1952, 1st ed., Chapter VIII.
(Bl55)   Blosser, Goodman, Handley, and Randolph, *Phys. Rev.* **100**, 429 (1955).
(Bl57)   J. Blok and C. C. Jonker, *Nuovo cimento* **6**, 378 (1957).
(Bl57a)   H. G. Blosser, *Oak Ridge Natl. Lab. Drawing* ORNL-LR-DWG: 13811 (1957), and private communication.
(Bl58)   Blosser, Goodman, and Handley, *Phys. Rev.* **110**, 531 (1958), and private communication.
(Bo36)   N. Bohr, *Nature (London)* **137**, 344 (1936).
(Bo51)   Bockelman, Miller, Adair, and Barschall, *Phys. Rev.* **84**, 69 (1951).
(Bo51a)   W. Bollmann and W. Zünti, *Helv. Phys. Acta* **24**, 517 (1951).
(Bo55)   Bostrom, Hudspeth, and Morgan, *Phys. Rev.* **99**, 643 (1955).
(Bo57)   Bostrom, Moore, and Morgan, *Bull. Am. Phys. Soc.* **2**, 104 (1957).
(Br49)   E. Bretscher and D. H. Wilkinson, *Proc. Cambridge Phil. Soc.* **45**, 141 (1949).
(Br51)   Brown, Bendel, Shore, and Becker, *Phys. Rev.* **84**, 292 (1951).
(Br52)   Brolley, Fowler, and Schlacks, *Phys. Rev.* **88**, 618 (1952).
(Br53)   J. E. Brolley, Jr., *Phys. Rev.* **89**, 877 (1953).
(Br55)   Brolley, Bunker, Cochran, Henkel, Mize, and Starner, *Phys. Rev.* **99**, 330 (1955).
(Br57)   G. Brown and H. Muirhead, *Phil. Mag.* **2**, 473 (1957).
(Br57a)   Brown, Morrison, Muirhead, and Morton, *Phil. Mag.* **2**, 785 (1957).
(Bu51)   S. T. Butler, *Proc. Roy. Soc. (London)* **208A**, 36 (1951).
(Ca57)   R. R. Carlson, *Phys. Rev.* **107**, 1094 (1957).
(Co56)   L. Colli and V. Facchini, *Nuovo cimento* **4**, 671 (1956).
(Co56a)   Cohen, Hyder, and White, *Nuclear Phys.* **1**, 278 (1956).
(Co56b)   A. V. Cohen and P. H. White, *Nuclear Phys.* **1**, 73 (1956).
(Co56c)   Cowan, Reines, Harrison, Kruse, and McGuire, *Science* **124**, 3212 (1956).
(Co57)   L. Colli and V. Facchini, *Nuovo cimento* **5**, 309 (1957).
(Co57a)   Colli, Facchini, and Micheletti, *Nuovo cimento* **5**, 502 (1957).
(Co57b)   Colli, Facchini, Marcazzan, and Pignanelli, Columbia International Conference on the Neutron Interactions with the Nucleus, New York, 1957.
(Co57c)   L. Colli, Piquauelli, Rytz, and Zurmühle, *Nuovo cimento* **9**, 280 (1958). private communication (1957).
(Co57d)   B. L. Cohen, *Phys. Rev.* **105**, 1549 (1957).
(Co58)   Coon, Davis, Felthauser, and Nicodemus, *Phys. Rev.* **111**, 250 (1958).
(Co58a)   Colli, Facchini, Iori, Marcazzan, and Sona, *Nuovo cimento* **7**, 400 (1958).
(Da53)   Darlington, Haugsnes, Mann, and Roberts, *Phys. Rev.* **90**, 1049 (1953).
(Da55)   J. Dabrowski and J. Sawicki, *Phys. Rev.* **97**, 1002 (1955).
(De56)   J. J. Devaney, *Los Alamos Sci. Lab. Report* LA-1960 (1956).
(Du54)   J. J. Dudley and C. M. Class, *Phys. Rev.* **94**, 807 (1954).

(Dz57)   Dzantiev, Levkovskiĭ, and Malievskii, *Doklady Akad. Nauk. S.S.S.R.*
         113, 537 (1957); *Soviet Phys. "Doklady"* **2**, 153 (1957).
(El55)   J. P. Elliott and B. H. Flowers, *Proc. Roy. Soc. (London)* **229A**, 536
         (1955), and private communication.
(El57)   Elpidinskii, Shapiro, and Shmranich, "Nuclear Reactions in Light
         Nuclei," *Soviet J. Atomic Energy* Suppl. 5, 75 (1957).
(Fe55)   H. Feshbach, "Report on the Brookhaven Conference on the Statistical
         Aspects of the Nucleus," *Brookhaven Natl. Lab. Report* BNL-331, p.
         59 (1955).
(Fi57)   G. J. Fischer, *Phys. Rev.* **108**, 99 (1957).
(Fo50)   J. L. Fowler and J. M. Slye, Jr., *Phys. Rev.* **77**, 787 (1950).
(Fo52)   S. G. Forbes, *Phys. Rev.* **88**, 1309 (1952).
(Fo54)   Fowler, Owen, and Hanna, *NYO Report* 3864 (1954).
(Fo55)   Fowler, Hanna, and Owen, *Phys. Rev.* **98**, 249(A) (1955).
(Fr54)   G. M. Frye, Jr., *Phys. Rev.* **93**, 1086 (1954).
(Fr55)   French, Halbert, and Pandya, *Phys. Rev.* **99**, 1387 (1955).
(Fr55a) Frye, Rosen, and Stewart, *Phys. Rev.* **99**, 1375 (1955).
(Fr56)   G. M. Frye, Jr. and J. H. Gammel, *Phys. Rev.* **103**, 328 (1956).
(Ga58)   Gabbard, Davis, and Bonner, *Phys. Rev.* **114**, 201 (1959),
(Gi49)   Gittings, Barschall, and Everhart, *Phys. Rev.* **75**, 610 (1949).
(Gi54)   G. von Gierke, *Z. Naturforsh.* **9a**, 164 (1954).
(Go56)   Gorlov, Gokhberg, Morozov, and Otroshchenko, *Doklady Akad. Nauk.
         S.S.S.R.* **111**, 791 (1956); *Soviet Phys. "Doklady"* **1**, 705 (1957).
(Go56a) Gorlov, Gokhberg, Morozov, and Otroshchenko, *Doklady Akad. Nauk.
         S.S.S.R.* **110**, 963 (1956); *Soviet Phys. "Doklady"* **1**, 598 (1957).
(Gr49)   L. L. Green and W. M. Gibson, *Proc. Phys. Soc. (London)* **62A**, 296
         (1949).
(Gr53)   E. R. Graves and L. Rosen, *Phys. Rev.* **89**, 343 (1953).
(Gr55)   E. R. Graves and R. W. Davis, *Phys. Rev.* **97**, 1205 (1955).
(Gr58)   Grundl, Henkel, and Perkins, *Phys. Rev.* **109**, 425 (1958).
(Gu54)   P. C. Gugelot, *Phys. Rev.* **93**, 425 (1954).
(Ha52)   W. Hauser and H. Feshbach, *Phys. Rev.* **87**, 336 (1952).
(Ha55)   Hayakawa, Kawai, and Kikuchi, *Progr. Theoret. Phys.* **13**, 415 (1955).
(Ha57)   Haling, Peck, and Eubank, *Phys. Rev.* **106**, 971 (1957).
(He54)   S. A. Heiberg, *Phys. Rev.* **96**, 856(A), (1954).
(Ho53)   J. R. Holt and T. N. Marsham, *Proc. Phys. Soc. (London)* **66A**, 1032
         (1953).
(Ho53a) J. Horowitz and A. M. L. Messiah, *J. phys. radium* **14**, 12, 695 (1953).
(Hu41)   P. Huber, *Helv. Phys. Acta* **14**, 163 (1941).
(Hu55)   D. J. Hughes and J. A. Harvey, "Neutron Cross Sections," *Brookhaven
         Natl. Lab. Report* BNL-325 (1955).
(Hu55a) T. Hürlimann and P. Huber, *Helv. Phys. Acta* **28**, 33 (1955).
(Hu57)   D. J. Hughes and R. B. Schwartz, "Neutron Cross Sections," *Brook-
         haven Natl. Lab. Report* BNL-325, Suppl. No. 1 (1957).
(Ja53)   J. D. Jackson and D. I. Wanklyn, *Phys. Rev.* **90**, 381 (1953).
(Je50)   J. V. Jelley and E. B. Paul, *Proc. Phys. Soc. (London)* **63A**, 112 (1950).
(Jo50)   C. H. Johnson and H. H. Barschall, *Phys. Rev.* **80**, 818 (1950).

(Jo51)   Johnson, Bockelman, and Barschall, *Phys. Rev.* **82**, 117 (1951).

(Jo51a)   Johnson, Petree, and Adair, *Phys. Rev.* **84**, 775 (1951).

(Jo54)   Johnson, Willard, and Bair, *Phys. Rev.* **96**, 985 (1954).

(Ke58)   B. D. Kern and W. E. Kreger, *Bull. Am. Phys. Soc.* **3**, 187 (1958).

(Kl48)   E. D. Klema and A. O. Hanson, *Phys. Rev.* **73**, 106 (1948).

(Ko57)   T. I. Kopaleishvili, *Zhur. Eksptl. i Teoret. Fiz.* **33**, 788 (1957); *Soviet Phys. JETP* **6**, 606 (1958).

(Ko58)   Kondaiah, Iyengar, and Badrinathan, *Nuclear Phys.* **5**, 346 (1958).

(Ku57)   Kumabe, Takakoshi, Ogata, Tsuneoka, and Ōki, *Phys. Rev.* **106**, 155 (1957).

(Ku58)   I. Kumabe, *J. Phys. Soc. Japan*, **13**, 325 (1958), and private communication.

(Ku58a)   Kumabe, Takekoshi, Ogata, Tsuneoka, and Ōki, *J. Phys. Soc. Japan*, to be published (1958), and private communication.

(La54)   J. M. B. Lang and K. J. LeCouteur, *Proc. Phys. Soc. (London)* **67A**, 586 (1954).

(La56)   J. R. Lamarsh and H. Feshbach, *Phys. Rev.* **104**, 1633 (1956).

(Le52)   K. J. LeCouteur, *Proc. Phys. Soc. (London)* **65A**, 718 (1952).

(Le56)   V. N. Levkovskiĭ, *Zhur. Eksptl. i Teoret. Fiz.* **31**, 360 (1956).

(Le57)   V. N. Levkovskiĭ, *Doklady Akad. Nauk. S.S.S.R.* **113**, 1032 (1957); *Soviet Phys. "Doklady"* **2**, 182 (1957).

(Li52)   A. B. Lillie, *Phys. Rev.* **87**, 716 (1952).

(Li53)   D. L. Livesey and C. L. Smith, *Proc. Phys. Soc. (London)* **66A**, 689 (1953).

(Lu50)   Lüscher, Ricamo, Scherrer, and Zunti, *Helv. Phys. Acta* **23**, 56 (1950).

(Ma52)   H. C. Martin and B. C. Diven, *Phys. Rev.* **86**, 565 (1952).

(Ma53)   H. C. Martin and R. F. Taschek, *Phys. Rev.* **89**, 1302 (1953).

(Ma54)   H. C. Martin, *Phys. Rev.* **93**, 498 (1954).

(Ma55)   J. B. Marion and R. M. Brugger, *Phys. Rev.* **100**, 69 (1955).

(Ma56)   Marion, Brugger, and Chapman, *Phys. Rev.* **101**, 247 (1956).

(Ma56a)   Marion, Weber and Mozer, *Phys. Rev.* **104**, 1402 (1956).

(Ma57)   P. V. March and W. T. Morton, Columbia International Conference on Neutron Interactions with the Nucleus, New York, 1957.

(Ma59)   Marion, Levin, and Cranberg, *Phys. Rev.* **114**, 1584 (1959).

(Mc52)   H. McManus and W. T. Sharp, *Phys. Rev.* **87**, 188(A) (1952).

(Mc55)   H. McManus, "Report on the Brookhaven Conference on the Statistical Aspects of the Nucleus," *Brookhaven Natl. Lab. Report* BNL-331, p. 68 (1959).

(Me52)   A. M. L. Messiah, *Phys. Rev.* **88**, 151 (1952).

(Ne52)   N. Nereson and S. Darden, *Phys. Rev.* **89**, 775 (1952).

(On54)   G. K. O'Neill, *Phys. Rev.* **95**, 1235 (1954).

(Os56)   Y. Oshima, *Ann. soc. sci. Bruxelles* **70**, No. 1, 73 (1956).

(Ov59)   O. E. Overseth, Jr. and R. A. Peck, Jr., *Phys. Rev.* **115**, 993 (1959).

(Pa53)   E. B. Paul and R. L. Clarke, *Can. J. Phys.* **31**, 267 (1953), and private communication.

(Pe51)   Petree, Johnson, and Miller, *Phys. Rev.* **83**, 1148 (1951).

(Pe51a) J. L. Perkin, *Phys. Rev.* **81**, 892 (1951).
(Pe52) M. Peshkin and A. J. F. Siegert, *Phys. Rev.* **87**, 735 (1952).
(Pe57) R. A. Peck, Jr., *Phys. Rev.* **106**, 965 (1957).
(Pe59) R. A. Peck, Jr. and J. Lowe, *Phys. Rev.* **114**, 847 (1959).
(Ph52) Phillips, Davis, and Graves, *Phys. Rev.* **88**, 600 (1952).
(Pr55) R. J. Prestwood, *Phys. Rev.* **98**, 47 (1955).
(Re54) J. B. Reynolds and K. G. Standing, *Phys. Rev.* **95**, 639(A) (1954).
(Re54a) Reines, Cowan, Harrison, and Carter, *Rev. Sci. Instr.* **25**, 1061 (1954).
(Re58) C. H. Reed, private communication (1958).
(Ri51) R. Ricamo, *Nuovo cimento* **8**, 383 (1951).
(Ri54) F. L. Ribe and J. D. Seagrave, *Phys. Rev.* **94**, 934 (1954).
(Ri55) F. L. Ribe and R. W. Davis, *Phys. Rev.* **99**, 331 (1955).
(Ri56) F. L. Ribe, *Phys. Rev.* **103**, 741 (1956).
(Ri57) F. L. Ribe, *Phys. Rev.* **106**, 767 (1957).
(Ro55) L. Rosen and L. Stewart, *Phys. Rev.* **99**, 1052 (1955).
(Ro57) L. Rosen and L. Stewart, *Phys. Rev.* **107**, 824 (1957).
(Sa55) Sattar, Morgan, and Hudspeth, *Phys. Rev.* **100**, 960 (1955).
(Sc59) J. P. Schiffer and L. L. Lee, Jr., *Phys. Rev.* **115**, 1705 (1959).
(Se55) J. D. Seagrave, *Phys. Rev.* **97**, 757 (1955).
(Se55a) J. Scitz and P. Huber, *Helv. Phys. Acta* **28**, 227 (1955).
(Si48) C. P. Sikkema, *Nature (London)* **162**, 698 (1948).
(Si50) C. P. Sikkema, *Nature (London)* **165**, 1016 (1957).
(Sm52) K. Smith and R. Henkel, Los Alamos Scientific Laboratory, private communication (1952).
(St48) A. Stebler and P. Huber, *Helv. Phys. Acta* **21**, 59 (1948).
(St51) P. H. Stelson and C. Goodman, *Phys. Rev.* **82**, 69 (1951).
(St56) K. G. Standing, *Phys. Rev.* **101**, 152 (1956).
(St57) P. H. Stelson and E. C. Campbell, *Phys. Rev.* **106**, 1252 (1957).
(Ta57) Taylor, Ashby, Catron, and Newkirk, Columbia Conference on the Neutron Interactions with the Nucleus, New York, 1957.
(Te58) J. Terrell and D. M. Holm, *Phys. Rev.* **109**, 2031 (1958).
(Th55) R. G. Thomas, *Phys. Rev.* **100**, 25 (1955).
(Th58) Thompson, Fergusson, and Kern, *Bull. Am. Phys. Soc.* **3**, 210 (1958).
(Ti57) E. W. Titterton and T. A. Brinkely, *Nature (London)* **179**, 368 (1957).
(To53) B. J. Toppel and S. D. Bloom, *Phys. Rev.* **91**, 473(A) (1953).
(Va54) I. Sh. Vashakidze and G. A. Chilashvili, *Zhur. Eksptl. i Teoret. Fiz. S.S.S.R.* **26**, 254 (1954).
(Va57) Vasilev, Komarov, and Popova, "Nuclear Reactions in Light Nuclei," *Soviet J. Atomic Energy*, Suppl. 5, 92 (1957).
(Ve57) Verbinski, Hurlimann, Stephens, and Winhold, *Phys. Rev.* **108**, 779 (1957).
(Wa50) H. Wäffler, *Helv. Phys. Acta* **23**, 239 (1950).
(Wa55) Way, King, McGinnis, and van Lieshout, Nuclear Level Schemes, *Natl. Research Council Nuclear Data Project Report* TID-3300 (1955).
(Wa57) Walton, Clement, and Boreli, *Phys. Rev.* **107**, 1065 (1957).
(Wa58) R. Wagner and P. Huber, *Helv. Phys. Acta* **31**, 89 (1958).

(We37)   V. Weisskopf, *Phys. Rev.* **52**, 295 (1937).

(We40)   V. F. Weisskopf and D. H. Ewing, *Phys. Rev.* **57**, 472 (1940).

(We54)   J. B. Weddell and J. H. Roberts, *Phys. Rev.* **95**, 117 (1954); **91**, 473 (1954).

(We55)   V. F. Weisskopf, "Report on the Brookhaven Conference on the Statistical Aspects of the Nucleus," *Brookhaven Natl. Lab. Report* BNL-331, p. 106 (1955).

(We56)   V. F. Weisskopf, *Physica* **22**, 941 (1956).

(We57)   V. F. Weisskopf, *Revs. Modern Phys.* **29**, 174 (1957).

(Wh51)   B. G. Whitmore and G. E. Dennis, *Phys. Rev.* **84**, 296 (1951).

(Wi58)   Williamson, Hudspeth, Morgan, and Moore, *Phys. Rev.* **110**, 139 (1958).

(Wo51)   L. Wolfenstein, *Phys. Rev.* **82**, 690 (1951).

(Wu52)   Wu, Rustad, Perez-Mendez, and Lidofsky, *Phys. Rev.* **87**, 1140 (1952).

(Wy58)   M. E. Wyman, *Bull. Am. Phys. Soc.* **3**, 187 (1958).

(Ya57)   S. Yasumi, *J. Phys. Soc. Japan* **12**, 443 (1957).

Neutron Threshold Measurements

J. B. MARION, *University of Maryland, College Park, Maryland*

T. W. BONNER,* *Rice University, Houston, Texas*

1. Introduction

Measurements of neutron threshold energies by charged-particle bombardment fall logically into two categories: the determination of nuclear Q-values for (a) ground states and for (b) excited states. Experiments of the first type are made primarily to establish precise ground-state Q-values and isotopic mass differences while those of the second type are concerned mainly with the location of excited states of nuclei and the accurate measurement of their energies. Obviously, only negative Q-values can be measured by the neutron threshold method.

In general, ground-state neutron thresholds in the light and medium-weight nuclei are relatively easy to detect. This is a result of the fact that at bombarding energies corresponding to most thresholds in the lighter nuclei the incident charged particle has a good probability of penetrating the Coulomb barrier of the target nucleus. Since there are no electrostatic forces inhibiting the outgoing neutron, only centrifugal barrier effects must be overcome. Consequently, when the neutron is not required to carry off any angular momentum (as is frequently the case), the onset of the neutron yield in the reaction occurs rapidly and the threshold is well defined. This sudden increase in the number of neutrons is usually not difficult to detect, since, in a properly designed experiment, there is a minimum of neutron background present below the ground state threshold. (A more complete discussion of ground state thresholds will be found in Section 3.)

The situation is appreciably different in the detection of neutron thresholds for excited states of the final nucleus. In experiments of

---

* Professor Bonner died suddenly on Dec. 6, 1961.

this type it is necessary to observe threshold neutrons in the presence of large numbers of fast neutrons which leave the residual nucleus in the ground state or in lower-lying excited states. Methods for meeting these difficulties are discussed in Sections 4 and 5. The use of γ-ray detection in measurements of neutron thresholds for excited states is discussed in Section 6.

2. Accelerator Energy Calibration

The measurement of Q-values for neutron-producing reactions by the threshold detection method does not involve the use of elaborate instruments for the determination of the energy of the outgoing particle,[1] as is the case in Q-value measurements for reactions involving charged particles (see, for example, Bu56). For this reason, the accuracy of threshold measurements is determined almost exclusively by the accuracy to which the energy of the bombarding particles is known. (The effects of target thickness and beam spread on the accuracy of threshold measurements are discussed in Section 3.B.)

Absolute instruments of the electrostatic (He49, Hu52, Bo58, Bo59) and magnetic (St57) types are in use as energy selectors for Van de Graaff beams. Also an ingenious devise for the absolute measurement of particle velocities has been described (Al49) which operates on the wave-guide principle. Most energy analyzers, however, are not of the absolute variety and detailed calibration is required if precise measurements are to be made.

A. Summary of Low-Energy Calibration Points

In a recent review article (Ma61) dealing with accelerator calibration data, an analysis was given of all current, precision data relating to those γ-ray resonances and neutron thresholds which are suitable for calibration purposes. The data were divided into three categories: (a) 5 energy points were classed as "primary calibration points," since considerable data, measured on an absolute basis, exist for these points; (b) 8 energy points were classed as "secondary

---

[1] Certain types of threshold measurements do require knowledge of the calibration of a secondary energy analyzer (or at least the *ratio* of the calibration constants of the two analyzers); see Jo54.

calibration points," since the available data consist largely of relative measurements which had to be corrected for the values of the standards used according to the weighted means adopted in (a); and (c) 12 energy points were classed as "other calibration points," which

Table I. Summary of primary calibration points (Ma61). (All contributing measurements made on an absolute basis.)

Reaction	Adopted resonance or threshold energy (Mev)[a]	Adopted Γ (kev)[b]
$B^{11}(p, \gamma)C^{12}$	0.1631 ± 0.0004	6.3 ± 1.0
$F^{19}(p, \alpha\gamma)O^{16}$	0.3405 ± 0.0002	2.7 ± 0.4
$F^{19}(p, \alpha\gamma)O^{16}$	0.8724 ± 0.0004	4.7 ± 0.3
$Al^{27}(p, \gamma)Si^{28}$	0.9920 ± 0.0005	0.08 ± 0.04
$Li^{7}(p, n)Be^{7}$	1.8807 ± 0.0004	Threshold

[a] Weighted mean value plus the larger of the internal and external probable error.

[b] Arbitrarily chosen.

Table II. Summary of secondary calibration points (Ma61). (Contributing measurements both absolute and relative; the latter have been corrected for the adopted values of the standards used.)

Reaction	Adopted resonance or threshold energy (Mev)[a]	Adopted Γ (kev)[b]
$Li^{7}(p, \gamma)Be^{8}$	$0.4412 \perp 0.0003$	12.2 ± 0.5
$Be^{9}(p, \gamma)B^{10}$	1.0839 ± 0.0006	3.8 ± 0.5
$F^{19}(p, \alpha\gamma)O^{16}$	1.3466 ± 0.0011	5 ± 1
$F^{19}(p, \alpha\gamma)O^{16}$	1.3735 ± 0.0006	11 ± 1
$C^{13}(p, \gamma)N^{14}$	1.7465 ± 0.0005	0.077 ± 0.012
$Ni^{58}(p, \gamma)Co^{59}$	$1.8432 + 0.0005$	0.1 ± 0.05
$Be^{9}(p, \alpha\gamma)Li^{6}$	2.5646 ± 0.0018	39 ± 2
$C^{13}(p, n)N^{13}$	3.2358 ± 0.0011	Threshold

[a] Weighted mean value plus the larger of the internal and external probable error.

[b] Arbitrarily chosen.

included only the most recent and most precise measurement of a resonance or threshold energy which helped to fill a gap left by the points falling into categories (a) and (b). These 25 calibration points are listed in Tables I, II, and III.

Table III. Other Calibration Points (Ma61)

Reaction	Resonance or threshold energy (Mev)	Γ(kev)	Method	Reference
$T(p, n)He^3$	1.0197 ± 0.0005	Thresh	Absolute Electric	Bo60
$Ni^{58}(p, \gamma)Co^{59}$	1.4241 ± 0.0007	0.050 ± 0.050	Absolute Electric	Bo59
$O^{16}(d, n)F^{17}$	1.8292 ± 0.0006	Thresh	Absolute Electric	Bo60a
$O^{18}(p, n)F^{18}$	2.5734 ± 0.0008	Thresh	Absolute Electric	Bo60b
$C^{13}(\alpha, n)O^{16}$	2.800 ± 0.003	~ 4	$Li^7(p, n)$, 1.8811	Wi60
$Si^{28}(p, p'\gamma)Si^{28}$	3.105 ± 0.006	12	Several Reactions	Wi60a
$Si^{28}(p, p'\gamma)Si^{28}$	3.340 ± 0.007	12	Several Reactions	Wi60a
$Na^{23}(\alpha, n)Al^{26}$	3.492 ± 0.003	<1	$Li^7(p, n)$, 1.8811	Wi60
$N^{15}(p, n)O^{15}$	3.7808 ± 0.0011	Thresh	$Li^7(p, n)$, 1.8811	Jo58b
$F^{19}(p, n)Ne^{19}$	4.2332 ± 0.002	Thresh	Absolute Magnetic	Be62
$Si^{28}(p, p'\gamma)Si^{28}$	4.240 ± 0.008	16	Several Reactions	Wi60a
$Si^{28}(p, p'\gamma)Si^{28}$	4.887 ± 0.010	12	Several Reactions	Wi60a

B. *Energy Measurements with Molecular Beams*

Since accurate measurements of resonance and neutron threshold energies are not available over the entire energy range which is attainable with present-day accelerators, it has been customary in some laboratories to calibrate beam energy analyzers by observing resonances or thresholds with molecular as well as atomic beams (see, for example, Ki55). Thus, it should be possible to obtain three calibration points by observing a given (p, γ) resonance or (p, n) threshold with the H+, HH+, and HHH+ beams. By properly taking into account the aggregate particle masses and the effective energy spreads in the beams due to the internal motion of the protons in the molecular ions (Ne57, An58), it would then be possible to obtain three calibration points with zero relative error. Recently, however, detailed measurements of resonance processes with molecular beams have been carried out by Bondelid and Kennedy (Bo58, Bo59), Anderson *et al.* (An58), and Dahl *et al.* (Da60), which indicate that asymmetrically shaped thick-target resonance curves are obtained with molecular beams, even though atomic beam experiments on the same targets and under otherwise identical conditions yield symmetrical curves. Furthermore, the resonance energy positions obtained with molecular beams are slightly lower for thick-target measurements than for thin-target measurements. This latter effect amounts to some 0.05

to 0.08 per cent (Bo58, Bo59, Da60). The reason for this effect appears to be associated with the Coulomb energy of the two protons which result from the stripping of the electron from the ion (Da60).

In view of the uncertainties concerning the behavior of molecular ions in matter, molecular-beam calibration points should probably not be used, except if very thin targets are employed, when accuracies approaching 0.1 per cent are desired.

C. Target Conditions

In the measurement of resonance or threshold energies it is important to insure that the target surface is clean. The contamination of targets by carbon buildup from the cracking of organic vapors in the vacuum system is a frequent cause of sizeable apparent energy shifts. Cold trapping in the immediate vicinity of the target is an effective means of preventing carbon deposits; these techniques have been discussed, for example, by Butler and Gossett (Bu57a) and by Richards (Ri60). In the case of α-particle bombardment, carbon buildup is extremely rapid and even a highly trapped target may show appreciable carbon deposits after short bombardments (Wi60). The only effective means of dealing with this problem at present seems to be frequent changes of the target spot or of the entire target.

In the measurement of γ-ray or neutron resonances the thickness of the target used in the experiment enters directly into the analysis of the data (see, for example, Fo48 and Ri60). Targets for resonance energy determinations may be divided into three thickness categories.

(a) *Thin targets.* If the thickness of the target is much less than the natural width of the resonance observed, then the position of the peak counting rate corresponds to the resonance energy. Some of the resonances listed in the preceding tables, however, have extremely small natural widths and the preparation of targets which have an even smaller energy loss for the bombarding particle beam is quite difficult, if possible at all. Therefore, as a general technique for precision experiments, the thin target method is not particularly useful, although in some cases, it is adequate.

(b) *Targets with thickness comparable to the natural resonance width.* If targets of this type are used, then it is necessary to measure the thickness to an accuracy (usually) of a fraction of a kev since the position of the peak counting rate will differ from the resonance energy by one-half of the target thickness. Hunt (Hu60) has determined target thicknesses by observing the difference in the position of the peak counting rate between a resonance curve measured with the particle beam striking the target at normal incidence and a curve measured with the beam striking the target at an angle of 60°. Since the effective target thickness is increased by a factor of 2 in the 60° rotation, the difference in the positions of the peak counting rates is equal to one-half of the target thickness. Results of these measurements were always checked with thicknesses calculated from a knowledge of the amount of material evaporated on the target backing (Hu60).

(c) *Thick or semi-thick targets.* Perhaps the easiest and most straightforward technique in the measurement of resonance energies is to use a target whose thickness is somewhat greater than the natural width of the resonance studied. If a measurement of the "thick-target step" is made, then the midpoint of the rise corresponds to the resonance energy (Fo48, Ri60). Furthermore, the natural width of the resonance can be obtained from an analysis of the shape of the thick-target step, even for extremely narrow resonances (see, for example, Bo58 and Bo59). Because of the ease with which targets may be prepared and because of the straightforward nature of data analysis, the use of semithick targets is to be recommended for resonance energy measurements.

3. The Measurement of Ground-State Threshold Energies

A. Energy Dependence of Cross Sections Near Threshold

The energy dependence of the total reaction cross section for neutron emission immediately above threshold can be deduced from a Born approximation or an R-matrix calculation (Wi48, Ba57, Br57a, Gu57, La58; see also Chapter V.E). The zero-order result is that the cross section is proportional to k_n^{2l+1}, where k_n is the neutron wave number and l is the relative angular momentum of the neutron and the final nucleus in units of $\hbar$. Since the neutrons from a reaction have relatively low velocities near threshold, centrifugal barrier effects make the $l = 0$ case dominant. In fact, it would not be possible to detect a threshold which did not proceed at least partially through s-wave since for $l > 0$ the yield curve has zero slope at threshold; for the $l = 0$ case the slope is infinite. The conditions

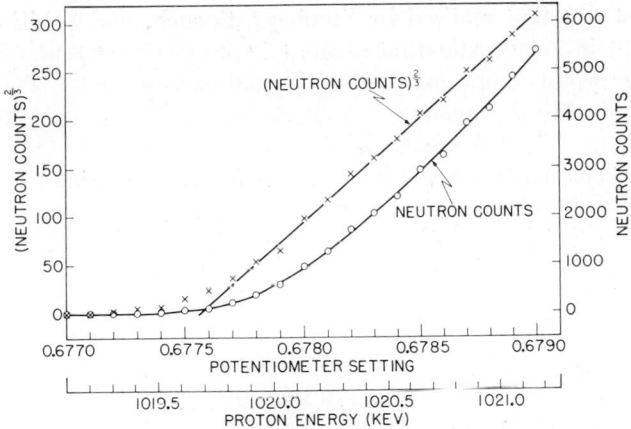

Figure 1. Extrapolation of the neutron yield from the $T(p,n)He^3$ reaction to obtain the threshold energy (Bo60).

for the validity of the k_n^{2l+1} law are that $\sigma \ll \pi \lambda_n^2$ where σ is the total reaction cross section and $\lambda_n^2 = k_n^{-2}$, and that $kR \ll 1$, where k is the wave number and R the interaction radius in the entrance channel. An additional requirement is that the density of levels in the compound nucleus be small, since otherwise the cross section would depend in a complicated manner on the level positions and the individual reduced level widths. In most reactions with light nuclei these conditions are fulfilled at the neutron threshold energy and the theory remains valid for many kev; for medium weight nuclei, however, the region of validity is only a few hundred ev above threshold.

The k_n^{2l+1} law implies that the total reaction cross section should vary approximately as $(E - E_{th})^{(2l+1)/2}$ in the region immediately above threshold. (E is the bombarding energy and E_{th} is the threshold energy; $E - E_{th} = \Delta E$.) Consequently a thick-target measurement of the total reaction cross section should produce a yield curve that varies as $(\Delta E)^{3/2}$ if only s-wave emission is important. This result indicates that in order to extrapolate linearly a yield curve to zero yield for the purpose of determining the threshold energy, a plot of $Y^{2/3}$ vs. ΔE must be made. The necessity of using a

$Y^{2/3}$ plot was first realized by Stephens, Spruch, and Schiff (quoted by Bo49) in an investigation of the $C^{14}(p, n)N^{14}$ reaction. The use of the $Y^{2/3}$ plot in obtaining the threshold energy for the $T(p, n)He^3$ is shown in Fig. 1 (Bo60).

B. Effect of Counter Geometry on Threshold Measurements

The discussion above relates to the *total* neutron yield from a thick target in the energy region immediately above threshold. Since the neutrons are confined to a narrow cone about the forward (beam) direction in this energy region, it is possible to measure the total yield with a single detector. A paraffin- or polyethylene-moderated $B^{10}F_3$ proportional counter is commonly used as a detector. Such a counter must be placed so that it subtends a half-angle at the target which is greater than the half-angle of neutron emission at the maximum bombarding energy used for the extrapolation to threshold.

The equation which gives the half-angle ψ of the cone which includes all of the neutrons is (Ha49):

$$\psi = \sin^{-1}[(M_2 M_4/M_1 M_3)(\Delta E/E)]^{1/2} \tag{1}$$

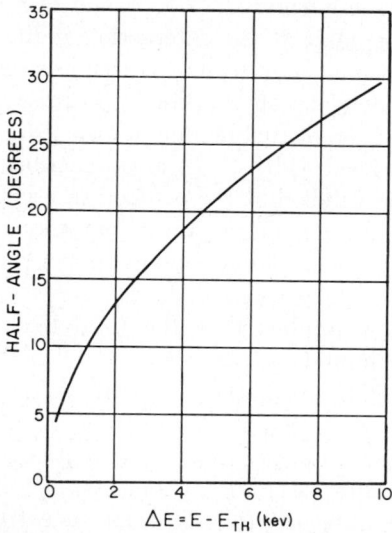

Figure 2. Calculated curve for the half-angle of the cone which contains all of the neutrons from the $Li^7(p, n)$ reaction as a function of $\Delta E = E - E_{th}$.

where E is the bombarding energy, $\Delta E = E - E_{th}$, and the subscripts 1, 2, 3, and 4 refer to the incident particle, target nucleus, emitted particle, and the residual nucleus, respectively.

Equation (1) is shown graphically in Fig. 2 for the case of the Li^7 (p, n) reaction, and gives as a function of ΔE the minimum half-angle which a detector must subtend at the target in order to intercept all of the neutrons emitted from this reaction near threshold. For example, if a measurement is to be made such that the extrapolation of the yield will be carried out over an energy region 5 kev above threshold, then the detector must be placed so that the half-angle subtended by its sensitive surface at the target is greater than 21°. In this statement the assumption is made that the detector is equally sensitive over the entire surface presented to the source and that the sensitivity is not dependent on the angle at which the neutrons strike this surface. Unfortunately, data concerning these latter effects are not available for most types of neutron detectors commonly used for threshold measurements.

C. Effects of Beam Spread on Threshold Energy Measurements

Another precaution to be considered in the measurement of neutron threshold energies is the energy spread or resolution of the bombarding beam. Newson et al. (Ne57) contend that if a bombarding beam with energy spread δ is used, then the apparent threshold energy will be found approximately $\delta/2$ below the true threshold energy. Their calculation, however, probably overestimates the effect, since when high resolutions are used ($E/\delta \approx 2000$) Browne et al. (Br60) and others (e.g., St60) have found no measurable difference in the extrapolated thresholds as the resolution is altered. However, high resolutions should be used whenever precision energy measurements are undertaken.

The recommended procedures for the measuring of neutron threshold energies are therefore: (a) bombarding beams with the highest possible resolution should be used; (b) the neutron detector should subtend a sufficiently large half-angle at the target to intercept all of the neutrons from the reaction in the energy range investigated; and (c) the extrapolation procedure for determining the threshold energy should utilize a plot of $Y^{2/3}$ vs. bombarding energy.

Table IV.   Ground State Threshold Energies

Reaction	Threshold energy (Mev)		Calibration	Ref.
$D(p, n)2H^1$	3.339	± 0.015	$Li^7(p, n)$, 1.882	Ri50
$T(p, n)He^3$	1.019	± 0.001	$F^{19} + p$, 0.8735	Ta49
	1.0203	± 0.0015	$Al^{27}(p, \gamma)$, 0.9933	Bo51
	1.0197	± 0.0005	Absolute	Bo60
$Li^6(He^3, n)B^8$	2.9661	± 0.0017	Absolute	Du58
	2.974	± 0.010	Several reactions	Fa59
$Li^7(p, n)Be^7$	1.8807	± 0.0004	See Table I	
$Li^7(\alpha, n)B^{10}$	4.379	± 0.006	$Li^7(p, n)$, 1.881	Bi57
$Be^9(p, n)B^9$	2.059	± 0.002	$Li^7(p, n)$, 1.882	Ri50
$B^{11}(p, n)B^9$	3.015	± 0.003	$Li^7(p, n)$, 1.882	Ri50
$C^{12}(d, n)N^{13}$	0.328	± 0.003	$F^{19} + p$, 0.485 and 0.8735	Bo49
$C^{12}(He^3, n)O^{14}$	1.4496	± 0.0028	$Li^7(p, n)$, 1.8816	Br57
	1.4362	± 0.0009	Absolute	Bo61
	1.4370	± 0.0009	$Li^7(p, n)$, 1.8807	Ba60
	1.4348	± 0.0016	$Li^7(p, n)$, 1.8807	To61
$C^{13}(p, n)N^{13}$	3.236	± 0.003	$Li^7(p, n)$, 1.882	Ri50
	3.2372	± 0.0016	Absolute	Bo59
	3.238	± 0.004	Several reactions	Ch57a
	3.2353	± 0.0015	Absolute	Be62
$C^{14}(p, n)N^{14}$	0.664	± 0.009	$Li^7(p, n)$, 1.883	Sh49
	0.6715	± 0.0005	$Li^7(p, n)$, 1.881	Sa56
$C^{14}(\alpha, n)O^{17}$	2.340	± 0.003	$Li^7(p, n)$, 1.8811	Sa56
$N^{15}(p, n)O^{15}$	3.776	± 0.008	Several reactions	Ki55
	3.7808	± 0.0011	$Li^7(p, n)$, 1.8811	Jo58b
$O^{16}(d, n)F^{17}$	1.832	± 0.004[a]	Several reactions	Ma55a
	1.836	± 0.003	$F^{19} + p$, 0.8735	Bo51
	1.8292	± 0.0006	Absolute	Bo60a
$O^{18}(p, n)F^{18}$	2.584	± 0.010	$Li^7(p, n)$, 1.8814	Ma56a
	2.577	± 0.008	Several reactions	Hi56
	2.590	± 0.004	$Li^7(p, n)$, 1.882	Ri50
	2.5734	± 0.0008	Absolute	Bo60b
$F^{19}(p, n)Ne^{19}$	4.240	± 0.008	Several reactions	Ki55
	4.235	± 0.005	Several reactions	Ma55
	4.240	± 0.005	Several reactions	Ch57a
	4.2332	± 0.002	Absolute	Be62

[a] These data have been corrected by the various authors and differ from the values appearing in the reference.

D. Results of Ground-State Threshold Measurements

Accurate determinations of ground-state neutron threshold energies have been made for almost 40 different reactions, including

Table IV (Continued)

Reaction	Threshold energy (Mev)	Calibration	Ref.
$Na^{23}(p, n)Mg^{23}$	5.053 ± 0.010	Several reactions	Ki55
	5.061 ± 0.007	Several reactions	Ch57a
$Mg^{25}(p, n)Al^{25}$	5.289 ± 0.025	Several reactions	Ki55
$Al^{27}(p, n)Si^{27}$	5.792 ± 0.010	Several reactions	Ki55
	5.798 ± 0.005^a	Several reactions	Ma55
$P^{31}(p, n)S^{31}$	6.417 ± 0.020	Several reactions	Go58a
$Cl^{37}(p, n)A^{37}$	1.640 ± 0.004	$Li^7(p, n), 1.882$	Ri50
	1.641 ± 0.002	$Li^7(p, n), 1.8822$	Sc52
$Sc^{45}(p, n)Ti^{45}$	2.908 ± 0.004	Several reactions	Br55
$Ti^{49}(p, n)V^{49}$	1.413 ± 0.005	Several reactions	Tr53
	1.412 ± 0.004	Several reactions	Jo58a
$V^{51}(p, n)Cr^{51}$	1.5656 ± 0.0015	$Li^7(p, n), 1.881$	Gi55
	1.564 ± 0.002	Several reactions	Go58
$Cr^{53}(p, n)Mn^{53}$	1.406 ± 0.008	$Li^7(p, n), 1.8822$	Lo52
$Cr^{54}(p, n)Mn^{54}$	2.202 ± 0.005	$Li^7(p, n), 1.8822$	Lo52
$Mn^{55}(p, n)Fe^{55}$	1.034 ± 0.005^a	Several reactions	Tr53
	1.031 ± 0.004	Several reactions	Jo58a
	1.034 ± 0.002	Several reactions	Go58
$Co^{59}(p, n)Ni^{59}$	1.889 ± 0.003	$Li^7(p, n), 1.882$	Mc51
	1.895 ± 0.005	Several reactions	Ch57
	1.887 ± 0.004	$Li^7(p, n), 1.8811$	Bu57
$Ni^{58}(p, n)Cu^{58}$	9.459 ± 0.070	Several reactions	Go58a
$Ni^{60}(p, n)Cu^{60}$	7.028 ± 0.020	Several reactions	Go58a
$Cu^{63}(p, n)Zn^{63}$	4.215 ± 0.004	Several reactions	Br55
	4.213 ± 0.008	Several reactions	Ki55
$Cu^{65}(p, n)Zn^{65}$	2.1646 ± 0.0009^b		
$Zn^{67}(p, n)Ga^{67}$	1.810 ± 0.005^a	Several reactions	Tr53
	1.805 ± 0.005	Several reactions	Ch57
$Zn^{68}(p, n)Ga^{68}$	3.753 ± 0.006^a	Several reactions	Br55
	3.762 ± 0.005	Several reactions	Ch57
$Zn^{70}(p, n)Ga^{70}$	1.457 ± 0.002	Several reactions	Go58
$As^{75}(p, n)Se^{75}$	1.670 ± 0.005^a	Several reactions	Tr53
	1.669 ± 0.002	Several reactions	Go58
	1.670 ± 0.004	Several reactions	Jo58a
$Se^{77}(p, n)Br^{77}$	2.175 ± 0.004	$V^{51}(p, n), 1.5656$	Jo58

[b] The experimental threshold energy is calculated from the weighted mean Q-value given by Ma56; see Chapter I.D.

(p, n), (d, n), (α, n), and (He^3, n) reactions. The most precise measurements are collected in Table IV. The method by which the energy selector was calibrated is noted, but no attempt has been made to reduce the data to a common reference energy. The accuracy of many of these measurements is such that they are suitable for the calibration of beam analyzers. In such cases, however, the difficulties discussed in Sections 2.B, 2.C, 3.B, and 3.C must be taken into account.

Most of the measurements listed in Table IV were obtained by straightforward techniques. A notable exception is the determination of the $N^{15}(p, n)$ threshold energy by Jones *et al.* (Jo58b). Since the threshold energy for this reaction (3.78 Mev), is almost exactly twice that for the $Li^7(p, n)$ reaction (1.88 Mev), these experimenters were able to make essentially a direct comparison of the two threshold energies by simultaneously employing the H^+ and HH^+ beams. The experimental arrangement is illustrated schematically in Fig. 3. The HH^+ beam is deflected through 62.5° and strikes the lithium target, while the H^+ beam is deflected through 90° onto the N^{15} target. As the beam energy is increased, the threshold for the Li^7 (p, n) reaction with the HH^+ beam is reached first, followed closely by the $N^{15}(p, n)$ threshold with the H^+ beam. The experimental results are shown in Fig. 4. In terms of the $Li^7(p, n)$ threshold at 1.8811 Mev, and apart from the uncertainty in the Li^7 threshold, the value for the $N^{15}(p, n)$ threshold energy is 3.7808 ± 0.0015 Mev.

Another interesting modification of the standard threshold techniques has been made by Gove *et al.* (Go58a) in connection with

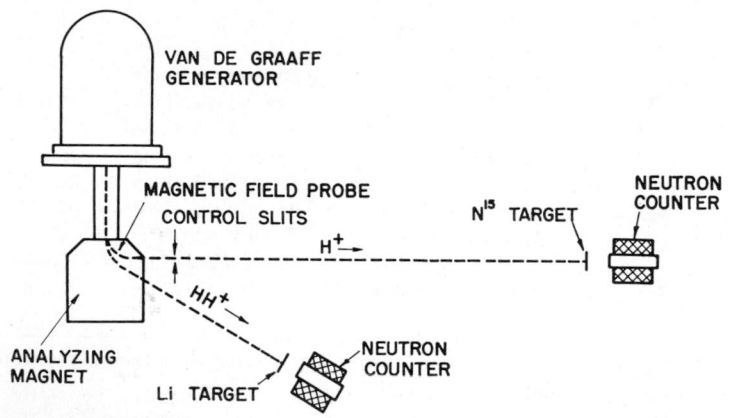

Figure 3. Schematic representation of the experimental arrangement for the comparison of the threshold energies for the Li^7 (p, n) and N^{15} (p, n) reactions using the H^+ and HH^+ beams (Jo58b).

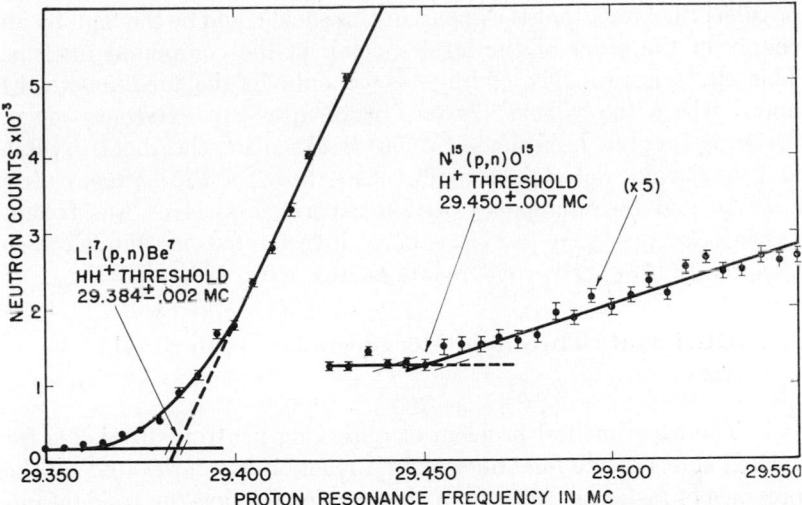

Figure 4. Results of the comparison of the threshold energies for the Li⁷ (p, n) and N¹⁵ (p, n) reactions (Jo58b).

the calibration of the new Chalk River Tandem Van de Graaff accelerator. Since accurately known threshold energies were not available above about 6 Mev, these workers accelerated quadruply and quintuply ionized O^{16} atoms and bombarded a deuterium target. They observed the threshold for the $D(O^{16}, n)F^{17}$ reaction, the energy for which (14.572 ± 0.030 Mev) can be easily calculated from that for the $O^{16}(d, n)F^{17}$ reaction (see Table IV). Using the calibration obtained from this and other reactions, this group was then able to measure the ground-state thresholds for the (p, n) reactions on P^{31}, Ni^{60}, and Ni^{58} which occur in the energy region from 6 to 9 Mev (see Table IV).

E. Effect of Resonances on Ground-State Thresholds

It has been pointed out (Br55) that the apparent threshold energy measured for a reaction may not correspond to the Q-value for the reaction if pronounced resonances occur in the compound nucleus. For example, if the theoretical threshold for a reaction falls in a low-yield valley between two resonances, there will be essentially no yield from the reaction until the next resonance is reached. It is possible, therefore, that the apparent threshold could be too high by an energy of the order of the level spacing in the compound nucleus. This effect is probably of importance only in the medium-weight nuclei where the valleys between resonances are extremely deep. A comparison has been made (Ma56) between the threshold Q-value and the Q-value determined by direct methods for the $Cu^{65}(p, n)Zn^{65}$ reaction and no discrepancy within experimental error was found. Other reactions have not yet been investigated in detail. (See Chapter I.D for further comments on this effect.)

4. Excited-State Threshold Measurements with Single Counters

The experimental problem of observing neutron thresholds for excited states of the final nucleus in a reaction is complicated by the presence of faster neutrons from the reaction leaving the residual nucleus in the ground state or in lower-lying excited states. Usually the number of these fast neutrons greatly exceeds the number of threshold neutrons, and therefore it is necessary to discriminate strongly against the fast neutrons in favor of the slower threshold neutrons.

The kinematics of the reaction assist in this discrimination, since just above threshold, the new group of neutrons is confined to the forward cone [see Eq. (1) and Chapter I.B], while the faster groups are emitted into the entire sphere. For a typical experimental arrangement, the favoring of the threshold neutrons may be a factor of the order of 50.

Further discrimination is obtained by constructing a detector with a sensitivity function that peaks at low neutron energies. The detector most commonly used for neutron threshold measurements is a $B^{10}F_3$ proportional counter surrounded by a moderator, and this detector can be made to respond strongly in favor of slow neutrons only at a sacrifice of efficiency and background discrimination. Consequently, one must compromise between efficiency and selectivity. One such compromise arrangement, developed by Bonner and Butler (Bo51), is shown in Fig. 5. The detector consists of a cylindrical BF_3 counter positioned laterally in a truncated cone of paraffin. The half-angle of the cone is 27°. This geometry was chosen, after various materials, sizes, shapes, and orientations of moderators were

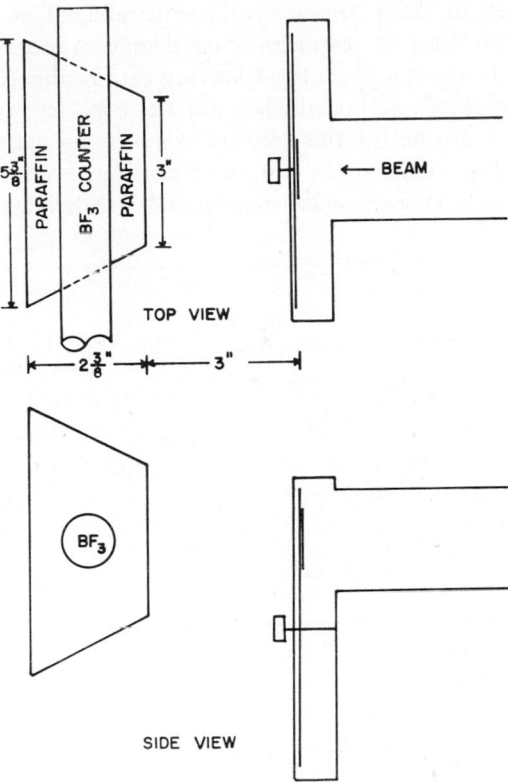

Figure 5. Geometry of the 27° - counter (Bo51).

tested, as that arrangement which yielded (a) a good counting rate relatively free from background neutrons and (b) the highest ratio of counting rate from threshold neutrons to that from fast neutrons.

The 27°-counter was tested by observing the neutrons from the $T(p, n)He^3$ reaction since the yield of neutrons from this reaction is smoothly varying and there are no low-lying excited states of the residual nucleus to give additional thresholds. The results are illustrated in Fig. 6. The counting rate rises smoothly until an energy of 15 kev above threshold is reached, after which the points fall slowly until an energy of 24 kev above threshold is reached. At the latter energy, the cone has opened to 27°, the half-angle of the counter, and any further increase in bombarding energy causes some of the neutrons to miss the detector entirely. The experimental results indicate that the counting rate decreases more rapidly after this point is reached. Since the counting rate begins to fall off after 15 kev above threshold, at which point the cone has opened to 21°, apparently the region of the counter cone between half-angles 21° and 27° is not as efficient as the inner portion. A comparison was made between the experimental points and a theoretical curve based

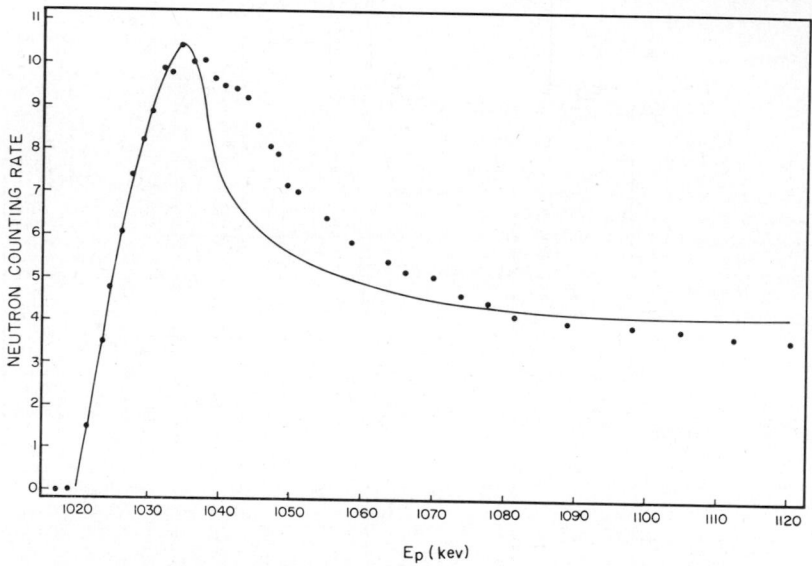

Figure 6. Neutrons from the T(p, n)He³ reaction. Circles give experimental points using the 27° - counter and a 4-kev target. The curve was calculated for an effective counter half-angle of 21° (Bo51).

on a uniform counter sensitivity out to 21° and zero sensitivity beyond that angle. The solid line of Fig. 8 shows the calculated curve. There is good agreement up to the point that the neutron cone has opened to 21° (15 kev above threshold), but the calculated curve then decreases more rapidly than the observed yield due to the fact that the counter cone between 21° and 27° does not have exactly *zero* sensitivity. In general, one may say that the performance of the 27°-counter may be calculated with fair accuracy for neutron energies up to about 1 Mev.

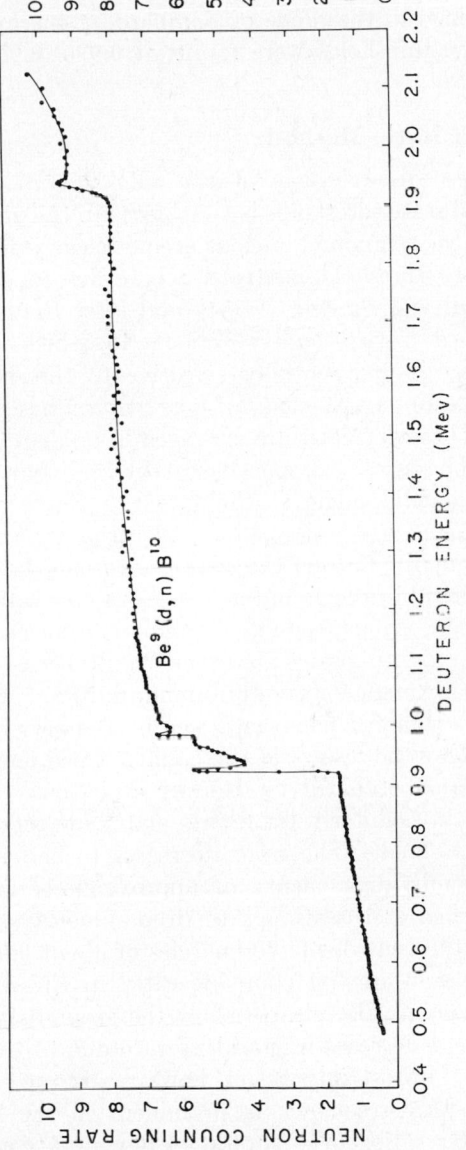

Figure 7. Neutrons from the Be⁹ (d,n)B¹⁰ reaction using the 27°-counter (Bo51).

Typical of the results obtained with the 27°-counter in a study of excited-state thresholds is the curve shown in Fig. 7 for the Be^9-$(d, n)B^{10}$ reaction. In the range of bombarding energy from 0.5 to 2.1 Mev, neutron thresholds were found at 0.920, 0.985, and 1.916 Mev (Bo51).

5. The Counter Ratio Method

The greatest disadvantage of the single-counter method for observing excited state thresholds is that peaks in the yield curve due to resonances in the compound nucleus are not clearly distinguishable from rises due to threshold neutrons. In order to eliminate this difficulty, Willard and Preston (Wi51) and later Bonner and Cook (Bo54) introduced a two-counter scheme in which one detector (the *slow counter*) is preferentially sensitive to threshold neutrons while the second counter (the *modified long counter*) has a more-or-less flat response. These detectors are arranged in tandem with the slow counter nearer the source and spaced so that they subtend approximately the same solid angle at the target. (Further geometrical details will be found in Section 5.A.) Neutron thresholds are detected by observing the ratio of the counting rate in the slow counter to that in the modified long counter. The counter ratio, then, to a first approximation, is independent of compound nucleus resonances, and since the two counting rates are taken simultaneously, compensation is automatically made for target nonuniformities. A brief survey of counter-ratio techniques has been given by Bonner (Bo60c).

Figure 8 shows the results of the counter ratio method for the $Li^7(p, n)Be^7$ reaction obtained by Bonner and Cook (Bo54). The solid circles are the counter ratio points and show the rapid rise at the 1.88-Mev threshold. The ratio decreases to half its maximum value when a bombarding energy of approximately 50 kev above threshold is reached and continues to drop smoothly to 0.1 of the maximum when the neutrons have energies of about 0.6 Mev. The open circles in Fig. 8 are the counting rates in the modified long counter. These points also clearly show the ground-state threshold and the subsequent decrease in counting rate due to the opening of the neutron cone. Most important, however, is the fact that, although the 2.25-Mev resonance is prominent in the long counter curve, the counter ratio curve shows no deviation from a smooth decrease. It is this fact which allows the counter ratio method to

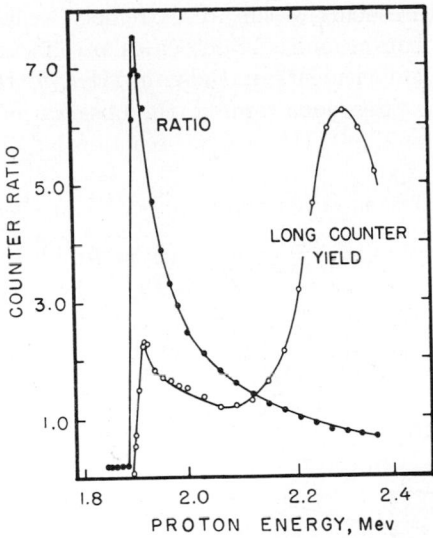

Figure 8. Neutrons from the Li⁷(p, n)Be⁷ reaction. The solid circles give the counter ratio and the open circles the neutron yield (Bo54).

distinguish between thresholds and resonances. (Situations in which resonances *do* affect the counter ratio are discussed in Section 5.C.)

When there are essentially no neutrons present below a threshold (i.e., for a ground-state threshold in a low background situation), the counter ratio will immediately rise to its maximum value at the threshold energy (see Fig. 8). For excited state thresholds, however, where there are appreciable counting rates in the counters below threshold, the counter ratio requires an energy interval approximately equal to the target thickness in order to reach its maximum value. This is a result of the fact that the rise of the counter ratio is due to the increase in the number of threshold neutrons relative to the fast neutron background and this ratio increases until the entire target is contributing to the yield of threshold neutrons. In those reactions in which the neutron cone opens slowly [e.g., in (α, n) reactions at high bombarding energies], the energy interval during which the counter ratio rises may be determined by the cone effect rather than the target thickness [see Eq. (1)].

In addition to its applicability in the detection of excited-state thresholds, the counter ratio method is also useful in the observation of groundstate thresholds which are extremely weak and are accompanied by large backgrounds. Such cases arise in (p, n) reactions in the medium-weight elements and also in (He^3, n) reactions even in the light nuclei. [See, for example, the observation of the groundstate threshold for the $C^{12}(He^3, n)N^{14}$ reaction by Br57.]

A. Geometrical Arrangements and Counter Efficiencies

The major requirement which must be fulfilled in order that the counter ratio method be successful is that the detectors must have different sensitivity functions, with one detector preferentially sensitive to slow neutrons. Obviously, there are many experimental

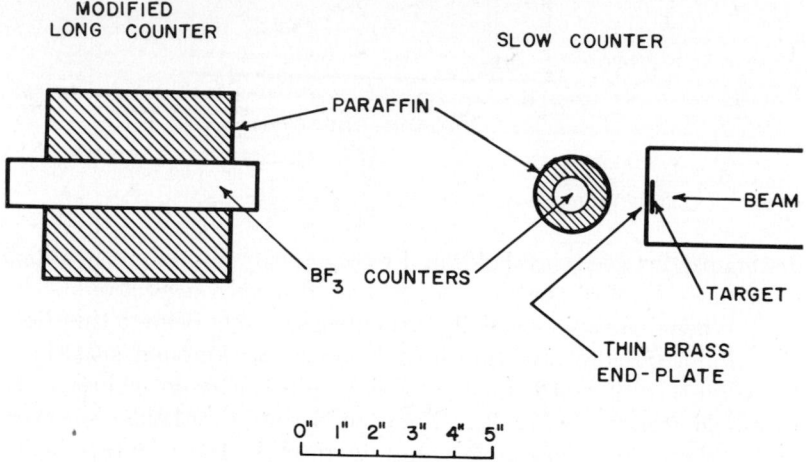

Figure 9. The geometry used by the Rice group for the observation of neutron thresholds by the counter ratio method.

arrangements which can satisfy this requirement. The Rice geometry (Br55, Ma55a) is shown in Fig. 9. The slow counter is a BF_3 detector surrounded by a $1/2$-inch layer of paraffin, 2 inches in length. The modified long counter is a similar BF_3 detector surrounded by a paraffin cylinder 5 inches in diameter and 5 inches in length. This detector is similar to the flat-response long counter (Ha47) except that the holes in the face have been eliminated.

The relative sensitivities as a function of the neutron energy for the counters in the Rice arrangement have been measured (Br55)

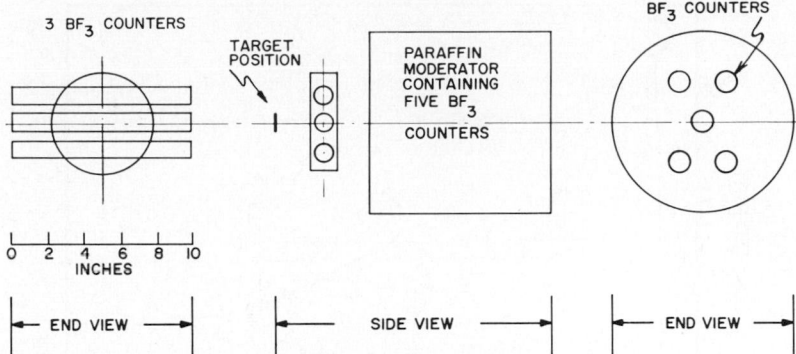

Figure 10. The geometry used by the Naval Research Laboratory group for the observation of neutron thresholds by the counter ratio method (Bu57).

by comparing the observed counting rates from the $Li^7(p, n)$ reaction with the differential cross section for the same solid angle measured by Taschek and Hemmendinger (Ta48). The response of the modified long counter is approximately flat for neutron energies between 0.3 and 2.0 Mev and has a reduced efficiency for detecting neutrons with energies below 0.2 Mev. The sensitivity of the slow counter decreases rapidly as the neutron energy is increased.

The counter geometries used for threshold measurements by the Wisconsin (Sa56), Saclay (Na56), Chalk River (Br57), Columbia (We57), and Aldermaston (To61) groups do not differ appreciably from that described above. The experimental arrangement at the Naval Research Laboratory (Bu57), however, is somewhat different and is shown in Fig. 10. The slow counter consists of three B^{10}-lined gas proportional counters placed in a paraffin disc and the modified long counter consists of five of these B^{10} detectors imbedded in a paraffin cylinder. This arrangement gives an increased detection efficiency over the single counters used in the Rice geometry. The sensitivity functions for the NRL detectors have not as yet been measured. (See also Go58.) Some more recent experiments at Chalk River (Br59) have been carried out with different geometries and with a variety of detectors, including scintillation counters.

B. Neutron Scattering Effects

Since the slow counter is placed between the target and the modified long counter, the counting rate in the latter depends not

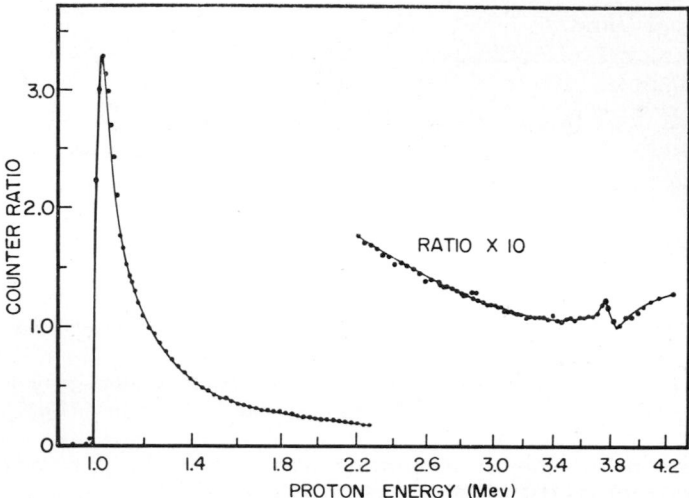

Figure 11. Counter ratio for the $T(p, n)He^3$ reaction showing the effect of the total cross section resonance in carbon (Ma55).

only on the yield of neutrons from the reaction under study but also on the neutron total cross section for the materials in the slow counter. The moderator for the slow counter is the most important of these materials since it forms the bulk of the interposed matter. If the total cross section of the moderator shows an increase at a particular neutron energy, the number of neutrons reaching the modified long counter will decrease and the counter ratio will increase. Hence, the shape of the counter ratio curve will be approximately the same as the total cross section curve.

When paraffin is used as the moderator, the total cross section resonances for carbon should appear in the counter ratio curve. Figure 11 shows the results obtained (Ma55) for the $T(p, n)He^3$ reaction. Since only one neutron group is present in this reaction, the counter ratio should be a smoothly decreasing function of the proton energy except for scattering effects. At a bombarding energy of 3.73 Mev, the neutrons have an energy of 2.95 Mev. This energy corresponds to that for a pronounced resonance in the carbon total cross section (Bo51a). The effect is evidenced in the experimental curve and the shape follows that of the total cross section. An additional carbon resonance in this energy region, due to 2.08-Mev neutrons (Bo51a), should occur at a bombarding energy of 2.80-Mev but was not observed because of the very narrow width of this resonance.

If moderators other than paraffin (e.g., lucite, LiH, D_2O, ZrH_2) are used, the scattering effects in these materials must be taken into account in the interpretation of threshold data.

C. Resonance Effects

If the counter ratio method is being used to study a reaction which is monoenergetic (i. e., only one neutron group is present), then one may make the following two statements: (a) if the effective solid angles subtended by the two counters at the target are equal for all neutron energies, then compound nucleus resonances in the reaction will not affect the counter ratio curve, and as the bombarding energy is increased, the ratio will decrease smoothly; and (b) if the effective solid angles subtended by the two counters at the target are *not* equal, but if the angular distribution of the neutrons is the same at all bombarding energies, then the counter ratio will decrease smoothly and will not be affected by compound nucleus resonances.

In the geometry of Figs. 9 and 10, the two detectors are arranged to subtend approximately the same solid angle at the target.

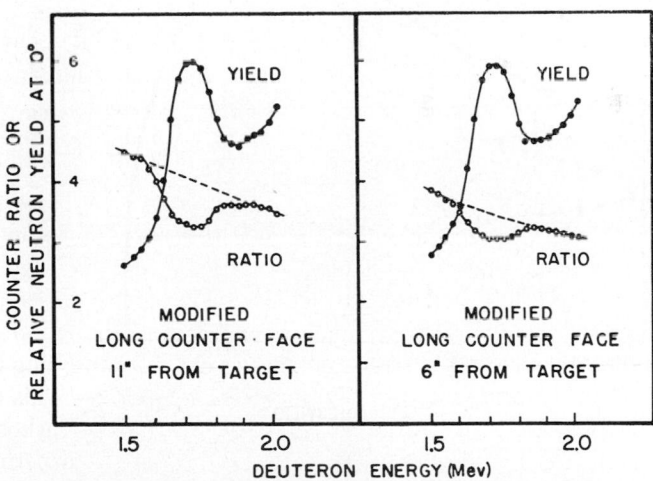

Figure 12. Counter ratio and yield of neutrons in the forward direction for the $C^{12}(d, n)N^{13}$ reaction near the 1.7-Mev resonance (Ma55c).

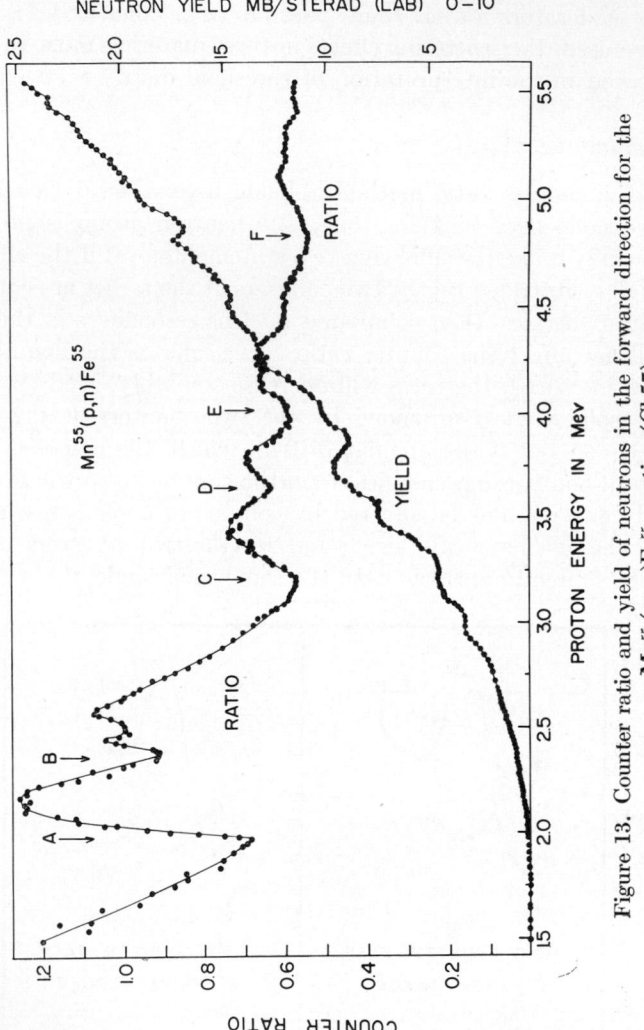

Figure 13. Counter ratio and yield of neutrons in the forward direction for the $Mn^{55}(p, n)Fe^{55}$ reaction (Ch57).

It is not known, however, what the relative *effective* solid angles are for various neutron energies. A demonstration that the effective solid angles in the Rice geometry are not equal for neutron energies near 1.5 Mev is afforded by a study of the $C^{12}(d, n)N^{13}$ reaction (Ma55c). In this reaction, a resonance occurs at a bombarding energy of 1.73 Mev at which the single group of neutrons present have an energy of 1.46 Mev. The neutrons are strongly peaked in the forward direction at this resonance (Bo49a), and the counter ratio is sensitive to differences in effective solid angle between the two counters. The counter ratio for this reaction and the relative yield of neutrons in the forward direction (as measured by the modified long counter) are shown in Fig. 12. The left-hand curves were obtained for the standard counter geometry (Fig. 9). The effect of the resonance is to lower the counter ratio by 19 per cent at resonance energy. Moving the modified long counter forward by 5 inches (right-hand curves of Fig. 12), reduces this effect to 12 per cent at resonance. Hence, the two solid angles are more nearly the same for the latter geometry for neutron energies near 1.5 Mev.

The above considerations are based on the assumption that the reaction is monoenergetic. If more than a single group of neutrons is present, however, an additional complication is possible. At a resonance, the spin and parity of the compound nucleus state involved may be such that the relative probabilities for neutron emission to the various energy levels of the residual nucleus may be quite different from those immediately off resonance. Since the relative numbers of slow and fast neutrons can therefore change appreciably in a comparatively small energy interval, the ratio curve may show certain irregularities. This type of resonance effect is most troublesome in the first 0.2–0.3 Mev above an excited-state threshold when the sensitivity of the slow counter is still relatively high. Figure 13 shows the effect of resonances on the counter ratio for the Mn^{55}-$(p, n)Fe^{55}$ reaction (Ch57). A pronounced dip in the ratio occurs following threshold B and several dips are found following thresholds E and F. Because of these effects, one must exercise considerable caution in the interpretation of threshold data for reactions which are strongly resonant. One method of at least partially overcoming these difficulties is to use targets thick enough to average over several compound nucleus resonances or to average several thin-target points to obtain each ratio point. The averaging over reso-

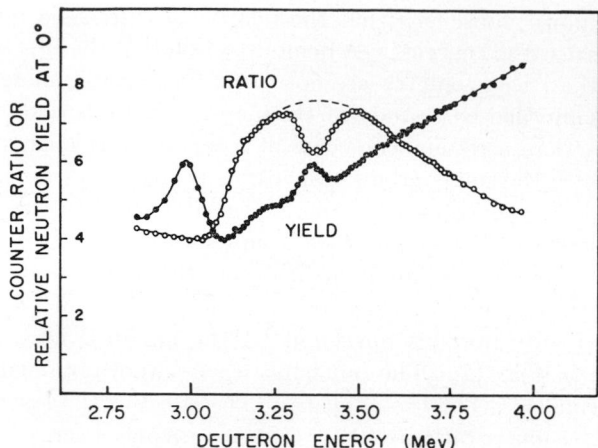

Figure 14. Counter ratio and yield of neutrons in the forward direction for the $C^{12}(d, n)N^{13}$ reaction near the threshold for the first excited state of N^{13} (Ma55b).

nances tends to reduce angular distribution effects and usually produces a much smoother counter ratio curve (Br55).

Although resonance effects can give rise to ambiguities in the interpretation of threshold data, under certain conditions these effects can be used to give information concerning the spin and parity of the resonance level. Figure 14 shows the counter ratio and neutron yield for $C^{12}(d, n)N^{13}$ reaction near the threshold for the first excited state of N^{13}(Ma55b). The counter ratio at this threshold requires approximately 200 kev, or 3 times the target thickness, to reach its maximum value. This strongly suggests (see the discussion in Section 5.E) that p-wave neutron emission is required to form the residual nuclear level, the 2.37-Mev state of N^{13}. Near the peak of the curve, there is a dip in the ratio, corresponding in energy and in width to the 3.36-Mev resonance in the total yield. The decrease in the ratio is caused by the fact that the slow neutron yield does not show this resonance at all. This implies that the yield from this resonance proceeds almost entirely to the ground state of N^{13}. This would be possible if s-wave neutrons could be emitted to the ground state but not to the first excited state. The ground and first excited states of N^{13} have $J = 1/2^-$ and $1/2^+$ respectively, and, therefore, the resonance state must have $J = 0^-$ or 1^- to allow s-wave neutron emission to the ground state but not to the first excited state. This is then consistent with p-wave character of the threshold rise in the counter ratio.

D. *Thresholds for Broad Levels*

The previous discussion of excited-state neutron thresholds has been limited to cases in which the final nuclear state is sharp, i.e., has only a radiation width. Thresholds have also been observed to excited states which are particle unstable and have widths ranging from a few kev to a few hundred kev.

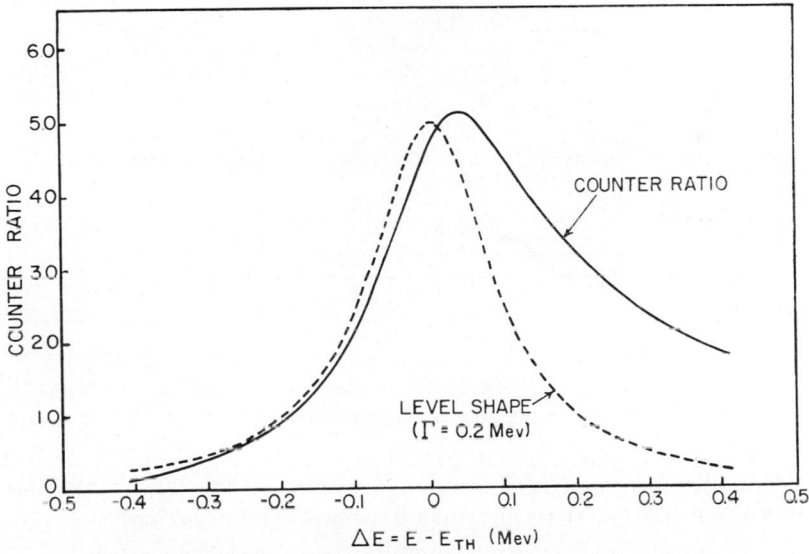

Figure 15. Effect of a broad final state on the counter ratio.

If the shape of the counter ratio curve is known for the case of a sharp level, then it is easy to compute the shape that would result from a final nuclear state of any width since the final state can always be represented as being composed of a large (strictly, infinite) number of sharp states. By using the shape of the counter ratio curve for the $Li^7(p, n)$ reaction (which is essentially monoenergetic[2]) (Ma55),

---

[2] Although a second neutron group is energetically possible for $E_p > 2.38$ Mev, it is very weak in this energy region (Ma55), leaving the $Li^7 (p,n)$ reaction essentially monoenergetic.

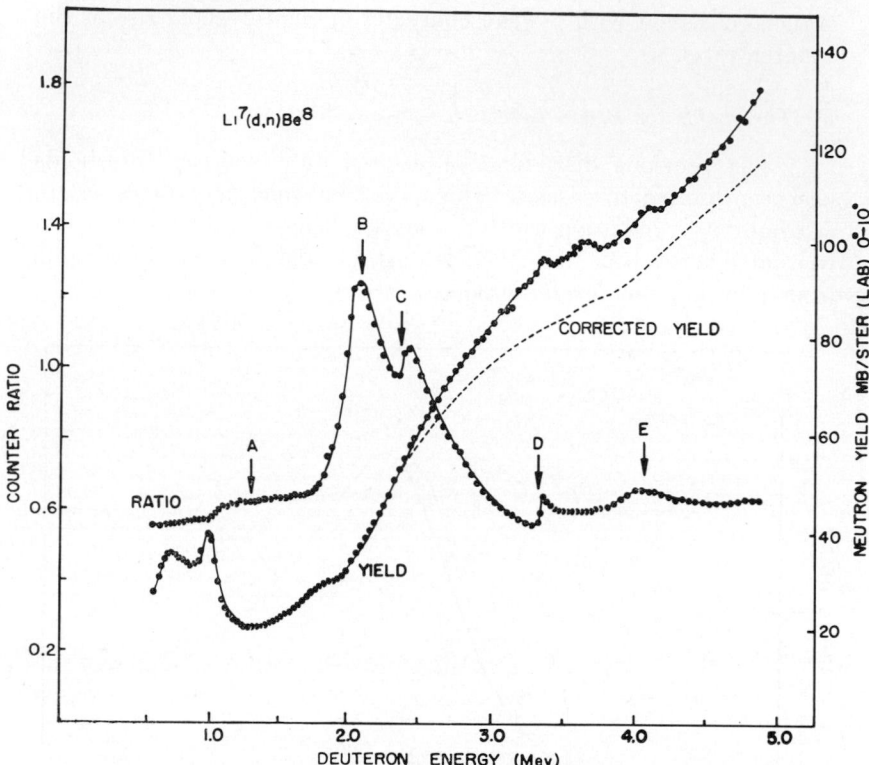

Figure 16. Counter ratio and yield of neutrons in the forward direction for the Li^7(d, n)Be^8 reaction showing the effect of broad states in Be^8 (Sl57). The "corrected yield" takes into account an oxygen contamination in the target.

the shape of the curve for a residual level with $\Gamma = 0.2$ Mev was computed. The result is presented in Fig. 15. The energy scale is given in terms of $E - E_{th}$, where E_{th} is the bombarding energy corresponding to the peak of the level shape. Strictly speaking, the shape of the computed curve should be in terms of the neutron energy obtained from the reference curve for the sharp level, but the shape is not sensitive to this approximation. Figure 15 shows that the counter ratio follows fairly closely the low energy side of the level, but that a severe distortion occurs for the high energy side. Furthermore, the peak of the ratio curve is displaced toward higher energies from the level peak, $E = E_{th}$. For broader levels, the distortion and the dis-

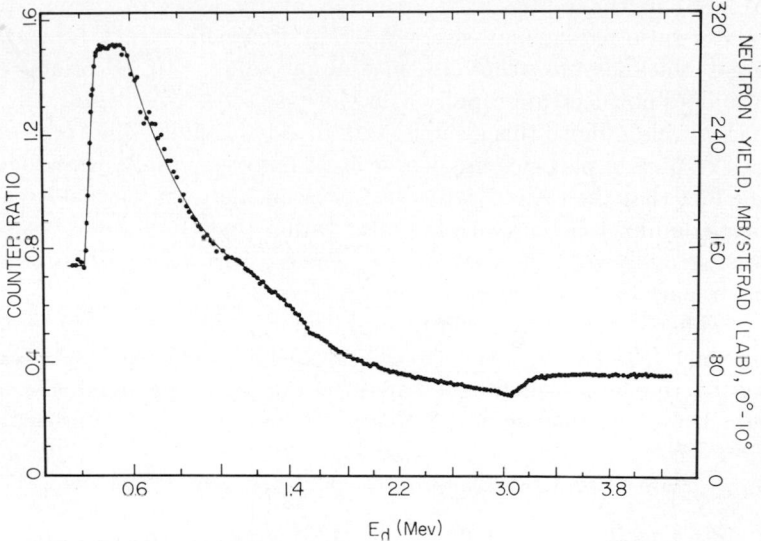

Figure 17. Counter ratio for the $C^{13}(d, n)N^{14}$ reaction (Ma55b).

placement of the peak are relatively smaller.   Experiments such as that on the $Li^7(d,n)Be^8$ reaction (Bo54, Sl57), shown in Fig. 16, confirm this predicted distortion for broad levels.

The distorted shape of the counter ratio curve, and particularly the displacement of the peak, must be taken into account in the assignment of Q-values and level widths from broad thresholds.

E. Thresholds with $l_n > 0$

It was pointed out at the beginning of Section 5 that the counter ratio at an excited-state threshold continues to rise for an energy interval approximately equal to the target thickness.   This statement holds when the threshold neutrons are emitted predominantly with $l = 0$.   For cases in which higher angular momenta are carried off by the neutron, the yield rises much more slowly (see Section 3.A), and the counter ratio can continue to increase for an energy interval even greater than target thickness.   Furthermore, unless there is some s-wave component, the onset of the slow neutron yield will not be sharp and the threshold will not be well-defined even though the residual level is sharp.   Figure 17 shows the strong threshold observed

(Ma55b) in the $C^{13}(d, n)N^{14}$ reaction at $E_d = 0.422$ Mev. The counter ratio requires an energy interval approximately 4 times the target thickness to reach its maximum value. In addition, the ratio does not decrease rapidly as is the case for s-wave thresholds at sharp levels. Since this excited state in N^{14} (at 5.68 Mev) is bound with respect to particle emission, it must have essentially zero width. The fact that the ratio requires such a large energy interval to reach its maximum, together with the observation that the decrease is also slow, strongly suggests that p-wave neutrons are responsible for the major part of the threshold yield.

There is as yet no experimental evidence for neutron thresholds for which $l_n > 1$. Such thresholds are expected to be extremely weak due to the large centrifugal barrier effect. No threshold was observed, for example, in the $Li^6(d, n)$ Be^7 reaction at a bombarding energy corresponding to the 4.59-Mev state in Be^7 under circumstances which probably required $l_n > 1$ to form this level (Sl57).

F. Gas Target Measurements

All of the measurements referred to in the preceding sections were carried out with solid target materials. Some experiments

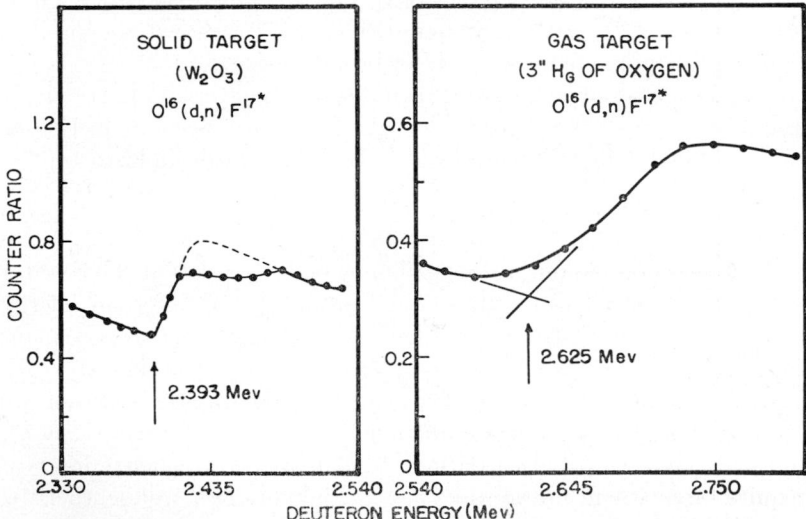

Figure 18. Counter ratio for the $O^{16}(d,n)F^{17}$ reaction near the threshold for the first excited state of F^{17} using solid and gas targets (Ma56b). The gas target was covered with an 0.0001-inch nickel foil.

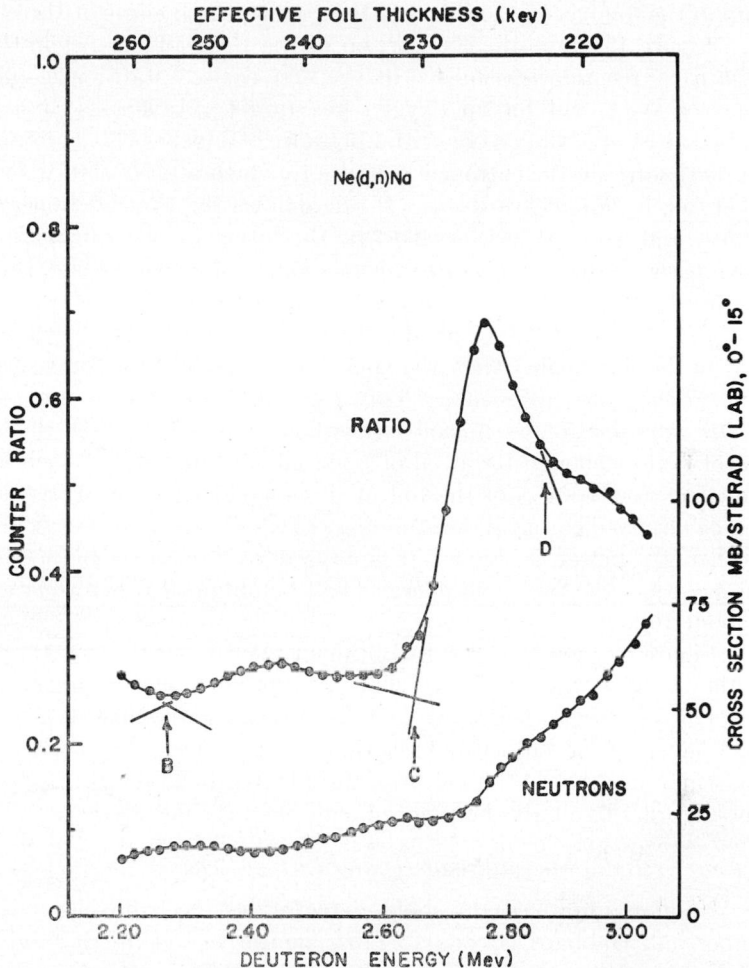

Figure 19. Counter ratio and yield of neutrons in the forward direction for the Ne(*d*, *n*)Na reactions using a gas target (Ma56b). The effective foil thickness (top scale) must be subtracted from the bombarding energy in order to obtain the energy of the beam incident on the neon gas.

require targets which cannot conveniently be prepared in solid form, e.g., the noble gases. Since the use of gaseous targets requires that the beam pass through a retaining foil before interacting with the target gas, it is important to know what effect the straggling of the beam in the foil has on the shape of the counter ratio curve at threshold. Figure 18 shows the comparison of the threshold shapes in the $O^{16}(d, n)F^{17}$ reaction leaving F^{17} in the first excited state for a solid target of W_2O_3 and for an oxygen gas target (Ma56b). The gas target consisted of tank oxygen at a pressure of 3 inches Hg contained in a platinum cell, the entrance aperture to which was covered with a nickel foil, 0.0001 inches thick. If one defines the threshold energy as measured with the gas target to be the intercept of straight lines drawn through the counter ratio curve above and below the rise, then the threshold in this case occurs at a bombarding energy (i.e., the energy of the beam before passing through the nickel foil) of 2.625 Mev, or 232 kev higher than the energy of the solid target measurement [2.393 Mev (Ma55a)]. This experiment serves to give an *effective thickness* for the nickel foil (which agrees to within 10 per cent of that calculated for a foil of nominal thickness 0.0001 inches). The effective thickness of the foil at other bombarding energies can then be obtained by using the stopping cross section curves for nickel. If other gas target reactions are analyzed by the same method of extrapolation, the threshold energies can be obtained to an accuracy of about 10 kev.

Figure 19 shows the results obtained (Ma56b) with a gas target for the $Ne(d, n)Na$ reactions. The thresholds B and D are interpreted as due to the $Ne^{22}(d, n)Na^{23}$ reaction and the strong threshold C as due to the $Ne^{20}(d, n)Na^{21}$ reaction. The effective foil thickness (top scale) must be subtracted from the bombarding energy (bottom scale) in order to obtain the energy incident on the neon gas.

G. Counter Ratio Measurements Using Li^{6}I Detectors

Another improved threshold detector has been developed by Bonner and Gabbard (Bo58a). This counter makes use of a small $Li^6I(Eu)$ scintillator surrounded by a polyethylene sphere. Light from the scintillator is piped to a photomultiplier tube by a styrene rod which is 6 inches long and $1/2$ inch in diameter. (Quartz rods were originally used but were discarded because of resonance scattering effects due to the oxygen content.) Polyethylene moderators in the form of spheres with diameters of from 1.75 to 2 inches have been used with good results. The Li^6I crystal should be small so that pulses from the $Li^6(n, \alpha)H^3$ reaction, $Q = 4.78$ Mev, will be larger than γ-ray pulses. Crystals 4 mm in diameter and 4 mm thick

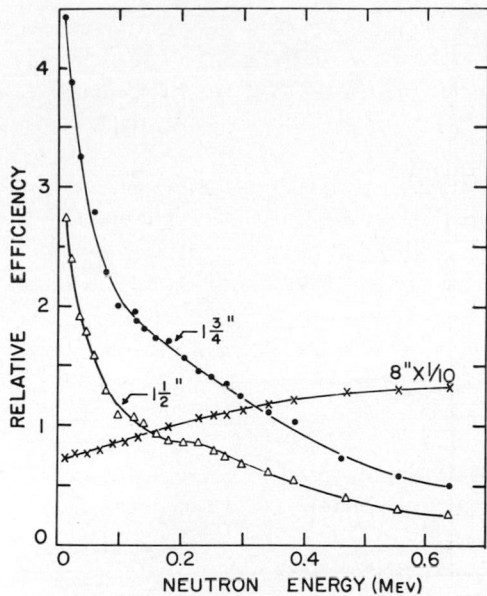

Figure 20. The relative counting rates obtained with Li⁶I scintillators at the center of polyethylene spheres with diameters of 1.5, 1.75, and 8 inches; all detectors at the same distance from the source (Bo58a). The absolute efficiency of the 1.75-inch detector is 0.2 per cent for 10-kev neutrons.

give pulses from the (n, α) reaction which are more than a factor of two larger than pulses obtained from γ radiation.

Since the Li⁶ (n, α)T reaction has a resonance at 0.250 Mev, a Li⁶I counter with no moderator will have a peak in its efficiency at this energy. A small amount of moderator can be used without giving an anomaly in the detection at 0.25 Mev if a thin layer of Li⁶I is used, since even a very thin layer of Li⁶ will absorb most of the moderated neutrons. In order to keep the efficiency as great as possible, the surface area should be kept large. A Li⁶I crystal 1 mm thick and 8 mm in diameter has been used by Bonner and Gabbard (Bo58a). The variation with neutron energy of the efficiency of a counter using a polyethylene sphere with a diameter of 1.75 inches is shown in Fig. 22. The efficiency decreases by a factor of 7.3 when the neutron energy increases from 10 kev to 600 kev. The efficiency of a counter with a moderator which has a diameter of 1.5 inches is also given in

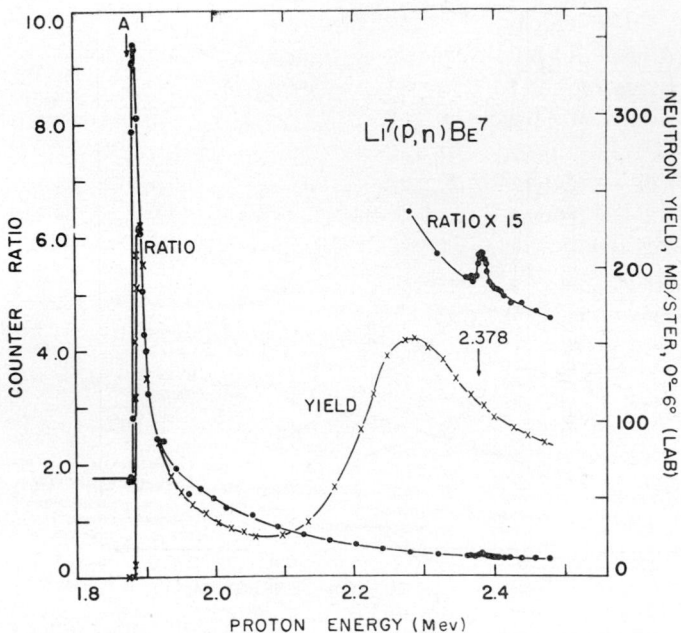

Figure 21. Thresholds in the Li⁷(p, n)Be⁷ reaction (Bo58a). The yield curve was obtained with a long counter and the ratio curve with Li⁶I detectors surrounded by 1.75 and 8-inch polyethylene spheres.

Fig. 20. The efficiency for this arrangement does not decrease monotonically with neutron energy but shows a maximum at 0.25 Mev.

The fast neutron counter need not have a flat response and, in fact, a certain increase in sensitivity in the detection of a weak threshold is obtained if the fast neutron counter has an efficiency which increases with neutron energy; the ratio of counts in the two counters will fall off more rapidly with energy above a threshold under these conditions. A fast neutron counter whose efficiency increases with neutron energy in the range from 20 kev to 600 kev has been constructed by surrounding a Li⁶I scintillator (1 mm × 8 mm) with a polyethylene sphere which has a diameter of 8 inches (Bo58a). The relative efficiency of this fast counter for a range of neutron energies is given in Fig. 20. Since this fast counter has spherical symmetry, its efficiency is expected to be essentially independent of the position on the surface of the moderator at which the neutron enters. The efficiency characteristics of such detectors has been treated in detail by Bramblett, Ewing, and Bonner (Br60a).

Experiments to detect thresholds in the $Li^7(p, n)Be^7$ reaction were carried out (Bo58a) with neutron detectors of the type which have just been described. The experimental results are given in Fig. 21. With this arrangement the ratio curve falls to half-value in 20 kev and to 0.1 of the peak value in 200 kev. The second neutron threshold from this reaction which leaves Be^7 in an excited state at 0.434 Mev is clearly shown on the ratio curve at 2.378 Mev.

H. Closed Geometry Techniques

All of the methods discussed above utilize an "open geometry," i.e., the target and the detectors are located as far away as possible from moderating and scattering surfaces. A completely different approach has been studied by Marion et al. (Ma60) who have detected neutron thresholds in a completely "closed" geometry. This method uses a 4π detector (Fig. 22) as the *fast counter*. Six $B^{10}F_3$ proportional counters are mounted in each of the two concentric rings which surround the target. The moderator is an 18-inch cube of paraffin. The slow neutron detector consists of a $Li^6I(Eu)$ crystal

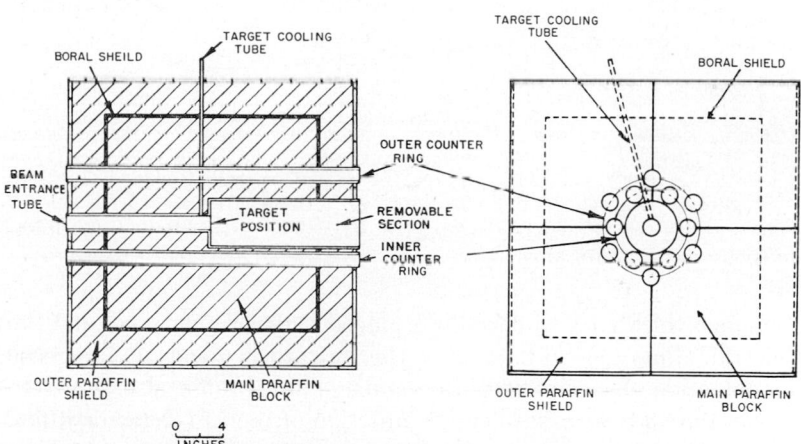

Figure 22. Schematic diagram of the 18-inch 4π neutron detector (Ma60). Each counter ring holds six 12-inch $B^{10}F_3$ counters. The Li^6I slow neutron counter and its B_4C shield are located in the "removable section" when threshold measurements are made.

(8 mm diam. × 1 mm thick) mounted directly on a phototube. This assembly is mounted at 0° with respect to the charged-particle beam. In order to suppress detection of slow neutrons moderated in the paraffin of the 4π detector, the Li^6I crystal is mounted in a B_4C shield which is placed in the removable section indicated in Fig. 22. The B_4C shield is a hollow cylinder of outside diameter 4 inches and inside diameter 2 inches. The slow neutron detector is located within this cylinder and at a distance of approximately 2 inches from the target.

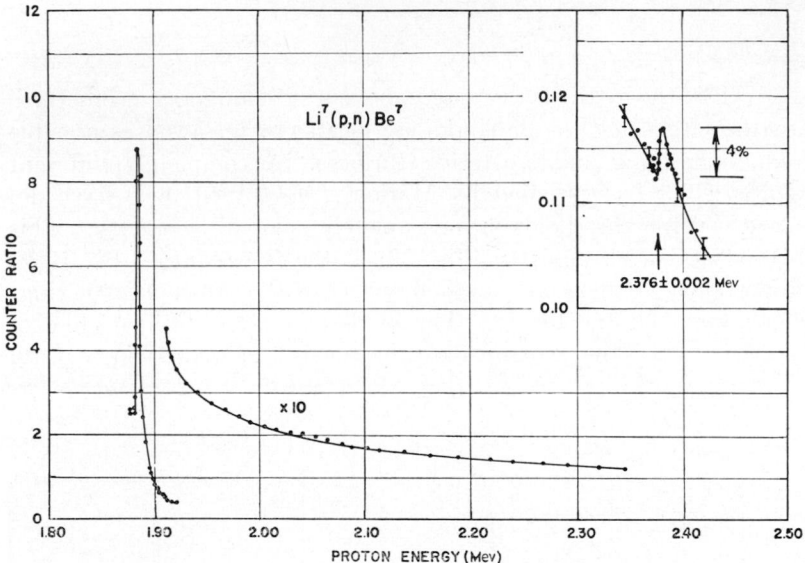

Figure 23. The counter radio for the $Li^7(p, n)Be^7$ reaction measured in closed geometry with the 4π neutron detector (Ma60). The first-excited-state threshold is observed at 2.376 Mev.

A $^1/_8$-inch thick piece of paraffin is placed between the target and the Li^6I crystal in order to thermalize the forward neutrons and increase the detection efficiency of the crystal. This paraffin also serves to smooth out the intrinsic efficiency function of the Li^6I detector which otherwise would show a maximum at a neutron energy of 0.25 Mev due to the resonance in the $Li^6(n,\alpha)T$ reaction at that energy. Therefore, with a forward counter sensitive only to low energy threshold neutrons and with the 4π detector having a response sensitive to the fast neutron component, the basic requirements of the counter ratio method are met.

As an illustration of the capabilities of this "closed geometry" system in the investigation of neutron thresholds Fig. 23 shows the results for the first two thresholds (ground state and first excited state) in the $Li^7(p,n)Be^7$ reaction. The ratio of the yield in the forward counter to that in the 4π detector shows the peak at 1.881 Mev corresponding to the ground-state threshold energy for this reaction. The ratio curve falls to half value in approximately 5 kev and to 0.1 of the peak value in approximately 17 kev. The energy resolution as determined by these fall-off distances is superior to that obtained in open geometry experiments (Bo58a; see Section 5.G above) where the corresponding energy values are 20 and 200 kev, respectively. The threshold for the first excited state neutron group is extremely weak but is clearly shown in the ratio curve at a proton energy of 2.376 ± 0.002 Mev. The magnitude of the effect observed at this excited-state threshold with the closed geometry system shows that this method is at present not as sensitive as the open geometry technique. The present results indicate a 4 per cent rise at the first excited state threshold whereas the Rice group (see Fig. 21) has observed an 8 per cent effect. It is anticipated that by utilizing a somewhat larger Li^6I crystal and by placing this detector at a greater distance from the target the sensitivity can be materially increased.

I. Additional Remarks on Counter Ratio Results

The most successful applications of the counter ratio method have so far been in studies of the (p, n) reactions in the light and medium-weight nuclei and in (d, n) reactions in the light nuclei. Some 75 excited states have been observed in reactions of these types. However, few thresholds have been observed in (α, n) reactions. These reactions are usually strongly resonant at moderate bombarding energies (see, for example, Bo56), and it is probable that resonance effects such as those discussed in Section 5.C tend to obscure expected thresholds.

It is also interesting to note that in the majority of the (d, n) reactions which have been studied, the most intense thresholds are found for levels having Q-values approximately equal to the binding energy of the deuteron (see, for example, Figs. 16 and 19). It seems possible that this effect could be the result of an increased probability for the capture of the proton by the excitation of the deuteron to its virtual level at or near the surface of the target nucleus. A theoretical investigation of this possibility and its consequences in general stripping theory would probably be worthwhile.

6. Measurement of Excited-State Thresholds by Gamma-Ray Detection

The method of observing excited-state neutron thresholds with neutron detectors suffers from two inherent disadvantages: (a) fast neutrons originating in the target can be degraded in energy by scattering from the target assembly, the walls and floor of the experimental room,[3] and by air scattering; these neutrons then become undesirable background in the slow counter; (b) the method of energy discrimination used in the counter ratio technique is a statistical one involving energy loss per collision in the moderator and the capture cross section as a function of energy in B^{10} or Li^6, and, hence, the energy selectivity of the detectors is severely limited.

A different technique for the observation of neutron thresholds which has not yet been widely used, is the detection of the γ rays that result from the decay of the residual excited state. This method by-passes the difficulties mentioned above and allows the use of positive electronic pulse-height discrimination, but, at the same time, the problem of contending with background produced by the neutrons is introduced. This undesirable γ radiation results from neutron inelastic scattering in the target assembly and in the detecting system and from neutron capture in the detecting crystal. The advantages of this method are that high-efficiency NaI crystals which subtend large solid angles may be used and that new γ rays corresponding to neutron thresholds may be identified by their characteristic spectra.

The γ-ray detection method has been used by Butler (Bu55) and Butler and Holmgren (Bu58) in studies of the $F^{19}(d, n\gamma)Ne^{20}$ and $O^{18}(d, n\gamma)F^{19}$ reactions, and by Levi and Papineau (Le57) in an investigation of the $Mo^{95}(p, n\gamma)Tc^{95}$ reaction. Bernstein and Lewis (Be57) used a conversion-electron spectrometer to detect a 54-kev γ ray from the $Cu^{65}(p, n\gamma)Zn^{65}$ reaction and found the threshold for its production at 2.223 Mev.

[3] The construction of a laboratory with a spacious area in which to perform neutron experiments can essentially eliminate the effects of floor- and wall-scattering. Several such laboratories are in existence. See also Chapter IV.F.

References

(Al49)   W. Altar and M. Garbuny, *Phys. Rev.* **76**, 496 (1949).
(An58)   Andersen, Gjotterud, Holtebekk, and Lönsjö, *Nuclear Phys.* **7**, 384 (1958).
(Ba57)   A. I. Baz', *Zhur. Eksptl i Teoret. Fiz.* **32**, 478 (1957); *Soviet Phys. JETP* **5**, 403 (1957).
(Ba60)   Bardin, Barnes, Fowler, and Seeger, *Phys. Rev. Letters* **5**, 323 (1960).
(Bc57)   E. M. Bernstein and H. W. Lewis, *Phys. Rev.* **107**, 737 (1957).
(Be62)   Beckner, Bramblett, Phillips, and Eastwood, *Phys. Rev.*, to be published (1962).
(Bi57)   H. Bichsel and T. W. Bonner, *Phys. Rev.* **108**, 1025 (1957).
(Bo49)   Bonner, Evans, and Hill, *Phys. Rev.* **75**, 1398 (1949).
(Bo49a) Bonner, Evans, Harris, and Phillips, *Phys. Rev.* **75**, 1401 (1949).
(Bo51)   T. W. Bonner and J. W. Butler, *Phys. Rev.* **83**, 1091 (1951).
(Bo51a) Bockelman, Miller, Adair, and Barschall, *Phys. Rev.* **84**, 69 (1951).
(Bo54)   T. W. Bonner and C. F. Cook, *Phys. Rev.* **96**, 122 (1954).
(Bo56)   Bonner, Kraus, Marion, and Schiffer, *Phys. Rev.* **102**, 1348 (1956).
(Bo58)   R. O. Bondelid and C. A. Kennedy, *U. S. Naval Research Lab. Report* NRL-5083 (1958).
(Bo58a) T. W. Bonner and F. Gabbard, unpublished results (1958).
(Bo59)   R. O. Bondelid and C. A. Kennedy, *Phys. Rev.* **115**, 1601 (1959).
(Bo60)   Bondelid, Butler, del Callar, and Kennedy, *Phys. Rev.* **120**, 887 (1960).
(Bo60a) Bondelid, Butler, and Kennedy, *Phys. Rev.* **120**, 889 (1960).
(Bo60b) Bondelid, Butler, and Kennedy, private communication (1960).
(Bo60c) T. W. Bonner, in *Nuclear Spectroscopy*, F. Ajzenberg-Selove, ed., Academic Press, 1960, Part A, p. 477.
(Bo62)   Bondelid, Butler, Kennedy, and del Callar, to be published (1962).
(Br55)   Brugger, Bonner, and Marion, *Phys. Rev.* **100**, 84 (1955).
(Br57)   Bromley, Almqvist, Gove, Litherland, Paul, and Ferguson, *Phys. Rev.* **105**, 957 (1957).
(Br57a) G. Breit, *Phys. Rev.* **107**, 1612 (1957).
(Br59)   Bromley, Ferguson, Gove, Kuehner, Litherland, and Almqvist, *Can. J. Phys.* **37**, 1514 (1959).
(Br60)   Browne, Galey, Erskine, and Warsh, *Phys. Rev.* **120**, 905 (1960).
(Br60a) Bramblett, Erving, and Bonner, *Nucl. Instr. and Meth.* **9**, 1 (1960).
(Bu55)   J. W. Butler, *Phys. Rev.* **98**, 241(A) (1955).
(Bu56)   W. W. Buechner, *Progr. in Nuclear Phys.* **5**, 1 (1956).
(Bu57)   Butler, Dunning, and Bondelid, *Phys. Rev.* **106**, 1224 (1957).
(Bu57a) J. W. Butler and C. R. Gossett, *Phys. Rev.* **108**, 1473 (1957).
(Bu58)   J. W. Butler and H. D. Holmgren, *Phys. Rev.* **112**, 461 (1958).
(Ch57)   R. A. Chapman and J. C. Slattery, *Phys. Rev.* **105**, 633 (1957).
(Ch57a) R. A. Chapman and H. Bichsel, unpublished results (1957).
(Da60)   Dahl, Costello, and Walters, *Nucl. Phys.* **21**, 106 (1960).
(Du58)   Dunning, Butler, and Bondelid, *Phys. Rev.* **110**, 1076 (1958).
(Fa59)   B. J. Farmer and C. M. Class, *Bull. Am. Phys. Soc.* **4**, 95 (1959).
(Fo48)   Fowler, Lauritsen, and Lauritsen, *Revs. Modern Phys.* **20**, 236 (1948).

(Gi55)   Gibbons, Macklin, and Schmitt, *Phys. Rev.* **100**, 167 (1955).
(Go58)   C. R. Gossett and J. W. Butler, *Phys. Rev.*, to be published (1958).
(Go58a)   Gove, Kuehner, Litherland, Almqvist, Bromley, Ferguson, Rose, Bastide, Brooks, and Connor, *Phys. Rev. Letters* **1**, 251 (1958).
(Gu57)   W. H. Guier and R. W. Hart, *Phys. Rev.* **106**, 296 (1957).
(Ha47)   A. O. Hanson and J. L. McKibben, *Phys. Rev.* **72**, 673 (1947).
(Ha49)   Hanson, Taschek, and Williams, *Revs. Modern Phys.* **21**, 635 (1949).
(He49)   Herb, Snowdon, and Sala, *Phys. Rev.* **75**, 246 (1949).
(Hi56)   H. A. Hill and J. M. Blair, *Phys. Rev.* **104**, 198 (1956).
(Hu52)   S. E. Hunt, *Proc. Phys. Soc.* (*London*) **65A**, 982 (1952).
(Hu60)   Hunt, Pope, Freck, and Evans, *Phys. Rev.* **120**, 1740 (1960).
(Jo54)   Jones, Douglas, McEllistrem, and Richards, *Phys. Rev.* **94**, 947 (1954).
(Jo58)   Johnson, Galonsky, and Ulrich, *Phys. Rev.* **109**, 1243 (1958).
(Jo58a)   C. H. Johnson and A. I. Galonsky, unpublished results (1958).
(Jo58b)   Jones, Lidofsky, and Weil, *Phys. Rev.* **112**, 1252 (1958).
(Ki55)   Kington, Bair, Cohn, and Willard, *Phys. Rev.* **99**, 1393 (1955).
(La58)   A. M. Lane and R. G. Thomas, *Revs. Modern Phys.* **30**, 257 (1958).
(Le57)   C. Levi and L. Papineau, *Compt. rend.* **244**, 1358 (1957).
(Lo52)   Lovington, McCue, and Preston, *Phys. Rev.* **85**, 585 (1952).
(Ma55)   Marion, Bonner, and Cook, *Phys. Rev.* **100**, 91 (1955).
(Ma55a)   Marion, Brugger, and Bonner, *Phys. Rev.* **100**, 46 (1955).
(Ma55b)   Marion, Bonner, and Cook, *Phys. Rev.* **100**, 847 (1955).
(Ma55c)   J. B. Marion, unpublished results (1955).
(Ma56)   J. B. Marion and R. W. Kavanagh, *Phys. Rev.* **104**, 107 (1956).
(Ma56a)   H. Mark and C. Goodman, *Phys. Rev.* **101**, 768 (1956).
(Ma56b)   Marion, Slattery, and Chapman, *Phys. Rev.* **103**, 676 (1956).
(Ma60)   Marion, Levesque, Ludemann, and Detenbeck, *Nucl. Instr. and Meth.* **8**, 297 (1960).
(Ma61)   J. B. Marion, *Revs. Modern Phys.* **33**, 139 (1961), and errata, **33**, 623 (1961).
(Mc51)   J. J. G. McCue and W. M. Preston, *Phys. Rev.* **84**, 384 (1951).
(Na56)   Naggiar, Roclawski-Conjeaud, Szteinsznaider, and Thirion, *Compt. rend.* **242**, 1443 (1956).
(Ne57)   Newson, Williamson, Jones, Gibbons, and Marshak, *Phys. Rev.* **108**, 1294 (1957).
(Ri50)   Richards, Smith, and Browne, *Phys. Rev.* **80**, 524 (1950).
(Ri60)   H. T. Richards, in *Nuclear Spectroscopy*, F. Ajzenberg-Selove, ed., Academic Press, New York, 1960, Part A, p. 99.
(Sa56)   R. M. Sanders, *Phys. Rev.* **104**, 1434 (1956).
(Sc52)   Schoenfeld, Duborg, Preston, and Goodman, *Phys. Rev.* **85**, 873 (1952).
(Sh49)   Shoupp, Jennings, and Sun, *Phys. Rev.* **75**, 1 (1949).
(Sl57)   Slattery, Chapman, and Bonner, *Phys. Rev.* **108**, 809 (1957).
(St57)   H. H. Staub, *Nuovo cimento Suppl.* **6**, 306 (1957).
(St60)   H. H. Staub and H. Winkler, *Nucl. Phys.* **17**, 271 (1960).
(Ta48)   R. F. Taschek and A. Hemmendinger, *Phys. Rev.* **74**, 373 (1948).
(Ta49)   Taschek, Argo, Hemmendinger, and Jarvis, *Phys. Rev.* **76**, 325 (1949).

(To61)   J. H. Towle and B. E. F. Macefield, *Proc. Phys. Soc. (London)* **77,** 1217 (1961).

(Tr53)   C. C. Trail and C. H. Johnson, *Phys. Rev.* **91,** 474(A) (1953).

(We57)   Weil, Jones, and Lidofsky, *Phys. Rev.* **108,** 800 (1957).

(Wi48)   E. P. Wigner, *Phys. Rev.* **73,** 1002 (1948).

(Wi51)   H. B. Willard and W. M. Preston, *Phys. Rev.* **81,** 480 (1951).

(Wi60)   Williamson, Katman, and Burton, *Phys. Rev.* **117,** 1325 (1960).

(Wi60a)   Willard, Bair, and Cohn, private communication (1960).

Neutron Spectroscopy

J. M. CALVERT AND A. A. JAFFE

The Physical Laboratories, University of Manchester, England

1. Introduction

The accurate analysis of a neutron energy spectrum presents a difficult experimental problem. None of the many methods available for the spectroscopy of charged particles is directly applicable. On the other hand, neutron spectroscopy can lead to much desirable information. One important application is in the study of those nuclear reactions where the outgoing particle is a neutron. When, as is generally the case, the reaction leads to more than one level of the final nucleus, it is essential to separate the reaction products into their component energies so that the properties of the individual neutron groups may be studied and information obtained about the individual levels involved. Neutron spectra may also be of great practical value as, for example, that of the fast neutrons emitted as a result of nuclear fission, since such information may be essential in the design of some types of nuclear reactors.

Many ingenious neutron spectrometers are available and the most important of these have already been described in this volume in some detail. However, because of their complicated nature, neutron spectrometers cannot be expected to be as versatile as charged particle spectrometers. Less latitude is therefore available in the choice of an instrument for any specific purpose and it is important to select somewhat carefully the type of instrument which gives the best compromise between the various properties required.

Generally, a spectrometer is required to produce a spectrum of resolved neutron groups with an efficiency which is as high as practicable from the design and which is a known function of the neutron energy. Not all spectrometers have this last feature but with those that do, it is possible to measure differential cross sections in reactions giving rise to neutrons. The analysis of such data is valuable in that it gives information on nuclear levels which may not be available from other sources, or it helps to confirm and supplement data obtained by other means.

2. Comparison of Experimental Methods

A. Requirements for Neutron Spectroscopy

(1) **Energy Resolution and Energy Measurement.** It is unnecessary to stress the importance of good energy resolution in the investigation of nuclear reactions; it is clearly required both for the separation of closely spaced groups and also it is essential for the accurate measurement of the neutron energy. Even low-lying nuclear levels often have separations of less than 100 kev and energy resolutions of 0.1 per cent or better could be regularly used.

Neutron spectrometers are conspicuous for their low counting rates and spectra are often obtained with poor statistics so that the deterioration in accuracy of neutron energy measurements with decreasing energy resolution is particularly marked. For example, if an instrument has a spectral line which is approximately Gaussian or triangular in shape having a width at half-height of ΔE, and consisting of a total of N recorded particles, it is possible to show that the accuracy with which its energy may be found by comparison with a similar calibration line is limited by statistical considerations alone to $\Delta E/\sqrt{N}$. Similarly, poor counting statistics may reduce the spectrometer's effective energy resolution. The latter might usefully be expressed as

$$\delta E = \Delta E[1 + \sqrt{2}(N_1^{-1/2} + N_2^{-1/2})] \qquad (1)$$

where N_1 and N_2 are the number of particles recorded in two adjacent groups. This may be written as

$$\delta E = \Delta E\{1 + (2/N)^{1/2}[(1 + \lambda^{-1})^{1/2} + (1 + \lambda)^{1/2}]\} \qquad (2)$$

where $N_1 + N_2 = N$, the total number of particles in the two groups and λ is the ratio of their intensities.[1]

[1] The authors are grateful to M. B. Priestley of the Statistical Laboratory, University of Manchester, for useful discussions on this subject.

(2) **Efficiency.** As stated above, the efficiency of a spectrometer may affect its energy resolution in practice if it results in poor counting statistics. In addition, there is often an instrumental connection between the two which has the opposite effect. For example, in time-of-flight spectrometers, increasing the flight path to improve resolution results in reduced efficiency. In proton recoil spectrometers with hydrogenous radiators, variation of the radiator thickness has the same effect.

If a spectrometer is capable of recording a large range of energies simultaneously, this will, in some applications, compensate for low efficiency. High intrinsic efficiency may be limited in practice by the labor and delay in analyzing results, as in the case of photographic emulsions.

(3) **Angular Distribution Measurements.** The value of such measurements will be described below. Only the photographic plate method has so far been used for simultaneous recording of neutrons at several angles, thus eliminating the difficulties of monitoring the incident beam. This apparent advantage is, however, negated by the poor accuracy with which even relative intensities may be measured from the plates. The economy in machine running time may also be outweighed by the subsequent lengthy analysis required. Other types of spectrometers, while requiring repeated exposure at different angles, are usually preferable for this purpose.

(4) **Measurement of Absolute and Relative Intensities.** This subject will be discussed in Sections 4 and 5 of this article. The ease with which intensity measurements can be made may be an important factor in the choice of spectrometer.

B. Summary of Experimental Techniques

Up to the present time, all neutron spectrometers have been based on one of two principles. The first is the measurement of the energy for detection of recoil particles after elastic scattering (usually n-p scattering). The second is the determination of the energies of the charged particles produced when the neutrons under investigation are made to undergo some specific nuclear reaction. Techniques representing all the major variations of these principles are listed in Table I in order to summarize and compare their performance.

Single proportional counters have not been included since they have not been used in the analysis of complex spectra (for which they

Table I. Performance of Fast Neutron Spectrometers

Type	Resolution	Efficiency	Useful energy range (Mev)
Time of flight	3.5% at 0.5 Mev 14% at 140 Mev	2×10^{-5}	0.5–140
Photographic plates [n-p scattering]	3% at 14 Mev (0.5 Mev constant half-width over fairly large range)	—	0.5–15
Photographic plates with external radiator [n-p scattering]	2% at 14 Mev (0.3 Mev half-width)	Very low below 2 Mev	2–20
Li⁶-loaded plates [Li⁶(n, t)He⁴ reaction]	0.2 Mev half-width	—	0–1.3
He³ proportional counter [He³(n, p)T reaction]	15% at 0.5 Mev 8% at 2.0 Mev		
Low pressure cloud chamber [n-p recoils in H₂]	0.2 Mev half-width	—	0.5–3.5
High pressure cloud chamber [n-p recoils in methane]	0.2 Mev half-width	—	2–8.5
Proportional counter telescope with radiator and absorbers	5% at 15 Mev	—	2.5–20

Table I (continued)

Method of recording and analyzing results	Remarks	Chapter ref.
Delay to pulse-height conversion combined with a multichannel pulse-height analyzer	Flight-paths vary between 0.5 and 26 meters	V.Q.
Measurement of recoil track length and three angles for each neutron counted.	Suitable for simultaneous exposure at several angles. Analysis extremely laborious. Difficult to find high energy neutrons amongst low energy background. Poor intensity measurement.	II.D
Measurement of recoil proton track lengths in emulsion.	More accurate absolute and relative intensity measurements than with plates alone.	II.D
Range of α and t and angle between is measured for each $Li^6(n, t)He^4$ event.	It is not necessary for incident neutrons to be collimated or to come from known direction.	II.D
Pulse-height analysis.	Background from (a) tritium impurities in He^3, (b) slow neutron capture, (c) He^3 recoils from high energy neutrons.	III.C
Measurement of length and direction of recoil proton tracks from cloud chamber photographs.		II.E
Integral range spectrum counted.		II.C

(continued)

Table I. Performance of Fast Neutron Spectrometers

Type	Resolution	Efficiency	Useful energy range (Mev)
Holt-Litherland triple ionization chamber. Time of arrival of ions from end of proton recoil track	5%	10^{-9}	5–25
Single Anthracene crystal	0.4 Mev	High	1–3
Li^{6}I(Eu) crystal [Li$^6(n, t)$He^4 reaction]	6% at 14 Mev	up to 10^{-3}	1–20
Recoil telescope with radiator. Collimated *n-p* recoils passing through two proportional counters into NaI crystal	6% at 14 Mev	3×10^{-9} at 14 Mev	2–20
Scintillation counter telescope. Proton recoils from anthracene passing through proportional counter into NaI crystal	6%	6×10^{-8} at 20 Mev	5–25
Scintillation counter spectrometer. Measurement of recoil proton energy and detection of recoil neutron at specific angle	20–28%	Very low	2–15

are not really suited); such devices are chiefly employed in the measurement of fast neutron fluxes rather than as differential spectrometers (see Chapter II.A).

The most difficult property to compare is the spectrometer efficiency since this may depend, for a given instrument, on the particular experiment. For instance, time-of-flight spectrometers

Table I (continued)

Method of recording and analyzing results	Remarks	Chapter ref.
Analysis of photographic record of oscillograph sweeps.	Only part of energy range may be studied at any given chamber pressure (range of 5 Mev or less in neutron energies). Resolution is not affected by high γ-ray backgrounds.	II.C
Multichannel pulse-height analysis giving integral spectrum.		II.B
Pulse-height analysis	No collimation required. For good resolution the crystal must be cooled to the temperature of liquid nitrogen.	III.B
Pulses from NaI crystal in coincidence with proportional counters are analyzed on multichannel analyzer.		II.C
NaI and anthracene pulse heights simultaneously recorded when in coincidence with proportional counter. Spectrum analyzed from film record.	Also used with anthracene as second crystal.	II.C
Pulse-height analysis of pulses from scintillator which are in coincidence with detected recoil neutron.		II.B

could have efficiencies approaching 100 per cent for a perfectly collimated beam of neutrons. The efficiencies quoted in Table I are therefore estimates of the fraction, which would be detected, of the total number of neutrons from a reasonably small source radiating uniformly in all directions. It is hoped that this will provide a useful basis for comparison in most applications.

It will be seen that photographic emulsions, particularly when used with external radiators, provide the best energy resolution in the analysis of complex spectra. It appears possible that they will eventually be superceded in this respect by improved time-of-flight spectrometers. It is often suggested that neutron spectra from nuclear reactions may best be determined with high resolution by measuring the energies of the resultant charged particles rather than that of the neutrons themselves. Although this has been attempted in the case of the $D(d, n)He^3$ and $T(d, n)He^4$ reactions, the high rate of energy loss of the recoiling nucleus makes the method difficult even with the lightest target nuclei. [The C^{13} recoils from the reaction $C^{12} (d, p)C^{13}$ has been observed by Kavanagh and Barnes using a 180° magnetic spectrometer (Ka58).]

3. Neutron Energy Spectra and Determination of Nuclear Energy Levels

A. Fast Neutrons from Fission

The importance of accurate knowledge of the spectra of fission neutrons in nuclear reactor design is obvious. The U^{235} spectrum has been investigated thoroughly and the earlier work on this subject is reviewed by Bonner et al. (Bo52). These authors determined the spectrum in the range from 0.05 to 0.7 Mev from measurements of recoil proton tracks in a hydrogen-filled cloud chamber. The fission neutrons were produced by placing a 0.10-inch thick U^{235} foil in a beam from the thermal column of the Los Alamos Water Boiler reactor (Fig. 1). Hill (Hi52) extended the spectrum up to about 7 Mev by means of a proportional counter telescope employing the absorber-range-measurement technique. The fraction of neutrons above 7 Mev is small and, in order to obtain higher thermal neutron fluxes, Watt (Wa52) inserted the U^{235} sample into the reactor, collimating the emergent fast neutrons with graphite and wood. A proportional counter telescope with interchangeable radiators of different thicknesses enabled the spectrum to be followed with significant intensity up to 17 Mev.

Watt has combined his results with those of Hill and Bonner et al., and they yield an excellent fit to a semi-empirical formula (Fig. 2) which indicates a distribution of energies in the center-of-mass

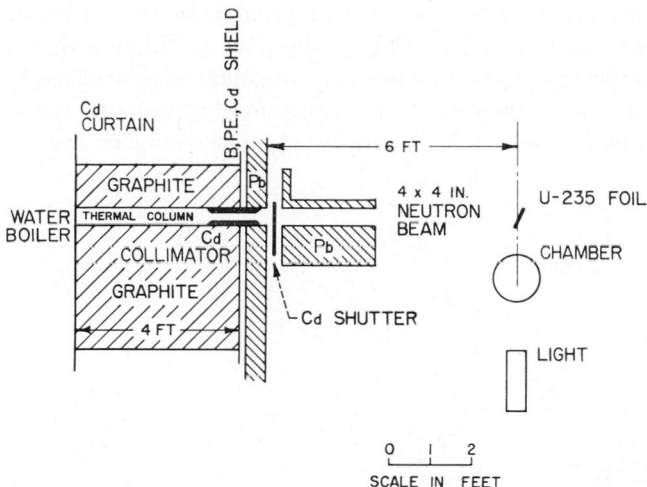

Figure 1. Measurement of the fission neutron spectrum in the range 0.05 to 0.7 Mev (Bo52).

system of the form $N(E)dE \propto \sqrt{E}\exp(-E/T)dE$ corresponding to an effective nuclear temperature of about 1.00 Mev for the fission fragments. This interpretation is not rigorous since no account is taken of the distribution of kinetic energies and masses of the fragments.

More recently, Cranberg *et al.* (Cr56) have redetermined the U^{235} spectrum, using different methods designed to provide an independent check on previous work and to reduce room background for energies below 2 Mev. The range from 0.18 to 2.7 Mev was covered by a time-of-flight spectrometer. Thermal neutrons were produced in a narrow cone by "tickling the threshold" of the Li^7-$(p, n)Be^7$ reaction and background in the fission neutron detector could be kept small without shielding by placing it outside the direct thermal neutron beam. Fissions, taking place in a spiral chamber, give the zero time pulse and the time of flight is measured by the arrival of a pulse from proton recoil in a plastic scintillator 50 cm away. From 0.35 to 12 Mev photographic plates were employed, care being taken to reduce the effect of background by minimizing sources of scattering and by making background exposures with a polythene absorber between the U^{235} foil and the plates. The results are in good agreement with those described above and can be fitted by the same relation, though with slightly different parameters.

The theory of the emission of prompt neutrons from fission is discussed by Leachman (Le56) who has calculated the expected neutron spectrum assuming isotropic angular emission of the neutrons. The best fit with the experimental results is again found for a nuclear temperature $T = 1.0$ Mev and discrepancies may be accounted for

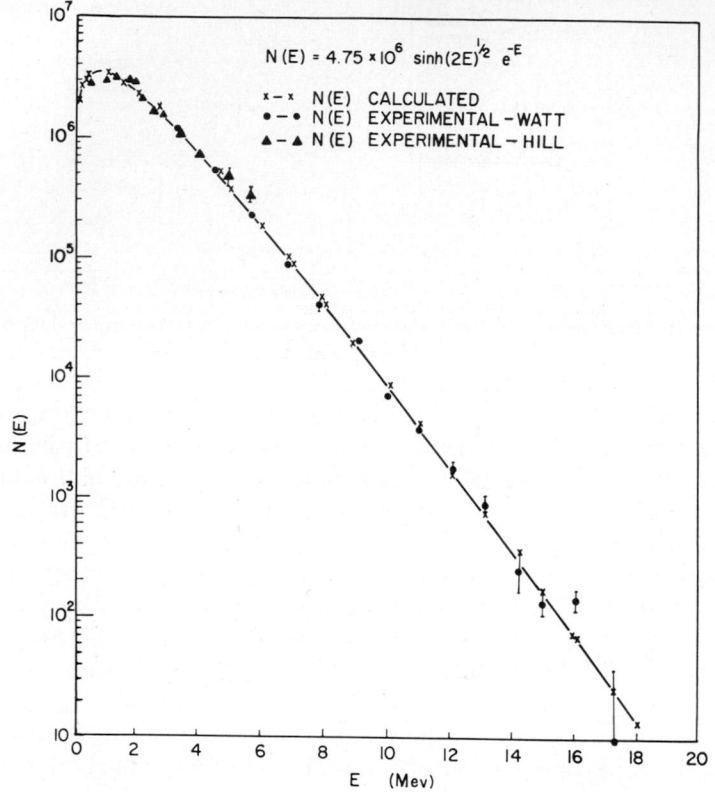

Figure 2. The spectrum of neutrons from U^{235} fission (Wa52).

by the expected preferential emission along the direction of motion of the fragment. The value of T, so found, is in poor agreement with the value 1.4 Mev which is obtained from $(n, 2n)$ excitation functions. The calculated fission spectrum is insensitive to the incident neutron energy; the difference in shape, for thermal neutrons and those with 3.0 Mev kinetic energy is slight.

B. The D(d, n)He³ and T(d, n)He⁴ Reactions

The reaction D(d, n)He³ first reported by Oliphant *et al.* (Ol34) has been intensively studied; it is of great importance as a readily available source of monoenergetic neutrons of known energy in the range from 2 Mev upwards (see Chapter I.C). The Q-value is thus of practical interest, and it may also be used to determine the mass of the He³ nucleus.

From the ranges of proton recoil tracks in a methane-filled cloud chamber, with a bombarding deuteron energy of 500 kev, Bonner (Bo41) found a Q-value of 3.31 ± 0.03 Mev. From this the He³ mass was calculated to be 3.01698 ± 0.00006 mass units. Later work by Livesey and Wilkinson (Li49), Dyer and Bird (Dy53), and Subotic and Maglic (Su55) using photographic plates, is in good agreement with this result, as is that of Bischel *et al.* (Bi52).

Greater accuracy is claimed, however, for methods in which the energy of the He³ recoils, rather than that of the neutrons, is measured. Argo (Ar48) observed He³ recoils at 90° to the direction of deuteron beams of up to about 330 kev incident on D₂O ice targets, with a 15-cm radius electrostatic analyzer capable of a resolution of 2 per cent. Thick and intermediate targets were used and the

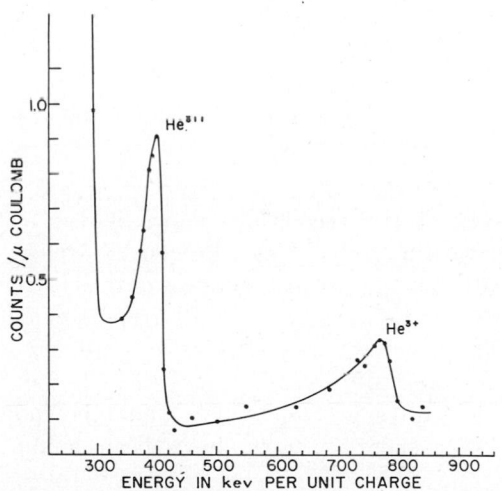

Figure 3. Spectrum of He³ recoils at 90° from D(d, n)He³, from 330-kev deuterons on D₂O ice target (Ar48).

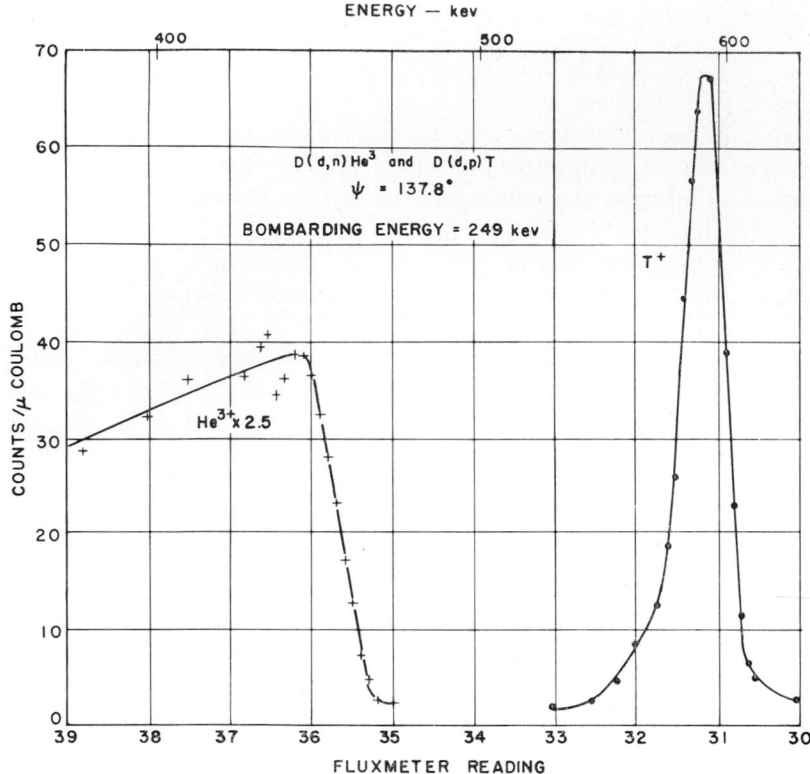

Figure 4. He³ recoils spectrum at 137.8° from D(d, n)He³ by magnetic analysis (To49).

resultant spectra of He³ recoils are shown in Fig. 3. The recoils were detected with a twelve-stage electron multiplier. Argo found $Q = 3.30 \pm 0.01$ Mev. Magnetic analysis of the He³ recoils emerging in the angular range 134.5° to 141.1° with respect to a deuteron beam of about 250 kev which was monoenergetic to 0.1 per cent was made by Tollestrup *et al.* (To49); see Fig. 4.

No excited states in He³, which would be indicated by the presence of lower energy groups, have been found through this reaction.

Another example in which analysis of the recoiling charged nucleus may lead to the most accurate determination of neutron energy, is that of the $T(d, n)He^4$ reaction; this reaction is a useful source of high energy neutrons.

Using photographic plates with an external radiator, Rosen (Ro53) found a Q-value of 17.7 ± 0.3 Mev. No neutron groups corresponding to excited states in He^4 were observed. Williamson *et al.* (Wi51) bombarded thin tritium targets prepared on zirconium backings, investigating the recoiling He^4 nuclei. They determined the position of the high energy edge of the recoils, using an electrostatic analyzer, finding a lower limit of 17.578 ± 0.030 Mev for the $T(d, n)$ Q-value; Mazari *et al.* (Ma57) find the value 17.580 ± 0.025 Mev from magnetic analysis. For excitation functions and angular distributions of these reactions, see the article by Brolley and Fowler (Chapter I.C).

C. Nuclear Energy Levels

(1) **Introduction.** The excitation energies of many nuclear levels have been found by the threshold detection technique, though this can only be used for reactions with negative Q-values (see Chapter V.O). Direct analysis of neutron groups has been employed in many cases and is often essential for the observation of low-lying levels and also when additional information is to be obtained by angular distribution or absolute cross section measurements.

Neutron spectra, indicating discrete excited states, have been found using protons, deuterons, tritons, He^3 particles, and α particles as bombarding particles producing nuclear reactions and, more recently, from inelastically scattered neutrons. Until now, deuteron reactions have proved the most interesting. This is partly because they often allow a direct comparison between corresponding states in mirror nuclei or isotopic spin multiplets if the (d, p) reaction has also been performed on the same target nucleus (as it usually has). The theory of deuteron stripping, which has proved successful, enables a ready interpretation of the results to be made. A review of such reactions, including a discussion of the methods of analyzing the results will be given in Sections 5 and 6. In this section, only the identification and energy measurement of the states will be considered and this will be done with the aim of giving examples only rather than a definitive list, since a complete bibliography of all nuclear reactions is readily available (Wa55, En57, Aj59).

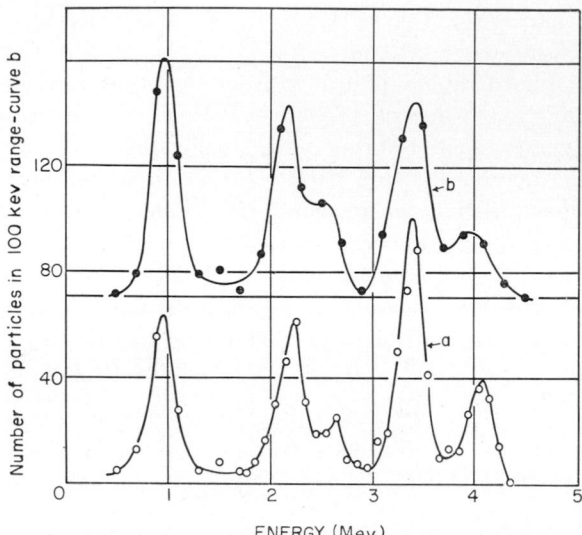

Figure 5.   Spectra of neutrons at 100° from the reaction Be⁹(d, n) for 500-kev deuteron bombarding energy, (a) photographic plate measurements; (b) cloud chamber measurements (Po42).

While neutron spectroscopy is often used as a method of supplementing information about levels which may be observed in several nuclear reactions, there are many low-lying levels which have only been observed by spectroscopy of out-going neutrons, since the choice of available target material and bombarding particles is limited. Such levels occur, for example, in C^{10}, C^{11}, C^{12}, O^{15}, Al^{25}, Si^{28}, etc. and have been observed using the (d, n) reaction at such excitations that it is equivalent to adding a proton of negative kinetic energy to the target nucleus.   [Since this article was prepared, some of these levels have also been observed in reactions induced by Mass-3 particles.]

(2) (d, n), (p, n), (α, n), and (He³, n) **Reactions.**   The first application of the photographic plate recoil proton technique to fast neutron spectroscopy was made by Powell (Po42) who investigated the Be⁹(d, n)B¹⁰ reaction with 500-kev deuterons and the F^{19}(d, n)-Ne^{20} reaction at 900 kev.   The results for the Be⁹ (d, n) spectrum, taken at 100° with respect to the incident deuteron beam, are in good agreement with previous work by Staub and Stephens (St39) and by

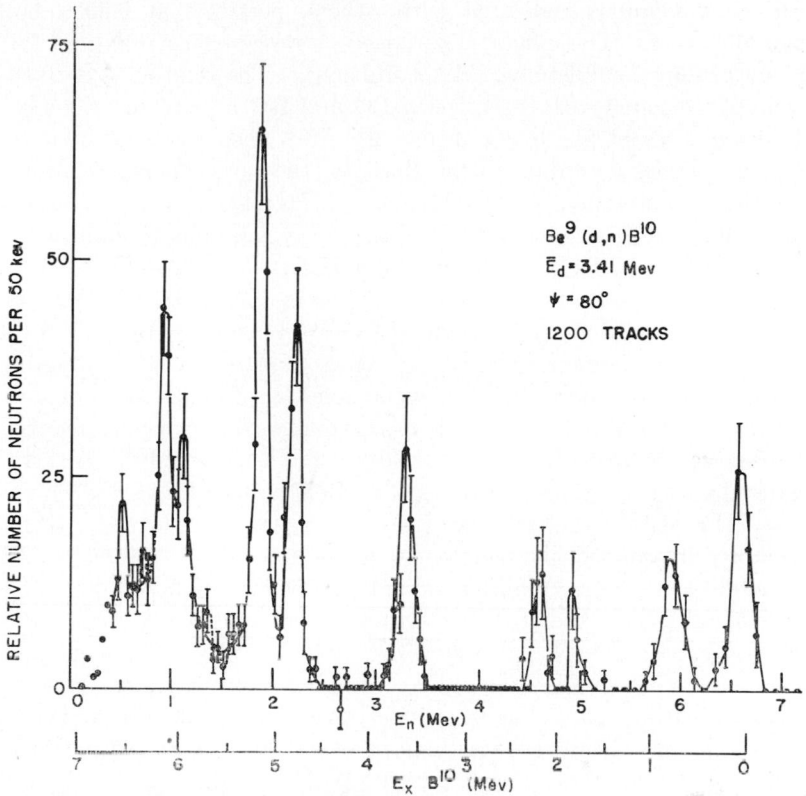

Figure 6.   Spectrum obtained using photographic plates of neutrons leading to states in B[10] (Aj51).

Bonner and Brubaker (Bo35) who investigated this reaction by measurements of recoil tracks in cloud chambers containing helium or ethane.   Powell found five neutron groups and somewhat better resolution was obtained than by the cloud chamber method (see Fig. 5).   These F^{19} (d, n) results were also found to be in agreement with previous cloud chamber spectra by Bonner (Bo40).   More recent work by Ajzenberg (Aj51) shows great improvement in resolution (Fig. 6), probably through the use of thinner targets and higher and more stable bombarding beam energies.   Figure 6 shows the results of an investigation of the $Be^9(d, n)B^{10}$ reaction;   excited states in B^{10} at 0.77, 1.79, 2.22, 3.59, 4.79, 5.12, 6.11, 6.57, and 6.81

Mev are definitely indicated with others, possibly, at 5.58, 5.68, and 6.38 Mev. These figures are based on range-energy relations for recoil protons for Eastman NTA emulsions. The relation is derived from points found with the $Li^7(p, n)Be^7$ and $Be^9(p, n)B^9$ reactions by Johnson et al. (Jo50, Jo50a) below 2.5 Mev and is extrapolated to higher energies according to the shape of the range-energy relations for Ilford emulsions given by Lattes et al. (La47). (For a detailed account of the measurement of range-energy relations in emulsions, see the article by R. S. White, Chapter II.D.)

Confirmation of the observed states in B^{10} up to 4.79 Mev is provided by inelastic proton and deuteron scattering (Bo53, Br53), indicating an average accuracy of about 30 kev in the measured neutron energies; no additional levels have been found in this region. Above about 5 Mev the level spacing is smaller than can conveniently be resolved by fast neutron spectroscopy but may readily be investigated by neutron threshold detection (Bo54).

The above account clearly shows that nuclear levels may be reliably determined by neutron spectroscopy alone, although the possibility of missing *multiplet* structure because of poor resolution cannot be overlooked. Hence, studies such as $B^{10}(d, n)C^{11}$, B^{11} $(d, n)C^{12}$, $C^{13}(d, n)N^{14}$, $N^{14}(d, n)O^{15}$, and $Mg^{24}(d, n)Al^{25}$ which, in fact, have all been investigated by the photographic emulsion technique must be regarded as of special importance (Pe49, Jo52, Be53, Ev53, Go53). Excited states in K^{41}, observed *only* in the reaction $A^{40}(d, n)K^{41}$ were found by Worth (Wo50) using a proportional counter telescope-absorber technique.

Similar results may also be obtained from (p, n) or (α, n) reactions, though the latter generally have negative Q-values so that the threshold detection technique may be used even for the low-lying final states.[2] Levels in C^{10} which is the member of the $A = 10$ triad having isotopic spin $T = -1$, have been determined by Ajzenberg and Franzen (Aj54) from $B^{10}(p, n)C^{10}$; in Cr^{51} from V^{51} (p, n) by Stelson et al. (St50); in S^{31} from P^{31} (p, n) by Rubin et al. (Ru56); again, photographic plates were used in all cases.

Neutron spectra from the reactions $B^{10}(\alpha, n)N^{13}$, $B^{11}(\alpha, n)N^{14}$, $F^{19}(\alpha, n)Na^{22}$, and $P^{31}(\alpha, n)Cl^{34}$ have been observed by Quinton and Doyle (Qu56, Do56), and from the reaction $Be^9(\alpha, n)C^{12}$ by Risser

---

[2] Difficulties associated with threshold measurements in (α, n) reactions are discussed in Chapter V.O.

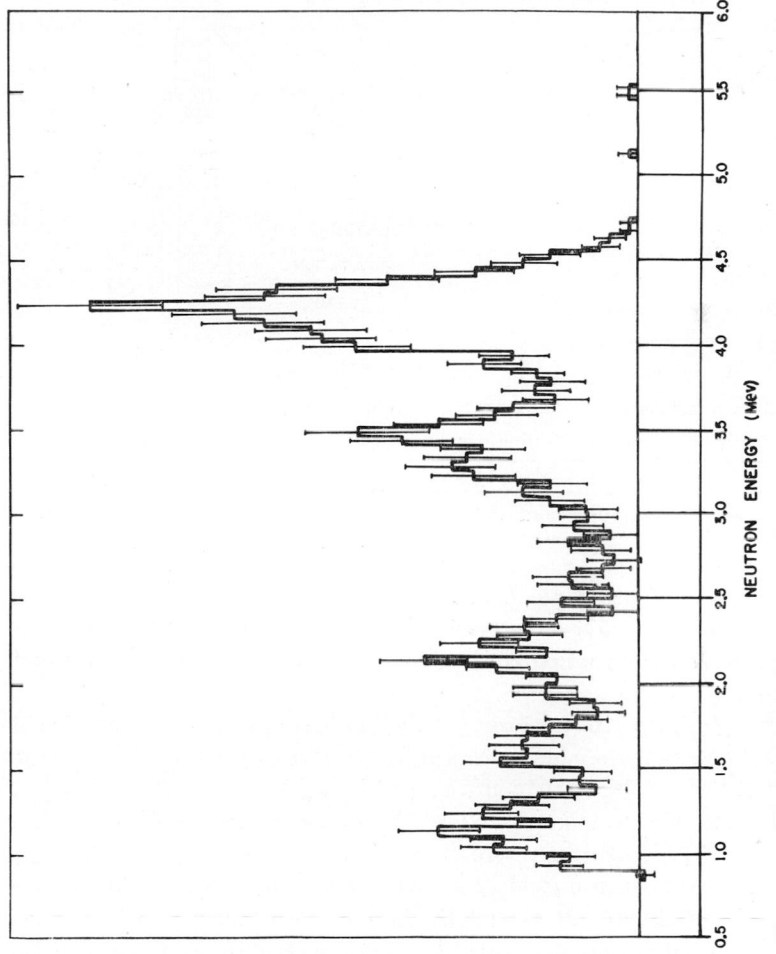

Figure 7.   Elastic and inelastic groups from scattering of 4.4-Mev neutrons by Fe^{56} (We56).

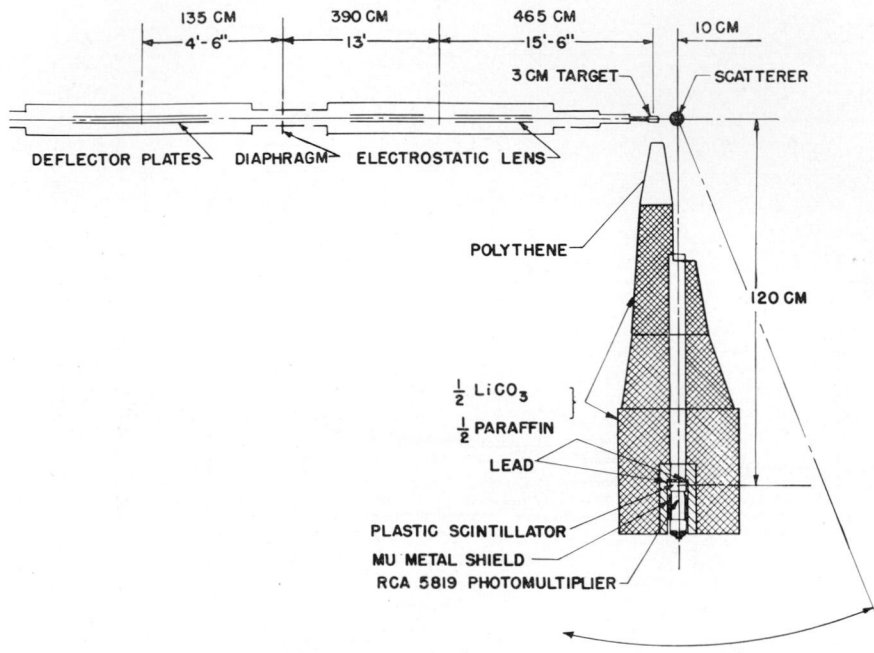

Figure 8. Beam-pulser and detector for time-of-flight neutron spectroscopy (Cr56a).

et al. (Ri57) using recoil proton telescopes. Recently, Ajzenberg-Selove *et al.* (Aj57) have resolved neutron groups from the reaction $B^{10}(He^3, n)N^{12}$ at a bombarding energy of 2.5 Mev, with photographic plates.

(3) (n, n') **Reactions.** Resolved groups of inelastically scattered neutrons were first successfully observed by Stelson and Preston (St52) who collimated neutrons of about 1.9 Mev from $Li^7(p, n)$ with paraffin and borax and scattered them from an iron target. The scattered neutrons were analyzed using photographic plates and an inelastic neutron group corresponding to an excited state in Fe^{56} was definitely present, though the intensity was fairly weak. Weddell *et al.* (We56, Je55) subsequently found several excited states in Fe^{56} from the photographic plate spectrum of inelastically scattered neutrons of 4.4 Mev incident energy (Fig. 7).

Great improvement in counting statistics has been achieved by Cranberg and Levin (Cr56a) with a time-of-flight spectrometer of

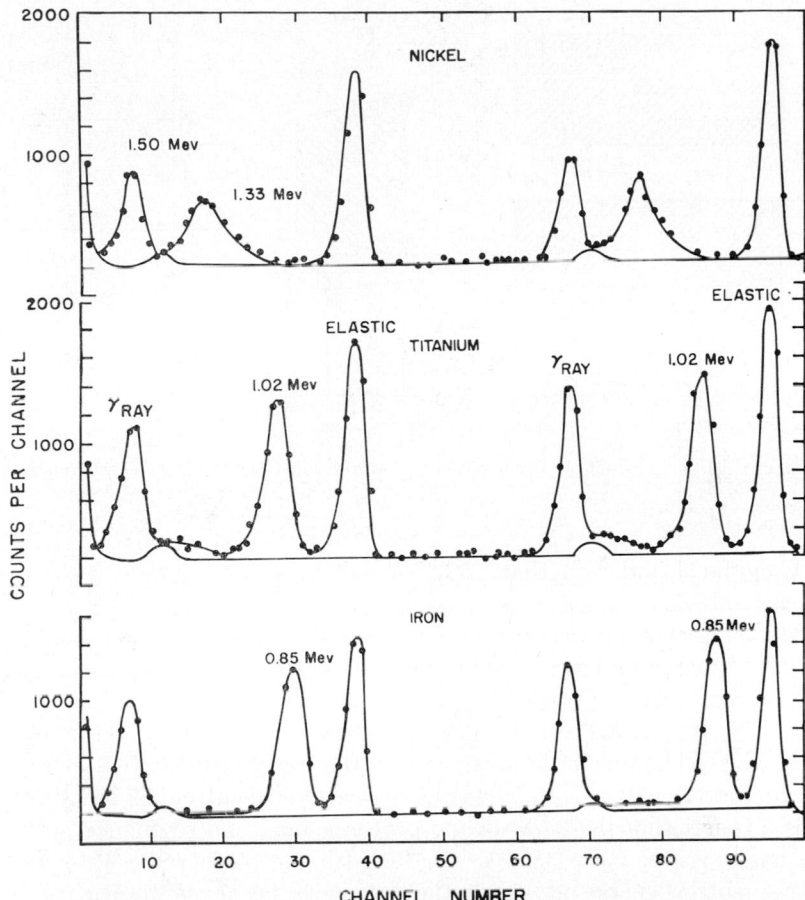

Figure 9.   Spectra found by time-of-flight measurements of scattering of 2.45-
Mev neutrons by nickel, titanium, and iron (Cr56a).

1.2–1.5 m flight path. Monoenergetic 2.45-Mev neutrons are
obtained from the $T(p, n)$ reaction with a pulsed proton beam.   Many
low-lying levels have thus been observed in nuclei from F^{19} to U^{235}
(see Figs. 8 and 9).

   (4) **Resonant Scattering Techniques.**   Low-lying states in
medium and heavy nuclei are difficult to observe by the threshold
detection technique since the cross sections are often very small near
the neutron threshold, even with negative ground state Q-values.

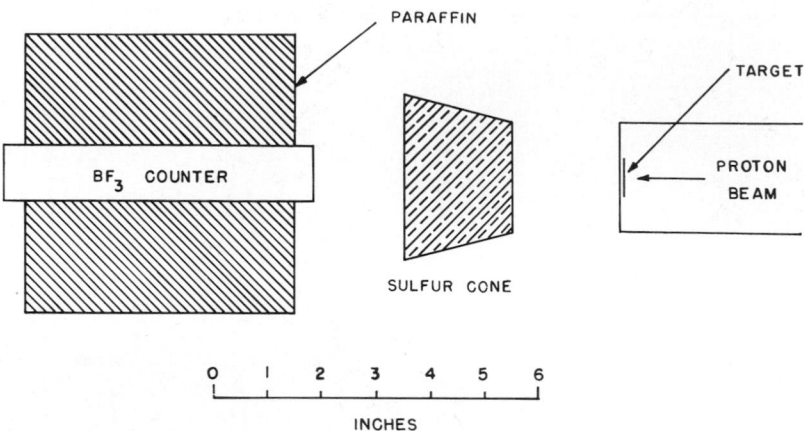

Figure 10. Experimental arrangement for resonant scattering measurements (Ma56).

A method similar to that of threshold detection, namely those of resonant scattering, has been used in the investigation of (p, n) reactions in medium-weight nuclei. The method depends on the selection of materials having large and well separated resonances in the total neutron cross section.

Stelson and Preston (St51) proposed the use of Li, Be, and S for this technique and investigated the reactions $Mn^{55}(p, n)Fe^{55}$ and $Be^9 (p, n)B^9$. The intensity of scattered neutrons is measured as a function of the bombarding proton energy and resonance peaks (sometimes as sharp as 4 kev half-width) are observed. Provided the neutron energy at which the resonance occurs is known (or is determined by a separate experiment using a monoenergetic neutron-producing reaction of known Q) the Q-value leading to ground and excited states may be found to within about 10 kev. Marion and Chapman (Ma56) used resonances in sulfur and beryllium at 585 kev and 620 kev respectively. With the arrangement shown in Fig. 10 they investigated the low lying levels in Zn^{65} by the reaction Cu^{65} $(p, n)Zn^{65}$, revealing an excited state at 118 ± 8 kev. The resonance curve with the Be scatterer is shown in Fig. 11. The sulfur scatterer which was used to find the ground state Q-value and to search for levels up to about 90 kev, was replaced by beryllium for higher bombarding energies since a second higher resonance exists in sulfur at

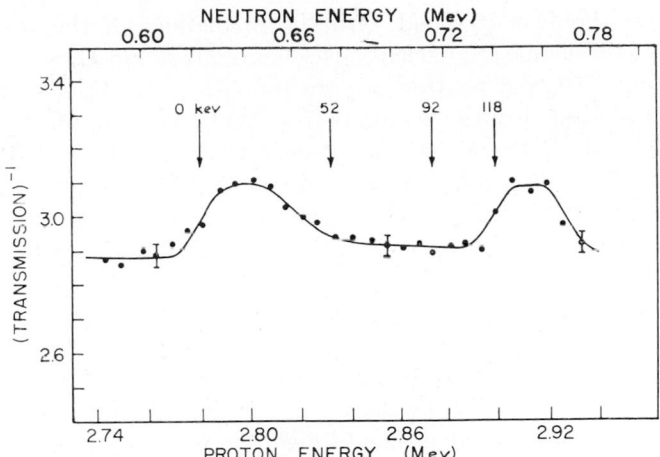

Figure 11. Results for resonant scattering of neutrons from $Cu^{65}(p, n)Zn^{65}$ showing an excited state in Zn^{65} at 118 kev (Ma56).

680 kev through which the ground state neutrons would pass, masking neutron groups of lower energy.

Threshold detection using resonant scattering has been further improved by Evans et al. (Ev59) and by Lee and Mooring (Le59). Instead of using only a single detector to measure the scattered neutrons, an additional detector is employed to measure the neutron flux transmitted through the scatterer. A plot of the ratio of the counting rates as a function of the bombarding energy is then made and resonant scattering of neutrons is indicated by peaks in the curve.

Using this technique, Ferguson and Paul (Fe59) have used the 258-kev resonance in Li^7 to investigate the energy levels of A^{37}, Sc^{48}, and Cr^{51} by the (p, n) reactions induced in targets of Cl^{37}, Ca^{48}, and V^{51}. Energy resolutions of better than 50 kev are attainable using this method.

D. Continuous Spectra

When large numbers of closely-spaced levels are excited in out-going neutron reactions and the neutron spectrum is observed with a resolution of a few per cent, individual levels cannot be distinguished but an apparently continuous spectrum is recorded. At fairly high bombarding energies with the heavier nuclei the observed spectrum should correspond with the predictions of the statistical model of the compound nucleus (see Chapters V.J and V.N).

Gugelot found neutron spectra from (p, n) reactions with 16-Mev protons on a range of targets from Be to Tl using photographic plates (Gu51). Above 2 Mev the spectra have the form $n(E)dE \propto E \exp(-E/T)dE$ where E is the observed neutron energy and T is a constant depending on the target nucleus. T is identified with the statistical model nuclear temperature, though the values found are lower than those predicted by Weisskopf (We37). The photographic plate technique has also been applied to the scattering of 14-Mev neutrons by Graves and Rosen (Gr53) who obtained spectra with numerous targets from carbon to bismuth having the above shape in the range $0.5 < E < 4.0$ Mev. Similar results have been found by O'Neill (ON54) using a time-of-flight spectrometer and 14.8-Mev neutrons from the $\mathrm{T}(d, n)\mathrm{He}^4$ reaction. The He^4 recoils were detected at a specific angle to give a zero-time pulse and to "collimate" the incident neutron beam. Continuous spectra of inelastically scattered neutrons of 2.45 Mev incident energy on bismuth and gold are given by Cranberg and Levin (Cr56a).

4. Measurements of Cross Sections

A. General Requirements

One of the important applications of a fast neutron spectrometer is in the measurement of cross sections of nuclear processes in which a neutron is one of the outgoing particles, e.g. (p, n), (d, n), (α, n), and (n, n') reactions. All such determinations depend on the measurement of four factors: (a) the intensity of the incident particles, (b) the nuclear density of the target, (c) the efficiency of the neutron detector and (d) the angular distribution of the neutrons.

Measurement of the first two factors is discussed elsewhere in this volume (see Chapter IV.D). The third factor is discussed here while the fourth is considered in detail in the next section.

The efficiency of most neutron spectrometers in use at present is extremely low (see Table I). Moreover, it is generally related to the resolution in such a way that increased efficiency can only be obtained at the expense of resolution, so it is usual to effect a compromise between the two. The efficiency can usually be determined with higher precision when the design giving the highest resolution is chosen. This follows from the reasons indicated below.

Neutrons leaving the target or source are observed by a primary process in what is essentially a *radiator*. This need not necessarily be thin as in the recoil telescope (Mo52, Jo56) but may be extensive as in the case of gas-filled counters or emulsions (see Chapter II.A, II.C, and II.D). The charged particles from the primary process are detected by their ionization or its effects. Thus the efficiency of detection depends on (a) the solid angle subtended at the source of neutrons by the radiator ω_r; (b) the collision cross section for producing a charged particle σ; and (c) the efficiency of detection of these charged particles, η. This latter factor will mainly be determined by geometry in an instrument but is in some cases also dependent on the process of energy selection; e.g., in the spectrometer of Calvert, Jaffe, and Maslin (Ca55), recoil protons within a certain solid angle are only recorded *provided* they give pulses above a prescribed level in a scintillation counter.

In principle the precision of cross-section measurements in neutron spectroscopy is limited by the accuracy of the scattering data (σ, the second factor above). In practice, the errors of measurement are usually governed rather by the uncertainty in the first and third factors. Usually it is the instrument of high resolution (and therefore of low efficiency) in which these factors can be determined with high precision.

Until recently, there were very few absolute measurements of cross sections in fast neutron spectroscopy, generally because of the unknown efficiency of detection, but most methods have given relative cross sections for the neutron groups in complex spectra.

B. Measurements of Cross Sections with Nuclear Emulsions

The nuclear emulsion, one of the oldest methods of neutron spectroscopy, has been applied in many cases for measuring relative cross sections (Aj51, Ev53, Go53, Mi53, El57), but in only very few instances so far, for absolute measurements (Ro53, Mi55; see also Chapter II.D).

Relative measurements of differential cross sections are made by simultaneous exposure of plates at set angles over the range under investigation. A typical arrangement used by Middleton *et al.* (Mi53) is shown in Fig. 12.

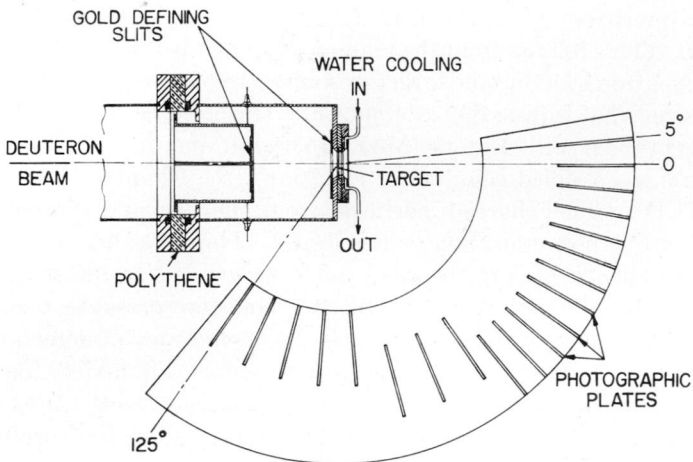

Figure 12.   Experimental arrangement, using photographic plates, for observing angular distribution of neutrons from (d, n) reactions (Mi53).

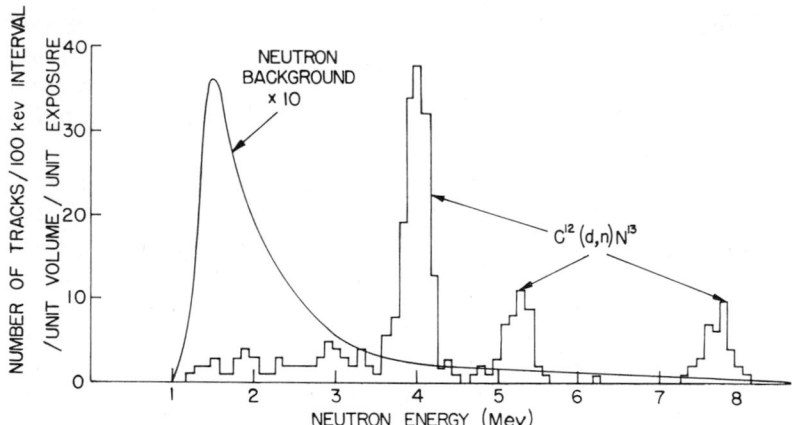

Figure 13.   Neutron groups from $C^{12}(d, n)N^{13}$ (Mi53).

A criterion of selection of recoil protons has to be adopted and usually only those tracks within a few degrees of the direction of incidence of the neutrons are accepted.   Knowing the volume of emulsion scanned on each plate, relative cross sections can be calculated.   It is an assumption of this method that all plates have the same hydrogen content and this is achieved in practice by using plates from the same batch which presumably have the same moisture content. One drawback of this method is the difficulty of assessing the number of recoils lost from the surfaces of the emulsion since this number may form a significant fraction of the whole when using thin emulsions.

The method can be made absolute by measuring the integrated beam current during the exposure and by knowing the solid angle subtended at the source or target by the individual emulsions. Alternatively, a monitor can be used to count charged particles originating from a reaction in the target of known cross section. One source of inaccuracy is the uncertainty in the direction of the incident neutrons which is reflected in the n-p scattering cross section applied in determining the efficiency of detection. Typical histograms are shown in Fig. 13.

C. Measurements of Cross Sections with Recoil Telescopes

A number of absolute measurements of differential cross sections have been made with instruments of this type in which essentially collimated recoil protons are counted from n-p scattering in a radiator (Ca55, Ca55a, Jo56). The efficiency of detection per neutron incident on the radiator is calculated from the radiator thickness, the geometry, and the differential cross section for n-p scattering (see Chapter V.T). Since the latter factor decreases monotonically with increase of neutron energy, instruments of this type usually have a selection of radiator thicknesses chosen so as to maintain the yield at higher energies. The spectrum is usually presented in the form of a histogram, generally from a multi-channel pulse-height analyzer (Fig. 14). In assessing the counts in a given group, attention must be paid to the line shape and to the background. These two are not completely separable. The background which may arise from chance coincidences or recoils from sources other than the radiator is usually assessed by a blank run, i.e., a measurement with no radiator in place. In such a measurement, Johnson and Trail (Jo56) found in examining the spectrum of the $T(d, n)He^4$ reaction (a single group of neutrons) that the background amounted to 6 per cent of the integrated peak. (This was with apparatus carefully redesigned after finding a value of 25 per cent when using a housing and radiator holders of aluminium.) This fraction was spread uniformly over the

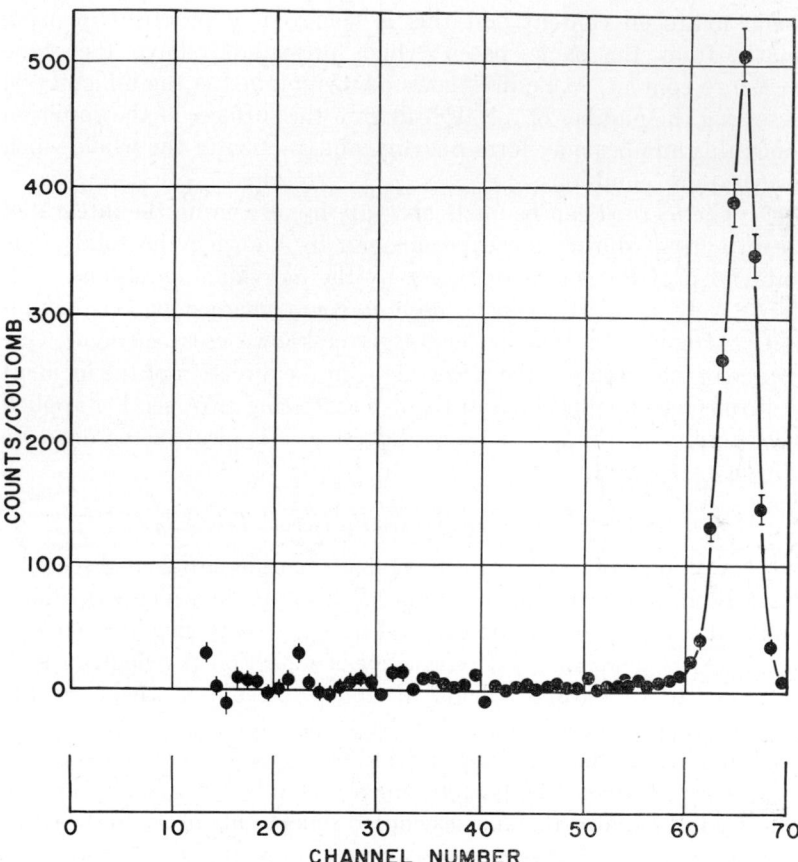

Figure 14. Performance of recoil telescope showing relatively low background for single neutron group from T(d, n)He⁴ (Jo56).

spectrum. The yield with the background subtracted was grouped in a single peak with a low energy tail, a feature of most spectrometers using counters. When several groups are present in a spectrum, it is difficult to assess the magnitude of the tails extending to low energies unless the behavior of the spectrometer has been determined previously at all energies. This feature, then, has limited the accuracy of some measurements (Ca55, Ca55a), but Johnson and Trail have shown that, with careful design, the tail can be reduced to the order of 1 per cent of the integrated peak.

Additional measurements to those already listed have been made by Trail and Johnson (Tr54), Galonsky and Judish (Ga55), and Johnson and Galonsky (Jo55). For instance, this type of spectrometer has been used for studying the differential cross section for n-p scattering at 14.1 and 17.9 Mev with an accuracy of 2 or 3 per cent (Ga55) and for examining the differential cross section of the reaction $T(d, n)He^4$ for deuteron energies from 1 to 6 Mev (Jo55, Fo56). The emphasis in these measurements was on accurate determinations of absolute cross sections, although this degree of accuracy is not always essential for gaining useful information (Ca55).

D. Measurements of Cross Sections Using Time-of-Flight Spectrometers

The introduction of time-of-flight techniques has made the study of reactions yielding neutrons much less laborious.

The experiment yields an intensity as the number of neutrons per specified time interval, this time interval being the channel width in a time sorter. This figure is usually translated into the units of a cross section by applying a calibration factor for the instrument. The calibration is determined in a subsidiary experiment. For example, Bogdanov et al. (Bo56) calibrated their spectrometer under fixed conditions of flight path, scintillator size, and detector threshold by using the known flux from the reaction $T(p, n)He^3$. A recalibration is made for any change in spectrometer details. The efficiency as a function of energy is shown in Fig. 15. The spectral sensitivity has the form

$$\eta(E) = A\sigma(E)(1 - V/E) \tag{3}$$

where $\sigma(E)$ is the neutron-proton scattering cross section at energy E, and V is the threshold energy of detection determined largely by a preset discriminator level. A and V are then determined empirically.

Cranberg and Levin (Cr56a) also used the $T(p, n)He^3$ reaction to calibrate their spectrometer and referred their yield to that determined by a radiator and proton recoil telescope for neutrons above 1.20 Mev; i.e., their efficiency is related to known n-p scattering data. Below this energy, the yield of the above reaction was referred to that measured by a long counter. This type of spectrometer has been applied to a variety of measurements of cross sections of which the following are typical.

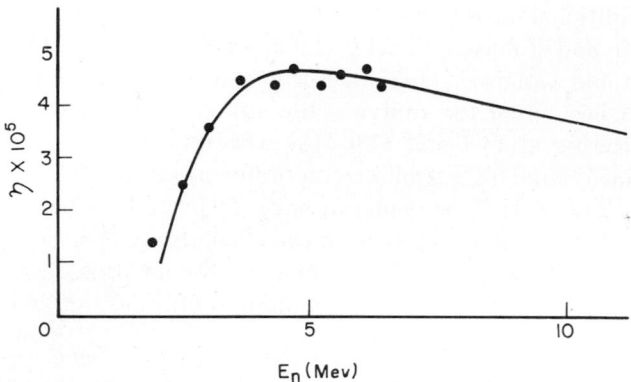

Figure 15. Efficiency of time-of-flight spectrometer as a function of neutron energy (Bo56a).

Scanlon *et al.* (Sc57) have measured the total cross section for *n-p* scattering to an accuracy of 3 to 5 per cent in the range of energies from 15 to 120 Mev. Cranberg and Levin (Cr56a) have measured the differential cross sections for inelastic scattering of neutrons for a number of elements. Typical results for $d\sigma/d\omega$ as a function of θ are shown in Fig. 16.

The technique has found little application, so far, in absolute measurements of reactions, although Grismore and Parkinson (Gr57) have measured the relative intensities of the groups of neutrons leading to low-lying levels of the residual nucleus in the reactions $Be^9(d, n)B^{10}$ and $O^{16}(d, n)F^{17}$.

Recently there have been a number of publications on neutron spectroscopy using the time-of-flight technique. The pulsed-beam method (Chapter IV.A) has been used for measuring differential cross sections (Ba59, Ba59a, Ne59, Ne59a) while the associated-particle method (Chapter IV.A) has been used for similar purposes and also for $(X,n\gamma)$ correlation measurements. The importance of the latter is mentioned below and is discussed more fully in Chapter V.G.

A useful development which can be applied to time-to-flight spectroscopy is the discrimination technique developed by Owen (Ow59) and Brooks (Br59) which depends on the difference in scintillator decay time under γ and neutron irradiation. Obviously it can be applied to reduce γ-ray background normally recorded by the neutron detector of a pulsed-beam arrangement, and similarly to

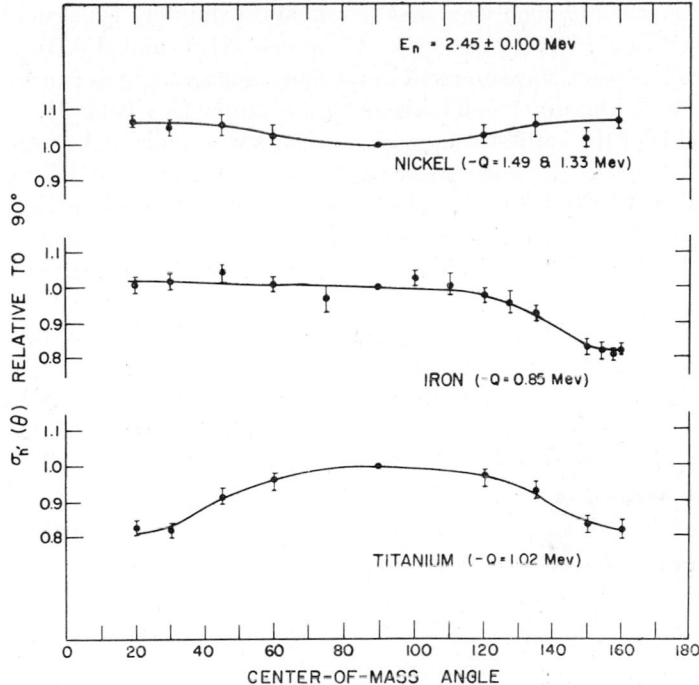

Figure 16. Differential cross-sections for inelastic scattering of 2.45-Mev neutrons by various elements (Cr56).

eliminate neutron and γ ray background from the appropriate detectors in an associated particle arrangement.

While the energy resolution of the time-of-flight technique is only moderate for high energy neutrons, its usefulness stems from its high efficiency and undoubtedly it will be widely employed (see Ne59a and Chapter V.Q).

E. Measurements using Other Techniques

As discussed elsewhere in this volume in detail (see Chapters II.A, II.B, and III.C), cross sections can also be determined by methods not mentioned here previously. These generally involve calibration using a neutron reaction of known yield for monoenergetic neutrons (for example, the D-D and D-T reactions or n-p scattering) or a standard source of neutrons for counters such as the long counter in which the efficiency is approximately constant with energy (Ha47, No54; see also Chapters III.A and IV.B). The accuracy of such measurements is usually not as high as can be obtained with a proton recoil telescope, for example (see Table I).

One of the earliest such measurements was made at Los Alamos by Taschek and Hemmendinger (Ta48) who measured the differential cross section of the Li^7 $(p, n)Be^7$ reaction for protons of energy 1.95 Mev to 2.25 Mev (at 50-kev intervals) and over an angular range of $0°$ to $135°$ (at $15°$ intervals). Absolute values were measured to an accuracy of 5 per cent by comparing the yield with a standard Ra-α-Be source. The uncertainty in the standardization of this (α, n) source was considered the main contribution to their error.[3]

Other workers have measured (p, n) (Br55, Ma55, Ma56, Sa56) and (α, n) (Bo56, Sa56) cross sections for many nuclei in a similar way, using either the Li^7 $(p, n)Be^7$ reaction[4] or a Ra-α-Be source as a standard.

5. Angular Distributions

One of the more important applications of fast neutron spectroscopy has been in the measurement of the angular distributions of neutrons from nuclear reactions. This has received more attention in the case of deuteron stripping because of the simple interpretation of the curves. However, recently interest has been extended to the distribution in (p, n), (He^3, n) and (α, n) reactions. Typical results are given below rather than an exhaustive survey.

A. (d, n) Angular Distributions

Almost the whole range of spectrometers has been applied to such measurements and typical results obtained by differing instruments at deuteron energies of a few Mev are shown in Fig. 17.

---

[3] Gabbard, Davis, and Bonner (Bo59, Ga59) have recently shown that the $0°$ cross sections of Taschek and Hemmendinger are low by approximately 50 per cent. This is probably a consequence of the fact that the differential cross sections were obtained by normalizing $\int(d\sigma/d\omega)d\omega$ to the total cross section obtained by a Mn-bath technique, while the differential cross sections found at backward angles were too high because of scattering.

[4] Measurements based on the $Li^7(p, n)$ data of Taschek and Hemmendinger should be increased by 50 per cent (Ga59).

As can be seen from these diagrams, most measurements have been limited to about ±50° with respect to the direction of the incident deuterons. This small angular range is in the cases presented sufficient for unambiguous interpretation on the stripping theory of Butler (Bu51, Bh52). It was this work which stimulated the detailed study of this reaction and its mirror (d, p) process. Surveys of stripping have been made by Huby (Hu53) and Butler (Bu57), and only the essentials of the theory will be described (see also Chapter V.D).

The process can be considered as the capture by the target nucleus of the proton constituent in a deuteron while the neutron does not enter the nucleus and plays little part in the interaction except for conserving energy and momentum. The differential cross section for the process depends on the relative velocity of deuteron and target nucleus, the internal state of the deuteron and the probability of capture of the proton by the target nucleus. This probability depends on the orbital angular momentum, $l\hbar$, of the proton added in a discrete energy state of the final nucleus (in the simple shell model, the l-value of this particle is unique) and so this contains a *centrifugal factor* which largely determines the direction of emergence of the outgoing neutron.

The theoretical curves of angular dependence of the differential cross section for a given reaction (but for the different assumed values of $l\hbar$, the orbital angular momentum transfer) are usually sufficiently different for an experiment of moderate accuracy to be able to determine the correct one. It seldom proves impossible to determine the correct l-value although at low bombarding energies and for low or negative Q-values, curves differing in l by one are less readily distinguishable.

In this way, many nuclear levels have been studied and the l-values for their formation by (d, n) stripping found. The angular momentum of the captured particle, $l\hbar$, is connected with the angular momenta of the initial and final nuclear states by the vector equation

$$\mathbf{J}_i = \mathbf{J}_f + \mathbf{l} + \tfrac{1}{2} \tag{4}$$

with the additional restriction that l is odd if there is a change of parity between initial and final states, and is even if there is no such change.

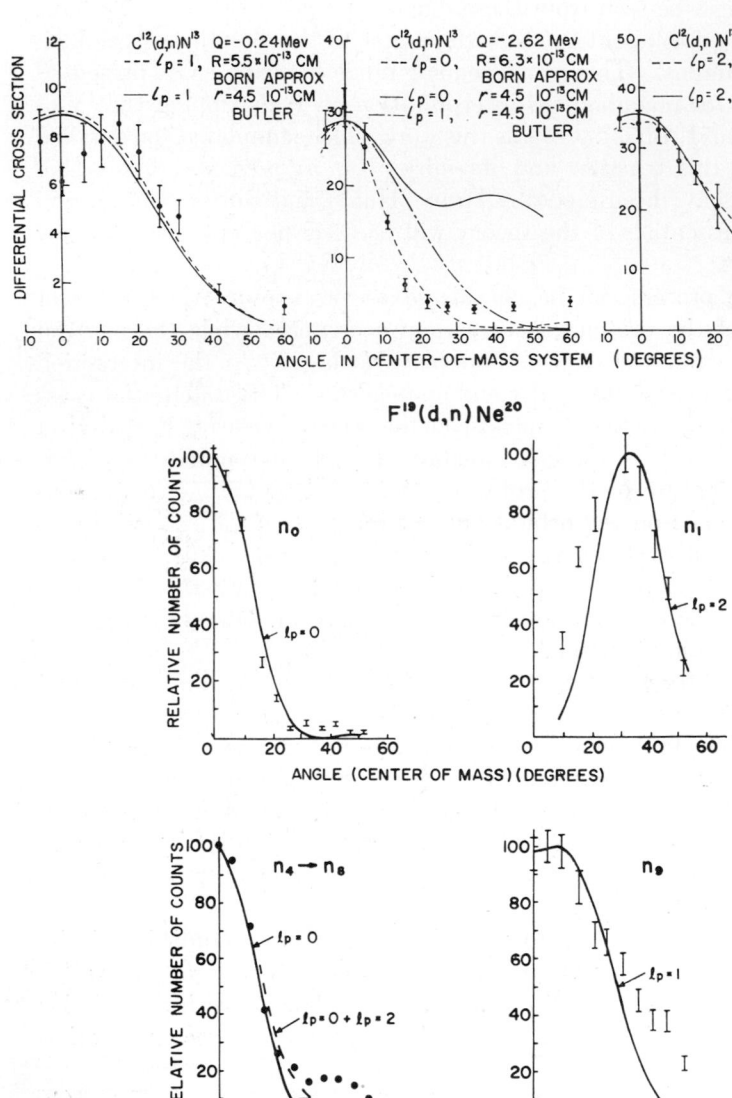

Fig. 17 continued on next page

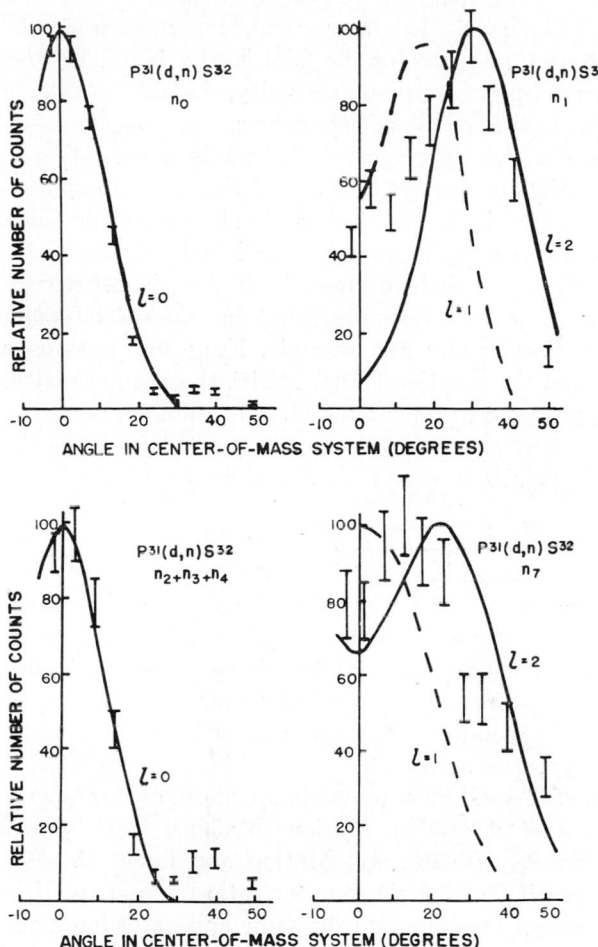

Figure 17. Angular distributions of neutrons from various (d, n) reactions using different methods of spectroscopy, (a) nuclear emulsions (Mi53); (b) double scintillator (Ca55a); (c) triple ionization chamber (Ca55).

If l is determined for a particular group of neutrons in a reaction and if the spin of the target nucleus is known, then limits to the spin of the residual level can be found. In the case of $J_1 = l = 0$ the result is unambiguous. In other cases, the measurement predicts possible alternative spins for the final level. However, the angular distribution does give, without ambiguity, the parity of the final state with respect to that of the initial nucleus.

For cases of J_i and J_f for which l can have more than one value as given by the above rules, it is found that the experimental distributions can be well fitted by a single l-value, since additional contributions from higher l-values would be reduced in intensity by a factor 7 to 10. The l-value which gives the best fit is not necessarily the lowest allowed by the selection rules but depends on the configurations of the nuclei involved. For example, King and Parkinson (Ki52) found that for the reaction $Cl^{35}(d, p)Cl^{36}$, the angular distribution of the protons leading to the ground state of the final nucleus indicated a value of $l = 2$ as would have been expected from the shell model theory, although $l = 0$ would be allowed by the selection rules.

B. (p, n) Reactions

(p, n) reactions have not been studied as extensively as (d, n) reactions because they have negative Q-values on the whole and also because their analysis is not so rewarding. As indicated previously, the deuteron reaction gives information on the parity and spin as well as on the energy of each excited state. It is only recently that attempts have been made to gain information other than on energy levels from (p, n) reactions.

Typical of such measurements are those of Ajzenberg (Aj55a), Bartholomew et al. (Ba55), Marion (Ma56a), Mark and Goodman (Ma56b), Sanders (Sa56), and Marion and Levin (Ma59). Many experimenters have used the counter ratio method for the accurate determination of Q-values and the same apparatus for angular distribution measurements although it is not truly energy selective (see Chapters III.A and V.O). In some cases, energy selection of the neutrons has been used (Aj55a, Ma59).

The general theory of nuclear reactions predicts that for a process going through a well-isolated resonance, i.e., a compound state of definite parity, then the angular distribution is symmetrical about $\theta = 90°$ in the center-of-mass system. Furthermore, the

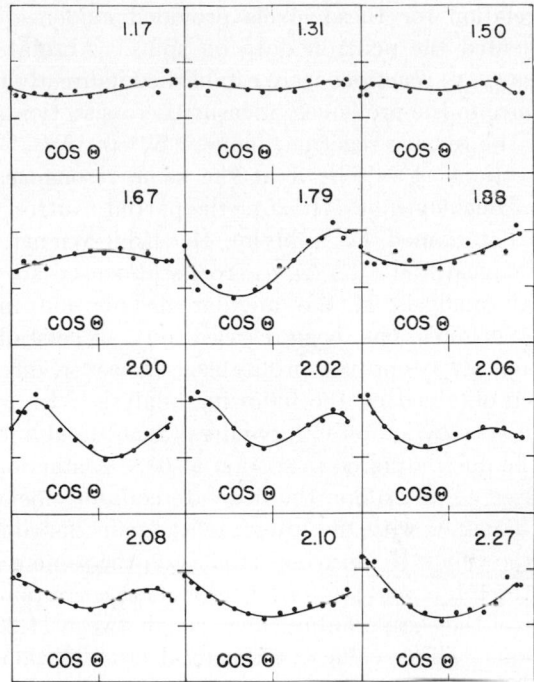

Figure 18. Experimental angular distributions of neutrons from $C^{14}(p, n)N^{14}$ at different proton energies plotted from $\cos \theta = +1$ to -1 (Ba55).

distribution for an unpolarized process has the form of a sum of Legendre polynomials (in which only even orders are present because of the requirement on symmetry), the highest index, ν, appearing in the sum being limited by the inequalities $\nu \leqq 2l_{\max}$ and $\nu \leqq 2J$ where $l_{\max}$ and J are the maximum orbital angular momentum of the partial wave and the total angular momentum of the compound state respectively. This analysis is well-established and has been applied by Bartholomew *et al.* (Ba55) to the angular distributions of neutrons from twelve resonances in the reaction $C^{14}(p, n)N^{14}$ at proton energies between 1.16 and 2.27 Mev (Fig. 18). A least-squares fit of the experimental points to a series of Legendre polynomials up to and including the fourth was carried out. The relative sizes of the coefficients of the different terms was sufficient evidence to determine the spins of the majority of the states. A measurement of the C^{14} (p, γ)

angular correlation for these levels provided evidence on parities and supplemented the neutron data on spins. Absolute cross sections for these (p, n) reactions were established indirectly by applying detailed balance to the previously measured cross section at a specific resonance of the reverse reaction, namely N^{14} $(n, p)C^{14}$. Since the total cross sections of $N^{14} + n$ at the same resonances had been measured by Hinchley *et al.* (Hi52a),[5] the partial neutron and proton widths were determined by applying the Breit-Wigner single-level formula to the measured total (p, n) cross sections.

Although analysis of the angular distribution in terms of Legendre polynomials has been carried out successfully in some cases, it has not always proved profitable. However, information on spins has been obtained by the following analysis. In an investigation of the (p, n) reaction on C^{14}, Sanders (Sa56) used a long counter to measure the differential cross section at $0°$. A standard Ra-α-Be source was used to determine the absolute counter efficiency. This information, together with the integrated angular distributions from the work of the Chalk River group (Ba55) on the same reaction, was used to find the total cross section at resonances corresponding to ten excited states of the compound nucleus, N^{15}, between 11.29 and 12.92 Mev excitation. These values of the total cross section were then applied to the resonance scattering of neutrons by N^{14} using the Breit-Wigner one-level formula.

At resonance

$$\sigma_{n,n} = 2\pi\lambda_n^2(2J + 1)\ \Gamma_n^2/3\Gamma^2 \tag{5}$$

where λ_n is the reduced neutron wavelength and Γ and Γ_n are the total width and partial neutron width respectively of the compound state of spin J.

Since

$$\sigma_{n,n}/\sigma_T = \Gamma_n/\Gamma$$
$$2J + 1 = 3\sigma_T^2/2\pi\lambda_n^2\sigma_{n,n} \tag{6}$$

σ_T was known from previous measurements and $\sigma_{n,n}$ was found by knowing σ_T, $\sigma_{n,p}$, and $\sigma_{n,\alpha}$:

$$\sigma_{n,n} = \sigma_T - \sigma_{n,p} - \sigma_{n,\alpha} \tag{7}$$

[5] Fortunately, the residual nucleus from the (p, n) reaction in this case is stable so that the parameters in the Breit-Wigner formula can be determined completely.

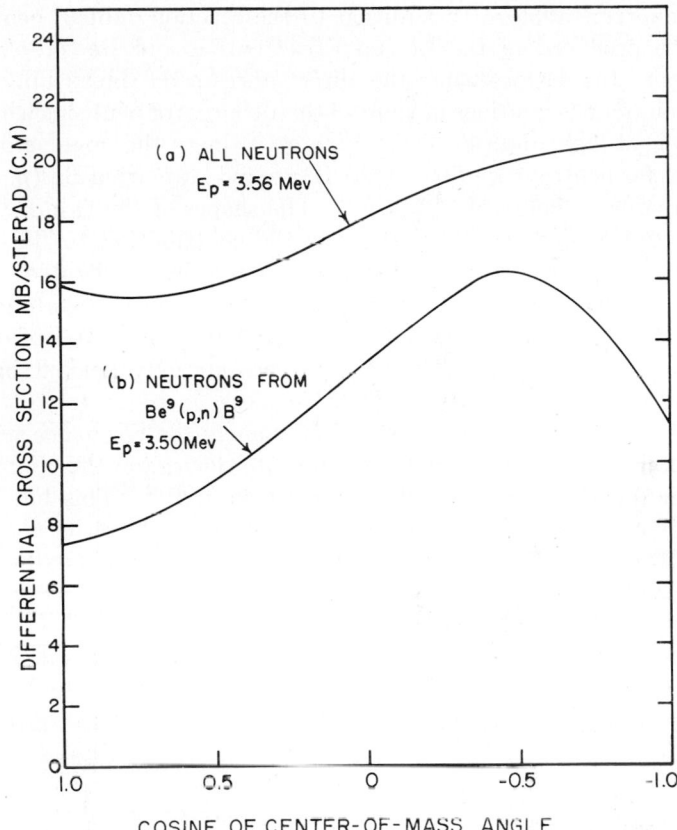

Figure 19. Experimental angular distributions of neutrons from Be⁹(p, n)B⁹ using (a) long counter, (b) time-of-flight, techniques (Ma56a, Ma59).

$\sigma_{n,p}$ for this equation was found from the measured $\sigma_{p,n}$ by the principle of detailed balance.

The nearest half-integer to the solution of J in Eq. (6) was taken for the spin of the compound state in N^{15}.

Marion and Levin have recently shown that observations made with detectors that have no energy discrimination may be misleading if neutrons can arise from more than one process. They have investigated the reaction Be⁹(p, n)B⁹ for proton energies of 2 to 5 Mev using a time-of-flight spectrometer (Ma59), while Marion had studied the reaction under similar conditions using a paraffin-moderated

BF_3 counter (Ma56). In addition to the reaction quoted, neutrons may be produced in the $Be^9(p, p')Be^{9*}(n)Be^8$ and $Be^9(p, p'n)Be^8$ reactions, the latter being the direct three-body break-up. The long-counter observations include all these sources of neutrons whereas the time-of-flight data do not. Figure 19 shows the angular distributions for neutrons leading to the B^9 ground-state from $Be^9(p, n)$ at a bombarding energy of 3.56 Mev. The shapes of the two distributions are significantly different while the contribution to the cross section from the continuum neutrons is not inconsiderable. The highly asymmetric character of the curve for the ground-state group of neutrons indicates interference between compound states of opposite parity. The continuum neutrons are strongly peaked in the forward direction, suggesting a direct process.

The data from this investigation, namely the resonance widths and total cross sections, have been used to determine the spins and isotopic quantum numbers of several levels in B^{10}. This has been done by analysis of the $Be^9(p, \alpha\gamma)Li^6$ reaction together with the Be^9-$(p, n)B^9$ reaction. Both reactions show resonances at bombarding energies of 2.56, 3.5, and 4.49 Mev. The $(p, \alpha\gamma)$ reactions proceed through the 3.57-Mev level in Li^6 which has $J = 0^+$, $T = 1$. Hence, the three states in B^{10} must have $T = 1$. The spins are found from consistency arguments between the fitting of possible values to the experimental data and the measured reduced widths of the equivalent levels in Be^{10}.

C. (α, n) and (He^3, n) Reactions

These measurements have not been made extensively, but nevertheless they have been carried out in a number of cases. It has proved useful to measure the differential cross section over a large angular range in order to determine the total cross section. The shape of the distribution and the size of the cross section help to fix the spin and parity of any intermediate state in the reaction and the spin-mixing of the outgoing channel.

Typical measurements are those of Sanders (Sa56), Risser et al. (Ri57), James et al. (Ja56), and Ajzenberg et al. (Aj57). Figure 20 shows distributions of experimental points with fitted curves. Theory of nuclear reactions suggests that an angular distribution should be a sum of Legendre polynomials, the coefficient of each term being determined by the mechanics of the process (Bl52).

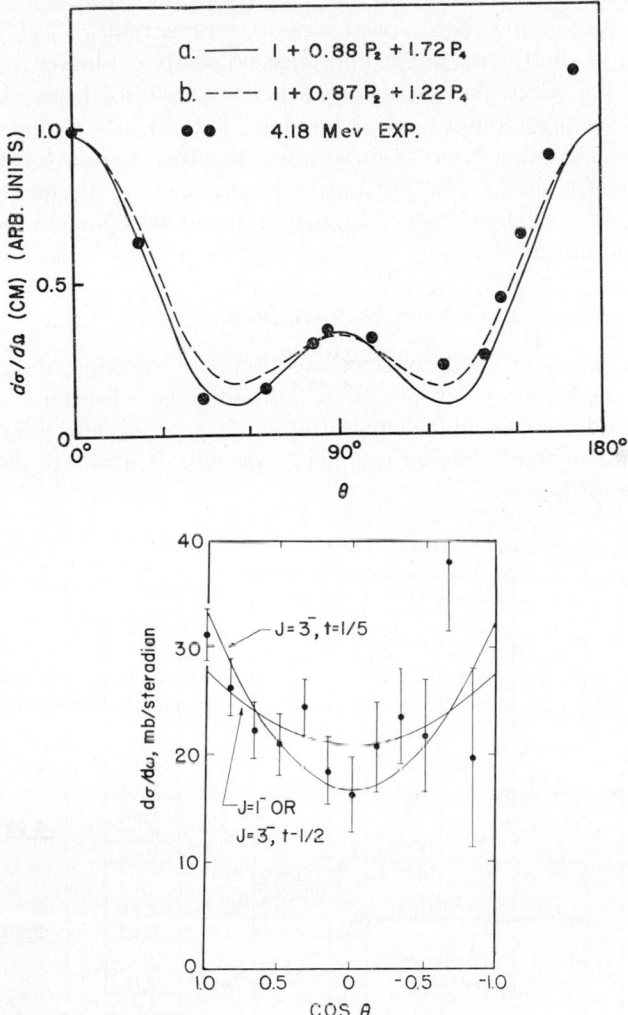

Figure 20. (α, n) angular distributions with fitted theoretical curves. (a) $Be^9(\alpha, n)C^{12}$; experimental points are for neutrons leading to ground state of C^{12}. The theoretical curves are calculated for a mixture of two compound-nuclear states of different J (Ri57). (b) $C^{14}(\alpha, n)O^{17}$; theoretical distributions are for given J of the compound state and outgoing-channel spin-mixing-ratio, t (Sa56).

So far, theory has not been as successful in fitting data for this process as stripping theory has for deuteron reactions. This may be the fault of the theory but it may also be partly explained by conditions in the particular experiments investigated to date. In some of these, the compound nucleus has been formed in a region of excitation where levels have been so close together that interpretation in terms of a single spin and parity is unrealistic. It may be that interpretation of these distributions in terms of direct interactions will be successful (Bu57).

6. Determination of Nuclear Level Properties

As indicated in the previous sections, information about spins, parities, and energy levels can be obtained by observing neutron spectra and their angular distributions. It is possible to supplement these data in the following manner, especially if absolute cross sections are measured.

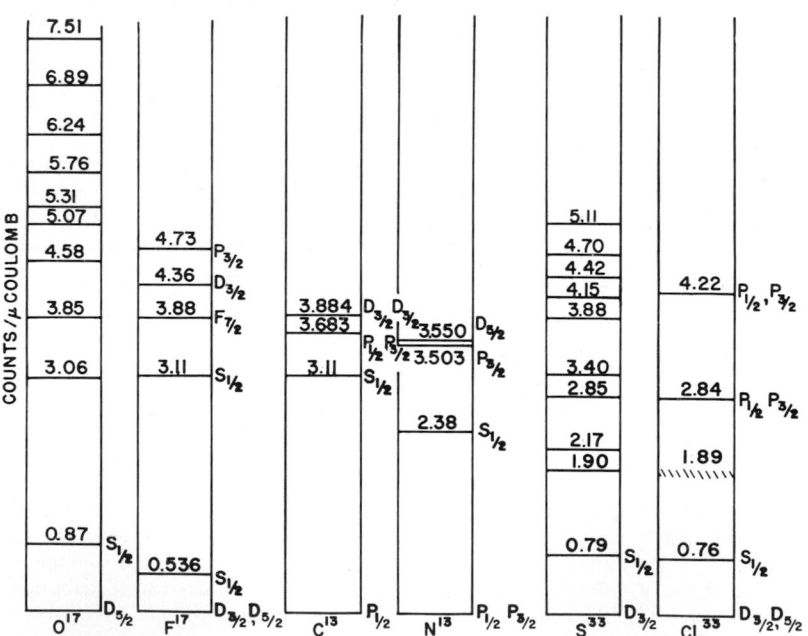

Figure 21. Comparison of level properties of mirror nuclei (Mi53).

A. Levels of Mirror Nuclei

In many cases, the (d, n) and (d, p) reactions have been performed on a nucleus with $A = 2Z$, leading to levels of mirror nuclei of mass number $(A + 1)$. In this way, the positions of energy levels in mirror nuclei have been compared (Mi53, En54) (Fig. 21).

Excitations found by the (d, n) reaction are not as accurate as the corresponding ones found by the (d, p) reaction (see discussion above). However, such comparisons give strong support to the hypothesis of charge-symmetry of nuclear forces. In fact, this belief is so accepted that close doublets observed in (d, p) reactions are assumed to be present in their mirror reactions although never observed because of the poorer resolution.

B. Reduced Widths

In deuteron stripping, measurements of absolute cross sections enable calculations to be made of the nucleon reduced widths appertaining to the captured particles. Butler's theory gives an expression for the differential cross section in the form:

$$d\sigma(\theta)/d\omega = \pi(K_n) \sum_l P_l L_l(k) \tag{8}$$

where $\pi(K_n)$ is a factor depending on the internal state of the deuteron, K_n being the wave number of the neutron; $L_l(k)$ measures the probability of finding a proton with the correct linear and angular momentum at the surface of the nucleus and so depends on the radius, R, at which the capture occurs; P_l represents the probability of capture of the proton when it has reached the nuclear surface. This, then, is proportional to the nucleon reduced width, $\gamma_p{}^2$, of the level which is a measure of the probability of finding a single nucleon at the nuclear surface for a given energy state with definite quantum numbers.

The summation is carried out over all values of l which satisfy the selection rules [see Eq. (4)].

The shape of the theoretical distribution depends on the parameter R and this is usually chosen to give the closest agreement between the theoretical and experimental curves. Generally, a value slightly greater than the nuclear radius is needed [see the discussion by Holt and Marsham on the (d, p) process (Ho53a)]. With R thus determined empirically, all quantities are known in Eq. (8) except $\gamma_p{}^2$ which can therefore be found.

Whether any value can be placed on a precise figure of $\gamma_p{}^2$ obtained in this way has been discussed at great length (Ho53, Fa54, Bo55, To55, Fr56, To56) but it does seem certain that the order of magnitude of $\gamma_p{}^2$ is a useful guide in describing the final level in terms of a shell-model of the nucleus. This has been done, for instance, by Holt and Marsham (Ho53a) quite extensively in the (d, p) cases, and by Calvert *et al.* and Middleton *et al.* in several (d, n) reactions (Ev53, Mi53, Ca55, Ca55a, Ma56c, Ca57). The reduced width found by stripping can be used as a guide to the single-particle or many-particle nature of a level. However, the *absolute* values must be treated with reserve because of the occasional large discrepancies when stripping measurements are compared with those made by resonance scattering or other experiments (La53, Bo55, Hi58). Detailed theoretical corrections applied to the stripping theory change the size of the reduced width significantly without very much changing the angular distribution but they do not remove the discrepancies mentioned above.

Although this question is still unsettled, Calvert, Jaffe, and Maslin, (Ca56) have shown that Butler's theory applied to mirror (d, n) and (d, p) reactions gives reduced widths for mirror levels which are

Table II. Comparison of (d, n) and (d, p) Cross Sections and Reduced Widths for Various Nuclei (Ca56)

Target nucleus	Final nucleus (d, p)	Final nucleus (d, n)	Levels compared	Stripping l-value	$\dfrac{\sigma_{\max}(d, p)}{\sigma_{\max}(d, n)}$	$\gamma_n{}^2/\gamma_p{}^2$
Be^9	Be^{10}	B^{10}	First $T = 1$ level	1	1.64 ± 0.25	2.16^{a}
C^{12}	C^{13}	N^{13}	Ground states	1	0.50 ± 0.05	0.86
N^{14}	N^{15}	O^{15}	Ground states	1	1.16 ± 0.14	1.71
O^{16}	O^{17}	F^{17}	Ground states	2	0.47 ± 0.08	1.30
Si^{28}	Si^{29}	P^{29}	Ground states	0	1.01 ± 0.15	0.58

[a] For this case, a ratio of 2 would be expected from consideration of isotopic spin (see Ad52).

of the same magnitude, as would be expected. They observed neutrons and protons simultaneously from the same target under deuteron bombardment having previously measured the separate angular distributions. The comparison found for various target nuclei is shown in Table II. Benenson *et al.* (Be56) came to a similar conclusion from measurements on the C^{12} $(d, n)N^{13}$ and C^{12} $(d, p)C^{13}$ reactions compared at two different energies. These topics have now been treated in great detail by MacFarlane and French (Ma60).

C. Other Level Parameters

More information can be obtained about excited final states by stripping if the correlation of γ rays with respect to the outgoing neutrons is observed. Relatively few cases have been measured because of the very low coincidence rates involved. Neilson and Warren (Ne56) have used the correlation in the Li^6 $(d, n\gamma)Be^7$ reaction to show that the first excited state in Be^7 at 0.429 Mev has spin and parity $\frac{1}{2}^-$. The neutron distribution alone is characteristic of $l = 1$ and therefore predicts possible spins of $\frac{1}{2}$, $\frac{3}{2}$, $\frac{5}{2}$. Since the n-γ correlation is isotropic, the spin must be $\frac{1}{2}$. (See Chapter V.Q for a further discussion of correlation measurements.)

The method of determining Q-values by using resonant scattering described above has also been applied to determining an upper limit to the width of a level by Stelson and Preston (St51). Sulfur has a sharp resonance (natural width $\sim$1.5 kev) at 585 kev in its total neutron cross section. Using a sulfur scatterer for the reaction Be^9 $(p, n)B^9$, the number of neutrons detected was plotted as a function of proton energy. The observed width of the peak of neutrons corresponding to B^9 formed in its ground state was 4 kev. This was accounted for by 3 kev due to target thickness and geometry and 1.5 kev for the sulfur width, leaving an estimated 2 kev for the width of the B^9 ground state. This was significantly smaller than earlier measurements had indicated.

References

(Ad52)   R. K. Adair, *Phys. Rev.* **87**, 1041 (1952).
(Aj51)   F. Ajzenberg, *Phys. Rev.* **82**, 43 (1951).
(Aj54)   F. Ajzenberg and W. Franzen, *Phys. Rev.* **95**, 1531 (1954).
(Aj55a) F. Ajzenberg, *Phys. Rev.* **95**, 1531 (1955).
(Aj57)   Ajzenberg-Selove, Bullock, and Almqvist, *Phys. Rev.* **108**, 1284 (1957).
(Aj59)   F. Ajzenberg-Selove and T. Lauritsen, *Nuclear Phys.* **11**, 1 (1959).

(Ar48)   H. V. Argo, *Phys. Rev.* **74**, 1293 (1948).

(Ba55)   Bartholomew, Brown, Gove, Litherland, and Paul, *Can. J. Phys.* **33**, 441 (1955).

(Ba59)   R. Batchelor and J. H. Towle, *Proc. Phys. Soc.* **73**, 307 (1959).

(Ba59a)   R. Batchelor and J. H. Towle, *Proc. Phys. Soc.* **73**, 193 (1959).

(Be53)   R. E. Benenson, *Phys. Rev.* **90**, 420 (1953).

(Be56)   Benenson, Jones, and McEllistrem, *Phys. Rev.* **101**, 308 (1956).

(Bh52)   Bhatia, Huang, Huby, and Newns, *Phil. Mag.* **43**, 484 (1952).

(Bi52)   Bischel, Halg, Huber, and Stoebler, *Helv. Phys. Acta* **25**, 119 (1952).

(Bl52)   J. M. Blatt and L. C. Biedenharn, *Revs. Modern Phys.* **24**, 258 (1952).

(Bo35)   T. W. Bonner and W. M. Brubaker, *Phys. Rev.* **47**, 910 (1935).

(Bo40)   T. W. Bonner, *Proc. Roy. Soc.* (*London*) **174A**, 339 (1940).

(Bo41)   T. W. Bonner, *Phys. Rev.* **59**, 237 (1941).

(Bo52)   Bonner, Ferrell, and Rinehart, *Phys. Rev.* **87**, 1032 (1952).

(Bo53)   Bockelman, Browne, Buechner, and Sperduto, *Phys. Rev.* **92**, 665 (1953).

(Bo54)   T. W. Bonner and C. F. Cook, *Phys. Rev.* **96**, 122 (1954).

(Bo55)   J. E. Bowcock, *Proc. Phys. Soc.* (*London*) **68A**, 512 (1955).

(Bo56)   Bogdanov, Kurashov, Rybakov, and Sidorov, *J. Nuclear Energy* **3**, 148 (1956).

(Bo56a)   Bonner, Kraus, Marion, and Schiffer, *Phys. Rev.* **102**, 1348 (1956).

(Br53)   C. P. Browne and C. K. Bockelman, *M.I.T. Lab. for Nuclear Science Progr. Report* May (1953).

(Br55)   Brugger, Bonner, and Marion, *Phys. Rev.* **100**, 84 (1955).

(Br59)   F. D. Brooks, *Nuclear Inst.* **4**, 151 (1959).

(Bu51)   S. T. Butler, *Proc. Roy. Soc.* (*London*) **208A**, 559 (1951).

(Bu57)   S. T. Butler, and O. H. Hittmair, *Nuclear Stripping Reactions*, Pitman, London (1957).

(Ca55)   Calvert, Jaffe, and Maslin, *Proc. Phys. Soc.* (*London*) **68A**, 1017 (1955).

(Ca55a)   Calvert, Jaffe, Litherland, and Maslin, *Proc. Phys. Soc.* (*London*) **68A**, 1008 (1955).

(Ca56)   Calvert, Jaffe, and Maslin, *Phys. Rev.* **101**, 501 (1956).

(Ca57)   Calvert, Jaffe, and Maslin, *Proc. Phys. Soc.* (*London*) **70A**, 78 (1957).

(Cr56)   Cranberg, Frye, Nereson, and Rosen, *Phys. Rev.* **103**, 662 (1956).

(Cr56a)   L. Cranberg and J. S. Levin, *Phys. Rev.* **103**, 343 (1956).

(Do56)   W. T. Doyle and A. B. Robbins, *Phys. Rev.* **101**, 1056 (1956).

(Dy53)   A. J. Dyer and J. A. Bird, *Australian J. Phys.* **6**, 45 (1953).

(El57)   F. A. El-Bedewi and M. A. Wahab, *Nuclear Phys.* **3**, 385 (1957).

(En54)   P. M. Endt and J. C. Kluyver, *Revs. Modern Phys.* **26**, 95 (1954).

(En57)   P. M. Endt and C. M. Braams, *Revs. Modern Phys.* **29**, 683 (1957).

(Ev53)   Evans, Green, and Middleton, *Proc. Phys. Soc.* (*London*) **66A**, 108 (1953).

(Ev59)   Evans, Kinsey, and Whitmore, *Can. J. Phys.* **37**, 396 (1959).

(Fa54)   W. M. Fairbairn, *Proc. Phys. Soc.* (*London*) **67A**, 564 (1954).

(Fe59)   A. T. G. Ferguson and E. B. Paul, *Nuclear Phys.* **12**, 426 (1959).

(Fo56)   J. L. Fowler and J. E. Brolley, Jr., *Revs. Modern Phys.* **28**, 103 (1956).

(Fr56)   J. B. French, *Phys. Rev.* **103**, 1391 (1956).
(Ga55)   A. Galonsky and J. P. Judish, *Phys. Rev.* **100**, 121 (1955).
(Ga59)   Gabbard, Davis, and Bonner, *Phys. Rev.* **114**, 201 (1959).
(Go53)   E. Goldberg, *Phys. Rev.* **89**, 760 (1953).
(Gr53)   E. R. Graves and L. Rosen, *Phys. Rev.* **89**, 343 (1953).
(Gr57)   R. Grismore and W. C. Parkinson, *Rev. Sci. Instr.* **28**, 245 (1957).
(Gu51)   P. C. Gugelot, *Phys. Rev.* **81**, 51 (1951).
(Ha47)   A. O. Hansen and J. L. McKibben, *Phys. Rev.* **72**, 673 (1947).
(Hi52)   T. L. Hill, *Phys. Rev.* **87**, 1034 (1952).
(Hi52a)   Hinchley, Stelson, and Preston, *Phys. Rev.* **86**, 483 (1952).
(Hi58)   Hinds, Middleton, and Parry, *Proc. Phys. Soc.* (*London*) **71**, 49 (1958).
(Ho53)   J. Horowitz and A. M. L. Messiah, *Phys. Rev.* **92**, 1326 (1953).
(Ho53a)   J. R. Holt and T. N. Marsham, *Proc. Phys. Soc.* (*London*) **66A**, 1032 (1953).
(Hu53)   R. Huby, *Progr. in Nuclear Phys.* **3**, 177 (1953).
(Ja56)   James, Jones, and Wilkinson, *Phil. Mag.* **1**, 949 (1956).
(Je55)   Jennings, Weddell, Alexeff, and Hellens, *Phys. Rev.* **98**, 582 (1955).
(Jo50)   Johnson, Laubenstein, and Richards, *Phys. Rev.* **77**, 413 (1950).
(Jo50a)   Johnson, Ajzenberg, and Laubenstein, *Phys. Rev.* **79**, 187 (1950).
(Jo52)   V. R. Johnson, *Phys. Rev.* **86**, 302 (1952).
(Jo55)   C. H. Johnson and A. Galonsky, *Phys. Rev.* **100**, 1252(A) (1955).
(Jo56)   C. H. Johnson and C. C. Trail, *Rev. Sci. Instr.* **27**, 468 (1956).
(Ka58)   R. W. Kavanagh and C. A. Barnes, *Phys. Rev.* **112**, 503 (1958).
(Ki52)   J. S. King and W. C. Parkinson, *Phys. Rev.* **88**, 141 (1952).
(La47)   Lattes, Fowler, and Cuer, *Proc. Phys. Soc.* (*London*) **59A**, 883 (1947).
(La53)   A. M. Lane, *Proc. Phys. Soc.* (*London*) **66A**, 977 (1953).
(Le56)   R. B. Leachman, *Phys. Rev.* **101**, 1005 (1956).
(Le59)   L. L. Lee and F. P. Mooring, *Phys. Rev.* **115**, 969 (1959).
(Li49)   D. L. Livesey and D. H. Wilkinson, *Proc. Roy. Soc.* (*London*) **195A**, 123 (1949).
(Ma55)   Marion, Bonner, and Cook, *Phys. Rev.* **100**, 91 (1955).
(Ma56)   J. B. Marion and R. A. Chapman, *Phys. Rev.* **101**, 283 (1956).
(Ma56a)   J. B. Marion, *Phys. Rev.* **103**, 713 (1956).
(Ma56b)   H. Mark and C. Goodman, *Phys. Rev.* **101**, 768 (1956).
(Ma56c)   Maslin, Calvert, and Jaffe, *Proc. Phys. Soc.* (*London*) **69A**, 754 (1956).
(Ma57)   Mazari, Castro, Alba, and Vazquez, *Rev. mec. fis.* **6**, 9 (1957).
(Ma59)   J. B. Marion and J. S. Levin, *Phys. Rev.* **115**, 114 (1959).
(Ma60)   M. M. MacFarlane and J. B. French, *Revs. Modern Phys.* **32**, 567 (1960).
(Mi53)   Middleton, El-Bedewi, and Tai, *Proc. Phys. Soc.* (*London*) **66A**, 95 (1953).
(Mi55)   R. M. Middleton and T. S. Green, private communication (1955).
(Mo52)   R. F. Mozley and F. C. Shoemaker, *Rev. Sci. Instr.* **23**, 569 (1952).
(Ne56)   G. C. Neilson and J. B. Warren, *Phys. Rev.* **103**, 1758 (1956).
(Ne59)   Neilson, Dawson, Johnson, and Sample, *Suffield Technical Paper No. 179*, unpublished (1959).

(Ne59a)   Neilson, Dawson, and Johnson, *Rev. Sci. Instr.* **30**, 963 (1959).

(No54)   Nobles, Day, Henkel, Jarvis, Kutarnia, McKibben, Perry, and Smith, *Rev. Sci. Instr.* **25**, 334 (1954).

(Ol34)   Oliphant, Harteck, and Rutherford, *Proc. Roy. Soc.* (*London*) **144A**, 692 (1934).

(ON54)   G. K. O'Neil, *Phys. Rev.* **95**, 1235 (1954).

(Ow59)   R. B. Owen, *Nucleonics* **17**, No. 9, 92 (1959).

(Pe49)   R. A. Peck, *Phys. Rev.* **76**, 1279 (1949).

(Po42)   C. F. Powell, *Proc. Roy. Soc.* (*London*) **181A**, 343 (1942).

(Qu56)   A. R. Quinton and W. J. Doyle, *Phys. Rev.* **101**, 669 (1956).

(Ri57)   Risser, Price, and Class, *Phys. Rev.* **105**, 1288 (1957).

(Ro53)   L. Rosen, *Nucleonics* **11**, No. 7, 32; No. 8, 39 (1953).

(Ru56)   Rubin, Johnson, and Reynolds, *Phys. Rev.* **104**, 1444 (1956).

(Sa56)   R. M. Sanders, *Phys. Rev.* **104**, 1434 (1956).

(Sc57)   Scanlon, Stafford, Thresher, and Bowen, *Rev. Sci. Instr.* **28**, 749 (1957).

(St39)   H. Staub and W. E. Stephens, *Phys. Rev.* **55**, 131 (1939).

(St50)   Stelson, Preston, and Goodman, *Phys. Rev.* **90**, 287 (1950).

(St51)   P. H. Stelson and W. M. Preston, *Phys. Rev.* **83**, 469 (1951).

(St52)   P. H. Stelson and W. M. Preston, *Phys. Rev.* **86**, 132 (1952).

(Su55)   S. Subotic and B. Maglic, *Phil. Mag.* **46**, 805 (1955).

(Ta48)   R. F. Taschek and A. Hemmendinger, *Phys. Rev.* **74**, 373 (1948).

(To49)   Tollestrup, Jenkins, Fowler, and Lauritsen, *Phys. Rev.* **75**, 1947 (1949).

(To55)   W. Tobocman and M. H. Kalos, *Phys. Rev.* **97**, 132 (1955).

(To56)   W. Tobocman, *Phys. Rev.* **102**, 588 (1956).

(Tr54)   C. C. Trail and C. H. Johnson, *Phys. Rev.* **95**, 1363 (1954).

(Wa52)   B. E. Watt, *Phys. Rev.* **87**, 1037 (1952).

(Wa55)   Way, King, McGinnis, and van Lieshout, "Nuclear level schemes (*A* = 40 to *A* = 92)," *Atomic Energy Comm. Report* TID-5300 (1955).

(We37)   V. Weisskopf, *Phys. Rev.* **52**, 295 (1937).

(We56)   J. B. Weddell, *Phys. Rev.* **104**, 1069 (1956).

(Wi51)   Williamson, Browne, Craig, and Donahue, *Phys. Rev.* **84**, 731 (1951).

(Wo50)   D. C. Worth, *Phys. Rev.* **78**, 378 (1950).

Coincidence Studies

G. C. Neilson and J. T. Sample, *University of Alberta, Edmonton, Alberta, Canada*

J. B. Warren, *University of British Columbia, Vancouver, British Columbia, Canada*

1. Introduction

There are numerous circumstances of interest in fast neutron physics in which a fast neutron appears in coincidence with radiation or some other particle and for which a satisfactory interpretation can be obtained only if the energies of the coincident pair are known. Up to the present time no neutron detector has been developed which combines the virtues of speed adequate for coincidence work together with a sufficiently precise and unambiguous selection of the neutron energy to enable coincidence studies to be made, for example, of the γ radiation accompanying neutron groups in $(d, n\gamma)$ reactions. This situation may change with the development of the He^3 gaseous scintillation detector described in Chapter III.D of this book. In the meantime it has proved possible to use the time-of-flight technique to measure and select the energy of the coincident neutrons and still preserve an adequate coincidence counting rate. This article is concerned specifically with this technique and the results which have so far been obtained.

The experimental arrangement in essence consists of one counter close to the source of the coincident events, which registers the radiation or other coincident particle, while the fast neutron detector is placed some distance away. The neutron energy is then determined from the neutron flight time or delay time between coincidences in the two counters. In order to achieve reasonably short duration experiments without too great an array of apparatus, the delayed coincidence time spectrum is converted into a pulse amplitude spectrum which can be sorted by a conventional pulse-height analyzer. In this manner the entire energy spectrum of neutrons in coincidence with other radiation may be obtained at one time with a single pair of counters. The chief practical difficulty has been in the very high counting rate in the scintillation counter placed close up to the source, which is necessary in order to achieve a reasonable coincidence counting rate and adequate neutron energy resolution, the latter being dependent on the flight distance.

Thus in reactions of the type $A(x, n\gamma)B$, where x may be p, d, He³, He⁴, etc., and if the close counter is a γ-ray detector, it is possible to measure: (a) the energies of the neutron groups, except that of the group proceeding to the ground state for which there is no corresponding γ ray; (b) the excitation functions of the neutron groups; (c) the angular distributions of the neutrons and the angular correlations of interest; (d) the lifetimes of the excited states of the product nucleus B, when these lie in the range 10^{-7} second $> \tau_{1/2}$ $> 5 \times 10^{-10}$ second.

Up to the present time the $A(d, n)B^*(\gamma)B$ type of reaction has received most attention since, in addition to the spin and parity data which may be deduced concerning the levels of the product nucleus B^* and the compound nucleus $(A + d)$ if formed, a more complete understanding of such surface reactions may be obtained. There is a lack of experimental information about such matters for example as "backward" or heavy particle stripping, polarization phenomena, and possible spin flip of the out-going neutron. Consequently the technique described in this chapter and most of its applications are concerned mainly with this type of reaction and the theoretical evaluation of the results of such studies. There is no problem however in applying the method to reactions such as $A(x, n\alpha)B$ leading to neutrons in coincidence with charged particles.

There are also a number of more difficult but possible applications of this technique, for example to the study of $(n, 2n)$ processes and to inelastic neutron scattering $(n, n'\gamma)$. It should also be mentioned that in the absence of coincident γ radiation or particles, the fast neutron energies can be determined by scattering from the close-up counter and measuring the flight time to the second counter at some selected scattering angle. In this way, too, the energy of a beam of neutrons may be defined quite precisely and, by the insertion of absorbers in the flight path, fast neutron total cross sections may be measured.

2. Experimental Technique

A. *Basic Requirements for Time-of-Flight Methods*

In all fast neutron time-of-flight work it is necessary to measure short time intervals (10–200 mμ sec) with precision. The early attempts to separate neutron groups by time-of-flight technique (Ja51) were unsatisfactory because of insufficient time resolution and poor efficiency. Although many practical circuits for the precise measurement of short time intervals were developed (Ga50, Be52a; see also Be55a or Le54 for a review of the development of coincidence techniques), these were not very suitable for direct application to time-of-flight methods because only one point in the time spectrum could be measured at one time. However for the study of a single neutron group at a time such single channel coincidence systems have been used successfully (Sh57a, Ow58a). The need for more efficient data collection was realized and several multi-channel coincidence analyzers were developed (Mc52, On55, Ke49). These multi-channel time-delayed coincidence analyzers, commonly called "chronotrons," are essentially single-channel coincidence units duplicated many times. Moreover these chronotrons, because of inherent pulse difficulties, are limited to a small number of fixed time channels. Recently a new type of chronotron, a vernier chronotron, has been developed (Le57) which overcomes the difficulties of fixed and limited number of time channels. A more detailed account of this circuit is given in Chapter IV.A. A different approach to the problem of measuring a time spectrum originated from the proposal of converting a time spectrum into a pulse-height spectrum (Mo52). Using this method several workers have developed practical "time-converters" for the milli-microsecond region (Fr54b, Ne55, Le55a, We56a, Jo56, Re57, Gr58). The operation of all these time-converters is dependent on the fact that many reliable multi-channel pulse-height analyzers are now available allowing the display of as many time channels as there are pulse-height-analyzing channels.

This time conversion principle outlined above has been applied successfully to coincidence studies of $(x, n\gamma)$ reactions (Ne55, Ne56, Ne58, Da58, Sa58). The apparatus is shown in schematic form in Fig. 1 as it would be used for measuring a neutron spectrum in coincidence with the γ rays from a $(d, n\gamma)$ reaction. Here the γ rays are used to give the initial pulse to the timing circuit. In using the γ ray

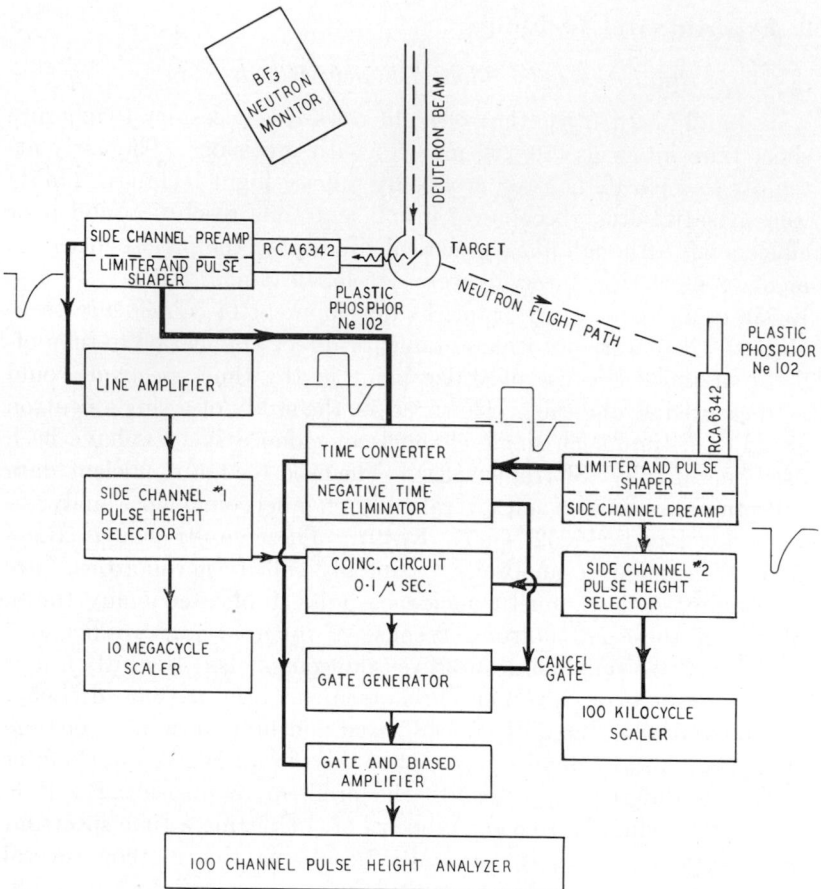

Figure 1. Block diagram of the complete coincidence time-of-flight spectrometer.

to give the initial pulse it is assumed, and in general it is true, that the lifetimes of the excited states emitting the γ rays are short compared to the time resolution of the spectrometer. It should be pointed out that if the lifetime of an excited state is not short compared to the resolving time of the spectrometer, then under favorable circumstances the lifetime of the excited state can be measured, as described for example in Section 3.B(2) of this chapter. The initial pulse from the γ-ray detector is followed by a terminal pulse from the neutron detector. The time interval between these two pulses is converted to a voltage pulse by the time-converter circuit. If the γ-ray and neutron detectors did not have a noise spectrum and all real pulses were large, then the pulse from the time-converter could be amplified and fed directly into the pulse-height analyzer. The two side-channels and the gated biased amplifier are required to eliminate the small pulses that would not operate the time-converter correctly. The two side-channels also serve another useful purpose in that they allow some energy selection, if the neutron and γ-ray spectra are complex.

B. Choice of Detectors for $(x, n\gamma)$ Coincidence Schemes

(1) **General Considerations.** In choosing the neutron and γ-ray detectors, the three factors of prime importance are high efficiency, millimicrosecond response, and large amplitude pulses. The only detectors available at this time that meet these requirements are scintillation counters using fast phosphors.

Table I shows the relative pulse heights and decay times for a number of available scintillators that could be used as neutron or γ-ray detectors.

Table I.   Comparison of Phosphors[a]

Phosphor	Light yield[b]	Decay time × 10^{-9} sec
Anthracene	1.0	30
Diphenyl-acetylene	0.8	4
Stilbene	0.65	8
Naphthalene	0.25	60
NaI(Tl)	2.0	250
Sintilon Plastic[c]	0.6	8
Pilot "B" Plastic[d]	0.9	4
N.E. 101 Plastic[c]	0.55	4
N.E. 102 Plastic[e]	0.65	3.5
N.E. 202 Liquid[e]	0.75	2

[a] Values quoted are mostly from suppliers of the materials.

[b] From β-rays, relative to anthracene.

[c] Manufactured by National Radiac, Newark, N. J.

[d] Manufactured by Pilot Chemicals Inc., Waltham, Mass.

[e] Manufactured by Nuclear Enterprises Ltd., Winnipeg, Canada.

(2) **The Neutron Detector.** The problem of efficiency requires that the neutron detector be an efficient organic scintillator

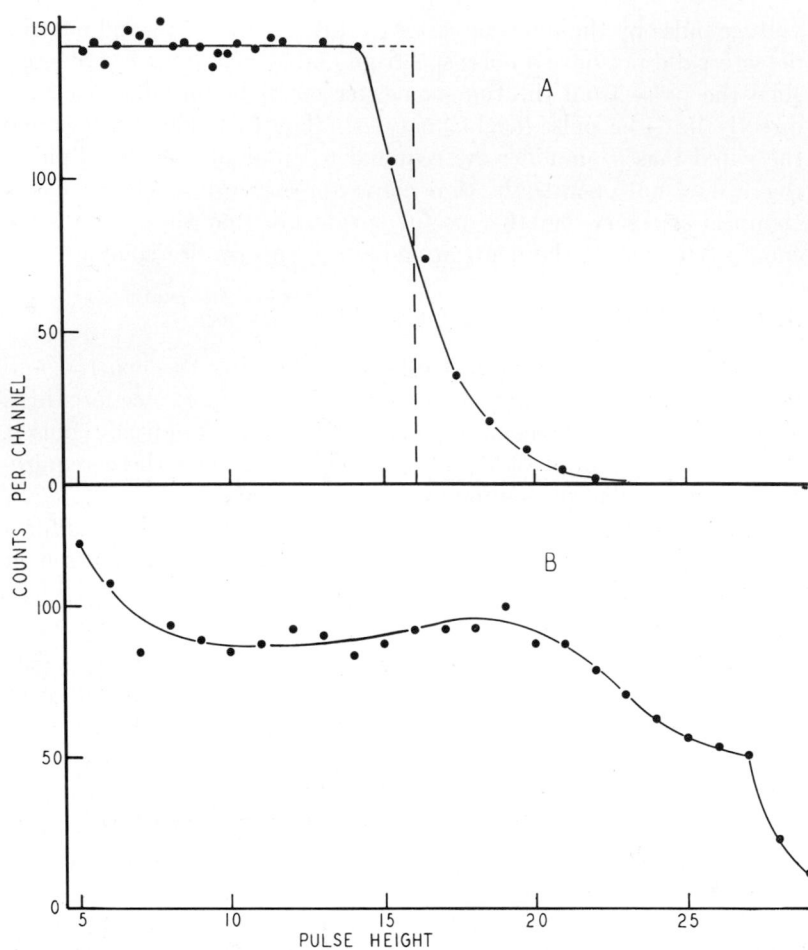

Figure 2. Pulse-height spectra of neutron detectors exposed to monoenergetic neutrons. A, 4 × 4 × 2 cm stilbene crystal, 2.67-Mev neutrons. The dashed line is the theoretical knock-on spectrum. B, 5 inch diam. × 2 inch thick liquid phosphor, 3.51-Mev neutrons (Ha57).

rich in hydrogen to take advantage of the relatively large n-p scattering cross section over a large range of neutron energy. Of the choices in Table I only liquid and plastic scintillators are available in the sizes required. Plastic phosphor has the added advantage of ruggedness

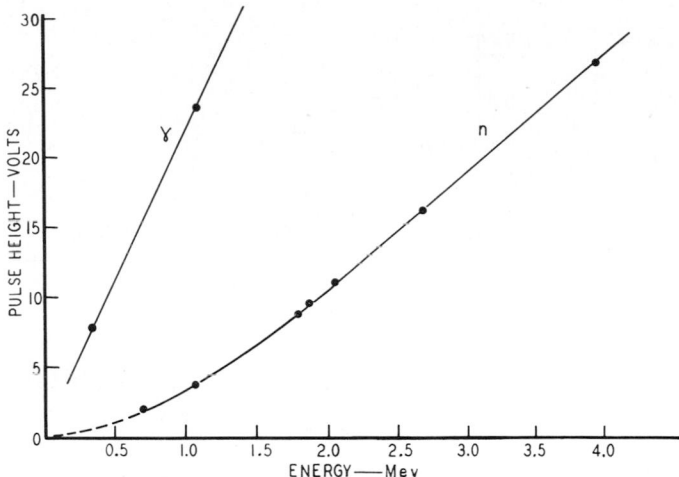

Figure 3. Response of stilbene to neutrons and γ rays.

and ease of handling but both liquid and plastic phosphors have been used successfully (Ha57, Ne58, Ne59a).

The response of a small stilbene crystal (4 × 4 × 2 cm) to mono-energetic neutrons of 2.67 Mev is shown in Fig. 2a, where the dashed line is the predicted recoil spectrum for single *n-p* scattering using a detector with perfect inherent resolution. The sloping front edge of the experimental spectrum is attributed to the imperfect resolution of the detector. The vertical dashed line in Fig. 2a, corresponding to the mean pulse height produced by a neutron losing all its energy to the recoiling proton, is plotted in Fig. 3 as a function of neutron energy. Figure 3 also shows the response of the stilbene crystal to Compton electrons of various energies. The large difference in light output for electrons and protons of the same energy is a very undesirable characteristic of the organic scintillators when used as neutron detectors. Owing to the non-linear response of organic phosphors to low-energy neutrons, special techniques must be used if they are to be detected. The response curve of stilbene to neutrons, Fig. 3, is in essential agreement with the work of Fowler and Roos (Fo55) who measured the response of stilbene to protons (see also Chapter II.B).

For large volume detectors the proton recoil spectrum is no longer closely approximated by a single interaction spectrum but is much

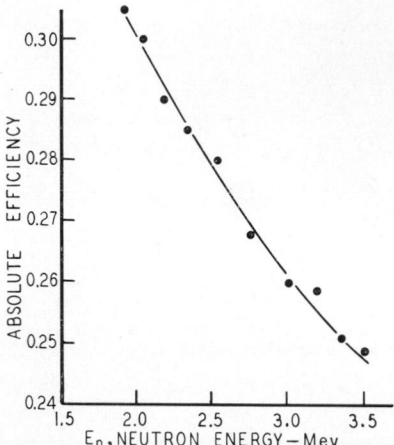

Figure 4. Absolute efficiency *vs.* neutron energy of a liquid phosphor (5 inch diam. $\times$ 2 inches thick), co-axial with neutron direction (Ha57). The curve is of the form, efficiency $= 0.146 + 0.45/(E_n + 0.82)$.

more complicated. The recoil spectrum shown in Fig. 2B (Ha57) was obtained using NE202 liquid phosphor[1] (5 inches diam. $\times$ 2 inches thick) exposed to 3.51-Mev neutrons. The neutron detection efficiency of the large liquid scintillator for fast neutrons, defined as the number of scintillations observed per neutron passing through the scintillator, has been measured, Fig. 4 (Ha58), for neutrons with energies from 2 to 3.5 Mev by measuring the differential cross section for the $D(d, n)He^3$ reaction and comparing with the cross section measured by Hunter and Richards (Hu49). The absolute neutron detection efficiency for 2.07-Mev neutrons was obtained by two methods: calculated from the target thickness (thin gas target) and beam current the efficiency is 29 $\pm$ 2 per cent; calculated from the neutron flux measured by a standard flat response BF_3 counter (see Chapter III.A) the efficiency is 32 $\pm$ 2 per cent. The increase in efficiency with decreasing neutron energy can be accounted for by the increase in the n-p scattering cross section (Fo56) at lower neutron energies.

(3) **Initial Detector.** The choice of the initial detector is dependent upon the type of radiation to be detected. If the neutrons

[1] Manufactured by Nuclear Enterprises Ltd., Winnipeg, Canada.

are measured in coincidence with an associated particle (Wa54, On54), e.g., reactions of the type $D(d, n)He^3$, $T(d, n)He^4$, etc., only a very thin section of fast scintillator is needed. For reactions of the type $(x, n\gamma)$ in which the detection of the coincident γ ray gives the initial pulse, the choice of detector is limited to the organic phosphors or, in some cases, to a NaI(Tl) crystal. The organic scintillators have the virtue of very short decay times but, unfortunately, since the absorption of γ rays (from 0.5 to 10 Mev) in organic scintillators is predominantly due to the Compton process (Ne53a, Da52b) it is impossible to select only one γ ray when there are higher-energy γ rays present. The inorganic scintillator, NaI(Tl), while it has a longer decay-time gives a much larger pulse and allows better selection of γ-ray energy. Selection of a particular γ ray is of importance if the complex decay schemes of most $(x, n\gamma)$ type reactions are to be completely resolved. The superiority of the NaI(Tl) scintillator for γ-ray energy discrimination is obvious but, as will be shown in the next section, one must sacrifice some time resolution if a NaI(Tl) crystal is used.

(4) **Effect of Photomultiplier and Scintillator Combinations on Time Resolution.** Table II contains the time resolutions obtained with different combinations of photomultiplier and scintillator. Test conditions were similar throughout with the following exceptions. The side-channel settings depended on the type of scintillator used. For plastic phosphors all pulses corresponding to an electron energy loss of greater than 150 kev were accepted while for NaI(Tl) only the photopeak was accepted. Magnesium oxide was used as a diffuse reflector for all scintillators except for the two largest plastic phosphors which were highly polished and covered with an aluminium reflector and relied on internal reflection for light collection. Initial rise and intrinsic time resolution are probably largely determined by the time spread of the light directly reaching the photomultiplier and the provision of a white reflector does not affect this very much, though of course it does affect the total light reaching the tube.

Tests of noise and gain characteristics on R.C.A. 6342 and R.C.A. 6810 photomultipliers indicate that roughly one-fifth of each type is capable of achieving the time resolutions shown in Table II. However, no selection of R.C.A. 7046 photomultipliers was made. The 6810 and 6810-A show appreciable fatigue under high counting

Table II. Time Resolution of Phototube-Phosphor Combinations

| | γ-ray counter | | | | Neutron counter | | | |
Phototube	Type	Phosphor diam., in.	Length, in.	Phototube	Type	Phosphor diam., in.	Length, in.	Resolution, mμ sec
6342	plastic	1.875	2	6342	plastic	1.875	2	1.50
6342	"	1	2	6342	"	1	2	1.37
6810	"	1.875	2	6810	"	1	2	3.6
6810	"	1	2	6810	"	1	2	2.8
6810A	"	1	2	6810A	"	1	2	1.88
6342	"	1.5	2	6342	"	1.5	4.5	1.53
6342	"	1.5	2	7046	"	3	6	1.47
6342	stilbene	1	1	7046	"	3 × 2 slab	10	1.7
6342	NaI(Tl)	1	0.5	7046	"	3	6	2.1
6342	NaI(Tl)	2	2	7046	"	3	6	2.7
7046	NaI(Tl)	4	3	6342	liquid	5	2	3.5

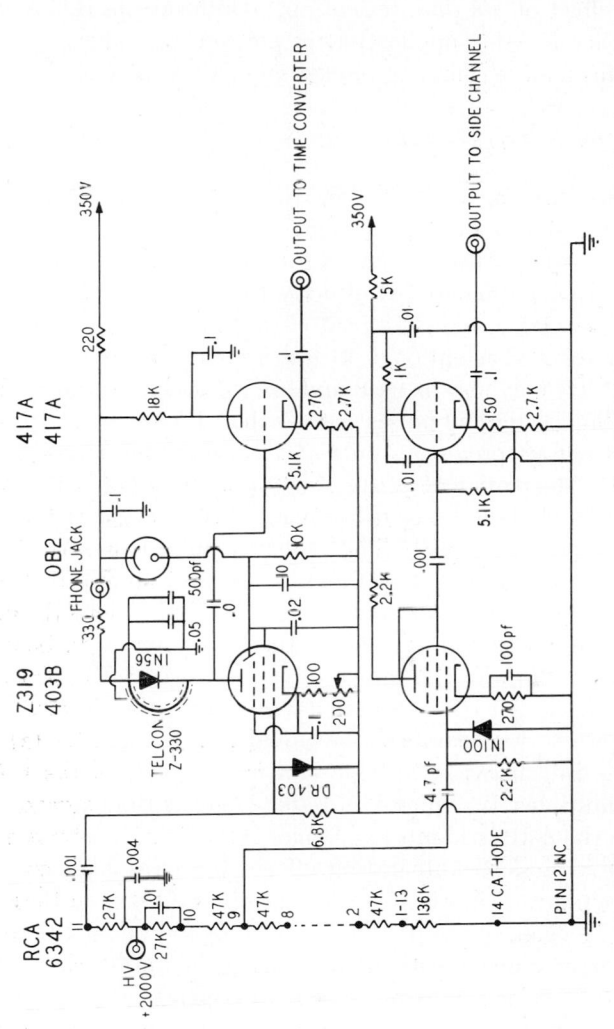

Figure 5. Pulse-shaping circuit and side-channel head amplifier. Resistance in ohms, capacitance in μf unless otherwise specified.

rates preventing their use as the initial detector in many cases. It is apparent from Table II that the relatively long transit time of the R.C.A. 7046 (40 mμ sec longer than that for the R.C.A. 6342) has no appreciable effect on its time resolution. Data on the R.C.A. 7264 photomultiplier for this application is not yet available. Chapter IV.A. contains a more complete discussion of these effects.

C. Circuitry for $(x, n\gamma)$ Correlation Studies

(1) **Detector and Pulse-Shaping Circuit.** The pulse-shaping circuit shown in Fig. 5 (Ne55) generates the fast positive pulses required to operate the time-converter. Negative pulses from the photomultiplier tube are fed directly to the grid of the Z-319,[2] a sharp cut-off secondary emission pentode with a mutual-conductance of 18 ma per volt. Conventional pentodes such as the Western Electric 404A, E180F may also be used and are rather more stable. With 18 ma. standing current all pulses greater than 1.5 volts will drive the tube beyond cut-off producing pulses of constant amplitude at the Z-319 anode. The plate load of the Z-319 is a section of Z-330[3] delay cable ($Z_0 = 330$ ohms, 1.7 μsec delay per 100 ft) shorted at the plate supply end with a capacitor. The reflected pulse is absorbed by a 1N56 crystal diode forming a rectangular pulse of amplitude 5 volts and duration $2t$ where t is the transit time of the pulse along the cable. Choice of cable length will depend on the time interval to be measured. Values of $2t$ up to 100 mμsec have been used successfully. A 417-A Western Electric triode is used as a low-loss cable driver.

There are several points to be noted in this circuit. (a) The large voltage drop between cathode and first dynode of the R.C.A. 6342 photomultiplier is required to reduce transit time spread. (b) The pulse on the Z-319 grid must be longer than $2t$ but must not be too long because of possible integrating effects from the high counting rates; the values used in Fig. 5 are a compromise between these two effects. (c) The gain of the photomultiplier should be set to produce the largest possible pulses without saturating the limiter circuit with noise pulses. This circuit, as described, will operate at 2×10^5 random pulses per second without appreciable distortion of the output pulse, which is flat-topped with rise and fall times of less than 5

[2] Manufactured by E.M.I. Ltd., Middlesex, England.
[3] Manufactured by Telcon Works, Greenwich, England.

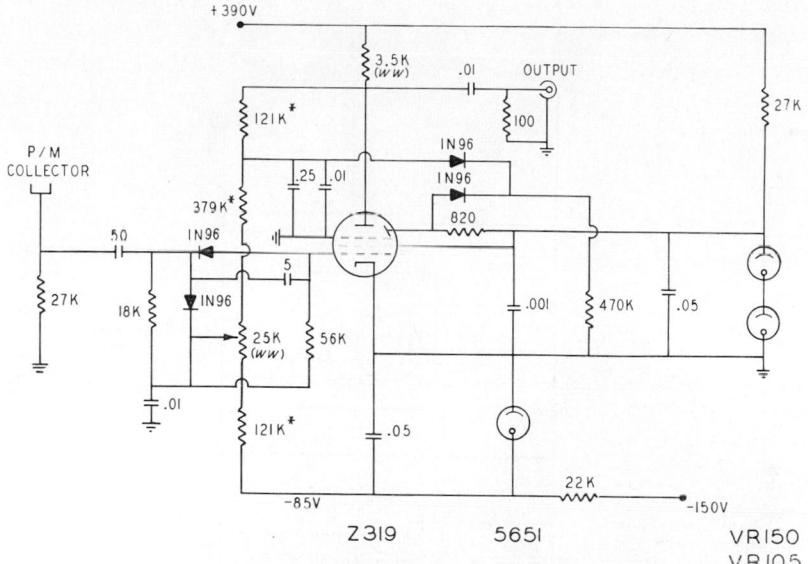

Figure 6. Highly stabilized pulse-shaping circuit (Jo57).

mμsec. The output pulse also has a large undershoot which does not affect the functioning of the time-converter but actually aids in DC restoration at high counting rates. The long-term stability of this limiter circuit can be improved by providing some anode current stabilization. Figure 6 shows such a circuit developed for use in the measurement of the short lifetimes of positrons in metals (Jo57) where long-term stability is of prime importance. Negative DC feedback is incorporated to provide long term stability but as this introduces a dependence of pulse amplitude on counting rate, an additional positive feedback loop is inserted which is operative only during the presence of a pulse at the grid of the pentode. Thus by adjustment of the positive feedback parameters the negative feedback is cancelled during the pulse and only applied when the circuit is in a truly DC condition in the absence of a pulse.

(2) **Time-to-Pulse-Height Converters.** The time-to-pulse-height converter circuit shown in Fig. 7 (Ne55) is simple and reliable and, as it is typical of time-converters, will be discussed in some detail. (For a more detailed discussion of time-converters applied to other special problems, see Chapter IV.A.) The time-converter in

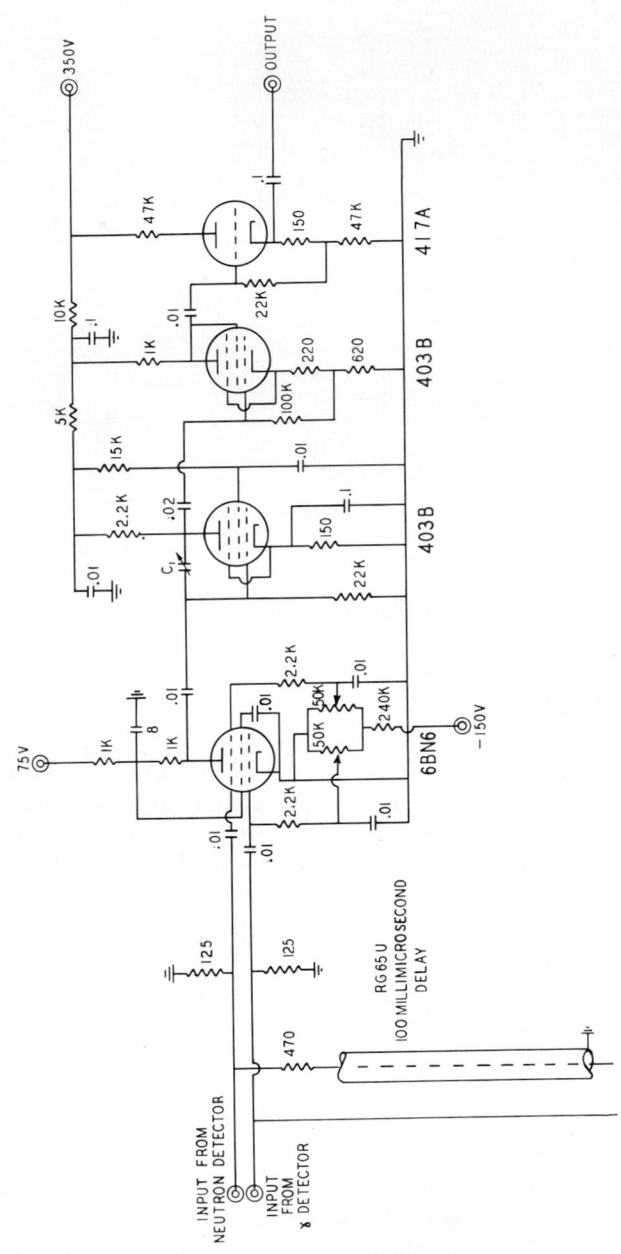

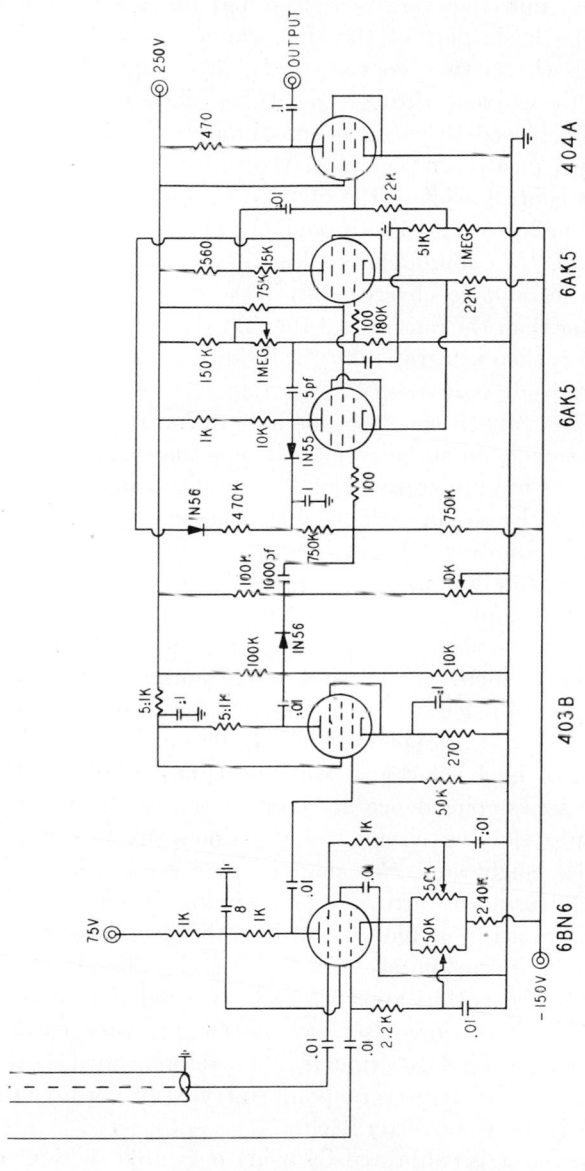

Figure 7. Time-to-pulse-height converter circuit. Upper portion of diagram is the time-converter, lower portion is the "negative time eliminator."

Fig. 7 will operate with very high random counting rates (up to 5×10^5 counts per sec) and therefore is well suited for use in coincidence studies. The basic part of the time converter is the 6BN6 gated-beam tube whose two control grids have approximately equal control on the current through the tube. The grids of the 6BN6 are normally biased to cutoff (approximately -2.5 to -3.0 volts). The shaped positive pulses from the pulse-shaping circuits are fed to the two control grids of the 6BN6. If the two pulses are coincident (to within $2t$) the current through the 6BN6 will be a function of their overlap. Maximum charge flows if there is no delay between the two pulses and no charge flows if the delay between the two pulses is greater than the duration of the first pulse. The current through the 6BN6 is then integrated by the following tube producing a pulse whose amplitude is inversely proportional to the time delay between pulses. The capacitor C_1 sets the integration time constant and also provides some gain stabilization. The actual value of C_1 is not critical as long as the integrating time constant is long compared to 100 mμsec. Since the circuits following the time-converter do not have to handle high counting rates or have good high frequency response they can be standard μsec design. Although the time-converter works best with input pulses 2.5 to 3.0 volts in amplitude, the circuit will function when these pulses are as small as 1.5 to 2.0 volts in amplitude. Measurements made using a fast pulser to drive the pulse-shaping circuits in place of the photomultipliers show the coincidence resolving time of this type of circuit to be much better than the 0.3 mμsec quoted by Fischer and Marshall (Fi52) who used the 6BN6 as a simple series coincidence detector. Using the fast pulser to operate the pulse-shaping circuit, all the time-converter pulses fall within one pulse-height analyzing channel, 10^{-10} sec in width (see Fig. 9). In fact by using a narrow sliding window in place of the pulse-height analyzer, it is possible to show that the electronic resolution of the circuit is approximately 2×10^{-11} sec. The electronic time resolution obtained is thus approximately two orders of magnitude better than the best time resolution obtainable with organic phosphors and present photomultipliers. Therefore, until better detectors become available, there is no point in trying to improve the time resolution of the time-converter itself.

The time-converter is calibrated by using measured sections of Telcon[3] AS-48 cable to delay the pulse from the neutron detector be-

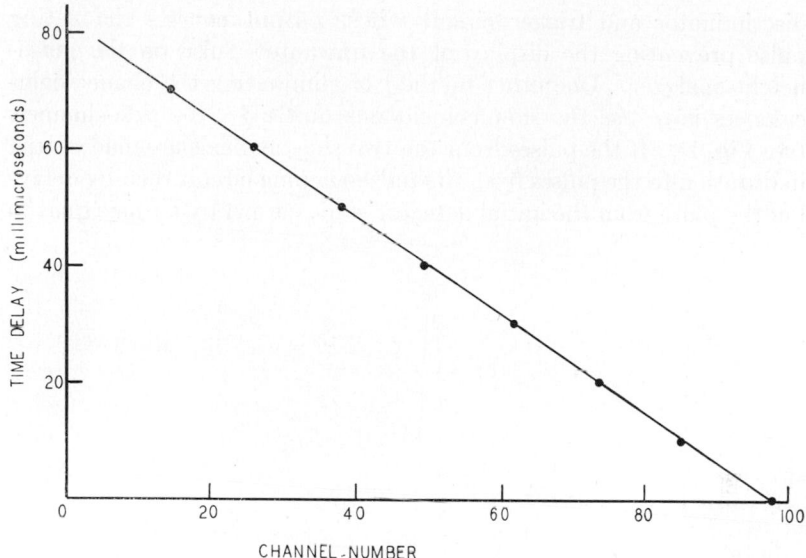

Figure 8. Time-to-pulse-height calibration curve of the spectrometer.

fore it reaches the time-converter. Figure 8 shows the time-to-pulse-height calibration curve for the spectrometer. The time calibration curve is very nearly linear over the entire time spectrum but for very accurate work the slight nonlinearities must be taken into account.

(3) **Further Improvements to the Time-of-Flight Spectrometer.** The basic time-converter described above when used in coincidence studies has the fault that the circuit is unable to reject those chance events in which the pulse from the neutron detector precedes the pulse from the initial detector. There are several possible methods of eliminating these chance coincidences. The circuit shown in Fig. 7 (locally called the "negative-time eliminator") eliminates the undesirable chance coincidences as follows. The pulse from the neutron detector is delayed by a length of RG-65U cable equivalent to one pulse length and fed to one grid of the lower 6BN6 in the circuit diagram Fig. 7, while the pulse from the initial detector is fed directly to the other grid of this tube which operates as a simple coincidence detector. With this arrangement the plate will produce an output pulse only when the pulses are coincident and the neutron pulse precedes the pulse from the initial detector. This pulse operates a

discriminator and trigger circuit whose output cancels the gating pulse preventing the display of the unwanted pulse on the pulse-height-analyzer. One other method of eliminating the chance coincidences is to use the slow coincidence unit after the side-channels (see Fig. 1). If the pulses from the two side-channels are made equal in duration to the pulses from the pulse-shaping circuit then by delaying the pulse from the initial detector side-channel by a time equal to

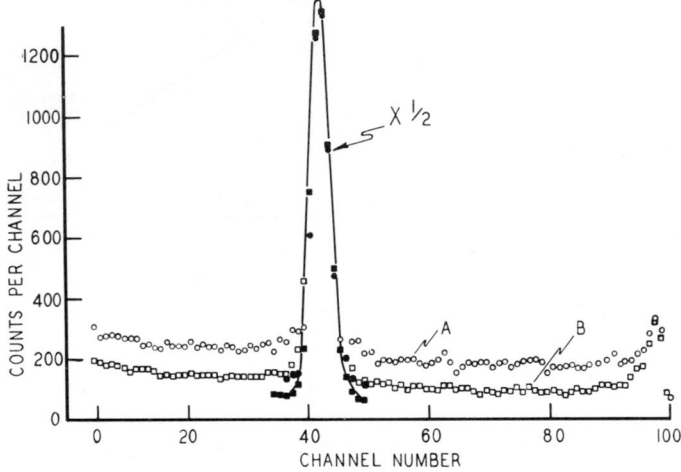

Figure 9. Effect of negative time eliminator on the true to chance ratio. A without, B with negative time eliminator in operation. The peak is from Co[60] γ rays, "neutron" channel delayed. The time per channel is 0.5 mμ sec.

this pulse duration there will be no coincidence output when the pulse from the neutron detector precedes the pulse from the initial detector. Green and Bell (Gr58) have developed a similar circuit for use in positron lifetime measurements.

The improvement in background realized by the use of the above circuits is shown in Figs. 9A and B. Figure 9A shows the background level using a large Co[60] source (the coincidence peak is in channel 42.5) without the negative time eliminator in operation. Figure 9B is a repeat of Fig. 9A with the negative time eliminator working, showing as expected, an improvement of nearly a factor or two in the true-to-chance ratio.

D. *Performance of Time-of-Flight Coincidence Spectrometer*

(1) **Resolution and Time Calibration.** The performance of the complete spectrometer can be checked using the coincident annihilation radiation from a Na[22] source. Figure 10 shows the coincidence resolution curve using large plastic phosphors coupled to R.C.A.

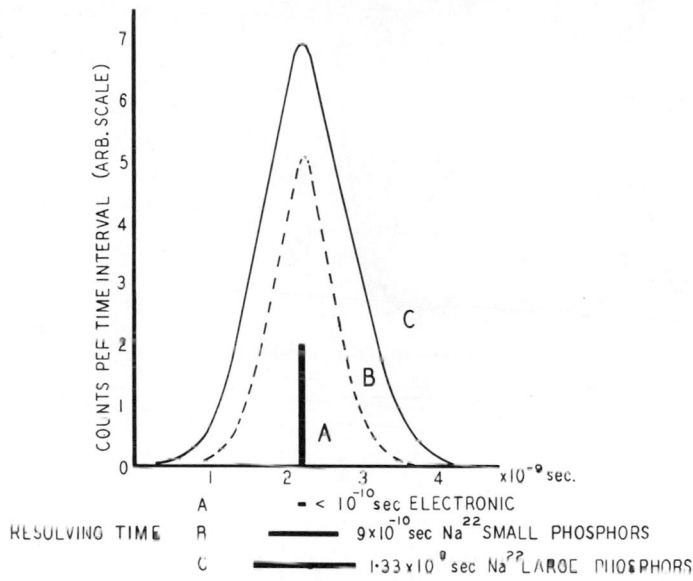

Figure 10. Time resolution curves.

6342 photomultipliers. The initial detector is a 1.5-inch diam. × 2-inch long cylinder of plastic phosphor, while the neutron detector is a 1.75-inch diam. × 4.5 inch long cylinder of plastic phosphor. By using smaller plastic phosphors (1-inch diam. × 2-inch long) on both detectors the 1.33 mμ sec time resolution for the 0.51-Mev annihilation radiation can be reduced to 9 × 10⁻¹⁰ sec. As can be seen by comparing the resolution curve using a Na[22] source with the resolution obtained with a pulser, almost all the time dispersion comes from the phosphor (Po50) and photomultiplier. The time resolution obtained with the spectrometer when used for $(x, n\gamma)$ correlation work is not so good as that obtained from the annihilation radiation, but this is expected because of the finite time dispersion due to the size of the neutron detector. Another factor decreasing the resolution is the change in rise time of the limited pulse depending on the pulse size from the photomultiplier. This effect is particularly important when the neutron energy is low and the side-channels are set to accept a

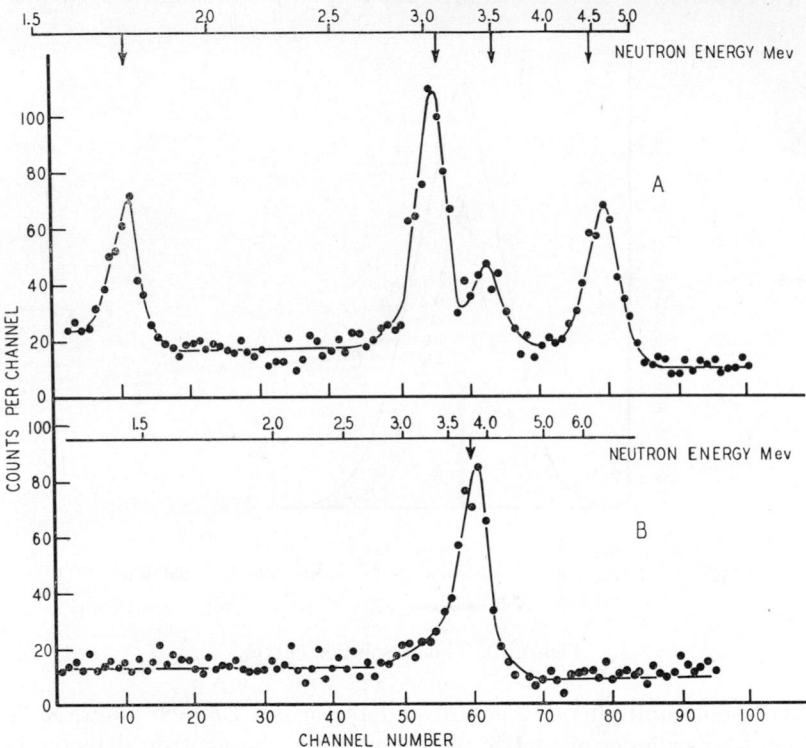

Figure 11. Neutron coincidence time-of-flight spectra. A, $Be^9(d, n\gamma)B^{10}$; B, $Li^6(d, n\gamma)Be^7$. Uncorrected experimental curves. Arrows indicate the position of groups calculated from published Q values. Spectrum A was taken in 30 minutes with 6630 microcoulombs of beam onto a thin target while spectrum B took 30 minutes with 1020 microcoulombs onto a target approximately 100 μgm/cm² thick.

broad energy spectrum. Ways of decreasing the pulse height sensitivity are discussed in Section 2.E. In practice a working resolution of 2 mμsec can be achieved with little difficulty. A resolution of 2 mμsec and a flight path of 1.5 meters corresponds to an energy resolution of approximately 5 per cent for neutrons of 2 Mev which is adequate for most neutron spectroscopy.

Figure 11 shows typical time-of-flight spectra for coincidence studies in $(x, n\gamma)$ reactions. The energies of neutron groups can be computed directly from the time calibration curve, Fig. 8, and the flight distance. Energy scales calculated from the time calibration curve (Fig. 8) and the flight distance are shown at the top of the figures. The arrows (Fig. 11A) indicate the energies of the neutron groups corresponding to the first four excited states of B^{10} calculated from the accepted Q-values (Aj59). The slight broadening and asymmetric shape of the highest energy group is attributed to the measurable lifetime of the 0.72-Mev state [see Section 3.B(2)]. To a lesser extent the other groups are affected by this lifetime as their associated γ rays cascade through the 0.72-Mev excited state.

It should be noted that all the curves in Fig. 11 are uncorrected experimental curves taken with the energy-selecting side-channels set to accept all the γ rays in coincidence with any neutron group. This means that one must take into account the number of cascade γ rays and the γ-ray detector efficiency, as well as the efficiency of the neutron detector, if the relative yields of the neutron groups are to be compared. There is also a large prompt peak from coincident γ rays which lies above channel 100. The true-to-chance ratio, i.e., peak-to-background ratio, depends mainly on target current and to a lesser extent on the room background. The true-to-chance ratio can be improved further by decreasing the target current and taking longer runs.

(2) **Stability.** When used in conjunction with a high voltage accelerator the coincidence spectrometer must not only be stable for times long compared to the time required for each run but must also not be affected by widely fluctuating counting rates. Once the spectrometer discussed above has been in operation for a day the position of the coincidence peak does not drift more than 1 mμsec in any subsequent twenty-four hour period, which is more than adequate considering that the normal time for one run is twenty minutes. Jones (Jo56, Jo57), using highly stabilized circuitry, claims a stability of 10^{-11} sec over a twenty-four hour period and hopes to measure lifetimes to $\pm 1 \times 10^{-11}$ sec. The stability to counting rate fluctuations is shown in Fig. 12. Curve 1 is the coincidence curves from the 0.51-Mev annihilation radiation using a small Na^{22} source. Curve 2

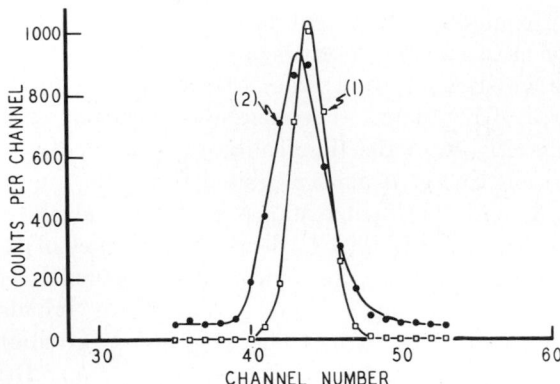

Figure 12. Spectrometer stability against count-rate fluctuations.   Curve 1: γ-ray channel count-rate very low.   Curve 2: γ-ray channel count-rate $5 \times 10^5 \text{sec}^{-1}$.

shows the effect of increasing the counting rate in the γ-ray detector with a Co^{60} source to 5×10^5 counts per sec.   At the highest counting rates the Na^{22} coincidence curve is broadened to approximately 1.7 $m\mu$sec, but up to counting rates of 2×10^5 counts per second as normally used there is no significant change in either the width or position of the coincidence curve.

E. Fundamental Limitations

Neutrons with an energy below 800 kev will not produce large enough pulses to operate the simple pulse-shaping circuit, Fig. 5, unless the photomultiplier gain is increased to such an extent that noise becomes troublesome.   One way of reducing noise difficulties is to use two photomultipliers in coincidence looking at the same phosphor.   This scheme has been used by Cranberg et al. (Cr57) to reduce the lower limit for neutron detection to 50 kev.   A similar circuit has been used by Neilson et al. (Ne59a) in conjunction with the time-converter previously described.   The pulse from this circuit can be fed directly to the time-converter and has no appreciable effect on the electronic resolving time, but by eliminating the photomultiplier noise the gain of the photomultipliers can be greatly increased.

It is evident that background counts from random events play a very important role in restricting the usefulness of any time-of-flight spectrometer.   In most practical applications a true-to-chance ratio of one-to-one can be tolerated; much below this level the accumulation of meaningful experimental data becomes increasingly difficult. For both pulsed beam and coincidence methods the neutron detector is the prime factor in background considerations because the real neutron counting rate is usually smaller than the undesirble background counting rate. Any decrease in the background counting rate will therefore result in an improved true-to-chance ratio and thus allow the measurement of lower intensity neutron groups. Most of the background in the neutron counter is due to low energy γ rays which, until recently, could not be conveniently differentiated from pulses initiated by neutrons. It has recently been shown (Ow58a) that there is a long-lived component in the fluorescent decay of some organic scintillators whose magnitude depends on the specific ionization of the detected particle. This immediately leads to the possibility of selecting only those pulses produced by heavy particles and thereby making the detector insensitive to γ rays. Circuits for this purpose, which work well for neutrons above about 3 Mev, have been developed by Owen (Ow58a, Ow58b), and Litherland et al. (Li59).

A circuit developed by Neilson (Ne59a) has been used successfully to give a tenfold improvement in the true-to-chance ratio when detecting neutrons of energies greater than 1 Mev. In this system the liquid scintillator glass cell is viewed by R.C.A. 7046 photomultipliers at each end. One photomultiplier operates the conventional pulse shaping and preamplifier circuits, while the other forms part of a circuit which discriminates between pulses initiated by heavy particles and γ rays.

Without some improvement in photomultipliers and scintillators it is hard to see how any significant improvement can be made to the time resolution now obtainable. The use of new photomultiplier tubes, like the R.C.A. 7046, and a larger plastic phosphor for a neutron detector have improved the efficiency and therefore, by using longer flight paths, the energy resolution.

3. $(x, n\gamma)$ Reaction Studies

A. Theoretical Considerations

(1) **Reaction Paths.** The measurement of n-γ correlations in reactions of the type $A(x, n\gamma)B$, where x may be a proton, deuteron, or heavier particle, can aid in determining the spins and parities of

states of the nucleus B, and of the compound nucleus $(A + x)$, if it is formed as a step in the reaction. The interpretation of such correlations depends on the assumed mechanics of the reaction. Two idealized reaction paths are compound nucleus formation and surface interaction; probably many actual reaction paths lie between these extremes (We56b). Reactions proceeding principally by compound nucleus formation are exemplified by the $(\alpha, n\gamma)$ reactions (for a possible exception see Ma55a). Theoretical n-γ angular correlation functions have been calculated (Bi53, Sh53), but little experimental work has been reported (Ja56).

(2) **Deuteron Stripping.** This process is the most widely studied example of surface reactions. In the case of $(d, n\gamma)$ reactions the proton of the loosely bound deuteron is captured by the target nucleus, the neutron passing so far away that its interaction with the nucleus may be neglected. Excited states of the residual nucleus then decay by γ-ray emission. Stripping reactions are characterized by strong forward maxima in the angular distributions of the outgoing particles. Explanation of such maxima by compound nucleus theory would call for improbably high values of the angular momentum transferred to the compound nucleus by the bombarding particle. Deuteron stripping, unlike most particle capture reactions, can proceed via the ground and first few excited states of the residual nucleus, whose properties are of great interest for comparison with the predictions of the shell model.

Since the work of Butler (Bu51) and of Bhatia *et al.* (Bh52) the usefulness of deuteron stripping theory in assigning the parities and spins of nuclear states has been proven by many experiments. The theory has undergone several refinements and extensions in the attempt to explain disagreements with experiment, particularly for low bombarding energies. Several reviews of stripping theory and its comparison with experimental results have been published (Hu53, Ho56a, Ho56b, Bu57; see also Chapter V.D).

The simple theory assumes that (a) all effects of Coulomb repulsion and nuclear scattering of the deuteron and outgoing particle may be neglected, (b) there is no compound nucleus formation, (c) the captured particle reacts with the target nucleus only on the surface of a sphere of radius R. The following sketch of the theory follows the development by Bhatia *et al.* (Bh52), the notation applying to (d, n) reactions. The shape of the angular distribution of emitted neutrons is strongly dependent on l_p, where l_p is the angular momentum with which the proton is captured. Conservation of angular momentum and parity restricts the possible value of l_p; if J_i and J_e are respectively the spins of the target nucleus and the particular state in which the residual nucleus is left, then

$$\left| J_i - J_e \right| - \frac{1}{2} \leq l_p \leq J_i + J_e + \frac{1}{2}$$

If the states i and e have similar (opposite) parities, l_p is even (odd).

The differential cross section in the center-of-mass system may be written

$$\sigma(\theta) = \Pi(K_n) \sum_{l_p} P_{l_p} L_{l_p}(k_p) \tag{1}$$

where $\Pi(K_n)$ is the probability that the neutron has the momentum contribution $\hbar K_n$ from the internal motion of the deuteron, L_{l_p} is the centrifugal barrier factor of a proton with angular momentum $\hbar l_p$ and linear momentum $\hbar k_p$, and P_{l_p} is the probability that a proton reaching the "surface" of the target nucleus with angular momentum $\hbar l_p$ will be captured. Using the zero range approximation to the deuteron wave function,

$$\Pi(K_n) = (\alpha/\pi^2)(\alpha^2 + K^2_n)^2 \tag{2}$$

$$\alpha = 2.3 \times 10^{12} \text{ cm}^{-1}$$

The barrier factor $L_{l_p}(k_p)$ is given by

$$L_{l_p}(k_p) = 4\pi(2l_p + 1)j_{l_p}{}^2(k_p R) \tag{3}$$

where j_{l_p} is a spherical Bessel function and R is the radius at which the proton is supposed to be captured. Within reasonable limits R may be regarded as a parameter in fitting experimental curves. P_{l_p} contains, as well as kinematical and statistical factors, a factor dependent on the properties of the initial and final nuclear levels.

The momenta K_n and k_p are related to θ and to the energies of the deuteron and neutron by conservation of momentum and energy. From Fig. 13,

$$\mathbf{K}_n = \mathbf{k}_n - \mathbf{k}_d/2 \tag{4}$$

$$K_n = [(k_n - k_d/2)^2 + 2k_n k_d \sin^2(\theta/2)]^{1/2} \tag{5}$$

$$\mathbf{k}_p = \mathbf{k}_d - (m_i/m_f)\mathbf{k}_n \tag{6}$$

$$k_p = [(k_d - (m_i/m_f)k_n)^2 + 4(m_i/m_f)k_n k_d \sin^2 (\theta/2)]^{1/2} \quad (7)$$

$$k_d = [m_i/(m_d + m_i)][2m_d E_d]^{1/2}/\hbar \quad (8)$$

$$k_n = [2m_n m_f/(m_n + m_f)][Q + E_d m_i/(m_i + m_d)]^{1/2}/\hbar \quad (9)$$

where m_i, m_f, m_n, and m_d are the masses of target nucleus, residual nucleus, neutron, and deuteron respectively, E_α is the bombarding energy (laboratory system), and Q refers to the particular state, e.

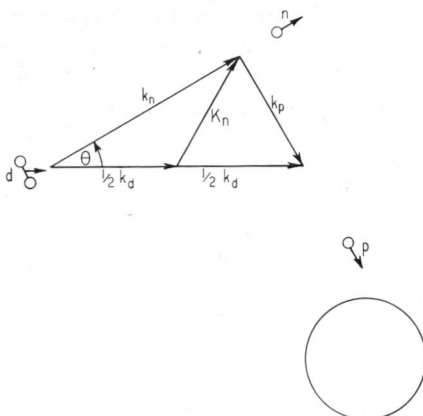

Figure 13. Momentum relations in stripping.

While Eq. (1) is a rather crude approximation, computation of the angular distribution for particular cases is relatively rapid, and it is usually possible to obtain a satisfactory fit to experimental curves if the bombarding energy is not too low. Then l_p, and hence the relative parity of states i and e, is determined, and limits are placed on the value of J_e if J_i is known. Usually only one value of l_p contributes appreciably to the cross section, but stripping reactions are known in which two l values appear to contribute (Ki52, Bi57).

By a process of joining wave functions smoothly at the radius R, Butler (Bu51, Bu57) obtains a more complicated form of L_{l_p} than that given by Eq. (3). The shape differs little from that given by Eq. (1), but a smaller value of R is usually needed to agree with experiment (Hu53). The Butler expression may be derived more simply by means of a Born approximation (Da52a, Ge53). Much computational labor is avoided by use of the tables of Butler cross sections prepared by Lubitz (Lu57), who presents a method of choosing the optimum value of R to fit experimental results.

It has been observed in some (d, n) reactions (Cl57, Ru57) that the neutron yield increases at angles greater than 90°, unlike that for deuteron stripping. While it may be possible in some cases to explain this on the basis of compound nucleus formation, Owen and Madansky (Ma55a, Ow57) have proposed an explanation within the framework of direct interactions. It may happen that the emitted neutron originates from the target nucleus, the incident deuteron being captured as a whole by the core of the target nucleus. This "heavy-particle stripping" has enhanced probability of producing neutrons at large angles, since the nuclei from which the neutrons are stripped are travelling in the direction opposite to the deuteron beam in the centre-of-mass system. In fact, an approximation to the differential cross-section is obtained from Eq. (1) by replacing θ with $\pi - \theta$ and changing the definitions of the momenta. $\Pi(K_n)$ is now of course the momentum distribution of a neutron in the outer shell of the target nucleus and instead of l_p, the angular momentum parameter is l_α, the angular momentum with which the deuteron is captured by the core. The form of $\Pi(K_n)$ depends on the nuclear model, the assumption that the neutron is in a square well whose parameters fit the neutron binding energy giving good qualitative agreement with experiment in the case of the B^{11} $(d, n)C^{12}$ ground state group (Ma55a). If the final state wave function describing the outgoing neutron and the residual nucleus is constructed to be antisymmetric under exchange of neutrons, the resulting differential cross section contains the deuteron and heavy-particle stripping terms, as well as a strong interference term (Ow57).

To explain a conflict in the spin assignments of the first excited states of B^{11} and C^{11}, Wilkinson (Wi57) has suggested that the outgoing particle in (d, n) and (d, p) reactions may suffer spin reversal, with the consequent addition of one unit of angular momentum to the residual nucleus. In the case cited, the shell model and some experimental evidence suggest that $J = 1/2^-$, whereas stripping angular distributions indicate $J \geq 3/2$. By a calculation similar to that of Owen and Madansky (Ow57), French and Evans (Fr57, Ev58; see also Ne58a) have shown that such an occurrence may be explained by nucleon exchange. In cases where the stripping cross section is abnormally small, it would seem that spin-flip must be considered in assigning limits to the spin of the final state.   (See Chapter V.D for further discussion of this point.)

Coulomb repulsion, nuclear scattering of the deuteron and outgoing particle, and compound nucleus formation all affect the form of the cross section for deuteron stripping and heavy particle stripping. The effects on heavy-particle stripping have not as yet been calculated, but several authors (Fr54a, Yo54, Gr55a, To55, Ho56b, Wi58, Wi60, Yo60) have considered the modifications to deuteron stripping. For deuteron energies exceeding 5 Mev these corrections in general change the angular distribution very little, broadening the peaks and filling in the minima somewhat.   The shift of the principal peak toward larger angles is insufficient to cause difficulty in choosing the value of l.   At lower bombarding energies near the Coulomb barrier height the corrections are much larger.   Even at energies where the shape of the angular distribution is little changed, the magnitude of the cross section is considerably reduced (To55, Bu57).   Resonances have been observed in some reactions where the angular distribution is in good agreement with stripping theory (Bo56, St55), the variations in yield sometimes being larger at the stripping maxima than at larger angles.   Since stripping is non-resonant, such effects are probably due to interference with compound nucleus formation.

The polarization of the outgoing particle is a sensitive measure of deviations from "pure" stripping, since it should be zero according to the Butler assumptions.   The degree of polarization arising from the various perturbations has been calculated (Ch54, Yo54, Gr55a, Ne53b, Hi56b, Ho56b), the maximum value of the polarization being 33 per cent for any form of perturbed stripping.   Proton polarizations as great as 58 ± 13 per cent have been measured in the reaction $C^{12}(d, p)C^{13}$ (Hi56a, Ju56), indicating compound nucleus formation in agreement with the presence of resonances in the yield (Bo56).

(3) $(n\text{-}\gamma)$ **Angular Correlation.**   Radiation from an excited state of the residual nucleus may show a nonisotropic directional correlation with the emitted particle corresponding to that state, depending on the angular momenta of the states involved and the coupling scheme (Bi52, Ga52, Sa52, Sa53).   If the Butler assumptions apply, the angular correlation in the plane containing the deuteron beam and the emitted particle is symmetric about the recoil direction of the residual nucleus.   In the case of pure multipole radiation of order L from a level formed by absorption of a particle with one value

of l and one value of $j = l \pm \frac{1}{2}$, the correlation function has the simple form

$$W(\phi) = \sum \eta_\nu (j\, j\, J_i\, J_e) F_\nu\, (L\, J_f\, J_e) P_\nu\, (\cos\, \phi) \qquad (10)$$

where ϕ is the angle of emission of th γ ray measured from the recoil axis, J_i = spin of the target nucleus, J_e = spin of the excited state, and J_f = spin of the final state. The η_ν are tabulated by Satchler (Sa53) and the F_ν by Biedenharn and Rose (Bi53). The summation is over even values of ν to $\nu_{max} \leqq$ min $(2j, 2L, 2J_e)$. In many cases a measurement of $W(\phi)$ is sufficient to determine J_e, if the assumptions leading to Eq. (10) are correct. The correlation in the plane normal to the recoil axis should be isotropic, according to this simple theory. Satchler (Sa53) has developed expressions for $W(\phi)$ when the γ ray is a mixture of multipoles and pure j-j coupling is not assumed.

The low energy corrections to pure stripping have strong effects on $W(\phi)$ (Ho54, Bu57). The recoil axis is, in general, no longer an axis of symmetry in the reaction plane, and there may be anisotropy in the plane perpendicular to the recoil axis. If there is appreciable compound nucleus formation, triple correlation functions must be used (Sh53). This, as well as involving much more calculation, introduces more arbitrary parameters. At 9 Mev bombarding energy, the p-γ correlation involving the first excited state in the reaction $Si^{28}(d, p\gamma)Si^{29}$ is symmetric about the recoil axis in the plane of the reaction and is anisotropic in the plane normal to the recoil axis (A156).

In the type of experiment described in Section 3.B, a coincident γ ray is used as a time reference to separate neutron groups. The n-γ coincidence rate of a particular group as a function of neutron detector angle is not necessarily equivalent to the neutron angular distribution, since, as discussed above, the n-γ correlation may be anisotropic. If the recoil axis is an axis of symmetry of the n-γ correlation the coincidence rate may be written in terms of the neutron differential cross section σ and the correlation function W thus: $n_c(\theta_n, \theta_\gamma) \propto \delta(\theta_n) W(\phi)$, where the angles are as shown in Fig. 14. Since $\phi = |\theta_r - \theta_\gamma|$ and the recoil angle θ_n is kinematically related to θ_n, δ (except for a constant multiplier) may be obtained from the measured quantities n_c and W by the relation $\delta(\theta_n) \propto n_c(\theta_n, \theta_\gamma) / W(\theta_n, \theta_\gamma)$. W usually varies much less than n_c in the region of the forward maximum, so that the correction factor W^{-1} does not greatly alter the shape of n_c. When the γ-ray detector is placed above the target, on the normal to the plane of Fig. 14, the correction is unnecessary since ϕ is then constant. When heavy-particle stripping contributes to the reaction, the n-γ angular correlations are much more complex than those given by Eq. (10) (Ed58).

As well as the applications to nuclear spectroscopy discussed above, stripping experiments promise more detailed information about nuclear energy levels. The factor P_{l_p} in Eq. (1) is the product of known factors and the reduced width of the excited state of the residual nucleus. A method of obtaining the reduced width from experimental curves of the differential cross section has been described by Bowcock (Bo55). According to the "j-j" shell model (Ma55b) the reduced width should be zero for all but single particle states.

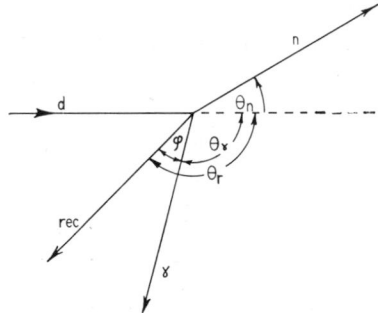

Figure 14. Angular relations in $(d, n\gamma)$ reactions.

Comparison of the reduced widths of levels then, in principle, gives a measure of the purity of states. In practice, the corrections to simple stripping theory restrict safe comparison to levels of the same nucleus, or at least to similar nuclei (Au55, Fr56). In many reactions, the stripping selection rules permit two or more l values for the captured particle, the smallest one giving the largest contribution to the cross section. If the shell model forbids the lowest l value, a measurement of the angular distribution is a sensitive check of the purity of the state (Be52b, Ki52). The departure of p-γ and n-γ angular correlations from Eq. (10) is another measure of the intermediate coupling parameter (Sa53), though the possibility of multipole mixtures adds a further parameter to the expression for $W(\phi)$. The particle detector should be placed at the forward maximum of the angular distribution to minimize the effects of compound nucleus formation.

B. Experimental Investigations

(1) $Li^6(d, n)Be^{7*}(\gamma)Be^7$. The reaction $Li^6(d, p\gamma)Li^7$ has been studied in great detail (Aj59) because of the relative ease, as compared to neutrons, of the detection of the proton and measurement of its energy. Measurements of the angular distributions of the protons (Ho53, Le55b) and the associated γ rays (Li50, Cl52) and of the angular correlation between the two (Cl52, Bu52) has led to an assignment of $J = \frac{1}{2}^-$ for the spin and parity of the first excited state of Li^7. Also from studies of the angular distributions of the protons it is evident that the formation of the first excited state of Li^7 proceeds by deuteron stripping with capture of p-wave neutrons even at very low deuteron energies (Wh50).

The mirror reaction $Li^6(d, n\gamma)Be^7$ has been studied less thoroughly owing to the experimental difficulty in detecting the neutron and measuring its energy. However, the study of this reaction is particularly easy with the coincidence time-of-flight apparatus described in Section 2 as there is only one neutron group in coincidence with a single γ ray for deuteron energies up to 1.7 Mev (Fig. 11B). It has been possible (Ne56), from the detailed study of the n-γ correlation in conjunction with previous measurements, to assign the spin and parity of the first excited state of Be^7 as $J = \frac{1}{2}^-$. This assignment is in agreement with the mirror relationship of Li^7 and Be^7.

The interpretation of the angular correlations obtained with the coincidence time-of-flight spectrometer will depend on the type of interaction taking place, i.e., compound nucleus, or surface interactions (cf. Section 3.A). For very low deuteron bombarding energies the formation of a compound nucleus is expected to be predominant with the possibility of resonances in the excitation curve. In fact, the excitation curve (Ne56), Figure 15A, when corrected for s-wave penetrability of the deuterons, shows a resonance, Fig. 15B, corresponding to an excited state of Be^8 at 22.6 Mev. This resonance has also been reported in the excitation curve for the reaction Li^6 and d using no neutron energy discrimination (Ba52, Wh49). The angular correlation of the neutron and γ ray for low energy deuterons is isotropic both in the plane containing the deuteron beam (Ne56)

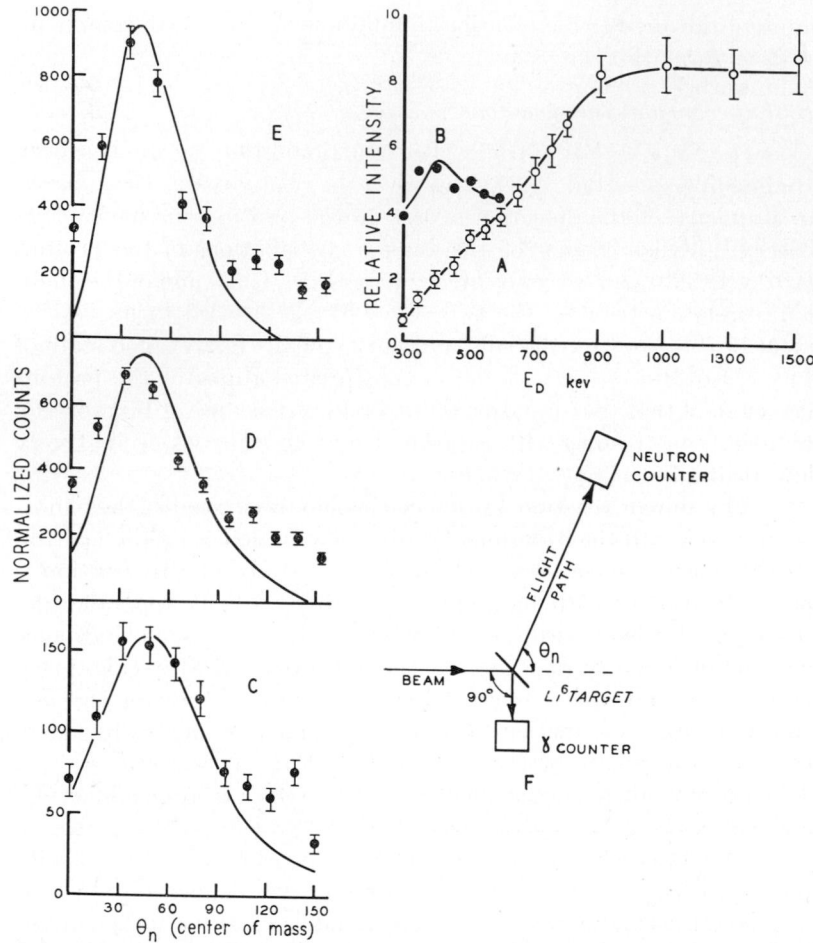

Figure 15. Li^6(d, $n\gamma$)Be^7, (0.430-Mev state).   A and B are excitation curves at $\theta_n = 45°$, with B corrected for s-wave penetrability.   C, D, and E are center-of-mass angular distributions for $E_d = 1.0$, 1.5, and 2.0 Mev, respectively.   F is the experimental configuration.

and in the plane perpendicular to the deuteron beam (Th53a).   The isotropic nature of the angular correlations and also the isotropy of the 430-kev γ rays (Cl52) is strong evidence that the first excited state of Be^7 is a $J = \frac{1}{2}$ state.

For deuterons of 3.5 Mev, the angular distributions (Aj52a) of the neutrons to the ground and first excited states of Be^7 are predominantly stripping in character, proceeding by capture of p-wave protons. Even for a deuteron energy of 600 kev, the angular correlations (Ne56, Ne58) are not isotropic but must be interpreted with the aid of surface interaction theory. The angular distribution of the γ rays about the recoil axis is still isotropic but the neutron distribution about the beam direction with the gamma counter at a fixed angle shows the strong peaking in the forward direction typical of stripping reactions. The neutron angular distributions for E_d equal to 1.0, 1.5, and 2.0 Mev are given in Fig. 15, and show clearly that the stripping peak moves in to smaller θ_n as the bombarding energy is raised. The data presented in these figures were taken with the γ-ray counter at 90° to the deuteron beam and the neutron detector in the plane containing the deuteron beam and the γ-ray detector. These points are corrected for detector efficiency and are in the center-of-mass frame. The solid curves in Figs. 15C, D, and E are the theoretical stripping curves (Bu57, Lu57) for p-wave capture of the protons assuming a radius of 5.2×10^{-13} cm for the Li^6 nucleus. From the good agreement between theory and experiment one can draw several conclusions: (a) the reaction is predominantly stripping above 1 Mev with the capture of p-wave protons; (b) in conjunction with the angular correlation work, the capture of p-wave protons uniquely determines the spin and parity of the 0.43-Mev state of Be^7 as $J = \frac{1}{2}^-$; (c) simple stripping theory is adequate to predict the shape of the stripping curves as a function of the deuteron energy even with 1 to 2-Mev deuterons.

(2) $Be^9(d, n)B^{10*}(\gamma)B^{10}$. At bombarding energies less than 2 Mev, seven excited states of B^{10} (Aj59) are associated with neutron groups sufficiently energetic to be detected with the coincidence time-of-flight spectrometer (Sa58, Ne58). Groups corresponding to the first four excited states are evident in the time spectrum, Fig. 11A. Decay by particle break-up ($Li^6 + \alpha$) is energetically possible in the case of the remaining three states, though γ rays have been assigned to two of them (Aj59, see however Mc57); only one of these levels has been detected by the n-γ coincidence method (Ne58).

The n-γ angular correlations, obtained by fixing the γ-ray counter and moving the neutron counter in the plane containing the deuteron beam and the γ-ray counter, are assumed to be neutron

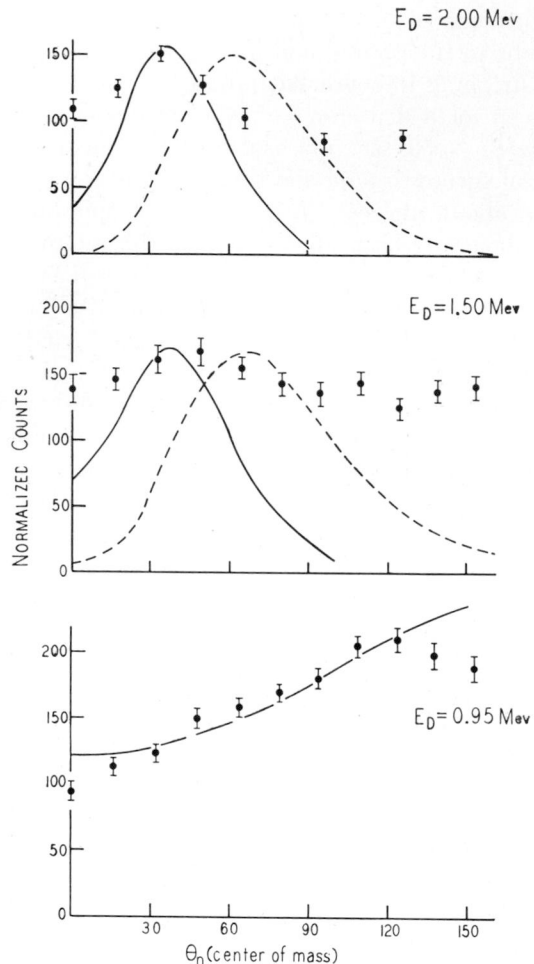

Figure 16. Be⁹$(d,\ n\gamma)$B¹⁰ (0.72 Mev-state) neutron angular distributions Solid curves for $E_d = 1.50$ and 2.0 Mev are calculated from Eq. (1) with $l_p = 1$, dotted curves with $l_p = 2$. Solid curve for $E_d = 0.95$ Mev is calculated for "heavy-particle stripping."

angular distributions with respect to the deuteron beam because (a) such correlations with one exception have been found to agree in shape with distributions measured by other methods, (b) the correlations have been found to be symmetric about the direction of

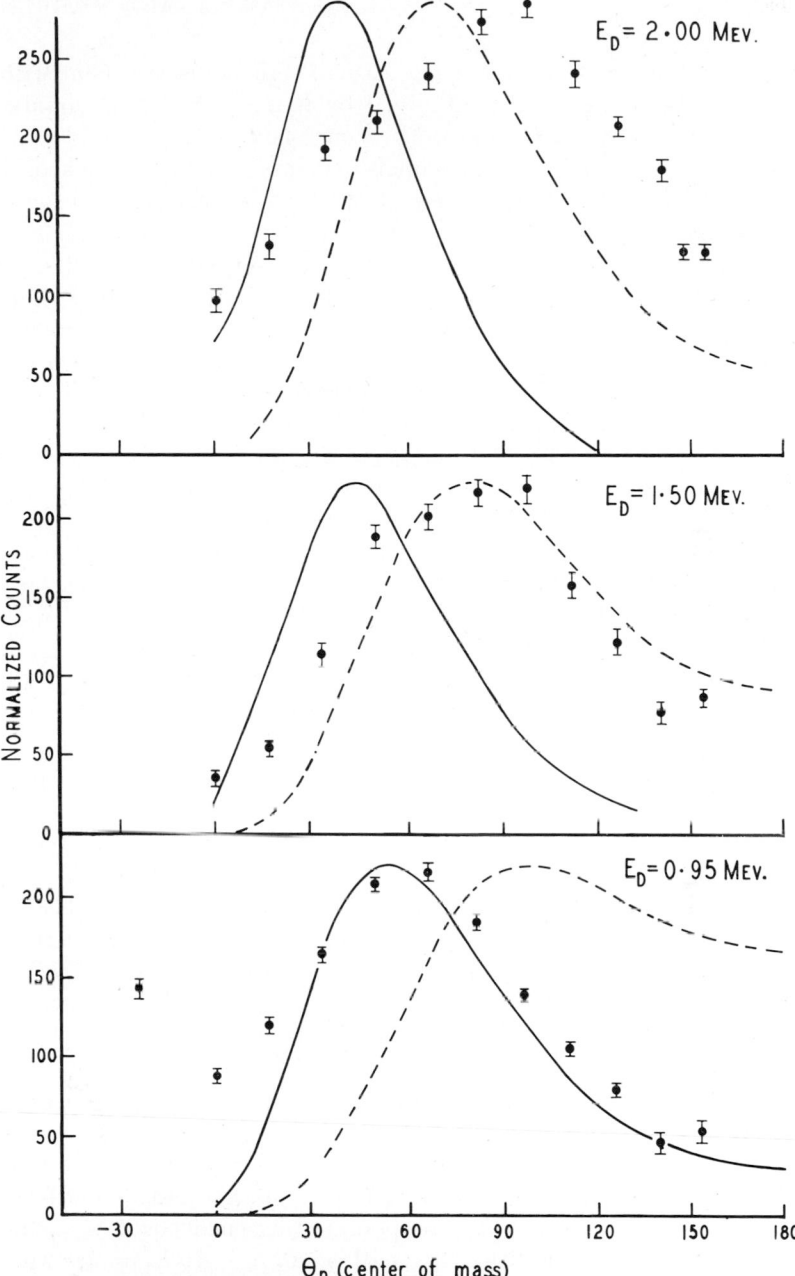

Figure 17. Be⁹(d, nγ)B¹⁰ (3.58-Mev state) neutron angular distributions. Solid curves are calculated from Eq. (1) with $l_p = 1$, dotted curves with $l_p = 2$

the deuteron beam, (c) in the one case of serious disagreement with other work, the correlation obtained by fixing the neutron counter and moving the γ-ray counter in the same plane has been found to be isotropic. (d) The coincidence measurements have been checked at some energies by the pulsed-beam method, with excellent agreement. The angular distribution in the center-of-mass system of the groups leaving B^{10} in its first and fourth excited states are shown in Figs. 16 and 17 for bombarding energies of 0.95, 1.5, and 2.0 Mev. The points have been corrected for solid angle variation and for energy variation in neutron counter efficiency. The γ-ray counter was fixed at 90° with respect to the deuteron beam during these runs. Points taken on both sides of 0° at $E_d = 0.95$ in the case of the 3.58-Mev level are shown in Fig. 17 to demonstrate the symmetry about the deuteron beam. Curves for $l_p = 1$ and 2 calculated from Eq. (1) with $R = 6.5 \times 10^{-13}$ cm are shown in the figures, with the exception of the 0.72-Mev state at $E_d = 0.95$ Mev. Here the curve represents heavy-particle stripping with $l_d = 0$ and $R = 4.1 \times 10^{-13}$ cm, the assumed model of the Be^9 nucleus being a p-state neutron in a square well of depth 38.5 Mev and radius 2.58×10^{-13} cm.

The experimental points in Fig. 16 for the 0.72-Mev level are in fair agreement with angular distributions measured by means of nuclear emulsions (Pr53, Gr55b, Sh57b). The angular distribution at $E_d = 0.95$ Mev is in qualitative agreement with the crude heavy-particle stripping model assumed, but compound nucleus formation cannot, of course, be ruled out as the cause of the rise at large angles (Gr55b). At $E_d = 2$ Mev a deuteron stripping peak with $l_p = 1$ is in evidence above a large isotropic background, presumably due to compound nucleus formation. The $l_p = 1$ assignment is in agreement with measurements at higher bombarding energies (Aj52b).

The angular distributions of the group to the 3.58-Mev level are shown in Fig. 17. The one case of fair agreement between theory and experiment, the similarity of a deuteron stripping distribution with $l_p = 1$ to the experimental distribution for $E_d = 0.95$ Mev, is probably fortuitous. When the bombarding energy is increased, the agreement is expected to improve. Instead, at $E_d = 1.5$ Mev, the best fitting curve is that for $l_p = 2$, violating the parity assignment from the 0.95-Mev results. When the bombarding energy is 2 Mev, the angular distribution is fitted by neither curve. At $E_d = 3.4$ Mev (Aj52b), the angular distribution is once again in fair agreement with

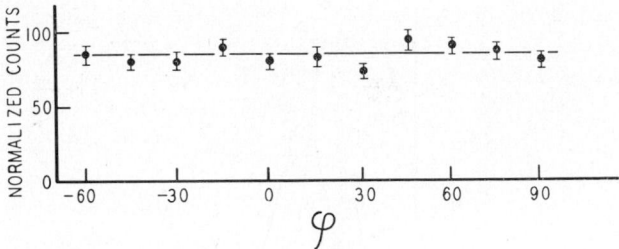

Figure 18. Be^9(d, $n\gamma$)B^{10} (3.58 Mev-state).   Gamma-ray angular distribution about recoil axis at E_d = 1.50 Mev.   Neutron detector fixed at 75° with respect to the deuteron beam.

p-wave stripping.   At E_d = 0.5 Mev, while there is a strong forward maximum in the angular distribution, no stripping curve fits it for reasonable values of the radius parameter (Ha57).   It is apparent that parity and spin assignments based on angular distribution measurements at only one energy are unreliable if that energy is not greater than 5 Mev.   Except for E_d = 0.95 Mev, the 3.58-Mev level angular distributions presented here differ from those of Shpetnyi (Sh57b), who has found angular distributions consistent with p-wave stripping at five bombarding energies between 0.8 and 1.6 Mev.

Measurements of the γ-ray angular distribution about the recoil axis show that the difference mentioned above cannot be explained by the existence of a strong n-γ angular correlation.   The correlation is isotropic in the case of the 3.58-Mev level at E_d = 1.50 Mev as shown by Fig. 18.   The neutron counter was fixed at the maximum of the neutron angular distribution.   To avoid modification of the angular correlation by cascade γ rays from the long-lived 0.72-Mev state, the γ-ray side-channel discriminator was set to accept only pulses due to dissipation of energies between 1.5 and 3.0 Mev in the γ-ray counter.   This setting strongly favors detection of the γ ray emitted in the 3.58–0.72 Mev transition, which is the most intense γ ray from the 3.58-Mev state (Aj59).   In a similar way, an isotropic angular correlation was found between the neutron group leaving B^{10} in the 3.58-Mev state and the 1.43-Mev γ ray from the 3.58–2.15 Mev transition.   In this case, about 25 per cent of the 1.43-Mev γ rays are due to the 2.15–0.72 Mev cascade transition (Aj59).   There are of course small contributions in both cases from the Compton "tails" of more energetic γ rays associated with the 3.58-Mev state.

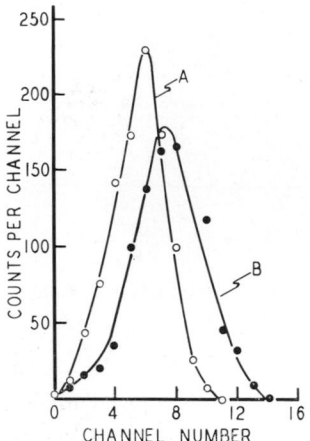

Figure 19. Mean life of the 0.72-Mev state. A prompt, B delayed resolution curves. Each channel corresponds to 5.57×10^{-10} seconds.

The correlation at $E_d = 0.5$ Mev is also isotropic (Ha57). The isotropic angular correlation is consistent with the assumptions that the 3.58-Mev state is formed by stripping with $l_p = 1$ and has $J = 2^+$, and that pure j-j coupling holds. Equation (10) then predicts isotropy for all multipole orders, since for $j = \frac{1}{2}$, $\nu = 0$ only and for $j = \frac{3}{2}$, η_2 ($\frac{3}{2}$, $\frac{3}{2}$, $\frac{3}{2}$, 2) is zero (Sa53). Provided that the state is formed by stripping, appreciable departure from j-j coupling should produce a measurable anisotropy.

The mean life of the 0.72-Mev state has been measured by the recoil time-of-flight method to be $(7 \pm 2) \times 10^{-10}$ (Th53b) and $(8.5 \pm 2) \times 10^{-10}$ sec (Se56). Using a pulsed proton beam to excite the 0.72-Mev level by inelastic scattering, Bloom et al. measured directly a lifetime of $(1.05 \pm 0.10) \times 10^{-9}$ sec (Bl57) while Holland et al. (Ho58) give $(0.90 \pm 0.1) \times 10^{-9}$ sec. The γ-ray cascade in coincidence with the neutron group leaving B^{10} in the 3.58-Mev state offers another means of measuring this lifetime. If the γ-ray side-channel discriminator is set first to accept predominantly pulses due to 0.72-Mev radiation, and then in a succeeding run is set to accept radiation of energy greater than 0.72 Mev (assumed prompt), the two time spectra of the neutron group are respectively the delayed and prompt resolution curves of the apparatus. Typical curves normalized to equal area are shown in Fig. 19. An instrumental

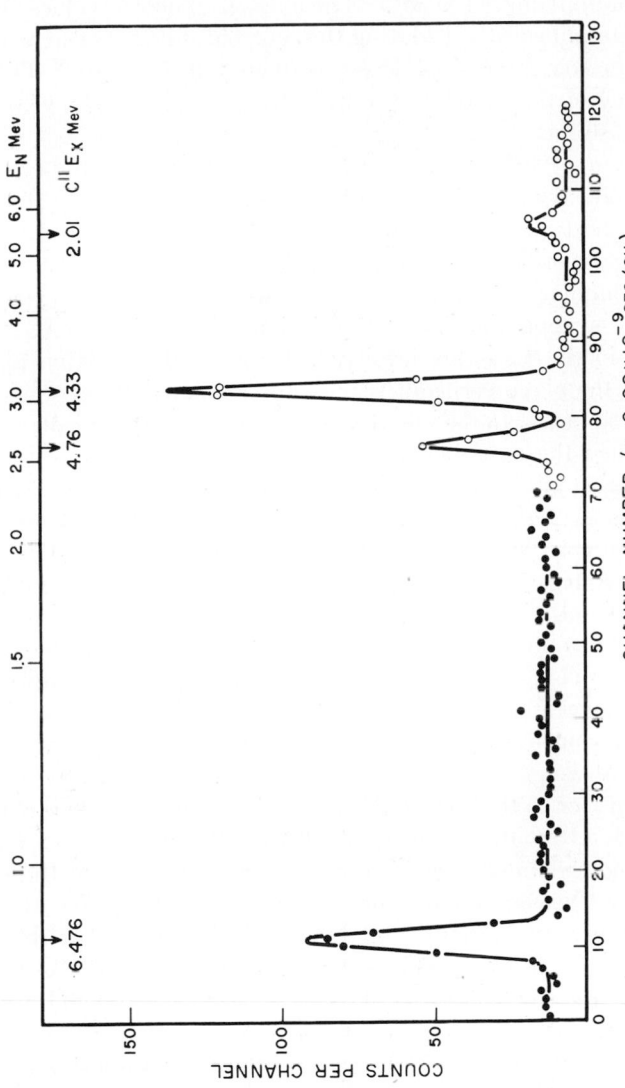

Figure 20. $B^{10}(d, n\gamma)C^{11}$. Neutron coincidence time-of-flight spectrum for $E_d = 1.00$ Mev. Uncorrected experimental curve for a flight distance of 200 cm. Arrows indicate the expected position of groups for the labeled excitation energy of C^{11}.

shift due to the different γ-ray side-channel discriminator settings has been removed by shifting the delayed curve until its maximum lies on the prompt curve (Ne50). The average of eleven values of the mean life determined by calculating the centroid shift between prompt and delayed resolution curves (Ba50) is $(0.96 \pm 0.10) \times 10^{-9}$ (Da58). The accuracy of the method is limited by errors in allowing for instrumental shifts.

(3) $B^{10}(d, n)C^{11*}(\gamma)C^{11}$. Hardy (Ha57) has studied the neutron spectra in coincidence with γ radiation and, with 500-kev deuterons, found that the transitions proceeding via the 4.23-Mev level in C^{11} are much more prolific than those via the 4.77-Mev and 1.90-Mev levels. Preliminary results show that with the neutron counter placed in the stripping peak the γ radiation coincident with neutrons leaving C^{11} in the 4.23-Mev level is isotropic in the reaction plane. However in the plane perpendicular to the recoil axis the coincident γ radiation appears to be slightly anisotropic; such anisotropy is expected when the outgoing neutron is polarized.

Further study of the reaction $B^{11}(d, n\gamma)C^{10}$ has been carried out by Neilson et al. (Ne59b). Figure 20 shows a typical neutron time-of-flight coincidence spectrum. Neutron groups to the first four excited states of C^{11} are apparent. The accuracy of energy level measurements obtained from time-of-flight technique is definitely inferior to that obtained when the same state can be reached with reactions involving the emission of charged particles. However, most energy level assignments for the low-lying levels of C^{11} are made from nuclear emulsion studies and, in this case for low energy neutrons, the precision obtained with the time-of-flight technique is probably superior to that obtained with nuclear emulsion as is shown in Table III. Recently, measurement with the much lower background brought about by cancellation of γ-ray pulses from the neutron detector (Ne59a) has revealed an excited state of C^{11} at 6.35 Mev, in agreement with Hi60 and Ja60. Thus the close doublet at 6.76 and 6.81 Mev in the mirror nucleus B^{11} is matched in C^{11}. Comparison of the relative intensities of the respective neutron and proton groups indicates a reversal of the level positions, the group to the lower level in C^{11} having about 6 per cent of the intensity of the group to the higher level.

The angular correlations involving the 4.33- and 6.474-Mev states show a characteristic deuteron stripping shape at all energies

Table III. Energy Levels of C^{11}

Level no.	Previous work E_x (Mev)	Ref.	Method	Data from neutron coincidence time-of-flight technique E_x (Mev)
2	4.23 ± 0.06	Jo52	Photoplate	4.33 ± 0.05
	4.24 ± 0.03	Gr56	Photoplate	
	4.28 ± 0.05	Cc56	Photoplate	
3	4.77 ± 0.06	Jo52	Photoplate	
	4.73 ± 0.03	Gr56	Photoplate	4.76 ± 0.05
	4.77 ± 0.05	Ce56	Photoplate	
	4.75 ± 0.03	Sa55	E_γ	
4	6.40 ± 0.04	Jo52	Photoplate	
	6.40 ± 0.04	Gr56	Photoplate	6.476 ± 0.020
	6.50 ± 0.03	Be55b	E_γ	
	6.52 ± 0.05	Sa55	E_γ	
	6.476 ± 0.010	Hi60	$B^{10}(He^3, d)C^{11}$	

from $E_d = 0.5$ to 2.00 Mev. At the higher energies there appears to be some heavy particle contribution (Ow57). The neutron angular correlation involving the 2.01-Mev level shows backward peaking presumably due to heavy-particle stripping (Fr57) or the exchange spin-flip interaction (Wi57).

(4) $B^{11}(d, n)C^{12*}(\gamma)C^{12}$. Only the neutron groups leaving C^{12} in excited states at 4.43 Mev and 12.76 Mev are observed to be coincident with γ rays (Ne59b), in agreement with gamma ray measurements (Ka58).

The angular distribution of the group corresponding to the 4.43-Mev state is shown in Fig. 21 for several bombarding energies (Sa58). The solid curves show the calculated relative cross section for heavy-particle stripping interfering with deuteron stripping (Ow57) for the given values of radii and angular momenta. The parameter λ is a measure of the relative amplitudes of deuteron and heavy particle stripping.

n-γ angular correlations are shown in Fig. 22 for several bombarding energies (Ne59b), the neutron counter being fixed at 45° with respect to the deuteron beam. While the experimental results qualitatively resemble the theoretical results of Edwards (Ed58),

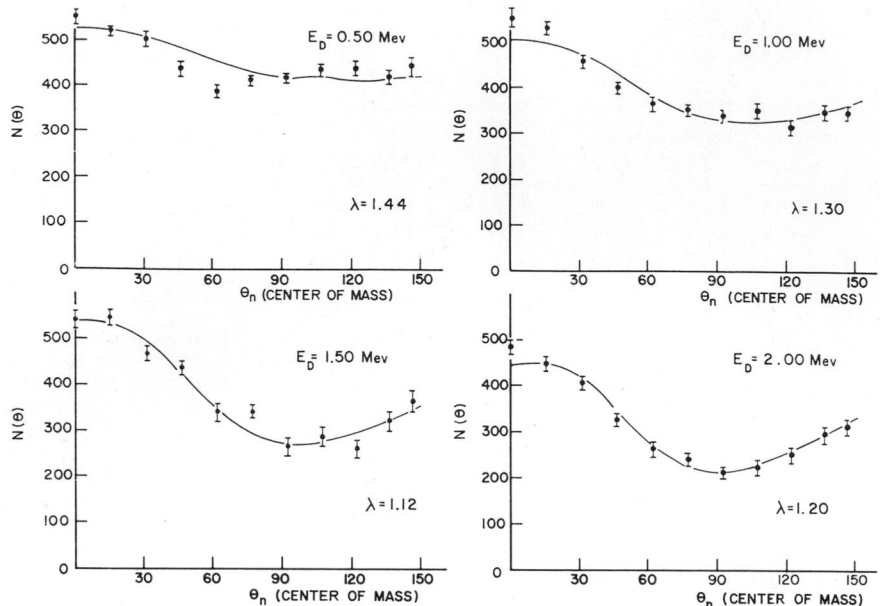

Figure 21. $B^{11}(d, n\gamma)C^{12}$. Angular distributions of neutrons leading to 4.43 Mev-excited state of C^{12}. The γ-ray counter is fixed below the target. The solid curves are calculated for the values $R^1 = 5.6 \times 10^{-13}$ cm; $l_p = 1$; $R^2 = 3.8 \times 10^{-13}$ cm; $l_d = 0$.

they differ quantitatively from each of the three simple cases for which he gives explicit results. Undoubtedly a combination of the different coupling schemes could be made to fit the experimental results. Similar results have been reported by Rask et al. (Ra57).

(5) $Be^9(\alpha, n)C^{12*}(\gamma)C^{12}$. James et al. (Ja56) describe some measurements on the angular distributions of the ground state neutrons, of the lower energy neutron group proceeding to the 4.43-Mev state in C^{12}, of the γ radiation, and of the angular correlation between the low energy neutron group and the 4.43-Mev radiation, over a range of bombarding energies from 0.4 to 1.3 Mev. The angular correlation was measured only in the plane perpendicular to the α-particle beam, but is very pronounced. Indeed the correlation is noteworthy in that, at the present time, this is the only example of a pronounced $(n-\gamma)$ angular correlation which has been established. The analysis of the results is not clear cut, but there is no indication

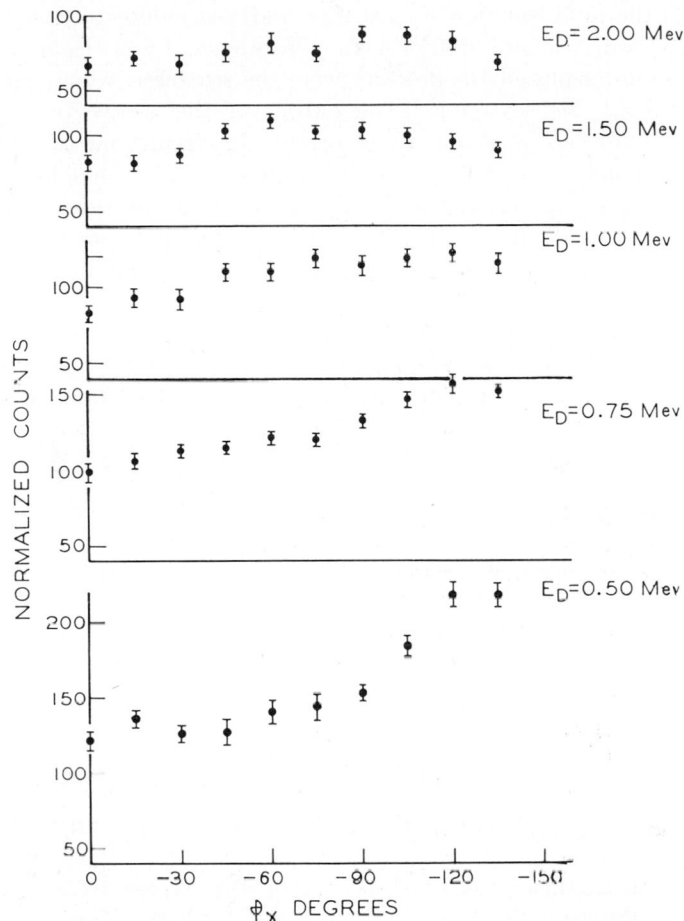

Figure 22. $B^{11}(d, n\gamma)C^{12}$. n-γ angular correlations for the neutron group leading to first excited state of C^{12}. The neutron counter is fixed at 45° with respect to the deuteron beam.

of heavy particle stripping as suggested by Ma55a. The reaction can be interpreted as arising from overlapping resonances.

(6) $Na^{23}(n, n')Na^{23*}(\gamma)Na^{23}$. Shipley, Owens, and Madansky (Sh57a) have applied delayed coincidence technique to the study of inelastic neutron scattering from Na^{23}. In their experiment a beam of fast neutrons is scattered from a sodium iodide crystal, which

performs the dual function of scatterer and γ-ray detector, and the scattered neutrons are detected in coincidence by a 1-cm thick stilbene counter placed 16 cm away from the scatterer, which can be rotated about the scatterer. The output of the γ-ray counter is rated by a 10^{-8} sec resolving time coincidence circuit and displayed on a pulse-height analyzer. A clear distinction can be made between the various processes occurring in the sodium iodide coincident with a neutron scattered into the stilbene counter. The light output from the sodium iodide arises from the γ radiation from the 439-kev excited state in Na^{23} plus a contribution from the recoiling sodium nucleus, as well as from excited states at 340 kev and 630 kev in iodine.

The total cross section for inelastic scattering of 3.9-Mev neutrons from the 439-kev state in sodium was found to be 0.14 barn.

References

(Aj52a) F. Ajzenberg, *Phys. Rev.* **87**, 205 (1952).

(Aj52b) F. Ajzenberg, *Phys. Rev.* **38**, 298 (1952).

(Aj59) F. Ajzenberg-Selove and T. Lauritsen, *Nuclear Phys.* **11**, 1 (1959).

(Al56) Allen, Collinge, Hird, Maglic, and Orman, *Proc. Phys. Soc.* (*London*) **69A**, 705 (1956).

(Au55) T. Auerbach and J. B. French, *Phys. Rev.* **98**, 1276 (1955).

(Ba50) Z. Bay, *Phys. Rev.* **77**, 419 (1950).

(Ba52) L. M. Baggett and S. J. Bame, *Phys. Rev.* **85**, 434 (1952).

(Be52a) Bell, Graham, and Petch, *Can. J. Phys.* **30**, 35 (1952).

(Be52b) H. A. Bethe and S. T. Butler, *Phys. Rev.* **85**, 1045 (1952).

(Be55a) R. E. Bell, in K. Siegbahn, ed., *Beta- and Gamma-ray Spectroscopy*, Interscience, New York, 1955, p. 494.

(Be55b) Bent, Bonner, McCrary, Ranken, and Sippel, *Phys. Rev.* **99**, 710 (1955).

(Bh52) Bhatia, Huang, Huby, and Newns, *Phil. Mag.* **43**, 485 (1952).

(Bi52) Biedenharn, Boyer, and Charpie, *Phys. Rev.* **88**, 517 (1952).

(Bi53) L. C. Biedenharn and M. E. Rose, *Revs. Modern Phys.* **25**, 729 (1953).

(Bi57) O. M. Bilaniuk and P. V. C. Hough, *Phys. Rev.* **108**, 305 (1957).

(Bl57) Bloom, Turner, and Wilkinson, *Phys. Rev.* **105**, 232 (1957).

(Bo55) J. E. Bowcock, *Proc. Phys. Soc.* (*London*) **68A**, 512 (1955).

(Bo56) Bonner, Eisinger, Kraus, and Marion, *Phys. Rev.* **101**, 209 (1956).

(Bu51) S. T. Butler, *Proc. Roy. Soc.* (*London*) **208A**, 559 (1951).

(Bu52) W. H. Burke and J. R. Risser, *Phys. Rev.* **85**, 741 (1952).

(Bu57) S. T. Butler and O. H. Hittmair, *Nuclear Stripping Reactions*, Wiley, New York, 1957.

(Ce56) M. Cerino, *Nuclear Phys.* **2**, 113 (1956).

(Ch54) W. B. Cheston, *Phys. Rev.* **98**, 1590 (1954).

(Cl52) C. M. Class and S. S. Hanna, *Phys. Rev.* **87**, 247 (1952).

(Cl57)   Class, Price, and Risser, reported by Ow57.
(Cr57)   Cranberg, Beauchamp, and Levin, *Rev. Sci. Instr.* **28**, 89 (1957).
(Da52a) P. B. Daitch and J. B. French, *Phys. Rev.* **87**, 900 (1952).
(Da52b) C. M. Davisson and R. D. Evans, *Revs. Modern Phys.* **24**, 79 (1952).
(Da58)   Dawson, Neilson, and Sample, *Bull. Am. Phys. Soc.* **3**, 323 (1958).
(Ed58)   S. Edwards, Jr., *Johns Hopkins Univ. Report* NYO-2054 (1958).
(Ev58)   N. T. S. Evans and A. P. French, *Phys. Rev.* **109**, 1272 (1958).
(Fi52)   J. Fischer and J. Marshall, *Rev. Sci. Instr.* **23**, 417 (1952).
(Fo55)   J. M. Fowler and C. E. Roos, *Phys. Rev.* **98**, 996 (1955).
(Fo56)   J. L. Fowler and J. E. Brolley, *Revs. Modern Phys.* **28**, 103 (1956).
(Fr54a) N. C. Francis and K. M. Watson, *Phys. Rev.* **93**, 313 (1954).
(Fr54b) J. S. Fraser and J. C. D. Milton, private communication (1954).
(Fr56)   J. B. French and B. J. Raz, *Phys. Rev.* **104**, 1411 (1956).
(Fr57)   A. P. French, *Phys. Rev.* **107**, 1655 (1957).
(Ga50)   R. L. Garwin, *Rev. Sci. Instr.* **21**, 569 (1950).
(Ga52)   L. J. Gallaher and W. B. Cheston, *Phys. Rev.* **88**, 684 (1952).
(Ge53)   E. Gerjuoy, *Phys. Rev.* **91**, 645 (1953).
(Gr55a) I. P. Grant, *Proc. Phys. Soc. (London)* **68A**, 244 (1955).
(Gr55b) Green, Scanlon, and Willmott, *Proc. Phys. Soc. (London)* **68A**, 386 (1955).
(Gr56)   A. Graue, *Phil. Mag.* **1**, 1027 (1956).
(Gr58)   R. E. Green and R. B. Bell, *Nuclear Instr.* **3**, 127 (1958).
(Ha57)   J. Hardy, M.A. Thesis, "Time-of-flight Neutron Spectrometry and the $Be^9(d, n\gamma)B^{10}$ Reaction," Univ. of British Columbia, unpublished (1957).
(Ha58)   J. Hardy, *Rev. Sci. Instr.* **29**, 705 (1958).
(Hi56a) P. Hillman, *Phys. Rev.* **104**, 176 (1956).
(Hi56b) O. H. Hittmair, *Z. Physik* **144**, 449 (1956).
(Hi60)   S. Hinds and R. Middleton, private communication (1960).
(Ho53)   J. R. Holt and T. N. Marsham, *Proc. Phys. Soc. (London)* **66A**, 1032 (1953).
(Ho54)   J. Horowitz and A. M. L. Messiah, *J. phys. rad.*, **15**, 142 (1954).
(Ho56a) J. R. Holt, *Physica* **22**, 1069 (1956).
(Ho56b) J. Horowitz, *Physica* **22**, 959 (1956).
(Ho58)   Holland, Lynch, and Hanna, *Phys. Rev.* **112**, 903 (1958).
(Hu49)   G. T. Hunter and H. T. Richards, *Phys. Rev.* **76**, 1445 (1949).
(Hu53)   R. Huby, *Progr. in Nuclear Phys.* **3**, 177 (1953).
(Ja51)   D. B. James and P. B. Treacy, *Proc. Phys. Soc. (London)* **64A**, 847 (1951).
(Ja56)   James, Jones, and Wilkinson, *Phil. Mag.* **1**, 949 (1956).
(Ja60)   A. James, private communication (1960).
(Jo52)   V. Johnson, *Phys. Rev.* **86**, 302 (1952).
(Jo56)   G. Jones and J. B. Warren, *J. Sci. Instr.* **33**, 429 (1956).
(Jo57)   G. Jones, private communication (1957).
(Ju56)   A. C. Juveland and W. Jentschke, *Bull. Am. Phys. Soc.* **1**, 193 (1956).
(Ka58)   R. W. Kavanagh and C. A. Barnes, *Phys. Rev.* **112**, 503 (1958).
(Ke49)   J. W. Keuffel, *Rev. Sci. Instr.* **20**, 197 (1949).

(Ki52)   J. S. King and W. C. Parkinson, *Phys. Rev.* **88**, 141 (1952).
(Le54)   I. A. D. Lewis and F. H. Wells, *Millimicrosecond Pulse Techniques*, 2nd ed., McGraw-Hill, New York, 1955.
(Le55a)   Lepri, Mezzetti, and Stoppini, *Rev. Sci. Instr.* **26**, 936 (1955).
(Le55b)   Levine, Bender, and McGruer, *Phys. Rev.* **97**, 1249 (1955).
(Le57)   H. W. Lefevre and J. T. Russell, "The Vernier Chronotron," *Hanford Report HW-496694* (1957).
(Li50)   R. M. Littauer, *Proc. Phys. Soc. (London)* **63A**, 294 (1950).
(Li59)   Litherland, Almqvist, Batchelor, and Gove, *Phys. Rev. Letters* **2**, 104 (1959).
(Lu57)   C. R. Lubitz, *Numerical Table of Butler-Born Approximation Stripping Cross-sections*, Randall Lab. of Phys., Univ. of Michigan (1957).
(Ma55a)   L. Madansky and G. E. Owen, *Phys. Rev.* **99**, 1608 (1955).
(Ma55b)   M. G. Mayer and J. H. D. Jensen, *Elementary Theory of Nuclear Shell Structure*, Wiley, New York, 1955.
(Mc52)   G. R. J. McLusky and N. F. Moody, *Electronic Eng.* **24**, 330 (1952).
(Mc57)   McCrary, Bonner, and Ranken, *Phys. Rev.* **108**, 392 (1957).
(Mo52)   N. F. Moody, *Electronic Eng.* **24**, 289 (1952).
(Ne50)   T. D. Newton, *Phys. Rev.* **78**, 490 (1950).
(Ne53a)   A. T. Nelms, *Natl. Bur. Standards Circular* 542 (1953).
(Ne53b)   H. C. Newns, *Proc. Phys. Soc. (London)* **66A**, 477 (1953).
(Ne55)   G. C. Neilson and D. B. James, *Rev. Sci. Instr.* **26**, 1018 (1955).
(Ne56)   G. C. Neilson and J. B. Warren, *Phys. Rev.* **103**, 1758 (1956).
(Ne58)   Neilson, Dawson, and Sample, *Bull. Am. Phys. Soc.* **3**, 323 (1958).
(Ne58a)   V. G. Neudachin, *J. Exptl. Theoret. Phys. (U.S.S.R.)* **35**, 1165 (1958).
(Ne59a)   Neilson, Dawson, and Johnson, *Rev. Sci. Instr.* **30**, 963 (1959).
(Ne59b)   Neilson, Dawson, Johnson, and Sample, "A Fast Neutron Time-of-flight Spectrometer with Applications," *Suffield Technical Paper No.* **176** (1960).
(On54)   G. K. O'Neill, *Phys. Rev.* **95**, 1235 (1954).
(On55)   G. K. O'Neill, *Rev. Sci. Instr.* **26**, 285 (1955).
(Ow57)   G. E. Owen and L. Madansky, *Phys. Rev.* **105**, 1766 (1957).
(Ow58a)   R. B. Owen, *Proc. I.R.E.*, *NS-5*, 198 (1958).
(Ow58b)   R. B. Owen, *Nucleonics* **16**, No. 6, 54 (1958).
(Po50)   R. F. Post and L. Schiff, *Phys. Rev.* **80**, 1113 (1950).
(Pr53)   Pruitt, Swartz, and Hanna, *Phys. Rev.* **92**, 1456 (1953).
(Ra57)   Rask, Ames, Edwards, Madansky, and Owen, *Bull. Am. Phys. Soc.* **2**, 351 (1957).
(Re57)   P. E. Remy and K. Winter, *J. phys. rad.* **18**, 112A (1957).
(Ru57)   A. G. Rubin, *Phys. Rev.* **108**, 62 (1957).
(Sa52)   G. R. Satchler and J. A. Spiers, *Proc. Phys. Soc. (London)* **65A**, 980 (1952).
(Sa53)   G. R. Satchler, *Proc. Phys. Soc. (London)* **66A**, 1081 (1953).
(Sa55)   Sample, Neilson, Chadwick, and Warren, *Can. J. Phys.* **33**, 828 (1955).
(Sa58)   Sample, Neilson, and Dawson, *Bull. Am. Phys. Soc.* **3**, 323 (1958).
(Se56)   J. C. Severiens and S. S. Hanna, *Phys. Rev.* **104**, 1612 (1956).

(Sh53) Sharp, Kennedy, Sears, and Hoyle, "Tables of Coefficients for Angular Distribution Analysis," *Chalk River Report* CRT-556 (1953).

(Sh57a) Shipley, Owen, and Madansky, *Bull. Am. Phys. Soc.* **2**, 357 (1957).

(Sh57b) A. I. Shpetnyi, *J. Exptl. Theoret. Phys. (U.S.S.R.)* **5**, 357 (1957).

(St55) Stratton, Blair, Famularo, and Stuart, *Phys. Rev.* **98**, 629 (1955).

(Th53a) J. Thirion, *Ann. phys.* **8**, 489 (1953).

(Th53b) J. Thirion and V. L. Telegdi, *Phys. Rev.* **92**, 1253 (1953).

(To55) W. Tobecman and M. H. Kalos, *Phys. Rev.* **97**, 132 (1955).

(Wa54) A. Ward, *Nature (London)* **173**, 771 (1954).

(We56a) Weber, Johnstone, and Cranberg, *Rev. Sci. Instr.* **27**, 166 (1956).

(We56b) V. F. Weisskopf, *Physica* **22**, 952 (1956).

(Wh49) Whaling, Evans, and Bonner, *Phys. Rev.* **75**, 688 (1949).

(Wh50) W. Whaling and T. W. Bonner, *Phys. Rev.* **79**, 258 (1950).

(Wi57) D. H. Wilkinson, *Phys. Rev.* **105**, 666 (1957).

(Wi58) D. H. Wilkinson, *Phil. Mag.* **3**, 1185 (1958).

(Wi60) D. H. Wilkinson, *Proceedings of the International Conference on Nuclear Structure*, D. A. Bromley and E. Vogt, eds., Univ. of Toronto Press, 1960, p. 20.

(Yo54) J. Yoccoz, *Proc. Phys. Soc. (London)* **67A**, 813 (1954).

(Yo60) S. Yoshida, *Proceedings of the International Conference on Nuclear Structure*, D. A. Bromley and E. Vogt, eds., Univ. of Toronto Press, 1960, p. 336.

Fission by Fast Neutrons

R. L. HENKEL

Los Alamos Scientific Laboratory, Los Alamos, New Mexico

1. Introduction

Soon after the discovery of the neutron, an active experimental study was made of neutron-induced nuclear transmutations, particularly by Fermi and his collaborators, which quickly resulted in the discovery of many new radioisotopes. The neutron bombardment of uranium and thorium initiated by this group was followed up by Meitner, Hahn, and Strassman (Me37, Me38) and by Curie and Savitch (Cu37, Cu38) and showed remarkable results. In particular, Hahn and Strassman (Ha40) demonstrated in 1939 that an isotope of barium resulted from such transmutations, and Meitner and Frisch (Me39) gave the name of *nuclear fission* to the process which resulted in the break-up of the nucleus into two large fragments accompanied by a considerable energy release. Within a short period of time, six experimental groups verified the existence of the fission process for uranium and thorium by the intense ionization produced in a gas by the fragments.

The new research field of nuclear fission was established by a year of productive international activity, resulting in the publishing of more than 100 papers. Turner has given a complete survey of this early work in 1940 (Tu40). The classic theoretical paper of Bohr and Wheeler (Bo39) and others developed the major fraction of the present knowledge of the fission process and gave striking predictions of the variations of fission cross sections with energy. A fairly good estimate of the U^{238} and Th^{232} fission cross sections below 3 Mev neutron energy was obtained, and the enhancement of the natural uranium fission cross section with moderated neutrons (due to thermal fission of U^{235}) was noted.

After 1940, however, the subject of fission became classified and essentially disappeared from the literature. A few articles appeared from Germany and other items appeared after 1946, but until the Geneva Conference of 1955, no appreciable amount of information was published for high energy neutron work. As a result of classification and procurement problems, very few laboratories have been active in experimental fission physics using high energy neutrons, and the situation persists at the present time (1958).

A partial survey of experimental results concerning fast neutron fission cross sections and associated topics will be given. It is not a complete survey since a large fraction of the many unpublished measurements made between 1940 and 1955 have been superseded by more recent work using improved experimental techniques. Much of the information included has been reported earlier by Allen and Henkel (A157).

The determination of the fast fission properties of fissionable nuclei has several aspects of interest. From the practical viewpoint, accurate fission cross sections are essential for the prediction and interpretation of results in fast reactors. Fission excitation functions give verification of the qualitative predictions of Bohr and Wheeler (Bo39) and Bohr (Bo40). In addition, small variations in fission cross sections which occur over relatively small energy intervals have received recent qualitative theoretical explanation by A. Bohr (Bo56) and Wheeler (Wh56). The fluctuations occur in a number of nuclei, but are particularly marked in even-even nuclei near threshold. These same nuclei show considerable variation in the angular distributions of fission fragments relative to the incident neutron beam direction. Perhaps the closest approach to the theoretical understanding of some phases of the fission process has come from the interpretation of the experimental data concerning angular distributions of fragments from neutron induced fission (Bo56, Wi56 Gr58).

2. Fission Cross Section Measurements

In principle, the measurement of a fission cross section is simple. It is determined by observing the number of fissions in a known number of fissionable nuclei exposed to a known neutron flux. To find the fission excitation curve, the absolute amount of fissionable material need not be known, and to increase counting rates a relatively large amount of material is usually employed. First, some absolute determinations will be discussed, and these will be followed by a consideration of relative measurements and excitation curves for fission.

A. Absolute Measurements of Fission Cross Sections

To measure absolute fission cross sections, it is convenient to use foils with thicknesses of the order of 50 to 250 $\mu g/cm^2$. Several methods have been used to prepare and estimate the mass of fissile material. The specific α activity of most fissionable nuclei is uncertain to only the order of 1 per cent and provides a mass determination by α-particle counting when the isotopic composition of the foil material is known. Foils have been prepared by a painting technique in which organic material is driven off by heating and the material remains as an oxide. A second mass determination is obtained by weighing such foils. A third method, applicable to uranium isotopes, is to dissolve the material from the foil and determine the mass by colorimetric techniques. Electroplating a known amount of material to a backing is a common practice which is particularly useful for highly α-active materials. An excellent way to obtain very uniform thicknesses of active material is by the evaporation of compounds, usually oxides or fluorides. This method is particularly well adapted to the deposition of material on very thin backings for coincidence studies using both fission fragments.

In favorable cases, the agreement between the several methods for mass determinations may approach 1 per cent. For some materials, however, only admixtures of several isotopes are available, the handling processes are not sufficiently developed, or the growth of daughter products produces complications such that high accuracy is not achieved.

Absolute neutron flux determinations are usually made by the observation of proton recoils from hydrogenous materials and the utilization of the accurately known n-p scattering cross section. Several types of proton recoil detectors have been employed. The general details of neutron flux determinations as well as the cross sections for n-p scattering are described in Chapter IV.B and Chapter V.T.

The absolute fission cross section of U^{235} for fast neutrons has been of particular interest since it has been used extensively as a

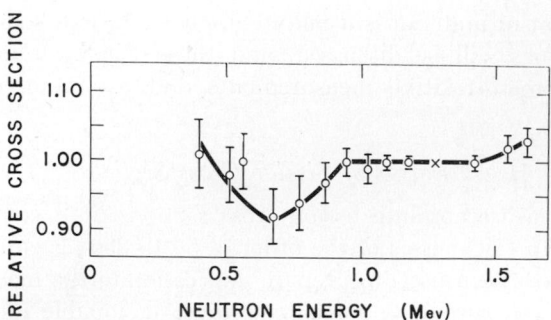

Figure 1. Variation of the relative U^{235} fission cross section with neutron energy. The points are normalized to unity at 1.27 Mev, and the errors shown are standard deviations of the ratio.

standard in the determinations of neutron flux and cross sections of other fissionable materials. Probably the first significant absolute fission cross section determination for U^{235} after the war was made by Diven in 1952 at a neutron energy of 1.27 Mev (Di57). In this experiment, the ratio of the fission cross section to the hydrogen scattering cross section was measured. A thin fission foil and a thin solid hydrogenous radiator were formed over the common wall of a double, concentric cylindrical counter. The outer counter was used as an ionization chamber for detecting fission fragments, and the neutron flux was determined by detecting proton recoils in the central proportional counter. With this system, errors due to distance uncertainties and neutron scattering were minimized. Considerable care was used in the determination of the number of nuclei in the foils and in the absolute counting of fission fragments and proton recoils. A fission cross section of 1.27 ± 0.04 barns was obtained for U^{235} at 1.27 Mev. This absolute measurement for U^{235} served as the standard for all United States fission cross sections for a number of years. Using thicker foils, relative measurements were made for neutron energies between 400 and 1600 kev. The relative measurements are shown in Fig. 1. Tabular values of both absolute and relative cross sections are given in Table I.

At Harwell in 1954, absolute determinations of fission cross sections were made at 550 kev and 1500 kev for U^{233}, U^{235}, and Pu^{239} by Allen and Ferguson (Al55). The neutron flux was measured by detecting proton recoils with a hydrogenous gas proportional counter.

Table I. Absolute and Relative Fission Cross Sections for U^{235}

E_n (Mev)	$\sigma_f (E_n) \div$ σ_f (1.27 Mev)	σ_f (barns)
1.620 ± 0.030	1.03 ± 0.02	1.31 ± 0.05
1.545 ± 0.032	1.02 ± 0.02	1.30 ± 0.05
1.424 ± 0.035	1.00 ± 0.01	1.27 ± 0.04
1.272 ± 0.035	1.00	1.27 ± 0.04
1.171 ± 0.037	1.00 ± 0.01	1.27 ± 0.04
1.095 ± 0.039	1.00 ± 0.01	1.27 ± 0.04
1.025 ± 0.039	0.99 ± 0.02	1.26 ± 0.05
0.944 ± 0.039	1.00 ± 0.02	1.27 ± 0.05
0.865 ± 0.039	0.97 ± 0.03	1.23 ± 0.06
0.770 ± 0.040	0.94 ± 0.04	1.19 ± 0.06
0.673 ± 0.041	0.92 ± 0.04	1.17 ± 0.06
0.562 ± 0.039	1.00 ± 0.04	1.27 ± 0.07
0.513 ± 0.039	0.98 ± 0.04	1.24 ± 0.07
0.403 ± 0.039	1.01 ± 0.05	1.28 ± 0.08

Analysis was made of the end effects and wall effects resulting from proton recoils which did not lie completely within the active volume of the counter. The main difficulties in the use of this counter were to account for small deviations from the theoretical distributions arising, for example, from lack of linearity in the ionizing power of the proton recoils. However, using gas of adequate purity, neutron flux determinations self-consistent to within 2 per cent were obtained with hydrogen and methane. As applied to fission measurements by Allen and Ferguson, the neutron flux was measured at a distance of one meter from the source and fission events were recorded by inserting a counter about 10 cm from the source. Checks of counting rate with $1/r^2$ indicated that errors from distance measurements were small. The chief uncertainty resulted from neutron scattering at both counters and was estimated to be 1 to 2 per cent. The absolute measurements at 550 and 1500 kev were extended with relative measurements between 30 and 3000 kev. In addition, a set of ratios between U^{233}, U^{235}, and Pu^{239} fission cross sections were determined which were self-consistent. The measurements for U^{235} are in agreement with Di57. The results are incorporated in the curves showing results from all laboratories (Figs. 7, 8, and 9).

Recently, absolute fission cross sections for U^{238} were measured for neutron energies between 1 and 22 Mev and for U^{235} between 2

and 10 Mev (Sm57).   Measurements were made with a fission foil
and a CH_2 foil, mounted back-to-back and irradiated in a neutron
flux of variable energy, using the $T(p, n)He^3$, $D(d, n)He^3$, and $T(d, n)$-
He^4 reactions for neutron sources.   Fission fragments were detected

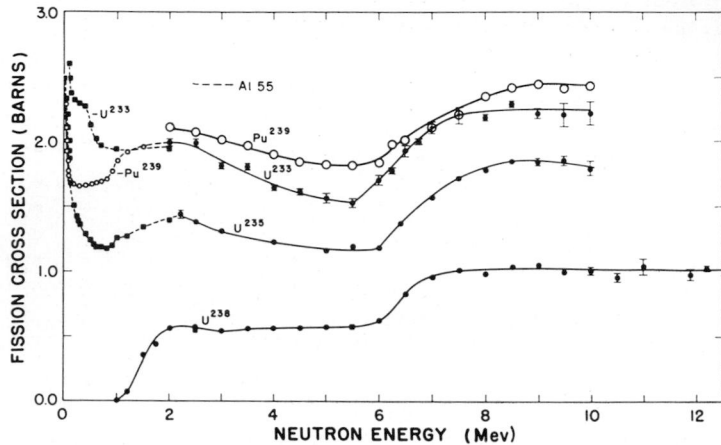

Figure 2. Fission cross sections for U^{233}, U^{235}, U^{238}, and Pu^{239}.   Results for
U^{235} and U^{238} are absolute determinations. U^{233} and Pu^{239} data are from ratio
measurements.

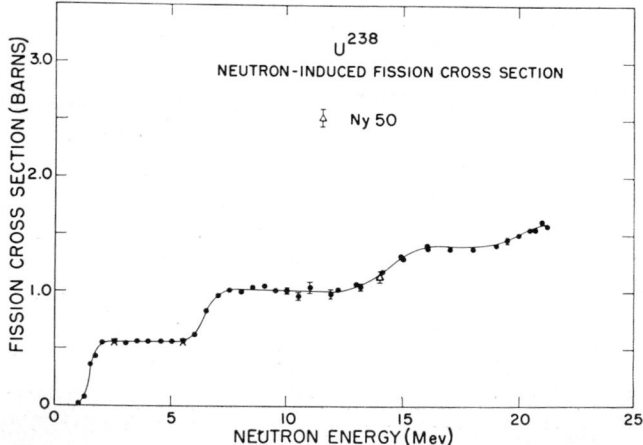

Figure 3. The absolute fission cross section for U^{238} from Sm57. The $\times$ symbols represent check points using thin fissionable foils having smaller mass uncertainties.   An earlier absolute measurement by Nyer is included at 14 Mev (Ny50).

in a parallel-plate ionization chamber and proton recoils were counted in a coincidence counter telescope using two proportional counters and a CsI(Tl) scintillator. At neutron energies between 8 and 10 Mev neutrons from the $D(d, n)He^3$ reaction were contaminated by those from the break-up of the deuteron $D(d, np)D$. Corrections were made for the effects of these neutrons by using the data given in Cr56a. Neutron flux determinations had uncertainties somewhat larger than 3 per cent. The uncertainties in fission cross section were about 5 per cent. In connection with the absolute measurements, the U^{233} and Pu^{239} fission excitation functions were obtained by determining ratios with U^{238} using back-to-back foils in a double ionization chamber. Most of these results are shown in Fig. 2 where low-energy results from Al55 have been included. The measurements for U^{238} are given in Fig. 3 for neutron energies up to 22 Mev.

B. Fission Ratio Measurements and Relative Excitation Curves

The determination of fission cross section ratio measurements is in principle simpler than absolute measurements since it is not necessary to know the neutron flux. Similarly, for fission excitation curves, only the relative neutron flux must be known as a function of energy, and the amount of fissionable material need not be known. These simplifications permit the use of thicker foils and consequently greater counting rates than in the absolute determinations.

Ratio measurements have been widely used by different laboratories for measuring or cross-checking fission cross sections. The two foils of fissionable material are usually placed back-to-back. Since the foils and supports are thin, the neutron flux passing through one foil is to a close approximation the same as the flux passing through the other. By rotating the foils through 180°, a second ratio may be obtained (usually within 1 or 2 per cent of the first). The mean ratio thus obtained is effectively corrected for the effects of neutron flux variations and center-of-mass motion.

An impressive set of ratio measurements has been made at Oak Ridge by R. W. Lamphere (La55, La56). Ratios of U^{233}, U^{234}, U^{236}, and U^{238} were measured with respect to U^{235}, and interpreted with the U^{235} fission cross section values reported in BNL-325 (Hu55). The $T(p, n)He^3$ reaction was used as the neutron source above 300 kev. At lower energies, the $Li^7(p, n)Be^7$ and $V^{51}(p, n)Cr^{51}$ reactions served as the sources of neutrons, and measurements to as low as 5

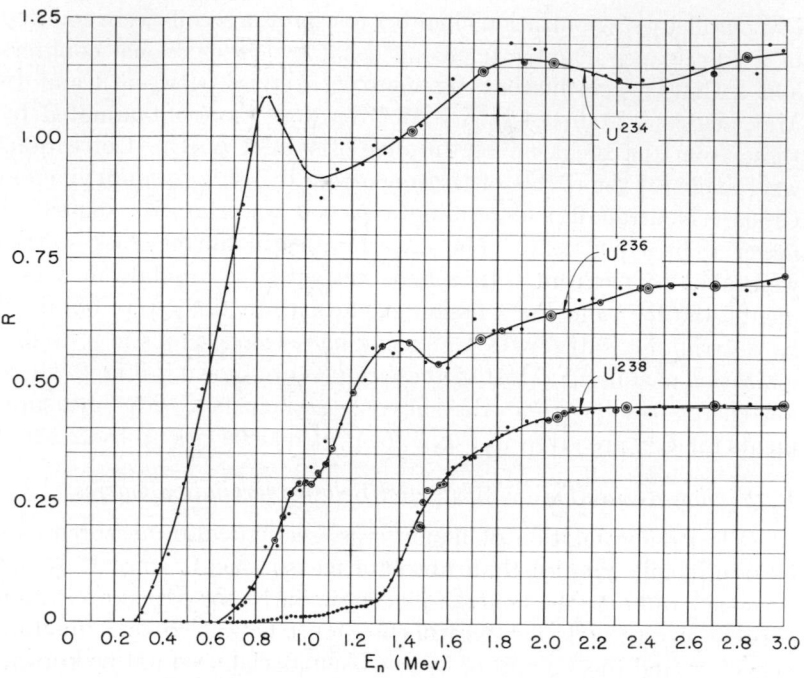

Figure 4. Ratio of U^{234}, U^{236}, and U^{238} fission cross sections to that of U^{235} (La56).

kev were made for U^{233}. For most of the work, back-to-back foils were irradiated in a double ionization chamber. However, for U^{238} at lower energies, a multiple foil chamber using U^{235} and U^{238} foils, and a spiral counter in conjunction with a long counter neutron monitoring system were used to increase counting rates. In general, the fission cross section ratios were believed to be accurate to about 2 per cent. Figure 4 shows the ratios for U^{234}, U^{236}, and U^{238}. The threshold region of the fission cross section for U^{238} was investigated quite carefully and is shown in Fig. 5. Fluctuations, which were also observed earlier, clearly appear in this excitation curve. These will be discussed later.

Similar ratio measurements have been made by a number of workers at Los Alamos. The results are incorporated in the composite curves shown and most of the results do not warrant separate description. However, perhaps the measurement of Am^{241} was sufficiently novel to be described (No55). The half-life for α decay of Am^{241}

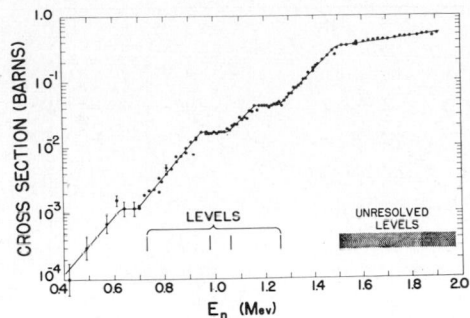

Figure 5. Fission cross section of U^{238} in the region of the threshold (La56). The indicated energy levels are from Cr58.

is 470 years and the resulting α-particle activity precludes measuring fission events with the normal techniques. The Am^{241} fission cross section was measured for several energies between 0.5 and 7 Mev by simultaneously counting fission events from known foils of U^{235} and Am^{241} irradiated in the same neutron flux. U^{235} fissions were counted in a conventional ionization chamber. Due to the high specific activity of Am^{241}, a fast counting system was developed to prevent difficulties caused by multiple pile-up of α-particle pulses. The Am^{241} fission pulses were detected in a zenon scintillation counter using a plastic film loaded with tetraphenylbutadiene to shift the ultra-violet radiation to the visible spectrum for viewing by an RCA-6342 photomultiplier. Pulse-height stability was achieved by maintaining the temperature of this counter at 0°C. The pulse output of the photomultiplier was delay-line clipped to 2×10^{-9} sec, amplified and sent to a fast crystal discriminator which was biased to remove α-particle pulses. The remaining fission pulses were lengthened to 1 μsec, amplified and counted with conventional circuits. Using the known U^{235} fission cross sections, the excitation curve for Am^{241} was determined.

The study of neutron-induced fission of Ra^{226} is particularly interesting for two reasons. First, radium has about the lowest fissionability which will still have a detectable fission cross section in the Mev neutron energy region. In addition, Fairhall and Jensen have made radio-chemical studies of the fission fragments from Ra^{226} fission induced by 11-Mev protons and have found a triple-peaked

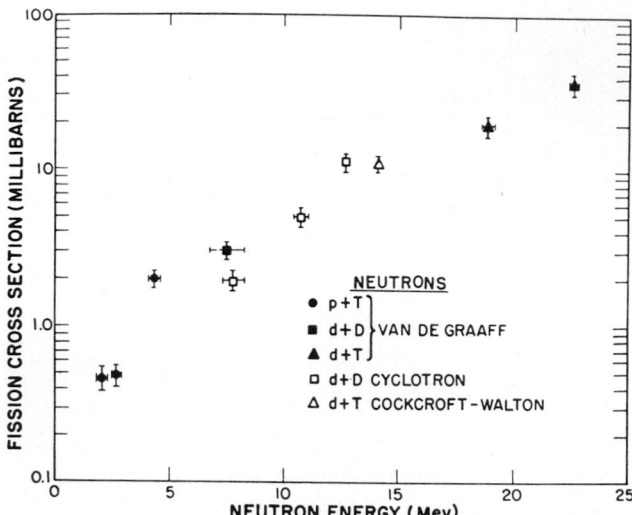

Figure 6. Fission cross section of Ra²²⁶.

mass distribution resulting from a combination of symmetric and asymmetric fission (Fa56, Fa58).

Recently, the neutron-induced fission of Ra²²⁶ has been studied by Nobles, Manley, and Leachman (No57, No58). Due to the high α activity of Ra²²⁶, a fast scintillation counter of xenon gas was used for detecting the pulse heights of fission fragments. The counter was similar to that described for the Am²⁴¹ measurements (No55). However, greater care was exercised to exploit linearity of response and stability of the counter in the radium experiment. The usual sources of neutrons were used with the large Los Alamos Van de Graaff accelerator, the Variable Energy Cyclotron, and the Cockcroft-Walton accelerator to cover the neutron range between 2 and 23 Mev. The combination of the small fission cross section and the high α activity for Ra²²⁶ made large fluxes of neutrons of 10⁹ neutrons/sterad-sec or larger necessary for reasonable observation times in the experiment. The cross section measurements were made by observing the fission rate for radium in the neutron fluxes calculated from existing differential cross sections of the source reactions used. The flux determinations were no better than ±10 per cent in most cases. The low fission rate resulted in additional 10 per cent statistical uncer-

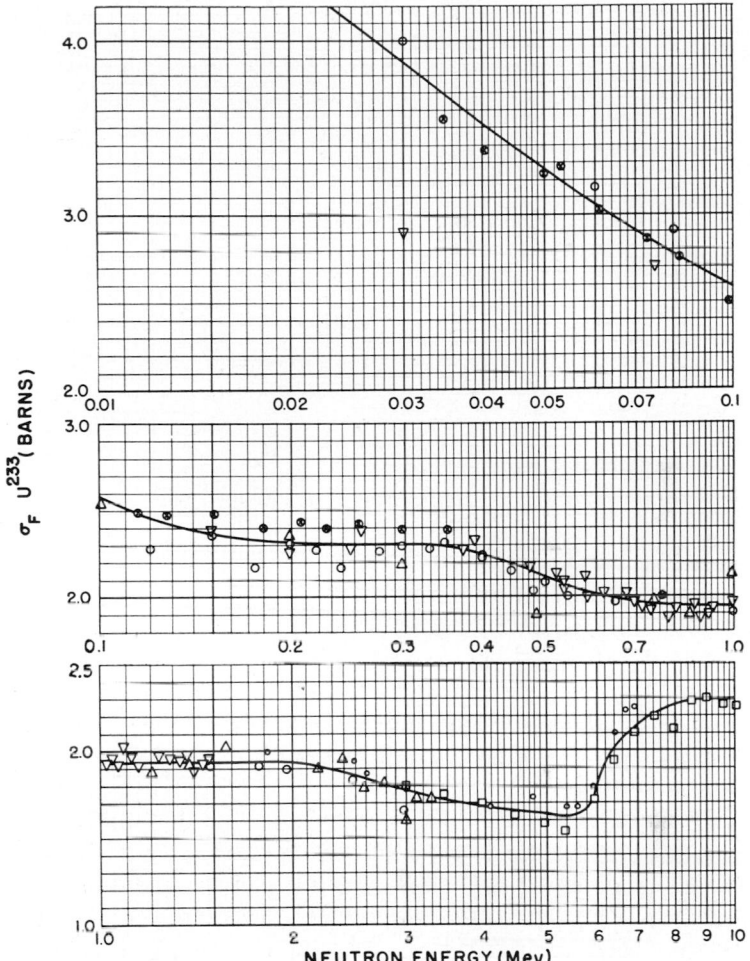

Fig. 7. Fission cross section of U^{233}: $\nabla \circ$ LASL—LA-1714, corrected for long counter efficiency effects; $\square$ LASL—From U^{233}/U^{238} ratios, Henkel, Nobles, Smith (private communication); $\otimes$ ORNL—Lamphere (La56); $\bigcirc$ Harwell; $\triangle$ Scalay.

tainty.   Figure 6 shows the fission cross section for Ra^{226} to increase from 0.5 millibarn at 2 Mev to 37 millibarns at 23 Mev.

The one experiment which serves to connect low energy data with the fast neutron measurements is the work of Yeater, Mills, and

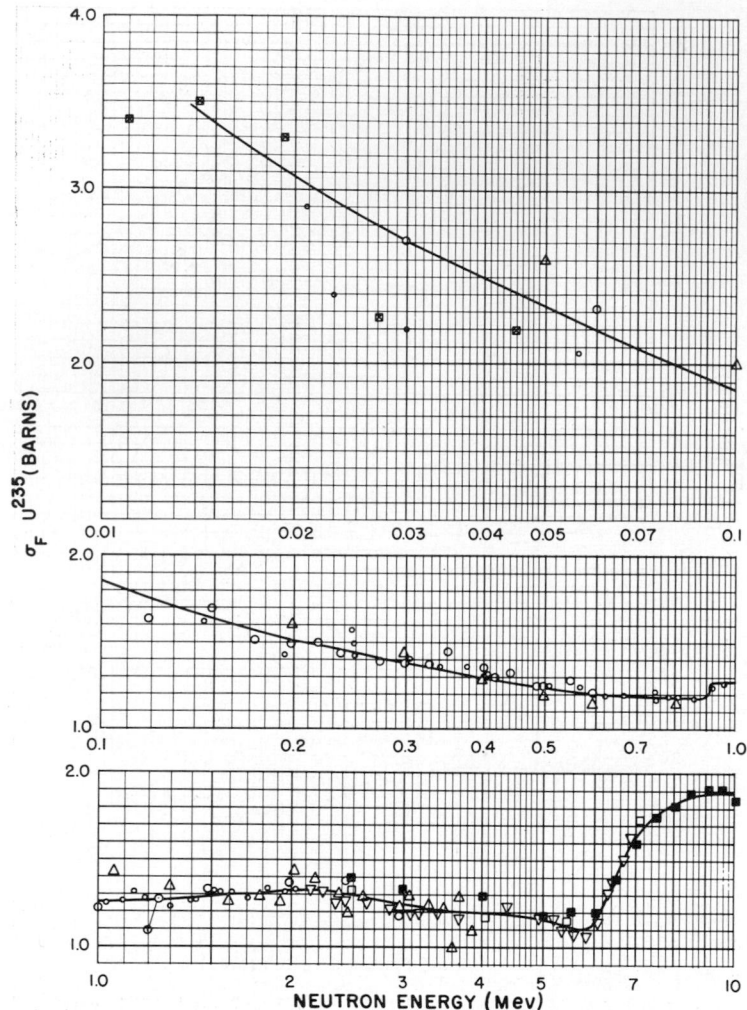

Figure 8. Fission cross section of U^{235}: $\nabla\circ$ LASL—LA-1714, corrected for long counter efficiency effects; $\square$ LASL—From U^{235}/U^{238} ratios, Smith, Nobles, Henkel (private communication); $\blacksquare$ LASL—Absolute values, Smith, Nobles, Henkel (private communication); $\oplus-\odot$ LASL—B. C. Diven, LA-1336 (basis of all LA-1714 and ORNL values); O Harwell; $\triangle$ Saclay; $\boxtimes$ KAPL.

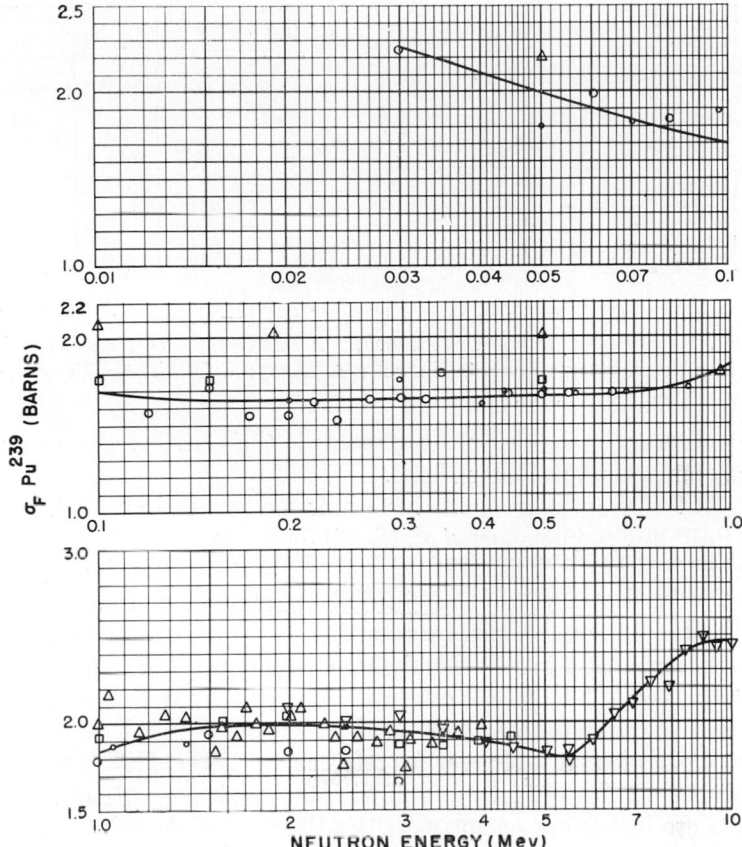

Figure 9. Fission cross section of Pu^{239}: O LASL—LA-1714, corrected for long counter efficiency effects; □ LASL—From Pu^{239}/U^{235} ratios, Henkel, Smith, and Nobles (private communication); ▽ LASL—From Pu^{239}/U^{238} ratios, Henkel Smith, and Nobles (private communication); O Harwell; △ Saclay.

Gaertner (Ye56) at Knolls Atomic Power Laboratories in which the U^{235} excitation function was measured for neutron energies between 6 ev and 2000 ev. A velocity selector was used in conjunction with the KAPL 100-Mev betatron as the neutron source, and the U^{235} fission cross section was measured relative to the B^{10} (n, α) cross sections, assuming that the latter obeys the $1/v$ law. The fission cross section was referred to the absolute value between 0.3 and 0.7 ev (Hu55).

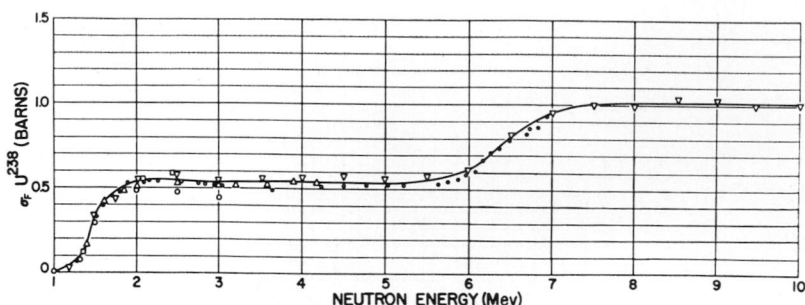

Figure 10. Fission cross section of U²³⁸: ▽ LASL—Absolute values, Smith, Nobles, Henkel (private communication); ○ LASL—LA-1714, corrected for long counter efficiency effects; ○ Harwell; △ Saclay; □ ORNL—Based on U²³⁵ values in Lamphere (La56).

The agreement with other measurements in the kilovolt energy range is only fair, as is indicated in Fig. 8.

At Saclay, measurements have been made with U²³³, U²³⁵, U²³⁸, and Pu²³⁹ by Szteinsznaider *et al.* (Sz55) for neutron energies between 50 and 2000 kev. This work was extended to 4 Mev by Netter, Julien, Corge, and Ballini (Ne56). The relative amounts of fissionable material were obtained by counting fission ratios of the various materials measured in a double fission chamber exposed to a thermal neutron beam. The fission excitation curves were determined with the use of a calibrated long counter (Ha47) using the published values (Hu55) of fission cross sections for references. Although this method involves a number of factors, each with their independent errors, the results are in fair agreement with the British and American results as shown on the composite cross section curves.

At Los Alamos measurements were made on Th²³², U²³³, U²³⁴, U²³⁵, U²³⁶, U²³⁸, and Np²³⁷ for neutron energies up to about 7 Mev (He52, Hu55). For this work, fission excitation curves were obtained using the long counter (Ha47) as a relative neutron flux monitor. In all but the U²³³ case, fission events were recorded with fission spiral counters (Ro49) having a relatively large amount of fissionable material. Normalization of the excitation curves was made with ratio measurements relative to U²³⁵, using Diven's absolute determination (Di57) as the reference. These data were corrected recently for long counter efficiency variations (He57).

The fission cross sections of greatest practical interest are those for U²³³, U²³⁵, Pu²³⁹, and U²³⁸ which are given in Figs. 7, 8, 9, and 10 re-

Table II. Fission Cross Sections in Barns of U^{233}, U^{235}, U^{238}, and Pu^{239}

E_n (kev)	U^{233}	U^{235}	Pu^{239}	E_n (Mev)	U^{238}
10		3.8		1.0	0.01
20		3.08		1.2	0.045
30	3.88	2.72	2.26	1.4	0.25
40	3.52	2.49	2.12	1.6	0.42
50	3.28	2.33	2.00	1.8	0.50
60	3.06	2.20	1.92	2.0	0.53
70	2.92	2.10	1.83	2.5	0.54
80	2.77	2.00	1.79	3.0	0.53
90	2.68	1.92	1.74	3.5	0.535
100	2.59	1.86	1.70	4.0	0.54
120	2.47	1.75	1.68	4.5	0.54
150	2.37	1.64	1.66	5.0	0.54
200	2.32	1.50	1.66	5.5	0.55
250	2.30	1.44	1.66	6.0	0.62
300	2.30	1.37	1.66	6.5	0.82
400	2.25	1.29	1.66	7.0	0.95
500	2.12	1.24	1.67	8.0	1.02
600	2.02	1.20	1.68	9.0	1.02
700	1.97	1.19	1.69	10.0	1.01
800	1.96	1.18	1.71		
900	1.94	1.20	1.77		
1000	1.94	1.26	1.85		
1200	1.94	1.27	1.92		
1500	1.94	1.29	1.98		
2000	1.94	1.33	1.99		
2500	1.86	1.30	1.98		
3000	1.79	1.23	1.94		
4000	1.69	1.20	1.89		
5000	1.65	1.16	1.83		
6000	1.78	1.12	1.92		
7000	2.15	1.65	2.15		
8000	2.27	1.82	2.34		
9000	2.30	1.88	2.45		
10000	2.30	1.89	2.50		

spectively. British, French, and American results available early in 1957 have been included (Al57, He57) and presumably give the best values available to date.[1] The data are plotted in a manner

[1] For Figs. 7, 8, 9, and 10 the Los Alamos Scientific Laboratory data are usually from Ba54a, He56, Sm57, or Di57. The Harwell data are from Al55. The Saclay data are from Sz55 and Ne56. KAPL points are from Ye56.

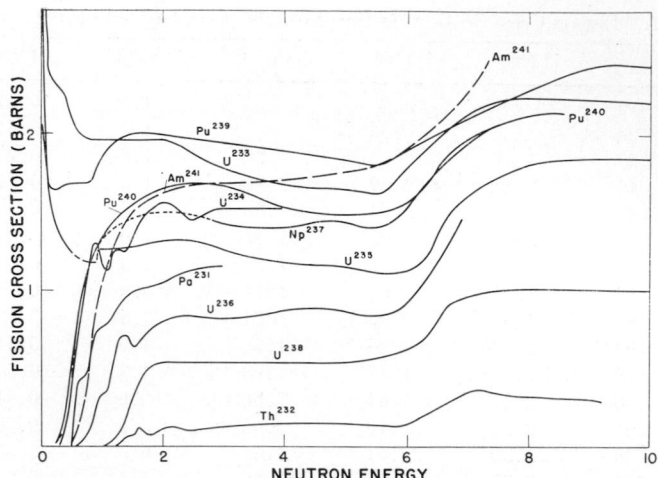

Figure 11. Compilation of fission excitation curves for 11 fissionable nuclei.

such that values may be read off with an accuracy comparable to the experimental accuracies.   In each case, the solid curve is meant to indicate the most probable cross section values.   The position of this curve has been influenced by the uncertainties in the results from the various measurements.   Table II gives a listing of "best values" taken from these curves.

A compilation of neutron-induced fission excitation functions for 11 fissionable nuclei is given in Fig. 11.   No data points are shown since only a comparison of general features was wanted.   Above 3 Mev, the curves are based upon Los Alamos data (He52, No55, Sm57, Hu55, He57).   Below 3 Mev, data are included from Al55, La56, Di57, and Sz55.

C. *Integral Fission Cross Section Measurements*

It is of interest to compare measurements made with mono-energetic neutron sources with the *integral* measurement of a fission cross section using a spectrum of fission neutrons.   Such a comparison gives an independent check of the product of the fission excitation curve and fission neutron spectrum.   The source of fission neutrons is usually produced at a reactor by a thermal neutron beam incident on a thermally fissile material.   Experimental difficulties are apparent in the determination of the cross section of a thermally fissile material in a fission spectrum. However, such difficulties do not arise for U^{238}, which has a fission threshold near 1 Mev. Two experimental methods have been developed for such measurements. In each of these methods, the errors in $\bar{\nu}$, the neutron multiplicity, are involved in the final result. The first was used in a careful measurement by Leachman and Schmitt (Le57) at Los Alamos. A disk of U^{235}, located at the center of a double hemispherical ionization counter, was placed in the thermal beam of the Los Alamos water boiler. The flux of fission neutrons was determined by placing next to the disk a U^{235} monitor foil from which fission fragments were detected in the inner chamber of the counter. U^{238}, depleted in U^{235}, was located in a thin layer on a hemisphere of the outer chamber of the counter in which the fission fragments were detected. The fission cross section of U^{238} measured in a U^{235} fission spectrum was thus found to be 0.307 ± 0.005 barns using a value of $\bar{\nu} = 2.46 \pm 0.03$ for U^{235}.

A different method, also involving $\bar{\nu}$, has been developed by Richmond (Ri57) at Harwell. He used back-to-back foils of U^{235} and enriched U^{238} exposed to a thermal neutron beam. Coincidences were detected between the fission fragments from U^{235} and from U^{238}, since fission in the U^{238} could arise only from U^{235} fission neutrons. Using the known geometry, the integral fission cross section was simply and accurately determined to be 0.304 ± 0.007 barns, in excellent agreement with the value obtained by Leachman and Schmitt.

The above results can be compared with the one obtained by multiplying the fission cross section excitation curve by the U^{235} fission spectrum. For this calculation, the expression used for the fission spectrum was $N(E) = 1765 \, E^{1/2} \exp (-0.775E)$, (Cr56), and the U^{238} fission cross section is that given in Fig. 3. The integral fission cross section was calculated to be 0.305 barn. The integral measurements and the calculated value from the spectrum and excitation curve thus agree to within the uncertainties present in both the fission excitation curve and the fission spectrum.

Richmond extended his measurements to the thermally fissile nuclei. For this work, it was necessary to insert a cadmium foil between the two fissile materials and use a gas scintillation counter so as to obtain maximum counter speed. This fast time resolution was required to discriminate against those fission neutrons which were slowed down and re-entered the target foil (with increased fission probability). The following cross section ratios were obtained:

$$\sigma_f(\mathrm{Pu}^{239})/\sigma_f(\mathrm{U}^{235}) = 1.42 \pm 2.1\%$$

$$\sigma_f(\mathrm{U}^{233})/\sigma_f(\mathrm{U}^{235}) = 1.45 \pm 2.2\%$$

$$\sigma_f(\mathrm{U}^{233})/\sigma_f(\mathrm{Pu}^{239}) = 1.02 \pm 2.0\%$$

A great many measurements have been made in the neutron spectra available at various types of moderated and unmoderated nuclear reactors. However, this work is very specialized in that the neutron spectrum used is determined by a specific position in a particular reactor configuration. These measurements will not be included in this summary.

3. Systematics and Fluctuations of Fission Cross Sections

A. Systematic Behavior of Fission Cross Sections

A comparison of the fission cross sections for eleven isotopes is shown in Fig. 12. The fission excitation functions for thermally fissile nuclei rapidly decrease at low energy and are approximately constant between 2 and 5 Mev. Similarly, for nuclei having positive

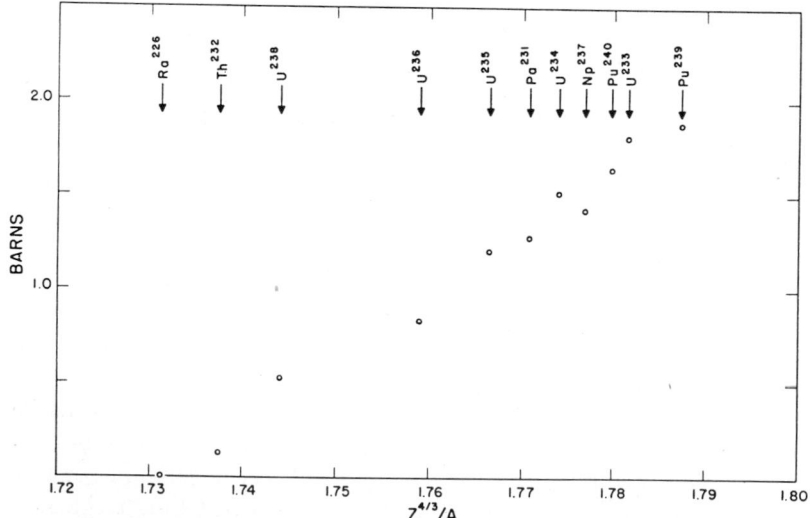

Figure 12. Fission cross sections as 3 Mev neutron energy as a function of $Z^{4/3}/A$.

energy thresholds, the excitation curves exhibit a plateau in this region. It may be noticed that near 6 Mev all cross sections rise toward a new plateau.   In the case of U^{238}, shown in Fig. 3, a similar step seems to occur after 12 Mev and possibly after 17 Mev.

The gross features of typical excitation curves were predicted by Bohr and Wheeler (Bo39) and by Bohr (Bo40) in 1939 and 1940 and accounted for the plateaus which were observed many years later. The basis of the description is the concept of *widths* for fission, neutron re-emission, *etc.*, which indicate the probability for the compound . nucleus to decay by one of several channels. These widths increase with energy as do the nuclear level densities. The partial cross section for fission can be written:

$$\sigma_f = \sigma_c \, \Gamma_f / \Sigma_i \Gamma_i = \sigma_c \, \Gamma_f / (\Gamma_n + \Gamma_f) = \sigma_c \, \Gamma_f / \Gamma \qquad (1)$$

where σ_c is the cross section for the formation of the compound nucleus and Γ_n, Γ_f, and Γ are the neutron re-emission width, fission width, and total width, respectively. Γ_γ for de-excitation by γ-ray emission is omitted since its effect is small in the Mev energy region. The theory assumes that there is a large number of overlapping levels and that statistical considerations apply. One might expect that well above threshold the widths for fission and neutron re-emission would increase similarly with energy. Then, since σ_c varies slowly with energy, σ_f would be fairly constant. In this way, the plateaus between 2 and 5 Mev were accounted for (Bo40).

If one compares the values for the fission cross section at 3 Mev, it is noticed that there seems to be a systematic variation with Z and A. Since the first considerations of fission theory, it has been known that the properties of fission are associated with the quantity Z^2/A which represents the ratio of the Coulomb energy to the surface energy of the nucleus as represented in the liquid drop model

$$Z^2/A = Z^2/A^{1/3} \div A^{2/3}$$

For example, correlations have been shown for spontaneous fission half-lives (Sw55), and fission thresholds (Ja56, Sw56). Early measurements of fission cross section in the Mev region suggested a correlation of plateau values with Z^2/A (Hu53). However, more recent and supposedly more reliable determinations do not show such a clear and simple correlation with Z^2/A, but have shown that different charge values give a family of curves for the correlation with Z^2/A

(Za57, Hu58). Barschall (Ba54) found an empirical correlation of 3-Mev fission cross sections with $Z^{4/3}/A$ which is shown in Fig. 12. There is no known significance for the parameter $Z^{4/3}/A$, although it behaves almost identically with Z and A as does the Coulomb energy per nucleon

$$Z^2/A^{1/3} \div A = Z^2/A^{4/3}$$

Figure 12 can be used to estimate 3-Mev fission cross sections and fission branching ratios (Γ_f/Γ) fairly reliably.

Jackson (Ja56) has used a different approach in which the critical parameter is $(E_{th} - B_n)$, where E_{th} is the observed or deduced fission threshold and B_n is the binding energy of the last neutron in the system. His conclusion is that, on the plateau, the probability of fission is a universal function of $(E_{th} - E_B)$.

Bohr (Bo40) predicted the step behavior in the fission excitation curves which occur above 6, 12, and 17 Mev. The step above 5 Mev is explained by the possibility of fission following the inelastic emission of a neutron which leaves the target nucleus sufficiently excited. The process may be written as a reaction

$$A + n \rightarrow (A + 1)^* \rightarrow n + f$$

or more simply as the $(n, n'f)$ process. Similarly, the emission of 2 or more neutrons may leave the residual nuclei sufficiently excited for additional fission contributions from the $(n, xn'f)$ processes. In this way, the fission cross section below 5 Mev is entirely composed of that due to the compound nucleus $(A + 1)$. Between 5 and 12 Mev, it is a combination of fission of the compound nucleus $(A + 1)$ and the original nucleus (A). Similarly, above 17 Mev, the nucleus $(A - 1)$ also contributes.

One can write down an estimate of the fission cross sections at the middle of the first several plateaus in terms of Eq. (1) since the neutron binding energies and fission thresholds are roughly equal:

$$\sigma_f(3 \text{ Mev}) = \sigma_c(3)(\Gamma_f/\Sigma\Gamma)_{A+1} \tag{2}$$

$$\begin{aligned}
\sigma_f(10) &= [\sigma_f(10)]_{A+1} + [\sigma_f(10)]_A \\
&= \sigma_c(10)(\Gamma_f/\Gamma)_{A+1} + \sigma_c(10)(1 - \Gamma_f/\Gamma)_{A+1}(\Gamma_f/\Gamma)_A \\
&= \sigma_c(10)\{(\Gamma_f/\Gamma)_{A+1} + [1 - (\Gamma_f/\Gamma)]_{A+1}(\Gamma_f/\Gamma)_A\} \tag{3}
\end{aligned}$$

$$\begin{aligned}
\text{and } \sigma_f(17) &= \sigma_c(17)(\Gamma_f/\Gamma)_{A+1} + (1 - \Gamma_f/\Gamma)_{A+1}(\Gamma_f/\Gamma)_A \\
&\quad + (1 - \Gamma_f/\Gamma)_{A+1}(1 - \Gamma_f/\Gamma)_A(\Gamma_f/\Gamma)_{A-1} \tag{4}
\end{aligned}$$

Making these estimates, one can calculate plateau values of fission cross section by using Γ_f/Γ which is found from Fig. 12 and making the simple assumption that this ratio stays constant with excitation energy. Using the σ_c from Beyster (Be57) and calculating plateau values for U^{238} for example, one obtains values almost within the experimental uncertainties of the measured values as shown in Table III. Since 5 or 10 per cent uncertainties are present in the σ_c values, uncertainties at least as large are present in the fission cross section estimates.

Table III. Comparison of Estimated and Calculated Plateau Values of the Fission Cross Section of U^{238}

E_n (Mev)	σ_c (barns)(Be57)	σ_f calculated (barns)	σ_f measured (barns) (Sm57)
3	3.3	0.55	0.55
10	2.7	0.93	1.01
17	2.8	1.48	1.37

If simple assumptions are made concerning the spectrum of the emitted neutrons using evaporation theory, one can let $E \exp(-E/t)$ represent the energy distribution of evaporated neutrons where E is the energy of the emitted neutron and t is the nuclear temperature. Inelastic neutron experiments like those of Rosen and Stewart (Ro57) and Cranberg (Cr56b) give a measure of t which is then assumed to vary as $E^{1/2}$. If one assumes that whenever energetically possible, particle emission or fission occurs, one can calculate the fission excitation curves over these steps associated with neutron emission. Such calculations for U^{238} compare favorably with experimental measurements. Jackson (Ja56) and Zamyatium (Za57) have also made similar calculations of the steps and excitation functions in fission.

B. *Fluctuations of Fission Cross Sections*

In the neighborhood of 1-Mev neutron energy, fluctuations are present in the fission excitation curves. In the thermally fissile nuclei, for example, there is a step increase for U^{235} at 920 kev, or over a broader range, a rise in σ_f of Pu^{239} near 1200 kev. The phe-

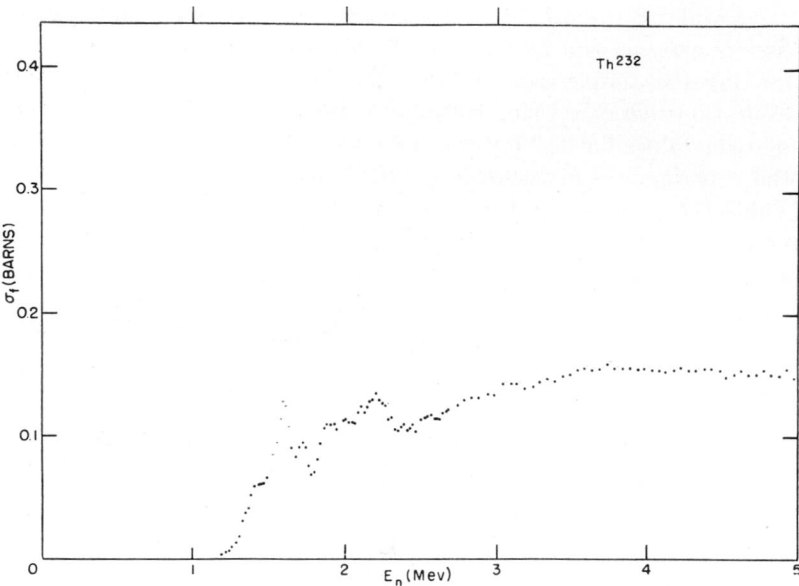

Figure 13. Fission cross section of Th²³² near threshold (He52).

nomena showing abrupt changes in cross section are clearer for the even-even nuclides, which have thresholds between 0.4 and 1.2 Mev. One example is shown by Fig. 5 in which the cross section of U²³⁸ rises through 3 short plateaus at 610, 950, and 1180 kev. More striking variations near thresholds are exhibited by the lighter nuclei, as shown in Fig. 13. While U²³⁸ shows plateaus, U²³⁶ gives a barely resolved peak near 1.4 Mev, U²³⁴ gives a more clearly resolved peak at 810 kev, and Th²³² shows structure similar to that found in the total neutron cross sections of light nuclei. It is thus clearly established that the fast neutron fission cross sections in some cases show abrupt changes in cross section and do not vary smoothly with energy.

Equation (1) can give a qualitative account for these variations. Γ_n fluctuates with energy as low-lying levels in the residual nucleus become excited by inelastic scattering. As each new level is excited, an increase in Γ_n appears which results in an increase in the denominator of Eq. (3) and a decrease in the fission cross section (Bo56). This competition between inelastic scattering and fission may account for fine structure in the fission excitation curves. Indeed, the known levels in U^{238} at 900 and 1680 kev probably correspond to the plateaus observed in the fission excitation curve near threshold (Fig. 5).

An alternative explanation leading to possible fine structure is given by a nucleus being *cold* at the time of fission.   That is, the binding energy and kinetic energy of the incoming neutron are absorbed in producing nuclear deformation, so that at the time of fission the excitation of the compound nucleus is near the ground state.   The spacing of low-lying levels is perhaps large enough to result in observable fine structure in the fission excitation curves.   Recent considerations of this idea (Wi57) suggest it is probably not an important contribution to fission fluctuations.

4. Angular Distribution of Fission Fragments

The angular distribution of fission fragments is isotropic at thermal neutron energies.   However, for energies greater than 1 Mev, marked anisotropies with respect to the incident neutron beam occur. These anisotropies have no direct bearing on reactor design and only indirect effects on fission cross section determination, but are of considerable interest and importance for theories of fission.   The

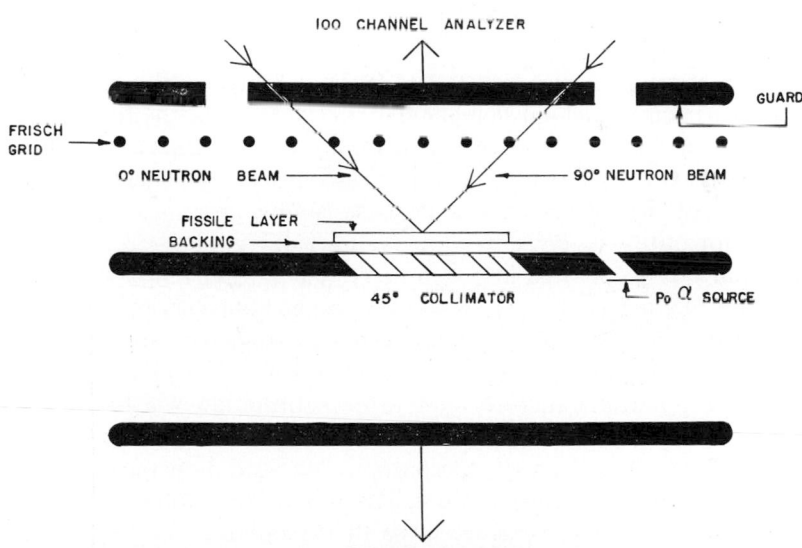

Figure 14. Schematic cross section of double fission chamber (Br55).

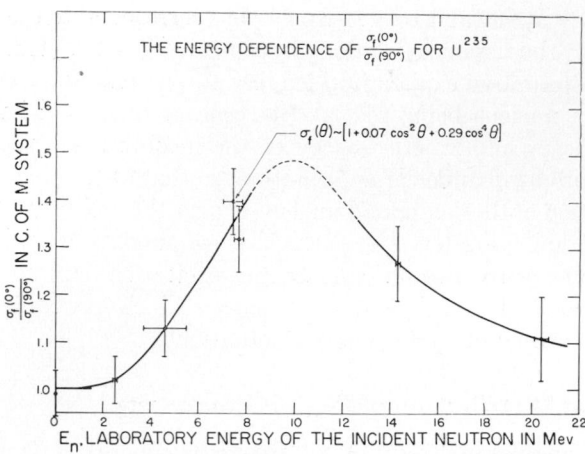

Figure 15. Energy dependence of the anisotropy for U^{235}.

measurements of angular distribution for neutron-induced fission are largely those of a group at Los Alamos (Di53, Br54, Br55, He56, Si57). For U^{238}, additional measurements have been made by Varfolomeev, Romantsera, and Kutukova (Va55) in Russia. Recently, more information has been obtained by Lamphere (La57) at Oak Ridge for U^{234}.

In the early work (Di53) for 14-Mev neutrons, it was shown that the fission fragment angular distribution was of the form $A + B \cos^2 \theta$ for five nuclides bombarded in a simple ionization chamber. (Here, θ is the angle of emission with respect to the incident neutron beam.) In view of the interest in these results, an improved coincidence apparatus was developed and is shown in Fig. 14 (Br55). Fissile material was evaporated in a thin layer (0.5 mg/cm²) on a thin gold backing (0.9 mg/cm²), and the fission fragments emerging from the foil on the side opposite the collimator were studied in an ionization chamber using a Frisch grid. The chamber was calibrated with standard α-particle sources, and after subtracting widths due to electronics, the residual energy resolution was about 1 per cent. With this chamber, good discrimination was obtained between the light and heavy fragments, and the possibility of finding different angular distributions for the two groups was investigated.

Three results arose from the first work with the improved chamber. The first, shown in Fig. 15, gives the anisotropy, $\sigma_f(0°,$

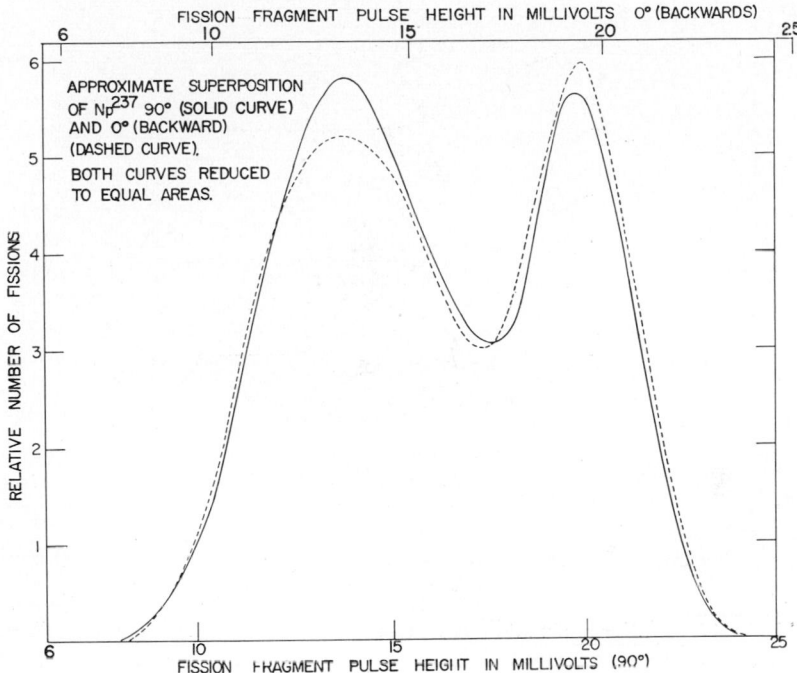

Figure 16. Superposition of $0°$ and $90°$ ionization spectra for Np^{237} at 14 Mev neutron energy.

$E_n)/\sigma_f(90°, E_n)$, in the center-of-mass system for U^{235} as a function of neutron energy where $0°$ represents the fission fragment proceeding along the neutron direction. It seemed clear that the anisotropy was a rising function up to 8 Mev. Insufficient data were taken to be certain about the anisotropy above this energy. Second, the relative differential cross section of Np^{237} at 14.3 Mev was fitted by an expression of the form $(1 + A \cos^2 \theta + B \cos^4 \theta)$, in which B was considerably greater than A. To a large extent, the same was true for the U^{235} distribution at 7.3-Mev neutron energy. Finally, the spectra of fission fragments at $0°$ and at $90°$ were obtained for Np^{237} at 14-Mev neutron energy. The curves, reduced to equal area and adjusted for center-of-mass motion, are shown superimposed in Fig. 16. These curves are interpreted to mean that the intensity of heavy fragments is 10 per cent greater in the forward direction than at $90°$. However, the conclusion that the heavy fragments may be

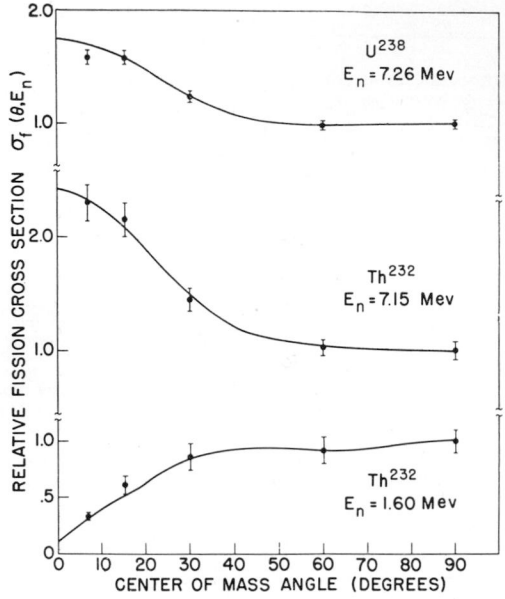

Figure 17. Relative differential fission cross sections for U²³⁸ and the Th²³².

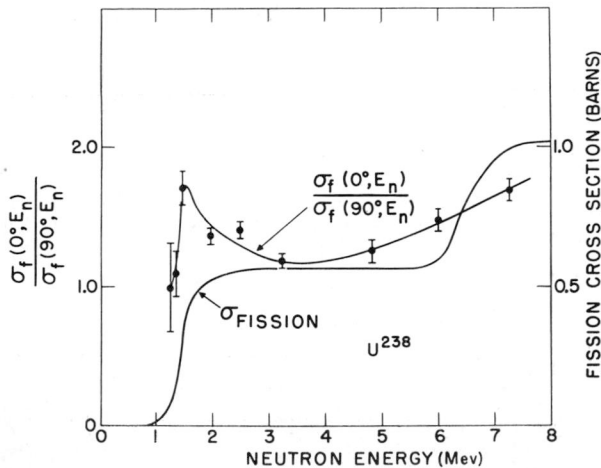

Figure 18. Energy dependence of the anisotropy of fission fragments and the total fission cross section for U²³⁸.

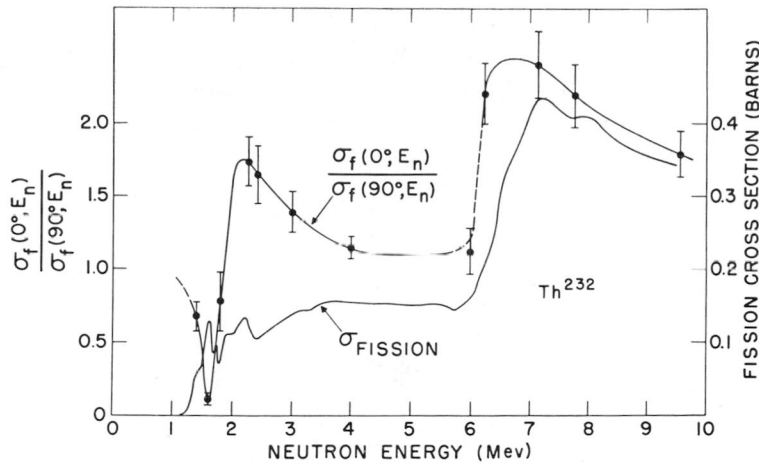

Figure 19. Energy dependence of the anisotropy of fission fragments and the total fission cross section for Th[232].

more forward peaked is only tentative. The results for the odd nuclides Np[237] and U[235] show anisotropies up to 1.5.

A more recent study (He56) of the even nuclides U[238] and Th[232] gave unexpected results, especially for Th[232]. At higher energies, U[238] behaves rather like U[235] in that the anisotropy climbs to a value of 1.69 at 7.26 Mev. Thereafter, the anisotropy declines but appears to show another increase near 20 Mev. Insufficient data were taken to show the complete curve shape above 7 Mev. At 7 Mev, both U[238] and Th[232] were studied at five angles (Fig. 17). Fitting the curves for the differential fission cross sections by a Legendre expansion of form $\Sigma_n A_{2n} P_{2n} (\cos \theta)$ required values of n up to 3. Near threshold, as has been shown, the fission cross section excitation function shows some evidence of structure. The anisotropy near threshold for U[238] however, is quite small but it rises steeply and reaches a fairly sharp peak at 1.6 Mev, from which it rapidly declines. The results are shown in Fig. 18.

For Th[232], the relationship of anisotropy to fission cross section is close and striking. In general the fission cross section is small while the fluctuations near threshold are marked. Unlike all nuclei previously discussed, Th[232] near threshold shows an anisotropy which is *less* than unity, i.e., the angular distribution has a minimum in the forward direction. At the first peak in the fission cross section at

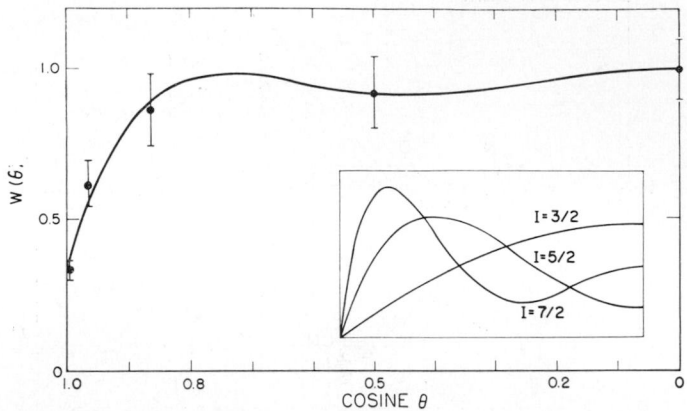

Figure 20. Angular distribution of fission fragments for Th²³² at 1.6 Mev neutron energy. The points represent experimental data (He56). The curve constitutes a least-squares fit based on assumption of a $K = {}^3/_2$ saddle-point rotational hand (Wi56). Inset: Plots of the normalized angular distribution functions for the saddle-points states $K = {}^3/_2, I = {}^3/_2, {}^5/_2, {}^7/_2$.

1.6 Mev, the anisotropy shown in Fig. 19 is very marked. While experimental conditions could not confirm that the forward and backward yield was actually zero, it was certainly small. As at higher energies, a detailed study of the angular distribution showed that terms of at least $n = 3$ were required in the Legendre expansion for a good fit to the experimental results. This suggests that even at this relatively low energy, neutrons of angular momentum $l = 3$ were taking part in the interaction. As the energy is increased, the Th²³² anisotropy sharply increases to a value of 1.74 at 2 Mev similar to the 1.6 Mev peak for U²³⁸, followed by a slow decline as the *plateau* of the fission cross section was reached. Above 6 Mev, another peak in the anisotropy occurs, corresponding to the threshold of the $(n, n'f)$ process. At higher energies the behavior of the anisotropy of Th²³² is similar to that of U²³⁸. The rise in anisotropy at 20 Mev may be associated with the $(n, 3n'f)$ process. Insufficient data were taken to prove the existence of a similar peak near 13 Mev associated with the threshold of the $(n, 2n'f)$ process.

These results furnish pertinent data to assist in the theoretical interpretation of the fission process (Hi53, Fo53, Bo56). At one time, fragment anisotropy was predicted on the basis of collective vibrations, but recently the Bohr-Mottelson theory of collective

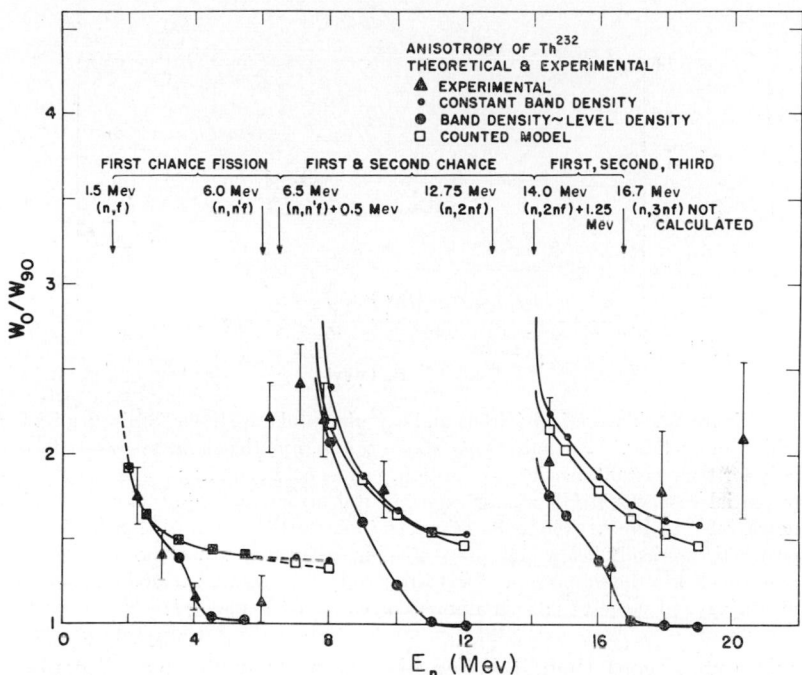

Figure 21. Theoretical (Gr58) and experimental (He56) fission fragment ani-sotropies for Th[232]. The first neutron emitted is assumed to have a kinetic energy of 0.5 Mev; the second, 0.75 Mev. The gaps in the calculation are regions where one expects too few levels for the average behavior to be relevant, and where the ef-fect of the distribution in energy of emitted neutrons will be significant.

motion, which has had impressive successes in other fields, offers an explanation of the observed anisotropies in terms of collective rotation (Bo56). Fission occurs if enough of the energy contributed by the incident neutron becomes concentrated in potential energy of de-formation to enable the nucleus to pass over the saddle-point shape. At the saddle point, the repulsive Coulomb forces balance the cohesive nuclear interactions (Hi53). For excitation energies just above the fission threshold, Bohr regards the nucleus to be essentially *cold* in passing over the saddle point so that only the lowest rotational states are excited. On this basis, it can be shown in general that the differential cross section will show a peak in the forward direction, and that the anisotropy will be greater for a target nucleus with zero

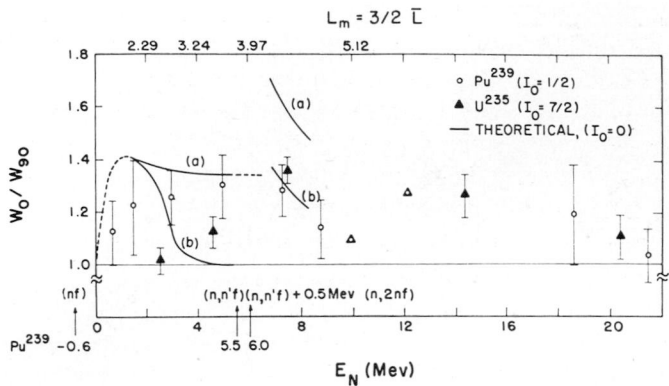

Figure 22. Theoretical (Gr58) and experimental (Br54, Si57) anisotropies for odd-even nuclides.   The anisotropy above the $(n, n'f)$ threshold has been plotted only for the constant density assumption.   The corresponding points for the exponential case would fall within experimental error for Pu^{239}.   The thresholds noted refer to Pu^{239}.   The open triangles indicate the qualitative behavior expected theoretically below and above the $(n, 2n'f)$ threshold.   The data for U^{235} indicate clearly the suppresion of the anisotropy for incoming orbital angular momenta $< I_0$ and suggest that this suppression ceases for values $\geqq I_0$.

spin (even-even) than it is for high spin.   However, an exception appears in the case of Th^{232} at 1.6 Mev, where the forward yield of fission fragments is almost zero.   This has been explained by Wilets and Chase (Wi56) on the assumption that only the lowest members of a single rotational band are excited.   With this assumption, it was possible to give a good account of the angular distribution observed for Th^{232} at 1.6 Mev as shown in Fig. 20.

At energies up to 20 Mev, Griffin has had considerable success in using Bohr's theory to explain qualitatively the energy dependence of the anisotropy (Gr58).   Reasonable assumptions were made about the energy dependence of the maximum value of K, the component of angular momentum along the nuclear symmetry axis.   In Th^{232}, for example, the sudden increase in anisotropy just above the $(n, n'f)$ threshold is attributed to *second-chance* fissions which occur through states of high angular momentum and relatively low excitation energy (low K).   Figure 21 shows the comparison of anisotropy calculations with experiment and indicates a similar increase of anisotropy for $(n, 2n'f)$ or *third-chance* fissions.   The comparison is impressive. Unfortunately insufficient experimental data are available to prove the existence of all of these effects. For several nuclei at 7 Mev, calculated anisotropies are substantially in agreement with experiment. Finally, calculations were given for Pu^{239} at low energy. The spin of $^1/_2$ for Pu^{239} is neglected, but the low energy anisotropy is still given qualitatively, suggesting that the target spin becomes a secondary effect when the incoming orbital angular momentum of the neutron is somewhat larger than the target spin. Comparison is made in Fig. 22 between Pu^{239} and for U^{235} wherein the anisotropy is suppressed for energies below 3 Mev.

Halpern has independently made an analysis of fission anisotropy with results very similar to those reported by Griffin (Ha58). The success of the Bohr theory in explaining the angular distributions of fission fragments in neutron-induced fission is the most impressive recent result in the theoretical understanding of the fission process.

5. Neutrons Associated with Fission

The study of the multiplicities of neutrons from neutron-induced fission is useful in understanding the energetics of the fission process. In addition, fission neutron multiplicity and its variation with neutron energy are of great importance in the potential application of fast reactors as breeders. The methods for measuring $\bar{\nu}$, the mean number of neutrons emitted per fission, are more complicated for fast neutron fission than for thermal fission. Since incident fast neutrons, as well as causing fission, may be scattered, they are then indistinguishable from those released in fission. Three methods for measuring $\bar{\nu}$ for fast neutrons have been developed. The first depends upon the detection of delayed coincidences of neutrons with respect to neutron events, the second uses prompt coincidences and the third involves sphere transmission measurements.

In the first method, a relatively low fission rate is used in conjunction with a neutron detector having high efficiency. A fission event is observed in a chamber placed at the center of the neutron detector, and neutrons are detected during the time required for slowing down and capture of the fission neutrons. Among these detected neutrons will be some which are scattered out of the incident beam by the chamber. These can be estimated by replacing the fission chamber with an identical one having no fissile material. Such a background, however, sets an upper limit to the neutron flux.

A system has been developed by Johnstone (Jo55) at Harwell, using a detector consisting of a number of BF_3 chambers in a water moderator. This detector had an efficiency of 10 to 20 per cent and a slowing-down and capture time of about 200 μsec.

A more efficient system has been used at Los Alamos by Diven, Martin, Taschek, and Terrell (Di56) using a liquid scintillator for the neutron detector. A diagram of the counter is shown in Fig. 23. The detectors consisted of 90 photomultiplier tubes mounted flush with the inside surface of the cylinder. Neutrons were slowed down in the scintillating liquid and were captured in a mean time of some 15 μsec after fission. The γ rays from the neutron capture in cadmium gave light flashes in the scintillator which were recorded by the photo-tubes. The capture efficiency was estimated to vary from 99.6 per cent for thermal neutrons to 74 per cent for 8-Mev neutrons, and for a fission spectrum the capture efficiency was 95 per cent. The efficiency of detection depended upon the bias of the photomultipliers and was about 80 per cent. A fission event started the time base on an oscilloscope, and subsequent signals from neutron detection were shown as pulses on the sweep. A novel feature of the method is that

Table IV. Typical 80-kev Neutron Multiplicities (Di56)[a]

Nuclide Fissions	U^{233}	U^{235}	Pu^{239}
Fissions analyzed	1632	10715	1376
ν	2.585 ± 0.062	247[b] ± 0.03	3.408 ± 0.079
$(\nu^2)_{av}$	7.84 ± 0.34	7.32 ± 0.15	10.62 ± 0.53
$(\nu^2)_{av} - (\bar{\nu}/\bar{\nu}^2)$	0.786 ± 0.013	0.795 ± 0.007	0.815 ± 0.017
P_0	0.010 ± 0.008	0.027 ± 0.004	−0.01 ± 0.01
P_1	0.151 ± 0.024	0.158 ± 0.010	0.11 ± 0.03
P_2	0.326 ± 0.037	0.339 ± 0.014	0.13 ± 0.06
P_3	0.301 ± 0.044	0.305 ± 0.015	0.56 ± 0.08
P_4	0.176 ± 0.041	0.133 ± 0.013	0.11 ± 0.08
P_5	0.042 ± 0.028	0.038 ± 0.009	0.06 ± 0.09
P_6	−0.010 ± 0.017	−0.001 ± 0.003	0.05 ± 0.08
P_7	0.006 ± 0.009	0.001 ± 0.002	0.00 ± 0.06
P_8	−0.002 ± 0.002	0.000 ± 0.000	−0.01 ± 0.03

[a] ν and $(\nu^2)_{av}$ are the average and the average square of the number of neutrons per fission; $P_0, P_1, P_2, \ldots$ are the respective probabilities of emission of 0, 1, 2, ... neutrons per fission.

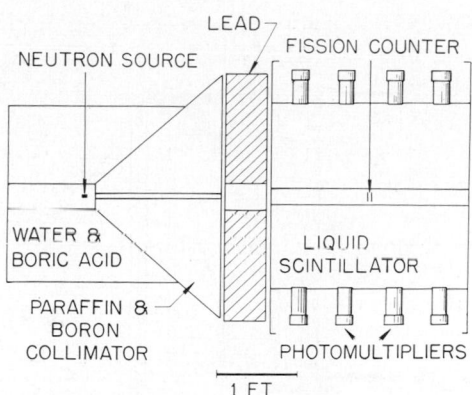

Figure 23. Schematic diagram of $\bar{\nu}$ experimental equipment (Di56).

it gives not only $\bar{\nu}$, but also the distribution in ν.   Table IV gives some typical distributions in ν as obtained from this experiment.

The prompt method for finding $\bar{\nu}$ uses a high fission rate and detects fission neutrons by coincidence proton recoils in a counter containing hydrogenous material.   The efficiency of such neutron counting, however, is necessarily low (about 10^{-3}) so that the advantage of a high fission rate, which is made possible by prompt coincidences, is off-set by the low neutron detection efficiency.   Non-fission neutrons are discriminated against by the bias setting of the fission neutron counter and requires a knowledge of the fission neutron spectrum.   The experimental arrangement used by Fowler (Fo55) is shown in Fig. 24 and that used by Hanna (Ha56) in Fig. 25. In each system, $\bar{\nu}$ for fast neutrons was compared with $\bar{\nu}$ for thermal neutrons by surrounding the counter with paraffin.   The method is essentially a ratio method based upon thermal values of $\bar{\nu}$.   The results from these two prompt coincidence experiments are in agreement within the rather large uncertainties although the neutron region in which they overlapped was relatively small.

The third method for $\bar{\nu}$ measurement involves sphere transmission measurements in which neutron multiplication is detected by neutron counters of several types (Be55).   Monoenergetic and fission neutrons as well as various (α, n) neutron sources have been employed.   The analysis of such apparently simple experiments is quite involved and requires a knowledge of the fission cross sections.

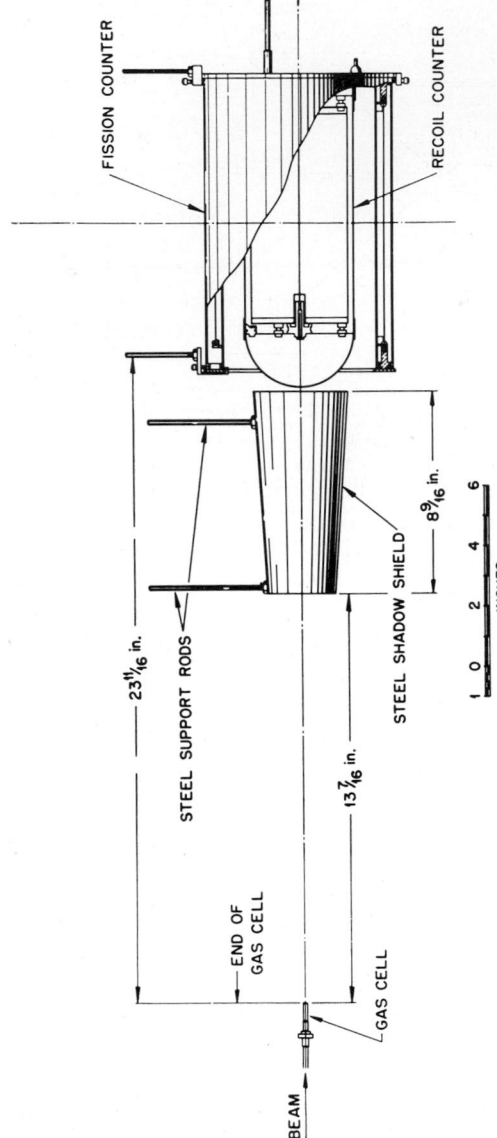

Figure 24. Schematic diagram of the fission neutron experiment made by Fowler (Fo55). The central neutron chamber detected proton recoils. Fissions were counted in the outer cylindrical ionization chamber.

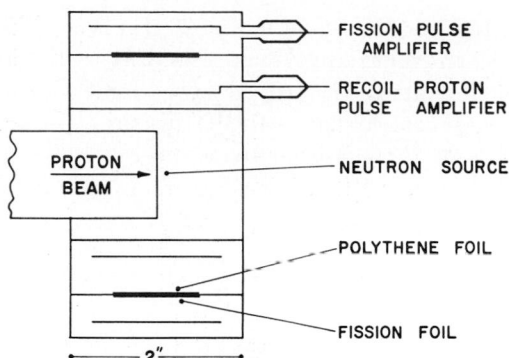

Figure 25. Schematic diagram of the apparatus used by Hanna for neutron multiplicity experiment (Ha56).

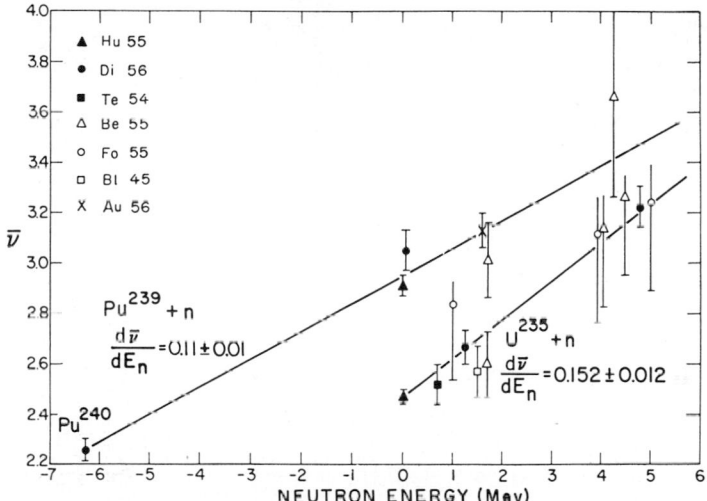

Figure 26. Experimental variation of the average number of neutrons from fission with incident neutron energy.   The straight lines represent least squares fit (Te57).

The results of these experiments are shown in Fig. 26 for U^{235} and Pu^{239} (Te57).   It appears that the increase in $\bar{\nu}$ with neutron energy is linear within experimental error.   The accuracy is insufficient to decide whether the difference in slopes is significant. The curves can be approximated by the expression:

$$\bar{\nu}(E_n) = \bar{\nu} \text{ (thermal)} + E_n/7$$

where E_n is in Mev, and the denominator (7 Mev) can be considered as the sum of the neutron binding energy and average kinetic energy of the evaporated neutron. Since the curve for Pu includes a value of $\bar{\nu}$ for the spontaneous fission of Pu^{240}, this simple expression holds for a range of about 10 Mev in neutron energy. More accurate experiments will be required to establish second-order deviations from this expression.

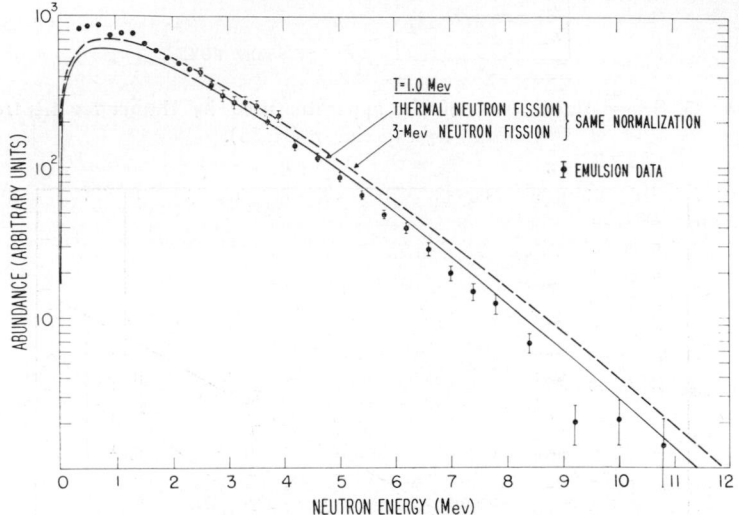

Figure 27. Calculations of the energy spectra of fission neutrons for $T = 1.0$ Mev (Le57). Data are from Frye and Rosen (Cr56).

The ν results and other features of fission have been satisfactorily accounted for by Leachman (Le55). The analysis begins by estimating the total energy of fission fragments. For a given fragment mass ratio, the mass of the fragments was found from mass systematics. By subtraction of the combined fragment masses from the mass of the initial compound nucleus the total energy from fission was obtained. The distribution in fragment kinetic energy was found from ionization chamber measurements in which corrections were made for dispersion and ionization defects. If the kinetic energy of the fragments is subtracted from the total energy available, the remainder is the excitation energy of the fragment nuclei, which is dissipated in γ radiation

and neutron emission. The probability of emission of 1,2,3. . .
neutrons from the fragment nuclei was then obtained from evaporation theory. In addition, the energy spectrum of the evaporated
neutrons was calculated using the assumption of isotropic emission
with respect to the moving fragments.

With this analysis, Leachman obtained qualitative agreement
with many of the known experimental data. The neutron emission
probabilities for spontaneous fission and neutron-induced fission show
agreement with experimental results. Similarly the calculated neutron spectra agree well with observation and indicate that little change
is expected as one changes from thermal to 3 Mev incident neutron
energy as is shown in Fig. 27. Considering the variation of $\bar{\nu}$ with
energy, recourse is made to the experimental observation of Wahl
(Wa54) that the kinetic energy of the fission fragments remains approximately constant with increasing incident neutron energy. The
significance of this had been first pointed out by J. L. Fowler (Fo52).
Since the kinetic energy remains constant, the excitation energy increases with increasing energy of the incident neutron and the theory
predicts a linear increase in $\bar{\nu}$ with a slope close to that experimentally
observed.

Recently, Terrell (Te57) has made similar calculations using
modified and usually simpler assumptions than those used by Leachman. In general, the results are similar concerning $\bar{\nu}$ predictions.
More extensive calculations of fission neutron spectra have been made
using evaporation theory. In addition, Terrell has studied the systematic behavior of the distribution of fission neutron numbers. He
found that the probability of observing ν neutrons is given by the
Gaussian distribution:

$$\sum_{n=0}^{\nu} P_n = (2\pi)^{-1/2} \int_{-\infty}^{(\bar{\nu} - \nu + 1/2 + b)/\sigma} \exp\left(-t^2/2\right) dt \qquad (5)$$

where P_n is the probability of observing n neutrons, $\bar{\nu}$ is the average
number of neutrons, b is a small adjustment $(<10^{-2})$, and σ is the
R.M.S. width of the total excitation distribution in units of the average excitation energy change per emitted neutron $(\sigma \approx 1.08)$. Figure
28 shows a comparison of experimental neutron emission probabilities
with the Gaussian distribution of Eq. (5). Table V shows a summary of the quantities describing the neutron multiplicity distributions for a number of nuclei as given by Terrell (Te57).

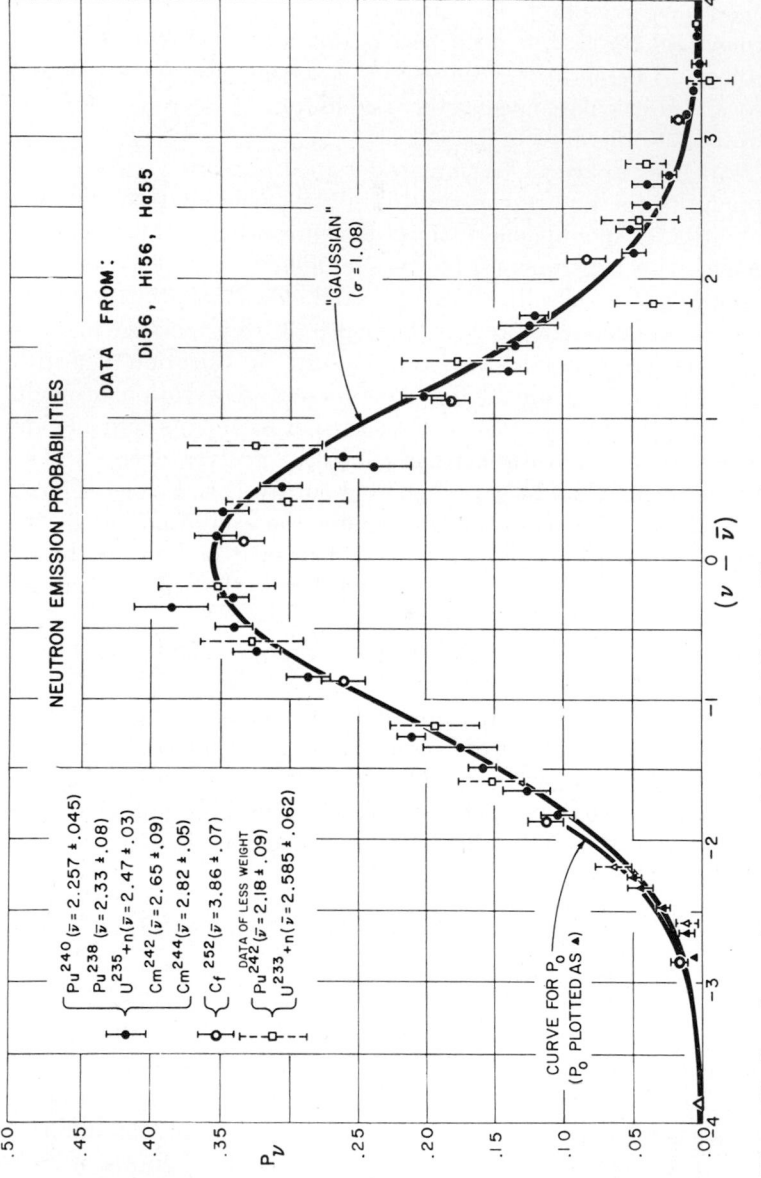

Figure 28. Experimental neutron emission probabilities. The continuous curves are for a "Gaussian" distribution (Te57).

Table V. Widths of Neutron Number Distributions from Fission[a]

Fissioning nuclide	Ref.	Experimental Data				Calculated[d]	
		$\bar{\nu}$	σ	D[b]	Γ_2[c]	D	Γ_2
Pu^{242}	H56	2.18 ± 0.09	1.069 ± 0.035	1.19 ± 0.07	0.792 ± 0.014	1.213	0.796
Pu^{240}	D56, H56, Ha55	2.26 ± 0.05	1.109 ± 0.012	1.28 ± 0.02	0.807 ± 0.005	1.218	0.796
Pu^{236}	H56	2.30 ± 0.19	1.11 ± 0.11	1.28 ± 0.21	0.807 ± 0.039	1.221	0.796
Pu^{238}	H56	2.33 ± 0.08	1.115 ± 0.023	1.30 ± 0.05	0.809 ± 0.009	1.223	0.796
$U^{235} + n$ (80 kev)	D56	2.47 ± 0.03	1.072 ± 0.021	1.22 ± 0.04	0.795 ± 0.007	1.231	0.797
$U^{233} + n$ (80 kev)	D56	2.58 ± 0.06	1.041 ± 0.041	1.16 ± 0.08	0.786 ± 0.013	1.236	0.798
Cm^{242}	H56	2.65 ± 0.09	1.053 ± 0.013	1.18 ± 0.03	0.791 ± 0.004	1.238	0.799
$U^{235} + n$ (1.25 Mev)	D56a	2.65 ± 0.07	1.04 ± 0.06	1.15 ± 0.12	0.786 ± 0.018	1.238	0.799
$U^{238} + n$ (1.5 Mev)	D56a	2.65 ± 0.09	1.23 ± 0.08	1.56 ± 0.18	0.845 ± 0.025	1.238	0.799
Cm^{244}	D56, H56	2.82 ± 0.05	1.036 ± 0.018	1.15 ± 0.05	0.790 ± 0.005	1.243	0.802
$Pu^{239} + n$ (80 kev)	D56	3.05 ± 0.08	1.14 ± 0.07	1.38 ± 0.14	0.821 ± 0.015	1.246	0.806
$U^{235} + n$ (4.8 Mev)	D56a	3.20 ± 0.08	1.20 ± 0.06	1.51 ± 0.13	0.835 ± 0.013	1.247	0.810
Cf^{252}	D56, H56	3.86 ± 0.07	1.207 ± 0.012	1.54 ± 0.04	0.844 ± 0.002	1.250	0.825
All			1.110 ± 0.006				
All but Cf^{252}			1.079 ± 0.007				

[a] For neutron-induced fission the energy of the neutrons is given. The quantities σ, D, and Γ_2 are measures of the widths of the neutron number distributions; σ has been derived from either D or Γ_2 on the assumption of a Gaussian distribution. Standard deviations are given for all experimental quantities.

[b] $D = (\nu^2)_{av} - \bar{\nu}^2$.

[c] $\Gamma_2 = [(\nu^2)_{av} - \bar{\nu}]/\bar{\nu}^2$.

[d] Calculated, assuming a Gaussian distribution with $\sigma = 1.08$.

6. $(n, 2n)$ Excitation Functions for Fissionable Nuclei

It is possible to make an estimate of the neutron emission probabilities for fissionable nuclei if one has some knowledge of the fission cross section. The estimate is based upon the assumption of the formation of a compound nucleus and the assumption that neutron re-emission and fission are the only important competing processes by which the compound nucleus will decay when both are energetically possible. The decay by (n, γ) deexcitation is sufficiently unimportant that it may be ignored. An example, using U^{238}, will be considered.

The cross section for the formation of the compound nucleus for U^{238} has been calculated using a diffuse-surface optical model of the nucleus by Beyster (Be57). The ideas of evaporation theory have been used for the decay of the compound nucleus by neutron emission in which the spectrum of inelastic neutrons may be represented by:

$$N(\varepsilon) = \varepsilon \exp\left(-\varepsilon/t\right)$$

where ε is the excitation energy of the residual nucleus (not the incident neutron energy) and t is the nuclear temperature. This temperature was determined by experiments (Cr56, Ro57) to be 1.0 Mev for an incident neutron energy of 14.1 Mev and was assumed to vary as $\varepsilon^{1/2}$. The competition between fission and neutron emission for various nuclei was determined from fission measurements at 3 Mev (Fig. 12) and was assumed to be independent of excitation energy. Fission thresholds were obtained from the systematics of the fission excitation functions, and multiple-neutron emission thresholds were found from known neutron binding energies (Hu55a). Finally, an estimate was made for the effects of direct interaction processes which lead in lower residual nuclear excitations than result when neutrons are evaporated. The estimate was based upon measurements at 14 Mev (Ro57).

Using such simple considerations, one can simply write down upper limits for multiple-neutron emission cross sections at the approximate energies where each cross section is maximum. Effects due to differences between fission threshold and neutron binding energies have been ignored.

At 3 Mev,

$$\sigma(n, n') = \sigma_c(3) \left(1 - \Gamma_f/\Gamma\right)_{A+1} = \sigma_c(3) \left(\Gamma_n/\Gamma\right)_{A+1} \qquad (6)$$

at 10 Mev,

$$\sigma(n,\,2n) \leqq \sigma_c(10)\,(\Gamma_n/\Gamma)_{A+1}(\Gamma_n/\Gamma)_A \qquad (7)$$

and at 17 Mev,

$$\sigma(n,\,3n) \leqq \sigma_c(17)(\Gamma_n/\Gamma)_{A+1}(\Gamma_n/\Gamma)_A(\Gamma_n/\Gamma)_{A-1} \qquad (8)$$

The manner in which the $(n,\,2n)$ excitation function rises above threshold can be estimated by simply multiplying Eq. (7) by the fraction of the evaporated neutrons which leave the residual nucleus sufficiently excited for the evaporation of the second neutron or $(n,\,n'f)$ fission to occur. For U^{238}, these thresholds are approximately identical. Then,

$$\sigma(n,\,2n) \approx \sigma_c(E)\,(\Gamma_n/\Gamma)_{A+1}(\Gamma_n/\Gamma)_A$$
$$\int_0^{E\,-\,E t}\,\mathcal{E}\,\exp\,(-\mathcal{E}/t)d\mathcal{E}/\int_0^{\infty}\,\mathcal{E}\,\exp\,(-\mathcal{E}/5)d\mathcal{E} \qquad (9)$$

$$= \sigma_c(E)\,(\Gamma_n/\Gamma)_{A+1}\,(\Gamma_n/\Gamma)_A t^{-2}\int_0^{E\,-\,E t}\,\mathcal{E}\,\exp\,(-\mathcal{E}/t)d\mathcal{E} \qquad (10)$$

where E is the incident neutron energy, $\mathcal{E}$ is the excitation energy of the residual nuclei, σ_c is the cross section for the formation of the compound nucleus, t is the nuclear temperature corresponding to the average excitation energy at the time of evaporation of the neutron, and

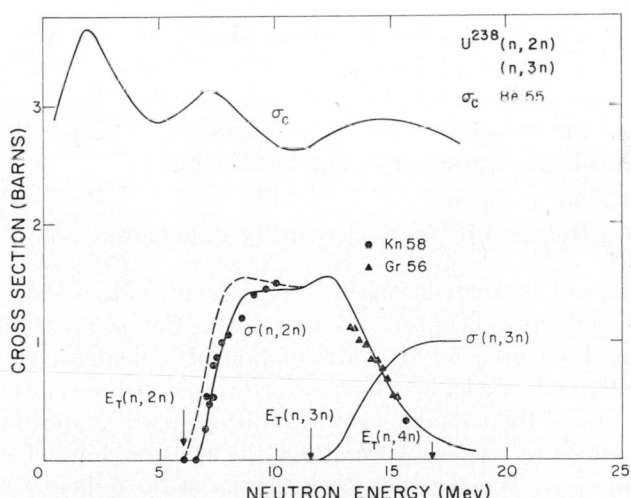

Figure 29. Comparison of calculated cross sections and experimental determinations for $U^{238}\,(n,\,2n)U^{237}$.

E_t is the threshold for the $(n, 2n)$ process.   Above the threshold for the $(n, 3n)$ process, competition occurs with $(n, 2nf)$ and $(n, 3n)$ processes which rapidly lowers the $(n, 2n)$ excitation curve.   The competition due to the $(n, 3n)$ process can be calculated from Eq. (8) by multiplying by the fraction of the residual nuclei which are sufficiently excited after emission of the second neutron to be above the threshold for the emission of the third neutron.   Similar calculations to find the effects of the $(n, 2nf)$ process can be made, or the measured cross sections may be used.

Figure 29 shows the results of such considerations in the case of U^{238}.   The σ_c curve is taken from the values calculated by Beyster (Be57).   For the effects of neutron emission by direct interaction (Ro57), this curve was reduced 10 per cent at 14 Mev, 0 per cent at 5 Mev, and in a proportional manner at other energies.   The calculated $(n, 2n)$ excitation functon is also shown (with no fitting to measurements being made).   Near threshold, several criteria are probably not satisfied well enough for such a calculation to be realistic: the (n, γ) process is not negligible near threshold, the excitation of the residual nucleus is insufficient to use the formula for the density of levels used in the evaporation model, and finally, the change in angular momentum required for the emission of the second neutron is probably quite high.

If one adds $^1/_2$ Mev to the neutron binding energy, the resulting calculated cross section is indicated by the solid line.   This change is essentially the same as applying the penetration function for an $l = 2$ neutron in the emission of the second neutron.   Comparisons with measurements are also shown in Fig. 29 (Kn58).

7. Fission Induced by (d, p) Stripping Reactions

There are alternate means of adding a neutron to a nucleus than that of direct neutron capture.   In particular, the (d, p) stripping reaction has been used for the introduction of a neutron of known energy into fissile nuclei by Stokes, Northrup, and Boyer (St58).   A novel feature of the technique is the ability to reach excitation levels in the compound nucleus lower than the neutron binding energy.   These states correspond to negative energies of the unbound neutron which are inaccessible to direct neutron interactions.   In this way, the (d, pf) experiments make it possible to investigate the thresholds of nuclei that fission with thermal neutrons. For excitation energies below the neutron binding energy, competition due to neutron emission is precluded. Hence, more detailed information of the properties of the fission barrier can be obtained than is possible from neutron-induced fission experiments.

The experiment used the 14-Mev deuteron beam from the Los Alamos 42-inch cyclotron to produce (d, p) reactions in fissionable nuclei. The energy spectra of the emitted protons are measured for those protons that are in coincidence with fission events. The energy relations are given by the equation:

$$E_d - \varepsilon_d = E_p + E_m = E_p + E_x - \varepsilon_n \tag{11}$$

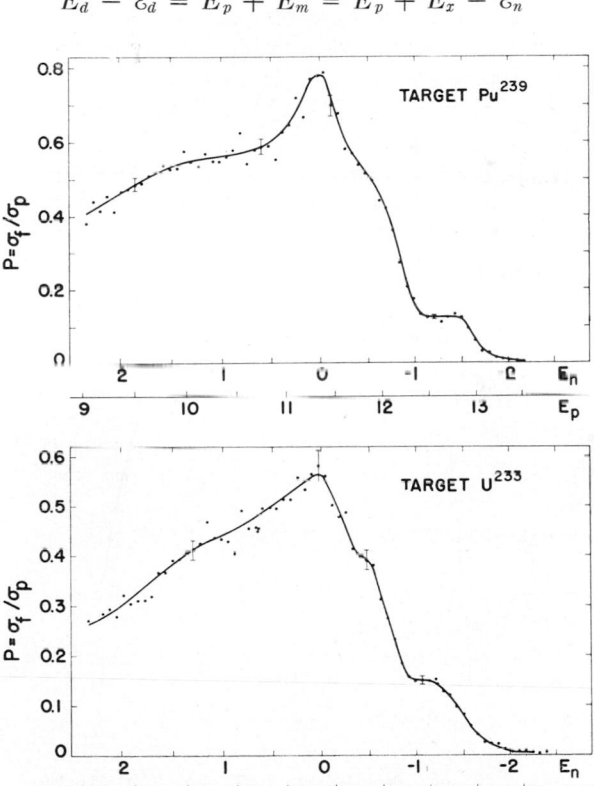

Figure 30. The probability P for $d(p,f)$ fission as a function of neutron energy for Pu²³⁹ and U²³³ targets.

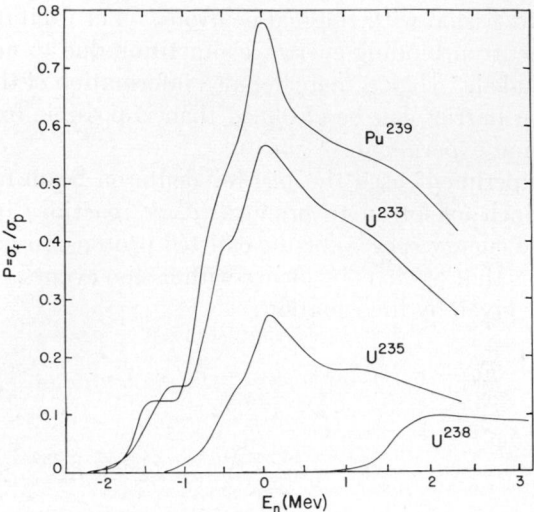

Figure 31. The probability P for fission as a function of neutron energy for $d(p, f)$ experiments.

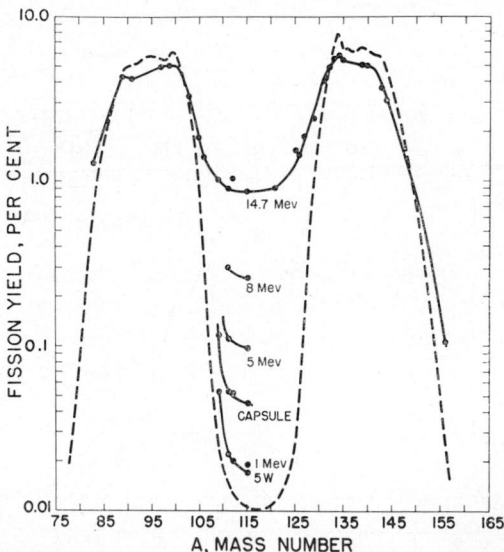

Figure 32. Fragment mass distribution in fission of U^{236}, showing change of distribution with neutron energy.

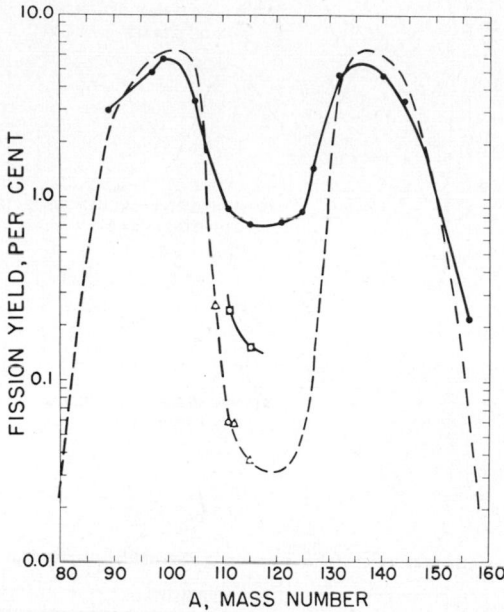

Figure 33. Fragment mass distribution in fission of U^{238}, showing change of distributions with neutron energy. The triangles represent the yield from degraded fission neutrons, the squares 8.1 Mev, and the circles 14.7 Mev.

E_d and $\mathcal{E}_d$ are the kinetic and binding energies of the deuteron, respectively. E_p is the kinetic energy of the emitted proton, and E_n is the equivalent kinetic energy of the incoming neutron. $\mathcal{E}_n$ and E_x are, respectively, the neutron binding energy and the excitation energy, both for the compound nucleus. Thus, the equivalent neutron energy is determined by measuring the proton energy and can be negative by an amount as large as the neutron binding energy. The energy spectrum coincident with fission is proportional to the probability for the (d, p) reaction to occur, multiplied by the probability for subsequent fission to take place. To obtain a cross section value characteristic of the fission process alone, the branching ratio for fission is found by dividing the coincidence proton spectrum by the total $(d, p($ proton energy spectrum. A particle identification system (St58) was developed to measure these spectra. It allows the whole proton spectrum to be identified in the presence of many elastically scattered deuterons. The system had the necessary properties of a large solid

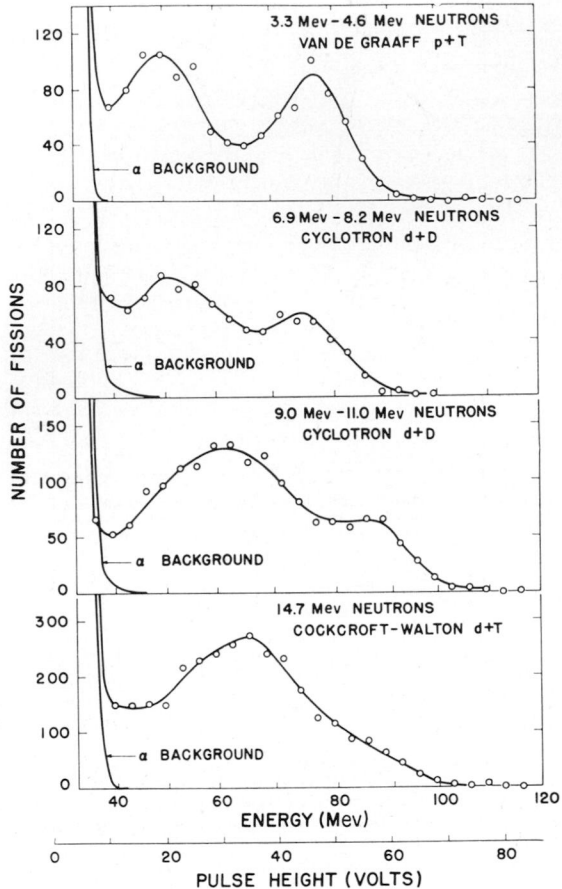

Figure 34. The energy distribution of fragments from neutron-induced fission of Ra²²⁶.

angle and the ability to collect data simultaneously in many channels over a wide energy range. In fact, this experiment is impressive in that many instrumentation problems were cleverly solved to make it successful.

Figure 30 shows the ratio of $\sigma(d, pf)$ to $\sigma(d, p)$ for Pu²³⁹ and U²³³ targets. The steps in the excitation curve can be reasonably associated with vibrational levels and nucleonic excitations (St58a). Figure 31 gives the compilation of excitation curves in which three negative thresholds are shown. The curve for U^{238} is very similar to that given by neutron-induced fission.

8. Mass Distribution of Fission Fragments

Since the early years of the study of the fission process, investigations have been made to determine whether the fragment mass distribution was a function of incident neutron energy (Fo47). A variation was reported by Spence (Sp49), Jungerman and Wright (Ju49), Friedland (Fr51), and more recently by Wahl (Wa54). For all of these studies except in Sp49, the mass distribution variation was inferred from ionization chamber studies of fission fragment energies. Recently, careful radiochemical studies have been made by the Los Alamos Radiochemistry Group (Fo56) for neutron energies below 14 Mev. The results for U^{235} and U^{238} are shown in Figs. 32 and 33. The probability for symmetric fissions rapidly becomes greater for increasing neutron energy, in agreement with the ionization chamber studies. In addition, there appears to be a higher probability for very asymmetric fission and the heavy mass peak seems to shift toward lower mass number for 14.7-Mev neutrons.

Confirmation of the increase in symmetric fission at higher neutron energies is given for the case of Ra^{226} (No57) in which a study was made of fission fragment pulses in a gaseous scintillation counter. Figure 34 shows the energy distribution of fragments from radium fission for several neutron energies. At 4 Mev, the familiar double-peak distribution characteristic of the asymmetric fission of the heavier nuclides is observed. For higher energies, a single peak becomes predominant, indicating an increasing yield from the symmetric mode of fission. The predominance of symmetric fission for Ra^{226} at 14 Mev is quite different from the asymmetry shown for heavy nuclei but is confirmed by the 11-Mev proton data of Fairhall and Jensen (Fa56, Fa58) and the systematics of fission asymmetry (Gr56, Jo55).

References

(Al55) W. D. Allen and A. T. G. Ferguson, *Atomic Energy Comm.* (*Gt. Brit.*) *Reports* NP/R 1667 and NP/R 1720 (1955). See also Al57.

(Al57) W. D. Allen and R. L. Henkel, *Progr. in Nuclear Energy*, Ser. *I*, **2** (1957).

(Au56) Auclair, Landon, and Jaboc, *Physica* **22**, 1187 (1956).

(Ba54) H. H. Barschall, private communication (1954).

(Ba54a)   H. H. Barschall and R. L. Henkel, *Los Alamos Sci. Lab. Report* LA-2099 (1954).

(Be55)   Bethe, Beyster, and Carter, *Los Alamos Sci. Lab. Reports* La-1495 and LA-1939 (1955).

(Be57)   J. R. Beyster, *Los Alamos Sci. Lab. Report* LA-2099 (1957).

(Bl45)   J. M. Blair, *Los Alamos Sci. Lab. Report* LAMD-89 (1945).

(Bo39)   N. Bohr and J. A. Wheeler, *Phys. Rev.* **55**, 426 (1939).

(Bo40)   N. Bohr, *Phys. Rev.* **58**, 864 (1940).

(Bo56)   A. Bohr, *Proc. Intern. Conf. Peaceful Uses Atomic Energy (Geneva)* **2**, 151 (1956).

(Br54)   J. E. Brolley, Jr. and W. C. Dickinson, *Phys. Rev.* **94**, 640 (1954).

(Br55)   Brolley, Dickinson, and Henkel, *Phys. Rev.* **99**, 159 (1955).

(Cr56)   Cranberg, Frye, Nereson, and Rosen, *Phys. Rev.* **103**, 662 (1956).

(Cr56a)   Cranberg, Armstrong, and Henkel, *Phys. Rev.* **104**, 1639 (1956).

(Cr56b)   L. Cranberg and J. S. Levin, *Phys. Rev.* **103**, 343 (1956).

(Cr58)   L. Cranberg and J. S. Levin, *Phys. Rev.* **109**, 2063 (1958).

(Cu37)   I. Curie and P. Savitch, *J. phys.* **8**, 385 (1937).

(Cu38)   I. Curie and P. Savitch, *J. phys.* **9**, 355 (1938).

(Di53)   W. C. Dickinson and J. E. Brolley, Jr., *Phys. Rev.* **90**, 388 (1953).

(Di56)   Diven, Martin, Taschek, and Terrell, *Phys. Rev.* **101**, 1012 (1956).

(Di56a)   Diven, Martin, Taschek, and Terrell (unpublished) quoted in Te57.

(Di57)   B. C. Diven, *Phys. Rev.* **105**, 1350 (1957).

(Fa56)   A. W. Fairhall, *Phys. Rev.* **102**, 1335 (1956).

(Fa58)   A. W. Fairhall and R. C. Jensen, *Phys. Rev.* **109**, 942 (1958).

(Fo47)   J. L. Fowler and L. Rosen, *Phys. Rev.* **72**, 926 (1947).

(Fo52)   J. L. Fowler, private communication (1952).

(Fo53)   Peter Fong, *Phys. Rev.* **89**, 332 (1953).

(Fo55)   J. L. Fowler, private communication (1955), quoted by Leachman, Geneva Conf. Paper P/592 (1955).

(Fo56)   Ford, Gilmore, Radiochemistry Group, *Los Alamos Sci. Lab. Report* LA-1997 (1956).

(Fr51)   S. S. Friedland, *Phys. Rev.* **84**, 75 (1951).

(Gr56)   E. R. Graves, Conner, Ford, and Warren (1956).

(Gr58)   J. Griffin, private communication (1958).

(Ha40)   O. Hahn and F. Strassmann, *Naturwiss.* **27**, 11 (1939).

(Ha47)   A. O. Hanson and J. L. McKibben, *Phys. Rev.* **72**, 673 (1947).

(Ha55)   J. E. Hammel and J. F. Kephart, *Phys. Rev.* **100**, 190 (1955).

(Ha56)   R. C. Hanna, private communication (1956).

(Ha58)   I. Halpern, private communication (1958).

(He52)   Henkel, Cranberg, Day, Hawkins, Jarvis, Lazar, Nobles, Perry, Smith, and Walt, *Los Alamos Sci. Lab. Report* LA-1495 (1952).

(He56)   R. L. Henkel and J. E. Brolley, Jr., *Phys. Rev.* **103**, 1292 (1956).

(He57)   R. L. Henkel, *Los Alamos Sci. Lab. Report* LA-2122 (1957).

(Hi53)   D. L. Hill and J. A. Wheeler, *Phys. Rev.* **89**, 1102 (1953).

(Hi56)   Hicks, Ise, and Pyle, *Phys. Rev.* **101**, 1016 (1956).

(He53)   J. R. Huizenga, *Argonne Natl. Lab. Report* ANL-5150 (1953).

(Hu55)   D. J. Hughes and J. A. Harvey, "Neutron Cross Sections," *Brookhaven Natl. Lab. Report* BNL-325 (1955).

(Hu55a) J. Huizenga, *Physica* **21**, 410 (1955).
(Hu58) J. Huizenga, *Phys. Rev.* **109**, 484 (1958).
(Ja56) J. D. Jackson, *Proc. Symposium on Physics of Fission*, held at Chalk River, Ontario, CRP-642A (1956).
(Jo55) I. Johnstone, private communication (1955).
(Ju49) J. Jungerman and S. C. Wright, *Phys. Rev.* **76**, 1112 (1949).
(Kn58) Knight, Smith, and Warren, *Phys. Rev.* **112**, 259 (1958).
(La55) R. W. Lamphere and R. E. Greene, *Phys. Rev.* **100**, 763 (1955).
(La56) R. W. Lamphere, *Phys. Rev.* **104**, 1654 (1956).
(La57) R. W. Lamphere, private communication (1957).
(Le55) R. B. Leachman, *Phys. Rev.* **101**, 1005 (1955).
(Le57) R. B. Leachman and H. W. Schmitt, *J. Nuclear Energy I* **4**, 38 (1957).
(Me37) Meitner, Hahn, and Strassman, *Z. Physik* **106**, 249 (1937).
(Me38) Meitner, Hahn, and Strassman, *Z. Physik* **109**, 538 (1938).
(Me39) L. Meitner and O. R. Frisch, *Nature (London)* **143**, 239 (1939).
(Ne56) Netter, Corge, and Gallini, *J. phys. radium* **17**, 565 (1956).
(No55) Nobles, Henkel, and Smith, *Phys. Rev.* **99**, 616(A) (1955).
(No57) Nobles, Manley, and Leachman, *Bull. Am. Phys. Soc.* **2**, 70 (1957).
(No58) R. A. Nobles and R. B. Leachman, *Nuclear Phys.* **5**, 255 (1958).
(Ny50) W. Nyer, *Los Alamos Sci. Lab. Report* LAMS-938 (1950).
(Ri57) D. R. Richmond, private communication quoted in Al57 (1957).
(Ro49) Rossi and Staub, *Ionization Chambers and Counters*, McGraw-Hill, New York, 1949, Vol. 2, p. 39.
(Ro57) L. Rosen and L. Stewart, *Phys. Rev.* **107**, 824 (1957).
(Si57) Simmons, Brolley, and Henkel, *Bull. Am. Phys. Soc.* **2**, 308 (1957).
(Sm57) Smith, Henkel, and Nobles, *Bull. Am. Phys. Soc.* **2**, 196 (1957).
(Sp49) R. W. Spence and G. P. Ford, *Ann. Rev. Nuclear Sci.* **2**, 339 (1953).
(St58) Stokes, Northrop, and Boyer, *Rev. Sci. Instr.* **29**, 61 (1958).
(St58a) Stokes, Northrop, and Boyer, private communication (1958).
(Sw55) W. J. Swiatecki, *Phys. Rev.* **100**, 939 (1955).
(Sw55a) W. J. Swiatecki, *Phys. Rev.* **101**, 97 (1955).
(Sz55) Sztcinsznaider, Naggiar, and Netter, *Proc. Intern. Conf. Peaceful Uses Atomic Energy (Geneva)* **4**, 245 (1956). See also Al57.
(Te54) J. Terrell and W. T. Leland, unpublished (1954).
(Te57) J. Terrell, *Phys. Rev.* **108**, 783 (1957), and private communication.
(Tu40) L. A. Turner, *Revs. Modern Phys.* **12**, 1 (1940).
(Va55) Varfolomeev, Romantsera and Kutukova, *Doklady Akad. Nauk. S.S.S.R.* **105**, 693 (1955).
(Wa54) J. A. Wahl, *Phys. Rev.* **95**, 126 (1954).
(Wh56) J. A. Wheeler, *Physica* **22**, 1103 (1956).
(Wi56) L. Wilets and D. M. Chase, *Phys. Rev.* **103**, 1296 (1956).
(Wi57) L. Wilets, private communication (1957).
(Ye56) Yeater, Mills, and Gaerttner, *Phys. Rev.* **104**, 479 (1956).
(Za57) S. Zamyatmin, *Physics of Nuclear Fission*, Pergamon Press, London, 1957.

Channel Analysis of Fission

John A. Wheeler

Lawrence Radiation Laboratory, University of California, Berkeley, California; Palmer Physical Laboratory, Princeton University, Princeton, New Jersey

1. Fission Channels

A. Reaction Rates in Chemistry and Nuclear Physics

The study of nuclear transmutations has brought some new insight into the theory of reaction rates. In nuclear physics it is possible to specify the energy of excitation of the reacting system. In chemistry, on the other hand, it is not usual to have this degree of detailed information. It is typical to know only the temperature, a certain average of the energy over a number of systems. There reaction rates are generally given (Gl41) by expressions of the form

$$c_1 T^n \exp(-c_2/T) \tag{1}$$

In this formula the quantity c_2 is related to the "energy of the activated complex" or the "transition state energy" or the energy of a potential energy barrier which must be surmounted to allow the interacting atoms to move to the new configuration. But how does the reaction rate depend upon energy when the energy is well determined?

B. The Channel Formula for Reaction Rate

The discovery of nuclear fission gave incentive in 1939 to ask and answer this question for a reaction governed by an almost impenetrable potential barrier (Bo39). Here semiclassical considerations can be applied, much like those employed in physical chemistry in deriving for monomolecular reactions an expression of the type (1). In this

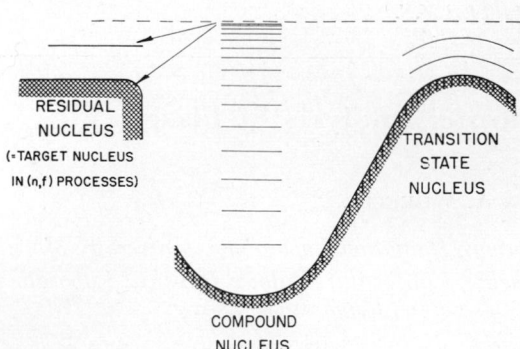

Figure 1. Distinction between levels of compound nucleus, transition state nucleus and residual nucleus. At the excitation of the compound nucleus indicated in the diagram, 3 fission channels and 2 neutron channels are accessible. The diagram is to be understood as referring only to those levels of the combined system which have a specified total angular momentum quantum number I and a specified parity π.

way it was possible to derive a semiclassical formula for the probability per second

$$A_f(\sec^{-1})$$

that a given level of the excited compound nucleus will undergo fission, and a formula for the associated level broadening

$$\Gamma_f = \hbar A_f \tag{2}$$

where

$$\hbar = 1.054 \times 10^{-27} \text{ erg sec} = 0.66 \times 10^{-15} \text{ ev sec}$$

This reaction rate formula has the form

$$\Gamma_f = (D/2\pi)N_f \tag{3}$$

Here D is the average spacing between those levels of the compound nucleus which have the specified angular momentum and parity (see Fig. 1). The quantity N_f was called in 1939 the "number of levels in the transition state available with the given excitation." Today the number N_f might more vividly be called the "number of channels effective for fission." A description of fission which examines into the properties of the individual channels may be called "a channel analysis of fission."

It was clear in 1939 that the number of channels available for fission increases roughly exponentially with energy in excess of the height of the lowest potential barrier against fission. It was possible along these lines to discuss the competition between neutron re-emission and fission in terms of an approximate formula of the form

$$\sigma(n, f) \approx \pi R^2 \frac{\Gamma_f}{\Gamma_f + \Gamma_n} = \pi R^2 \frac{(2\pi\Gamma_f/D)}{(2\pi\Gamma_f/D) + (2\pi\Gamma_n/D)}$$

$$= \pi R^2 \frac{N_f}{N_f + N_n}$$

It was possible to understand qualitatively why for example the cross section for neutron induced fission of Th^{232} or U^{238} varies only slowly with energy for energies well above the fission threshold. It was not clear that one would be able to see individual jumps in the fission cross section as the neutron energy is increased and as new individual fission channels become accessible.

C. Channel Widths and Fission Widths

Several developments have occurred in recent years which have led to a deeper understanding of the part played by a single channel in the fission process. In 1953, a formula was given (Hi53) for the "width" or "degree of opening" of a single fission channel. The formula is based on the assumption that the potential barrier against fission through the given channel is approximately representable by the inverse of a harmonic oscillator potential appropriate for vibrations of circular frequency $\omega_b = 2\pi\nu_b$. Then the channel opening is

$$W(E - S_b) = \frac{1}{1 + \exp[2\pi(S_b - E)/\hbar\omega_b]} \tag{4}$$

This expression (see Appendix A) is unity far above the barrier or "saddle point" height S_b, is 0.5 exactly at the barrier, and falls off in a closer and closer approximation to a simple exponential as the energy drops more and more below S_b. The effective number of channels is given then by a "carpeted staircase" function of energy

$$N_f = \sum_{b=1}^{\infty} W(E - S_b) \tag{5}$$

as illustrated in Fig. 2 and intrepreted semiclassically in Fig. 3.

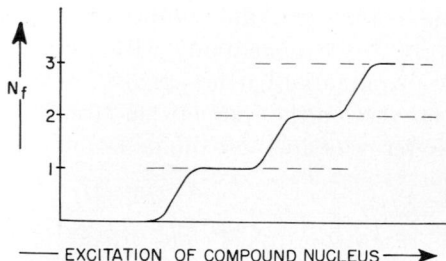

— EXCITATION OF COMPOUND NUCLEUS —▶

Figure 2. Yield-effective number of accessible fission channels as a function of the excitation of the compound nucleus. The low energy tail of the lowest step governs the rate of spontaneous fission. The diagram refers to levels of the compound nucleus of a specified angular momentum quantum number I and specified parity π.

In 1955 Lamphere and Green (La55, La56) observed dramatic rises and falls in the cross section for neutron induced fission of U^{234}, which Aage Bohr (Bo56) was the first to explain in terms of the channel description of fission. The cross section rises, he pointed out, when a new fission channel becomes accessible, and falls when a new neutron channel becomes energetically available.

Aage Bohr also pointed out that the angular distribution of fission fragments can be expressed as the sum of contributions from individual channels. To account for the contribution of a given channel it is necessary to characterize that channel not only by the angular momentum $I\hbar$ of the compound nucleus and its projection $M\hbar$ along a preferred direction in space, but also by the angular momentum $K\hbar$ of the elongated transition state configuration about an axis of approximate symmetry, at least at not too high excitations. It has become possible to determine K for some channels from the angular distribution in fission.

Further evidence for the effects of individual channels comes from the distribution in mass of the fission fragments, particularly from the abundance ratio between fragments of comparable mass and fragments with mass ratio roughly 2:1. The abundance ratio was first found to vary in an unusual way with energy by Fairhall, Halpern, and Winhold (Fa54) in photofission. This effect was explained by Aage Bohr (Bo56) in terms of the channel description of fission. A similar effect was predicted in slow neutron fission (Wh56) and since detected by several observers (see Section 3).

In addition to effects of single channels at thermal energies and in the range 0.5 to 3 Mev, it has been possible to see effects of a *statistical distribution of channels* at higher energies. From the angular distribution of fission fragments it has been possible to infer the statistical distribution of levels as a function of total angular momentum quantum number I and of the angular momentum $K\hbar$ about the symmetry axis.

At the same time that the quantity N_f on the right hand side of the reaction rate Eq. (3) has acquired through the channel analysis of fission a deeper significance, the level width on the left hand side has been stripped of some sharpness. No longer should there appear in Eq. (3) the fission width of any individual level, but only the average fission width $\langle \Gamma_f \rangle$ of a number of levels of the same spin and parity and nearly the same energy:

$$\langle \Gamma_f \rangle = (D/2\pi)N_f \qquad (6)$$

Individual widths fluctuate (Po56) about this average value percentage-wise the more, the fewer the number of channels which contribute to the width.

D. Neutron Width Without Regard to Angular Momentum

Nuclear reaction rate studies have an advantage over analogous chemical investigations—that the energy is sharply measurable. But the two fields still have in common this handicap—that the angular momentum of the compound system in any individual reaction is often not known. A neutron of 1 Mev (wave number $k = 2\pi/\lambda = 1/\lambda = 2.197 \times 10^{12}$ cm^{-1}) brings into a nucleus of effective interaction radius

$$R_{\text{inter}} = 1.5 \times 10^{-13} \text{ cm } A^{1/3}$$

$$= 9.3 \times 10^{-13} \text{ cm for } A = 236$$

an orbital angular momentum which can be 0, 1, 2, or 3 with substantial probability. Conversely, a 1-Mev neutron which emerges from the nucleus takes away an amount of angular momentum which is not normally measured. No attempt was made to look into the distribution in angular momentum of the neutron in the early analysis of the competition between fission and neutron re-emission. Based on con-

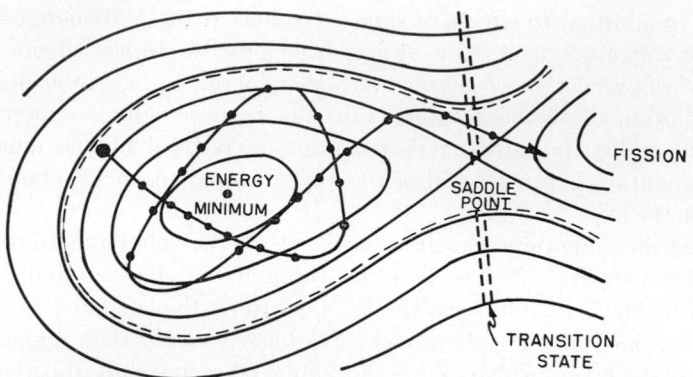

Figure 3. The representative point of the system moves about in the region of configuration space allowed by its energy (dashed curve) much like a marble rolling on a plaster surface, until almost as if by chance it passes over the saddle to fission (nucleus) or dissociation (molecule). The smooth curves represent contours of equal energy. Orthogonal to fission is a $(2N-2)$-dimensional "transition state phase space." Its volume divided by h^{2N-2} gives N_+ (semiclassical value).

siderations of detailed balance a formula was given for neutron width of the form

$$\Gamma_n = \sum_k \Gamma_{n_k} \approx D(8\pi M_n R^2/h^2) \sum_k E_k \qquad (7)$$

Here Γ_{n_k} is the partial width associated with a re-emission process leading to the kth level of the residual nucleus and E_k is the kinetic energy of the neutron given off in this process. The quantity D is the average spacing of *all* levels of the compound nucleus which come into play, as contrasted to the spacing D of levels of specified angular momentum and parity as considered in Eqs. (3) and (6).

According to Eq. (7) the relative intensities of each neutron group in the emergent spectrum will be proportional to the kinetic energy E_k of that group. The number of neutrons dn emergent in an interval of kinetic energy dE will be proportional to E and to the number of levels

$$\rho_{\text{resid}}(E_{\text{resid}})dE = \rho_{\text{resid}}(E_{\text{compound}} - B_n - E)dE$$
$$(B_n = \text{binding energy of neutron})$$

of the residual nucleus in the energy interval dE:

$$dn/dE = \text{const } E\rho_{\text{resid}}(E_{\text{comp}} - B_n - E) \qquad (8)$$
$$= \text{quasi-maxwellian distribution}$$

This formula provided one of the starting points in the development of the evaporation model, which was carried so far by Feshbach and Weisskopf and others.

E. Neutron Width for a Specified Angular Momentum

Today, the theory of nuclear reactions has come to the point where it is appropriate to recognize in Eq. (7) an expression for neutron width averaged over states of many different angular momenta. More useful now is an expression for the neutron width associated with levels of a particular angular momentum. Such an expression is derived most easily when the residual nucleus has zero angular momentum. Then the spin I of the compound nucleus can be identified with the angular momentum j of the outgoing neutron. The derivation of the more specialized formula follows arguments of microscopic reversibility like those used in the deviation of the original expression (7) for neutron widths. The reasoning is given here (a) because analogous reasoning will enter into the discussion of fission widths, and (b) because the similarities and differences between the theories of Γ_n and Γ_f will then come more readily into view.

Many identical systems are considered, each at the center of a large spherical box of its own, each with energy between E_{comp} and $E_{\text{comp}} + dE$. Some are in the combined state, a compound nucleus of angular momentum $I\hbar = j\hbar$. Many more are in the dissociated state: (a) a residual nucleus of zero angular momentum and excitation E_0, plus (b) a neutron of angular momentum quantum number j and of energy between E and $E + dE$. Here

$$E = E_{\text{comp}} - B_n - E_0$$

An initial state of affairs is considered in which there are as many systems of each kind as there are quantum states of each kind. Then the transitions which go on as time proceeds will preserve this state of affairs (Vo55). Accordingly the number of break-up processes per sec will equal the number of formation processes per second.

The rate of break-up is found by multiplying the chance per second that one system will emit a neutron, $\Gamma_n/\hbar$, with the number of systems, that is, by the number of quantum states of the given properties which lie within dE. Let $D_{I\pi}$ denote the average spacing between levels of angular momentum quantum number I and parity π in the absence of a magnetic field. The presence of a magnetic field will reveal that the actual number of states is

$$(2I + 1)dE/D_{I\pi} = (2j + 1)dE/D_{j\pi}$$

Accordingly the number of relevant neutron emission processes per second is

$$(\Gamma_n/\hbar)(2j + 1)dE/D_{j\pi} \tag{9}$$

The number of processes per sec of formation of the compound nucleus, under conditions of complete interception, is found by multiplying the interception cross section by the number density and by the velocity. If the neutron had no spin, classical impact parameters between $l\lambda$ and $(l + 1)\lambda$ would be considered to lead to formation of a system with angular momentum quantum number l provided (a) that this impact parameter is smaller than the dimensions of the nucleus, and (b) that the nuclear opacity is large. Then the cross section would be $\pi\lambda^2(2l + 1)$. However, the spin of the neutron has to be oriented properly. The cross section is therefore cut down by a factor of approximately 2. The correct expression for the cross section (see Table I) is

$$\pi\lambda^2(2j + 1)/(2s + 1)$$

Table I. Factors affecting break-up (and formation) of a state of the compound nucleus into (and from) a neutron plus a spin zero state of a residual nucleus in the ideal case where the classical impact parameter is small enough compared to nuclear dimensions and the nuclear opacity is great enough so that complete interception results. Note that for each value of l there are two partial cross sections, the sum of which is $(2l + 1)\pi\lambda^2$. The individual partial cross section is $[(2j + 1)/(2s + 1)]\pi\lambda^2$

Angular momentum $I\hbar$ of compound nucleus		$\frac{1}{2}$	$\frac{1}{2}$	$\frac{3}{2}$	$\frac{3}{2}$	$\frac{5}{2}$	$\frac{5}{2}$	$\frac{7}{2}$
$\begin{pmatrix}\text{Parity of}\\\text{compound}\\\text{nucleus}\end{pmatrix} \times \begin{pmatrix}\text{Parity of}\\\text{residual}\\\text{nucleus}\end{pmatrix}$		+	−	−	+	+	−	−
Quantum numbers of emitted neutron								
j		$\frac{1}{2}$	$\frac{1}{2}$	$\frac{3}{2}$	$\frac{3}{2}$	$\frac{5}{2}$	$\frac{5}{2}$	$\frac{7}{2}$
l		0	1	1	2	2	3	3
Partial cross section divided by $\pi\lambda^2$		1	1	2	2	3	3	4

The number of quantum states—and hence the number of systems—per unit volume of coordinate space is the product of the following factors:

(a) the number of translational states per unit volume of phase space: $1/h^3$

(b) the volume of momentum space between the energy E and $E + dE$ or between the corresponding momenta p and $p + dp$: $4\pi p^2 dp$

(c) the number of spin states per translational state, 2 or: $(2s + 1)$

Multiplying this product with

(d) the velocity of the neutrons: $v(= dE/dp)$

and

(e) the ideal cross section for interception of neutrons with specified angular momentum quantum number j and specified parity: $[(2j + 1)/(2s + 1)]\pi\lambda^2$

one finds for the number of formation processes per second the expression

$$(4\pi p^2/h^3)dE(2j + 1)\pi\lambda^2 \tag{10}$$

Now let the number of break-ups per second (9) be equated to the ideal rate of formation (10). In this way one arrives at an expression for the ideal neutron width of a level of a well defined angular momentum and parity—or rather, the partial width with respect to break up into a neutron and a residual nucleus in a particular state of spin 0:

$$\Gamma_{n,\,ideal} = D_{j\pi}/2\pi \tag{11}$$

This expression for the neutron width agrees in form with the uncorrected expression for the fission width associated with a single fission channel. As in the case of fission, a correction must be applied for the fact that the neutron channel is usually not fully open. Let W_n, a number between 0 and 1, represent the channel opening or channel width. Also, recall that the quantity Γ_n is to be thought of, not as the partial width associated with any given level, but as the average of the partial width over a number of nearby levels of the compound nucleus of the given spin and parity. Then the corrected expression for the partial width has the form

$$\langle\Gamma_n\rangle = (D_{j\pi}/2\pi)W_{n,i} \tag{12}$$

for a single channel leading to a single spin 0 level—the ith level—of the residual nucleus.

Table II. Channel formulas for neutron widths and fission widths compared and contrasted. It is assumed that level widths are less than level spacings. All entries refer to states of the compound nucleus of a given spin J and parity π. (J is used instead of the more familiar symbol I so as to distinguish the spin of the compound system from the spin of the target.) The average spacing between these levels is $D_{J\pi}$. The energy of a selected one of these levels is written as E_0. The target of the neutron bombardment, or the residual nucleus after neutron escape, has spin I_1, parity π_1, when in its lowest state (neutron channel number 1). The spin of the neutron is written as $s = {}^1/_2$, and its reduced wave length as λ. [For 1 Mev, $\lambda = 0.455 \times 10^{-12}$ cm, $\pi\lambda^2 = 0.651 \times 10^{-24}$ cm^2]

	n-emission	Fission
$\hbar$ times probability per second for compound nucleus to go to particular level i of residual nucleus (*n*-emission) or level b of transition-state nucleus (fission)	$\langle\Gamma_{n,i}\rangle = (D_{J\pi}/2\pi)W_{n,i}$	$\langle\Gamma_{f,b}\rangle = (D_{J\pi}/2\pi)W_{f,b}$
Factors governing channel width or opening W.	Energy $E_{n,i}$ of emergent neutron and its angular momentum; also nuclear radius; also effective potential felt by neutron inside.	Difference between energy E of compound nucleus and saddle point energy S_b of barrier associated with bth state of transition state nucleus. In an improved analysis the shape of the potential surface may have to be taken into account.
Simple model for estimation of channel opening under appropriate circumstances.	Residual = target system is an even-even nucleus of spin 0 whose probability to take up a neutron is described by optical model potential. Radial part of neutron wave function in this potential has asymptotic form $-(-1)^l \exp(-ikr) + \eta_l \exp(ikr)$ when neutron spin is neglected. When spin is taken into account, analogous expression contains $\eta_{j\pi}$ (here $j = J$).	Barrier against fission representable as inverse of a harmonic oscillator potential of characteristic circular frequency ω, quantum level spacing $\hbar\omega$.
Formula for channel opening under this idealization.	$W_{n,0} = 1 - \left|\eta_{j\pi}\right|^2$ (for $^1/_2$ + neutron at low energies is proportional to neutron velocity times	$W_{f,b} = \dfrac{1}{e^{\,2\pi(E - S_b)\hbar\omega} + 1}$

Table II. (*continued*)

	n-emission	Fission
	a Barschall-Ramsauer resonance factor that depends strongly upon the ratio of nuclear radius to neutron wave length inside.)	
Typical reaction where channel analysis can be put to use.	Inelastic neutron scattering to a particular state, 2, of the residual nucleus.	Fission through a particular channel, *b*, of the transition state nucleus.
Cross section for this reaction to take place through an isolated resonance of angular momentum $J\pi$.	$\pi\lambda^2 \dfrac{(2J+1)}{(2s+1)(2I_1+1)}$ $\times \dfrac{\Gamma_{n1}\,\Gamma_{n2}}{(E-E_0)^2+(\Gamma/2)^2}$	$\pi\lambda^2 \dfrac{(2J+1)}{(2s+1)(2I_1+1)}$ $\times \dfrac{\Gamma_{n1}\,\Gamma_{f,b}}{(E-E_0)^2+(\Gamma/2)^2}$
Average of cross section over a number of isolated resonances of this particular type (ratio of averages of Γ's approximately equal to average of ratio).	$\pi\lambda^2 \dfrac{(2J+1)}{(2s+1)(2I_1+1)}$ times $\dfrac{2\pi}{D_{J\pi}}\left\langle \dfrac{\Gamma_{n1}\,\Gamma_{n2}}{\Gamma}\right\rangle$ or approximately $\left(\dfrac{W_{n1}\,W_{n2}}{N_n+N_f+\ldots}\right)_{J\pi}$	$\pi\lambda^2 \dfrac{(2J+1)}{(2s+1)(2I_1+1)}$ times $\dfrac{2\pi}{D_{J\pi}}\left\langle \dfrac{\Gamma_{n1}\,\Gamma_{fb}}{\Gamma}\right\rangle$ or approximately $\left(\dfrac{W_{n1}\,W_{fb}}{N_n+N_f+\ldots}\right)_{J\pi}$
Relation between effective number of channels and channel opening (all quantities understood to carry labels $J\pi$).	$N_n = \sum\limits_{i} W_{ni}$	$N_f = \sum\limits_{b} W_{fb}$
Total cross section for compound nucleus reactions which go through levels of the compound nucleus of type $J\pi$.	$\pi\lambda^2 \dfrac{(2J+1)}{(2s+1)(2I_1+1)}\,W_{n1}$	
Special case of this cross section for compound nucleus reactions when target nucleus has spin $I_0 = 0 \ (J = j)$.	$\pi\lambda^2 \dfrac{2j+1}{2s+1}\,W_{n0}$	
Another equivalent and quite general expression for this cross section.	$\pi\lambda^2 \dfrac{2j+1}{2s+1}\,(1-\lvert\eta_j\rvert^2)$	

The channel opening goes to zero for particles whose classical impact parameter

$$b = (l + \tfrac{1}{2})\lambda$$

is large compared to the effective radius of the nucleus for interaction, R_{inter}, as will be the case for large λ (low energy) or large l or both. The situation changes when the energy is above about $\tfrac{1}{2}$ Mev or 1 Mev, so that λ is *small* compared to nuclear dimensions, and when in addition $(l + \tfrac{1}{2})$ is small enough $(R_{\text{inter}}/\lambda$ or less) so that the classical impact parameter is less than R_{inter}. Then it is reasonable to speak of an impact of the neutron on the nucleus. If the energy of impact on the spin zero residual (= target) nucleus is not too high compared to 10 Mev, the probability of interception will be comparable to unity. The channel opening W_n is then of the order of 1.

The formula [Eq. (12)] for contribution of a single channel to the average neutron width makes no direct reference to the nuclear radius, whereas the nuclear surface appears as a very evident proportionality factor in the 1939 estimate [Eq. (7)] for the neutron width. To obtain that earlier expression it is only necessary to sum (10) for the number of formation processes over all relevant values of j

$$\sum_j (2j + 1)\pi\lambda^2 = \pi R^2$$

and to sum (9) for the number of break-up processes

$$\sum_j (2j + 1)/D_{j\pi} = 1/D_{\text{effective}}$$

Equate the number of formation processes which take place per second to the number of disintegration processes in the same time:

$$2(4\pi p^2/h^3)dE(\pi R^2) = (\Gamma_n/\hbar)(dE/D_{\text{effective}}) \tag{13}$$

The resulting expression for Γ_n is proportional to the energy of the outgoing neutron and agrees with Eq. (7). It is not so useful as the simpler Eq. (11): (a) because it does not tell how Γ_n depends on angular momentum, (b) because the average quantities R and $D_{\text{effective}}$ cannot be defined so well as the channel width or channel opening $W_{j\pi}$ associated with levels of a well specified angular momentum and parity, and (c) because it does not agree in form—as does Eq. (11)— with the simple formula (6) for fission widths:

$$\langle \Gamma_f \rangle = (D_{J\pi}/2\pi)N_f \tag{6}$$

Therefore in studying reaction rates it is appropriate to seek for a channel-by-channel analysis both of neutron and of fission widths, in line with Eqs. (6) and (11). The analogy between the two processes shows in more detail in Table II.

2. Theory of the Fission Width

Before applying the formula

$$\hbar\langle A_{f,b}\rangle = \langle \Gamma_{f,b}\rangle = (D_{J\pi}/2\pi)W_{f,b} \tag{14}$$

that connects probability per second of fission through a given channel, $A_{f,b}$, with the width or opening of that channel, $W_{f,b}$, it is appropriate to look more in detail at the ideas and assumptions that underlie this formula.

A. Separation of Intrinsic and Collective Degrees of Freedom

The passage of the nucleus from its original configuration over a potential barrier, its subsequent tearing or "scission" into two or more pieces, and the separation of the fragments constitute phases in the dynamical evolution of a quantum system endowed with an enormous number of degrees of freedom. It is practical to trace out the dynamics of so many particles only by limiting attention to the most significant features of the system. The most important feature is the approximate separation which is possible between nucleonic or intrinsic degrees of freedom on the one hand, and on the other such collective degrees of freedom as rotation and vibration or deformation of shape. Experience has shown that the nucleons can be idealized as moving in an effective average potential. This potential takes into account the major part of the nucleon-nucleon interaction. The weaker residual part of the interaction, not taken into account in this average potential, is responsible for the so-called pairing energy and for other special features of the pattern of nucleonic energy levels.

The state of the nucleonic motion is thus described by (a) the shape of the average potential, (b) the quantum numbers appropriate to the orbits of the individual nucleons in this average potential, and (c) further quantum numbers that describe the coupling of these nucleons to each other.

In addition to this motion of the individual nucleons there ordinarily take place collective motions, in which the shape of the effective

Table III. Molecules and nuclei compared and contrasted with respect to division of degrees of freedom into those associated with slow and fast motion

	Molecules	Nuclei
Individual particle degrees of freedom	Individual electronic states	Individual nucleonic states
Potential in which individual particle motion goes on defined by	Interatomic distances: $V = V(x_{\text{elec}}; r_{12}, r_{13}, r_{23})$	Parameters like α_λ that measure shape and extension of effective average nuclear potential: $V = V(x_{\text{nucleon}}; \alpha_2, \alpha_3, \ldots)$
"Particle" states resulting from interaction of individual particle degrees of freedom.	Electronic state of system; numbered by collection of quantum numbers e	Nucleonic or "intrinsic" state of system; numbered by collection of quantum numbers n.
Sum of kinetic energies of these particles and energy of interaction between them defines a storehouse of energy which (a) depends upon the vibrational coordinates, and (b) serves as potential energy function for that vibration.	Curve or surface for potential energy as a function of interatomic distances: $V = V_e(r_{12}, r_{13}, r_{23})$	Surface for potential energy as a function of deformation coordinates: $V = V_n(\alpha_2, \alpha_3, \ldots)$
Energy available for kinetic energy of vibration when total energy of system has a specified value E	$E - V_e$	$E - V_n$
Expression for this kinetic energy in terms of a single vibrational coordinate in a case of special simplicity	$(\tfrac{1}{2})\left(\dfrac{\text{reduced}}{\text{mass}}\right)\dot{r}_{12}^2$ for a diatomic molecule	$(\tfrac{1}{2})(\tfrac{3}{10})MR_0^2\dot{\alpha}_2^2$ for α_2 or cigar-pancake-cigar mode of capillary oscillation
Expression in general	$(\tfrac{1}{2})\Sigma_{\text{atoms}}M_k\dot{\mathbf{x}}_k^2$	$(\tfrac{1}{2})\sum_{\mu,\nu} B_{\mu,\nu}(\alpha)\dot{\alpha}_\mu\dot{\alpha}_\nu$
Dependent on quantum numbers n or e?	No	Yes, but not different in order of magnitude from one n value to another.

Table III. (continued)

	Molecules	Nuclei
Characteristic time for a single particle to move from an outer part of particle potential to an inner part and back out again.	$\sim 0.7 \times 10^{-15}$ sec in H_2	$\sim 0.3 \times 10^{-21}$ sec for nucleon at top of Fermi sea in U^{236}
Characteristic period of simplest mode of vibration	8×10^{-15} sec for vibrations of H_2	$\sim 5 \times 10^{-21}$ sec for α_2 mode of U^{236}
Factor distinguishing in example between fast and slow vibrations	~ 10	~ 15
Very rough order of magnitude figure for effect of a 10% extension of a typical dimension such as r_{12} (molecule) or $R_0(1 + \alpha_2 P_2 (\cos \theta))$ (nucleus)	$\delta V \sim 2$ ev	$\delta V \sim 2$ Mev
Differ greatly from one particle state to another?	Yes; even in sign	Yes; even in sign
Statistical description appropriate for V_e or V_n averaged over e or n?	No; the very few valence electrons are too drastically affected by changes of e to make any average useful except under conditions of very high pressure.	Yes; calculation of potential from surface tension and electric energy of liquid drop model.
Statistical description appropriate for inertial parameters associated with vibrations?	Unnecessary; the effective atomic masses M_k are independent of e to 1 part in 10^3 or better.	Yes; inertial parameters from liquid drop model more and more appropriate for higher states of excitation; may be wrong by factor 2 or more for lowest state of even-even nucleus.

average potential or its orientation in space or both change systematically with time (Table III). When the amplitudes of these collective motions are small compared to the nuclear radius, they can be described approximately as the superposition of nearly independent modes of vibration and rotation.

Associated with the rotation is a moment of inertia $\mathfrak{J}$ which depends upon the nucleonic state in question. Associated with each vibrational degree of freedom ($\lambda = 1, 2, 3 \ldots$) is not only an equilibrium amplitude α_λ, but also an inertial parameter B_λ defined by the relation

$$\left(\begin{array}{c} \text{kinetic energy of} \\ \text{collective motion} \end{array} \right) = (B/2)\dot{\alpha}_\lambda{}^2 \qquad (15)$$

and a restoring force constant C:

$$\left(\begin{array}{c} \text{potential energy of} \\ \text{collective deformation} \end{array} \right) = (C_\lambda/2)(\alpha_\lambda - \alpha_{\lambda\,\mathrm{eq}})^2 \qquad (16)$$

The constants $\alpha_{\lambda\,\mathrm{eq}}$, β_λ, and C_λ ($\lambda = 1, 2, \ldots$), like the moment of inertia $\mathfrak{J}$, all depend upon the nucleonic state of the system. In physical terms, the nucleonic orbits exert pressures upon the "wall" of the nucleus which ordinarily are not spherically symmetrical. As a consequence, the equilibrium configuration of the effective average potential is not itself spherically symmetrical either.

B. Droplet Model

It is possible to compare the collective motions of the nucleus with the vibrations and rotations of a droplet of an ideal incompressible liquid endowed with a mass density ρ_m, a volume density of electrification ρ_e, and a surface tension σ. The energy of such a droplet is

$$(\rho_m/2) \int v^2 d^3x + (\rho_e{}^2/2) \int \frac{d^3x_1 d^3x_2}{r_{12}} + \sigma \int dS \qquad (17)$$

When the surface of such a droplet is deformed in a finite way and at a definite rate, the energy of the fluid motion is least when it is irrotational:

$$\mathbf{v} = -\mathbf{grad}\ u;$$
$$\mathbf{curl}\ \mathbf{v} = 0. \qquad (18)$$

Any additional kinetic energy over and above this minimum value may be attributed to internal motions like turbulence and vortices. This form of energy may be compared loosely with the energy of intrinsic or nucleonic excitation of the nucleus.

Small deformations of the droplet are often described in terms of parameters $\alpha_{\lambda\mu}$ so defined and so normalized that $|\alpha_{\lambda\mu}|^2$ measures the integral over all solid angle of the square of the fractional departure of the typical point $R(\theta, \varphi)$ of the actual surface from the configuration of a sphere of radius R_0:

$$R(\theta, \varphi) = R_0 \left[1 + \sum_{\lambda=2}^{\infty} \sum_{\mu=-\lambda}^{\lambda} \alpha_{\lambda\mu} Y_{\lambda\mu}(\theta, \varphi) \right] \qquad (19)$$

Here $Y_{\lambda\mu}$ is a spherical harmonic proportional to $P_\lambda^{(\mu)}(\theta)e^{i\mu\varphi}$, so normalized that

$$\int |Y_{\lambda\mu}(\theta, \varphi)|^2 \sin\theta d\theta d\varphi = 1 \qquad (20)$$

The mean square fractional departure of the surface from sphericity is

$$\frac{\int |\delta R/R_0|^2 \sin\theta d\theta d\varphi}{\int \sin\theta d\varphi} = (1/4\pi) \sum_{\lambda,\mu} |\alpha_{\lambda\mu}|^2 \qquad (21)$$

In terms of such parameters $\alpha_{\lambda\mu}$ the velocity of the irrotational fluid motion at the point r, θ, φ is

$$v_r = -\partial u/\partial r = \sum \dot{\alpha}_{\lambda\mu} Y_{\lambda\mu}(\theta, \varphi)(r^{\lambda-1}/R_0^{\lambda-2})$$

$$v_\theta = -r^{-1}\partial u/\partial\theta = \sum (\dot{\alpha}_{\lambda\mu}/\lambda)(\partial Y_{\lambda\mu}/\partial\theta)(r^{\lambda-1}/R_0^{\lambda-2}) \qquad (22)$$

$$v_\varphi = -(r\sin\theta)^{-1}\partial u/\partial\varphi = \sum (\dot{\alpha}_{\lambda\mu}/\lambda\sin\theta)(\partial Y_{\lambda\mu}/\partial\varphi)(r^{\lambda-1}/R_0^{\lambda-2})$$

The volume integral of $(\rho_m/2)v^2$ gives for the kinetic energy the expression (Bo52)

$$(\tfrac{1}{2}) \sum_{\lambda\mu} B_\lambda |\dot{\alpha}_{\lambda\mu}|^2 \qquad (23)$$

with

$$B_\lambda = (1/4\pi)(3/\lambda)AM_pR_0^2$$

Similarly the potential energy is

$$(\tfrac{1}{2}) \sum_{\lambda\mu} C_\lambda |\alpha_{\lambda\mu}|^2$$

with

$$C_\lambda = (1/4\pi)\left[(\lambda-1)(\lambda+2)4\pi R_0^2\sigma - 6\frac{\lambda-1}{2\lambda+1}\frac{Z^2e^2}{R_0} \right] \qquad (24)$$

For larger deformations the potential and kinetic energies no longer can be represented as a simple sum of squares; or in other words, the degrees of freedom of collective motion become inextricably coupled with each other. The dependence of energy upon shape for large deformations has been explored in any detail to date only for axially symmetric deformations. Such deformations require for their description only the simple Legendre polynomials, most conveniently in the familiar unnormalized form. Each $P_\lambda (\cos \theta)$ takes on the value unity for $\theta = 0$ ("north pole" of figure). Therefore α_λ signifies in first approximation the fractional extension of the figure at the north pole due to a deformation of order λ. Three ways of representing large amplitude deformations have been employed. In the first,

$$R(\theta) = R_0 \left[1 + \alpha_0 + \sum_{\lambda=1}^{\infty} \alpha_\lambda P_\lambda(\cos \theta) \right] \qquad \text{(I)(25)}$$

and in the second

$$R(\theta) = R_0 a_0 \left[1 + \sum_{\lambda=1}^{\infty} \alpha_\lambda P_\lambda(\cos \theta) \right] \qquad \text{(II)(26)}$$

the quantity α_0 or a_0 is chosen so as to guarantee that the new figure has the same volume as the original sphere. In the third description, the cylindrical coordinates of the typical point on the surface z, ρ, are expressed in terms of prolate spheroidal coordinates

$$z = a_1 \zeta_{\text{surf}} \, \eta$$
$$\rho = a_1(\zeta^2_{\text{surf}} - 1)^{\frac{1}{2}}(1 - \eta^2)^{\frac{1}{2}} \qquad (27)$$

The length a_1 is again fixed by the requirement of volume normalization. The quantity ζ_{surf} is a constant for a figure which is exactly a prolate spheroid, but for more general shapes is written in the form

$$\zeta_{\text{surf}} = \zeta_0 \left(1 + \sum_{\lambda=3}^{\infty} \alpha_\lambda P_\lambda(\eta) \right) \qquad \text{(III)(28)}$$

In this third description it is convenient to retain a quantity called α_2, now defined however as $1/3\zeta_0^2$.

The expansion of the deformation energy agrees to terms of the second order for all three definitions. However, higher order terms naturally depend upon the choice of definition. Of course all physically significant results here, as in Riemannian geometry, are invariant with respect to choice of coordinate system! For small deformations one can make the identification

$$\alpha_\lambda P_\lambda (\cos\theta) = \alpha_{\lambda_0} Y_{\lambda_0}(\theta, \varphi) = \alpha_{\lambda_0}[(2\lambda + 1)/4\pi]^{1/2} P_\lambda (\cos\theta)$$

or

$$\alpha_{\lambda_0} = [4\pi/(2\lambda + 1)]^{1/2}\alpha_\lambda \qquad (29)$$

In the variables α_λ the leading terms in the kinetic energy, surface energy, and coulomb energy associated with the λ-th mode of axially symmetric capillary oscillation have the form

$$[3AM_pR_0^2/2\lambda(2\lambda + 1)]\dot{\alpha}_\lambda^2$$
$$+ 4\pi R_0^2\sigma[(\lambda - 1)(\lambda + 2)/2(2\lambda + 1)]\alpha_\lambda^2$$
$$- (3Z^2e^2/5R_0)[5(\lambda - 1)/(2\lambda + 1)^2]\alpha_\lambda^2 \quad (30)$$

in any of the three representations. For larger amplitudes, where this decomposition of the potential energy into a sum of squares is no longer possible, the first few terms in the more extended expansion of the potential energy in representation III [see Eq. (28)] (Bo39) are

$$V(\alpha) = 4\pi R_0^2\sigma\{[1 + \tfrac{2}{5}\alpha_2^2 + {}^{116}\!\!/\!_{105}\alpha_2^3 + {}^{101}\!\!/\!_{35}\alpha_2^4 + \cdots$$
$$+ \tfrac{5}{7}\alpha_3^2 + \cdots$$
$$+ \tfrac{9}{9}\alpha_4^2 + \cdots$$
$$+ \tfrac{2}{35}\alpha_2^2\alpha_4 + \cdots$$
$$+ \cdots]$$

$$+ x[2 - \tfrac{2}{5}\alpha_2^2 - {}^{128}\!\!/\!_{105}\alpha_2^3 - {}^{116}\!\!/\!_{35}\alpha_2^4 - \cdots$$
$$- {}^{20}\!\!/\!_{49}\alpha_3^2 - \cdots$$
$$- {}^{30}\!\!/\!_{81}\alpha_4^2 - \cdots$$
$$- {}^{16}\!\!/\!_{35}\alpha_2^2\alpha_4 - \cdots$$
$$- \cdots]\} \qquad (31)$$

Here the coefficient of the second, bracketed, series is written as

$$4\pi R_0^2\sigma x$$

This expression represents half the Coulomb energy of the undeformed sphere,

$$\tfrac{1}{2}(3Z^2e^2/5R_0)$$

For U^{236} this quantity is estimated to be in the neighborhood of

$$972 \text{ Mev}/2 = 486 \text{ Mev}$$

and the effective surface energy is estimated to be about 680 Mev.

The *fissility parameter* x has the value

$$x = \left(\frac{\text{half the Coulomb energy}}{\text{surface energy}}\right)_{\text{sphere}} = \frac{(3Z^2 e^2/10R_0)}{(4\pi R_0^2 \sigma)}$$

$$= \frac{(\text{charge})^2}{10 \text{ volume} \times \sigma} = \frac{\text{volume} \times (\text{charge density})^2}{10\sigma}$$

$$= \frac{(Z^2/A)}{2(4\pi r_0^2 \sigma)/(3e^2/5r_0)} = \frac{(Z^2/A)}{(Z^2/A)_{\text{crit}}} \tag{32}$$

or about

$$x \cong Z^2/50A \qquad \text{in general and}$$
$$x \cong 486 \text{ Mev}/680 \text{ Mev} = 0.72 \tag{33}$$

for U^{236}.

For nuclei comparable to U^{236} and heavier, the Coulomb part of the deformation energy is evidently quite substantial in comparison with the effective surface tension energy.

The surface energy increases with deformation but the electric energy decreases. Furthermore, for larger distortions—what is not immediately obvious from the mathematical expression [Eq. (31)] for the deformation energy—the Coulomb energy eventually decreases faster than the surface energy increases. In other words, a point is reached at which the energy of the system begins to go down hill. This simple consideration (Me39) even without further analysis suggests that there exists a saddle or transition point configuration of the droplet. This shape of course has slightly more energy than the original spherical form. Both forms have enormously more energy than the two or more fragments into which the droplet is destined to divide. This circumstance implies that fission, like many chemical reactions, is essentially a trigger phenomenon. The input of a small amount of energy brings about the release of a much larger amount of energy.

The reasonableness of a saddle point configuration is most readily argued by considering the drop to have a shape something like a peanut shell. The surface tension around the waist of this figure, $2\pi r_{min}\sigma$, pulls against the electric forces of repulsion between the two halves of the droplet. The surface tension wins out in the original spherical form. In the necked-in figure the two opposing forces—supplemented by hydrostatic pressure within the fluid—just balance. However, the balance is unstable. If the elongation is slightly diminished, the neck thickens. Surface tension gains the upper hand. The droplet moves more and more rapidly towards a spherical configuration. On the other hand, when the elongation is slightly increased beyond the saddle point value, the neck becomes too thin to stand the strain, electric repulsions win, and fission ensues.

C. Swiatecki's Analysis of Equilibrium Forms.

Recent important and unpublished investigations by W. J. Swiatecki show that for values of the fissility parameter x between about $x = 0.67$ and $x = 0.74$ the situation is more complicated than this simple account might seem to imply. By electronic computer evaluation of the energy as a function of deformation he finds *two* configurations of unstable equilibrium. In one (configuration A) the neck is thick. The attraction of surface tension is able to act over a substantial equator. However, the effective electrical centers of the two nascent fragments are close enough together to counterbalance this attraction. The other configuration (C) is much more extended. The electrical repulsion is therefore much less. But the neck is also much thinner; and again the countervailing forces are balanced.

Between the two configurations of unstable equilibrium is a slight hollow, configuration B, depressed by something of the order of 1 Mev or 2 Mev with respect to the one critical energy or the other. Whether B represents a completely stable point of equilibrium, or whether it is unstable with respect to asymmetric deformations, is not known at present. Table IV summarizes available information about points of equilibrium. One of them was known in part from past work but the most novel and interesting of them have been brought to light entirely through the work of Swiatecki.

D. Classical Analysis of Crossing of Barrier

How does the probability of fission depend upon energy when there is enough energy to surmount the fission barrier—when there is

Table IV. Known points of equilibrium of a uniformly charged liquid drop, over and above the spherical form, as determined by the mathematical analysis and electronic calculations of W. J. Swiatecki, according to a kind personal communication by him of preliminary results. The corresponding equilibrium forms all possess an axis of rotational symmetry and a plane of reflection symmetry. The extremal dimensions of the typical equilibrium form are written as R_{max} (distance from center to tip) and R_{min} (radius of neck). The quantity R_0 represents the radius of the original sphere. The quantity x is the fissility parameter defined by Eq. (32) and subject to estimation by Eq. (33). The quantity ζ measures the energy required to go from the sphere to the given equilibrium form, relative to the surface energy $4\pi R_0^2 \sigma$ of the sphere. This factor is estimated to have a value not far from 700 Mev for nuclei near uranium. The quantities α_2, α_4, and α_6 give more detail about the shape. Alternate definitions of these quantities (I, II, and III) are given in Eqs. (25), (26), and (28). Details of the analytic behavior near the two limits $x = 1$ and $x = 0$ are taken from Bo39

x	Saddle A (dumbbell shaped figure with thick neck)	Saddle B (dumbbell with neck of intermediate thickness)	Saddle C (extended dumbbell with thin neck)
1.000	Sphere; $\alpha_2 = \alpha_4 = \alpha_6 = 0$; $R_{max}/R_0 = R_{min}/R_0 = 1.000$; $\zeta = 0.0000$	Nonexistent	Nonexistent
Very close to 1	Near prolate spheroid $\alpha_2\,(\mathrm{III}) = (7/3)(1-x)$; $\alpha_4\,(\mathrm{III}) = -(189/85)(1-x)^2$ $R_{max}/R_0 = 1 + (7/3)(1-x)$; $R_{min}/R_0 = 1 - (7/6)(1-x)$; $\zeta = (98/135)(1-x)^3$ $- (11368/34425)(1-x)^4$	Nonexistent	Nonexistent
0.74	$\alpha_2\,(\mathrm{II}) = 0.74$; $\alpha_4 = 0.22$; $\alpha_6 = 0.01$; $R_{max}/R_0 = 1.765$; $R_{min}/R_0 = 0.636$; $\zeta = 0.01360$ *(continued)*		B and C just coming into existence simultaneously at a point of bifurcation (point of inflection just developing on outer portion of curve of energy as a function of deformation) at or near $x = 0.74$: $\alpha_2\,(\mathrm{II}) = 1.55$; $\alpha_4 = 1.33$; $\alpha_6 = 0.46$; $R_{max}/R_0 = 2.652$; $R_{min}/R_0 = 0.355$; $\zeta = -0.0001$

This is still the saddle point whose height governs the energy required for fission.

	Column A	Column B	Column C
0.70 (near that value of x at which A and C have same height)	α_2 (II) = 0.92 α_4 = 0.295 α_6 = -0.02 R_{max}/R_0 = 1.868 R_{min}/R_0 = 0.559 ζ = 0.0222	α_2 (II) = 1.35 α_4 = 0.955 α_6 = 0.146 R_{max}/R_0 = 2.394 R_{min}/R_0 = 0.442 ζ = 0.0191 (about 0.35 Mev below C)	α_2 (II) = 1.69 α_4 = 1.282 α_6 = 0.414 R_{max}/R_0 = 2.610 R_{min}/R_0 = 0.302 ζ = 0.0196
0.68	α_2 (II) = 0.99 α_4 = 0.34 α_6 = -0.04 R_{max}/R_0 = 1.901 R_{min}/R_0 = 0.536 ζ = 0.02713	α_2 (II) = 1.20 α_4 = 0.59 α_6 = -0.04 R_{max}/R_0 = 2.088 R_{min}/R_0 = 0.481 ζ = 0.02650	α_2 (II) = 1.72 α_4 = 1.21 α_6 = 0.35 R_{max}/R_0 = 2.566 R_{min}/R_0 = 0.291 ζ = 0.02923

A and B just about to fade out of existence simultaneously at a point of bifurcation (point of inflection of inner portion of curve of energy as a function of deformation) which is definitely lower in energy than C:

	Column A	Column B	Column C
Very close to 0	Nonexistent	Nonexistent	ζ = 0.260 - 0.215x
0	Nonexistent	Nonexistent	α_2 (II) = 1.585 α_4 = -0.44 α_6 = 0.133 R_{max}/R_0 = 1.5874 R_{min}/R_0 = 0 ζ = 0.260

Table V. Dimensions relevant to use of a wave packet to describe nucleon emission or fission.   The dimensions are compared for the purely illustrative situation where the kinetic energy at emergence from the nucleus and the kinetic energy at passage over the fission barrier are both 1 Mev

	Neutron or proton	Fission degree of freedom
Coordinate	r (cm)	α_2 (dimensionless) or pole extension $R_0\alpha_2$ (cm)
Inertial parameter	M_p	$(3/10)\ MR_0^2$ (g-cm^2) or $(3/10)\ M$ (g) or $71M_p$ for U^{236} for not too great a departure from sphere
Momentum p associated with a kinetic energy of 1 Mev	$(2M_pE)^{1/2} = 2.3 \times 10^{-15}$ g-cm/sec	20×10^{-15} g-cm/sec
Reduced wave length $\lambda = \lambda/2\pi = \hbar/p = (1.05 \times 10^{-27}$ g-cm^2/sec$)/p$ associated with this momentum —an order of magnitude estimate of size of wave packet which can be constructed from waves of energies between 0 and 1 Mev	4×10^{-13} cm	0.5×10^{-13} cm

one saddle—or to pass over the higher saddle when there are two or more saddles?   Can the dynamics of division even be described by probability concepts?

The coordinates α_2, α_3, . . . associated with collective vibrations and with fission differ from the coordinates associated with nucleon evaporation or alpha-particle emission in this decisive respect, that the associated mass is very great.   The de Broglie wave length is very short (Table V).   A wave packet can be constructed which will follow to a reasonable approximation the laws of classical mechanics. Therefore it is appropriate to consider the classical problem of a system with potential $V(\alpha_2, \alpha_3, . . .)$ and energy E a little in excess of the rate-determining saddle point of V.

E. Statistical Formula for Reaction Probability

Figure 3 gives a schematic representation of the dynamics of a system which moves about in a restricted region of configuration space until as if by chance it comes to that narrow region in which it can proceed over a saddle to a quite new region of configuration space. Under some conditions the motion in the region to the left of the barrier is nearly random. Then the motion can be discussed in statistical terms, and a probability A can be defined for passage from the region to the "left" of the barrier through the transition state to the region on the "right,"

$$A(\sec^{-1}) = \frac{\begin{pmatrix} \text{number of systems per second which pass over} \\ \text{saddle in direction of dissociation} \end{pmatrix}}{(\text{number of systems remaining on "left"})} \quad (34)$$

This quantity has the dimensions

$$A \sim \frac{1}{(\text{time})} \sim \frac{(\text{energy})}{(\text{coordinate}) \times (\text{momentum})} \quad (35)$$

It is possible to derive for this quantity the formula (Be63)

$$A = \frac{\begin{pmatrix} \text{that volume of a certain } (2N-2)\text{-dimensional} \\ \text{subspace of phase space which is accessible with ener-} \\ \text{gies between } E_0 \text{ and } E\text{—that subspace which at the} \\ \text{saddle point is dynamically orthogonal to dynamical} \\ \text{coordinates } x_{\text{diss}} \text{ and } p_{\text{diss}} \text{ which lead in the direction of} \\ \text{fission or dissociation} \end{pmatrix}}{d\begin{pmatrix} \text{volume in } 2N\text{-dimensional phase space to left of} \\ \text{barrier included within a hypersurface of energy } E \end{pmatrix}/dE} \quad (36)$$

under certain conditions, among which one of the most important is the requirement of true randomness. How can a mechanical system be random?

F. Always 3N First Integrals?

There was a day when it might have been thought that every holonomic conservative mechanical system with N degrees of freedom possessed N independent first integrals of the equations of motion. Judging from the example of an electron in a central field, where these integrals may be taken to be the energy E, total angular momentum M, and angular momentum M_z about the z-axis, one would have been led to think of this program as leading also in the general problem to simple integrals to determine the N configuration coordinates of the system as a function of (a) the numerical values of the N first integrals, (b) the numerical values of N further constants of integration, and (c) the time. With the technique of separation of variables, so fully developed by Stäckel (St35), it was possible to carry through this program to completion for many interesting and important problems. However, the very exhaustiveness of Stäckel's analysis showed that the method of separation of variables definitely would not go through in the general dynamical problem; it is suited only to problems with potential functions of special categories. It might have been tempting at the time of Stäckel's analysis to hold to the hope that $3N$ first integrals always exist, even when they cannot be found by the method of separation of variables. How different from this vision the general state of affairs really is came especially clearly to the fore in the famous problem of three bodies. It was not necessary to analyze this problem in its general form. The important features showed already in the primitive version known as "Hill's limiting case of the restricted problem of three bodies" (Po99, Li49, Wi41). A point planet is idealized to revolve about a distant sun in a circular orbit. About the planet in the plane of its revolution circulates a rocket of negligible mass at a distance negligible in comparison with the distance to the sun. The equations of motion of the rocket take a simple form in a frame of reference (OX, OY) which is centered on the planet with its OX-axis pointing always toward the sun. The content of the equations is most compactly summarized in Lagrange's function

$$L(x, y, \dot{x}, \dot{y}) = \underbrace{\tfrac{1}{2}(\dot{x}^2 + \dot{y}^2)}_{\text{(kinetic)}} + \underbrace{(x\dot{y} - y\dot{x})}_{\text{(Coriolis)}} - \underbrace{U(x, y)}_{\text{(potential)}} \qquad (37)$$

Here the effective potential U includes not only the influence of gravitational forces but also that of centrifugal force:

$$U = -(x^2 + y^2)^{-1/2} - 3/2x^2 \qquad (38)$$

The equations of motion themselves have the form

$$\ddot{x} - 2\dot{y} = -\partial U/\partial x$$
$$\ddot{y} + 2\dot{x} = -\partial U/\partial y \qquad (39)$$

In the alternative Hamiltonian form of the equations there appear the momenta

$$p_x = \partial L/\partial \dot{x} = \dot{x} - y$$
$$p_y = \partial L/\partial \dot{y} = \dot{y} + x \tag{40}$$

and the Hamiltonian function

$$
\begin{aligned}
H &= \dot{x}p_x + \dot{y}p_y - L \\
&= \tfrac{1}{2}[(p_x + y)^2 + (p_y - x)^2] + U(x, y)
\end{aligned} \tag{41}
$$

thus

$$\dot{x} = \partial H/\partial p_x; \quad \dot{p}_x = -\partial H/\partial x$$
$$\dot{y} = \partial H/\partial p_y; \quad \dot{p}_y = -\partial H/\partial y \tag{42}$$

The equations of motion possess one simple integral, the energy

$$E = \tfrac{1}{2}(\dot{x}^2 + \dot{y}^2) + U(x, y) \tag{43}$$

However, it has been proven that there exists no other independent analytic function of the four variables x, y, $\dot{x}$, $\dot{y}$ which, like E, is conserved in time as a consequence of the equations of motion: no other first integral of the equations.

G. Lessons from the Problem of Three Bodies

What can be learned from the restricted problem of three bodies relevant to a statistical description of transformation processes? A complete discussion would lead outside the bounds of present knowledge, but from widely known results three points stand out. (a) There exist periodic orbits. For such an orbit there exists a time T (different for different orbits) such that

$$x(t + T) = x(t)$$
$$y(t + T) = y(t) \tag{44}$$

However, such an orbit is exceptional. It is analogous to the path of an ideal billiard ball which is started out upon an ideal (square!) billiard table with a *rational* inclination to one side:

$$\frac{(dy/dt)}{(dx/dt)} = \frac{dy}{dx} = \frac{\text{integer } m}{\text{integer } n} = \text{rational fraction} \tag{45}$$

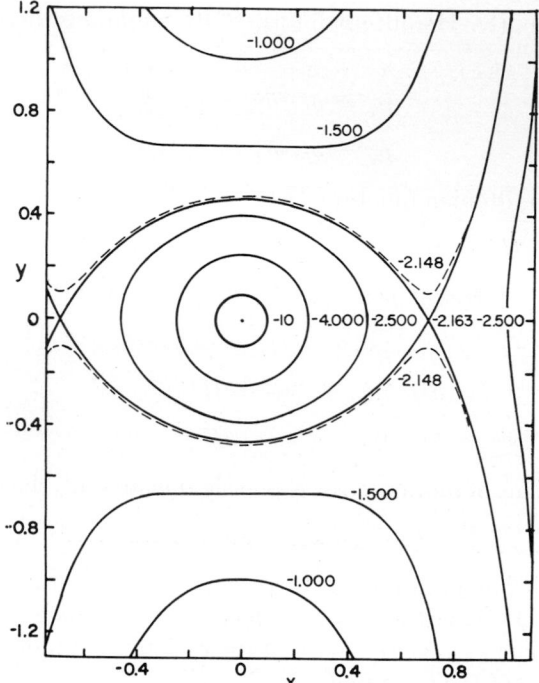

Figure 4. Illustration of ideas relevant to passage over barrier to fission or dissociation in a case where the analytic form of the potential is fully known: Hill's limiting case of the restricted problem of three bodies. The diagram gives contour lines of the effective potential function

$$U(x,y) = -(x^2 + y^2)^{-1/2} - 3/2\ x^2$$

The planet (or moon) is located at $x = 0$, $y = 0$ and the much more massive sun (or earth) about which it revolves is far away to the right at large positive x. The dipole component of the pull of that massive center is cancelled out (Einstein's equivalence principle!) by the continual "fall" of the planet (or moon) toward the sun (or earth). The quadrupole gravitational and quadrupole centrifugal parts of the force (tide producing component) are not so cancelled; hence the term in $-3/2x^2$. If the rocket (unit mass) that moves in the field of the local mass has energy E less than $E_{\text{crit}} = -3^{4/3}/2 = -2.163$, the rocket can never escape. If it is randomly launched and has for example the energy $E = -2.148$, then typically it will circulate about within the dashed boundary almost at random for a long time, but eventually escape over the left hand or right hand saddle through the one or the other of the two narrow mouths that are seen in the diagram for this energy. *Details:* The Taylor series expansion of the potential about the right hand saddle, through terms of the second order, is

$$U(x,y) = E_{\text{crit}} - 9/2(x - x_{\text{saddle}})^2 + 3/2y^2 + \dots$$

(*caption continued on facing page*)

where $x_{\text{saddle}} = 3^{-1/3}$. Equating this expression to the available energy, $E = E_{\text{crit}} + \epsilon$, one finds for the opening of the mouth at $x = x_{\text{saddle}}$ the result $y_{\text{mouth}} = \pm(2\epsilon/3)^{1/2}$. The chance to escape is proportional to opening of the mouth, that is, to the volume of phase space at the throat orthogonal to the dynamical coordinates x and p_x which lead to escape. This volume is

$$\int\int dy\, dp_y = \int\int dy\, d\dot{y}$$

where the integral is extended over the region within the ellipse $(\dot{y}^2/2) + (3y^2/2) = \epsilon$. This "volume" is

$$\pi\,(\text{semi major axis})(\text{semi minor axis})$$
$$= \pi(2\epsilon/3)^{1/2}(2\epsilon)^{1/2} = 2\pi\,\epsilon/3^{1/2}$$

$$= \frac{(\text{energy in excess of saddle})}{(\text{frequency of y-vibration at saddle})}$$

Translated into quantum terms, this phase space integral has the value

$$h \times \begin{pmatrix}\text{number of states of vibration in}\\ \text{y-direction accessible at saddle})\end{pmatrix}$$
$$= 2\pi\,\hbar N$$

where N is the number of accessible channels. To say that a particular system escapes in the third channel is to say that it has 2 quanta of vibration in the y-direction as it passes over the saddle. The probability of escape, summed over all channels, is thus in the present case proportional to the energy ϵ in excess of the saddle. The constant of proportionality [Eq. (36)] is inversely proportional to the volume of four dimensional phase space per unit of energy:

$$(d/dE) \int_{\text{allowed region}} dp_x dp_y dx\, dy = (d/dE)\int dx\, d\dot{y}\, dx\, dy$$
$$= (d/dE) \int \pi v^2_{\text{max}} dx\, dy = (d/dE)2\pi\int [E-U(x,y)]dx\, dy$$
$$\cong 2\pi \int_{\text{region inside curve } U=E_{\text{crit}}} dx\, dy = 2\pi\,(4/3^{2/3})\,[(\pi^{1/2}/2)$$
$$- (\ln 2)/3^{1/2}]$$
$$= 5.6_4$$

In the quantum transcription of this result the number of quantum states in the region of trapping per unit of energy near $E = E_{\text{crit}}$ will be said to be $5.64/h^2$; in other words, the level spacing D is $h^2/5.64$. The probability per unit time of escape from the zone of trapping over the right hand saddle is

$$A_{\text{right}}(\sec^{-1}) = (2\pi\,\epsilon/3^{1/2})/5.6_4$$
$$= 0.64_3\epsilon$$

or for the energy illustrated by the dashed line in the diagram

$$A_{\text{right}}(\sec^{-1}) = 0.64_3[(-2.148) - (-2.163)] = 0.0096_5$$

A like figure applies to the left hand saddle. The total escape probability is

$$A = A_{\text{right}} + A_{\text{left}} = 0.0193$$

The corresponding mean time, $A^{-1} = 52$, is long enough for a particle of unit velocity to travel 52 distance units in the diagram. The connection with the quantum formula for level widths—the formula first used to treat fission—is seen from the relations

$$\Gamma = \hbar A = (D/2\pi)N = \hbar h N/h^2/D$$

$$= \hbar\,\frac{(\text{two dimensional phase integral at the mouth})}{(d/dE)(\text{four dimensional phase integral in zone of trapping})}$$

It is known that the rational numbers between 0 and 1, for example, form a set of measure zero amongst all the numbers in this interval. Similarly there is zero probability that an orbit picked out with full randomness will turn out to be periodic. Therefore, such orbits can be disregarded in statistical discussion. (b) There exists a critical energy,

$$E_{\text{crit}} = -3^{4/3}/2$$

A rocket in a nonperiodic orbit with more than this energy will eventually escape from the influence of the planet. The chance that it will ever return is inversely proportional to some power of the distance from the planet to the sun. This chance is zero in the idealized limit represented by Hill's limiting case of the restricted problem of three bodies. (c) For an energy less than E_{crit} there exists an allowed region of configuration space of finite extent, bounded by the closed branch of the curve

$$E = U(x, y) = -(x^2 + y^2)^{-1/2} - 3/2x^2 \qquad (46)$$

For a value of E much more negative than $E_{\text{crit}} = -3^{4/3}/2$, this curve is nearly a circle of radius $1/(-E)$. The rocket will remain in this region for all time if it once starts off in this region. Let any point P be selected in this allowed region and let a circle of radius ϵ (within the allowed region!) be circumscribed about this point. Select any nonperiodic and nonsingular orbit of energy E. Then, no matter how small ϵ is, there exists a time T_ϵ—possibly very great—such that within this time the orbit will pass within the distance ϵ of P. Nonperiodic but bounded orbits are in this sense "quasi-ergodic." They are not ergodic; it cannot be guaranteed that the orbit will actually pass through the point P.

Beginning as far back as with Liouville and Gibbs, it has been natural to associate with quasi-ergodic motion a probability to come into one or another elementary volume of the four dimensional phase space defined by the variables x, y, p_x, p_y. The circumstance that the motion is confined to a three-dimensional subspace of this four-dimensional space—to the "energy shell"

$$H(x, y, p_x, p_y) = E \qquad (47)$$

—makes it more convenient in dealing with this probability to consider not one particle but a collection of particles distributed with uniform probability over an energy shell of finite thickness, extending from E to $E + \Delta E$. Then familiar arguments (La58) say that the probability d^4W to find a particle in a cell of size

$$dx \, dy \, dp_x \, dp_y \tag{48}$$

in the four-dimensional momentum space is the same wherever this cell is located within the finite energy shell; or

$$d^4W/dx \, dy \, dp_x \, dp_y = \text{constant} \tag{49}$$

In principle the situation changes when the energy E exceeds the critical energy $E_{\text{crit}} = -3^{4/3}/2$ by even a small quantity ϵ:

$$E_{\text{crit}} = E + \epsilon$$

Then the otherwise trapped system is no longer fully circumscribed. A small doorway opens up through which it can escape from the zone of trapping to a completely different region of configuration space, passing over or near a saddle point in the process (see Fig. 4). In an ensemble of randomly prepared systems of energy E this escape process depletes the number of trapped orbits. When the excess energy ϵ is very small, the mean time required to escape is very large compared to the typical "period" required to pass from one side of the zone of trapping to the other and back again. The orbit of each lost system perhaps looked special in one or another way at the time it was passing over the saddle. However, followed back in time for a few periods, through the randomizing processes illustrated in Fig. 3, it looks not significantly different from any other orbit. In other words, the existence of a long mean time before escape means that it is reasonable to treat the escape process on an elementary statistical basis. The probability distribution in phase space in the zone of trapping is taken to be unaffected by the depletion except for an everywhere identical exponential fall off:

$$d^4W/dx \, dp \, dp_x \, dp_y = \text{constant} \exp{(-At)}$$

$$\text{(in zone of trapping)} \tag{50}$$

On this basis all those trapped systems are considered which have energy from E to $E + dE$. Their efflux from the mouth is calculated and compared with the number of systems still present to determine the decay rate A:

$$A(\sec^{-1}) = \frac{\left(\begin{array}{c}\text{number of systems lost per sec from zone of} \\ \text{trapping}\end{array}\right)}{(\text{number still present})} \tag{51}$$

Apart from the quantity "constant $\exp(-At)$" in expression (50), which cancels out of the numerator and denominator of Eq. (51), the denominator is given by the integral

$$\int dp_x\, dp_y\, dx\, dy \tag{52}$$

extended over the region which satisfies the energy requirement

$$E \le H(x, y, p_x, p_y) \le E + dE \tag{53}$$

and lies within the zone of trapping. The numerator—apart from the factor that is to be dropped, "constant $\exp(-At)$"—is obtained by summing up the product of the following quantities:

(1) The velocity with which systems located near the saddle pass to the right. (This quantity is evaluated at $x = x_{\text{saddle}}$ for particles of a given total energy E and given y and given p_y.)

This gives: $\qquad\qquad \dot{x}(E,\, x_{\text{sad}},\, y,\, p_y)$

(2) The number of systems per unit interval of x which lie in the interval $dy\, dp_x\, dp_y$. (Note that fixing $x = x_{\text{sad}}$, y, and p_y would completely specify p_x if the energy E were sharply defined. However, an energy interval dE is envisaged. Therefore there is a spread in values of p_x given by the very general formula $dp_x = (dE)/\dot{x}$.)

This gives: $\qquad\qquad dy\, dp_x\, dp_y$
Thus, the product is: $\quad dy\, dp_y\, dE$

This product represents the number of systems in dE lost per second in a particular way. The systems in question cross the escape line $x = x_{\text{saddle}}$ with vibration coordinate in the interval y to $y + dy$ and vibration momentum in the interval p_y to $p_y + dp_y$. This degree of specification of the total energy and of the vibration energy leaves no freedom in the kinetic energy with which these particular systems pass over the barrier. This kinetic energy is fully determined, apart from the latitude dE introduced in order to have an energy shell of finite but small thickness. The particular class of systems under consideration form the closest classical analogue one has to quantum systems which undergo fission or dissociation in a particular channel. The quotient

$$d^2N = dy \, dp_y/h \tag{54}$$

is the semiclassical expression for the number of vibrational quantum states—and therefore for the number of channels—in the indicated interval of the dynamical coordinates. The total flux over the saddle is obtained by summing up over all available channels:

$$\text{efflux} = dE \iint dp_y \, dy \tag{55}$$

A little can be added to clarify the range of integration. The coordinate x has already been fixed at x_{saddle}; and with y also fixed for the moment, the momentum p_y goes over the entire range which is allowed by the fixed value E for the energy. The momentum p_x—which now does not even enter into the integration—has to adjust itself so as to take up any left over energy. In the present example, the limits of the integration are set by the equation

$$\tfrac{1}{2}(\dot{x}^2 + \dot{y}^2) + U(x_{\text{sad}}, y) =$$

$$\tfrac{1}{2}[(p_x + y)^2 + (p_y - x_{\text{sad}})^2] + U(x_{\text{sad}}, y) = E \tag{56}$$

In other words, the momentum p_y in Eq. (55) runs uniformly over the interval from

$$p_{y \, \min}(E, y) - x_{\text{sad}} - \sqrt{2} \, [E - U(x_{\text{sad}}, y)]^{1/2} \tag{57}$$

(at which limit no kinetic energy is left for motion in the x-direction; $\dot{x} = p_x + y = 0$) through the value

$$p_y = x_{\text{sad}} \tag{58}$$

which leaves over the maximum kinetic energy for translation over the barrier, up to the limit

$$p_{y \, \max}(E, y) = x_{\text{sad}} + \sqrt{2}[E - U(x_{\text{sad}}, y)]^{1/2} \tag{59}$$

where again no energy is left for translation over the barrier. After the integration over p_y is done there remains the integration over the vibration coordinate y itself; it evidently goes between those two values y_1 and y_2 of the vibration coordinate at which the potential energy matches the energy:

$$E - U(x_{\text{sad}}, y_1) = E - U(x_{\text{sad}}, y_2) = 0. \tag{60}$$

The result of this statistical analysis is the classical formula for escape probability

$$A(\sec^{-1}) = \frac{\iint \text{accessible channels } dp_y \, dy}{(d/dE) \iiiint_{\substack{\text{trapped} \\ \text{states}}} dp_x \, dp_y \, dx \, dy} \qquad (61)$$

or its quantum transcription

$$(\text{level width}) = \Gamma = \hbar A$$

$$= \hbar \, \frac{h \times \begin{pmatrix} \text{number of accessible } y\text{-vibrational} \\ \text{states or number } N \text{ of channels} \end{pmatrix}}{(d/dE)h^2 \times \begin{pmatrix} \text{number } n \text{ of bound quantum} \\ \text{states below the energy } E \end{pmatrix}}$$

$$= \frac{1}{2\pi} \frac{N}{dn/dE} = (D/2\pi)N \qquad (62)$$

H. When Are All Orbits Depleted at the Same Rate?

The question arises, what kind of difficulties can there be in the assumption that all the nonperiodic, nonsingular orbits in the energy interval dE undergo depletion at a constant fractional rate $A(\sec^{-1})$? What is the possibility that the motions may divide themselves into classes characterized by different A values? In this eventuality a plot of the logarithm of the number of undissociated systems as a function of time will not follow a straight line curve, but will show the familiar curvature characteristic of a mixture of radioactive species. This question of classification of orbits into families defined by one or more parameters additional to the energy E is closely related to the question whether any first integrals of the equations of motion exist over and above the energy. Comparison and contrast of four examples may bring some of the essential points to the fore (Table VI).

In the first of the examples in the table, Hill's limiting case of the problem of three bodies, it is well known that there exists no last first-integral. On this account a statistical analysis can be carried out to evaluate an escape probability as a function of energy, $A = A(E)$, as just outlined. The second example in Table VI appears to be nearly like the first one except for the replacement of a quadrupole perturbation by a dipole perturbation. However, this apparently minor change completely changes the character of the problem. There

Table VI. Comparison and contrast of four systems characterized by a trapped state from which escape is possible when the energy exceeds a critical amount. The collaboration of J. W. Benoit and R. A. Haberstroh (Be63) in the preparation of this table is gratefully acknowledged

System; number of degrees of freedom in present idealized version of problem; and first integrals of equations of motion.	Is statistical analysis of escape rate reasonable for energies very little in excess of saddle?
I. Rocket. Unit mass in central field plus special kind of quadrupole potential: $V = -(1/r) - \frac{3}{2}x^2$. Two degrees of freedom: x, y. Only one first integral: the energy E.	Yes; motion for energy just below saddle is known to be quasi-ergodic.
II. Field ionization. Electron subject to potential $V = -(Ze^2/r) - Fez$. Three degrees of freedom. Three first integrals: E, p_φ and Z_1.	No. Problem separates completely in parabolic coordinates ζ, η, φ. No randomness left of kind relevant for statistical description of reaction rates. The ζ degree of freedom is either trapped forever or goes over top on first try.
III. Charged particle in Størmer-Van Allen belt. Charged particle in field of ideal magnetic dipole of vector potential $A_\varphi = \mu \sin^2 \theta/r$, $A_r = A_\star = 0$. Three degrees of freedom. Only two first integrals of the equations of motion: the total momentum p and the total angular momentum p_φ (kinetic plus potential) about the symmetry axis.	No third first-integral exists. Suitable choice of p_φ determines narrow mouth where escape is possible. Statistical analysis can be carried through completely. However, this analysis is now realized normally to be irrelevant because there has been discovered to exist an approximate third first integral $p_{\text{adiabatic}}$. To the extent that p_a remains constant in time the situation resembles case II. The particle escapes or not according to the value of p_φ. The issue decisive for the escape rate is here very different from that in the foregoing statistical analysis; it is the gradual change with time of this third "constant" of integration.
IV. Fission of classical liquid drop. $V = V(\alpha_2, \alpha_3, \ldots)$. An infinite number of degrees of freedom. Every reason to believe that there are only three first integrals that commute exactly with the Hamiltonian: energy E; square of total angular momentum, M^2; angular momentum p_φ about space-fixed z-axis.	Statistical analysis as in example I appropriate to determine probability of passage over barrier *provided* that there exists no additional (approximate) first integral. The angular momentum K about the approximate symmetry axis of the extended fission form is an approximate first integral during passage over the barrier and scission, according to the evidence on angular distribution of fission products, but it has always seemed unreasonable to believe that any such quantity remains constant during the complicated vibrations and evolutions of shape that take place in the compound nucleus before it arrives at the fission saddle.

Table VII. Details of the problem of field ionization to illustrate a situation where a statistical description of escape is *not* appropriate

Properties of dynamical system	Potential and other details
Electron (1) circulating around a proton in an orbit of quantum number n so great that a classical discussion is appropriate, and (2) subject also to a uniform electric field $\mathbf{E} = (0, 0, -F)$.	$V = -(Ze^2/r) - Fez$ Saddle at $x = y = 0$, $z = (Ze^2/Fe)^{1/2}$. Critical energy $E_b = -2(Ze^2/Fe)^{1/2}$.
Any component of angular momentum conserved?	Component p_φ about symmetry axis.
Any third integral?	Yes! call it G_1.
Consequence of existence of as many first integrals as degrees of freedom	Problem separable into three separate problems.
Coordinate transformation to bring about this separation	$\rho = \zeta\,\eta$; $z = \frac{1}{2}(\zeta^2 - \eta^2)$; $r = \frac{1}{2}(\zeta^2 + \eta^2)$.
Nature of motion in φ coordinate	Rotation about z-axis with uniform angular momentum.
Nature of motion in η coordinate	Oscillation back and forth between two limits specified by the values of E, p_φ and Z_1, under influence of effective potential $\dfrac{p_\varphi^2}{2m\eta^4} - \dfrac{(Z - Z_1)e^2}{\eta^2} + \dfrac{Fe\eta^2}{2}$
Effective potential for motion in ζ-coordinate	$\dfrac{p_\varphi^2}{2m\zeta^4} - \dfrac{(Z + Z_1)e^2}{\zeta^2} - \dfrac{Fe\zeta^2}{2}$
Nature of potential (for field strength) F between 0 and $F_{\text{crit}} = \frac{8}{27}(m^2e^5/p_\varphi^4)(Z + Z_1)^3$	Highly repulsive at very small ζ. Minimum at small ζ. Maximum at intermediate ζ. Continual fall-off at very large ζ.
Value of barrier height or critical energy E_{crit}	$E_{\text{crit}} = E_{\text{crit}}(p_\varphi, Z_1, F)$
Nature of motion for E less than barrier height and particle to left of barrier.	Trapped; oscillates at well defined frequency for all time.
Motion for E just above barrier.	Particle escapes at first try.
Is statistical description or concept of an "escape probability" relevant?	No!

are now as many first integrals as there are degrees of freedom. The problem is completely separable. A statistical description of the escape process does not make sense (see Table VII).

I. Charge Trapped in Field of Magnetic Dipole

The third example in Table VI, charged particles trapped in the magnetic field of an ideal dipole, is one where only two exact first integrals exist. For certain values of these constants

$$\frac{\left(\begin{array}{c}\text{total angular momentum } P_\varphi \\ \text{(kinetic plus potential)} \\ \text{about symmetry axis}\end{array}\right)}{2(\text{linear momentum, } p)(e\mu/cp)^{1/2}} = \lambda > 1 \tag{63}$$

there exists a zone of trapping from which the charged particle can never escape. When the parameter λ is a very little less than 1, a small hole develops in the outer boundary of this zone, out of which particles can slowly leak (Table VIII).

Not in connection with the escape of trapped electrons through such a small mouth in the barrier, but in connection with the trapping of cosmic rays by their scattering in the magnetic field of the earth and other objects, calculations have been made (Ka49) which treat the motion as quasi-ergodic. The quantities p and P_φ were treated as constant before and after the scattering, and the motion in the allowed region of the ρ^*, z^* plane was analyzed by simple phase space considerations. Proceeding along this line, the channel theory of escape would have given for the rate of leakage through the mouth the result

$$A(\sec^{-1}) = A(p, P_\varphi) = \frac{\iint_{\substack{\text{accessible channels} \\ \text{near mouth}}} dz\, dp_z}{(d/dE)\iiiint_{\substack{\text{zone of} \\ \text{trapping}}} dp_\rho\, dp_z\, d\rho\, dz} \tag{63}$$

Here both integrals are extended over coordinates orthogonal to the dynamic variables φ and P_φ associated with motion around the symmetry axis. The accessible region in the momentum space p_ρ, p_z at any given point ρ, z is bounded by the circle

$$p_z{}^2 + p_\rho{}^2 = p^2 - (p_\varphi/\rho)^2$$
$$= p^2 - (P_\varphi - e\mu\rho^2/cr^3)^2/\rho^2 \tag{64}$$

The integral in the denominator has already been evaluated (Ka49), and a simple calculation also gives the numerator. However, this method of analysis of escape is not appropriate. The motion is not so random as has been assumed. A trapped particle "remembers" dur-

Table VIII. Charged particles trapped in an ideal dipole magnetic field—a problem where the simple channel analysis of escape probability at first seemed appropriate. The picture changed with the discovery of an approximate third integral of the equations of motion through the theoretical work of Alfvèn, Fermi, and Kruskal and the experimental observations of the Argus effect: fission product decay electrons trapped for an unexpectedly long time in the magnetic field of the earth

The system and its properties	Quantitative aspects
Charged particle moving in magnetic field of an ideal dipole. Two and only two exact first integrals of the equation of motion: cp and P_φ	(1) Momentum p; (2) total angular momentum (kinetic *plus* potential) about symmetry axis: $$P_\varphi = p_\varphi + (e/c)A_\varphi$$ $$= p_\varphi + (e\mu/cr)\sin^2\theta$$
Expression for angular momentum integral in units of the Størmer length R = radius of an exactly circular orbit in the equatorial plane = $(e\mu/cp)^{1/2}$, with $\rho/R = \rho^*$; $z/R = z^*$; $r/R = r^*$; $\rho^{*2} + z^{*2} = r^{*2}$; here χ = angle between momentary direction of motion of particle and exactly eastward direction of circulation about the common axis of μ and z; and λ = total angular momentum/$2pR$.	$\rho^* \cos\chi + (\rho^{*2}/r^{*3}) = 2\lambda$
Allowed region of motion	That portion of (ρ^*, z^*) plane within which the value of $\cos\chi$ as derived from the above formula lies between -1 and 1.
Character of region of trapping in (ρ^*, z^*) plane for λ greater than unity (electron spiralling about a line of force)	Crescent shaped region in (ρ^*, z^*) plane approximately centered about that magnetic line of force which has the equation $(\rho^{*2}/r^{*3}) = 2\lambda$ or $r^{*3} = \sin^2\theta/2\lambda$
Approximate formula for two boundaries (B_1 and B_2) of crescent	$$r^* \cong \frac{\sin^2\theta}{2\lambda} \pm \frac{\sin^5\theta}{8\lambda^3}$$
Nature of motion within this region of trapping	Quasi-ergodic (except for the periodic orbits, which constitute a set of measure zero relative to the set of all typical orbits)
Alternative region where a particle with same momentum and angular momentum integral (or λ) can move.	From boundary B_3 all the way to infinity (unlimited space).

Table VIII. (continued)

The system and its properties	Quantitative aspects
Approximate formula for boundary B_3	$\rho^* \cong 2\lambda$
Reason particle cannot get from zone of trapping to outer free region.	Barrier between B_2 and B_3 where motion with specified energy and angular momentum is not possible.
Thickness of this barrier at place where it is thinnest (equatorial plane, $z^* = 0$)	From $r^*(B_2) = \lambda - (\lambda^2 - 1)^{1/2}$ to $r^*(B_3) = \lambda + (\lambda^2 - 1)^{1/2}$
Nature of barrier when angular momentum parameter is a very little less than 1.	Barrier remains except for a small hole pierced through it centered on equatorial plane
Nature of motion of trapped particle in this case	Almost quasi-ergodic motion in zone of trapping until as if by chance the particle escapes through the hole to the outside.
Location of mouth of hole (where B_2 meets B_3) for λ a very little less than 1	$\rho^* = 1$; $z^* \cong \pm(4/3)^{1/2}(1 - \lambda)^{1/2}$
Statistical description of leakage process (Ka49)	Leakage probability A (sec^{-1}) given by (v/R) times a dimensionless function of λ, proportional to the mouth opening or to $(1 - \lambda)^{1/2}$ for λ close to 1.
Any question about appropriateness of a statistical description in this particular problem?	Yes! There has been discovered to exist an approximate third integral of the equations of motion [calculations of Alfven (Al50), Kruskal (Kr57), Fermi (Fe49), Hellwig (He55), and others; observations in Argus effect (Po59) of particles trapped for a long time].
Nature of approximate third integral	Kinetic angular momentum $p_{\text{adiabatic}}$ of particle about the local axis of gyration (this axis tangent to the line of force $r^* = \sin^2 \theta / 2\lambda$)
Nature of motion of particles of specified p and λ if this third integral were exact (analog of problem of field ionization).	Particles with values of $p_{\text{adiabatic}}$ in one range would escape on the first proper try. Particles with values of $p_{\text{adiabatic}}$ in the remaining range would never escape.
Useful to define statistical probability for escape A (sec^{-1}) in this extreme situation?	No.
Question requiring exploration before a proper theory of the rate of leakage of trapped electrons is possible.	Rate of change of the approximate third integral p_{ad}. Statistical analysis of changes in p_{ad}.

ing many turns about a magnetic line of force information which would have been "forgotten" in the first few periods of motion in a less regular field of force. The kinetic angular momentum $p_{\text{adiabatic}}$ of the gyration of the particle is nearly constant in time, according to Fermi (Fe49), Alfven (Al50), Hellwig (He55), and Kruskal (Kr57):

$$\begin{pmatrix} \text{momentum perpendicular} \\ \text{to magnetic field} \end{pmatrix} \times \begin{pmatrix} \text{radius of} \\ \text{gyration} \end{pmatrix} = p_{\text{adiabatic}} \cong \text{constant}$$

or

$$p_\perp(cp_\perp/eH) = p_{\text{adiabatic}} \cong \text{constant} \tag{65}$$

In consequence the particle goes faster and faster in the direction perpendicular to the lines of force as it moves into a region of stronger magnetic field H:

$$p^2{}_\perp = eHp_{\text{adiabatic}}/c \tag{66}$$

The momentum $p_\parallel$ available for translation parallel to the field falls in accordance with the equation

$$p_\parallel{}^2 = p^2 - p_\perp{}^2 = p^2 - eHp_{\text{adiabatic}}/c \tag{67}$$

and goes to zero where the magnetic field reaches the critical value

$$H = H_{\text{crit}} = cp^2/ep_{\text{adiabatic}} \tag{68}$$

In other words the particle spirals about a line of force from the equator northward, is turned about at a critical northern latitude fixed by $p_{\text{adiabatic}}$, spirals back southward across the equator to an equal southern latitude, and turns northward again. It continues this north and south vibration between the same two limits as long as the quantity $p_{\text{adiabatic}}$ keeps the same value. That is, a particle of

    (1) fixed momentum, p;

    (2) fixed true total angular momentum, P_φ; and

    (3) assigned adiabatic invariant $p_{\text{adiabatic}}$

does *not* move in a nearly random way throughout the region of the ρ, z plane allowed by the given p and $P\varphi$. Instead it remains confined to a subspace of this space. From this subspace it either escapes promptly as its north-south excursion carries it past the mouth of the zone of trapping or it does not escape at all. Under these circumstances an elementary statistical description of the rate of leakage according to Eq. (63) is out of the question.

J. Importance of Approximate First Integral

The statistical analysis now required is of a much more sophisticated type. The rate of leakage is controlled by the rate at which the value of the approximate first integral $p_{\text{adiabatic}}$ drifts or slowly fluctuates with time. A detailed theoretical analysis of this point is still lacking. However, observations are relevant which were made at the time of the Argus test of a nuclear device in the region high above the earth (Po59). The electrons set free circulated about the magnetic lines of force for a time far longer than had been anticipated. This result is now understood in the following way: An average decay constant $A(\text{sec}^{-1})$ is not an appropriate way to describe the escape. Some groups of electrons (high $p_{\|}$, low $p_{\text{adiabatic}}$) travel far north or south along the lines of force and are lost by collision with the atmosphere. Others, with lesser $p_{\|}$, or higher $p_{\text{adiabatic}}$, cannot move so far north and south and remain in orbit for a very much longer time than would otherwise have been expected.

One turns from these examples to fission (Table IX) aware that the central issue concerns exact and approximate first integrals of the equations of motion.

K. Channel Formula for Fission Rate

If there are no (approximate) first integrals of the equations of motion that commute with E, M^2, and p_6, and if the rate of leakage is low enough not to destroy the nearly ideally random distribution of orbits in phase space, then it is appropriate to evaluate the partial radioactive decay constant associated with fission from the formula

$$A_{\text{fiss}}(E, M^2) = \frac{\left\{ \begin{array}{l}\text{integral over all phase space accessible at} \\ \text{saddle with given energy and angular mo-} \\ \text{mentum, omitting differentials } d\alpha_{\text{fiss}} \text{ and} \\ dp_{\text{fiss}} \text{ relevant to translation over barrier and} \\ \text{omitting differentials } d\theta\, d\varphi\, dp_\theta\, dp_\varphi \text{ associated} \\ \text{with rotations of extended fission form} \\ \text{about axes perpendicular to axis of exten-} \\ \text{sion} \end{array} \right\}}{(d/dE) \left\{ \begin{array}{l}\text{integral over all of phase space corre-} \\ \text{sponding to undissociated configura-} \\ \text{tions with angular momentum pa-} \\ \text{rameters } M^2 \text{ and } p_\varphi \text{ and with energy} \\ E \text{ or less, omitting differentials } d\theta\, d\varphi \\ dp_\theta\, dp_\varphi \end{array} \right\}} \tag{69}$$

Table IX. Features of the classical liquid drop model relevant to a statistical description of the probability for fission

Properties of system	Quantitative aspects
Features of model	Incompressible liquid, free of viscosity, with uniform charge density, ρ_e, surface tension σ, in irrotational flow.
Dynamical coordinates	α_γ: parameters used to describe shape of surface; here ν stands for the pair of labels λ, μ mentioned in the text.
Potential energy	$V = V(\alpha_2, \alpha_3, \ldots)$
Conditions for an extremum in the potential (maximum, minimum, saddle, etc.)	Coordinates α_ν so chosen that simultaneously $\partial V/\partial \alpha_2 = 0$, $\partial V/\partial \alpha_3 = 0$, etc.
Energy of lowest saddle which will lead to fission, relative to energy of undeformed and nonrotating sphere.	E_b
Integrals of the equations of motion	(1) Total energy E (2) Square M^2 of the total angular momentum (3) Projection p_φ of this angular momentum on the space-fixed z-axis.
Any further exact integrals of the equations of motion which commute with (1), (2), and (3), that is, whose Poisson brackets with (1), (2) and (3) vanish?	None believed to exist
Consequence of existence of integrals M, p_φ in addition to the energy E itself.	Barrier relevant for fission probability is not in general the E_b above but an E_b which depends upon M: $E_b(M)$.
Relation between general $E_b(M)$ and the elementary E_b	$E_b(\text{elementary}) = E_b(M = 0)$.
Behavior of $E_b(M)$ for small M	$E_b(M) \cong E_b(0) + \text{const}_1 M^2$
Minimum energy which undivided droplet of angular momentum M can have (relative to energy of undeformed nonrotating sphere)	$E_{\min}(M)$
Approximate expression for this energy for small M	$E_{\min}(M) \cong \text{const}_2 M^2$
Maximum angular momentum which droplet can have without falling apart immediately	$M = M_{\max}$
Equation defining this maximum angular momentum	$E_{\min}(M_{\max}) = E_b(M_{\max})$
Rough order of magnitude approximation to $M_{\max}$	$M_{\max} \sim \left[\dfrac{E_b(0)}{\text{const}_2 - \text{const}_1} \right]^{1/2}$

Table IX. (*continued*)

Properties of systems	Quantitative aspects
Statistical formula for probability of fission of droplet of specified M^2 and $p\varphi$ when energy E is only slightly in excess of the barrier energy $E_b(M)$	$A_f = \dfrac{\left(\begin{array}{l}\text{Integral over the } 2(3N\text{-}3) \text{ dimensional phase space of channels accessible at saddle with given } M^2, M_\varphi, \text{ and } E\end{array}\right)}{\dfrac{d}{dE}\left(\begin{array}{l}\text{Integral over the } 2(3N\text{-}2) \text{ dimensional phase space of bound states of given } M^2 \text{ and } M_\varphi \text{ with energy less than } E\end{array}\right)}$
A shorthand way of writing this equation [equivalent to Eq. (69) of text], with $d^{6N}\Omega$ symbolizing the entire phase space	$A_f = \dfrac{\displaystyle\int^{(6N-6)} \dfrac{d^{6N}\Omega}{d\alpha_{\text{fiss}}dp_{\text{fiss}}d\theta\;d\varphi\;dp_\theta\;dp_\varphi}}{\dfrac{d}{dE}\displaystyle\int^{(6N-4)}\dfrac{d^{6N}\Omega}{d\theta\;d\varphi\;dp_\theta\;dp_\varphi}}$
Is this fraction a well defined quantity in the case of an ideal fluid with its continuously infinite number of degrees of freedom (limit $N \to \infty$)?	Presumably not, because the more degrees of freedom there are available, the more ways there are to divide up the energy, and the less chance it will ever be concentrated on the mode of motion leading to fission. (Compare infinite heat capacity of black body cavity in strictly classical continuum treatment, where each degree of freedom sops up energy kT).
Conclusion from argument that $A_f \to 0$ in strict limit of classical continuum?	Necessary to take into account fact that system is actually composed of only a finite number of particles, or take into account quantum principle, or both.
Quantum transcription of formula for fission rate of systems with a given energy E and angular momentum I.	$\Gamma_{\text{fiss}}(E, I) = \hbar A_f$ $= \dfrac{1}{2\pi}\dfrac{N(E, I)}{(d/dE)n(E, I)} = (D/2\pi)N$ where N is number of channels and D is level spacing.
Any *approximate* integral of the equations of motion which might make simple channel theory of fission rate as inappropriate here as it is for escape of charged particles trapped in magnetic field?	Angular momentum K about approximate symmetry axis of extended fission form conserved—or nearly so—in act of scission and would be important if conserved for whole time of existence of compound nucleus. However, there is as yet no known evidence for such a conservation of K during the vibrations leading up to the fission saddle.

Transcribed into quantum language this expression takes the form

$$A_{\text{fiss}} = \frac{h^{3N-3}\begin{pmatrix}\text{number of channels accessible at energy } E \\ \text{with angular momentum quantum numbers } I \\ \text{and } I_z\end{pmatrix}}{(d/dE)h^{3N-}\begin{pmatrix}\text{number of states of compound system} \\ \text{with energy } E \text{ or less with angular mo-} \\ \text{mentum quantum numbers } I \text{ and } I_z\end{pmatrix}} \quad (70)$$

or

$$\Gamma_{\text{fiss}}(E, I) = \hbar A_f = \frac{1}{2\pi}\frac{N(E, I)}{(d/dE)n(E, I)} = (D/2\pi)N \quad (71)$$

Not knowing how to tell from theory whether there exists any appropriate first integral which would invalidate the simplest statistical approach, one is driven to test the channel analysis of fission by its consequences, of which this decay rate formula is one, and a prediction about the angular distribution of fission products is another.

3.   Distribution of Fission Products in Angle and in Mass

A. Quantum, Semiclassical, and Classical Descriptions of Angular Distribution

There is not a great difference between the considerations that govern the angular distribution of fission products and those that tell how those electrons will be distributed in direction which come out of a central potential with angular momentum l and magnetic quantum number m. The electron is described by a wave function of the form

$$Z(r, \theta, \varphi) = f(r)Y_{lm}(\theta, \varphi). \quad (72)$$

The probability to emergy into a unit solid angle in the direction specified by the polar angles θ and φ is proportional to the quantity

$$\left| Y_{lm}(\theta, \varphi) \right|^2 \quad (73)$$

independent of the details of the radial factor $f(r)$ and of the dependence of force upon distance. The angular distribution is spherically symmetric in the simplest case $l = 0, m = 0$

$$\left| Y_{00}(\theta, \varphi) \right|^2 = 1/4\pi \quad (74)$$

and spherically symmetrical only in this case. What is more, there is a simple classical interpretation for the angular distribution in the opposite limiting case of large l. In that limit the so-called Jeffrey-Wentzel-Kramers-Brillouin (JWKB) of large l. In that limit the so-called Jeffrey-Wentzel-Kramers-Brillouin (JWKB) treatment (Ke-37) gives the asymptotic formula

$$Y_{lm} \cong \frac{\exp(im\varphi)}{\pi[\sin^2\theta - m^2/(l + \frac{1}{2})^2]^{1/4}}$$
$$\times \sin\left\{(\pi/2) + \int_\theta^{\theta = \sin^{-1}[m/(l + 1/2)]} [(l + \frac{1}{2})^2 - m^2/\sin^2\theta]^{1/2} d\theta\right\} \qquad (75)$$

inside the classical limit of the motion

$$\sin\theta > m/(l + \frac{1}{2}),$$
$$-[1 - m^2/(l + \frac{1}{2})^2]^{1/2} < \cos\theta < [1 - m^2/(l + \frac{1}{2})^2]^{1/2} \qquad (76)$$

and Y_{lm} very small outside these limits. When the rapidly oscillating $\sin^2$ function in $|Y_{lm}|^2$ is replaced by its average value of $\frac{1}{2}$, expression (75) reduces to a formula which can be deduced directly (Fig. 5) from classical considerations:

$$|Y(\theta, \varphi)|^2_{\substack{\text{local} \\ \text{average}}} \cong \frac{1}{2\pi^2[\sin^2\theta - m^2/(l + \frac{1}{2})^2]^{1/2}} \qquad (77)$$

The mechanics of the separation of the two fission fragments is similar to the mechanics of the electron moving away from the center of force in this respect, that the elementary two body problem—through use of relative coordinates and a reduced mass—can always be reduced to an equivalent one body problem. However, the dividing nucleus differs from that elementary example in another regard: it is typically endowed with an angular momentum K about the separation axis, and an angular momentum which does not enter into the problem of a point particle. This angular momentum, when present, arises from

(1) angular momentum of collective rotation about the axis of extension, and

(2) angular momentum about the axis of extension due to individual unpaired nucleons.

In principle, there may exist also in the extended fission form

(3) angular momentum perpendicular to the axis of extension due to individual unpaired nucleons, and

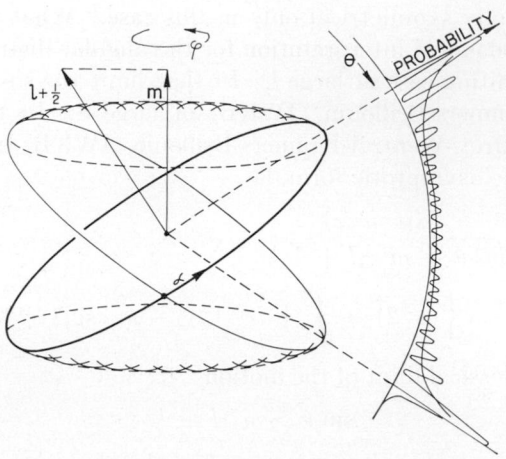

Figure 5. Angular distribution of particles emergent from a central field according to quantum mechanics (oscillatory dependence upon θ) and according to classical mechanics (smooth dependence upon θ in allowed region, zero value outside) for large values of the quantum numbers l and m. Details: The angular momentum $p_\varphi = m\hbar$ about the z-axis is fixed, so the angle φ is completely indeterminate, and all azimuths for the orbit are equally probable. It is enough to consider one orbit to derive the classical distribution in θ. The angle θ is connected with angle α of revolution in this orbit by the trigonometric relation

$$\cos\theta = [1 - m^2/(l + 1/2)^2]^{1/2}\sin \alpha$$

All values of α are equally probable. Normalized to the range $\alpha = -\pi/2$ to $\alpha = +\pi/2$ the element of probability is therefore

$$d(\text{probability}) = d\alpha/\pi = (d\alpha/d\theta)(d\theta/\pi)$$

$$= \frac{2\pi \sin\theta d\theta}{2\pi^2[\sin^2\theta - m^2/(l + 1/2)^2]^{1/2}}$$

The equivalent semiclassical value for the probability of emergence into a unit solid angle is

$$\left| Y_{lm} \right|^2_{\text{local average}} = (1/2\pi^2)[\sin^2\theta - m^2/(l + 1/2)^2]^{-1/2}$$

(4) lack of rotational symmetry about the axis of extension, as in the familiar mechanical problem of a rotor whose three moments of inertia are unequal.

However, both of these effects have been neglected in accounts to date of the angular distribution in fission (Bo56, Wi56, St57a, Ha58, Gr59). They are occasionally significant in the much less extended configurations of nuclei in their ground states or in states of low excitation (Ke56). However there is no evidence for either effect in any angular distributions of fission products observed to date.

In the absence of effects 3 and 4 the dynamics of the dividing nucleus is compared with the dynamics of a symmetric top. The axis of symmetry of the top is identified with the axis of extension of the fission form before scission, and after scission with the direction of separation. In other words, the probability distribution in direction of fission fragments is taken to be the same as the probability distribution in direction of the symmetry axis of a symmetric top which has

(1) the same total angular momentum quantum number I,

(2) the same quantum number M for the component of the angular momentum about the space-fixed Z-axis (to be distinguished from the symbol M^2 used for the square of the total angular momentum in Table IX), and

(3) the same quantum number K for the component of the angular momentum about the symmetry axis (top) or the axis of extension (fission form).

Effects on the direction of the fission fragments due to neutron evaporation and α-particle emission are neglected.

There is an important difference between K and the other two quantum numbers, I and M. The constancy of I and M throughout the act of fission is guaranteed by the law of conservation of angular momentum. However, the quantity $K\hbar$, "the angular momentum about an axis of approximate rotational symmetry in the nucleus," is not even defined for shapes which depart greatly from such symmetry. Moreover, it is natural to suppose that the nucleus typically has to go through many vibrations, many changes of shape, and much redistribution of energy and angular momentum before it arrives at the transition state or saddle point. Therefore, insofar as K might have had a meaning for the original compound nucleus, and insofar as it does have a meaning for the dividing nucleus, the initial and final K-values may have no relation to each other. The migration of the system from the original K-value to the final one is a quantum mechanical process. This process has a classical analog. This analog is the migration of the representative point of a classical mechanical system in configuration space as illustrated in the example of Fig. 3. The opening in the figure from which trapped particles may escape corresponds in the case of fission to the collection of channels which are accessible from the given state of the compound nucleus—a state specified by given E, I, M, and parity.   Each channel has a K-value of its own.   If each channel were open ($W = 1$), the contribution of that channel to the average fission width $\langle \Gamma_f \rangle$ of levels of the compound nucleus of the given character (E, I, M, π) would be $(1/2\,\pi)$ times the average spacing of levels of that character.   For any specific level of this character in the compound nucleus the relevant partial width for fission will typically be greater or less than this average—even for a fully open channel.   Moreover, the channel opening W will drop significantly below unity when the barrier height for the channel in question exceeds about $E - (\tfrac{1}{4})$ Mev, where E is the available energy.

So much for entry into a channel of a given K-value a little before the saddle point for fission!   But once at or past the summit of the barrier and on the way towards scission, the nucleus has a highly deformed shape which is reasonably considered as nearly axially symmetric, in the sense that K remains a good quantum number.   That K is conserved upon entry into a fission channel is also suggested by the success of this assumption in accounting for the angular distribution in fission.

The concept of a well defined K-value is not normally reasonable to apply to the history of the compound nucleus before the time of passage over the barrier in a specific fission channel.   Even in spontaneous fission (Wh55) out of the ground state of an odd-even or odd-odd nucleus it is not believed that the angular momentum K about the axis of extension is conserved during the process of tunneling through the barrier.   Only during barrier penetration from the ground state of an even-even nucleus does it appear that K remains constant $(K = 0)$.

So much for the mechanics of the choosing of the channels through which fission is going to occur and the significance of K for such a channel.   Now for the angular distribution of the fission associated with one of these channels!

It might be thought that the distribution in direction of the symmetry axis of the top (described by polar angles θ and φ) would depend not only upon the numbers I, M, and K but also upon the moments of inertia $I_{\parallel}$ about the symmetry axis and $I_{\perp}$ about any perpendicular axis.   However, this is not the case.   The probability distribution is given by a function $D_{MK}^{I}(\varphi, \theta, \chi)$,

$$d(\text{probability}) = \frac{2I + 1}{4\pi} \left| D^I_{MK}(\varphi, \theta, \chi) \right|^2 2\pi \sin \theta \, d\theta \qquad (78)$$

which is universal, in the sense that it is independent of the moments of inertia. The square of its absolute value depends on θ but not on φ nor on the angle χ of rotation about the symmetry axis. It is true that the moments of inertia enter into the expression for the energy and therefore also for the wave equation of the rotator:

$$\frac{\hbar^2}{2I_\perp} \left[\frac{1}{\sin \theta} \frac{\partial}{\partial \theta} \left(\sin \theta \frac{\partial \psi}{\partial \theta} \right) + \frac{\left(\cos \theta \dfrac{\partial}{\partial \chi} - \dfrac{\partial}{\partial \varphi} \right)^2 \psi}{\sin^2 \theta} \right] + \frac{\hbar^2}{2I_\parallel} \frac{\partial^2 \psi}{\partial \chi^2}$$

$$+ \, E\psi = 0 \quad (79)$$

However, the solution of this equation by the method of separation of variables (Pa35)

$$\psi = D^I_{MK}(\varphi, \theta, \chi) = e^{iM\varphi} \, d(\theta) e^{iK\chi}, \qquad (80)$$

with

$$E = \frac{\hbar^2 [I(I + 1) - K^2]}{2I_\perp} + \frac{\hbar^2 K^2}{2I_\parallel} \qquad (81)$$

leads to an equation for the decisive factor $d(\theta)$ which is free of $I_\parallel$ and $I_\perp$:

$$\sin \theta \, \frac{d}{d\theta} \, \sin \theta \, \frac{d \, d(\theta)}{d\theta}$$

$$+ \, [I(I + 1)\sin^2 \theta - M^2 - K^2 + 2MK \cos \theta](d\theta) = 0 \quad (82)$$

For large values of the quantum number I of total angular momentum, the solution of this equation within the classically allowed region of motion is given to good approximation by the JWKB or semiclassical expression

$$d(\theta) = \frac{(2/\pi)^{1/2}}{[\quad]^{1/4}} \sin \left\{ (\pi/4) + \int_{\theta_{\min}}^{\theta} [\quad]^{1/2} \, (d\theta/\sin \theta) \right\} \quad (83)$$

Here the square bracket is an abbreviation for the quantity

$$[\quad] = (I + \tfrac{1}{2})^2 \sin^2\theta - M^2 - K^2 + 2MK \cos \theta \qquad (84)$$

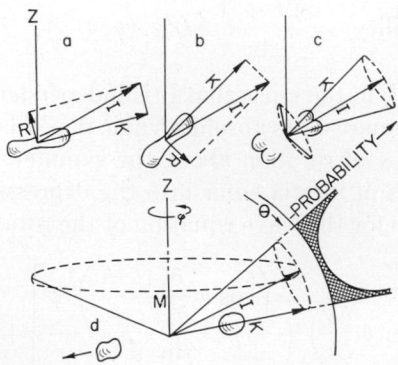

Figure 6. Semiclassical account of probability distribution in angle of fission fragments from nucleus of given quantum numbers, I of total angular momentum and M of angular momentum about the Z-axis, passing over the fission barrier in a channel of angular momentum $K\hbar$ about the axis of extension—and undergoing division with this same angular momentum. All diagrams refer to the special case where K constitutes a large part of I and where the angular momentum $R\hbar = \hbar[I(I+1) - K^2]^{1/2}$ about an axis at right angles to the symmetry axis is small by comparison. (a) Orientation of angular momentum vectors at one moment of time. The rotation of the extended fission form about the axis R by a small angle is equivalent to a rotation of the same figure about the axis I by a small angle. Continuation of this rotation carries the fission form to the orientation of (b) In consequence the angular momentum vectors K and R precess about I as shown in (c). If the orientation of I in space were well determined, then, according to this analysis, the fission fragments from one end of the fission form would go into a well-defined circle in space, of angular radius $\alpha = \cos^{-1}(K/I)$. However, the angular momentum $M\hbar$ about the Z-axis is well determined. Consequently, all values of the conjugate azimuthal angle φ occur with equal probability. The angular distribution to be expected semiclassically is therefore (d) that due to a circular spray of angular radius α, whose center is swung around the dashed arc centered on the Z-axis. This probability distribution, on being calculated, leads to [Eq. (85)] of the text.

The normalization is such that the probability (78) integrates to 1. That the JWKB approximation is not bad for a value of I as low as 1 is shown by the comparison of the semiclassical and accurate value of D_{00}^1 in Fig. 7. However, more valuable for insight into the physics of the angular distribution is the limiting value for large I, when the rapidly fluctuating $\sin^2$ function can be replaced for many purposes by the average value of $\frac{1}{2}$. Then one finds for the probability for that fission fragment which stands at the positive end of the vector **K** to go into the interval $d\theta$ the result

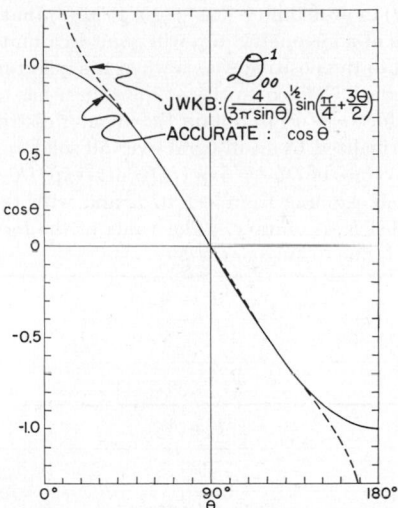

Figure 7. Semiclassical or JWKB formula for the angular distribution factor D_{00}^{1} compared with the accurate value, showing that the high quantum number approximation is not very bad for a value of the total angular momentum quantum number I as low as 1. For $I = 0$ the agreement is worse; the exact value of D_{00}^{1} is 1, whereas the JWKB value is $(4/\pi \sin\theta)^{1/2} \sin (\pi/4 + \theta/2)$, with the values listed here:

θ	10°	20°	30°	40°	50°	60°	70°	80°	90°
D_{00}^{1}(JWKB)	2.08	1.58	1.38	1.28	1.21	1.17	1.15	1.14	1.13

$$d(\text{probability}) = \frac{(2I + 1)}{4\pi} d^2(\theta) 2\pi \sin d\theta$$

$$\cong \frac{(d\theta/\pi)}{\left[1 - \dfrac{M^2 + K^2 - 2MK \cos \theta}{(I + \frac{1}{2})^2 \sin^2 \theta}\right]^{1/2}} \tag{85}$$

[Insert in Eq. (85) $(\pi - \theta)$ for θ, add to Eq. (85), and divide by 2 to get the properly symmetrized angular distribution.] This probability distribution has a simple classical interpretation (Bo56, Wi56, St57, Ha58, Gr59; see also Fig. 6). Table X lists formulas for the angular distribution and Table XI gives a thumbnail summary of the simplest ideas about angular distribution. Figure 8 gives the same conclusions in diagrammatic form. (See Mu30, Mu31, and Mu32 for a discussion of the corresponding molecular problem.)

Table X. Factor d(θ) in probability $[(2I + 1)/4\pi]d^2(\theta)$ that specified end of symmetry axis of a symmetric top will point in a unit solid angle at the inclination θ to the positive Z-axis when the quantum numbers I, M, and K are specified. This quantity at the value θ has to be supplemented by the value for $(\pi - \theta)$ to obtain the angular distribution of fission fragments, normalized to an integral over all solid angles equal to 2. The matrix of values of $D^I_{MK} = \exp(iM\varphi)d(\theta)\exp(iK\chi)$ for fixed I, with the row label M running from $-I$ to I, and with the same range for the column label K, is unitary. The value of the factor $d(\theta)$ for general I, M, and K is due to Wigner (Wi59).

$I = 0$	
$M \backslash K$	0
0	1

$I = \frac{1}{2}$		
$M \backslash K$	$\frac{1}{2}$	$\frac{1}{2}$
$-\frac{1}{2}$	$\cos(\theta/2)$	$-\sin(\theta/2)$
$\frac{1}{2}$	$\sin(\theta/2)$	$\cos(\theta/2)$

$M \backslash K$	$I = 1$		
	-1	0	1
-1	$(1 + \cos\theta)/2$	$-(\sin\theta)/2^{1/2}$	$(1 - \cos\theta)/2$
0	$(\sin\theta)/2^{1/2}$	$\cos\theta$	$-(\sin\theta)/2^{1/2}$
1	$(1 - \cos\theta)/2$	$\sin\theta/2^{1/2}$	$(1 + \cos\theta)/2$

$I = \,^3/_2$ with c $= \cos(\theta/2)$, s $= \sin(\theta/2)$

$M \backslash K$	$-\frac{3}{2}$	$-\frac{1}{2}$	$\frac{1}{2}$	$\frac{3}{2}$
$-\frac{3}{2}$	c^3	$-3^{1/2}c^2s$	$3^{1/2}cs^2$	$-s^3$
$-\frac{1}{2}$	$3^{1/2}c^2s$	$c^3 - 2cs^2$	$s^3 - 2c^2s$	$3^{1/2}cs^2$
$\frac{1}{2}$	$3^{1/2}cs^2$	$2c^2s - s^3$	$c^3 - 2cs^2$	$-3^{1/2}c^2s$
$\frac{3}{2}$	s^3	$3^{1/2}cs^2$	$3^{1/2}c^2s$	c^3

$I = 2$ with c $= \cos(\theta/2)$, s $= \sin(\theta/2)$

$M \backslash K$	-3	-1	0	1	2
-2	c^4	$-2sc^3$	$6^{1/2}s^2c^2$	$-2s^3c$	s^4
-1	$2sc^3$	$c^4 - 3s^2c^2$	$6^{1/2}(s^3c - sc^3)$	$3s^2c^2 - s^4$	$-2s^3c$
0	$6^{1/2}s^2c^2$	$6^{1/2}(sc^3 - s^3c)$	$(c^4 - 4c^2s^2 + s^4)*$	$6^{1/2}(s^3c - sc^3)$	$6^{1/2}s^2c^2$
1	$2s^3c$	$3s^2c^2 - s^4$	$6^{1/2}(sc^3 - s^3c)$	$c^4 - 3s^2c^2$	$-2sc^3$
2	s^4	$2s^3c$	$6^{1/2}s^2c^2$	$2sc^3$	c^4

* Or $(3\cos^2\theta - 1)/2$.

Table X (continued)

---

(1) General $d(\theta) = \sum_n (-1)^n \dfrac{[(I + K)!(I - K)!(I + M)!(I - M)!]^{1/2}}{(I - M - n)!(I + K - n)!n!(n + M - K)!}$

$$\times \cos^{2I + K - M - 2n}(\theta/2) \sin^{2n + M - K}(\theta/2).$$

In the classically allowed region for large I

$$d^2(\theta)_{\substack{\text{local} \\ \text{average}}} \cong \frac{1}{\pi[(I + \frac{1}{2})^2 \sin^2 \theta - M^2 - K^2 + 2MK \cos \theta]^{1/2}}$$

The belt of intensity extends from $\theta_{\min}$ = the smallest of θ_1 and θ_2 to $\theta_{\max}$ = the largest of θ_1 and θ_2, and is most concentrated at these limits. Here

$$\theta_1 = |(I^*K) - (I^*M)| \text{ modulo } \pi$$

and

$$\theta_1 = |(I^*K) + (I^*M)| \text{ modulo } \pi$$

with

$$\cos (I^*M) = M/(I + \tfrac{1}{2}) \text{ and } \cos (I^*K) = K/(I + \tfrac{1}{2}).$$

---

(2) Case $M = I$: $d(\theta) = \left[\dfrac{2I!}{(I - K)!(I + K)!} \right]^{1/2} \cos^{I+K} (\theta/2) \sin^{I-K} (\theta/2)$

For large I, concentrated in a sharp ring near $\cos \theta = K/I$. For $|K|$ not too close to 1,

$$d(\theta) \cong \frac{(I/\pi)^{1/4}}{(I^2 - K^2)^{1/4}} e^{-I^3(\cos \theta - K/I)^2/2(I^2 - K^2)}$$

---

(3) Case $M = 0$: $d(\theta) = (-1)^K [4\pi/(2I + 1)]^{1/2} Y_{IK}(\theta, \chi)/e^{iK\chi}$; and in the classically allowed region, for large I,

$$d^2(\theta) \cong \frac{1}{\pi[(I + \frac{1}{2})^2 \sin^2 \theta - K^2]^{1/2}}.$$

The belt of intensity extends north and south from the equator to limits at $\sin \theta = K/(I + \frac{1}{2})$, or $\theta = (\pi/2) \pm \sin^{-1}[1 - K^2/(I + \frac{1}{2})^2]^{1/2}$, and is strongest at these limits.

For $K = I$, sharp concentration in equatorial plane:

$$d^2(\theta) \cong \frac{1}{\pi^{1/2}I^{1/2}} e^{-I(\theta - \pi/2)^2}$$

---

(4) Case $M = -I$: $d(\theta) = (-1)^{I+K} \left[\dfrac{2I!}{(I - K)!(I + K)!} \right]^{1/2}$

$$\times \cos^{I-K} (\theta/2) \sin^{I+K} (\theta/2)$$

Table X (continued)

For large I, concentrated in a sharp ring near $\cos \theta = -K/I$.
For $|K|$ not too close to 1,

$$d(\theta) \cong (-1)^{I+K} \frac{(I/\pi)^{1/4}}{(I^2 - K^2)^{1/4}} e^{-I^3(\cos \theta + K/I)^2/2(I^2 - K^2)}$$

---

(5) Case $K = I$: $d(\theta) = (-1)^{I+K} \left[\frac{2I!}{(I - M)!(I + M)!} \right]^{1/2}$

$$\times \cos^{I+M} (\theta/2) \sin^{I-M} (\theta/2)$$

Sharp ring near $\cos \theta = M/I$; refer to case 2 and in it replace K by M.

---

(6) Case $K = 0$: $d(\theta) = [4\pi/(2I + 1)]^{1/2} Y_{IM}(\theta, \varphi)/e^{iM\varphi}$;
belt of intensity reaching north and south from equator to limits
$\theta = (\pi/2) \pm \sin^{-1}[1 - M^2/(I + \frac{1}{2})^2]^{1/2}$, or from $\sin \theta = 1$ to $\sin \theta = M/(I + \frac{1}{2})$. See case (3). For $M = I$, sharp concentration in equatorial plane:

$$d^2(\theta) \cong \frac{1}{(\pi I)^{1/2}} e^{-I(\theta - \pi/2)^2}$$

---

(7) Case $K = -I$: $d(\theta) = \left[\frac{2I!}{(I - M)!(I + M)!} \right]^{1/2} \cos^{I-M} (\theta/2) \sin^{I+M} (\theta/2)$

For large I sharp ring near $\cos \theta = -M/I$.

---

(8) Case $K = 0$, $M = 0$. $d(\theta) = P_I(\theta)$. For large I this reduces at small θ to $J_0([I + \frac{1}{2}]\theta)$, going over for $\sin \theta \gg 1/(I + \frac{1}{2})$ to

$$\left[\frac{2}{\pi(I + \frac{1}{2}) \sin \theta} \right]^{1/2} \sin [(\pi/4) + (I + \frac{1}{2})\theta].$$

Also

$$\underset{\substack{\text{local} \\ \text{average}}}{d^2(\theta)} \cong \frac{1}{\pi(I + \frac{1}{2}) \sin \theta}$$

The classical picture is emission in the plane $\varphi = \text{const.}$ with all values of θ equally probable, and then the superposition of such emission patterns for all values of φ.

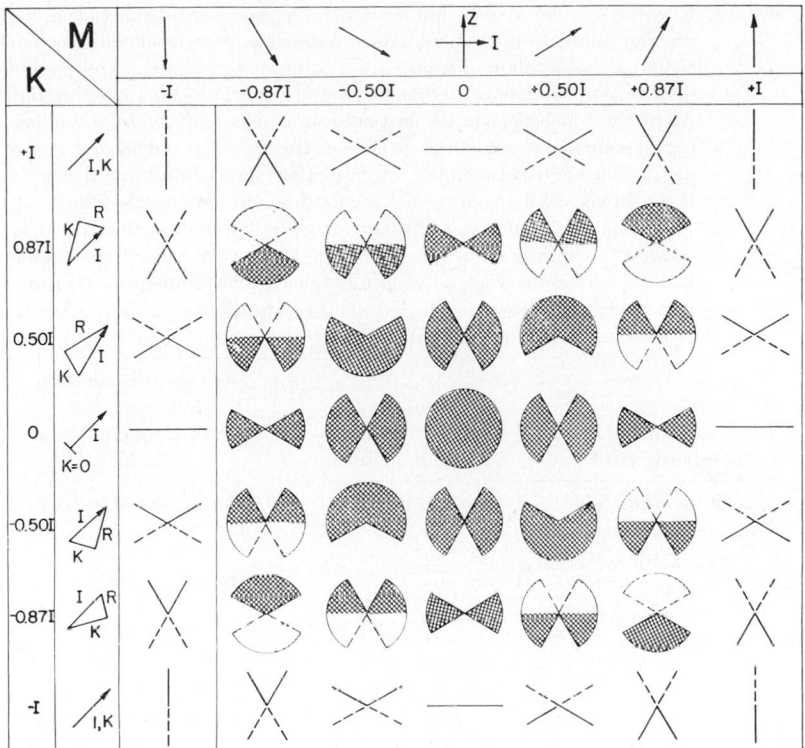

Figure 8. Angular region allowed for fission fragment emission as calculated semiclassically. The more darkly shaded areas indicate the allowed region as given by [Eq. (85)]. The more lightly shaded areas or dashed lines indicate the allowed region as given by the same formula with θ replaced by $\pi - \theta$. The two have to be added to give the angular distribution of *either* the heavy fragments *or* the light fragments; there is no difference in the angular distribution of the two kinds of fission products.

B. Large Anisotropy Just Above Threshold

Angular anisotropies in the emission of fission fragments were first observed in photofission by Winhold, Demos, and Halpern (Wi52) and then in fission induced by neutrons in the range of 1 Mev by Henkel and Brolley (Br55, He56). In both cases the observed anisotropies are large and striking when the target has *even-even* character and when the bombarding energy is near or not much greater than

Table XI. Effect of angular momentum brought in by bombarding particle and of
angular momentum K about axis of extension, associated with the particular channel followed from barrier summit to scission, upon angular
distribution of fission fragments in the semiclassical approximation.
All of the conclusions in the last column can be derived by the following sequence of arguments: (a) From the specified values of I and M
deduce the angle between the total angular momentum I and the space-
fixed Z-axis. All azimuths of I about this axis are equally likely. (b)
From the values of I and K deduce the angle between the axis of extension—and ultimate fission—of the nucleus and I. (c) Perpendicular
to K in the right triangle IKR stands the angular momentum R of rotation about an axis perpendicular to the extension axis. All azimuths
of K about I are equally probable

Conditions of bombardment	Orientation of total angular momentum	Angular distribution associated with fission through channel of specified K
(1) None–spontaneous fission of even-even nucleus; $I = 0$.	Unorientable	Uniform. In addition $K = 0$.
(2) Spontaneous fission of nucleus with $I \gg 0$.	Unoriented	Uniform, regardless of K.
(3) Spontaneous fission of nucleus with $I \gg 0$.	I oriented along Z- or $-Z$-axis by external magnetic field or by quadrupole electric field internal to a molecule ($M = \pm I$).	(a) For $K = I$, sharp concentration of fragments along $\pm Z$ directions (north and south poles) because K is parallel to I. (b) For $K = 0$, sharp concentration of products in equatorial plane. (Almost all of angular momentum is in component R of rotation which in nucleus is perpendicular to axis of extension, and which in space is nearly parallel to I—or nearly parallel or antiparallel to the Z-axis.) (c) For intermediate K, concentration in one sharp ring at an intermediate angle between north pole and equator and a symmetrically located ring in southern hemisphere.

Table XI (continued)

Conditions of bombardment	Orientation of total angular momentum	Angular distribution associated with fission through channel of specified K
(4) Spontaneous fission of nucleus with $I \gg 0$.	I oriented perpendicular to Z axis by quadrupole electric field internal to a molecule ($M = 0$).	(a) For $K = I$, sharp concentration of emission into equatorial plane.
		(b) For $K = 0$, all values of θ are equally likely: d (probability) $= d\theta/\pi = \dfrac{d(\text{solid angle})}{2\pi^2 \sin \theta}$; fore and aft concentration of intensity.
		(c) For intermediate K, a tropical belt of intensity reaching north and south from the equator to an intermediate angle, and strongest at those two limits.
(5) Incident particle brings in zero or a very small angular momentum because it is slow or because it makes a head-on impact.	Analysis similar to cases (1, 2, 3, 4) of spontaneous fission	Only those channels are accessible for which K is less than or equal to I. The quantity I in turn is governed almost entirely by the spin of the target nucleus.
(6) Incident particle brings in by peripheral impact an angular momentum I which is so big that the original angular momentum of the nucleus is negligible by comparison.	I large. $M \sim I$. (Angular momentum vector pointing perpendicular to Z-axis, in random azimuth.)	Analysis similar to case (4) of spontaneous fission.

the threshold value. Wilets and Chase (Wi56) explained this result in terms of the channel picture of fission (Bo39, Bo56) in this way: At an energy near the fission threshold typically only one fission channel is accessible. This channel has its own particular K-value.

The very special angular distribution associated with this one channel shows up clear and free of interference from contributions from other channels. For this purpose energy discrimination is required narrower than the energy interval between the lowest channel and the next higher channel.

The spacing between channels at the point of passage over the fission barrier is expected to be qualitatively similar for a given nucleus to the spacing between low-lying energy levels of the same nucleus. In particular, the lowest channel of an *even-even* nucleus, like the lowest energy level, will be anticipated to be of the order of 1 Mev below the next highest level. This energy separation is quite sufficient to allow the lowest channel to be picked out cleanly in γ-ray irradiation of an even-even target, despite the fact that the γ-ray spectrum used in such studies has the character of a descending step rather than a delta function of energy.

Why then should it not be even easier with monoenergetic neutron irradiation of an even-odd nucleus (U^{233}, U^{235}, Pu^{239}) to pick out sharply the lowest channel of the resulting even-even compound nucleus? Because the heat of condensation of the neutron is so great, due to formation of a new neutron pair, that it typically exceeds the fission barrier by an amount of the order of 1 Mev or more, thereby presumably making two or more channels accessible. Moreover, the calculated contribution of a new channel to the yield effective channel number, N_f (Fig. 2), rises sharply over a few times 0.1 Mev nearly to its full value of 1. Therefore the contribution of the additional channels to the angular distribution is mixed in to full force—or to some substantial fraction of full force—with the angular distribution due the lowest channel, $K = 0$, even under irradiation with neutrons of the lowest possible energy.

Neutron bombardment of an even-even target (Th^{232}, U^{234}, U^{236}, U^{238}, Pu^{240}) is much more favorable to seeing the contribution of the lowest channel to the angular distribution of fission fragments. The saddle point energy E_f of the lowest channel is anywhere from $\frac{1}{2}$ Mev to $1\frac{1}{2}$ Mev greater than the excitation made available by the addition of the neutron—the neutron binding B_n. To pass over the saddle the nucleus must be provided with the supplementary energy of the order of 1 Mev through kinetic energy of bombardment. At such an energy the energy resolution is adequate to distinguish the contribution of the lowest channel from that of a channel above it by

0.2 Mev or 0.3 Mev or more.   Whether the actual spacing of the lowest two fission channels in any given odd-A nucleus will be greater
than or less than 0.2 Mev or 0.3 Mev cannot be predicted in advance.
The remarkable discovery in U^{235} of a $I = \frac{1}{2}{}^+$ level raised above the
$I = \frac{7}{2}{}^-$ ground state by only a few *tens* of ev (Fr57, Mi57, As57,
Si57) is warning enough of the statistical character of level spacings!
But available evidence indicates that the average distance to the first
level of nucleonic or intrinsic excitation in odd-A nuclei in the region
of the fissile nuclei is of the order of 0.2 Mev.   With a similar spacing
for the two lowest fission channels in odd-A nuclei there is good chance
by neutron bombardment of appropriate even-even nuclei (U^{234},
U^{236}, U^{238}, Th^{232}) to see the effect of the lowest channel by itself, in
conformity with the strong anisotropies which have been observed in
the angular distribution near threshold (He56, La60).

C. Energy Levels of Saddle Point Nucleus

In any account of the angular distribution associated with
specific channels it is appropriate to look in more detail at the pattern
of states to be expected in the transition state configuration.   Two
differences between this pattern and the spectrum of normal nuclei
stand out at once.   (a) With respect to the degree of freedom which
leads to fission the energy presents a maximum, not a minimum.   This
coordinate for the normal nucleus is associated with vibrations which
come into the count of energy levels.   At the saddle there is no such
vibration in this coordinate.   The spectrum of the transition state
nucleus will differ from that of a typical nucleus near its ground state
in not having any of the vibrational levels that are normally associated with the coordinate α_2 in the expression

$$R(\theta) = R[1 + \alpha_2 P_2(\cos \theta)] \tag{85a}$$

The count of channels up to a given energy in excess of the lowest
barrier on this account will be less than might otherwise have been
expected.   The degree of freedom α_2 plays its part, but does so in a
way quite different from that of any of the other configuration coordinates.   The dynamics of α_2 and of the conjugate momentum p_2
have *already* been taken into account in the theory of the reaction rate
in the derivation of the formula

$$\langle \Gamma_f \rangle = N_f D/2\pi \tag{86}$$

Table XII. Moments of inertia of heavy *even-even* nuclei about an axis perpendicular to the axis of the equilibrium extension.* Data for column 2, based on the observed rotational spectra, taken from the summary of E. K. Hyde (Hy59; see also St58, Mo59). In the last column the moment of inertia for a rigid sphere has been calculated from the formula $\Im_{\text{rigid sphere}} = \frac{2}{5}$ (mass) (radius)^2 = $\frac{2}{5}A^{5/3}M_p r_0^2$ with r_0 = 1.216×10^{-13} cm. The figures in the last two rows refer to the liquid drop model, and to the transition state configuration of a droplet with fissility parameter $x = 0.74$, corresponding approximately to nuclei like uranium. Swiatecki (communication of results not yet published) finds for the saddle point configuration for this x, including harmonics up to the sixth order,

$$R(\theta) = R_0 a_1(1 + \alpha_2 P_2 + \alpha_4 P_4 + \alpha_6 P_6)$$

with $\alpha_2 = 0.70$, $\alpha_4 = 0.19$, $\alpha_6 = 0.01$ and hence (for normalization) $a_1 = 0.906$. For a rigid body of this shape the moment of inertia around an axis perpendicular to the axis of symmetry can be calculated to be $\Im = 2.12\Im_{\text{rigid sphere}}$.

Nucleus	$\hbar^2/2\Im\perp$	$\hbar^2/2\Im_{\text{rigid sphere}}$	$\Im\perp/\Im_{\text{rigid sphere}}$
Ra^{222}	18.67 kev	4.34 kev	0.232
Ra^{224}	14.08	4.28	0.304
Ra^{226}	11.27	4.21	0.374
Ra^{228}	9.7	4.15	0.428
Th^{226}	12.02	4.21	0.350
Th^{228}	9.58	4.15	0.433
Th^{230}	8.73	4.09	0.468
Th^{232}	8.33	4.03	0.484
Th^{234}	8.00	3.98	0.498
U^{230}	7.83	4.09	0.522
U^{232}	7.92	4.03	0.509
U^{234}	7.25	3.98	0.549
U^{236}	7.55	3.92	0.519
U^{238}	7.50	3.87	0.516
Pu^{236}	7.2	3.92	0.544
Pu^{238}	7.37	3.87	0.525
Pu^{240}	7.16	3.81	0.532
Pu^{242}	7.43	3.76	0.506
Cm^{242}	7.02	3.76	0.536
Cm^{246}	7.15	3.66	0.512
Cm^{248}	7.23	3.61	0.499
Cf^{250}	7.00	3.56	0.509

* Liquid drop model, constants of Table XIII, rigid body moments of inertia, evaluated for U^{236} assuming $x = 0.74$:

Normal sphere	3.92 kev	3.92 kev	1.00
Saddle shape	1.85	3.92	2.12

(b) The second difference from normal nuclei is this, that the transition state nucleus is much more extended, and—about an axis perpendicular to the direction of extension—has a greater moment of inertia than do normal nuclei. The low-lying levels associated with the collective rotation of heavy even-even nuclei are represented to a good approximation (Hy59, Da58, Da59, Sh60) by the formula of A. Bohr (Bo52, Al56),

$$E = \hbar^2 I(I + 1)/2\Im_\perp (I - 0, 2, 4, \ldots .) \qquad (87)$$

with the values of the inertial parameter summarized in the following table. For the sake of definiteness the nuclear constants of Green have been adopted (Table XIII). The normal nucleus (U^{236}, for example) has rotational energy states at excitations of the order $E = 0$ kev ($I = 0$); 45 kev ($I = 2$) (observed 44.2 kev); 150 kev ($I = 4$); 320 kev ($I = 6$). The transition state configuration of the same nucleus, on the other hand, is calculated from the liquid drop model (last row of table) to have rotational excitations at the saddle, of 0 kev ($I = 0$); 11 kev ($I = 2$); 37 kev ($I = 4$); etc.

It might be asked if it is right to add these quantities to the energy of the saddle for $I = 0$ in order to obtain the channel energies for other values of I. Will not the extra pull of centrifugal force in a rotating configuration depress the base-line figure E_f itself, upon which one proposes to add the rotational energy? No! The effect of the centrifugal forces is already included in an extra term in the potential energy:

$$V_{\text{effective}} (\alpha) = V_{\text{surf}}(\alpha) + V_{\text{elec}}(\alpha) + \frac{\hbar^2 I(I + 1)}{2\Im(\alpha)} \qquad (88)$$

The generalized force associated with any given coordinate—as for example an appropriate extension coordinate—is found by taking the negative of the derivative of this expression with respect to that coordinate. The effect of centrifugal forces does not have to be added as still another term! Or, in other words, the effect of the rotational perturbation upon the barrier energy is found in first approximation by evaluating the perturbation energy at the position of the unperturbed barrier, as was just done (Pi58).

D. *Contribution of One Rotational Band to N_f*

Do the different levels of collective rotation of the extended saddle point form that belong to the same rotational band all con-

Table XIII. Conventional values for average properties of nuclear matter adopted in the present article, based on Green's evaluation of the constants in the semiempirical mass formula (Gr54). If fission thresholds as calculated by the liquid drop model are to be given substantial weight in any readjustment of the constants, then the new value of x for nuclear near uranium will be closer to $x = 0.77$, for which the dimensionless measure of barrier height $\zeta(x) = 0.0080$ (Swiatecki) or $E_f \sim (680 \text{ Mev}) \times (0.0080) = 5.45$ Mev

Physical quantity	Relevant constant	General expression	Value for U^{236} ($A^{1/3} = 6.1797$)
Radius	$r_0 = 1.216 \times 10^{-13}$ cm	$A^{1/3} r_0$	7.515×10^{-13} cm
Mass	$M_1{}^* = 1.660 \times 10^{-24}$ g	$A M_1$	3.918×10^{-22} g
Moment of inertia	$\frac{2}{5} M_1 r_0^2 = 0.982 \times 10^{-70}$ g-cm^2	$\frac{2}{5} M_1 r_0^2 A^{5/3}$	8.850×10^{-47} g-cm^2
Rotational energy	$\dfrac{\hbar^2}{\frac{4}{5} M_1 r_0^2} = 35,340$ kev	$\dfrac{\text{This}}{A^{5/3}}$	3.921 kev
Surface energy	$4\pi r_0^2 \sigma = 0.01912$ AMU $= 17.80$ Mev	This $\times A^{2/3}$	679.8 Mev
Coulomb energy	$3e^2/5r_0 = 7.628 \times 10^{-4}$ AMU $= 0.710$ Mev	This $\times (Z^2/A^{1/3})$	972.4 Mev
Fissility parameter	$\left(\dfrac{Z^2}{A}\right)_{\text{crit}} = 50.13$	$x = \dfrac{(Z^2/A)}{(Z^2/A)_{\text{crit}}}$	0.7154
Energy $\hbar\omega_2$ of lowest mode ($\lambda = 2$) of vibration	$\left(\frac{8}{3} 4\pi r_0^2 \sigma \dfrac{\hbar^2}{M_1 r_0^2}\right)^{1/2} = 36.63$ Mev	This $\times \left(\dfrac{1-x}{A}\right)^{1/2}$	1.272 Mev

tribute to the number of channels N_f available for fission? Yes and no!

It will be recalled in using the reaction rate formula that the average level width $\langle \Gamma_f \rangle$ is associated with a well-defined region E of the spectrum and with a sharply specified quantum number of total angular momentum I (and parity π) of the compound nucleus; similarly for the level spacing D and the number of channels N_f:

$$\langle \Gamma_f(E, I, \pi) \rangle = [D(E, I, \pi)/2\pi]N_f(E, I, \pi) \qquad (89)$$

In other words, a given rotational band contains only one level of the given spin and parity, and makes only a unit contribution to N_f—if it makes any contribution at all (see Table XIV).

Table XIV. Contribution of the lowest rotational band ($K = 0$) of an even-even nucleus to the number of channels N_f effective for fission. Here $W(E - E_b)$ is the channel opening [Eq. (4) and Appendix A] associated with a barrier or channel of energy E_b.

Spin and parity of the compound nucleus	Contribution of lowest band to N_f	Height E_b of given channel	Angular distribution of fission in case $M = 0$
0^+	$W(E - E_{b_0})$	E_f	$1/4\pi$
0^-	none	—	—
1^+	none	—	—
1^-	none	—	—
2^+	$W(E - E_{b_2})$	$E_f + 6(\hbar^2/2\mathfrak{I}_{\text{saddle}})$	$(5/4\pi)P_2^2(\cos\theta)$
2^-	none	—	—
3^+	none	—	—
3^-	none	—	—
4^+	$W(E - E_{b_4})$	$E_f + 20(\hbar^2/2\mathfrak{I}_{\text{saddle}})$	$(9/4\pi)P_4^2(\cos\theta)$
etc.			

So far it has been supposed that the even-even compound nucleus has been formed in a state of well-defined E, I, π. Consider in contrast the case where the compound nucleus comes into being by union of a nucleus of *even Z-odd N* with a neutron of 1 Mev. Let the target nucleus be one of small spin—for example, $\frac{1}{2}^+$—so that most of the angular momentum of the compound nucleus is contributed by the incoming neutron ($l_{\max} \approx R_0/\lambda \approx 7.5 \times 10^{-13}/4.55 \times 10^{-13} \approx 2$). Then compound nuclei will be formed in states of the type

listed in the first six or eight rows of Table XIV, and with small
M-value. The angular distribution of fission fragments will be given
approximately by a linear combination of the expressions in the last
column of the table for $I = 0^+$ and $I = 2^+$, insofar as other channels
do not contribute. Other channels will not contribute appreciably if
the excitation E is close to or only a few hundred kev above the fission
threshold E_f. Under these conditions one can say that two channels—or two states in the lowest rotational band at the saddle—are
contributing to fission, even though any one nucleus of any one
I-value passes over the barrier through only one of these channels.

Can not the contribution of the two channels in question be
distinguished by proper selection of the energy of the bombarding
neutrons? Only with great difficulty or not at all! The conditions
will be most favorable for a distinction between the two contributions
when the channel openings $W(E - E_{b_0})$ and $W(E - E_{b_2})$ differ by
the greatest factor. The factor of difference is least well above the
barrier, because then both openings approach the limiting value
$W_{\max} = 1$; and greatest well below the barrier, where the simple exponential formula becomes applicable:

$$\frac{W(E - E_{b_2})}{W(E - E_{b_0})} \cong \exp\left[-2\pi \frac{(E_{b_2} - E_{b_0})}{\hbar\omega_{\text{inverted}}}\right]$$

$$\cong \exp\left[-\frac{E_{b_2} - E_{b_0}}{\text{energy interval over which experimental cross section increases by a factor } e = 2.718 \ldots \text{ for energies well below threshold}}\right] \quad (90)$$

Experimental (n, f) cross sections well below threshold increase by a
factor $e = 2.718 \ldots$ for an increase in the neutron energy anywhere
from $(1/30)$ Mev to $(1/10)$ Mev. The quantity $E_{b_2} - E_{b_0}$, on the other
hand, is only about 11 kev. Therefore, one expects to be able to alter
the ratio of the contributions of the two channels in question by only
about

$$\sim 11 \text{ kev}/50 \text{ kev} \quad (91)$$

by going from neutron energies well below threshold to neutron
energies well above threshold. In other words, the difference in
the channel energies E_{b_2} and E_{b_0} is so small relative to the
characteristic width $(\hbar\omega_{\text{inverted}}/2\pi)$ of any jump in the carpeted stair-

Table XV. Two contrasting and inequivalent ways to use the term "channel for fission." Which is meant in any given discussion depends upon the context. The term "definite K-value" used in the table to characterize a channel is actually to be understood as a shorthand way to imply a specification not only of the value of K itself—the angular momentum about the axis of extension—but also of a complete set of nucleonic quantum numbers, so as to distinguish different channels that happen to have the same K-values.

Use of term "channel"	Synonyms suggested to eliminate ambiguity	Case of compound nucleus formed in state of definite I-value	Bombardment producing compound nuclei of many I values
"Broad" sense: definite K-value; whole band of I-values associated with that K-value	"Band of channels" or "K-channel"	The combination of data fixes both I and K, and therefore also the channel energy: $$E_{bKI} = E_{IiK} + \frac{[I(I+1) - K^2]\hbar^2}{2\mathfrak{I}_{\perp \text{ saddle}}};$$ not very different from E_{0iK} for small $I - K$.	Spread in channel energies unimportant if spread in I-values is small compared to $\sim(50 \text{ kev}/2 \text{ kev})^{1/2}$ ~5. For larger spread in I-values the separate pure channels in the band of channels begin to become distinguishable.
"Narrow" sense: definite I-value and definite I-value.	"Pure channel" or "(K,I)-channel"	Same sharp barrier energy.	Numerous pure channels contribute to fission yield; they are in principle distinct, and have distinct angular distributions associated with them, but ordinarily (low I_{max} of bombardment) these contributions cannot be distinguished from each other by varying the bombarding energy.

case function that the energies of the two channels can be identified
for many purposes. Moreover, only one of them shows up in a
nucleus of any one I-value. Therefore, it is often appropriate to use
the term channel (Table XV) in the "broad" sense to speak of the
collection or band of "pure channels" (different I-values that belong
to the same K-value).

No *even Z-odd N* nucleus is known which illustrates these considerations. The three most important fissile nuclei, U^{233}, U^{235}, and
Pu^{239} would all serve but for one circumstance: the threshold E_f instead of being high enough to demand neutrons of ~ 1 Mev to bring
about fission, is well below even the energy B_n made available by the
addition of a neutron of zero kinetic energy. The energy difference
$B_n - E_f$ is great enough so that apparently two or more "K-channels"
or "bands of channels" are accessible. This circumstance makes it
natural to ask about the higher "bands of channels" associated with
even-even compound nuclei at the saddle.

E. Collective Vibrations

As guide in predictions about these saddle point bands one has
considerable information about the bands of normal nuclei in the
neighborhood of uranium, information summarized by Davydov and
Filippov (Da58, Da59), Hyde (Hy59), and Sheline (Sh60). The low-
lying bands of *even-even* nuclei are built upon collective vibrations.
These vibrations are most readily visualized in terms of the liquid

Table XVI. Dimensionless measure of square of vibration frequency for ideal
liquid drop given by second line in Eq. (92). The value $x = 0.74$ is
believed to correspond roughly to nuclei in the neighborhood of uranium. The constants of Table XIII—which are used to obtain the
last column of the present table—would give $x = 0.71$ for U^{236}. A
value closer to $x = 0.77$ would be given by identifying liquid drop
and observed barrier heights, without any correction for anomalies
in the ground state energy

Order λ	$(3\omega^2 A M_p/32\pi\sigma)$ for general x	$x = 0.74$	$\hbar\omega_\lambda$ for $x = 0.74$ and constants of Table XIII
1	0	0	0 (translation)
2	$1 - x$	0.26	1.2 Mev (cigar-pancake)
3	$3.75 - 2.143x$	2.16	3.5 Mev (pear up—pear down)*
4	$9.00 - 3.333x$	6.54	6.1 Mev ($P_4 (\cos \theta)$)

* Sometimes termed "octupole" vibration.

drop model. The characteristic quantum energy associated with one quantum of excitation of an ideal spherical droplet by mode of vibration of order λ is given by the formula (Bo39, Hi53):

$$\hbar^2\omega_\lambda^2 = \hbar^2(C_\lambda/B_\lambda) = (1/A)(8\hbar^2/3M_p r_0^2)(4\pi r_0^2\sigma)$$
$$\times [\lambda(\lambda - 1)/8]\{(\lambda + 2) - [20x/(2\lambda + 1)]\} \quad (92)$$

Here the factor on the second line has the values indicated in Table XVI.

To what extent do any of these vibrations partake of the character of a rotation? The vibrations $\lambda = 2$, $\mu = 2$ and $\lambda = 2$, $\mu = -2$ can be given such amplitudes and phases that the linear combination of the two describes a *rotatory* vibration:

$$\delta R(\theta, \varphi, t) = \text{constant} \times \{ [\sin^2\theta \exp(2i\varphi)][\exp(-i\omega t)]$$
$$+ [\sin^2\theta \exp(-2i\varphi)][\exp(i\omega t)]\} \quad (93)$$
$$= \text{constant} \times \sin^2\theta \cos(2\varphi - \omega t).$$

This vibration is endowed with rotational angular momentum. However, the energy of the motion does not increase with quantum number—or with angular momentum—in accordance with the quadratic law of a rigid rotor

$$E = n_{22}^2\hbar^2/2\mathfrak{J} \quad (94)$$

Instead, the energy increases only linearly with quantum number

$$E = n_{22}\hbar\omega_{22} \quad (95)$$

This result can be understood qualitatively in the following way (Bo52). The moment of inertia relevant for the rotatory motion is not the entire rigid body moment of inertia for the sphere. The rotational advance of the fluid is only a fraction of the rotational advance of the wave upon the surface of the fluid. This wave travels around the equatorial belt of the droplet at the angular velocity $d\varphi/dt = \omega/2$. The transport of momentum in the wave motion is proportional to the square of the amplitude and to the first power of the velocity; or here

$$\begin{pmatrix} \text{angular} \\ \text{momentum} \end{pmatrix} \sim \begin{pmatrix} \text{radius} \\ \text{of drop} \end{pmatrix}\begin{pmatrix} \text{momentum} \\ \text{transported by wave} \end{pmatrix}$$

$$\sim \begin{pmatrix} \text{radius} \\ \text{of drop} \end{pmatrix}\begin{pmatrix} \text{velocity} \\ \text{of wave} \end{pmatrix}\begin{pmatrix} \text{mass of} \\ \text{drop} \end{pmatrix}\begin{pmatrix} \text{fraction of mass in motion—} \\ \text{a fraction} \propto (\text{amplitude/radius})^2 \end{pmatrix}$$

$$\sim R^2\omega M(\text{amplitude}/R)^2 \sim M(\text{amplitude})^2\omega \quad (96)$$

In other words, *the effective moment of inertia is proportional to the square of the amplitude.* Moreover, the square of the amplitude here, as for any oscillator, is proportional to the first power of the energy, or to the first power of the quantum number n_{22} of the rotatory vibration:

$$(\text{mass})(\text{velocity})^2 \sim (\text{energy})$$

or

$$M\omega^2(\text{amplitude})^2 \sim n_{22}\hbar\omega$$

or

$$\mathfrak{I}_{\text{effective}} \sim n_{22}\hbar/\omega \tag{97}$$

Thus the energy of the rotatory vibration can still be estimated from the usual equation (94) for a rotor provided one inserts there the excitation—dependent moment of inertia [Eq. (97)]. This analysis gives a first approximate account of the lowest vibrational levels of nuclei of spherical form.

Many of the nuclei of interest in fission are far from spherical. They are deformed from ideality by the unbalanced pressure of nucleons against the nuclear wall (Ra50, Bo50, Bo52, Ga51, Ga51a, Ga53, Hi53). The influence of such a perturbation can be discussed to a certain approximation—particularly for even-even nuclei—even within the framework of the liquid drop model. For this purpose it is necessary to supplement the normal potential by extra terms which describe the effect of the specific nucleonic forces upon the normal deformation potential. The effect of these forces is somewhat analogous to that of a coiled spring placed inside the surface, pushing against surface tension, and deforming the drop away from sphericity. The deformation changes the character of the energy level spectrum from one that is purely vibrational to one that is a combination of rotation and vibration.

The rotational levels are given as before by an equation of the form (94), only now the moment of inertia is due primarily to the deformation produced by the nucleons. Only secondarily does it depend upon any additional average extension that is associated with vibration. Thus the rotational levels have the approximately $I(I + 1)$—proportional energy that is familiar from molecules. Superposed on these rotations are vibrations that are closely connected in form and frequency with the vibrations of the ideal spherical droplet.

To trace out in detail the correlation between the individual energy levels in the two limiting cases of large deformation and ideal sphericity demands considerable analysis (Je55, Da58, Da59, Sh60) The primary principles are these: (a) levels with a given I-value are always $(2I + 1)$—degenerate because of the equivalence of all directions in space; (b) different levels with the same I-value never cross. Without going into detail it is possible to illustrate some of the simpler features of the correlation diagram by considering collective vibrations of order $\lambda = 2$.

There are five modes of vibration of an ideal liquid drop, vibrations built out of spherical harmonics of order 2:

$$\delta R = R_0[\alpha_{2,-2} Y_{2,-2}(\theta, \varphi) + \ldots + \alpha_{2,2} Y_{2,2}(\theta, \varphi)] \qquad (98)$$

All have the same circular frequency ω_2 when sphericity obtains. There are therefore five ways to give the system one quantum $\hbar\omega_2$ of vibrational energy. They are associated with angular momentum $M_z\hbar$ about the space-fixed Z-axis, with M_z equal respectively to -2, -1, 0, 1, 2. One is thus in possession of the five independent magnetic substates of a state $E_2 = \hbar\omega$ of angular momentum quantum number $I = 2$. These states describe a rotatory vibration of quantum number $n = 1$.

When the drop is deformed by internal forces, so that the effective moment of inertia due to the "lumps,"

$$\mathfrak{I}_{\text{irrotational fluid motion in deformed droplet}} \qquad (99)$$

is larger than the moment of inertia contributed by the excitation of waves

$$\mathfrak{I}_{\text{eff}} \sim n_2\hbar/\omega \qquad (100)$$

then the character of the motion changes from a vibratory rotation to something much more nearly like an ordinary rotation.

The next higher state of $\lambda = 2$ excitation of the ideal spherical droplet has two quanta of vibrational energy. The two quanta can be disposed among the five independent oscillators of order $\lambda = 2$ in 15 ways. Out of the 15 degenerate states thus obtained one can construct linear combinations which describe

(1) the nine magnetic substates $M_z = -4, \ldots +4$ of a state $E_4 = 2\hbar\omega$ of $I = 4$;

(2) the five magnetic substates of a state $E_\gamma = 2\hbar\omega$ of $I = 2$; and

(3) one state with $E_\beta = 2\hbar\omega$ and $I = 0$.

The distinction between these modes becomes clearer when the restoring force parameters within the droplet are modified so that the fluid takes on an extended form of equilibrium. This change does not alter the symmetry of the problem with respect to direction in space. Therefore, the magnetic substates of any given level stay together in energy. However, the energy E_4 falls—and falls from something of a vibrational order of magnitude to the value appropriate to the a state of collective rotation of angular momentum $I = 4$. This is the origin of that state! In other words, E_4 and E_2, previously in the ratio

$$E_4/E_2 = 2\hbar\omega/\hbar\omega = 2 \tag{101}$$

not only decrease in absolute value, but also approach the ratio

$$E_4/E_2 = (4\cdot5\hbar^2/2\mathfrak{I}_\perp)/(2\cdot3\hbar^2/2\mathfrak{I}_\perp) = 3.33 \ldots \tag{102}$$

The state E_β is associated in an extended nucleus at a stable point of equilibrium with one quantum of vibration in that coordinate—here called β—that describes increases in the extension. It is not an error in the assignment that the energy of this mode is $2\hbar\omega$ for the ideal sphere. The energy goes over to $\hbar\omega_\beta$ for the extended nucleus in its normal state. At the saddle the restoring force constant associated with this mode is no longer positive, but negative. Thus this is the fission mode. It does not come into the count of channels.

The remaining energy level, E_γ, has also dropped in energy, but not so far as have E_4 and E_β. *It describes a collective rotation with $K = 2$ units of angular momentum about the axis of extension.* It is assumed here that this axis is an axis of rotational symmetry. Then in the rotation in question a pair of wave crests moves around the axis of symmetry. Let the axis of symmetry be conceived as coinciding at a certain instant with the space-fixed Z-axis. Then, complicated as may be the dependence of δR upon θ, its dependence upon φ is described by a factor of the form

$$\sin(2\varphi - \omega t + \text{phase constant}) \tag{103}$$

The travelling wave describes a rotatory vibration, a so-called "γ-vibration." The observed energy of the state identified as E_γ in normal nuclei ranges from about $E_\gamma \sim 950$ kev near Th^{228} up to ~ 1200 kev at Cm^{244} and down again as low as ~ 850 kev near Fm^{254}.

Turn now from normal nuclei to nuclei at the saddle. The moment of inertia of a rigid body similar in shape to the extended fission form, about the approximate symmetry axis, is evidently smaller than the moment of inertia of the normal shape about the same axis. The nucleus does not behave as a rigid body, of course, with respect to the rotatory or γ-vibration, but every relevant parameter that one can think of, whether moment of inertia or average circumference about the axis—and therefore average wave length of the waves of rotatory vibration—suggests that the quantity E_γ will be greater at the saddle point than for normal nuclei. A guess of $E_\gamma \sim$ 1.5 or 2 Mev might serve for an order of magnitude estimate.

Collective rotations can be superposed upon these rotatory or γ-vibrations, just as general rotations of a molecule can be superposed upon rotations internal to a molecule. The total angular momentum I in these more general states is greater than or equal to $K = 2$. The energy is given to a first approximation by the formula

$$E = \hbar\omega_\gamma + (\hbar^2/2\Im_{\shortparallel})[I(I+1) - K^2]$$
$$(I = K, K+1, K+2, \ldots) \tag{104}$$

The higher states $(I = K+1, K+2, \ldots)$ of the deformed system correlate with states of vibration of the spherical droplet which contain more than two quanta of action. This correlation will not be traced out here. However, two points deserve a closer look. First, there is rotational energy even when $I = K$ energy that might be called "zero-point" rotational energy. The angular momentum about an axis perpendicular to the axis of rotatory vibration would be

$$R\hbar = \hbar(I^2 - K^2)^{1/2}$$

according to a semiclassical analysis, but is actually

$$R\hbar = \hbar[I(I+1) - K^2]^{1/2}$$

according to the quantum mechanical version of the Pythagorean theorem. Therefore the energy of the state $I = K = 2$ is not $\hbar\omega_\gamma$, as the previous discussion could have been taken to imply, but

$$E(I = 2; K = 2) = (\hbar\omega_\gamma) + (\hbar^2/\Im_\perp) \tag{105}$$

where the second term can be taken to represent zero-point rotational energy. Second, the angular momentum of the rotatory vibration is

$2\hbar$. The lower conceivable value $K = 1$ is forbidden because inversion of the droplet in the origin in a state $K = 1$ would return the droplet to its original configuration but reverse the sign of the wave function and therefore demand that $\psi = -\psi$.

In summary to this point—where only vibrations of order $\lambda = 2$ have been considered—there appear in a deformed even-even nucleus (a) collective rotations without collective vibrations; (b) collective motions in the deformation coordinate β which endowed with small energy describe more-cigar-like-less-cigar-like-more-cigar-like vibrations about $\beta = \beta_{\text{normal}}$, but which with more energy are able to pass over the barrier to fission; (c) rotatory or γ-vibrations, with an angular momentum about the axis of extension equal to $K = 0$ (unexcited), $K = 2$ (first state of excitation), $K = 4, 6, \ldots$; and (d) combinations of these kinds of excitation. The channels for fission are built out of (a) the rotations, (c) the γ-vibrations, and combinations of (a) and (c).

Additional channels important for fission contain excitations genetically related to the vibrations of the undeformed sphere of order $\lambda = 3$. Before the law of force is changed and the degeneracy is broken up, there are seven such modes of vibration all of the same frequency ω_3, which make the following contributions to the fractional extension $\delta R(\theta, \varphi)/R_0$:

$$(7/4\pi)^{1/2}(5/16)^{1/2} \sin^3 \theta [-\alpha_{33} \exp(3i\varphi) + \alpha_{3-3} \exp(-3i\varphi)] \quad (106)$$

(progenitor of rotations and of mixtures of rotations with vibration);

$$(7/4\pi)^{1/2}(15/8)^{1/2} \sin^2 \theta \cos \theta [\alpha_{32} \exp(2i\varphi) + \alpha_{3-2} \exp(-2i\varphi)] \quad (107)$$

(progenitor of rotations and of mixtures of rotations with vibrations);

$$(7/4\pi)^{1/2}(3/16)^{1/2}(4 \sin \theta - 5 \sin^3\theta)$$
$$\times [-\alpha_{31} \exp(i\varphi) + \alpha_{3-1} \exp(-i\varphi)] \quad (108)$$

(progenitor of bending vibrations of the extended nucleus, like the bending vibrations of a linear molecule); and

$$(7/4\pi)^{1/2}(1/2)(5 \cos^3 \theta - 3 \cos \theta)\alpha_{30} \quad (109)$$

(progenitor of a pear shaped vibration of the extended form).

No attempt will be made here to consider all of the quantum states which come into being on placing one, two or more quanta in the seven modes of order $\lambda = 3$ and then allowing the forces to change and the equilibrium form to become extended. Instead, attention can be limited to those states which develop which have low frequency and which contribute to the number of low-lying channels. Now for the distinction between the modes of high frequency and those of low frequency!

The vibrations of an extended form are described more appropriately by polar coordinates referred to the axis of extension than by polar coordinates fixed in space. Therefore for a qualitative impression of the modes of vibration let the angle θ in (106), (107), (108), and (109) be thought of as referred to the axis of extension. Let the angular dependence be corrected in whatever way is appropriate to the extended form. Then such modes of vibration as possess the qualitative form (106) and (107) have primarily the character of circulation about the axis of extension. The quantum energy $\hbar\omega$ associated with modes of this kind is expected to rise for the extended form as compared to the estimated figure $\hbar\omega_3 \sim 3$ Mev (Table XVI) for the spherical form. Therefore these modes will be passed by in any count of low-lying channels. Not so for the other two modes, (108) and (109)! One is a bending vibration of quantum energy $\hbar\omega_b$. The other is a vibration in which material sloshes back and forth from one end of the extended form to the other, a vibration of quantum energy $\hbar\omega_s$. The bending vibration has apparently not received any attention to date. The evidence for the sloshing vibration, on the other hand, came from experiment (Asaro, Stephens, and Perlman, As53; see also St54, St55, St57a) before the theoretical interpretation was apparent (Christy, Ch56a). The identification between observed energy levels of normal nuclei and the sloshing vibration was made by way of the odd parity observed and expected for this mode.

F. Coupling Between Vibration and Rotation as Diagnostic Parameter

Now that two modes of vibration of odd parity are recognized, either one or both of which may have low frequency, it is not clear which is to be identified with the observed vibration. This is an interesting question for the future. The coupling between vibration and rotation here as in molecular spectra (Te34, Jo35, Te38, He42, He45, Go48, He50, Ni51), and the subleties of effective moments of inertia and transition probabilities, would seem to offer one of the most fruitful ways to clear up the assignment of vibrations. In the meantime it may be appropriate to refer to the observed vibration as the *sloshing mode*, with the understanding that this widely accepted assignment might conceivably later have to be changed.

Not only the sloshing mode $\hbar\omega_s$ but also the bending mode $\hbar\omega_b$ and all the modes of order $\lambda = 3(\mu = -3, -2, \ldots, +3)$ are of odd parity in this sense, that in the spherical drop a reversal of the coordinates $\alpha_{\lambda\mu}$ produces a change in shape which also can be brought about—and brought about more directly—by inversion at the origin:

$$
\begin{aligned}
x &\to -x \\
y &\to -y \\
z &\to -z
\end{aligned}
\tag{109a}
$$

In the deformed drop the coordinates are somewhat different, but there is one coordinate α_s connected with the sloshing vibration. This degree of freedom can be unexcited, of course ($n_s = 0$), or in its first ($n_s = 1$) or second ($n_s = 2$) or higher quantum state, just as is the case for any other oscillator.

When the system has a spherical form of equilibrium, the wave function for the ground state can be written in the form

$$
\text{constant} \times \exp[-(B_3 C_3)^{1/2} \alpha_s{}^2 / 2\hbar]
\tag{110}
$$

and the wave function for the first excited state similarly,

$$
\text{constant} \times \alpha_s \exp[-(B_3 C_3)^{1/2} \alpha_s{}^2 / 2\hbar]
\tag{111}
$$

The potential has another form when the droplet has a deformed position of equilibrium, but it is still expected to be symmetric with respect to change in the sign of α_s. Consequently the ground state, like (110), is still even with respect to the reversal $\alpha_s \to -\alpha_s$; and the first excited state is still odd.

The reversal of the pear which is brought about by a change in the sign of α_s can be undone by a rotation of $180°$ about an axis perpendicular to the axis of symmetry. In such a rotation the rotational wave function is multiplied by $(-1)^I$. The system is brought back to its original configuration, so the overall wave function must return to its original value. Normally there is no parity-changing factor to be considered in low states of even-even nuclei other than the factors associated with the degree of freedom α_{30} and the rotational angular momentum. Consequently this condition must be satisfied:

$$
(-1)^I (-1)^{n_{30}} = 1
\tag{112}
$$

Table XVII. Low-lying rotational states of even and odd parity in a few even-even nuclei. All energies in kev. The observed energies for the states of odd parity are written—when the breakdown can be estimated—as the sum of two parts, one the quantum energy $\hbar\omega_z$ of the sloshing (or bending?) vibration, the other a rotational energy. The effective moment of inertia calculated from the odd levels is of the same order as the effective moment calculated from the even levels, but different in value—a circumstance probably helpful to a future decision as to whether the observed mode of odd parity is due to sloshing or to bending. The data are taken from the review article of Hyde (Hy59) with supplements kindly supplied by F. Asaro, S. Bjornholm, and F. Stephens. In several cases it is known that the levels with $I = 1 -$ have $K = 0$; in these cases the interpretation as a bending vibration is excluded, and the sloshing mode is a more reasonable assignment. In another case, however (Th230) these does occur a band containing a level with $I = 1-$ and $K = 1$. This band could be interpreted as associated with the first excited state of bending vibration. Question marks besides certain levels indicate doubt, not about the energy, but about the I-value.

	0+	1-	2+	3-	4+	5-	6+	8+
Em218	0	(794)	325		850			
Em220	0	(650)	241					
Em222	0	(610)	187					
Ra222	0	242*	111		310			
Ra224	0	(203 + 14)*	84	(203 + 86)	210			
Ra226	0	(240 + 13)*	68	(240 + 89)	226	(240 + 205)	416	
Th226	0	230*	72		186			
Th228	0	(314 + 14)*	58	(314 + 82)	180	(314 + 200)	378?	
Th232	0	~1060	50		157			
U232	0	(551 + 13)†	48	(551 + 79)				
U234	0	788**	44		143?		296?	499?
U236	0	(688)	45					
U238	0	~665	45					
Pu238	0	605*	44		146?		304?	514?
Pu240	0	600	43		142?		292?	

* The K-value associated with these $I = 1^-$ levels is established as $K = 0$ (A156, p. 541, Table V.8). **$(I, K) = (1^-, 0)$: (Wo60). †$(I, K) = (1^-, 0)$: (Bj63).

In other words, the lowest rotational states of quantum number $I = 0, 2, 4, 6, \ldots$ are unaccompanied by the sloshing vibration of pear type and have even parity; while those of quantum number $I = 1, 3, 5, \ldots$ are accompanied by one vibrational quantum of this mode and have odd parity. Table XVII gives observational data on some low-lying levels of odd parity.

G. Order of Magnitude of Sloshing and Bending Frequencies

What can be said about the expected frequencies of the bending and sloshing vibrations in their dependence upon elongation? The stiffness of the normal spherical droplet against the bending mode—against a deformation proportional to

$$(5 \cos^2 \theta - 1) \sin \theta \cos \varphi \qquad (112a)$$

is great, as evidenced by the calculated quantum energy $\hbar\omega_3 \sim 3$ Mev. However, with increasing elongation the effective inertial constant associated with a rate of bending $d(\text{bending angle})/d(\text{time})$ goes up, and the restoring torque, or generalized force constant, goes down. Therefore the frequency of this mode can be expected to have dropped considerably at the extended form appropriate for normal nuclei near uranium, and to have dropped much further still for nuclei at the saddle. Therefore, there should exist low-lying channels built on the bending vibration $\hbar\omega_b$, alone and in combination with states of collective rotation.

For the sloshing vibration the difference between the ground state, $n_s = 0$, and the first excited state, $n_s = 1$, can be as low as the observed values (200 kev to 600 kev in Table XVII) without its being necessary to assume a harmonic oscillator potential of abnormally low force constant. It is conceivable (Ch56) that the effective potential for this degree of freedom is qualitatively of the form

$$V(\alpha_s) = -(a/2)\alpha_s{}^2 + (b/4)\alpha_s{}^4 \qquad (113)$$

A potential of this type has two minima, at

$$\alpha_s = \pm(a/b)^{1/2} \qquad (114)$$

The potential is still symmetric with respect to change in the sign of α_s. The distinction between states odd in α_s and states even α_s is maintained. The energy levels are not equally spaced, but instead have a pattern which is most easily symbolized by the following Table XVIII. The spacing between the two lowest levels can be very small when the barrier separating the two minima is high. The spacing is governed by the same exponential factor which controls the probability of penetration through the barrier, just as in the

Table XVIII. Spacing of levels of the sloshing vibration for a potential of the form (113). The levels approach regularity of spacing when the energy rises above the energy $E_s = 0$ of the barrier that separates the two minima

Parity	+	−		+	−		+	−		+	−
n_s	0	1		2	3		4	5		6	7

familiar umbrella vibrations of the molecule NH_3. It is not known whether the small separation of the two lowest states of the sloshing mode in Table XVII—if it is the sloshing mode—comes about through the blocking effect of such a barrier or through a nearly harmonic potential of very low force constant.

H. Relation of Sloshing Vibration to Asymmetry of Fission

Of significance to the channel analysis of fission is the pear-shaped vibration, not of normal nuclei, but of nuclei at the saddle point. Here the equilibrium configuration looks something like a dumbbell, according to the liquid drop model. The coordinate α_s assigns more mass to one part of this figure and less mass to the other. In other words, it changes the position of the indentation that one calls the neck of the fission form. This type of change would seem to be related to asymmetry in the division of mass in fission in the most direct possible way (Bo56, Wh56). In other words, the probability of a given value of α_s would appear likely to have a strong correlation with the probability for a certain mass ratio—or range of mass ratios—for the fission products. However, the connection between mass ratio and α_3 is not so simple that one is justified to say (a) asymmetric fission is overwhelmingly more probable than symmetric fission; therefore (b) values of α_s substantially different from zero are overwhelmingly more probable than values near zero; consequently (c) the factor in the over-all wave function which is associated with this coordinate has two maxima; hence (d) the potential

Table XIX. Channels expected to be accessible in the fission of U²³⁴, U²³⁵, and Pu²³⁹ by slow neutrons. Only the lowest channels are included and some may well be omitted which are accessible even at the low energy (the neutron binding energy B_n) which is made available by the addition of a slow neutron. The thresholds E_f for all three nuclei lie below B_n, so they cannot be observed in the neutron capture reaction itself. However, they can be inferred from the steps in the yield of fission as a function of deuteron energy in such reactions as U²³⁵($d; p, f$) as observed by Northrup, Stokes, and Boyer (No59). For this purpose the curve for (number of fissions)/(number of protons with and without fission) has been compared with the standard curve $W(E - E_b)$ for the opening of a fission channel and estimates have been made by eye of the value of E_b at which W takes on the value ½. Two channels can be seen fairly distinctly in the curve for U²³⁹, two less distinctly in Pu²³³, and in U²³⁵ it is not clear just where the channel or channels are located. The angular momentum quantum number I and parity π of the ground state of the target nucleus is given in every case. The K-value of the target nucleus is identical with I, but this circumstance is believed to be irrelevant to the choice of (K, I)-channel taken by the nucleus in passing over the fission barrier, because of all the vibrations and internal exchanges of energy and angular momentum which take place between the time of formation of the compound nucleus and the time of fission. The asterisks in the table indicate those among the listed channels which are expected to be relevant for fission in the given compound nucleus for the given I-value *provided* that sufficient energy is available to make the channel opening $W(E - E_b)$ appreciable and *neglecting* other—presumably higher—channels.

Description of channel	I^π	K	Estimate of $E_b - E_f$	Probability of symmetric fission	Target nucleus — $Z^A(I, \pi)$ / Heat of condensation of added neutron — B_n / Compound nucleus — $\begin{cases}E_{b_1}\\E_{b_2}\end{cases}$ (I^π) : U²³³(5/2 +) 6.8 Mev; ~5.3 Mev; ~6.1 Mev?; 2+ 3+	U²³⁵(7/2 -) 6.5 Mev; -6.0 Mev?; —; 3- 4-	Pu²³⁹(1/2 +) 6.4 Mev; ≅4.8 Mev; ~5.7 Mev; 0+ 1+
No collective vibration	0+	0	0 kev	normal	—	—	*
	2+	0	11.1 kev	normal	*	—	—
	4+	0	37.0 kev	normal	—	—	—
	6+	0	77.7 kev	normal	—	—	—
One quantum of sloshing vibration	1-	0	~100 to 600 kev plus rotational energy	extra low	—	—	—
	3-	0		extra low	—	*	—
	5-	0		extra low	—	—	—

				energy								
One quantum of bending vibration	1⁻	1	~500 to 1500 kev plus rotational energy	normal								—
	2⁻	1		normal								—
	3⁻	1		normal				*				—
	4⁻	1		normal						*		—
	5⁻	1		normal	*							—
One quantum of gamma vibration	2⁺	2	~1000 kev plus rotational energy	normal			*					—
	3⁺	2		normal								—
	4⁺	2		normal								—
	5⁺	2		normal								—
One quantum sloshing plus one quantum gamma	2⁻	2	~1500 kev plus rotational energy	extra low			*					—
	3⁻	2		extra low						*		—
	4⁻	2		extra low								—
	5⁻	2		extra low								—

If the indicated channels and no others are accessible in slow n-capture, and if slow neutron resonances of the two different spins are compared, then one expects:

(a) Yield-effective number N_f of channels	2	1	3	2	1	0
(b) Very different (>3 fold) fissibility?	No		No	No	Yes	
(c) Very different ratio of symmetric to asymmetric fission?	No		No	?		

Experimental findings:

(a) Fairly clear division of observed resonances into two groups of rather different widths? — No — No — Yes

(b) Ratio of symmetric to asymmetric fission for one resonance, divided by same ratio for another resonance.
(Fl58,Ro57a, Re59) | (La57a,Na57, Ro58,Co61) | (Au56,Re60)

(c) Yield effective number of channels $2\pi\langle\Gamma_f\rangle/D$, when D is taken to be twice the average spacing of levels in the composite spectrum (spectrum containing both $I = I_{target} - 1/2$ and $I = I_{target} + 1/2$)

$\langle\Gamma_f\rangle = 0.19$ ev | $\langle\Gamma_f\rangle = 0.042$ ev | $\langle\Gamma_f\rangle = 0.099$ ev
$\langle D\rangle = 2.0$ ev | $\langle D\rangle = 1.4$ ev | $\langle D\rangle = 5.8$ ev
$N_f \sim 1.2$ | $N_f \sim 0.17$ | $N_f \sim 0.11$

(d) Also information on angular distribution and on fluctuations in level widths.
(Fl58,Mo60, Vo60,Ro60) | (Ha58a,Sh58, Ha59,Vo60,Ro60) | (Bo58,Vo60, Fr62)

energy at the saddle values with α_{30} in accordance with an equation qualitatively of the form

$$V(\alpha_{2\text{saddle}},\ \alpha_{30}) = c^* - (a^*/2)\alpha_{30}^2 + (b^*/4)\alpha_{30}^4 \qquad (115)$$

and finally (e) there are *two* saddles, one at $\alpha_2 = \alpha_{2\text{ saddle}}$, $\alpha_{30} = (a^*/b^*)^{1/2}$, the other at $\alpha_2 = \alpha_{2\text{ saddle}}$, $\alpha_{30}^{\cdot} = -(a^*/b^*)^{1/2}$, with energy

$$E_f = c^* - (a^{*2}/4b^*) \qquad (116)$$

Far too many questions still surround the issue how the asymmetry of fission comes about to permit a final stand for or against this line of reasoning. However, a simpler and more straightforward conclusion seems safe: *In a channel with vibrational quantum number* $n_s = 1$, *for which the wave function vanishes at* $\alpha_s = 0$ *(odd parity), the chance for symmetric fission will be expected to be substantially less than the chance for symmetric fission—usually itself small—in a channel with vibrational quantum number* $n_s = 0$. (A state of even parity for which the wave function does not vanish at $\alpha_s = 0$.)

The difference in vibrational energy between the two kinds of channels, 0^+, 2^+, ... versus 1^-, 3^-, ..., is completely unknown, but presumably lies somewhere in the range from a few tens of kev to a few hundred kev.

I. Summary of Expected Low-Lying Channels

In addition to the channels so far listed, built out of combinations or rotation and $\hbar\omega_\gamma$ and $\hbar\omega_{\text{slosh}}$ and $\hbar\omega_{\text{bend}}$, there will exist higher channels built on multiple combinations of $\hbar\omega_\gamma$, $\hbar\omega_s$ and $\hbar\omega_b$ and higher modes of collective vibration and rotation, and also channels in which the nucleonic structure itself is excited. No attempt is made to include these higher channels in the following tabulation of some of the channels expected to be accessible in the fission of the three technically most important nuclei by slow neutrons (Table XIX).

J. Fission of Aligned Nuclei

The distribution in direction of fission products from aligned U^{233} and U^{235} nuclei has been observed by Dabbs, Walter, Roberts, and Parker (Da58a, Da58b, Da59a). The dividing nucleus was located in the anisotropic crystalline lattice of $UO_2\ Rb(NO_3)_3$ and aligned by the quadrupole electric field of the surrounding electrons and ions. The direction of alignment was determined by looking at anisotropy in α-particle emission. The argument was used (Hi53) that the rate of emission of α particles should be an order of magnitude greater near the tips of the elongated nucleus than near the equator. Unexpectedly, the α particles of both U^{233} and U^{235} were observed to come off preferentially perpendicular to the c-axis of the crystal. It was concluded that the proposed target nucleus before neutron capture has its symmetry axis also preferentially oriented in the plane perpendicular to the c-axis, or Z-axis, of the crystal. A study of possible molecular orbitals for the bonding electrons showed that it was not unreasonable to have an asymmetry in the electron cloud such as would produce this type of alignment.

The alignment observed by way of α-particle emission implies that, out of all the values M_z which might occur for the Z-projection of the angular momentum quantum number I (M_z from $-\frac{5}{2}$ to $+\frac{5}{2}$ for U^{233}, and M_z from $-\frac{7}{2}$ to $+\frac{7}{2}$ for U^{235}), the values $M_z = \pm\frac{1}{2}$ are favored before neutron uptake.

The incoming neutron brings no orbital angular momentum and has a Z-projection of spin angular momentum of only $\pm\frac{1}{2}$. The compound nucleus thus ends up with magnetic substate populations which are related to the original substate populations through the square of a Clebsch-Gordan coefficient. Because of the small neutron Z projection, and regardless of the angular momentum I of the compound state, whether $I = 2^+$ or 3^+, 3^-, or 4^-, the tendency thus persists for the nuclei to be aligned in the plane perpendicular to the space-fixed Z-axis. Not so the direction of extension of the dividing nucleus! In what direction it prefers to point depends upon the K-value of the channel through which the nucleus goes over the barrier. The two extreme cases are (a) a channel with $K = 0$, and (b) a channel with $K = 1$.

In case (a) the angular momentum I is expected to be all in the component R (Figs. 6 and 8) of rotation about an axis perpendicular to the axis of extension. In semiclassical language, the nascent fission fragments whirl about in a plane which is perpendicular to I and which therefore contains the Z-axis. All values of θ are equally probable

$$d(\text{probability}) = d\theta/\pi = (2\pi^2 \sin\theta)^{-1} 2\pi \sin\theta\, d\theta$$
$$= (2\pi^2 \sin\theta)^{-1} d(\text{solid angle}) \tag{115}$$

or on a per-unit-solid-angle basis the emergent fission fragments came off preferentially parallel and antiparallel to the c-axis (Z-axis) of the crystal. The transition state fission form and the target nucleus evidently have very different orientations. This change in orientation comes about between the stage of taking up the neutron and the stage of passage over the barrier. During this interval many vibrations typically take place, much internal reapportionment of energy and angular momentum goes on, and the change in orientation is the consequence. These rearrangements have been further discussed by Strutinski (St56a). Of course I is conserved throughout this development.

In the opposite limiting case (b) of a channel with $K = I$, there is no component R of angular momentum. However much the nuclear shape changes between capture of the neutron and passage over the barrier, the system ends up going through the transition state with its axis of extension once again parallel to the angular momentum vector I. Or to return to a quantum mechanically justified way of speaking, one can say that the probability distribution of fission fragments in case (b) must be somewhat concentrated in the equatorial plane, perpendicular to the c-axis of the crystal.

To translate into quantitative terms these qualitative predictions about the angular distribution associated with particular channels, it would be enough to use the values for the orientation function $\left| d_{MK}^I(\theta) \right|^2$ listed in Table X—if the compound nucleus were prepared in a state of definite M-value. Roberts, Dabbs, and Parker (Ro57) proceed as follows in the case of a distribution of M-values: (a) Sum terms $\left| d_{MK}^I(\theta) \right|^2$ over the different M-values which can occur with appropriate weighting factors (Tolhoek and Cox, To53; Rose, Roberts, and Dabbs, Ro56). (b) Develop the resulting expression for the angular distribution in a series of the form

$$a_0 P_0(\cos\theta) + a_2 P_2(\cos\theta) + \ldots \tag{116}$$

(c) Omit terms of order higher than the second. They derive the following formula for the relative intensity of fission fragment emission as a function of the angle θ with the c-axis of the crystal:

constant $\times\ d(\text{probability})/d\Omega$

$$= 1 + [I(I + 1) - 3K^2]f(I, I_{\text{target}})(P/kT)P_2(\cos\theta) \tag{117}$$

Here f is a dimensionless but positive function of the spins of the target nucleus of the compound nucleus, P is a measure of the coupling between the quadrupole moment of the target nucleus and the quadrupole component of the field in which it is immersed, and kT is the energy parameter of thermal excitation. The quadrupole coupling constant had been evaluated in another experiment. Thus the angular distribution due to any given channel is completely determinate:

$$\text{constant} \times d(\text{probability})/d\Omega = 1 + (T_{I,K}/T)P_2(\cos \theta) \quad (118)$$

The coefficient $T_{I,K}$ in this formula is measured in degrees Kelvin, and has been calculated by Roberts, Dabbs, and Parker (Ro57, Ro60) with the following results (Table XX).

Table XX. Factor $T_{I,K}$ (degrees Kelvin) in the formula for the angular distribution of fission products from $U^{233}(5/2^+)$ and $U^{235}(7/2^-)$ in the case of alignment in the crystalline field of $UO_2Rb(NO_3)_3$. A value of $T_{I,K}$ of $0.15°K$ implies 15 per cent more than average emission parallel (and antiparallel) to the c-axis of the crystal, and 7.5 per cent less than average emission in the equatorial plane at $1°K$. Values from Ro60. The asterisked items are associated with the channels starred in Table XIX.

K-value of channel	Target nucleus: I of compound nucleus:	U^{233} ($5/2^+$)		U^{235} ($7/2^-$)	
		2^+	3^+	3^-	4^-
0	(most intense at equator)	$\|0.115^*$	$\|0.173$	$\|0.108^*$	$\|0.108$
1		$+0.058$	$+0.129$	$+0.081^*$	$+0.092^*$
2		-0.115^*	0^*	0^*	$+0.043^*$
3	(most intense parallel and		-0.216	-0.135	-0.038
4	antiparallel c-axis)				-0.151

The observations (Ro60) give an *isotropic* angular distribution of fission fragments from thermal neutron-induced fission of U^{233}. This result appears not to contradict the assignment of channels starred in Table XX although it is of course far from providing anything like a test of that assignment. For a more complete investigation it would be natural to think of looking at specific slow neutron resonances, some of spin 2^+, others of spin 3^+.

Preliminary results (Ro60) on the thermal neutron-induced fission of U^{235} give an angular distribution proportional to

$$1 + (0.035°K/T)P_2(\cos \theta) \quad (119)$$

This preference for emission towards the c-axis and the $-c$-axis, plus evidence from α emission that I lies preferentially in the equatorial plane, together indicate that the direction of fission—or the direction of K—is more nearly perpendicular to I than parallel to it. Simple trigonometry of the triangle (I, K, R) therefore implies that K is closer in value to zero than it is to I(3 or 4). This result, too, is not incompatible with the assignment of low-lying channels starred in Tables XIX and XX—though again no proof of that assignment.

In contrast to U^{233} and U^{235}, the third fissile nucleus of technical importance, Pu^{239} ($\frac{1}{2}^{+}$) is not subject to alignment in a quadrupole electric field. Spin $I_{\text{target}} = 1$ is the minimum value for which such alignment is in principle possible.

K. Angular Distribution in Photofission

So much for the angular distribution associated with specific channels of even-even nuclei created by slow neutron irradiation; now for even-even nuclei excited by γ radiation (Bo56, Gr59, Co59). The target nucleus is in the state $I = 0$, $M = 0$ completely unaligned. Let the direction of propagation of the radiation be called the Z-axis, and let the radiation be assumed to be circularly polarized in the positive (right hand) sense about this axis. Then the ratio of angular momentum about this axis brought in by the photon to energy brought in by the photon is 1/(circular frequency of the radiation). In other words, by whatever mechanism the photon is absorbed, it carries the nucleus to a state of magnetic quantum number $M = 1$. Unpolarized radiation—or linearly polarized—radiation results in a mixture of states—or a linear combination of states—with $M = \pm 1$.

The spin I of the excited state must be one or more. The principal mechanisms of absorption lead to $I = 1^{-}$ (electric dipole transition) or $I = 2^{+}$ (electric quadrupole mechanism).

Electric dipole absorption of energy near or only a little above threshold gives the nucleus access to only two low-lying channels, $I = 1^{-}$, $K = 0$, according to Table XIX. The nucleus goes over the barrier in one channel with one quantum of excitation of the pear shaped vibration; in the other channel with one quantum of bending vibration. The probability for symmetric fission is expected to be extra low (Wh56). The predicted angular distribution (Bo56) is

$$d(\text{probability})/d\Omega = (3/4\pi)\left|D_{10}^{1}\right|^{2} = 3/8\pi \sin^{2}\theta \qquad (120)$$

peaking at $\theta = 90°$; that is, at right angles to the beam.

Electric quadrupole absorption leads to states $I = 2^+$, $M = 1$. Among channels with $I = 2^+$, according to Table XIX, one is lower by $\sim$1.5 Mev than any other. It is associated with complete absence of collective vibration, and endowed with two units of collective rotation, and with angular momentum $K = 0$ about the axis of extension. The angular distribution calculated for this channel is

$$d(\text{probability})/d\Omega = (5/4\pi)\left|D_{10}^2\right|^2 = (15/16\pi)\sin^2 2\theta \quad (121)$$

This function peaks at $\theta = 45°$ and $\theta = 135°$, and vanishes at $\theta = 0°$, $90°$, and $180°$.

The absolute cross section for quadrupole absorption of photons of $\sim$5 or 6 Mev from the ground state of an even-even nucleus is expected to be considerably less than that for dipole absorption. However, the natural preference for dipole absorption might conceivably be compensated or even over-compensated, Griffin points out, if the $(1^-, 0)$ channel is well above the $(2^+, 0)$ channel; that is, if the quantum energy of the vibration of the pear type at the saddle is several hundred kev or more.

Anisotropic distribution in angle of the fragments from photofission was first observed by Winhold, Halpern, and Demos (Wi52) for Th^{232} and U^{238}. More fragments came off per unit solid angle of directions perpendicular to the beam than parallel to it, provided that the energy of the photon did not exceed threshold by more than a few Mev. At higher energies the angular distribution became more and more isotropic. In other words, when the relative angular distribution was represented as a function of the form

$$1 + \alpha \sin^2 \theta \quad (122)$$

the factor $\alpha(E)$ was found to be a decreasing function of energy. More recent studies of photofission by many workers are summarized by Katz, Baerg, and Brown (Ka58) who themselves have measured the angular distribution near threshold in even-even nuclei with sharper energy resolution and still more striking results. They find no evidence for an angular distribution of the type predicted for quadrupole absorption; an expression of the form (122) is adequate to describe the data. They recall that out of states $I = 1^-$, $M = 1$ only those channels can lead which have $K = 0$ or $K = 1$. The two angular distributions are

$$\sin^2 \theta \ (K = 0) \quad (123)$$

and

$$2 - \sin^2 \theta \qquad (K = 1) \tag{124}$$

A mixture of the two kinds of channels with equal probability leads to an isotropic angular distribution: $\alpha = 0$. Thus the magnitude of α measures the contribution of channels with $K = 0$ relative to channels with $K = 1$. Katz and collaborators find $\alpha \approx 25$ for Th^{232} with a continuous γ-ray spectrum which terminates sharply at $\hbar\omega_{peak} = 6.5$ Mev, and $\alpha = 13 \pm 1$ for $\hbar\omega_{peak} = 7.0$ Mev. The anisotropy coefficient falls approximately as

$$\alpha \approx 68/(E - 5)^{2.3} \tag{125}$$

In other words, the $K = 0$ channel dominates at and near threshold, but with rising energy, channels with $K = 1$ make a contribution more and more nearly equal to the contribution of channels with $K = 0$.

In the case of U^{238} Katz and collaborators find the anisotropy coefficient behaves much as in the case of Th^{232}, falling as

$$\alpha \approx 40/(E - 4)^{2.6} \tag{126}$$

This result too is reasonable from the point of view of the statistics of the channels which become available at higher energies.

L. *Statistics of K-Values for Channels*

At energies well above the threshold, channels in even-even nuclei become more and more numerous. Their spacing falls to a value less than the characteristic energy ("widening energy") $\hbar\omega_{inverted}/2\pi$, in which one channel widens out to its full opening. Therefore it begins to make sense no longer to distinguish the contributions of individual channels, but to speak about the resultant of a statistical distribution of channels. This approach becomes appropriate even sooner in odd-A nuclei. In these nuclei channels at even a little energy above the threshold are more closely spaced than they are in *even-even* nuclei. This conclusion can be drawn because as regards intrinsic or nucleonic excitations, nuclei at the saddle point cannot differ greatly from normal stable deformed nuclei.

In heavy *even-even* nuclei the first level of nucleonic or intrinsic excitation typically lies a Mev or more above the ground state (Bo58a, De58). In heavy odd-A nuclei, on the other hand, the average distance between low-lying levels of intrinsic excitation is only of the order of 200 kev (Er58a, Er59b), comparable to the ~50 kev or 100 kev "widening energy"; and spacings between are occasionally much smaller.

To sort out the contributions of individual channels in odd-A nuclei is therefore difficult. It is still more difficult in photofission experiments where the irradiation is made with a continuous β-ray spectrum rather than a line spectrum of adjustable frequency. Consequently it is understandable, in line with the original ideas of Aage Bohr (Bo56) that odd-A systems have not been found to show anisotropy in photofission. Katz and collaborators obtained the following results for five odd-A nuclei (Table XXI).

M. Possibility of Anisotropy in Photofission of an $I = \frac{1}{2}$ Nucleus

It is not excluded in principle that some odd-A nuclei may show anisotropy. Griffin notes (Gr59):

"For a target with spin $\frac{1}{2}$ ... a measurable fragment anisotropy might result if the low-lying spectrum at the barrier were favorable. In such a case dipole absorption of the photon would yield compound states $(I, M) = (\frac{3}{2}, \pm\frac{3}{2}), (\frac{3}{2}, \pm\frac{1}{2}), (\frac{1}{2}, \pm\frac{1}{2})$ in the proportion 3, 1, 2. Then the anisotropy just above threshold would depend on whether a $K = \frac{3}{2}$ band or a $K = \frac{1}{2}$ lies lower; one calculates

$$W(0°)/W(90°) = 2.0 \qquad (127)$$

for fission through the $K = \frac{3}{2}$ band only, and

$$W(0°)/W(90°) = 0.572 \qquad (128)$$

for fission through the $K - \frac{1}{2}$ band only. If both $K = \frac{3}{2}$ and $K = \frac{1}{2}$ states lie low (a not unlikely situation), the anisotropy would be considerably less than either of these maximal estimates. Moreover the observation of this anisotropy would require a rather precise definition of the energy of the photon causing fission, since the spacing between bands of different K just above threshold is probably $<\frac{1}{4}$ Mev, in contrast to the even-even case...."

N. Anisotropy in Neutron-Induced Fission; Analysis in Terms of Statistical Distribution of K-Values

Fission induced by neutrons of several hundred kev or more is like photofission in this sense: that individual channels only rarely show up, and then only when the energy in excess of the barrier is small. Typically so many channels contribute that they can be discussed statistically (Bo56, Ha58, Gr59). Halpern and Strutinski idealize the distribution in K-values at the saddle, where the distribution in K is being frozen in, as Gaussian

$$d \text{ (number of channels)} = \text{constant} \times \exp\left(-K^2/2K_0^2\right)dK \quad (129)$$

Here K_0^2 is the mean value of K^2. The spread K_0 in the probability distribution of angular momentum about the axis of extension depends upon the excitation, $E - E_f$, available in excess of the barrier. The parameter K_0 required to account for the observed anisotropy increases from roughly $K_0 \approx 1$ in the neighborhood of 1 Mev to roughly $K_0 \approx 12$ at 20 Mev.

Not all K-values in this distribution are accessible, because of the condition $K \leqslant I$. A compound nucleus with a given value for the quantum number of total angular momentum I is idealized to have a distribution in K-values following the Gaussian law from $K = 0$ to $K = I$, and necessarily zero beyond this limit.

The value of I itself is not uniquely determined for neutrons in the Mev range. If the impact of a neutron of momentum p is pictured classically, then impact parameters between b and $b + db$ are associated with angular momenta between

$$I\hbar = bp$$

and

$$(I + dI)\hbar = (b + db)p$$

and with a target area

$$d\sigma = 2\pi b\,db$$
$$= 2\pi(\hbar/p)^2 I\,dI = (\pi\lambda^2)(2I\,dI) \quad (130)$$

A distribution in I-values is expected like a single saw tooth:

$$d\begin{pmatrix} \text{probability of} \\ I\text{-value between} \\ I \text{ and } I + dI \end{pmatrix} = \begin{cases} \dfrac{2I\,dI}{I_{\max}^2} & \text{for } I < I_{\max} \\ 0 & \text{for } I > I_{\max} \end{cases} \quad (131)$$

The mean value of I^2 for this distribution is

$$\langle I^2 \rangle = I_{\max}^2/2 \quad (132)$$

Halpern and Strutinski calculated the distribution in I-values in more detail not only for neutron bombardment but also for α-particle impact, assuming that the angular momentum of the target is negligible in comparison with the angular momentum brought in by the projectile.   They find for heavy nuclei in the neighborhood of uranium

$$\langle I^2 \rangle = \begin{cases} 2.5 \ (E_n/1 \text{ Mev}) \text{ for neutron bombardment} \\ 10.3\,[(E_\alpha/1 \text{ Mev}) - 17.6] \text{ for } \alpha \text{ particles of } 25 \\ \qquad\qquad\qquad\qquad\qquad \text{Mev or more} \end{cases} \quad (133)$$

In the evaluation of the angular distribution for both bombarding agencies they idealize the distribution as having a sawtooth character like (131). Also in both cases they take the angular momentum I of the compound nucleus to lie perpendicular to the direction of bombardment; that is, they idealize the projection M of the angular momentum along this axis to be zero.

For many purposes it is convenient to think of the angular distribution as expanded in a series of Legendre functions

$$\frac{d(\text{probability})}{d(\text{solid angle})} = (1/4\pi)[1 + c_2 P_2 (\cos \theta) + c_4 P_4 (\cos \theta) + \ldots] \quad (134)$$

with most interest attaching to the coefficient of the principal term in the asymmetry, c_2. The value of this "anisotropy" coefficient is easily evaluated for the semiclassical distribution associated with $M = 0$ and arbitrary I and K:

$$\frac{d(\text{probability})}{d(\text{solid angle})} = \frac{1}{2\pi^2(\sin^2 \theta - K^2/I^2)^{1/2}} \quad (135)$$

One finds

$$c_2 = \tfrac{5}{4}(1 - 3K^2/I^2) \quad (136)$$

In other words, under normal circumstances, where the angular distribution can be well fitted by a curve of the form

$$1 + c_2(3 \cos^2 \theta - 1)/2$$

$$= \begin{cases} 1 + c_2 \text{ at } 0° \text{ and } 180° \\ 1 - (c_2/2) \text{ at } 90° \end{cases} \quad (137)$$

the angular distribution will (a) peak forward and backward when $K < I/3^{1/2}$ (positive c_2); (b) be nearly uniform for $K = I/3^{1/2}$ (zero c_2); (c) peak at the equator for $K > I/3^{1/2}$ (negative c_2). The physical reasons for these three alternative types of distribution when I and K

have well-defined values apply equally well when I and K have standard *distributions* in values, as assumed by Halpern and Strutinski. They have calculated the angular distribution of fission fragments on the basis of these distributions in I and K and find that the results depend only on the ratio between K_0^2 and $\langle I^2 \rangle$, just as Eqs. (136) and (137) depend only on the ratio between K^2 and I^2.

When K_0^2 is very small compared to $\langle I^2 \rangle$, the angular momentum of the transition state nucleus lies primarily in the component $R = (I^2 - K^2)^{1/2}$ at right angles to the line of extension. In other words (a) I is perpendicular to the direction of bombardment; (b) the vector R is nearly parallel to I; (c) the rotation of the fission form is nearly all about R—and therefore nearly all about I—a direction nearly at right angles to the direction of extension; (d) all values of the angle θ between the direction of bombardment and the direction of emergence of the fission fragments are about equally probable; (e) therefore, the distribution in *solid* angle is approximately proportional to $1/\sin \theta$. This kind of distribution is not represented with great accuracy by an expression of the form (137), but in this extreme the calculated asymmetry coefficient has its maximum value $c_2 = \frac{5}{4}$, corresponding (if taken literally) to a ratio of intensities at $0°$ compared to $90°$ equal to $1\frac{8}{8}/\frac{3}{8} = 6$.

When the asymmetry coefficient is significantly smaller than 1, then the results of Halpern and Strutinski are well represented by expression (137) with

$$c_2 = \langle I^2 \rangle / 6K_0^2 \tag{138}$$

in other words, by the angular distribution

$$\frac{d(\text{probability})}{d(\text{solid angle})} = (1/4\pi)\left[1 + \frac{\langle I \rangle^2}{6K_0^2} \times \frac{3\cos^2 \theta - 1}{2} \right] \tag{139}$$

The important feature of the angular distribution [Eq. (139)] is this: that it never peaks in the equatorial direction ($\theta = 90°$). The distribution does not include enough cases where K is greater than $I/3^{1/2}$—enough cases where the extension is nearly along the direction of I—to show up, no matter *how large* K_0^2 happens to be in comparison with $\langle I^2 \rangle$. Even an infinite value of K_0^2 corresponds only to a distribution in values of K uniform from $K = 0$ to $K = K_{\max} = I$—and for such a distribution the asymmetry merely vanishes, it does not change sign.

The qualitative behavior of anisotropy as a function of bombarding energy in the statistical region can be read from an expression of the form (138). Consider 2-Mev neutrons incident on Th^{232}, so that the compound nucleus has odd A and closely spaced channels. The fission threshold lies at about 1.1 Mev. The excitation is far enough above threshold (≈ 0.9 Mev) so that at the same time many channels are accessible in this odd-A nucleus, but the parameter K_0 that measures the spread in their K-values is only of the order of unity. The total angular momentum, on the other hand, is significantly larger [$\langle I^2 \rangle$ of the order of 5, according to Eq. (133)]. Consequently there is a marked preference [Eqs. (137) and (138)] for emission of fragments at $0°$ and $180°$. With increasing excitation the quantity K_0^2 rises faster than does $\langle I^2 \rangle$, and the anisotropy decreases. The distribution of fission fragments becomes more and more uniform in angle.

O. Anisotropy Jumps Back to High Value at Onset of "Second Try" Fission

So far the energy has been supposed so low that fission and neutron re-emission were mutually exclusive alternatives for the compound nucleus. Of these two processes neutron evaporation is about 24 times more probable than fission (Va58) in the compound nucleus $Th^{232} + n = Th^{233}$. The reason is simple: the barrier against fission, E_f, ≈ 6.0 Mev, is about 1.1 Mev higher than the energy required for neutron emission, $B_n = 4.9$ Mev. However, when the energy of the bombarding neutrons rises to about 7 Mev, the 24 out of 25 nuclei which fail to divide at the first opportunity get a "second try" at fission (Bo40). The neutron that comes out at the first failure typically takes with it a kinetic energy only of the order of 1 Mev, so that the residual Th^{232} nucleus is left with an excitation of the order of $E_{ex} = 6$ Mev. Moreover, the likelihood that this second try will be successful is much greater than was the chance of success on the first try. The energy to dislodge a neutron is now $B_n = 6.3$ Mev whereas the fission barrier is now *smaller*, $E_f \approx 5.5$ Mev. Consequently, the fission that occur for neutron energies of 7 Mev are largely "second try" fissions.

What about angular momentum and angular distribution in second try fissions? The value of $\langle I^2 \rangle$ according to Eq. (133) is about $2.5 \times (7 \text{ Mev}/1 \text{ Mev}) = 17.5$. Moreover, the angular momentum of the Th^{233} is so large that the angular momentum taken away by the evaporated neutron is normally negligible by comparison. So I-values of 3, 4, 5 occur for the 6 Mev excited residual Th^{232} nucleus with substantial probability. As this nucleus elongates and goes over the barrier, however, it has available only ~ 0.5 Mev for nucleonic excitation. Only the lowest-lying channels are accessible. For them the spread of K-values will be small: $K_0^2 \approx 1$. Consequently, the angular momentum I will reside principally in rotation R about the "$\perp$-axis" of the fission form. This axis will be nearly parallel to I. The angular distribution will approach something like

$$\frac{d \text{ (probability)}}{d \text{ (solid angle)}} = \frac{1}{2\pi^2 \sin\theta} \tag{139a}$$

The asymmetry will become very large. At still higher energies channels with a wider variety of K-values become accessible, and the anisotropy gradually fades away, only to come in again at energies high enough for "third try" fission.

P. The Discovery of Anisotropy

Anisotropy in the direction of emergence of fission fragments was discovered by Dickinson and Brolley (Di53). In subsequent measurements of the energy dependence of the anisotropy of Th^{232} by Henkel and Brolley (He56) the first evidence was found that the anisotropy coefficient c_2 falls off fast from $E_n = 2$ Mev to $E_n = 6$ Mev, then suddenly becomes large at $E_n = 7$ Mev and again falls off, in accord with the subsequent predictions of the channel analysis.

More recent studies of the angular distribution in the fission of other nuclei are compatible with this same type of statistical account. An account of measurements in $U^{233}(n, f)$ and $Pu^{239}(n, f)$ appears in a paper of Blumberg and Leachman (Bl59a) who also give references to work on other nuclear species.

Q. Individual Channel Seen in $Th^{232}(n, f)$ Near Threshold for "First Try" Fission

The original observations of Henkel and Brolley showed the saw-tooth dependence of anisotropy upon energy above $E_n = 2$ Mev which is so striking for this and other nuclei and which is expected from the smallness of K_0^2 relative to $\langle I^2 \rangle$ just above a fission threshold.

Table XXI. The angular distribution of fragments from photo-fission of nuclei of odd A shows no evidence of anisotropy (Katz, Baerg, and Brown, Ka58). It follows that the contributions to the anisotropy from the $K = 0$ channels (proportional to $\sin^2\theta$) and the $K = 1$ channels (proportional to $2-\sin^2\theta$) are nearly equal. Of course the total *number* of fissions that then occur by way of the two kinds of channels are not then equal, but instead stand in the ratio of $\langle\sin^2\theta\rangle = \frac{2}{3}$ to $\langle 2-\sin^2\theta\rangle = \frac{4}{3}$. The table lists the ratio (number of fission fragments observed at $90°$ to the x-ray beam)/(number of fragments at $0°$).

$\hbar\omega_{peak}$ I	U^{233} $5/2+$	U^{35} $7/2-$	Np^{237} $5/2+$	Pu^{239} $1/2+$	Am^{241} $5/2-$
8 Mev	1.048 ± 0.07	1.024 ± 0.05	1.024 ± 0.10	1.002 ± 0.06	0.958 ± 0.07
10	1.032 ± 0.04			1.013 ± 0.05	
20	0.994 ± 0.03			0.952 ± 0.03	

Table XXII. Channel analysis of angular distribution of fission fragments from 1.6 Mev neutrons on Th^{232}. Observations by Henkel and Brolley (He56); interpretation by Wilets and Chase (Wi56). The calculated value of R/λ at this energy is $I_{\text{class max}} = 2.4$ for $R = 1.42 \times 10^{-13} A^{1/3}$ cm. The value of I^2 from Eq. (133) is 4. Therefore partial waves with $l = 4$ are judged to contribute significantly less to the formation of the compound nucleus than partial waves with $l = 3$. Not all of the observed angular distribution is accounted for by the listed channels; Chase and Wilets find an isotropic component amounting to 23 per cent of all the fissions

l of incident neutron	0^+	1^-		2^+		3^-		4^+	
I of compound nucleus (Th^{233})	$\tfrac{1}{2}^+$	$\tfrac{1}{2}^-$	$\tfrac{3}{2}^-$	$\tfrac{3}{2}^+$	$\tfrac{5}{2}^+$	$\tfrac{5}{2}^-$	$\tfrac{7}{2}^-$	$\tfrac{7}{2}^+$	$\tfrac{9}{2}^+$
Any channel of this (I, π) built on $K = \tfrac{3}{2}$, odd parity?	No	No	Yes	No	No	Yes	Yes	No	No
Per cent of fission through this channel required by least squares analysis of Chase and Wilets to account for observations of Henkel and Brolley			43			12	22		
Relevant angular distribution (to be averaged over $M = -\tfrac{1}{2}$ and $M = +\tfrac{1}{2}$)		$(d^{\tfrac{3}{2}}_{\pm \tfrac{1}{2},\tfrac{3}{2}}(\theta))^2$		$(d^{\tfrac{5}{2}}_{\pm \tfrac{1}{2},\tfrac{3}{2}}(\theta))^2$		$(d^{\tfrac{7}{2}}_{\pm \tfrac{1}{2},\tfrac{3}{2}}(\theta))^2$			
Angle where this function peaks	$90°$	$(47°, 133°)$		$(33°, 90°, 147°)$					
Minima	$(0°, 180°)$	$(0°, 90°, 180°)$		$(0°, 66°, 114°, 180°)$					
Properly normalized distribution	$(3/8\pi) \sin^2 \theta$	$(3/32\pi) \sin^2 \theta$ $(1 + 15 \cos^2 \theta)$		$(15/64\pi) \sin^2 \theta$ $(1 - 6 \cos^2 \theta + 21 \cos^4 \theta)$					

However, when Henkel and Brolley bombarded with 1.6-Mev neutrons, the fission fragments came off in greatest number 90° to the direction of bombardment, contrary to the predictions of the statistical analysis. Evidently the energy is so little above the ~1.1-Mev threshold that only a few channels are accessible, and a statistical description is not trustworthy. Wilets and Chase pointed out that a more detailed analysis was appropriate (Wi56). They found that they could account for the anisotropy on the assumption that almost all of the participating channels belong to a rotational band—at the saddle—with $K = \frac{3}{2}$ and odd parity (Table XXII).

R. Interference Between Contributions from Different Channels and Different K-Values

Chase and Wilets calculated the number of fission fragments per unit solid angle at a given angle by adding the intensities of the effects produced by way of different channels (one of $K = \frac{3}{2}$ and odd parity; the other responsible for an isotropic component in the angular distribution). Would it not be more reasonable to add the *amplitudes*? Yes, if one were focusing attention upon fissions in which for example (a) no neutrons happen to be released, (b) Sr^{95} is formed in a state of spin $I = \frac{7}{2}$ and odd parity—and specifically in the 19th excited state of this spin and parity, and with magnetic quantum number $M = \frac{1}{2}$—and (c) $_{54}Xe^{141}$ is formed in a state specified with similar detail! Let this narrowly described choice of products be designated by the letter p. Then the probability of having such a fission, with the heavy fragment emitted into a unit solid angle at the angle θ, will be given by an expression of the form

$$I_p(\theta) = \Big| \sum_K A_{pK}(\theta) \exp{(i\delta_{pK})} \Big|^2 \qquad (140)$$

The fact that there is an interference between amplitudes is emphasized here by the writing down explicitly of a phase δ_{pK} associated with each product and each channel.

It would be out of place to discourage any experiment designed to detect this kind of interference effect, with an angular distribution for Sr^{95} and Xe^{141} in one pairing of energy levels (one set of A's and δ's) very different from the angular distribution for another pairing of quantum states (another set of A's and δ's). However, experiments to date sum intensities over an enormous number of such pairings of quantum states:

$$I(\mathrm{Sr}^{95}, \mathrm{Xe}^{141}, \theta) = \sum_{\substack{\text{(over all } p\text{'s that} \\ \text{give Sr}^{95},\ \mathrm{Xe}^{141})}} I_p(\theta)$$

$$= \sum_p \sum_K \sum_K A_{pK} A_{pK'} \cos(\delta_{pK} - \delta_{pK'}) \tag{141}$$

It is reasonable to assume that the phases vary virtually at random from one pairing of levels to another. On this assumption the terms in Eq. (141) which describe interference between channels (K' different from $K;$ random values of $\delta_{pK} - \delta_{pK'}$) add up virtually to zero. The angular distribution is virtually what it would have been had there been no interference at all between channels of different K-values:

$$I(\theta) = \sum_p \sum_K \left| A_{pK}(\theta) \exp(i\delta_{pK}) \right|^2 \tag{142}$$

(incoherent addition of intensities). Therefore Chase and Wilets have to be judged correct in treating the contribution of each K-channel to the angular distribution in and by itself.

For a given K-channel the angular distribution of symmetry axes of dividing nuclei was further assumed by Chase and Wilets to be the incoherent sum of contributions coming from neutrons incident with different l-values (Table XXII). Moreover, the strengths with which the partial waves of orbital angular momentum $l = 1^-$ and 3^- contribute was evaluated from data fitting rather than from first principles. In both respects Hittmair (Hi60) has introduced new considerations.

Hittmair notes that the partial waves of different l-values have well defined relative phases before they enter into the formation of the compound nucleus. He further notes that on passage over the fission barrier toward scission what counts is the K-channel in which the division is occurring and the orientation in space (polar coordinates θ and φ) of the approximate symmetry axis of the extended nucleus—not the spin I or magnetic quantum number of the compound nucleus. In other words, the contributions of different l-values—that is to say, of different I-values—add *amplitude*-wise, not *intensity*-wise. For every one of the following alternative histories which leads all the way to fission there is a complex amplitude:

$$\begin{pmatrix}\text{incident}\\ \text{plane}\\ \text{wave}\end{pmatrix} \begin{array}{l}\nearrow (\text{higher partial waves}) \nearrow \\ \rightarrow (\text{partial wave } l = 1^-) \Big\langle \begin{array}{l}\nearrow (I = \tfrac{3}{2}^-)\\ \searrow (I = \tfrac{1}{2}^-)\end{array}\\ \searrow (\text{partial wave } l = 0^+) \rightarrow \underbrace{(I = \tfrac{1}{2}^+)}\end{array} \begin{array}{l}\nearrow (\text{higher } I\text{-}\\ \quad\uparrow\\ \text{values})\\ \end{array} \begin{array}{l}(\text{passage over barrier in}\\ \rightarrow \text{channel with } K = \tfrac{3}{2}^- \text{ into}\\ \nearrow \text{fission fragment detectors}\\ \text{set at a particular orien-}\\ \text{tation in space})\end{array}$$

compound
nucleus   (143

These amplitudes (more detail in Table XXII) have to be added with due account of their relative phases.

Consider a bombarding energy sufficiently low, of the order of a few thousand ev, to be in the region of well-separated slow neutron resonances. Let the spectrum be broad enough to span a substantial number of these fairly well defined states of the compound nucleus. Then at one energy in this band most of the fissions will occur by way of one state of the compound nucleus; at another energy, most by way of another state; and so on. Under these conditions the different I-values will contribute practically incoherently. The type of analysis outlined in Table XXII will be appropriate.

A weight factor will be assigned to each I-value to measure its contribution to the fission intensity.

The situation has changed at the 1.6 Mev bombarding energy used by Henkel and Brolley. The states of the compound nucleus are closer than their natural widths. The spectrum is continuous. All the types of states of the compound nucleus—all the I-values—which are going to contribute still contribute when small changes are made one way or the other in the bombarding energy. For these I-values it is necessary to add amplitudes according to the scheme of (143).

We conclude that the angular distribution of fission fragments ought to present new features when studied in the region of over-lapping resonances by bombarding with neutrons of *monochromatic* energy.

There is no evidence that the energy spectrum in experiments to date was sufficiently sharp to bring these new features to light. When the energy spectrum is broad, the interference effects under discussion should not appear. The *relative* phases of the contributions to a given K-channel that proceed by way of states of different angular momentum I of the compound nucleus will vary by an amount of the order of π over a spread of energies of the order of a certain characteristic width W. When the spread in neutron energy is large compared to W, the phases of the outputs from the several I-values are sufficiently at random so that each I-value yields its own characteristic angular distribution of *intensity*. Under these conditions the analysis of Chase and Wilets is appropriate. When the spread in energy is small compared to W, a different type of analysis is required which no one has yet had occasion to give.

One estimate of the energy interval W can be made as follows. Note that the change W in energy makes a change in the phase of the wave function of the order of $\pi(W/D_I)$ for states of the compound nucleus which have the average separation D_I; and at the same time produces a change of the order of $\pi(W/D_{I+1})$ for states of angular momentum $I + 1$. Equate the difference in these two phases to π, and find

$$W \sim \left| (1/D_I) - (1/D_{I+1}) \right|^{-1} \qquad (144)$$

Recall that the levels of U^{239} with spin $I = \frac{1}{2}$ and even parity formed by capture of a slow neutron in U^{238} have a spacing of about 18 ev. Assume a comparable figure for Th^{233} formed by slow neutron irradiation of Th^{232}. Use as definition of temperature T "that interval of energy over which the density of energy levels multiplies itself by the factor $e = 2.718$" Adopt for T the rough figure of ~ 0.5 Mev over the interval of excitations which is obtained by increasing the bombarding energy from 0 to 1.6 Mev. Thus for the density of levels of spin $\frac{1}{2}$ and even parity in the experiment of Henkel and Brolley estimate

$$(1/D_{1/2+}) \sim (\tfrac{1}{20} \text{ ev}) \exp(1.6 \text{ Mev}/0.5 \text{ Mev}) \sim 1/\text{ev} \qquad (145)$$

For levels of higher rotational angular momentum estimate a reduction in density proportional to $\exp\left(- \text{ rotational energy}/T \right)$, with a rotational energy of the order of

$$E_{\text{rot}} \sim (5 \text{ kev})I(I + 1) \qquad (146)$$

Thus find estimates of the level density and critical energy interval W for constructive interference from states of the compound nucleus of different I-values as listed in Table XXIII. The estimated values of W are evidently all small compared to any sharpness of definition of the energy of the compound nucleus which is obtainable by means of experimentation so far conceived. Therefore in in-

Table XXIII. Critical energy interval W for constructive interference between contributions from adjacent I-values. When the energy spread of the bombarding neutrons and the Doppler velocities of the target nuclei together cause a variation in energies of the compound nuclei large compared to W, then the contributions—to fission through a given K-channel—from states of the compound nucleus of adjacent I-values contribute with phases so much randomized that addition of intensities (with respect to I) rather than addition of amplitudes is the appropriate method to calculate the angular distribution. The following rough estimates have been made for Th^{232} bombarded by neutrons with an energy of 1.6 Mev

I		$\frac{1}{2}$	$\frac{3}{2}$	$\frac{5}{2}$	$\frac{7}{2}$	$\frac{9}{2}$	$1\frac{1}{2}$	$1\frac{3}{2}$	$1\frac{5}{2}$	$1\frac{7}{2}$
$(1/D_I)$ or levels per ev of one parity		1.0	1.9	2.8	3.4	3.9	4.2	4.3	4.3	4.0
W (ev)			1.1	1.2	1.5	2.1	3.3	5	14	5

terpreting the observations of Brolley and Henkel, it is appropriate to consider the contribution of each I-value in and by itself and add the intensities associated with each, as done by Chase and Wilets.

These investigators determined the contributions of different I-values to the intensity by curve fitting (Table XXII). Hittmair (Hi60), in a further development of the theory, goes back to first principles to determine the relative intensities. It is appropriate to sketch out his considerations here because they can be modified easily to take into account interference between different I-values when the spectrum of states of the compound nucleus is continuous and when the spread of energies is small compared to the critical energy W.

S. Factoring the Reaction Matrix

Let the amplitudes which are to be added be normalized according to the following principle: the square of the absolute value of the sum shall give the differential cross section for a fission. Then it can be read out of the work of Hittmair that the amplitude associated with any individual one of the histories in (143) is given by the product of the following factors:

(1) Amplitude associated with that partial wave in the incident plane wave (a wave of reduced wave length $\lambda = \lambda/2\pi = \hbar/Mv$, of orbital angular momentum $m = 0$ about the z-axis or axis of bombard-

ment, and of spin $s = \frac{1}{2}$) which has orbital angular momentum l and a projection μ of spin angular momentum along the z-axis:

$$\pi^{1/2}(2l + 1)^{1/2}(2s + 1)^{-1/2}\lambda$$

(2) Element of reaction matrix—or probability amplitude—associated with transition from (a) the state associated with original even-even nucleus in its ground state and the incident neutron in the state with the quantum numbers $(ls0\mu)$, to (b) the particular exit channel which has (i) certain quantum numbers of intrinsic or nucleonic motion which are not written down here, and (ii) the quantum numbers IKM: $\langle IKM | R | ls0\mu \rangle$

(3) Probability amplitude for passage from the specified exit channel to a state where a specified end of the axis of approximate rotational symmetry of the extended nucleus (symmetrization between the two ends is overlooked here for the sake of simplicity) lies in the element of solid angle $2\pi \sin \theta \, d\theta$:

$$(2\pi \sin \theta d\theta)^{1/2}(2I + 1)^{1/2}(4\pi)^{-1/2}d^I_{MK}(\theta) \tag{147}$$

The product of all three factors may be said to represent "the amplitude for a given fission history." This amplitude automatically vanishes—because the second factor vanishes—except when the angular momentum about the axis of bombardment satisfies the conservation relation $M = m + \mu = \mu$. It also vanishes except when the parity π of the state (I, π) of the compound nucleus is even (for an even value of l) or odd (for an odd value of l).

Let attention be limited hereafter to the case of primary interest, where the bombarding particle is a neutron. Also let attention be focussed on the amplitude for a history that goes through a particular type of level—particular (I, π)—of the compound nucleus. To find from this amplitude the differential cross secton for fission proceed as indicated in Table XXIV.

Hittmair simplifies the analysis by factoring the element of the reaction matrix into one part which is independent of orientation in space and another part which is completely specified by considerations of rotational symmetry (Fa59):

$$\langle IKM | R | ls0\mu \rangle = \langle IK | R | ls \rangle (ls0\mu | IMls) \tag{148}$$

Table XXIV. Combination of amplitudes for individual fission histories to find the differential cross setion for fission (a) in the case when only a single well-isolated resonance level of the compound nucleus of specified angular momentum I and parity π contributes significantly to the cross section, (b) in the case of a continuous spectrum of levels when the spread of excitation energies is broader than the critical energy spread W (the case considered by Chase and Wilets and by Hittmair), and (c) in the case of a continuous spectrum of levels when the excitation is specified substantially more narrowly than the critical spread W

Case	(a)	(b)	(c)
Level spacing versus width	$D > \Gamma$	$D < \Gamma$	$D < \Gamma$
Spectrum	Discrete	Continuous	Continuous
E sharply defined?	Yes	$\Delta E > W$	$\Delta E < W$
Focussing on contribution of channel of specified K and specified nucleonic quantum numbers?	Yes	Yes	Yes
Temporarily consider also a specified (I, π) of compound nucleus?	Yes	Yes	Yes
Conditions which determine that single l-value of incident neutron which contributes to this (I, π)	$(-1)^l = \pi$ $l = I \pm \frac{1}{2}$	$(-1)^l = \pi$ $l = I \pm \frac{1}{2}$	$(-1)^l = \pi$ $l = I \pm \frac{1}{2}$
Do what with amplitude for fission history which is thus specified in order to get differential cross section for fission through the given K-channel?	Square absolute value, then sum over both values of spin projection μ of incident neutron	Square absolute value, then sum over I and over μ	Sum over I, then square and sum over μ

Here $(lsm\mu | IMls)$ is the Clebsch-Gordan vector coupling coefficient (see, for example, Wi59, pp. 189, 289, 351–353); that is, the amplitude with which the product $\psi_m^{(l)}\psi_\mu^{(s)}$ of normalized wave functions appears in a normalized state $\psi_M^{(I)}$ built exclusively out of the two angular momenta l and s. These real coefficients satisfy the relations

$$\sum_m (lsm, M - m | IMls)(lsm, M - m | I'Mls) = \delta_{II'} \qquad (149)$$

and

$$\sum_I (lsm, M - m | Imls)(lsm', M - m' | IMls) = \delta_{mm'} \qquad (150)$$

Table XXV. Clebsch-Gordan coefficients suitable for the case where the incident particles travel parallel to the z-axis (that is, have zero component m of orbital angular momentum about this axis), impinge on an even-even nucleus in its ground state, have spin $s = \frac{1}{2}$ and a projection μ of s along the z-axis, have orbital angular momentum l, and lead to the formation of a state of the compound nucleus with angular momentum I and with projection M of this angular momentum along the z-axis

I	μ	M (set $m = 0$)	Value of vector coupling coefficient (set $m = 0$)
$l - \frac{1}{2}$	$-\frac{1}{2}$	$(m - \frac{1}{2})$	$(l + m)^{1/2}/(2l + 1)^{1/2} = (l + M + 1)^{1/2}/(2I + 2)^{1/2}$
	$+\frac{1}{2}$	$(m + \frac{1}{2})$	$-(l - m)^{1/2}/(2l + 1)^{1/2} = -(l - M + 1)^{1/2}/(2I + 2)^{1/2}$
$l + \frac{1}{2}$	$-\frac{1}{2}$	$(m - \frac{1}{2})$	$(l - m + 1)^{1/2}/(2l + 1)^{1/2} = (l - M)^{1/2}/(2I)^{1/2}$
	$+\frac{1}{2}$	$(m + \frac{1}{2})$	$(l + m + 1)^{1/2}/(2l + 1)^{1/2} = (l + M)^{1/2}/(2I)^{1/2}$

Explicit formulas for these coefficients are given by Wigner (Wi59, p. 193), and a table of those values of interest here is given in Table XXV.

Is not something being missed by summing over both values of the projection μ of the spin of the neutron along the axis of bombardment? Could one not detect a fore-aft asymmetry (difference between $d\sigma/d\Omega$ at θ and at $\pi - \theta$) if the incident neutrons were polarized and if at the same time the detectors of fission products were made capable of distinguishing between the light fission fragment and the heavy one? No, Hittmair shows, so long as attention is limited to case (b) in Table XXIV and so long as the target nucleus has spin 0, which is of course an assumption essential to all of the analysis given by him and by Chase and Wilets.

T. Final Expression for the Cross Section

In the factored notation of Hittmair the differential cross section per unit solid angle (say for heavy fission fragments—to exclude double counting!) associated with a given K-channel for fission and with a given (I, π) of the compound nucleus is

$$d\sigma/d\Omega = (I + \tfrac{1}{2})\pi\lambda^2 |\langle IK \, |R| \, I \pm \tfrac{1}{2}, \tfrac{1}{2}\rangle|^2$$

$$\times [(2I + 1)/8\pi[(d^I_{\frac{1}{2}K})^2 + (d^I_{\frac{1}{2}K})^2] \quad (151)$$

Table XXVI. Angular distribution factor for fission of *even-even* nuclei bombarded by neutrons (product of the last two factors in square brackets in Eq. (151). The normalization is such that this distribution factor, multiplied by $2\pi \sin \theta d\theta$, and integrated from $\theta = 0$ to $\theta = \pi$, gives unity. See last row of Table XXII for $K = \frac{3}{2}$, $I = \frac{3}{2}, \frac{5}{2}, \frac{7}{2}$. Extensive numerical tables of these angular distribution factors and those for other (I,K) combinations have been prepared by R. W. Lamphere and the Oak Ridge National Laboratory.

I	K	Angular distribution factor
$\frac{1}{2}$	$\frac{1}{2}$	$1/4\pi$
$\frac{3}{2}$	$\frac{1}{2}$	$(1/8\pi)(4 - 3 \sin^2 \theta)$
$\frac{3}{2}$	$\frac{3}{2}$	$(1/8\pi) 3 \sin^2 \theta$
I	K	$\dfrac{(2I + 1)}{8\pi} [(d^I_{-\frac{1}{2}K})^2 + (d_{\frac{1}{2}K})^2]$

This result applies whether the parity of the relevant state of the compound nucleus is $\pi = (-1)^{I-1/2}$ (in which case the orbital angular momentum of the incoming neutron is $l = I - \frac{1}{2}$) or whether the parity is $\pi = (-1)^{I+1/2}$ (with $l = I + \frac{1}{2}$). In both cases the first factor in $d\sigma/d\Omega$ is the geometrical target area; that is, $(l + 1)\pi\lambda^2$ in the first case and $l\pi\lambda^2$ in the second case. These numbers total to the familiar $(2l + 1)\pi\lambda^2$ that would come in for a reaction for which spin is irrelevant. The second factor comes from the reduced reaction matrix. The third factor (product of square brackets) determines the angular distribution (Table XXVI).

U. Reduced Matrix Element as a Function of I

Consider passage over the fission barrier in a given K-channel. The moment of inertia of the transition state nucleus will be large (Table VIII). The energy taken up in collective rotation about an axis perpendicular to the axis of extension will therefore be small, and of the order of

$$
\begin{aligned}
&\sim (2 \text{ kev}) \times [I(I + 1) - K^2] \\
&\sim 3 \text{ kev} \quad \text{for } I = \tfrac{3}{2}, \quad K = \tfrac{3}{2}, \text{ i.e.,} \\
&\sim 13 \text{ kev} \quad \text{for } I = \tfrac{5}{2}, \quad K = \tfrac{3}{2} \\
&\sim 27 \text{ kev} \quad \text{for } I = \tfrac{7}{2}, \quad K = \tfrac{3}{2} \\
&\sim 45 \text{ kev} \quad \text{for } I = \tfrac{9}{2}, \quad K = \tfrac{3}{2}
\end{aligned}
\tag{152}
$$

It is reasonable to think of the probability of passing over the barrier as not changing much over an energy interval of 45 kev *provided* that the energy of the compound nucleus exceeds the energy of the K-channel in question by substantially more than 100 kev. Hittmair assumes that this breakup probability is approximately the same for all the I-values of the compound nucleus that can go through the given K-channel to fission. On this basis he argues that the square of the element $\langle I_\pi K | R | l = I + [(-1)^{I+1/2}/\pi], \frac{1}{2}, s = \frac{1}{2}\rangle$ of the reduced reaction matrix should be proportional to the wave mechanical penetration factor for the partial wave in question. He therefore writes

$$
|\langle IK | R | ls \rangle|^2 \text{ is proportional to } 1/[F_l^2(R) + G_l^2(R)] \tag{153}
$$

where $F_l(r)$ and $G_l(r)$ are the regular and irregular solutions of the Schoedinger equation for the given angular momentum and R is the effective radius of the nucleus.

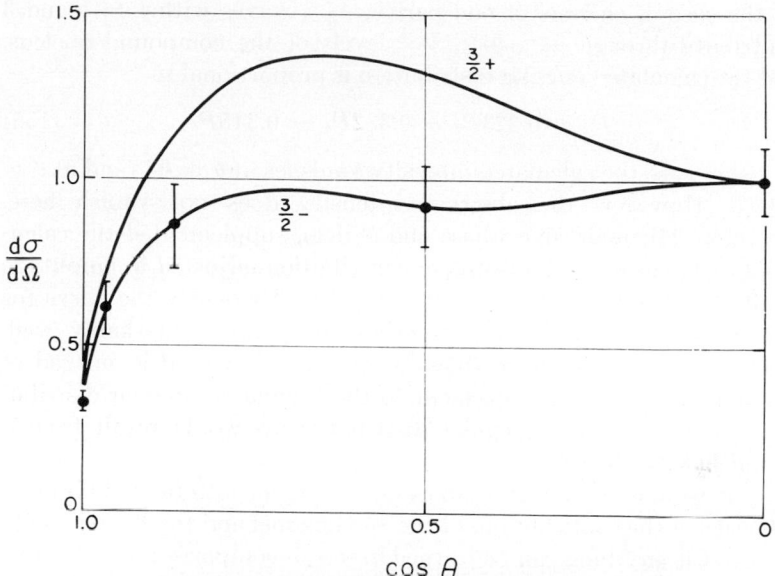

Figure 9. Angular distribution of fission fragments from Th^{232} bombarded by neutrons with an energy of 1.6 Mev. Points: measurements of Henkel and Brolley (He56). Curves: calculations of Hittmair assuming that the fission takes place mainly through a channel $K = \frac{3}{2}^+$ or mainly through a channel $K = \frac{3}{2}^-$, and supplementing angular distribution so calculated by an isotropic distribution of strength so chosen as to reproduce the observed intensity at 0°- ($\cos\theta = 1$) where there is a vanishing contribution from a channel which has either parity and an angular momentum $K = \frac{3}{2}$ about the axis of approximate rotation symmetry of the extended fission form.

Hittmair also gives a formula for decomposing into a sum of spherical harmonics the differential cross section calculated in case (b) (Table XXIV).

Hittmair has carried through the calculations in detail for the case of 1.6-Mev neutrons incident on Th^{232} and causing fission through a channel with $K = \frac{3}{2}$. If this channel has positive parity the incoming waves with $l = 2$ and $l = 4$ cause fission through levels of the compound nucleus with $(I, \pi) = \frac{3}{2}^+, \frac{5}{2}^+, \frac{7}{2}^+$, and $\frac{9}{2}^+$, and give rise (he calculates) to an angular distribution of fission

$$d\sigma/d\Omega = \text{constant } (P_0 - 0.128P_2 - 0.708P_4$$

$$- 0.096P_6 - 0.078P_8) \quad (154)$$

In the case of channel of odd parity, $\frac{3}{2}^-$, waves with $l = 1$ and 3 contribute through $\frac{3}{2}^-$, $\frac{5}{2}^-$, $\frac{7}{2}^-$ levels of the compound nucleus, and the calculated angular distribution is proportional to

$$P_0 - 0.323P_2 - 0.332P_4 - 0.345P_6 \qquad (155)$$

In either case the calculated intensity vanishes at $\theta = 0°$ (and at $\theta = 180°$). However, the observed intensity does not vanish here. Therefore Hittmair, like Chase and Wilets, supplemented the calculated distribution by an isotropic contribution adjusted in amplitude to fit the observations at $\theta = 0°$ (Fig. 9). Evidently the curve for $(K, \pi) = (\frac{3}{2}, -)$ fits the experimental points remarkably well. Hittmair finds that the goodness of fit is not impaired if, instead of assuming an *isotropic* supplement to the calculated angular distribution, he adds such an angular distribution as would result from a channel $(K, \pi) = (\frac{1}{2}, -)$.

It would be interesting to examine further into (a) the absolute intensity of the contributions of the $\frac{3}{2}^-$ channel and the $\frac{1}{2}$ channel to see what if anything can be learned from this comparison about agreement between theory and observation on the channel opening, and (b) the effect of allowing for spin orbit coupling and for nuclear deformation in the calculation of the penetration factors which go into Hittmair's analysis. In any case it is satisfying that he arrives at the same identification of the dominant channel as that which was reached by Chase and Wilets on a more empirical basis.

V. Well-Isolated Fission Channel in U^{235} Evidenced in the Reaction $U^{234}(n, f)$

Chase and Wilets argue that specificities in the angular distribution of fission fragments like those seen in $Th^{232}(n, f)$ may be expected from the neutron bombardment of other even-even nuclei near threshold. The details will depend upon the K-value of the lowest channel in the resulting odd-A nucleus, and upon the question whether the channel differs sufficiently in energy from higher channels to show up clearly. In this connection it is interesting to see the anisotropies in the distribution of fission fragments observed by Lamphere (La60) in the neutron bombardment of U^{234} (Fig. 10). Evidently individual channels show up even more distinctly in the angular distribution of fission fragments than they do in measurements on the total cross section itself as a function of energy.

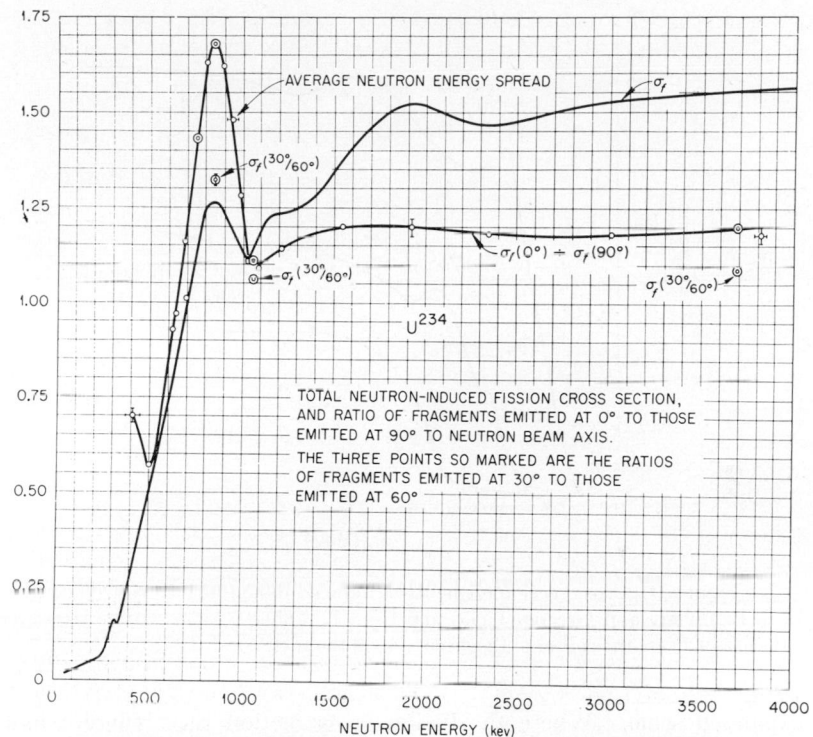

Figure 10. Cross section σ_f (in 10^{-24} cm²) for neutron induced fission of U²³⁴ and ratios of the quantity d(number of fission fragments)/d(solid angle) at 0° and 90°—and at 30° and 60°—as observed by Lamphere (La60).

4. Steps in the Number of Channels and Rises and Falls in the Cross Section for Fission

A. Competition Between Neutron Re-emission and Fission Changes as New Channels Become Accessible

In default of evidence from angular distribution to identity the angular momentum K about the axis of extension for individual fission channels, one can still see in some cases that channels are present simply from certain characteristic rises and falls in the fission cross section as a function of energy. Figure 11 shows the cross section for U²³⁴, U²³⁶, U²³⁸ from Lamphere and Greene (La55) and from Lamphere (La56); Fig. 12 shows the low energy portion of the U²³⁸ curve on an

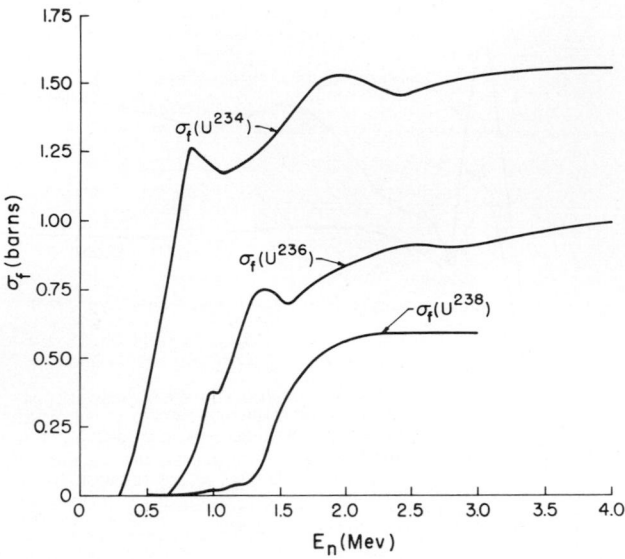

Figure 11. Cross section for neutron induced fission of U^{234}, U^{236}, and U^{238} from Lamphere and Greene (La55) and from Lamphere (La56). The rises and falls in $\sigma(n,f)$ are the center of the discussion in the text.

expanded scale. Where the fission cross section rises, there a new fission channel normally is to be considered as coming into play. Where it drops, there a new channel for neutron emission ordinarily is opening up. The analysis of these rises and falls leads straight into questions of intensity, of channel opening, of effective number of channels, and of competition between fission and neutron emission. Some of these points are clearly understood, others today have been treated only in part. Consider, for example, the angular distribution of fission fragments from Th^{232} (n,f), as discussed in the previous section. The relative number of fragments which emerge in channels $(K,\pi) = \frac{3}{2}^-$, $\frac{5}{2}^-$ and $\frac{7}{2}^-$ was determined by calculating the penetration factors for partial waves of the neutron with orbital angular momenta $l = 1$ and $l = 3$. No account was taken of the competition of various allowable neutron re-emission processes in determining the yield. A fuller account would allow for this competition from the start. Unfortunately neither in this example nor in general is it easy to calculate in detail the openings of the various channels which

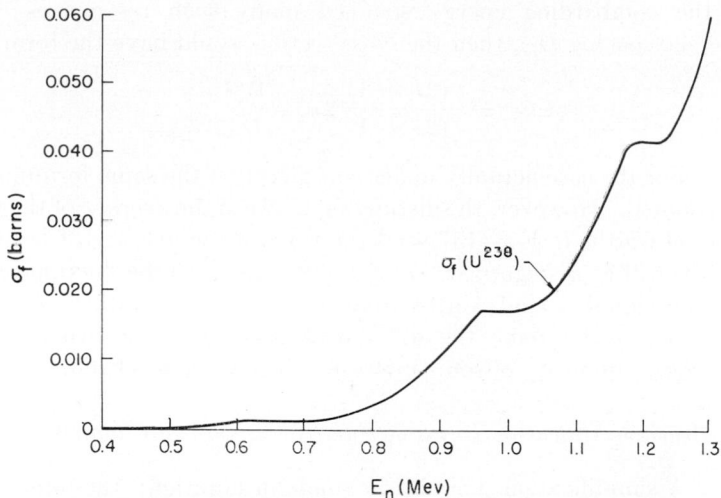

Figure 12. Low energy portion of fission cross section of U^{238} from R. W. Lamphere (La56), showing evidence for suddenly increased competition from neutron re-emission processes just above 0.96 Mev and at other energies.

compete for the output from the excited compound nucleus. Therefore the considerations in this section will have to be largely schematic and approximate.

B. Limitation to Reactions in the Continuous Spectrum

Attention will be limited throughout to the case described in the middle column of Table XXIV. The target nucleus has zero spin. The excitation of the compound nucleus is high enough—and the spread in the energy of the incoming neutrons is great enough—to allow the differential cross section $d\sigma/d\Omega$ and the total cross section σ_f to be represented as the sum of independent contributions. Each of these partial cross sections is associated with a definite fission channel (definite K-value and definite set of nucleonic or intrinsic quantum numbers) and a definite (I,π) of the compound nucleus. If one were dealing with the contribution of an isolated resonance, one would write for this partial cross section the expression

$$\sigma = \pi\lambda^2 \frac{(2I+1)}{(2s+1)} \frac{\Gamma_{n1}/\Gamma_f}{(E-E_0)^2 + (\Gamma/2)^2} \tag{156}$$

If the bombarding energy spanned many such resonances, with average spacing $D_{I\pi}$, then the cross section would have the form

$$\sigma = \pi\lambda^2 \frac{(2I + 1)}{(2s + 1)} 2\pi \left\langle \frac{\Gamma_{n1}\Gamma_f}{D_{I\pi}\Gamma} \right\rangle_{\text{ave}} \tag{157}$$

For the case actually under consideration the same formula will be adopted. However, the distinction between the average of the ratio of level widths in Eq. (157) and the ratio of the average of the level widths will be disregarded. In actuality there will be fluctuations of the individual partial widths from one energy to another of such a character as to make the differences between these two kinds of averages a quantity of some interest in its own right (Er60).

C. Reaction Matrix in Terms of Effective Number of Channels

A simplification will also be made in notation; the dimensionless quantity N_n or N_f, "yield-effective number of channels" for neutron emission or fission, will be used instead of the relevant partial widths; thus

$$N_n(I, \pi) = 2\pi\Gamma_n(I, \pi)/D_{I\pi}$$
$$N_f(I,\pi) = 2\pi\Gamma_f(I,\pi)/D_{I\pi} \tag{158}$$

Thus finally the partial cross section in question will be discussed in terms of the approximate formulas

$$\sigma_f(I\pi K) = (I + \tfrac{1}{2})\pi\lambda^2 \frac{N_{n1}N_f(I\pi K)}{N_n + N_f + N_\gamma + \ldots} \tag{159}$$

and

$$d\sigma(I\pi K)/d\Omega \doteq (I + \tfrac{1}{2})\pi\lambda^2 \frac{N_{n1}N_f(I\pi K)}{N_n + N_f + N_\gamma + \ldots}$$
$$\times [(2I + 1)/8\pi][(d^I_{-\frac{1}{2}K})^2 + (d^I_{\frac{1}{2}K})^2] \tag{160}$$

In other words, the element of the reduced reaction matrix in the treatment of Hittmair has been replaced by an expression in terms of effective number of channels:

$$|\langle IK|R|I \pm \tfrac{1}{2}, \tfrac{1}{2}\rangle|^2 \sim N_{n1} \frac{N_f(I\pi K)}{N_n + N_f + N + \ldots} \tag{161}$$

Here the quantity N_{n1} measures the chance for the compound nucleus to break up into a neutron plus the residual nucleus in its ground state, whereas N_n measures the yield effective number of channels for all processes of emission of a neutron from a compound nucleus of the given (I, π) and excitation. Similarly the quantity $N_f(I, \pi, K)$ in the numerator is but one of the contributions to the quantity $N_f(I, \pi)$ in the denominator.

D. "Competition Factor": Old and New

It follows from the form of Eq. (161) that, insofar as the quantity N_{n1} is proportional to any "neutron penetration factor," the fission cross section cannot be a strictly linear function of this penetration factor. Instead, the fission cross section is proportional to the opening of the neutron channel N_{n1}—a measure of the chance of forming the compound nucleus—multiplied by the "competition factor" $N_f(I, \pi, K)/(N_n + N_f + N_\gamma + \ldots)$—the probability that the compound nucleus, once formed, will undergo fission—a quantity which is *reduced* when the neutron channel opens wide.

The account of fission cross sections given by Eqs. (159) and (160) is finer grained than that given by the older and less detailed formula (Bo39)

$$\sigma_f \sim \pi R^2 \, \frac{\Gamma_f}{\Gamma_f + \Gamma_n + \ldots} \tag{162}$$

There the same "competition factor" was adopted for states of all angular momenta $I = \frac{3}{2}, \frac{1}{2}, \ldots$, up to the largest readily attained by fast neutron impact, $I \sim R/\lambda$. The older formula and the present ones [Eqs. (161) and (162)] are similar in this respect, that a rise in Γ_f produces a rise in σ_f, whereas a rise in Γ_n produces a drop in the fission cross section. Behind the older formula is a statistical approach, which treats channels as numerous and overlooks particularities due to any one channel or any one angular momentum. In keeping with that approach, the quantities Γ_n and Γ_f were envisaged as smoothly rising functions of energy. The observation of rises and falls in the fission cross section cannot be accounted for properly within the framework of such a statistical analysis. On the other hand, Eqs. (160) and (161) leave room for individual fission channels to show themselves in rises in the cross section and for individual neutron channels to produce drops in the fission yield.

E. *Structure Not Due to Barschall-Ramsauer Resonances*

This explanation for the rises and falls in the fission cross section did not come at once. It was first proposed (Wh56a) to try to account for the oscillations in the fission yield as due to rises and falls in the cross section

$$\sigma_{\text{compound}} \ (I,\pi) \ = \ (I \ + \ \tfrac{1}{2}) \pi \lambda^2 N_{n1} \tag{163}$$

for formation of the compound nucleus.

Barschall and collaborators (Wa54) and others (see summary of data in We56) have observed striking large scale resonances in the cross section of nuclei from Al to Pb for interaction with neutrons from $\sim$1 Mev up to $\sim$4 Mev to 10 Mev. Could not such resonances account for the peaks and dips in the fission cross section?

The Barschall-Ramsauer resonances do have a significant effect upon the fission cross section in its dependence upon energy. However, a closer investigation shows that the width of these resonances is too broad (a few Mev) to account for the scale (a few hundred kev) of the structure of immediate concern here.

A neutron wave resonating in a nonabsorptive potential well will escape much more readily if it has a zero or a small angular momentum than if it has a large angular momentum. In neither case is there any Coulomb barrier such as makes it so hard for an α particle to escape from one of the traditional α-radioactive nuclei. In the case of small angular momentum the nucleon escapes quickly, the decay rate

$$A_n(\text{sec}^{-1}) \ = \ \Gamma_n/\hbar$$

is large, and the resonance has a breadth of several Mev. But in the case of a large angular momentum will not the centrifugal barrier be large ($\sim$3 Mev for $l \ = \ 4$) and will not a 1-Mev neutron, for example, have a difficult time to escape? The estimated penetration factor is of the order

$$\exp \ (-2 \times \text{Gamow penetration integral})$$

$$= \exp \ (-2I) \sim \exp \ (-3) \sim \tfrac{1}{20} \quad (164)$$

Consequently the neutron—in the absence of absorption—will move back and forth between r_{min} and r_{max} about 20 times before escaping. Here it has been assumed, as an example, that the energy of this

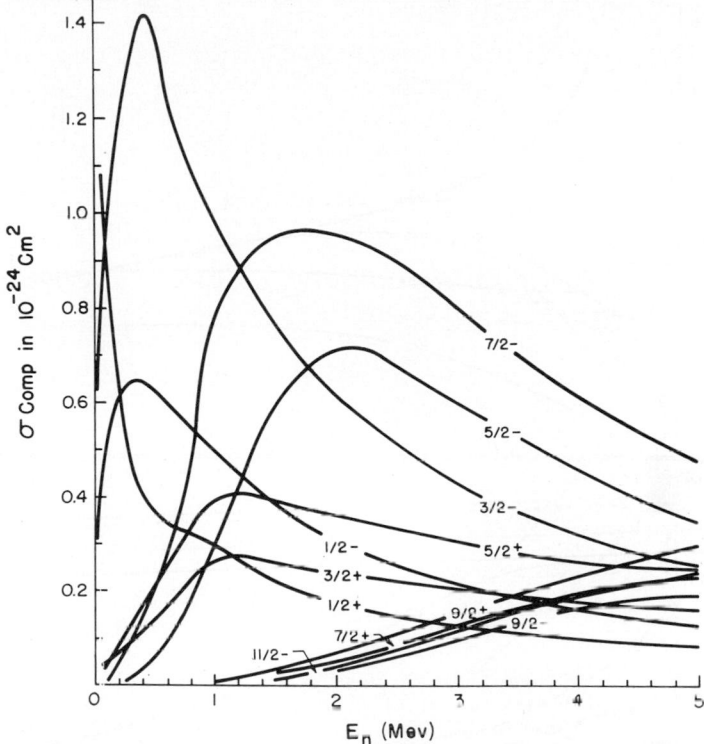

Figure 13. Partial cross sections for formation of the compound nucleus $U^{239} = U^{238} + n$ (or $U^{236} = U^{235} + n$) on bombardment with neutrons of specified i-values and parity as calculated from the optical model by Beyster (Be56). Spin orbit coupling was not taken into account in this work, but the σ_l of Beyster has nevertheless here been divided (R. W. Fuller) into parts

$$\sigma_{j=l-1/2} = l\sigma_l/(2l+1) \qquad \text{and} \qquad \sigma_{j=l+1/2} = (l+1)\sigma_l/(2l+1)$$

for comparison (Fig. 14) with optical model calculations at higher energies which do take into account such coupling. The structure in the $l = 0$ ($j = \frac{1}{2}^+$) partial wave near 1 Mev is the closest to anything like a large scale resonance that is easily to be seen in these results. The sum of the partial cross sections in the idealized case of complete opacity and geometrical optics is

$$\pi R^2 \cong \sum_{l=0}^{R/\lambda} (2l+1)\pi\lambda^2.$$

In this limit the cross section associated with a particular l-value is zero up to a certain critical energy characteristic of that l-value, then suddenly jumps to the value $(2l+1)\pi\lambda^2$, and then falls off inversely as the first power of the energy. Qualitative traces of this type of behavior are seen in the curves.

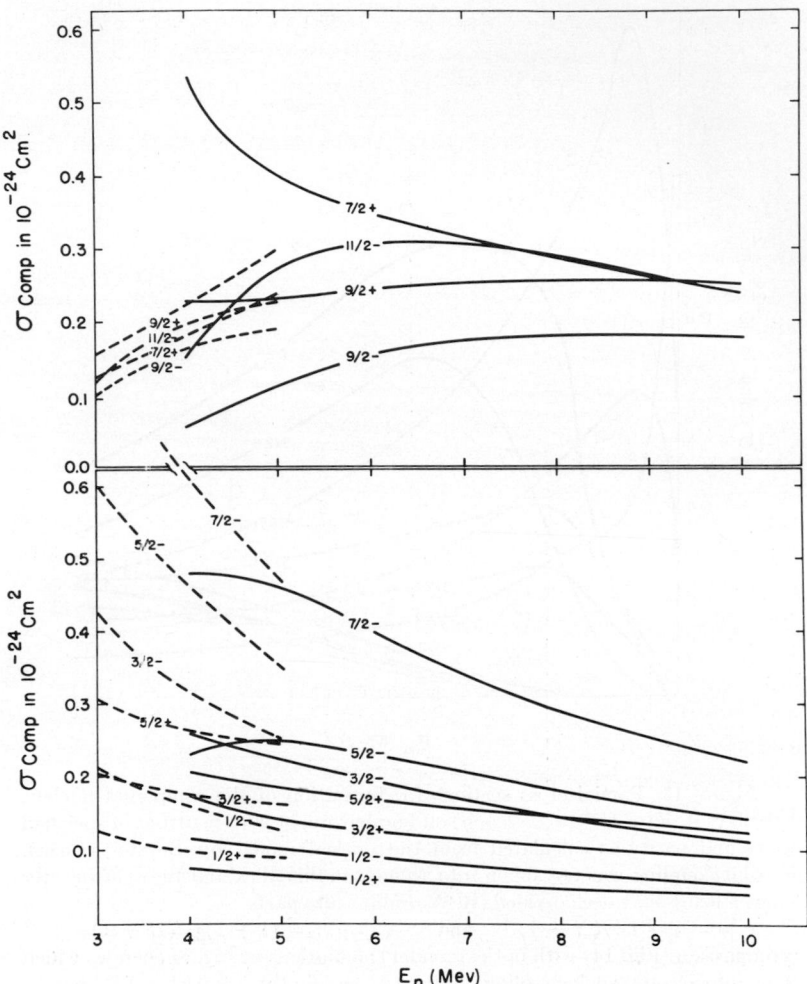

Figure 14. Partial cross sections for formation of a compound nucleus by neutron bombardment of uranium as calculated (a) by Beyster (Be56) (dashed curved) without allowance for spin orbit coupling, and (b) by Bjorklund with inclusion of spin orbit coupling. Appreciation is expressed to Dr. Frank Bjorklund for his having these calculations made and for allowing them to be published here. They followed the plan of calculations on other nuclei outlined by him in his discussion of the nuclear optical model (Bj59). The cross section for neutron-induced fission of the target nucleus U^{238} is to be calculated as a sum of the form

$$\sum_{I,\pi} \sigma_{\text{compound}} (I,\pi,E) \; \frac{N_f(I,\pi,E)}{N_f(I,\pi,E) + N_n(I,\pi,E) + \ldots}$$

nearly stationary state happens to exceed the neutron binding by about 1 Mev. Then the energy width of this state will be of the order of

$$\Gamma_n \sim \begin{pmatrix} \text{spacing between} \\ \text{single particle} \\ \text{levels of given } l \end{pmatrix} \exp\,(-2I)$$

$$\sim 10 \text{ Mev}/20 \sim \tfrac{1}{2} \text{ Mev} \tag{165}$$

Such a resonance would contribute to structure in the curve of fission cross section as a function of energy.

Any such sharpness of resonance is quite out of the question, according to the information which has been gained by comparing the optical model with observation. The absorption encountered by the neutron—its rate of exchange of energy with nuclear matter—is so great that the nucleon is fortunate if it makes the vibratory round trip once, let alone 20 times! This absorption is so great that it increases the effective width even of resonances of high angular momentum to a figure like that for resonances of low angular momentum—some substantial fraction of 10 Mev.

Figures 13 and 14 show some of this large scale structure in calculated curves for formation of a compound nucleus like U^{235} or U^{239} as a function of energy. The variations in $\sigma_{\text{compound}}(I,\pi)$ are interesting and significant. However, it is clear that they are not responsible for the $\sim\tfrac{1}{4}$ Mev structure observed in $\sigma(n,f)$ cross sections (Figs. 9, 10, 11, 12).

F. Competition Between Neutron Emission and Fission

Competition between neutron emission and fission is the explanation put forward by Aage Bohr (Bo56) for the rises and falls in the cross sections $U^{234}(n,f)$ and $U^{236}(n,f)$ as functions of energy as observed by Lamphere and Greene. This competition can be illustrated (Fig. 15; Wh56) by a schematic plot of N_f and N_n and the "competition factor" $N_f/(N_n + N_f)$ as functions of energy. This factor—either alone, or multiplied by the partial cross section for formation of the compound nucleus—shows rises and falls very like those observed in the experimental cross sections. Moreover, no alternative explanation for the observed structure presents itself. Therefore it must be concluded that a sudden rise in σ_f indicates the

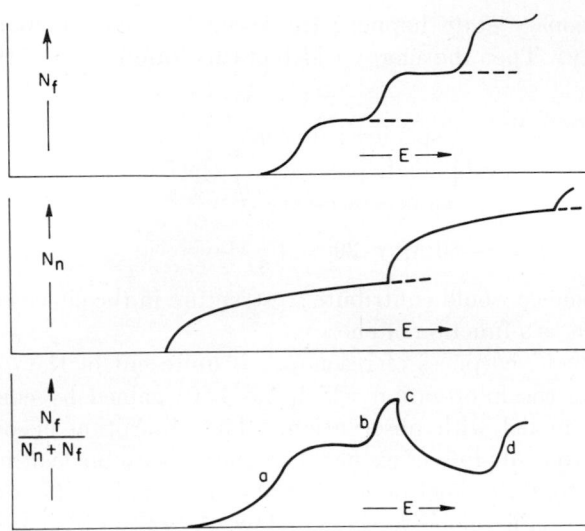

Figure 15. Competition between neutron re-emission and fission. The diagram deals with the break-up of a compound nucleus of specified spin and parity (I, π) and how the chance for fission (lowest curve) varies as a function of the excitation E of this compound nucleus. The upper curve gives as a function of energy the effective number of channels N_f for fission. This function is the superposition of three "channel width functions" W (Appendix A). The point of half of full rise on each of these channel width functions has special physical significance. It represents the energy associated with the effective top of the fission barrier in that particular channel. In other words, it marks the saddle point energy associated with that particular state of nucleonic excitation of the dividing nucleus. The full height of the rise in the channel number N_f contributed by any one fission channel is unity. Far below its saddle energy any fission channel gives a contribution to N_f which is very small compared to unity and which varies exponentially with energy. In contrast, the effective number of channels N_n for neutron emission receives a contribution from any one channel which definitely vanishes when the compound nucleus has insufficient energy to break up into (neutron) + (residual nucleus in specified state of excitation). When the angular momenta and parities of the compound nucleus and residual nucleus are such that the neutron can emerge in an s-wave, then the opening of the neutron channel varies with energy E of the compound nucleus as $(E - E_{\mathrm{resid}})^{1/2}$ near threshold. This type of situation is assumed here (for simplicity) for both neutron thresholds. The threshold energy of the lower neutron channel is identical with the energy of binding of the neutron in the compound nucleus. This energy is less in the present example than the energy of the first fission saddle. In other words, the situation depicted here is like that in the odd-even compound nuclei formed by neutron bombardment of Th^{232}, U^{234}, U^{236}, and U^{238}. Lower

opening out of a new fission channel. Similarly a sudden drop marks the threshold for a new channel for neutron emission, in which the residual nucleus is left in a new excited state.

The time has not yet come when a detailed account of the energy dependence and angular dependence of the fission cross section of any one *even-even* nucleus can be given along the above lines. (a) The relevant levels of the residual nucleus are not known in sufficient detail (see Table XIX for present expectations about some of these levels). (b) The opening of the neutron channels leading to these levels is not known as a function of energy. (c) The cross section for formation of the compound nucleus is subject to significant uncertainty. Nevertheless in unpublished work R. W. Lamphere has taken important steps towards working out and putting together these details. One can hope along these lines to gain a knowledge greatly improved over that available today about the competition between neutron reemission and fission.

All of the elements required to account for the cross section for neutron-induced fission of an *even-even* nucleus in its dependence upon angle and energy in the Mev energy range have been touched upon in at least general terms, so far as one today is able to judge, in the present account of the channel analysis of fission. Nevertheless some further detail can be supplied and the steps of the analysis can be recapitulated.

G. Recapitulation of Channel Analysis in Continuum

The differential cross section and the total cross section are ex-

---

curve: The "competition factor" which measures the probability for the compound nucleus of given (I,π) and E to undergo fission. This factor multiplied by the cross section for formation of a compound nucleus of the given spin and parity—a slowly varying function of energy—gives the partial fission cross section associated with the given (I,π). In the example this competition factor rises exponentially at a. It reaches a plateau as the fission channel becomes fully open. It rises again at b as a second fission channel starts to open. It drops suddenly at c as a new neutron channel first becomes accessible. It rises again at d as a third fission channel opens out. The actual fission cross section is a superposition of partial cross sections associated with all values of the spin and parity of the compound nucleus. The location of the channels in these various partial cross sections are shifted one with respect to another by amounts from which one can in principle deduce the moment of inertia of the critical saddle point fission form.

pressed as the sum of contributions that proceed by way of states of the compound nucleus characterized by a definite angular momentum I and parity π. Any one such contribution, regarded as a function of energy, has the form of the "competition curve" shown at the bottom of Fig. 15. Such a curve rises as a new fission channel becomes available and may fall as a new channel for neutron emission opens out, provided that it opens out sufficiently rapidly with increasing excitation energy.

The location in energy of these channels differs a certain amount from one of these "competition curves"—from one of these (I,π) values—to another. Consider, for example, the fission channels built upon a $(K,\pi) = \frac{3}{2}^-$ state of the extended fission form. Such a state will be characterized not only by this specific value of the angular momentum K about the approximate symmetry axis of the system but also by a definite set of intrinsic or nucleonic quantum numbers. The channel so selected for attention will not show at all in the "competition curves" for $(I,\pi) = \frac{1}{2}^+, \frac{1}{2}^-, \frac{3}{2}^+$, etc. It *will* lead to rises—with increasing energy—in the partial fission cross section for $(I,\pi) = \frac{3}{2}^-, \frac{5}{2}^-, \frac{7}{2}^-$, etc. The rise is governed by the channel width factor W (Appendix A). As parameters in this function there enters the nuclear excitation E and a characteristic energy interval $\hbar\omega$, which depends upon the effective curvature of the top of the barrier against fission. The value of this quantity is probably best found by examining the exponential tail of the fission cross section at energies well below threshold. It is not anticipated that the quantity $\hbar\omega$ will differ importantly from one fission channel to another. The third and final parameter in the width W of the channel for fission is the energy of this channel. For the given K-value, $\frac{3}{2}^-$, this energy differs [see Eq. (152)] appreciably ($\sim$40 kev) in going from $(I,\pi) = \frac{3}{2}^-$ and $\frac{5}{2}^-$ to $\frac{7}{2}^-$ and $\frac{9}{2}^-$. Consequently in the several partial cross sections that have to be added to get the total fission cross section, the upward steps are slightly displaced, one with respect to another. Therefore the width of rise in the resultant total cross section will be greater than it is for any of the partial cross sections individually.

H. Partial Untangling of Partial Fission Cross Sections by Analysis of Angular Distributions

Something can be done to untangle these separate rises from

each other. Each is characterized by its own distinct angular distribution (last row in Table XXII). Therefore it is appropriate to measure the angular distribution at each of several energies in the region of rise (with an energy discrimination of the order of 3 kev). Each such distribution can be analyzed into parts belonging to the relevant (I,K) values plus a background due to other channels. In this connection the author is kindly informed by Dr. R. W. Lamphere that the Oak Ridge National Laboratory has prepared an extensive table of the angular distributions for specified values of I and K. The strength of a specified (I,K) component, obtained from such an analysis, and plotted as a function of energy, should rise most rapidly at an energy some kev different from the energy of most rapid rise of a component with the same K-value but a different I-value. The difference should measure the moment of inertia of the extended fission form.

I. Moment of Inertia of Extended Fission Form

In actuality it will be necessary to proceed more cautiously to obtain a reliable value for this interesting parameter of the saddle point configuration. The multiplier of the normalized angular distribution of Tables XXII and XXVI

$$[(2I + 1)/8\pi][(d^I_{\frac{1}{2}K})^2 + (d^I_{-\frac{1}{2}K})^2] \tag{166}$$

as it contributes to the differential cross section, is not the fission channel opening $W(I, \pi, K, E)$ itself, but the quantity [see Eq. (160)]

$$\sigma_{\text{compound}, I\pi} (E) \frac{W(I, \pi, K, E)}{N_n(I, \pi, E) + N_f(I, \pi, E) + N_\gamma(I, \pi, E)} \tag{167}$$

The cross section for formation of the compound nucleus will vary differently with energy for one I-value than for another. Also the total effective number of channels available for breakup of the compound nucleus [denominator of (167)] will have a different value, and a different dependence upon energy, for $I = \frac{9}{2}^-$ than for $I = \frac{3}{2}^-$. Correction must be made for both circumstances before one can determine reliably from the observations the point of most rapid opening of the fission channel, and how this point differs for $I = \frac{9}{2}^-$ and for $I = \frac{3}{2}^-$.

J. Information Needed for Channel Analysis

From what has been said it is evident that the channel analysis of fission calls for an extensive collection of complicated information plus a sophisticated type of curve fitting. Specifically, it requires first and most importantly accurate measurement of the fission cross section as a function of angle and energy.

Second, the cross section for the formation of the compound nucleus with a specified spin and parity must be known as a function of energy for each (I, π) that contributes significantly to the fission cross section. This information is probably most readily acquired from calculations based on the optical model. Improvements have been and are being made in the optical model so that curves for $\sigma_{compound,\,I\pi}\,(E)$ more accurate and more reliable than those in Figs. 13 and 14 should soon be available. In this connection it would seem important to allow not only for spin orbit-coupling but also for the substantial departure from spherical symmetry in the effective nuclear potential.

Third, the saddle point energy S of each fission channel and the characteristic energy interval $\hbar\omega$ over which it opens out must be determined. This determination is probably best accomplished by simply trying different values of these two parameters and finding which best fit the data. It is a great simplification that there are only two parameters to be adjusted. Would that the opening of a neutron channel could be characterized as a function of energy by an equally small number of parameters!

Fourth, the effective number of fission channels leading out from a compound nucleus of given spin and parity is found by adding up the openings of all the channels which are accessible from that (I, π):

$$N_f(I, \pi, E) =$$
$$\sum_{K \leqslant I} \sum_{\substack{\text{nucleonic} \\ \text{quantum} \\ \text{numbers}}} W\left\{[E - S\,(K, \text{nucleonic quantum numbers})]/\hbar\omega\right\} \quad (168)$$

K. Opening of Neutron Channel

Fifth, a part of the effective number of neutron channels accessible to a compound nucleus of given spin and parity is found by dividing the cross section for forming the compound nucleus with that spin and parity by the ideal target area that goes with that (I, π):

$$W_{n1}(I, \pi, E) = N_{n1}(I, \pi, E) = \sigma_{\text{compound}, \, I\pi}(E)/[(I + \tfrac{1}{2})\pi\lambda^2] \quad (169)$$

This quantity represents the opening of the lowest neutron channel—the channel that leads to the ground state of the residual nucleus. This quantity is of the order of unity when the classical impact parameter of the neutron, $l\lambda = (I \pm \tfrac{1}{2})\lambda$, is less than the effective nuclear radius. In the opposite limiting case where the wave length of the neutron is long or its velocity v is low, the channel opening varies as v^{2l+1}.

Sixth and last, the other levels of the residual nucleus must be known and the opening of the channel leading to each of them must be obtained as a function of energy. This is the most difficult point in the entire analysis. Reference is made to other chapters in this book for some aspects of this problem. Some additional comments may be made here. Consider for definiteness a compound nucleus of spin and parity $(I, \pi) = \tfrac{7}{2}^-$. Ask for the width of the neutron channel leading to a state of the residual nucleus with such and such nucleonic quantum numbers and with an angular momentum about the axis of approximate rotational symmetry of $K = 1^-$. In reality there is not one state, but a whole collection of states, or bands, built upon this K-value. These states have angular momenta and parities $(I, \pi) = 1^-, 2^-, 3^-, \ldots$. All of them are in principle accessible, insofar as energy allows, from the $\tfrac{7}{2}^-$ state of the compound nucleus. The outgoing neutron takes away an amount of angular momentum determined by the familiar addition laws. For example, when the lowest of these states, $I = 1^-$ is formed by neutron evaporation from the state $\tfrac{7}{2}^-$, the wave function of the emergent neutron is a linear combination of the partial waves listed in Table XXVII. When the

Table XXVII. Partial waves relevant to a process of neutron emission which starts with the $\tfrac{7}{2}^-$ state of the compound nucleus and ends on a 1^- state of the residual nucleus.

Angular momentum j of partial wave	$\tfrac{5}{2}$	$\tfrac{7}{2}$	$\tfrac{9}{2}$
Parity of partial wave	+	+	+
Orbital angular momentum l of partial wave	2	4	4

energy of the neutron is low, the opening of this channel will be governed by the partial wave of lowest orbital angular momentum, $l = 2$, and will vary with velocity as $v^{2l+1} = v^5$. Thus the effects of this channel will not set in sharply. If this channel alone were relevant, it is questionable whether any resulting dip in the fission cross section could be seen.

Consider by way of contrast the channel which leads to the state $(K, I) = (1^-, 3^-)$ (higher band number) of the residual nucleus. The partial wave dominant for low energy of the outoing neutron has total angular momentum $j = \frac{1}{2}$ and even parity—and therefore has orbital angular momentum $l = 0$. The channel opening in this case varies as v or as $(E - E_{1^-, 3^-})^{1/2}$. This function jumps up sharply, with infinite slope, at threshold. Therefore the partial fission cross section associated with an $(I, \pi) = \frac{7}{2}^-$ of the compound nucleus will drop sharply at the energy of the state with $I = 3^-$. Likewise it will drop sharply at the band member $I = 4^-$. However, the fission yield through the specified variety of compound nucleus will not drop sharply at the energies of those states of the residual nucleus which have $I = 1^-, 2^-, 5^-, 6^-, 7^-, \ldots$.

So much for the limiting behavior of typical neutron channel openings for low energies of the emergent particle. What about the case of energies so high that the reduced wave length λ is small compared to nuclear dimensions? Then a simple result for the channel opening can be derived by applying the principle of microscopic reversibility and in addition assuming (to obtain an upper limit) that in the inverse reaction

(neutron) + (residual nucleus in state I_{res})
$$\rightarrow \text{(compound nucleus in state } I_{comp}) \quad (170)$$

the residual nucleus acts as a completely opaque target. The calculation proceeds along the line described earlier in this article for the case of a residual nucleus of spin zero (the original even-even target nucleus?), with the following changes. The angular momentum required for the incoming neutron is no longer uniquely specified; this quantity has only to lie between the two limits

$$j_{\min} = \left| I_{comp} - I_{resid} \right| \quad (171)$$

and

$$j_{\max} = \left| I_{comp} + I_{resid} \right| \quad (172)$$

Consider a definite j-value between these two limits. When a neutron with this j-value is absorbed by a nucleus with angular momentum I_{res}, what is the chance that a compound nucleus will be formed with angular momentum I_{comp}?   Proceeding semiclassically, denote by θ the angle between the two angular momentum vectors, so that

$$I_{comp}{}^2 = I_{res}{}^2 + j^2 + 2I_{res} j \cos \theta \qquad (173)$$

and

$$I_{comp}d(I_{comp}) = I_{res} jd(\cos \theta) \qquad (174)$$

The chance for the inclination between the two vectors to lie in such an angular interval $d\theta$ as will produce the desired I_{comp} is

$$\begin{aligned} \text{(probability)} &= (2\pi \sin \theta d\theta)/4\pi \\ &= I_{comp}/2I_{res} j \end{aligned} \qquad (175)$$

or, to the same degree of accuracy (analysis still semiclassical!)

$$\text{(probability)} = (2I_{comp} + 1)/(2I_{res} + 1)(2j + 1) \qquad (176)$$

Consider as before an ensemble of systems so great that each possible quantum state in the energy interval dE is occupied by one system. Then in the course of time dissociated systems will combine and compound nuclei will dissociate, but the numbers of the two countervailing reactions will be equal.   The number of formation processes of the type of interest here is given by the product of the following factors:

$\pi\lambda^2 \dfrac{(2j + 1)}{(2s + 1)}$,	cross section for neutron to come in with specified angular momentum and parity
$(2s + 1)4\pi p^2(dp/dE)dE/h^3$,	number of neutron states per unit volume
$(2I_{res} + 1)$,	number of states of residual nucleus of the specified kind
$v = dE/dp$,	velocity factor
$\dfrac{(2I_{comp} + 1)}{(2I_{res} + 1)(2j + 1)}$,	chance to come in aligned right to make specified I_{comp}
$(2I_{comp} + 1)dE/2h$,	product, gives number of formation processes per second due to neutrons of specified j-value

$(2I + 1)$ or $(2I_{comp} + 1)$, whichever is smaller	number of j-values for which the same type of considerations apply
$(2I_{min} + 1)$ $\times (2I_{comp} + 1)dE/2\pi\hbar$	product, total number of processes per second in which the target ($=$residual nucleus) in state I_{res} absorbs a neutron to produce a compound nucleus in a state I_{comp} in the energy interval dE

The number of break-up processes of the given character, in which a state of the compound nucleus in the energy interval dE, with spin and parity (I, π), breaks up to form a residual nucleus in the specified state, is

$$h^{-1}\Gamma_n(E, I_{comp}, \pi_{comp} \to I_{res}, \pi_{res}, K_{res}, \text{other quantum}$$
$$\text{numbers})(2I_{comp} + 1)dE/D_{I\pi} \quad (178)$$

or

$$N_n(2I_{comp} + 1)dE/2\pi\hbar \quad (179)$$

Here

$$N_n = 2\pi\Gamma_n/D_{I\pi} \quad (180)$$

is by definition the effective number of channels for the type of neutron emission process in question. Equating the number of formation and break-up processes, one finds the limiting formula

$$N_n \text{ (for the particular channel)} = \begin{cases} (2I_{res} + 1) \text{ or} \\ (2I_{comp} + 1), \text{ whichever} \\ \text{is smaller} \end{cases} \quad (181)$$

for the case of short wave length and ideally high nuclear opacity.

The result [Eq. (181)] can be made reasonable in the following way when the spin of the compound nucleus is larger than the spin of the residual nucleus. Presence of a magnetic field would show that the channel in question actually consists of $(2I_{res} + 1)$ distinct channels. Each of these channels has the ideal channel opening of unity. Therefore the effective number of channels is $(2I_{res} + 1)$.

The actual channel number may be less than the ideal value [Eq. (181)] by a factor as much as two even for a kinetic energy of the emergent neutron of several Mev, simply because the residual nucleus is not completely opaque to a neutron seeking to produce the reverse reaction.

Between the evidently rough limit [Eq. (181)] for high kinetic energies (1 to 10 Mev) and the limiting behavior v^{2l+1} at low velocities it is difficult to make anything more than a crude interpolation unless one is prepared to enter upon a rather elaborate calculation. It would be preferable if possible to determine $N_n(I, \pi, E)$ as a function of energy from the reaction cross section itself.

L. Neutron Channels Evidenced in Cross Section for Radiative Capture

Dr. John Huizenga has kindly pointed out (Hu60) that some evidence can be obtained on the partial width Γ_n for neutron emission—or in the present language, on the effective number N_n of neutron channels—by studying the cross section for radiative capture of neutrons in the continuum region under conditions where fission is of negligible importance:

$$\sigma(n, \gamma) - \sum_{I, \pi} \sigma_{\text{compound}, I\pi} (E) \frac{N_\gamma(I, \pi, E)}{N_n(I, \pi, E) + N(I, \pi, E)} \quad (182)$$

The term N_γ in the denominator measures the probability of radiative transitions. It will be negligible compared to the effective number N_n of neutron channels in the cases of interest here—as also in cases where fission occurs—and will therefore be dropped.

In Eq. (182), the cross section for formation of the compound nucleus and the effective number of radiative channels are smoothly varying functions of energy. On the other hand, the quantity N_n will suddenly rise when certain channels for neutron emission become energetically available. Than the cross section for radiative capture will suddenly drop.

The cross sections for radiative capture of a neutron by Th^{232} and U^{238} have been studied at energies below the saddle point energy of the lowest fission channel. The observed cross sections $\sigma(n, \gamma)$ (La57; Hu57, pp. 315, 342) show the first reasonably well-defined drop only at an energy of the order of $\sim$0.7 Mev in Th^{232} and $\sim$1 Mev in U^{238}. There would seem to be no escape from saying that this energy marks an excited state in the residual nucleus. Here then the effective number of channels for neutron emission from Th^{233} or U^{239} takes a sudden rise. In this connection it is satisfying to note how the fission cross section of U^{238} stops its rapid rise at about 0.96 Mev (Fig. 12). Again one has to say this is due to the increasing competition of neutron re-emission with fission.

M. Width of Neutron Channel Leading to State of Collective Excitation

Now for a central issue! Are the states of collective excitation of the residual nucleus to be counted on the same basis as all other states? Do they make a contribution to the number N_n of channels effective for neutron emission as great in order of magnitude as do levels of nucleonic or intrinsic excitation? Are the channels leading from $(I_{comp, \pi}) = \frac{7}{2}^-$ to higher members $(I_{res, \pi}) = 2^-, 3^-, 4^-, 5^-, \ldots$ of the band built on $(K_{res, \pi}) = 1^-$ (to take a hypothetical example already discussed) as widely open as the channel leading to the lowest state of this band—a state $(I_{res, \pi}) = 1^-$ unendowed with collective rotation? Yes! This is the answer given by the statistical analysis. This answer relies on the assumption that a compound nucleus has indeed been formed.

This assumption about formation of a compound nucleus can be expected to fail for processes in which states of collective rotation are excited which are built on the *ground* state of the residual (= target) nucleus. It is not necessary for the incoming neutron to be assimilated into a compound nucleus in order to excite such low-lying rotational states. The wave function of the neutron has only to be modulated ("rotational Raman effect") by the rotation of the deformed potential well presented by the target nucleus. There is experimental and theoretical evidence for such transitions (Dr55, Dr56, Dr58, Ch56, In56, Ch58, Bl59, Bl60). They are closely related to processes of excitation of nuclear rotation in the course of α-particle emission (Hi53, Ra53, Wh55a, Ch55, Ra56, St56b, Fr57a, Ga57, Ra58, Ra59, Ch59, Pe58). It is not obvious whether this modulation effect can be fitted into the theoretical framework used here for the channel analysis of fission. This analysis adds incoherently the effects which come by way of levels of the compound nucleus with different (I, π) values. It is conceivable that the nuclear rotational Raman effect cannot be described except by way of coherent addition of amplitudes from different (I, π) values. In this event the concept of effective channel opening for transition from a given (I, π) state of the compound nucleus to a given low-lying level of collective rotation will not make sense. The rest of the channel analysis will not be affected by this exception. However, it is also conceivable that the concept of channel opening and effective number of neutron channels can be employed for transitions to states of collective rotation built on the ground level with almost the same degree of validity which this concept possesses for other transitions. This will be the case, for example, if the modulation effects are weak in comparison with processes that proceed directly through the compound nucleus. It is interesting in this connection to note that no one has found evidence for a sudden drop in the capture cross section $\sigma(n, \gamma)$ of Th^{232} or U^{238} at the low energies, of a few kev, where the first low-lying rotational levels appear. This is not surprising. Only an s-wave incoming neutron contributes importantly to the cross section. If it were to excite the state with two units of collective rotation with appreciable probability, it would have to *emerge* with zero orbital angular momentum. This would only be possible if the neutron arrived in the partial wave with two units of orbital angular momentum—a wave which is too weak to contribute significantly to any reaction probability.

In summary, the channel analysis of nuclear fission calls on almost all branches of nuclear reaction theory, and offers ways to gain new information about nuclear reaction rates.

Thanks are expressed to the Physics Department of the University of California and the Lawrence Radiation Laboratory, where part of this account was written, for their hospitality; and to Frank Bjorklund, Harry Bowman, J. W. T. Dabbs, Robert Fuller, J. J. Griffin, E. Guth, I. Halpern, John Huizenga, Earl Hyde, R. W. Lamphere, I. Perlman, John Rasmussen, Louis Roberts, W. Swiatecki, Stanley Thompson, L. Wilets, and other colleagues for valuable discussions.

Appendix A. Channel Opening for a Fission Barrier Describable as an Inverted Harmonic Oscillator Potential

The channel width W is given [see Eq. (4) of text] by the probability of penetrating the barrier. The probability depends upon the energy at the top of the barrier; that is, upon the saddle point energy S in the case of fission; upon the energy E available in the one degree of freedom under consideration; and upon the curvature of the barrier near its maximum. Imagine the barrier inverted to make a harmonic oscillator potential. Determine the characteristic separation $\hbar\omega$ of the resulting vibrational energy levels. This energy measures the curvature of the barrier. The probability of barrier penetrations depends upon E, S, and $\hbar\omega$, not individually, but only in the combination

$$\epsilon = (E - S)/\hbar\omega$$

The accurate penetration formula

$$W(\epsilon) = 1/[1 + \exp(-2\pi\epsilon)]$$

is derived by Hill and Wheeler (Hi53), (Fig. 44). Earlier considerations exist relevant to the inverted harmonic oscillator potential: (a) Kramers and Ittman (Kr29a, Kr29b, Kr30) studied the problem of the rigid rotator with three unequal moments of inertia. They noted

Table XXVIII. Ideal fission channel opening

$\epsilon = E/\hbar\omega$	$W = F$	$\epsilon = E/\hbar\omega$	$W = F$
$-\infty$	$\exp(2\pi\epsilon)$	0.0	0.5000
-1.0	0.0017	0.1	0.6516
-0.9	0.0035	0.2	0.7743
-0.8	0.0067	0.3	0.8473
		0.3183	$W^*_{\text{extrap}} = 1$
-0.7	0.0121	0.3497	0.9000
-0.6	0.0225	0.4	0.9249
-0.5	0.0415	0.5	0.9585
-0.4	0.0751	0.6	0.9775
-0.3497	0.1000	0.7	0.9879
-0.3183	$W^*_{\text{extrap}} = 0$		
-0.3	0.1527	0.8	0.9933
-0.2	0.2257	0.9	0.9965
-0.1	0.3484	1.0	0.9983
0	0.5000	$+\infty$	$1 - \exp(-2\pi\epsilon)$

W_{extrap} refers to a straight line tangent to W at the point of inflection; that is, tangent at the point $W = \frac{1}{2}$, $\epsilon = 0$.

that the energy levels can be found only numerically, in contrast to the analytic formula possible for the symmetric rotator. They discussed an approximate solution of this problem by way of the semiclassical or JWKB approximation. They showed that there are many situations in this problem where there are two allowed regions in (φ, θ, χ) space separated by a potential barrier. They derived for the first time a formula which connects the JWKB approximations in the two potential minima with the JWKB approximation for barrier penetration. They considered the idealization of an inverted harmonic oscillator potential and applied the parabolic cylinder functions to solve the wave equation for this problem and to derive *energy levels*, but did not give an explicit expression for the *penetration factor*. (b) Voes (Vo33) considered the problem of an electron with orbital angular momentum moving in the atomic field of force. He showed that an effective potential results which can be idealized near its maximum as an inverted harmonic oscillator potential. He too applied parabolic cylinder functions, but used them to evaluate *phase shifts* for electron scattering (Ramsauer effect) and did not give an explicit expression for the barrier penetration. (c) Guth and Mullin (Gu41, Gu42) considered the extraction of electrons from a metal by very strong electric fields and idealized the barrier relevant for this problem as an inverted harmonic oscillator potential with corrections. They allowed for interference effects in the region to the left of the barrier as well as for the barrier penetration itself. They got a formula for the rate of electron escape which is therefore more complicated than the "*F*" tabulated here, but *F* can be seen as a factor in one of their terms. (d) The Kramers–Ittman JWKB approximate treatment of barrier penetration was applied to the case of the inverted harmonic oscillator potential by Kemble (Ke37), who thus derived the formula used here for barrier penetration without however proving that it is completely accurate and that it applies as well above as below the barrier. (e) Ford, Wakano, and Wheeler (Fo59) analyze the relation between the barrier penetration factor and the anamolous phase shift near a barrier maximum. Table XXVIII was calculated by R. W. Fuller.

References

(Al50)   H. Alfvén, *Cosmical Electrodynamics*, Clarendon Press, Oxford, 1950.
(Al56)   Alder, Bohr, Huus, Mottelson, and Winther, *Revs. Modern Phys.* **28**, 432 (1956).
(As53)   Asaro, Stephens, and Perlman, *Phys. Rev.* **92**, 1495 (1953).
(As57)   F. Asaro and I. Perlman, *Phys. Rev.* **107**, 318 (1957).
(Au56)   Auclair, Jacob, and Landon, *J. phys. rad.* **71**, 563 (1956).
(Be56)   J. R. Beyster, Los Alamos Sci. Lab. Report 2099 (1956).
(Be63)   Benoit, Haberstroh, and Wheeler, work as yet unpublished.
(Bj59)   F. Bjorklund, *Proc. International Conf. on the Nuclear Optical Model*, Florida State University, 1959.
(Bj63)   S. Bjornholm, A. Knutsen, and O. B. Nielsen, unpublished work kindly communicated by Dr. Bjornholm.

(Bl59)   J. S. Blair, *Phys. Rev.* **115**, 928 (1959).
(Bl59a)   L. Blumberg and R. B. Leachman, *Phys. Rev.* **116**, 102 (1959).
(Bl60)   Blair, Sharp, and Wilets, *Bull. Am. Phys. Soc.* **5**, 34 (1960).
(Bo39)   N. Bohr and J. A. Wheeler, *Phys. Rev.* **56**, 426 (1939).
(Bo40)   N. Bohr, *Phys. Rev.* **58**, 864 (1940).
(Bo52)   A. Bohr, *Dan. Mat. Fys. Medd.* **26**, No. 14 (1952).
(Bo56)   A. Bohr, *Proc. United Nations International Conf. on Peaceful Uses of Atomic Energy, Geneva* **2**, 151, 220–229 (1956).
(Bo58)   Bollinger, Coté, and Thomas, *Proc. Second United Nations International Conf. on the Peaceful Uses of Atomic Energy, Geneva* **15**, 127 (1958).
(Bo58a)   Bohr, Mottelson, and Pines, *Phys. Rev.* **110**, 936 (1958).
(Br55)   Brolley, Dickinson, and Henkel, *Phys. Rev.* **99**, 159 (1955).
(Ch55)   R. F. Christy, *Phys. Rev.* **98**, 1205 (1955).
(Ch56)   D. M. Chase, *Phys. Rev.* **104**, 838 (1956).
(Ch56a)   R. F. Christy, unpublished communication cited by Alder, Bohr, Huus, Mottelson, and Winther, *Revs. Modern Phys.* **28**, 432 (1956).
(Ch58)   Chase, Wilets, and Edmonds, *Phys. Rev.* **110**, 1080 (1958).
(Ch59)   R. R. Chasman and J. O. Rasmussen, *Phys. Rev.* **115**, 1257 (1959).
(Co59)   Conner, Henkel, and Simmons, *Bull. Am. Phys. Soc.* **4**, 234 (1959).
(Co61)   G. A. Cowan *et al.*, *Phys. Rev.* **122**, 1286 (1961).
(Da58)   A. S. Davydov and G. F. Filippov, *Nuclear Phys.* **8**, 237 (1958).
(Da58a)   Dabbs, Roberts, and Parker, *Bull. Amer. Phys. Soc.* **3**, 6 (1958).
(Da58b)   Dabbs, Roberts, and Parker, *Physica* **24**, S69 (1958).
(Da59)   A. S. Davydov and G. E. Filippov, *Nuclear Phys.* **10**, 654 (1959).
(Da59a)   Dabbs, Walter, Roberts, and Parker, *Bull. Am. Phys. Soc.* **5**, 22 (1959).
(De58)   C. De Dominicis and P. C. Martin, *Bull. Am. Phys. Soc.* **3**, 224 (1958).
(Di53)   W. C. Dickinson and J. E. Brolley, Jr., *Proc. Cambridge Meeting of the American Physical Society* **2** (January 24, 1953).
(Dr55)   S. I. Drozdov, *J. Exp. and Theor. Phys.* **28**, 734 and 736 (1955); translation *JETP*, **1**, 588 and 591 (1955).
(Dr56)   S. L. Drozdov, *J. Exp. and Theor. Phys.* **30**, 786 (1956); translation *JETP*, **3**, 759 (1956).
(Dr58)   S. L. Drozdov, *J. Exp. and Theor. Phys.* **34**, 1288 (1958); translation *JETP*, **7**, 889 (1958).
(Er58)   T. Ericson, *Nuclear Phys.* **6**, 62 (1958).
(Er58a)   T. Ericson, *Nuclear Phys.* **8**, 265 (1958).
(Er58b)   T. Ericson, *Nuclear Phys.* **9**, 697 (1958/59).
(Er60)   T. Ericson, *Phys. Rev. Letters* **5**, 430 (1960).
(Fa54)   Fairhall, Halpern, and Winhold, *Phys. Rev.* **94**, 733 (1954).
(Fa59)   U. Fano and G. Racah, *Irreducible Tensorial Sets*, Academic Press, New York, 1959.
(Fe49)   E. Fermi, *Phys. Rev.* **75**, 1169 (1949).
(Fl58)   Fluharty, Moore, and Evans, *Proc. Second United Nations International Conf. on the Peaceful Uses of Atomic Energy, Geneva*, **15**, 111 (1958).
(Fo59)   Ford, Hill, Wakano, and Wheeler, *Ann. of Phys.* **7**, 239 (1959).

(Fr57)   Freedman, Porter, Wagner, and Day, *Phys. Rev.* **108**, 836 (1957).

(Fr57a) P. O. Fröman, *Mat. Fys. Skr. Dan. Vid. Selsk.* **1**, No. 3 (1957).

(Fr62)   J. S. Fraser and R. B. Schwartz, *Nuclear Phys.* **30**, 269 (1962).

(Ga51)   S. Gallone and C. Salvetti, *Phys. Rev.* **84**, 1064 (1951).

(Ga51a) S. Gallone and C. Salvetti, *Nuovo Cimento* **8**, 970 (1951).

(Ga53)   S. Gallone and C. Salvetti, *Nuovo Cimento* **10**, 145 (1953).

(Ga57)   C. J. Gallagher, Jr. and J. O. Rasmussen, *J. Inorg. and Nucl. Chem.* **3**, 333 (1957).

(Gl41)   Glasstone, Laidler, and Eyring, *The Theory of Rate Processes*, McGraw-Hill, New York, 1941. See also K. J. Laidler, *The Chemical Kinetics of Excited States*, Clarendon Press, Oxford, 1955; E. P. Wigner, *Trans. Faraday Soc.* **34**, Part 1, 29 (1938); and James Keck, *A Statistical Theory of Chemical Reaction Rates*, Research Report 20, AVCO Manufacturing Corp., 1958.

(Go48)   S. Golden, *J. Chem. Phys.* **16**, 78 (1948).

(Gr54)   A. E. S. Green, *Phys. Rev.* **95**, 1006 (1954).

(Gr59)   J. J. Griffin, *Phys. Rev.* **116**, 107 (1959).

(Gu41)   E. Guth and C. J. Mullin, *Phys. Rev.* **59**, 575 (1941).

(Gu42)   E. Guth and C. J. Mullin, *Phys. Rev.* **61**, 339 (1942).

(Ha58)   I. Halpern and V. M. Strutinski, *Proc. Second United Nations International Conf. on the Peaceful Uses of Atomic Energy, Geneva* **15**, 408 (1958). See also St56a, St56b, and St57.

(Ha58a) W. W. Havens, Jr. and E. Melkonian, *Proc. Second United Nations International Conf. on the Peaceful Uses of Atomic Energy, Geneva* **15**, 99 (1958).

(Ha59)   W. W. Havens, Jr., *et al., Phys. Rev.* **116**, 1538 (1959).

(Hc42)   G. Herzberg, *Revs. Modern Phys.* **14**, 219 (1942).

(He45)   G. Herzberg, *Infrared and Roman Spectra*, D. Van Nostrand, New York, 1945.

(He50)   G. Herzberg, *Spectra of Diatomic Molecules*, D. Van Nostrand, New York, 1950.

(He55)   G. Hellwig, *Zeits. Naturforschung* **10a**, 508 (1955); see also F. Hertweg and A. Schlüter, *Zeits Naturforschung* **12a**, 844 (1957).

(He56)   R. L. Henkel and J. E. Brolley, Jr., *Phys. Rev.* **103**, 1292 (1956).

(Hi53)   D. L. Hill and J. A. Wheeler, *Phys. Rev.* **89**, 1102 (1953).

(Hi60)   O. Hittmair, *Nuclear Phys.* **18**, 346 (1960).

(Hu57)   Huizenga, Rao, and Engelkemeir, *Phys. Rev.* **107**, 319 (1957).

(Hu58)   D. J. Hughes and R. B. Schwartz, editors, *Neutron Cross Sections*, Brookhaven Nat'l. Lab. Report BNL-325, U.S. Govt. Print. Off., Washington, D. C., 2nd ed. (1958).

(Hu60)   J. R. Huizenga, personal communication of August, 1960.

(Hy59)   E. K. Hyde, Lawrence Radiation Laboratory Report UCRL-8783 (1959).

(In56)   E. V. Inopin, *J. Exp. Theor. Phys.* **31**, 901 (1956); translation, *JETP* **4**, 764 (1957).

(Jc55)   M. Jean and L. Wilets, *Acad. Sci. Paris C. R.* **241**, 1108 (1955); *Phys. Rev.* **102**, 788 (1956).

(Jo35) M. Johnston and D. M. Dennison, *Phys. Rev.* **48**, 868 (1935).

(Ka49) Kane, Shanley, and Wheeler, *Revs. Modern Phys.* **21**, 51 (1949).

(Ka58) Katz, Baerg and Brown, *Proc. Second United Nations International Conf. on the Peaceful Uses of Atomic Energy, Geneva* **15**, 188 (1958).

(Ke37) E. C. Kemble, *The Fundamental Principles of Quantum Mechanics*, McGraw-Hill Book Co., New York, 1937, Sections 21 and 31e.

(Ke56) See, for example, A. K. Kerman, *Mat. Fys. Medd. Dan. Vid, Selsk.* **30**, No. 15 (1956).

(Kr29a) H. A. Kramers and G. P. Ittmann, *Zeits. f. Physik* **53**, 553 (1929).

(Kr29b) H. A. Kramers and G. P. Ittmann, *Zeits. f. Physik* **58**, 217 (1929).

(Kr30) H. A. Kramers and G. P. Ittmann, *Zeits. f. Physik* **60**, 663 (1930).

(Kr57) M. Kruskal, *Proc. of Third International Congress on Phenomena of Ionization in Gases, Venice*, 562 (1957). See also R. Kulsrud, *Phys. Rev.* **106**, 205 (1957); S. Chandrasekhar, in *The Plasma in a Magnetic Field*, ed. by R. K. M. Landshoff, Stanford Univ. Press, Stanford, Calif., 1958; and H. C. Brinkman, *Physica*, **25**, 1016 (1959).

(La55) R. W. Lamphere and R. E. Green, *Phys. Rev.* **100**, 763 (1955).

(La56) R. W. Lamphere, *Phys. Rev.* **104**, 1654 (1956).

(La57) A. M. Lane and J. E. Lynn, *Proc. Phys. Soc. (London)*, **70A**, 557 (1957).

(La57a) Los Alamos Radiochemistry Group, *Phys. Rev.* **107**, 325 (1957).

(La58) L. D. Landau and E. M. Lifshitz, *Statistical Physics*, Addison-Wesley Press, Reading, Mass., 1958.

(La60) R. H. Lamphere, Oak Ridge National Laboratory Annual Physics Division Information Annual Meeting, 14 April 1960 (unpublished).

(Li47) A. M. Liapunov, *Probleme general de la stabilité du mouvement*, Princeton Univ. Press, Princeton, N. J., 1947; see also A. M. Ljapunow, *Stabilitäts probleme der Bewegung* by J. L. Geronimus, VEB Verlag Technik, Berlin, 1954.

(Me39) Lise Meitner and O. R. Frisch, *Nature (London)* **143**, 239 (1939).

(Mi57) Michel, Asaro, and Perlman, *Bull. Am. Phys. Soc.* **2**, 394 (1957).

(Mo59) B. R. Mottelson and S. G. Nilsson, *Dan. Nat.-Fys. Skrifter*, **1**, No. 8 (1959).

(Mo60) M. S. Moore and C. W. Reich, *Phys. Rev.* **118**, 718 (1960).

(Mu30) R. S. Mulliken, *Revs. Modern Phys.* **2**, 60 and 506 (1930). For Λ-type doubling, see especially the references cited by Mulliken on p. 100.

(Mu31) R. S. Mulliken, *Revs. Modern Phys.* **3**, 89 (1931).

(Mu32) R. S. Mulliken, *Revs. Modern Phys.* **4**, 1 (1932).

(Na57) Nasuhoglu, Raboy, Ringo, Glendenin, and Steinberg, *Phys. Rev.* **108**, 1522 (1957).

(Ni51) H. H. Nielsen, *Revs. Modern Phys.* **23**, 102 (1951).

(No59) Northrop, Stokes, and Boyer, *Phys. Rev.* **115**, 1277 (1959).

(Pa35) L. Pauling and E. B. Wilson, Jr., *Introduction to Quantum Mechanics*, McGraw Hill, New York, 1935. This reference treats the formulation and solution of the problem of the symmetric rotator. For the properties of the functions $D^I{}_{KM}$ and their use in transforming wave functions for a variety of problems to a rotated frame of reference, see Wi59.

(Pe58) E. Pennington and M. A. Preston, *Can. J. Phys.* **36**, 944 (1958).

(Pi58)   G. A. Pik-Pichak, *J. Exp. and Theor. Phys.* **34**, 341 (1958); translation *JETP*, **7**, 238 (1958).

(Po56)   C. E. Porter and R. G. Thomas, *Phys. Rev.* **104**, 483 (1956).

(Po59)   Porter, Christofilos, Van Allen *et al, Proc. Nat. Acad. Sci. U.S.* **45**, 1141 (1959).

(Po99)   H. Poincaré, *Les methodes nouvelles de la mécanique céleste*, Gauthier-Villars, Paris, 1892–99, 3 vols.

(Ra50)   J. Rainwater, *Phys. Rev.* **79**, 432 (1950).

(Ra53)   J. O. Rasmussen, University of California Report UCRL-2431 (1953).

(Ra56)   J. O. Rasmussen and B. Segall, *Phys. Rev.* **103**, 1298 (1956).

(Ra58)   J. O. Rasmussen and E. R. Hansen, *Phys. Rev.* **109**, 1656 (1958).

(Ra59)   J. O. Rasmussen, *Phys. Rev.* **113**, 1593 (1959) and **115**, 1675 (1959).

(Re59)   Regier, Burgus, and Tromp, *Phys. Rev.* **113**, 1589 (1959).

(Re60)   Regier, Burgus, Tromp, and Surenson, *Phys. Rev.* **119**, 2017 (1960).

(Ro56)   Rose, Roberts, and Dabbs, *Bull. Am. Phys. Soc.* **1**, 207 (1956).

(Ro57)   Roberts, Dabbs, and Parker, *Oak Ridge National Laboratory Physics Semiannual Progress Report* (September 10, 1957), p. 51.

(Ro57a)   Roeland, Bollinger, and Thomas, *Bull. Am. Phys. Soc.* **2**, 352 (1957).

(Ro58)   L. W. Roeland, University of Amsterdam Ph.D. thesis, *Massaverdelingen bij Splijting*, Drukkerij Wed. G. Van Soest, Amsterdam, 1958.

(Ro60)   L. D. Roberts *et al., Proc. Kingston Conf. Nuclear Structure*, D. A. Bromley and E. W. Vogt, eds., Univ. of Toronto Press, 1960. See also L. D. Roberts and J. W. T. Dabbs, "Nuclear Orientation," in *Annual Review of Nuclear Science*, **11**, 175 (1961); Oak Ridge National Laboratory reports ORNL 2430 and 2910.

(Sh58)   F. J. Shore and V. L. Sailor, *Proc. Second United Nations International Conf. on the Peaceful Uses of Atomic Energy*, Geneva, **15**, 118 (1958).

(Sh60)   R. K. Sheline, *Revs. Modern Phys.* **32**, 1 (1960).

(Si57)   Simmons, Henkel, and Brolley, *Bull. Am. Phys. Soc.* **2**, 308 (1957).

(St35)   P. Stäckel, *Habilitationschrift*, Halle, 1891. Summarized with much additional relevant material in the article of G. Prange, *Die allgemeine Integrationsmethoden der analytische Mechanik*, in *Enzyklopädie der mathematischen Wissenschaften*, B. G. Teubner, Leipzig, 1904-1935, Band IV, Teilband 2, p. 651.

(St54)   Stephens, Asaro, and Perlman, *Phys. Rev.* **96**, 1568 (1954).

(St55)   Stephens, Asaro, and Perlman, *Phys. Rev.* **100**, 1543 (1955).

(St56a)   V. M. Strutinski, *J. Exp. and Theor. Phys.* **30**, 606 (1956); translation *JETP*, **3**, 638 (1956–57).

(St56b)   V. M. Strutinski, *J. Exp. and Theor. Phys.* **30**, 411 (1956); translation *JETP*, **3**, 450 (1956–57).

(St57)   V. M. Strutinski, *Atomic Energy (USSR)*, **2**, 508 (1957).

(St57a)   Stephens, Asaro, and Perlman, *Phys. Rev.* **107**, 1091 (1957).

(St58)   Strominger, Hollander, and Seaborg, *Revs. Modern Phys.* **30**, 585 (1958).

(Te34)   E. Te er, *Hand und Jahrbuch der Chemischen Physik*, 1934, Vol. 9, Part II, p. 134.

(Te38)   E. Teller and J. A. Wheeler, *Phys. Rev.* **53**, 778 (1938).

(Va58)   R. Vandenbosch and J. R. Huizenga, *Proc. Second United Nations International Conf. on Peaceful Uses of Atomic Energy, Geneva* **15**, 284 (1958).

(Vo33)   W. Voes, *Zeits. f. Physik*, **83**, 581 (1933).

(Vo55)   J. von Neumann, *Mathématical Foundations of Quantum Mechanics*, Princeton Univ. Press, Princeton, N. J., 1955.

(Vo60)   E. Vogt, *Phys. Rev.* **118**, 724 (1960).

(Wa54)   M. Walt and H. H. Barschall, *Phys. Rev.* **93**, 1062 (1954).

(We56)   V. Weisskopf, *Proc. United National International Conf. on the Peaceful Uses of Atomic Energy, Geneva*, **2**, 23 (1956).

(Wh55)   J. A. Wheeler, in *Niels Bohr and the Development of Physics*, W. Pauli, ed., McGraw Hill, New York, 1955.

(Wh55a) J. A. Wheeler, in *Proc. 1954 Glasgow Conference on Nuclear and Meson Physics*, E. H. Bellamy and R. G. Moorhouse, eds., Pergamon Press, London, 1955, p. 38.

(Wh56)   J. A. Wheeler, *Physica* **22**, 1103 (1956).

(Wh56a) J. A. Wheeler, *Proc. United Nations Conference on Peaceful Uses of Atomic Energy, Geneva* **2**, 155 and 220 (1956).

(Wi41)   A. Wintner, *The Analytic Foundations of Celestial Mechanics*, Princeton Univ. Press, Princeton, N. J., 1941, Chapter VI.

(Wi52)   Winhold, Demos, and Halpern, *Phys. Rev.* **87**, 1139 (1952).

(Wi56)   L. Wilets and D. M. Chase, *Phys. Rev.* **103**, 1296 (1956).

(Wi59)   E. P. Wigner (translated by J. J. Griffin), *Group Theory and Its Application to the Quantum Mechanics of Atomic Spectra*, Academic Press, New York, 1959, Chapter 19. On p. 215 of this book are given references to the original literature on the symmetric and the asymmetric rotator.

(Wo60)   G. T. Wood, *Phys. Rev.* **119**, 2004 (1960).

The n-p Total and Differential Cross Sections in the Energy Range 0–40 Mev*

J. L. GAMMEL[1]

Los Alamos Scientific Laboratory, Los Alamos, New Mexico

1. Introduction

The following notation will be used in this paper.

E_{LAB}	The laboratory energy of the incident neutron in n-p scattering.
k	Wave number of incident neutron [see Eq. (2)].
$\sigma_n(E_{\text{LAB}})$	The n-p total cross section as a function of E_{LAB}.
$\sigma_n(\theta, E_{\text{LAB}})$	The n-p differential cross section as a function of E_{LAB}.
$\sigma_p(\theta, E_{\text{LAB}})$	The p-p differential cross section as a function of E_{LAB}.
$^3S_1$, $^3S_0$, $^3P_0$, etc.	States of the two nucleon system; usual notation. The superscript is $2s + 1$, where s is the spin angular momentum; the subscript is the total angular momentum J. S, P, D, etc., refer to values of the orbital angular momentum $L = 0,1,2$, etc., respectively, according to the usual spectroscopic notation.
δ	A phase shift. The Blatt-Biedenharn (Bl52) phase shifts are used in this paper. For a

* Since the time this article was prepared (late 1957), the author has become convinced that his arguments that the singlet shape-dependent parameter ^1P is negative is incorrect. Thus, the article must be read very critically. The fit to the n-p total cross section, however remains valid as an interpolation.

[1] This paper was prepared while the author was Fulbright Lecturer at the University of Utrecht, The Netherlands. The author is indebted to members of the Institute for Theoretical Physics of the University for their hospitality and to the Fulbright Committee and the Los Alamos Scientific Laboratory for financial support.

description of these phase shifts see also the appendix of the paper of Stapp, Ypsilantis, and Metropolis (St57). Their most useful property is that the contribution of a given state to the total cross section is simply given in terms of them [B152, Eq. (4.12)].

$\delta(^3S_1)$ The $^3S_1$ phase shift, for example.

a, ^3a, ^1a Scattering length

ρ, $^3\rho$, $^1\rho$ Effective range

P, ^3P, ^1P Shape dependent parameter

The superscript, when given, refers to triplet or singlet states.

A knowledge of the n-p total and differential cross sections is of importance in the use of fast neutron detectors of the recoil type. Wherever experimental data are lacking, this knowledge must be supplied by theoretical methods. For the total cross section, all that is required is an interpolation of the precise experimental data. This interpolation can be made with precision by using the effective range expansion, which is not based on a detailed knowledge of the nucleon-nucleon interaction. For the differential cross section, the problem is more difficult. Only relative values of the differential cross sections at angles confined to the backwards hemisphere in the center-of-mass system are measured with a precision approaching that of the total cross section data. Theoretical predictions of angular distributions are based on a detailed knowledge of the nucleon-nucleon interaction, and the experimental data are too fragmentary to determine the precision of these predictions. One main purpose of this paper is to discuss these problems of filling in gaps in the experimental data, and to show their solution or the difficulties which prevent a solution.

It is a happy circumstance that these problems go hand in hand with the problem of deducing knowledge of the nucleon-nucleon interaction from the data. The values of the effective range expansion parameters are a source of valuable, if not detailed, information about the nucleon-nucleon interaction and must be determined as accurately as possible from the data. The fragmentary data on the n-p differential cross sections in the backwards hemisphere is also a source of information about the singlet odd parity part of the n-p interaction. Another purpose of this paper is to discuss knowledge of the nucleon-nucleon interaction derived from data in this energy region.

The analysis of the total cross section data presented in this paper is very similar to previous analyses (Fi54, Sn52) based on the effective range expansion. A comparison with earlier work appears in Section 5.C. The article of Hulthen and Sugawara (Hu57) is quoted frequently as a source of information about previous analyses, the effective range expansion, and the effective range parameters. A novel aspect of this paper is the application of the effective range expansion for energies as high as 42 Mev.

Use of this expansion for $E_{LAB} > 14$ Mev requires an estimate of the contribution to $\sigma_n(E_{LAB})$ of states of the n-p system with orbital angular momentum $L \geqq 1$. A calculation of these contributions using phenomenological potentials (Si58, Ga57a, Ga57b) recently derived from high energy ($E_{LAB} < 310$ Mev) nucleon-nucleon scattering data[2] is reported in Section 2. The results are disappointingly inconclusive; nevertheless, definite values are settled on. An alternate method of obtaining estimates of these contributions from low energy ($E_{LAB} < 20$ Mev) p-p differential cross section data is discussed in Section 7.D. The results of applying this method agree with the values settled on in Section 2.

Use of this expansion for $E_{LAB} > 14$ Mev also requires an investigation of its convergence. The investigation reported in Section 3 and the Appendix, Section 8, is based on a modified effective range expansion which has a much greater radius of convergence than the usual expansion. This convergence is illustrated for a model, but realistic, potential and the singlet even parity potential of Gammel and Thaler (Ga57a). (For this latter potential, the usefulness of the modified expansion in calculating shape dependent parameters from high energy data is illustrated. See also p. 2195.) It is shown that even if the (say) $^1S_0$ phase shift were known with much greater precision than at present in the energy range $0 < E_{LAB} < 310$ Mev, all that could be learned from this information would be the values of four parameters (the singlet scattering length, effective range, shape dependent parameter, and one other parameter, which, like the shape dependent parameter, is most easily determined from the high energy

---

[2] An adequate summary of this data will not be attempted here. There is a useful collection of some total and differential cross section data by Wilmot N. Hess (He56), but for more recent polarization and triple scattering data it is necessary to consult the original papers; the paper of Stapp, Ypsilantis, and Metropolis (St57), the paper of Signell and Marshak (Si58); and recent reports of Rochester Conferences (Ro56, Ro57) are useful guides to the original papers.

data).   Finally, it is shown that the usual effective range expansion can be cut off after three terms in the energy range $0 < E_{LAB} < 50$ Mev.

Section 4 contains some remarks on the probable values of the effective range parameters based on theoretical calculations and previous data analyses.   Of particular interest is the fact that in view of the repulsive core hypothesis, the shape dependent parameters should be small and negative (Section 4.A).   It is remarked that the high energy ($E_{LAB} = 310$ Mev) p-p data prove that the singlet shape dependent parameter is negative (Section 4.A), and that the analyses of the low energy ($10 < E_{LAB} < 40$ Mev) p-p data from which it has been concluded that the singlet shape dependent parameter is positive are based on inadmissable hypotheses [Section 4.B(2)].   It is satisfying that one result of the experimental data reported in Section 5 is that the shape dependent parameters must be negative.

The most accurate data on $\sigma_n(E_{LAB})$ now (January, 1958) available are summarized in Table I.   A derivation of the effective range parameters from this data is reported in Section 5.   This derivation makes full use of the results of Sections 2–4.   Particular attention is given to the problem of the singlet effective range ($^1\rho$).   This problem is whether or not there is any evidence that the n-p $^1\rho$ is less than the p-p $^1\rho$.   The two $^1\rho$'s should be equal if the nucleon-nucleon interaction is charge independent.   (Of course, there is undeniable evidence that the n-p and p-p singlet even parity potentials are not quite the same.   However, the two $^1\rho$'s should be equal if the n-p and p-p singlet even parity potentials have the same range, even if (or perhaps because) they have slightly different depths.   The depths may differ by two per cent or so, and perhaps the ranges do also, but the effective ranges should be equal to within one or two per cent.).   From an analysis of the low energy ($E_{LAB} < 5$ Mev) p-p data employing a negative shape dependent parameter [Section 4.B(1)] and from an analysis of the n-p total cross section data in the same energy range employing a larger value of the triplet scattering length recently suggested (Br57), it is concluded[3] that the two are equal to well within even the error in the p-p $^1\rho$.

Finally, this work makes it possible to interpolate Table I with

[3] Fields, Becker, and Adair (Fi54) reached the conclusion that there is no difference in the two $^1\rho$'s, but the p-p $^1\rho$ lay at the upper limit of the value allowed by the large error in the n-p $^1\rho$.   For more details, see Section 5.

the precision of the data which it contains.   This interpolation, which is of importance in the use of fast neutron detectors of the recoil type, is discussed in Section 6.

The status of present theoretical interpretations of the high energy ($40 < E_{\text{LAB}} < 100$ Mev) data on $\sigma_n(\theta, E_{\text{LAB}})$ is discussed in Section 7.B.   It is pointed out that there still remain details of the data at $E_{\text{LAB}} = 42$ and 90 Mev which present phenomenological potentials do not explain.   Therefore, the precision of any extrapolation to lower energies is not certain, especially since there is no precise data to check the extrapolation against.   However, the circumstance that the $^3S_1$ phase shift is near 90° throughout the energy region $14 < E_{\text{LAB}} < 20$ Mev is made the basis of two final remarks about the *n-p* differential cross section in this lower energy region.   One of these remarks is that the *n-p* differential cross section can be calculated with some confidence at 90° in the center-of-mass system.   The other is that the contributions of the ^3P_J states to $\sigma_n(E_{\text{LAB}})$ also play a role in this calculation.   It is shown how the experimental *p-p* angular distributions can help determine the contributions of the ^3P_J states to the *n-p* total cross section (Section 7.D).

2. Contributions to $\sigma_n(E_{\text{LAB}})$ from States of the *n-p* System with Orbital Angular Momentum $L \geq 1$

The phenomenological potentials of Gammel and Thaler (Ga57a, Ga57b; referred to as GT in the following) and Signell and Marshak (Si58; referred to as SM in the following) are used to calculate these contributions up to $E_{\text{LAB}} = 40$ Mev.   The accuracy of these results can be estimated by comparing the predictions of GT and SM where possible.   It is also of interest to compare these predictions with older predictions, for example predictions calculated from the potential of Gammel, Christian, and Thaler (Ga57c), which did not have a spin-orbit term.

Table I shows the contributions of various states to $\sigma_n(E_{\text{LAB}})$ for various potentials.   The cross sections shown include the factors π/k^2 and the statistical weights $2J + 1$.

Table I shows that there is no detailed agreement about the contributions of various states.

However, if the contributions of all states are summed for $E_{\text{LAB}} = 40$ Mev, the result is 17.1 mb for SM, and 19.4 mb for GT.

Table I. Contributions to $\sigma_n(E_{LAB})$ (in mb) from Various States for Various Potentials

Triplet P states

E_{LAB} (Mev)	SM (Si58) $^3P_0$	$^3P_1$	$^3P_2$	GT (Ga57a) $^3P_0$	$^3P_1$	$^3P_2$	GCT (Ga57c) $^3P_0$	$^3P_1$	$^3P_2$
10	0.37	0.74	0.45	2.47	1.48	0.52	3.04	0.31	0.39
20				4.07	2.96	1.36	7.42	0.70	1.17
30				4.17	3.80	2.40	10.75	0.96	1.95
40	1.43	2.36	2.08	3.62	4.35	3.25	12.13	1.14	2.47

$^1P_1$ state

E_{LAB} (Mev)	SM $^1P_1$	GT $^1P_1$ ($^1V_C^- = -70$ Mev[a])	GCT $^1P_1$ ($^1V_C^- = -113$ Mev[a])
10	2.73	1.37	1.48
20			3.16
30			4.19
40	6.55	2.30	4.93

Triplet D states

E_{LAB} (Mev)	SM $^3D_1$	$^3D_2$	$^3D_3$	GT $^3D_1$	$^3D_2$ (4100[b])	$^3D_3$	GCT $^3D_1$	$^3D_2$	$^3D_3$
10	0.23	0.20	0.00	0.35	0.59	0.00	0.31	0.52	0.00
20							1.35	2.34	0.27
30							2.50	4.60	0.61
40	1.79	2.76	0.10	1.48	4.00	0.09	3.04	6.73	0.86

$^1D_2$ state

E_{LAB} (Mev)	SM $^1D_2$	GT $^1D_2$	GCT $^1D_2$
10	0.00	0.00	0.00
20		0.00	0.00
30		0.09	0.09
40	0.10	0.20	0.20

[a] $^1\mu_C^- = 1.0$; for notation see Ga57c. [b] See Table IV.

This agreement is good compared to the possible 7 mb error in the measurement at 42 Mev.   The old potential of Gammel, Christian, and Thaler gives 31 mb.   This last result is too large; phenomenological even parity potentials which fit the deuteron data, the triplet scattering length, and the singlet scattering length and effective range, give a contribution from the $^3S_1$ and $^1S_0$ states to $\sigma_n(42$ Mev) which cannot be reduced below 190 mb even if the potentials have repulsive cores.   Gammel, Christian and Thaler therefore found it impossible to fit the total cross section data at 42 Mev.   It is good that the recent phenomenological potentials with spin orbit terms have reduced the contribution of the triplet odd parity states by about 11 mb.

For $E_{\rm LAB} = 20$ Mev, summing the contributions of all states gives 6 mb for SM and 12 mb for GT.   Unfortunately, the difference is larger than the possible experimental error at 19.66 Mev.   This difference is not due to the D-state contributions whose total is less than 1 mb at 20 Mev; it is due entirely to the P-state contributions.

The criticism that the SM potentials do not fit the deuteron data (see Section 7.B), a criticism which also applies to the published GT potentials, is not relevant.   Actually, the triplet even parity potential used in preparing Table II for the GT case is not the published GT potential but a new potential which does fit the deuteron data (Ch57; potential 4100 in Table IV of this article).   Comparison with the published GT potential shows no change in the D-state contributions.

Table II.   Comparison of Experimental and Calculated Values of $\sigma_n(E_{\rm LAB})$

| | $\sigma_n(E_{\rm LAB})$ (barns) | | |
$E_{\rm LAB}$ (Mev)	Calculated (Eq. 30)	Experimental	Ref.
Thermal	20.34	20.36 ± 0.10	Me49
1.005	4.232	4.228 ± 0.018	Fi54
1.315 ± 0.003	3.671	3.675 ± 0.020	St54a
2.540	2.523	2.525 ± 0.009	Fi54
4.749 ± 0.009	1.683	1.690 ± 0.006	Ha53
14.10 ± 0.05	0.688	0.689 ± 0.005	Po52
14.12 ± 0.04	0.687	0.686 ± 0.007	Co52
19.655 ± 0.035	0.494	0.495 ± 0.003	Da55
25	0.381	$0.39 \ \pm 0.03$	Sh45
42	0.202	0.203 ± 0.007	Hi50

Neither is the singlet odd parity potential the one published by GT. This potential was modified after the triplet even parity potential was modified to fit the deuteron data (Ch57).

There is other evidence that the GT values are more nearly correct. The evidence given in Section 5.B(1) (last paragraph) to the effect that the results are unpleasant if the SM values are used, is not in itself convincing, unless these contributions are used for other purposes, as in Section 7.C; this point is referred to again in the last paragraph of Section 7.D. The evidence given in Section 7.D is based on experimental data, and actually suggests a contribution to σ_n(20 Mev) from the ^3P_J states larger than the GT value.

In the analysis reported in Section 5, the following contributions to $\sigma_n(E_{\text{LAB}})$ from states with $L \geqq 1$ have been subtracted from the experimental values of $\sigma_n(E_{\text{LAB}})$ shown in Table II.

$$\begin{array}{ll} 6 \text{ mb at } 14.1 & \text{Mev} \\ 12 \text{ mb at } 19.66 & \text{Mev} \\ 20 \text{ mb at } 42 & \text{Mev} \end{array} \tag{1}$$

3. The Convergence of the Effective Range Expansion

A. The Usual Expansion (Ch49a, Ch49b)

For simplicity the complication of the tensor force is not included in the following. It is not difficult to include the tensor force, especially with the paper of Christian (Ch49b) in hand; nothing is modified in an essential way. [See the first two sentences following Eq. (30.26) in the article of Hulthen and Sugawara (Hu57).]

The usual expansion (for $L = 0$) is

$$k \cot \delta = -{}^1/a + {}^1/_2\rho k^2 - P\rho^3 k^4 + \ldots \tag{2}$$

where the wave number k is given by

$$k^2 = 0.01206\, E'_{\text{LAB}} \times 10^{26}\ \text{cm}^{-2} \tag{3}$$

and the other parameters are the scattering length (a), the effective range (ρ), and the shape dependent parameter (P). The mathematical basis of Eq. (2) is outlined in Section 8.

The simple, but realistic, potential which is sometimes called the *sticky hard sphere* model is useful in understanding the result contained in Eq. (2), and in studying the convergence of the right hand side of

Table III. Comparison of δ's Calculated from the Modified Effective Range Expansion Described in the Text with Exact δ's, for Two Potentials

E_{LAB}(Mev)	Sticky Hard Core Potential		G-T Singlet Even-Parity Potential	
	Exact	Approximate	Exact	Approximate
0	1.571	1.571	0	0
5	1.334	1.334	1.105	1.105
10	1.243	1.243	1.036	1.036
40	0.914	0.914	0.711	0.711
100	0.533	0.533	0.378	0.378
160	0.257	0.257	0.175	0.175
200	0.102	0.102	0.067	0.067
228.8	0.000	0.000	0.000	0.000
260	-0.103	-0.102	-0.068	-0.067
300	-0.228	-0.220	-0.146	-0.143

Eq. (2). This potential consists of a hard core of radius r_c outside of which there is an attractive potential of zero range, so that the usual condition that the wave function (u_R) vanishes at $r = r_c$ is replaced by the condition that the logarithmic derivative of u_R has a finite, energy independent value at $r = r_c$. Of course, u_R must still vanish for $r < r_c$. Also, the potential is assumed to vanish outside of the attractive, zero range potential;[4] that is, for $r > r_c$.

The core radius and the value of the logarithmic derivative can be chosen to fit the scattering length and effective range. However, the value zero for the logarithmic derivative leads to simple equations and realistic results, as will be shown now.

For $r > r_c$, for which there is no potential, u_R has its asymptotic form

$$u_R = A \, (\sin kr + \tan \delta \cos kr), \qquad r > r_c \tag{4}$$

The condition that the logarithmic derivative, and therefore the derivative, vanishes for $r = r_c$ gives

$$k \cot \delta = k \tan kr_c \tag{5}$$

[4] Feshbach and Lomon (Fe56) have used a similar boundary condition, but prefer not to be explicit about the potential for $r \leq r_c$. They also eventually relaxed the condition that the logarithmic derivative be energy independent.

Table III shows a comparison of phase shifts calculated from this equation for $r_c = 0.9457 \times 10^{-13}$ cm and the $^1S_0$ phase shifts of GT. The core radius is chosen so that the model and GT phase shifts vanish at the same energy ($E_{\mathrm{LAB}} = 228.8$ Mev). Table III proves that the model potential is realistic.

The right hand side of Eq. (5) can be expanded in a power series

$$k \cot \delta = r_c k^2 + {}^1/_3 r_c{}^3 k^4 + {}^2/_{15} r_c{}^5 k^6 + \ldots \qquad (6)$$

Comparison with Eq. (2) shows that the scattering length is infinite, the effective range is $2r_c$; and $P = -{}^1/_{24}$, for the model potential. Equation (6) is the effective range expansion for the model potential.

The right hand side of Eq. (6) does not converge for $kr_c > \pi/2$ which corresponds to $E_{\mathrm{LAB}} = 228.8$ Mev for the value of r_c used in preparing Table III. Thus it is impossible to relate the results of phase shift analyses of high energy data ($E_{\mathrm{LAB}} > 150$ Mev) and the values of the effective range parameters by using the usual effective range expansion.

B. A Modified Expansion.

However, there is another way of expanding the right hand side of Eq. (5); namely

$$k \tan kr_c = k \sin kr_c / \cos kr_c$$
$$= k \left(kr_c - k^3 r_c{}^3/6 + k^5 r_c{}^5/120 + \ldots\right)/$$
$$\left(1 - k^2 r_c{}^2/2 + k^4 r_c{}^4/24 + \ldots\right) \qquad (7)$$

The power series in the numerator and denominator in Eq. (7) converge for all values of E_{LAB}; that is, all values of kr_c.

It is shown in Section 8 that there exists such an expansion for any potential.

The polynomial consisting of the first three terms in the denominator of Eq. (7) has two roots:

$$kr_c = 1.592 \equiv r_c/\beta_1 \qquad (8)$$

$$kr_c = 3.076 \equiv r_c/\beta_2$$

whereas the first two exact roots of the denominator in Eq. (7) are

$$kr_c = 1.571 \approx r_c/\beta_1 \qquad (9)$$

$$kr_c = 4.713$$

From the near equality of 1.592 and 1.571 it may be judged that retaining the first three terms gives a good approximation to the denominator for values of kr_c even somewhat greater than the first root.

Corresponding to these three terms in the denominator, the first two terms in the numerator of Eq. (7) should also be retained. For a potential for which the scattering length is not infinite, three terms in the numerator are retained.

The resulting expansion has the form

$$k \cot \delta = -1/a + \tfrac{1}{2}\rho k^2 - P\rho^3 k^4/(1 - \beta_1^2 k^2)(1 - \beta_2^2 k^2) \quad (10)$$

That this is so follows from the fact that if Eq. (10) is further expanded to have the same form as Eq. (2) (strict power series in k^2), then the result must agree with Eq. (2) to terms of order k^4. Equation (10) obviously satisfies this condition.

The announced modification of the effective range expansion results if the term $(1 - \beta_2^2 k^2)$ is put equal to unity and β_1 is taken from the exact root given in Eq. (9). From Eq. (9) it can be estimated that $(1 - \beta_2^2 k^2)$ varies from 1 to 0.9 as E_{LAB} varies from 0 to 310 Mev. It is not likely that it will be possible to detect such a variation in the near future. Thus, finally

$$k \cot \delta = -1/a + \tfrac{1}{2}\rho k^2 - P\rho^3 k^4/(1 - \beta_1^2 k^2) \quad (11)$$

is the form of the effective range expansion on which this paper is based.

The accuracy of this expansion can be estimated by comparing the exact values of δ's calculated from Eq. (5) and approximate values of δ's calculated from Eq. (11), which is, for the model potential

$$k \cot \delta = r_c k^2 + r_c^3 k^4/\{3[1 - (4/\pi^2)k^2 r_c^2]\} \quad (12)$$

For the value of r_c used in preparing Table III, this comparison is shown in Table III. There is no difference in the two sets of numbers.

As a final test of the validity of the expansion Eq. (11), it is used to analyze the energy dependence of the $^1S_0$ phase shifts calculated from the singlet even parity potential of GT (Ga57a). GT gives $^1a = -23.68 \times 10^{-13}$ cm, $^1\rho = 2.7 \times 10^{-13}$ cm, but not P. As an illustration of the usefulness of the modified expansion, we may calculate P and β_1^2 from Table IV of GT. The condition $\delta(^1S_0) = 0$ for

Table IV. Triplet Even Parity Potentials which Fit the Binding Energy and Electric Quadrupole Moment of the Deuteron and $^3a = 5.39 \times 10^{-13}$ cm

Code	$^3r_C{}^+$ (10^{-13} cm)	$^3V_C{}^+$ (Mev)	$^3\mu_C{}^+$ (10^{13} cm^{-1})	$^3V_T{}^+$ (Mev)	$^3\mu_T{}^+$ (10^{13} cm^{-1})	$^3V_{LS}{}^+$ (Mev)	$^3\mu_{LS}{}^+$ (10^{13} cm^{-1})	^3P	Per cent D-State
3100	0.3	56.066	1.0515	162.26	1.0515	0	—	−0.005	5.86
3105		58.504	1.1287	221.44	1.1287	5,000	3.7	−0.015	5.64
3300		701.93	1.9376	34.939	0.64585	0	—	−0.004	3.59
3305		851.40	2.0549	42.958	0.68497	5,000	3.7	−0.008	3.40
4100	0.4	87.724	1.2183	272.87	1.2183	0	—	−0.023	6.68
4105		84.086	1.2850	356.13	1.2850	5,000	3.7	−0.027	6.40
4109		75.046	1.3253	421.24	1.3253	9,000	3.7	−0.029	6.24
4113		66.245	1.3634	488.10	1.3634	13,000	3.7	−0.031	6.15
4200		726.69	1.9554	121.04	0.97772	0	—	−0.028	5.46
4205		877.39	2.0909	159.46	1.0454	5,000	3.7	−0.031	5.28
4210		966.23	2.2326	214.87	1.1163	10,000	3.7	−0.033	5.25
4300		1593.5	2.2754	52.435	0.75847	0	—	−0.022	4.27
4305		1964.4	2.4247	67.106	0.80823	5,000	3.7	−0.024	4.03
4400		2019.9	2.3259	22.719	0.58147	0	—	−0.007	3.31
4403		2202.5	2.3801	24.732	0.59500	3,000	3.7	−0.008	3.15
4407		2474.3	2.4606	28.354	0.61616	7,000	3.7	−0.01	3.04
5100	0.5	121.94	1.4112	498.73	1.4112	0	—	−0.029	7.38
5103		150.83	1.4480	504.02	1.4480	3,000	3.7	−0.031	7.22
5107		96.552	1.4884	671.45	1.4884	7,000	3.7	−0.034	7.05
5200		1587.7	2.3576	238.38	1.1788	0	—	−0.035	6.40
5205		1785.0	2.5322	333.23	1.2661	5,000	3.7	−0.037	6.29
5300		4480.0	2.8112	102.64	0.93708	0	—	−0.033	5.23
5305		5788.4	3.0337	141.42	1.0112	5,000	3.7	−0.035	5.14
5400		6780.2	3.0026	49.522	0.75064	0	—	−0.026	4.24
5403		8020.7	3.1352	58.543	0.78380	3,000	3.7	−0.028	4.15
5405		8782.1	3.2075	64.037	0.80188	5,000	3.7	−0.028	4.09
5407		9536.0	3.2742	69.512	0.81854	7,000	3.7	−0.029	4.05
5410		10,937	3.3901	79.639	0.84752	10,000	3.7	−0.031	4.03

E_{LAB} = 228.8 Mev (interpolated from their table) gives[5] β_1^2 = 0.36245×10^{-26} cm². From Eq. (10) it is easy to derive by differentiating that

$$d\delta/d(k^2) = \beta_1^2/P\rho^3 k^3, \qquad k^2 \neq 0, \quad \delta(k^2) = 0 \qquad (13)$$

where this equation is valid only for a nonzero value of k^2 for which $\delta = 0$ that is, at E_{LAB} = 228.8 Mev for the potential of GT. Using Table IV [the $\delta(^1S_0)$'s] of GT, the value of β_1^2 given above, and the $^1\rho$ value given by GT, one finds $P = -0.022$ for the singlet even parity potential of GT. This illustrates the remark that the shape dependent parameter is best calculated from high energy data. When the p-p triple scattering data at 150 Mev (Ta57, Wi57) is phase shift analyzed, the $\delta(^1S_0)$ from this analysis, the $\delta(^1S_0)$ from the analysis of the 310–Mev data by Stapp *et al.* (St57; solution 1 is currently thought correct), and the low energy p-p scattering data will determine the four parameters for p-p scattering, and hence the p-p $\delta(^1S_0)$ in the energy range $0 < E_{LAB} < 310$ Mev. From Table III, it is the author's opinion that nothing more can be determined from this data; some sort of investigation will have to be carried out to see to what extent the values of these four parameters determine a potential shape.

Approximate values of δ calculated from Eq. (11) with these four values of a, ρ, P, and β_1^2 are compared with the exact $\delta(^1S_0)$'s taken from GT's Table IV in Table III. There is again no difference in the two sets of numbers.

The mathematical basis of Eq. (11) for any potential is discussed in Section 8. It is shown that the use of a Fredholm expansion of the solution of an integral equation instead of the usual iteration procedure at one point in the mathematical derivation of the effective range expansion leads to Eq. (11).

C. Convergence of the Effective Range Expansion for E_{LAB} as Large as 40 Mev

For E_{LAB} = 40 Mev, $k^2 = 0.4824 \times 10^{26}$ cm⁻², and for values of β_1^2 similar to 0.36×10^{-24} cm², Eq. (11) is really no different from the first three terms of Eq. (2), especially from the data analysis point of

---

[5] This value is the same as that given by Eq. (9) for $r_c = 0.9457 \times 10^{-13}$ cm, of course. See the remark after Eq. (4) concerning the choice of r_c.

view.   It is hard enough to say anything about P from this data, and impossible to detect a 17 per cent variation in P.   For $E_{LAB} < 50$ Mev, Eq. (2) may be cut off after three terms.

The $^3S_1$ phase shift is not nearly so well understood as the $^1S_0$ phase shift; it may vanish for a much lower energy than $E_{LAB} = 228.8$ Mev or so, and the first three terms of Eq. (2) may not be a good approximation to Eq. (11).   However, the $\delta(^3S_1)$ of SM (Si58) does not vanish for $E_{LAB} < 310$ Mev, and the $\delta(^3S_1)$ of GT vanishes only for some $E_{LAB} > 150$ Mev.   For $E_{LAB} = 14.1$ or 19.66 Mev, the value of $k \cot \delta(^3S_1)$ is so near zero that any uncertainty in the $\delta(^3S_1)$ at these energies does not matter anyway.   It might be hoped that, because the theoretical value of the $^3S_1$ contribution to $\sigma_n(E_{LAB})$ for $E_{LAB} = 19.66$ Mev is precisely known, $^1\rho$ could be learned from the experimental value of $\sigma_n(E_{LAB})$ at this energy.   However, the $^3S_1$ contribution is about 400 mb, and the experimental error plus the uncertainty in estimating the contributions to $\sigma_n(E_{LAB})$ from states with $L \geq 1$ is large compared to the remaining 95 mb, so that this hope is not realized in the analysis reported in Section 5.   If the $\delta(^3S_1)$ vanishes much sooner than it does for the GT or SM phenomenological potentials, the analysis of the $\sigma_n(E_{LAB})$ data for $E_{LAB} = 42$ Mev may be affected.

4. Remarks on the Probable Values of the Effective Range Parameters based on Theoretical Calculations and Existing Analyses

A. The Shape Dependent Parameters and the Repulsive Core

The repulsive core plays a dominant role in determining the value of the shape dependent parameter.   This role is well known (Hu57, Figs. 14 and 16, and sentence preceding Section 32), but has not been sufficiently emphasized.   Nor has it been sufficiently emphasized that the negative $\delta(^1S_0)$ found by Stapp et al. (St57) at 310 Mev almost certainly[6] implies that the singlet shape dependent parameter is negative.

There is numerical evidence that any potential model which fits the singlet scattering length and effective range and the 310 Mev

---

[6] The arguments in this section are not proofs but plausibility arguments. Perhaps there are strangly shaped potentials for which these assertions fail.   The author knows of no examples.

$\delta(^1S_0)$ of Stapp *et al.*, has a negative P. For example, it has just been shown that GT's singlet even parity potential has $P = -0.022$. It is interesting to look at Fig. 16 in Hulthen and Sugawara's article (Hu57) with this value for P in mind. The potentials for which Fig. 16 is prepared are all displaced [see Eq. (19.4) in Hu57]; that is, the Yukawa potential is infinite at the core edge. The value $P = -0.022$ for $r_c = 0.4 \times 10^{-13}$ cm (as GT use) falls on the exponential curve, as it should for GT's undisplaced Yukawa. Were there a curve for an undisplaced Yukawa potential on Fig. 16, it would approach the curve for the exponential potential much more rapidly than the curves for the displaced Yukawa. Finally to get a $\delta(^1S_0)$ of $-10°$ at 310 Mev requires a core radius of about 0.1×10^{-13} cm even if there is no attractive potential outside the core. For all except the displaced Yukawa potential, $r_c = 0.1 \times 10^{-13}$ cm is already in the region of negative P's in Fig. 16.

Certainly the $\delta(^1S_0)$ of Stapp *et al.* shows that $\delta(^1S_0)$ passes through zero for $E_{\text{LAB}} < 310$ Mev. For any potential for which Eqs. (11) and (13) are valid, P must then be negative, otherwise Eq. (13) says that $\delta(^1S_0)$ is increasing as it passes through zero, a behavior which is impossible to reconcile with any reasonable view of the energy dependence of $\delta(^1S_0)$.

The presence of the tensor term in the triplet even parity potential does not change the conclusion that for triplet even parity potentials with hard cores of radius greater than 0.3×10^{-13} cm³ P should be negative. (In the last sentence before their Section 32, Hulthen and Sugawara (Hu57) mention the possible effects of a repulsive core on the triplet shape dependent parameter even when a tensor force is present. As it turns out, their Fig. 19 is irrelevant when $r_c \geqq 0.3 \times 10^{-13}$ cm, for in this case ^3P depends only on r_c and not at all on any other properties of the triplet even parity potential.) This conclusion is based on recent unpublished calculations of Christian, Gammel, and Thaler (Ch57), who have found a number of triplet even parity potentials with central, tensor, and spin-orbit terms, and several different hard core radii, which fit the data on the bound state of the deuteron and a triplet scattering length of 5.39×10^{-13} cm. These potentials, together with their shape dependent parameters, are shown in Table IV. For $r_c > 0.3 \times 10^{-13}$ cm, ^3P is negative.

For a fixed potential shape, P is a function of ρ/a (see Fig. 13 of Hu57). Many previous analyses have been based on the particular form of this function for Yukawa, exponential, Gauss, and square wells (see Tables 9 and 13 of Hu57). With the assumption of the hard core hypothesis, these curves of P versus ρ/a have no relevance whatsoever, and future analyses should not be based on them. The tables are still useful because they show how the results depend on the *assumed* value of P. (In reading Table 13 of Hulthen and Sugawara (Hu57), for example, one just ignores the columns headed Well Shape, b, and s, reads the column headed P first, and then looks at the results in the columns headed r_0 herein referred to as ρ and a.)

B. Analyses of the p-p Data in the Energy Range 0–40 Mev

   (1) The Effect of the Sign of the Shape Dependent Parameter on the Results of Analyses of Low Energy ($E_{LAB} < 5$ Mev) **p-p Data.** Figures like 17 and 18 of Jackson and Blatt (Ja50) are the result of an analysis of the *p-p* data. There has been much data published since 1950,[7] however, and the theoretical work of Foldy and Eriksen (Fo55) ought not be ignored in new analyses which include the new data. The analysis of Hulthen and Sugawara (Hu57) did not allow for the effects of polarization of the vacuum calculated by Foldy and Eriksen; presumably the former work just preceded the completion of the latter work, an unfortunate circumstance. Foldy and Eriksen's own analysis of the K [see Eq. (22.8) of Hu57] values they found[8] assumes that the singlet shape dependent parameter is positive, but it has just been argued that ^1P is not positive. Hulthen and Sugawara's Table 13 gives a result for a negative, although small, ^1P; namely, $^1P = -0.003313$. From the analyses of Hulthen and Sugawara and Foldy and Eriksen for $^1P = +0.05$, it appears that the value of the p-p $^1\rho$ which results from the analysis is not sensitive to Foldy and Eriksen's slight corrections. Thus it might be reasonable to extrapolate Hulthen and Sugawara's Table 13 to $^1P = -0.02$, except for the final unfortunate circumstance that in Table 13 the entry $r_0 = 2.559 \times 10^{-13}$ cm for $P = -0.003313$ definitely looks out of line with the other entries in the table, and also Jackson and Blatt's Fig. 18.

   [7] For a summary of this data, see the paper of Foldy and Ericksen (Fo55).
   [8] The K values of Foldy and Ericksen before correction for the effects of polarization of the vacuum are very nearly the same as those of Hulthen and Sugawara. Compare Table II in Fo55 with Table 2 in Hu57.

These analyses ought to be looked at again, with the repulsive core in mind. In the meantime, it seems advisable just to go back to Jackson and Blatt's Fig. 18, on which the points of Hulthen and Sugawara and Foldy and Eriksen fall very nicely anyhow, with the exception noted. One then finds

$$p\text{-}p \ ^1\rho = 2.62 \pm 0.07 \text{ for } ^1P = -0.02 \qquad (14)$$

If charge independence holds, the n-p $^1\rho$ should be equal to this p-p $^1\rho$.

(2) **Inadmissable Hypotheses in the Analysis of p-p Data for $10 < E_{\text{LAB}} < 40$ Mev.** In the last paragraph of their Section 23, Hulthen and Sugawara (Hu57) mention an apparent difficulty, namely, that the analyses of the p-p data including data for energies as large as 40 Mev (see their Fig. 18) indicate that the p-p singlet shape dependent parameter is positive. The probable origin of this difficulty is in the phase shift analyses of the data which include no (or perhaps one) triplet P phase shift (see Table 3 of Hulthen and Sugawara and the footnote labeled with a double asterisk). When the three triplet P phase shifts are split, they affect even the p-p differential cross section at $90°$ in the center of mass system, as is well known. The results of analyses employing no (or perhaps one) triplet P phase shift need not be accepted,[9] especially since it is known that GT (Ga57a) had no difficulty fitting the p-p data at $E_{\text{LAB}} = 18.3$ Mev,[10] and their singlet even parity potential has a negative shape dependent parameter. There is no convincing evidence from the p-p data in the energy range $10 < E_{\text{LAB}} < 40$ Mev that the p-p ^1P is positive. In my opinion, the only reliable evidence comes from the high energy data (see Section 4.A), and this evidence is that the p-p ^1P is negative.

C. The n-p Coherent Scattering Length, f

The analysis reported in Section 5 makes no use of measurements of the n-p coherent scattering length (Hu57, Section 18), except that the range of triplet and singlet scattering lengths (^3a and ^1a) consid-

---

[9] For low energies ($E_{\text{LAB}} < 4$ Mev) for which the only effect of the ^3P_J phase shifts appears in the interference between the triplet odd parity nuclear scattering amplitude and the Coulomb scattering amplitude, it is perfectly correct to use an average ^3P_J phase shift.

[10] See their footnote 11 in addition to their Fig. 1.

Table V. The Contribution of the $^3S_1$ to $\sigma_n(E_{LAB})$ (barns) for Various Triplet Effective Range Parameters.

Case	^3a (10⁻¹³ cm)	$^3\rho$ (10⁻¹³ cm)	^3P	E_{LAB} (Mev)						
				1.005	1.315	2.540	4.749	14.1	19.66	42
1	5.40	1.7329ᵃ	0	2.2106	2.0813	1.6890	1.2458	0.54961	0.39682	0.16510
2		1.7442	−0.02	2.2121	2.0846	1.6917	1.2488	0.55054	0.39623	0.16054
3		1.7562	−0.04	2.2137	2.0865	1.6944	1.2515	0.55138	0.39543	0.15556
4	5.38	1.7075	0	2.1954	2.0687	1.6787	1.2395	0.54888	0.39705	0.16613
5		1.7182	−0.02	2.1968	2.0705	1.6812	1.2424	0.54984	0.39658	0.16185
6		1.7297	−0.04	2.1984	2.0723	1.6838	1.2454	0.55074	0.39592	0.15715
7	5.36	1.6815	0	2.1802	2.0547	1.6683	1.2331	0.54811	0.39723	0.16717
8		1.6918	−0.02	2.1816	2.0564	1.6707	1.2358	0.54910	0.39687	0.16315
9		1.7027	−0.04	2.1830	2.0581	1.6732	1.2387	0.55003	0.39633	0.15874

ᵃ The error in $^3\rho$ due to the error in α is ±0.0025.

ered is determined by analyses of measurements of f and $\sigma_n(0)$. These analyses give

$$^3a = 5.38 \pm 0.02 \times 10^{-13} \text{ cm} \tag{15}$$

$$^1a = -23.69 \pm 0.06 \times 10^{-13} \text{ cm}$$

[(Hu57); Eqs. (18.16) and (18.17)]; or

$$^3a = 5.412 \pm 0.012 \times 10^{-13} \text{ cm} \tag{16}$$

$$^1a = -23.806 \pm 0.028 \times 10^{-13} \text{ cm}$$

(Br57).

The results of the analysis reported in Section 5 are not affected by the widest variation in ^1a permitted by Eqs. (15) and (16). The two values of ^1a considered in Section 5 are -23.63 and -23.87×10^{-13} cm; these values completely cover the range suggested by Eqs. (15) and (16), yet lead to the same results in Section 5. It is not hard to understand why this is so; the explanation is given in Section 5.

The ^3a values considered in Section 5 are 5.36, 5.38, and 5.40 $\times$ 10^{-13} cm. The results for $^3a = 5.42 \times 10^{-13}$ cm may be obtained by extrapolation of the results for these three values. Nothing in the results of Section 5 distinguishes among these possible values of ^3a. At either the high end or the low end there is difficulty with charge independence, however, as will be seen in Section 5.

D. The Connection Between ^3a, $^3\rho$, and ^3P

In this section, another well understood point is emphasized.

This point is that the triplet parameters are not independent of each other but must satisfy a relation imposed by the existence of the bound state of the deuteron; namely,

$$-\alpha = -\frac{1}{3}a - \frac{1}{2}\,^3\rho\alpha^2 - {}^3P\,({}^3\rho)^3\alpha^4 \tag{17}$$

where $\alpha^2 = M\epsilon/\hbar^2$ [see Eq. (19.1) of Hu57]. Equation (17) follows from Eq. (2) with $k \cot \delta = -\alpha$ and $k^2 = -\alpha^2$ [see Eq. (16.34) of Hu57, and also their Eq. (30.26), after which it is remarked that the presence of a tensor term in the potential does not alter Eq. (17)].

In view of this Eq. (17), Eq. (19.2) of Hulthen and Sugawara (Hu57) must be used with care. If it is deduced from experimental data that

$$^3a = 5.377 \pm 0.021 \times 10^{-13} \text{ cm} \tag{18}$$

Table VI.   Values of $k \cot \delta(^1S_0)$ in 10^{13} cm^{-1}

Case	E_{LAB}(Mev)						
	1.005	1.315	2.540	4.749	14.1	19.66	42
1	0.05876	0.06208	0.08335	0.1160	0.2558	0.3570	1.1165
2	0.05886	0.06240	0.08407	0.1180	0.2591	0.3535	0.9446
3	0.05896	0.06259	0.08480	0.1199	0.2620	0.3486	0.7996
4	0.05776	0.06082	0.08056	0.1116	0.2533	0.3583	1.1644
5	0.05786	0.06100	0.08123	0.1136	0.2566	0.3554	0.9894
6	0.05796	0.06118	0.08195	0.1156	0.2597	0.3516	0.8419
7	0.05675	0.05950	0.07771	0.1072	0.2507	0.3592	1.2160
8	0.05685	0.05958	0.07837	0.1091	0.2540	0.3573	1.0374
9	0.05694	0.05976	0.07906	0.1111	0.2573	0.3540	0.8880

it can be deduced[11] from Eq. (17) that

$$^3\rho = 1.704 \pm 0.028 \times 10^{-13} \text{ cm} \qquad (19)$$

but this last statement suppresses the relation expressed in Eq. (17). It is better to express $^3\rho$ as a function of ^3a and ^3P. This is done in Table V. Equation (19) expresses some fraction of the information which Table V contains.

5. Analysis of $\sigma_n(E_{LAB})$ for the Energy Range $0 < E_{LAB} < 42$ Mev

A. Plan of the Analysis

For each of the cases shown in Table V, the contribution of the $^3S_1$ state to $\sigma_n(E_{LAB})$ is calculated from

$$3\pi \sin^2 \delta(^3S_1)/k^2 = 3\pi/\{k^2 + [k \cot \delta(^3S_1)]^2\} \qquad (20)$$

where $k \cot \delta(^3S_1)$ is calculated from Eq. (2), and the result is shown in Table V. These contributions together with the contributions of all states for $L \geq 1$ estimated in Section 2, when subtracted from the experimental value of $\sigma_n(E_{LAB})$ shown in Table II, give the contribution of the $^1S_0$ state [this contribution is denoted by $\sigma_n(^1S_0)$] to $\sigma_n(E_{LAB})$.

[11] The value assumed for ^3P in deducing Eq. (19) has a negligible influence on the result for a wide range of ^3P values; Table V illustrates this. Also, the error in $^3\rho$ shown in Eq. (19) is due almost entirely to the error in ^3a because the experimental error in α is so small; this is also shown in Table V.

For each of the cases in Table V, Table VI shows the value of k cot $\delta(^1S_0)$, calculated from

$$\sigma_n(^1S_0) = \pi/\{ k^2 + [k \cot \delta(^1S_0)]^2 \} \tag{21}$$

where the plus sign must be used in taking a square root to get k cot $\delta(^1S_0)$.

For an assumed value of ^1a, $^1\bar{p}$ is calculated from

$$^1\bar{p} \equiv (2/k^2)[(1/^1a) + k \cot \delta(^1S_0)] \tag{22}$$

The value of $^1\bar{p}$ does not depend very much on which of the two extreme values for ^1a decided on in Section 4.C is used. The reason is that Eq. (22) suffers most from close cancellation at $E_{\text{LAB}} = 1.005$ Mev, for which

$$^1/_2 \, ^1\bar{p}k^2 \approx 0.014 \times 10^{13} \text{ cm}^{-1} \tag{23}$$

which is not particularly small compared to

$$1/^1a \approx 0.042 \times 10^{13} \text{ cm}^{-1} \tag{24}$$

The two extreme values of ^1a differ by only 1 per cent; the factor three between the right hand sides of Eqs. (23) and (24) means that the two values of $^1\bar{p}$ calculated from Eq. (22) will differ by only 3 per cent. This ± 1.5 per cent is small compared to the 10 per cent or greater uncertainty in $^1\bar{p}$ which arises from the experimental errors in the measurement of $\sigma_n(E_{\text{LAB}})$, and could have been ignored, but is not. The 3 per cent difference is actually exhibited in Table VII.

The results of using Eq. (22) for the two extreme values of ^1a decided on in Section 4.C and the k cot $\delta(^1S_0)$ values shown in Table VI are shown in Table VII. The error shown for $^1\bar{p}$ corresponds to the experimental error in $\sigma_n(E_{\text{LAB}})$. A decrease in $\sigma_n(E_{\text{LAB}})$ results in an increase in $^1\bar{p}$. The uncertainty in estimating the contributions to $\sigma_n(E_{\text{LAB}})$ of states with $L \geq 1$ for $E_{\text{LAB}} > 14$ Mev should perhaps be added to the experimental error, but it is not.

B. *Discussion of the Results*

(1) **The Shape Dependent Parameters Are Negative.** The 42-Mev data prove that the triplet and singlet shape dependent parameters are negative. Table VII shows that the 42-Mev value of $^1\bar{p}$ depends mainly on the triplet shape dependent parameter. A

Table VII. Values of $^1\bar{\rho}$ in 10^{-13} cm

Case	^1a 10^{-13} cm	E_{LAB}(Mev)						
		1.005	1.315	2.540	4.749	14.1	19.66	42
1	23.87	2.784	2.546	2.707	2.588	2.516	2.659	4.244
	23.63	2.713	2.492	2.679	2.573	2.511	2.656	4.244
2	23.87	2.800	2.587	2.754	2.658	2.554	2.630	3.564
	23.63	2.719	2.532	2.726	2.643	2.550	2.627	3.564
3	23.87	2.816	2.615	2.801	2.723	2.588	2.587	2.989
	23.63	2.746	2.556	2.774	2.708	2.583	2.584	2.989
4	23.87	2.619	2.387	2.525	2.434	2.486	2.670	4.432
	23.63	2.548	2.333	2.497	2.419	2.481	2.667	4.432
5	23.87	2.635	2.410	2.569	2.504	2.525	2.646	3.741
	23.63	2.564	2.356	2.541	2.489	2.520	2.643	3.741
6	23.87	2.652	2.433	2.616	2.574	2.561	2.614	3.158
	23.63	2.581	2.378	2.588	2.559	2.557	2.610	3.158
7	23.87	2.452	2.208	2.339	2.280	2.456	2.677	4.636
	23.63	2.382	2.166	2.311	2.265	2.451	2.673	4.636
8	23.87	2.469	2.231	2.382	2.347	2.494	2.662	3.930
	23.63	2.398	2.177	2.354	2.332	2.490	2.659	3.930
9	23.87	2.483	2.254	2.427	2.417	2.533	2.634	3.340
	23.63	2.412	2.199	2.399	2.402	2.528	2.631	3.340
Error	±0.20	0.20	0.25	0.20	0.15	0.25	0.17	a

a For $^1\rho = 2.989$, the error is $+0.9$, -0.6. For $^1\bar{\rho} = 4.244$, the error is $+1.5$, -1.0.

reasonable value of $^1\rho$ results only if the triplet shape dependent parameter is less than -0.02. By "reasonable" is meant that $^1\bar{\rho}$ at 42 Mev is not so much larger than $^1\bar{\rho}$ at $1 - 5$ Mev that a singlet shape dependent parameter less than -0.04 is needed to explain the results. On the other hand, Table VII also shows that no matter what is assumed about the triplet effective range parameters, provided the triplet shape dependent parameter is greater than -0.05, which is certainly the case for any reasonable interaction,[12] $^1\bar{\rho}$ is larger at 42 Mev than at $1 - 5$ Mev, so that the singlet shape dependent parameter is negative. Of course, it is impossible to fix the values of the shape dependent parameters accurately from this data. However, the results do not conflict with

$$^1P = -0.02, \quad ^3P = -0.04 \tag{25}$$

It will be noticed that the 19.66 Mev data is barely consistent with $^1\rho$ increasing with energy. In the author's opinion, this is evidence that the estimate settled on in Section 2 of a 12-mb contribution to $\sigma_n(19.66 \text{ Mev})$ from states with $L \geqq 1$ is not too large. If less is subtracted, $^1\bar{\rho}$'s smaller than those shown in Table VII would result. Of course, there is other evidence (Section 7.D) that 12 mb is about correct.

(2) **The Singlet Effective Range: Comparison with Previous Analyses.** Table VII shows that the values of $^1\bar{\rho}$ for $E_{\text{LAB}} = 1$ to 5 Mev increase with increasing ^3a. In this connection it is interesting to recall the work of Brimberg (Br57) and Fields, Becker, and Adair (Fi54). Fields, Becker, and Adair's analysis of the 1 to 5-Mev data is exactly the same as in this paper except that they did not consider different possible values for ^3a and $^3\rho$ (the value of ^3P does not matter), but only $^3a = 5.377 \times 10^{-13}$ cm, $^3\rho = 1.704 \times 10^{-13}$ cm, $^1a = -23.69 \times 10^{-13}$ cm, which they took from Burgy, Ringo, and Hughes (Bu51). They found

$$n\text{-}p \ ^1\rho = 2.48 \pm 0.20 \times 10^{-13} \text{ cm (Fi54)} \tag{26}$$

which is what Table VII shows for the ^3a and $^3\rho$ values they used. But Brimberg's recent analysis of f and $\sigma_n(0)$ suggests larger values

[12] See Table IV of this paper, the paper of Kalos, Biedenharn, and Blatt (Ka56), and Figs. 16 and 19 of Hulthen and Sugawara (Hu57).

for ^3a, and thus even larger values of $^1\rho$.   For $^3a = 5.40 \times 10^{-13}$ cm, $^3P = -0.04$, Table VII gives

$$n\text{-}p \ ^1\rho = 2.60 \pm 0.20 \times 10^{-13} \text{ cm} \qquad (27)$$

which agrees with the p-p value given in Section 4.B(1) to within the error in the p-p value, and well within the error in the n-p value.

Snow (Sn52) made an analysis of the data for $E_{\text{LAB}} = 14.1$ Mev. His result for $^1\rho$; namely,

$$n\text{-}p \ ^1\rho = 2.1 \pm 0.3 \times 10^{-13} \text{ cm (Sn52)} \qquad (28)$$

is low because he estimates that states of orbital angular momentum $L \geqq 1$ contribute less than 1 mb to $\sigma_n(14.1 \text{ Mev})$. [The reason why the estimate is low is that Snow considered central potentials only. The contribution to the total cross section of the ^3P_J states is related to the average over the three possible J states of the squares of the phase shifts.   For central potentials $\bar{\delta}^2 = (\bar{\delta})^2$, but for noncentral potentials $\bar{\delta}^2 > (\bar{\delta}).^2$]   His analysis is not sensitive to any assumptions about the $^3S_1$ contribution, which is nearly $3\pi/k^2$ at 14.1 Mev.   He states results for simply shaped potentials in a way which must be considered archaic in view of the repulsive-core hypothesis (see Section 4.A; last paragraph).

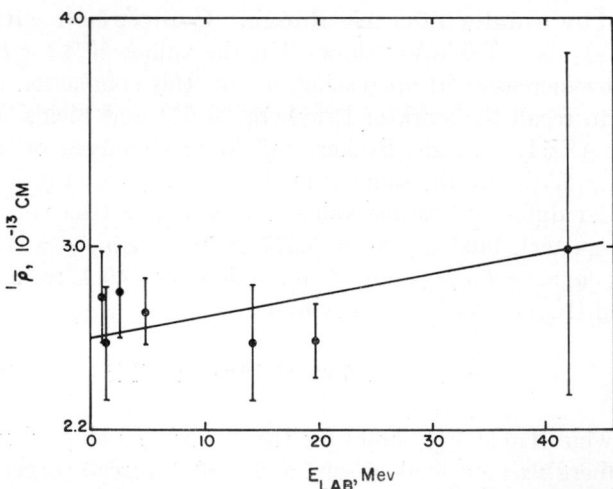

Figure 1. $^1\bar{\rho}$ $vs.$ E_{LAB}.   The solid curve corresponds to $^1\rho = 2.60 \times 10^{-13}$ cm, $^1P = -0.02$.

(3) **The Scattering Lengths.** Nothing in Table VII discriminates among the possible values of ^3a or ^1a. It might appear that the $^1\bar{\rho}$ value at 19.66 Mev for $^3P = -0.04$ is so low that it might not be advisable to consider ^3a's much larger than 5.40×10^{-13} cm, but again a slightly larger value than 12 mb for contributions to $\sigma_n(19.66 \text{ Mev})$ from states with $L \geqq 1$ would bring this $^1\rho$ value up, and no definite conclusion is possible. However, for ^3a's much larger than 5.40×10^{-13} cm, the $^1\rho$'s for $E_{\text{LAB}} = 1$ to 5 Mev become larger. than the p-p $^1\rho$, and so $^3a > 5.40 \times 10^{-13}$ cm might be ruled out by charge independence.

(4) **Values of the Effective Range Expansion Parameters.** A graph of $^1\bar{\rho}$, corresponding to Fig. 9 of Fields, Becker, and Adair (Fi54), but covering the entire energy range from 0 to 42 Mev, is shown in Fig. 1. Values of the effective range parameters which fit the data, seem in line with theoretical expectations and charge independence, and compromise between the Brimberg ^3a and ^1a values and older values, are

$$^3a = 5.40 \times 10^{-13} \text{ cm} \qquad ^1a = -23.75 \times 10^{-13} \text{ cm}$$
$$^3\rho = 1.7562 \times 10^{-13} \text{ cm} \qquad ^1\rho = 2.60 \times 10^{-13} \text{ cm} \qquad (29)$$
$$^3P = -0.04 \qquad\qquad ^1P = -0.02$$

Adequate indications of possible errors are given elsewhere in this article.

6. Interpolation of Table II

Sometime ago, the author participated in an effort to find a fit to the experimental data on $\sigma_n(E_{\text{LAB}})$ shown in Table II. The fit was needed to interpolate Table I; it is this interpolation which is of importance in the use of fast neutron detectors of the recoil type.

It is natural to attempt to use an analytical form based on effective range theory, and as a matter of fact such a fit was found. The fit is:

$$\sigma_n(E) = 3\pi \left[1.206\, E + (-1.86 + 0.09415\, E + 0.0001306\, E^2)^2\right]^{-1}$$
$$+ \pi\left[1.206\, E + (0.4223 + 0.13\, E)^2\right]^{-1} \quad (30)$$

The terms[13] $1.206\, E_{\text{LAB}}$ arise from the k^2's, given by Eq. (3) in terms of E_{LAB}, which appear in the denominators of the right hand

---

[13] E is used instead of E_{LAB} to shorten the long equations.

sides of Eqs. (20) and (21). The terms in the parentheses in the denominators of Eq. (30) are $k \cot \delta(^3S_1)$ and $k \cot \delta(^1S_0)$, respectively.

The numerical coefficients inside the parentheses correspond to the following values for the effective range expansion parameters

$$^3a = 5.376 \times 10^{-13} \text{ cm} \qquad ^1a = -23.68 \times 10^{-13} \text{ cm}$$
$$^3\rho = 1.56 \times 10^{-13} \text{ cm} \qquad ^1\rho = 2.156 \times 10^{-13} \text{ cm} \qquad (31)$$
$$^3P = -0.03 \qquad\qquad ^1P = 0$$

These values do not agree with the values adopted in Section 5.B(4). The reasons for this difference are that contributions to $\sigma_n(E_{\text{LAB}})$ of states with $L \geqq 1$ and the condition Eq. (17) were ignored in working out the fit Eq. (30). All that was required of the numerical coefficients in Eq. (30) was that the values of the effective range expansion parameters shown in Eq. (31) should be roughly realistic, as they are.

The accuracy of the fit Eq. (30) is of interest to users of fast neutron detectors of the recoil type. Because $\sigma_n(E_{\text{LAB}})$ has nearly a

Table VIII. Comparison of Values of $\sigma_n(E_{\text{LAB}})$ Calculated from the Fit Eq. (30) and from a Physically More Realistic Approach

E_{LAB} (Mev)	$^3S_1 + {}^1S_0$ Contribution (mb)	Contribution from States with $L \geqq 1$ (barns)	Sum (barns)	Eq. (30) (barns)
0	20.468	0	20.468	20.340
0.1	12.776	0	12.776	12.790
0.2	9.669	0	9.669	9.700
0.4	6.894	0	6.894	6.919
0.6	5.579	0	5.579	5.596
0.8	4.792	0	4.792	4.801
1.0	4.256	0	4.256	4.259
2.0	2.912	0	2.912	2.903
4.0	1.905	0	1.905	1.893
6.0	1.429	0	1.429	1.421
8.0	1.138	0	1.138	1.135
10.0	0.9393	0	0.9393	0.9408
14.1	0.6795	6	0.6855	0.6882
19.66	0.4794	12	0.4914	0.4940
25	0.3633	18	0.3813	0.3812
30	0.2897	20	0.3097	0.3096
35	0.2365	20	0.2565	0.2575
42	0.1833	20	0.2033	0.2020

$1/E_{\text{LAB}}$ dependence for $E_{\text{LAB}} > 1$ Mev, it is difficult to imagine that the fit is less accurate than the data in Table II at any $E_{\text{LAB}} > 1$ Mev. The region $E_{\text{LAB}} < 1$ Mev is most in doubt. However, the whole region $E_{\text{LAB}} < 40$ Mev may be tested by comparing values of $\sigma_n(E_{\text{LAB}})$ calculated by using the most probable effective range expansion parameters adopted in Section 5.B(4), together with the estimates of contributions to $\sigma_n(E_{\text{LAB}})$ from states with $L \geq 1$ from interpolation of Table I, where necessary, with values of $\sigma_n(E_{\text{LAB}})$ calculated from the fit Eq. (30). Such a comparison, shown in Table VIII, proves that the fit is as accurate as the data in Table II.

Extensive tables of $\sigma_n(E_{\text{LAB}})$ calculated from the fit Eq. (30) appear in Table XI. The fit is compared with the experimental data in Table II.

7. The n-p Differential Cross Section in the Energy Range 14 $< E_{\text{LAB}} \leqq 42$ Mev

A. An Old Fit to the Data

At the time the work described in Section 6 was done, a fit to the data on $\sigma_n(\theta, E_{\text{LAB}})$ was also made. The fit was based on the assumption that $\sigma_n(\theta, E_{\text{LAB}})$ is symmetrical about $90°$ in the center-of-mass system, and more specifically that it has the form[14]

$$\sigma_n(\theta, E_{\text{LAB}}) = [\sigma_n(E_{\text{LAB}})/4\pi] \; [(1 + b \cos^2\theta)/(1 + \tfrac{1}{3} b)] \quad (32)$$

It was further assumed that b is proportional to E_{LAB}^2; in fact,

$$b = 2(E_{\text{LAB}}/90)^2 \quad (33)$$

leads to the fit shown in Table IX to the experimental data in $\sigma_n(180°, E_{\text{LAB}})/\sigma_n(90°, E_{\text{LAB}})$.

This fit has practically no theoretical basis. In the first place, there is really no reason to suppose the $\cos \theta$ term is missing. At 42 Mev, $\cos^3 \theta$ and $\cos^4 \theta$ terms must be present and large.

In this paper, this problem of the angular dependence of $\sigma_n(\theta, E_{\text{LAB}})$ is reexamined. Because the phenomenological potentials of

---

[14] It is sometimes convenient to express differential cross sections in the laboratory system and in terms of the proton recoil angle Θ. The necessary expression is

$$\sigma_{\text{LAB}}(\Theta, E_{\text{LAB}}) = 4\sigma_n(\pi - 2\Theta, E_{\text{LAB}}) \cos \Theta.$$

Table IX. Comparison of Experimental and Calculated Values of $\sigma_n(180°, E_{\text{LAB}})/\sigma_n(90°, E_{\text{LAB}})$

| | $\sigma_n(180°, E_{\text{LAB}})/\sigma_n(90°, E_{\text{LAB}})$ | | |
E_{LAB} (Mev)	Calculated (Eq. 33)	Experimental	Ref.
1	1.0002		
4	1.003		
8	1.016		
10	1.025		
14.1	1.049	1.06 ± 0.023	Se55
		1.04 ± 0.05	Al53
		1.06 ± 0.06	Ba49
17.9	1.079	1.08 ± 0.03	Ga55a
19.66	1.095	1.09 ± 0.03	Pe57
22	1.119		
27.2	1.183	1.28 ± 0.10	Br51
42	1.441	1.55 ± 0.20	Ha49
91	3.044	3.15 ± 0.10	St54b

GT and SM do not explain some details of the 90-Mev data, and, worse yet, because these potentials do not fit the deuteron data and the triplet scattering length, the precision of predictions of differential cross sections based on these potentials is not certain. Phenomenological potentials are discussed in Section 7.B. However, for $14 < E_{\text{LAB}} < 20$ Mev, useful results follow from the qualitative properties of these potentials and the fact that $\delta(^3S_1)$ is near 90° throughout this energy region.

It is shown in Section 7.C that $\sigma_n(90°, E_{\text{LAB}})$ can be predicted with some confidence. The best estimates which can be made give values of $\sigma_n(90°, E_{\text{LAB}})$ slightly higher (38.65 mb at 19.66 Mev) than calculated from Eqs. (32) and (33) (38.19 mb at 19.66 Mev). As an extreme example of an angular distribution different from Eq. (32), we may consider

$$\sigma_n(\theta, E_{\text{LAB}}) = [\sigma_n(E_{\text{LAB}})/4\pi]$$
$$[(1 - \tfrac{1}{2}\,b\cos\theta + \tfrac{1}{2}\,b\cos^2\theta)/(1 + \tfrac{1}{6}\,b)] \quad (34)$$

In the author's opinion this example is extreme because, while angular distributions of this general shape result from the best available phenomenological potentials, the potentials give angular distributions for which $\sigma_n(0°, E_{\text{LAB}}) > \sigma_n(90°, E_{\text{LAB}})$. Also, while Eq. (34) is in agreement with fragmentary experimental evidence that $\sigma_n(\theta, E_{\text{LAB}})$ is not symmetrical about 90° (see Fig. 2 in Fo56), Eq. (31) gives values of $\sigma_n(90°, E_{\text{LAB}})$ slightly higher (38.79 mb at 19.66 Mev) than the best estimates of this quantity which can be made.

A comparison of the predictions of Eqs. (32) and (34), both combined with Eq. (33), after both are normalized to the same value of $\sigma_n(90°, E_{\text{LAB}})$ shows that the maximum difference in the differential cross sections in the backwards hemisphere is 1.25 per cent at $E_{\text{LAB}} = 19.66$ Mev, and this maximum occurs at $\theta = 120°$. Of course, possible experimental error in the measurement[14] of the ratio $\sigma_n(180°, E_{\text{LAB}})/\sigma_n(90°, E_{\text{LAB}})$ also affects the predictions of differential cross sections in the backwards hemisphere. While this error is three per cent for $E_{\text{LAB}} = 19.66$ Mev, only $^3/_8$ of this at most is present at 120°. There is little point in pursuing the details of possible errors in Eq. (32) further. Suffice it to say in summary that the results of Eq. (32) should be normalized to the precise and slightly higher values of $\sigma_n(90°, E_{\text{LAB}})$ arrived at by the methods discussed in Section 7.C. The resulting differential cross sections for $\theta > 120°$ are at least as accurate as the measurements of the ratio $\sigma_n(180°, E_{\text{LAB}})/\sigma_n(90°, E_{\text{LAB}})$, while for $\theta < 120°$, especially for $\theta = 90°$, the resulting differential cross sections are more accurate.

B. Phenomenological Potentials

The SM and GT potentials do not fit the deuteron binding energy (ϵ) and the triplet scattering length (^3a). SM started from the triplet even parity potential of Gartenhaus (Ga55b), which was adjusted to fit ϵ and ^3a, and added a spin-orbit term without readjusting the central and tensor terms to fit ϵ and ^3a. GT did the same thing starting from the triplet even parity potentials of Gammel, Christian, and Thaler (Ga57c). GT did not predict a low energy ($E_{\text{LAB}} < 90$ Mev) *n-p* angular distribution. SM's phase shifts for $E_{\text{LAB}} = 18$ Mev give a total cross section which is 100 mb or 25 per cent too low, which proves the inadvisability of applying these potentials in this energy range.

It is interesting that the shape of the *n-p* angular distributions calculated by SM for $E_{\text{LAB}} = 18$ and 42 Mev, are not symmetrical about 90° with less forward than backward peaking. Unfortunately, it must be noted that the SM and GT potentials also predict angular distributions at 90 Mev which have less forward than backward peak-

Table X. The Problem of the *V*-Shaped Angular Distribution at 90 Mev

Code[a]	$\sigma_n(\theta,$ 90 Mev) in mb				σ_n(90 Mev) (mb)
	$\theta = 0°$	$\theta = 90°$	$\theta = 130°$	$\theta = 180°$	
Experimental	13.5	4.0	7.2	13.5	76 ± 7
3100	14.58	4.72	9.10	14.15	93.3
3105	13.96	4.57	8.86	13.65	90.7
3300	14.63	3.96	10.66	15.03	94.8
3305	14.69	3.82	10.53	15.08	94.4
4100	13.44	4.86	8.31	13.16	88.8
4105	12.99	4.72	8.17	12.80	86.8
4109	12.86	4.56	7.97	12.74	85.5
4113	13.72	4.22	8.00	13.26	85.3
4200	12.81	4.43	8.85	12.90	87.7
4205	12.55	4.30	8.57	12.69	86.0
4210	13.05	4.10	8.24	13.18	85.4
4300	12.87	4.05	9.50	13.28	87.9
4305	12.90	3.91	9.42	13.27	87.6
4400	13.06	3.82	9.70	13.23	87.5
4403	13.14	3.74	9.68	13.86	87.6
4407	13.66	3.58	9.71	13.65	88.4
5100	12.78	5.06	7.85	12.59	86.4
5103	12.46	4.98	7.73	12.35	85.3
5107	12.28	4.85	7.58	12.17	83.6
5200	12.12	4.70	8.16	11.87	84.8
5205	11.90	4.61	7.97	11.65	83.5
5300	11.90	4.29	8.66	12.27	84.2
5305	11.85	4.20	8.51	12.21	83.5
5400	11.87	3.93	9.12	12.10	82.5
5403	11.90	3.88	9.11	12.12	82.5
5405	11.99	3.82	9.05	12.21	82.5
5407	12.16	3.75	9.02	12.29	82.5

[a] Triplet even-parity potentials of Table IV. The triplet odd and singlet even-parity potentials are those of GT. The singlet odd-parity potential is zero; if this potential is adjusted to increase σ_n(180°, 90 Mev) the differential cross section at other angles will change slightly, in particular σ_n(130°, 90 Mev) will increase by one or two tenths of a mb.

ing, whereas the experimental data at 90 Mev is more nearly consistent with equal forward and backward peaking [Fig. 2 (Fo56)].

The triplet even parity potentials of Table IV fit the deuteron data and $^3a = 5.39 \times 10^{-13}$ cm. However, an extensive search for a fit to the 90-Mev *n-p* angular distribution using these potentials, the singlet even and triplet odd parity potentials of GT, and any singlet odd parity potential whatsoever, has ended in failure (Ch57). The problem of the excessively V-shaped calculated angular distributions cannot be solved. Briefly stated, this problem is that the data on $\sigma_n(130°, 90\ \mathrm{Mev})$ is very difficult to fit. The experimental value, after the experimental angular distribution is smoothed graphically, is $\sigma_n(130°, 90\ \mathrm{Mev}) = 7.2$ mb. However, values like 8.8 mb, and at best 8.2 mb, except in a few rare cases for which $\sigma_n(90°, 90\ \mathrm{Mev})$ is much larger than the experimental value 4.0 mb, result from combinations of potentials which fit the backwards ($170°$–$180°$) and $90°$ data in the center-of-mass system. Some idea of the difficulty may be obtained by studying Table X. GT and SM did not encounter the problem of the V-shaped angular distribution because their potentials do not fit the deuteron data or ^3a. Because of this difficulty, it is also very difficult to fit the total cross section data at 90 Mev, especially since, unlike the GT and SM fits, the forward cross sections are not low. This difficulty is also shown in Table X.

For these reasons, it is not advisable to rely on the details of predictions of present phenomenological potentials. It is interesting to look at the qualitative features of predictions of these potentials, however. This section ends with an account of what is found in attempting to fit the 42-Mev data, and what is found in calculations of angular distributions for $E_{\mathrm{LAB}} = 19.66$ Mev.

The 42-Mev data can be fit if the data is normalized to a larger value of $\sigma_n(90°, 42\ \mathrm{Mev})$. [The backward scattering data is not very smooth as a function of angle. While it is possible to fit any value of $\sigma_n(180°)/\sigma_n(90°)$ by adjusting the singlet odd parity potential, the data on this ratio at 14–20 Mev also has to be fit, as does the data at 90 Mev. An experimental value 1.55 ± 0.20 is shown for this ratio at 42 Mev in Table IX. This value is difficult to fit with potentials which also fit the 14 to 20 and 90-Mev data. One wonders to what extent this value depends on the roughness of the data.] The data is given by Hess (He56) is normalized to the total cross section by assuming that the angular distribution is symmetrical about $90°$, which results in a low value $\sigma_n(90°, 42\ \mathrm{Mev}) = 14$ mb. When the search program referred to above was extended to 42 Mev, values of $\sigma_n(90°, 42\ \mathrm{Mev})$ nearer 14.7 mb were found. While it appears that the 42-Mev angular distribution might not be symmetrical about $90°$, the calculated angular distributions are nearly symmetrical, with perhaps 5 per cent fewer neutrons going into the forward hemisphere than the backwards, depending on which potential in Table IV and what sing-let odd parity potential is used in the calculations. Also, it should be noted that 14.7 and 14.0 differ by only 5 per cent, whereas the possible experimental error in the total cross section is 3.5 per cent.

At 19.66 Mev, a wide variety of potentials which fit the 42 and 90-Mev data, except for the difficulties noted, were found to give shapes for the angular distribution similar to and between the shapes predicted by Eqs. (32) and (34). The similarity was not detailed; there was considerable evidence of cos $^3\theta$ and higher terms in some cases. But the minimum in the differential cross section always occurred at a center-of-mass angle less than 90°, and the forward peaking was less than the backward peaking.

Most interesting of all, it was observed that the calculated value of $\sigma_n(90°, 19.66 \text{ Mev})$ did not depend on which of the potentials in Table IV is used, and, of course, not at all on the singlet odd parity potential. Because the potentials to which $\sigma_n(90°, 19.66 \text{ Mev})$ is sensitive also determine the p-p angular distribution, there is reason to believe that the cross section at 90° in the center-of-mass system can be calculated with precision and confidence. The possible use of this 90° cross section in measuring absolute neutron fluxes led to an attempt to put this observation on a solid foundation. The attempt is reported in the next two Sections.

Those who calculate n-p differential cross sections from potentials would be stimulated to look at the energy region $14 < E_{\text{LAB}} < 42$ Mev more closely if they were in the possession of a precision measurement of $\sigma_n(\theta, E_{\text{LAB}})$ for $E_{\text{LAB}} = 32$ or 42 Mev. The question of the shape of the angular distribution in the forward hemisphere and the question of whether or not the problem of the V-shaped angular distributions persists at these lower energies are of great interest. The forward scattering is particularly sensitive to the central term in the triplet odd parity potential. [Calculations of the binding energy of nuclear matter from the theory of Brueckner (Br58) are particularly sensitive to the value of this term because of the high statistical weight of the triplet odd parity states (isotopic spin $T = 1$, spin $s = 1$). The tensor and spin orbit terms do not contribute to the binding energy of nuclear matter in Born approximation.]

Our present knowledge of this central term is largely derived from the 310-Mev p-p scattering; the low values of the forward differential n-p cross section found by GT at 90 Mev caused them to investigate a possible velocity dependence of this term (see their foot-note 6). It would, of course, be interesting to trace this apparent velocity dependence to still lower energies.

The n-p data in the energy range 0–42 Mev does not contribute much to our knowledge of the nucleon-nucleon interaction. The ratio $\sigma_n(180°, E_{\text{LAB}})/\sigma_n(90°, E_{\text{LAB}})$ for $E_{\text{LAB}} = 14$ to 20 Mev does help determine the singlet odd parity potential.[15] Beyond this, all that is ordinarily fit is the triplet scattering length, which is determined from the zero energy data alone; the potentials are adjusted to fit the p-p singlet scattering length and effective range. (The triplet effective range is not fit; it is determined by the triplet scattering length and deuteron binding energy and these two quantities are fit [see Eq. (17)]. The n-p singlet scattering length is sometimes fit by allowing a slight charge dependence of the singlet even parity potential; see Ga57c. The n-p singlet scattering length does contribute the knowledge that the singlet even parity potential is not charge independent. For the rest, the p-p singlet effective range is fit, and with a suitable singlet odd parity potential, and a repulsive core, the n-p angular distributions look good, especially graphically, up to $E_{\text{LAB}} = 90$ Mev. At 90 Mev, there are details which cause trouble, but at 40 Mev and below, the data is so fragmentary that it is too easy to fit; it tells nothing.)

It is to be hoped that the development of bubble chamber and other techniques will put us in the possession of n-p data which will change the situation.

C. The Energy Range $14 < E_{\text{LAB}} < 20$ Mev

The values of $\sigma_n(90°, 19.66 \text{ Mev})$ found were 38.65 ± 0.15 mb (± 0.4 per cent). The variation shown is the variation which results from the use of all potentials in Table IV with the GT singlet even and triplet odd parity potentials. The singlet odd parity potential plays no role because the odd spherical harmonics $Y_L°$ vanish at 90°.

The reason that the value of $\sigma_n(90°, 19.66 \text{ Mev})$ is insensitive to the triplet even parity potential is less obvious, although not difficult to understand. The reason depends on the fact that the $^3S_1$ phase

[15] See p. 2213. The fact that the potentials described in Section 7.B are adjusted to fit the data has as a consequence, of course, that the potentials cannot be used to predict the ratio.

shift passes through and remains near $90°$ in the energy range 14 $< E_{\text{LAB}} < 20$ Mev.   If we define

$$R(\delta) \equiv [\exp (2i\delta) - 1]/2i \tag{35}$$

then

$$R(\delta(^3S_1)) \approx 0 + i\,1 \tag{36}$$

in this energy range, while for any other state,

$$R(\delta) = \delta + i\delta^2 + O(\delta^3) \tag{37}$$

The terms in the expression for the differential cross section resulting from the interference of $^3S_1$ scattering with the scattering in any other state will be small and of the same order as the square of the phase shift for this latter state.   Were the $^3S_1$ phase shift not near $90°$, the interference term would be of the same order as the phase shift (not squared) so the special role of the near-$90°$ value of the $^3S_1$ phase shift is clear.   The ^3D_J phase shifts are so small that the $^3S_1$–^3D_J interference nearly disappears for $\delta(^3S_1) \approx 90°$.

There is no $^3S_1 - {}^3P_J$ interference for $\theta = 90°$.

Thus the value $\sigma_n(90°, 19.66 \text{ Mev}) = 38.65$ mb may be expressed as the sum of a triplet even parity contribution, a triplet odd parity contribution, and a singlet even parity contribution.   The relative magnitudes of these contributions are like 31 mb, 0.7 mb, and 7 mb, approximately.

As calculations based on the potentials in Table IV show, the triplet even parity contribution can be calculated to within ± 0.15 mb.

The triplet odd parity contribution is very small, and can be calculated with confidence.   Assuming charge independence, this contribution is $1/4$ of the contribution of the triplet odd parity states to the proton-proton differential cross section at $90°$ $[\sigma_p(90°, E_{\text{LAB}})]$. The factor $1/4$ arises from the Pauli principle.   Table III in the paper of Gammel, Christian, and Thaler (Ga57c) shows 2.80 mb for the core radius used by Gammel and Thaler (Ga57a).   One fourth of this is 0.70 mb.   A still better estimate is obtained by subtracting the singlet even parity contribution to $\sigma_p(90°, E_{\text{LAB}})$ calculated from the best p-p effective range parameters and a $^1D_2$ phase shift from the GT phenomenological potential from the experimental value of $\sigma_n(90°, E_{\text{LAB}})$.

The singlet even parity contribution can be calculated from the best values of the *n-p* effective range parameters and a $^1D_2$ phase shift from a phenomenological potential. It can be seen that errors in the calculation of the triplet odd parity contribution and the singlet even parity contribution tend to cancel; $\sigma_p(90°, E_{\text{LAB}})$ serves as a fixed point and the effective range expansion amounts to a correction for Coulomb effects.

Since GT did fit the *p-p* differential cross section at 18.3 Mev, the value $\sigma_n(90°, 19.66 \text{ Mev}) = 38.65$ mb cannot be much in error beyond the uncertainty in the triplet even parity contribution, which is small.

These points require further investigation, but it looks as though the *n-p* differential cross section at 90° in the center-of-mass system can be calculated with precision. This fact may be of use in the measurement of absolute neutron fluxes.

D. The p-p Differential Cross Section and the Contribution of the ^3P_J States to $\sigma_n(E_{\text{LAB}})$

It can be shown that the contribution of the triplet odd parity states to the *n-p* differential cross section at 90° is approximately

$$\frac{1}{2\pi} \frac{9}{20} \sigma_n(^3P_J) \tag{38}$$

where $\sigma_n(^3P_J)$ is the contribution of the ^3P_J states to $\sigma_n(E_{\text{LAB}})$.

The mathematical origin of the contribution of the triplet odd parity states to $\sigma_n(90°, E_{\text{LAB}})$ is in the squares of two of the spin flip scattering amplitudes; namely M_{01} and M_{10} (As48, St57). Equation (38) is derived by assuming that the ^3P_J phase shifts are due to a tensor term in the triplet odd parity potential *only;* this is nearly the case for either the GT or SM potentials. The GT triplet odd parity potential has no central term, and the central term in the triplet odd parity potential of SM is short ranged; also, the spin orbit terms in both the GT and SM potentials are short ranged, and so cannot affect the ^3P_J phase shifts at these low energies (14–20 Mev).

From the point of view of Section 2, Eq. (38) might be used in the following way. Equation (38) also gives $^1/_4$ of the contribution of the triplet odd parity states to $\sigma_p(90°, E_{\text{LAB}})$. For the core radius used

J. L. GAMMEL

Table XI. $\sigma_n(E_{\text{LAB}})$ in barns. A linear interpolation between two cross sections is accurate to within 0.1 per cent of the interpolated value.

E_{LAB} (Mev)	$\sigma_n(E_{\text{LAB}})$ (barns)	E_{LAB} (Mev)	$\sigma_n(E_{\text{LAB}})$ (barns)	E_{LAB} (Mev)	$\sigma_n(E_{\text{LAB}})$ (barns)
0.0	20.340	3.3	2.146	6.6	1.321
0.1	12.790	3.4	2.105	6.7	1.306
0.2	9.700	3.5	2.067	6.8	1.291
0.3	8.003	3.6	2.029	6.9	1.277
0.4	6.919	3.7	1.993	7.0	1.262
0.5	6.161	3.8	1.959	7.1	1.249
0.6	5.596	3.9	1.925	7.2	1.235
0.7	5.156	4.0	1.893	7.3	1.221
0.8	4.801	4.1	1.862	7.4	1.208
0.9	4.507	4.2	1.832	7.5	1.195
1.0	4.259	4.3	1.803	7.6	1.183
1.1	4.045	4.4	1.775	7.7	1.170
1.2	3.858	4.5	1.747	7.8	1.158
1.3	3.693	4.6	1.721	7.9	1.146
1.4	3.546	4.7	1.695	8.0	1.135
1.5	3.414	4.8	1.670	8.1	1.123
1.6	3.293	4.9	1.646	8.2	1.112
1.7	3.183	5.0	1.623	8.3	1.101
1.8	3.082	5.1	1.600	8.4	1.090
1.9	2.989	5.2	1.578	8.5	1.080
2.0	2.903	5.3	1.557	8.6	1.069
2.1	2.822	5.4	1.536	8.7	1.059
2.2	2.747	5.5	1.515	8.8	1.049
2.3	2.676	5.6	1.495	8.9	1.039
2.4	2.609	5.7	1.476	9.0	1.029
2.5	2.547	5.8	1.457	9.1	1.020
2.6	2.487	5.9	1.439	9.2	1.010
2.7	2.431	6.0	1.421	9.3	1.001
2.8	2.378	6.1	1.403	9.4	0.9922
2.9	2.327	6.2	1.386	9.5	0.9833
3.0	2.279	6.3	1.369	9.6	0.9745
3.1	2.232	6.4	1.353	9.7	0.9659
3.2	2.188	6.5	1.337	9.8	0.9574
				9.9	0.9490
				10.0	0.9408
				10.1	0.9327
				10.2	0.9248
				10.3	0.9169
				10.4	0.9092
				10.5	0.9016
				10.6	0.8941
				10.7	0.8867
				10.8	0.8795
				10.9	0.8723
				11.0	0.8652
				11.1	0.8583
				11.2	0.8514
				11.3	0.8447
				11.4	0.8380
				11.5	0.8314
				11.6	0.8250
				11.7	0.8186
				11.8	0.8123
				11.9	0.8061
				12.0	0.8000
				12.1	0.7939
				12.2	0.7880
				12.3	0.7821
				12.4	0.7763
				12.5	0.7706
				12.6	0.7649
				12.7	0.7593
				12.8	0.7538
				12.9	0.7484
				13.0	0.7430
				13.1	0.7377

13.2	0.7325	16.5	0.5905	19.8	0.4903	23.1	0.4159
13.3	0.7273	16.6	0.5869	19.9	0.4877	23.2	0.4139
13.4	0.7222	16.7	0.5834	20.0	0.4851	23.3	0.4120
13.5	0.7172	16.8	0.5800	20.1	0.4826	23.4	0.4101
13.6	0.7122	16.9	0.5775	20.2	0.4801	23.5	0.4081
13.7	0.7073	17.0	0.5731	20.3	0.4776	23.6	0.4063
13.8	0.7024	17.1	0.5698	20.4	0.4751	23.7	0.4044
13.9	0.6976	17.2	0.5664	20.5	0.4727	23.8	0.4025
14.0	0.6929	17.3	0.5631	20.6	0.4703	23.9	0.4007
14.1	0.6882	17.4	0.5599	20.7	0.4679	24.0	0.3988
14.2	0.6836	17.5	0.5566	20.8	0.4655	24.1	0.3970
14.3	0.6790	17.6	0.5534	20.9	0.4631	24.2	0.3952
14.4	0.6745	17.7	0.5503	21.0	0.4608	24.3	0.3934
14.5	0.6700	17.8	0.5471	21.1	0.4585	24.4	0.3916
14.6	0.6656	17.9	0.5440	21.2	0.4562	24.5	0.3898
14.7	0.6613	18.0	0.5409	21.3	0.4539	24.6	0.3881
14.8	0.6569	18.1	0.5379	21.4	0.4516	24.7	0.3863
14.9	0.6527	18.2	0.5349	21.5	0.4494	24.8	0.3846
15.0	0.6485	18.3	0.5319	21.6	0.4471	24.9	0.3829
15.1	0.6443	18.4	0.5289	21.7	0.4449	25.0	0.3812
15.2	0.6402	18.5	0.5260	21.8	0.4428	25.1	0.3795
15.3	0.6361	18.6	0.5231	21.9	0.4406	26.0	0.3648
15.4	0.6321	18.7	0.5202	22.0	0.4384	27.0	0.3496
15.5	0.6281	18.8	0.5174	22.1	0.4363	28.0	0.3354
15.6	0.6241	18.9	0.5145	22.2	0.4342	29.0	0.3221
15.7	0.6202	19.0	0.5117	22.3	0.4321	30.0	0.3096
15.8	0.6164	19.1	0.5090	22.4	0.4300	31.0	0.2979
15.9	0.6125	19.2	0.5062	22.5	0.4279	32.0	0.2869
16.0	0.6088	19.3	0.5035	22.6	0.4259	33.0	0.2765
16.1	0.6050	19.4	0.5008	22.7	0.4238	34.0	0.2668
16.2	0.6013	19.5	0.4981	22.8	0.4218	35.0	0.2575
16.3	0.5977	19.6	0.4955	22.9	0.4198		
16.4	0.5941	19.7	0.4928	23.0	0.4178		

by GT, Table III of (Ga57c) gives 2.80 mb for this contribution, as mentioned already, and this gives

$$\sigma_n(^3P_J) = 9.78 \text{ mb} \qquad E_{\text{LAB}} = 18.3 \text{ Mev} \qquad (39)$$

in good agreement with the GT value shown in Table 1.

From the point of view of Section 7.C, the argument might be reversed, and stated in the following way.   Only a value $\sigma_n (^3P_J) \gtrsim 8$ mb leads to results in Section 5 consistent with theoretical expectations, so that the contributions of the triplet odd parity states to σ_n-(90°, 1966 Mev) must be about 0.7 mb, as it is for the GT potential.

8. Appendix: The Mathematical Basis of the Modified Effective Range Expansion

1. Outline of the Chew and Goldberger (Ch49a) Derivation of the Effective Range Expansion

The original paper (Ch49a) should be consulted for the details omitted in the brief outline in this Section 1, which is inserted here only to facilitate the discussion in Section 2.

The effective range parameters (a, ρ, and P) can all be expressed in terms of solutions of Schrodinger's equation for $E_{\text{LAB}} = 0$ (and $L = 0$, of course):

$$d^2u/dr^2 + (M/\hbar^2) \, V \, u = 0 \qquad (40)$$

and the corresponding equation with $V = 0$:

$$d^2v/dr^2 = 0 \qquad (41)$$

An outline of the derivation of these expressions for a, ρ, and P follows.   In the course of this derivation, the effective range expansion is also derived, of course.

Any solution of Eq. (40) is asymptotically equal to a solution of Eq. (41), because as $r \to \infty$, $V(r) \to 0$, so that the two equations become the same for large r.

Chew and Goldberger define *the* regular solution (u_{R}) of Eq. (41) as that regular solution which is asymptotically equal to a certain (necessarily) irregular solution (v_{I}) of Eq. (41); namely

$$u_{\text{R}} \approx v_{\text{I}} = -(r/a) + 1 \qquad (42)$$

This equation is, in fact, the definition of the scattering length. It is easily verified that v_I is a solution of Eq. (41) by differentiating. Chew and Goldberger also define the irregular solution (u_I) of Eq. (40) as that irregular solution which is asymptotically equal to a certain (by choice) regular solution of Eq. (41); namely

$$u_I \approx v_R = -r \tag{43}$$

Chew and Goldberger prove that a certain regular solution (u_R') of Schrodinger's equation for $E_{\text{LAB}} \neq 0$,

$$d^2u'/dr^2 + k^2u' + (MV/\hbar^2)u' = 0 \tag{44}$$

and a certain irregular solution $(v_I'$, defined so that $u_R' = v_I')$ of the corresponding equation with $V = 0$,

$$d^2v'/dr^2 + k^2v' = 0 \tag{45}$$

satisfy a set of two coupled integral equations; namely

$$u_R' = u_R + k^2 \left\{ u_I \int_0^r u_R u_R' - u_R \int_0^r u_I u_R' + \right.$$
$$\left. u_R \int_0^\infty (u_I u_R' - v_R v_I') \right\} \tag{46}$$
$$v_I' = v_I + k^2 \left\{ v_R \int_r^0 v_I v_I' - v_I \int_0^r v_R v_I' - v_R \int_0^\infty (v_I v_I' - u_R u_R') \right\}$$

In these coupled integral equations, the unprimed functions, the functions for $E_{\text{LAB}} = 0$, are the known functions. The integral equations determine the primed, or unknown, functions, in terms of the known functions and k^2.

Finally, Chew and Goldberger prove that

$$k \cot \delta = -1/a + k^2 \int_0^\infty (v_I v_I' - u_R u_R') \tag{47}$$

This equation is exact. If the integral equations Eq. (46) are solved and the solutions v_I' and u_R' substituted into Eq. (47), the result is an exact expression for $k \cot \delta$ in terms of k^2 and the known functions.

The effective range expansion is obtained by solving the integral equations Eq. (46) by an iteration procedure. The result is the well known Eq. (2) and the equations

$$\rho = 2 \int_0^\infty (v_I^2 - u_R^2) \tag{48}$$

$$-P\rho^3 = 2 \int_0^\infty [(u_R^2 - v_I^2) \int_0^r v_I v_R] + 2 \int_r^\infty [(v_I v_R - u_R u_I) \int_0^r u_R^2]$$

2. Derivation of the Modified Expansion from the Fredholm Theory of Integral Equations

An expansion like Eq. (7) may be obtained for any potential by solving the integral equations Eq. (46) by the procedure of Fredholm instead of by iteration. In particular, it can be shown that if Eq. (46) is solved by the procedure of Fredholm for the *sticky hard core* potential, the result is Eq. (7). This will be shown now. Only the denominator of the Fredholm expansion need be studied, since such a study suffices to prove these assertions, and anyhow the integral expressions for the parameters which appear in the numerator of Eq. (11) have already been given in Eq. (48).

Equation (46) can be written

$$u_R' = u_R + k^2 \int_0^\infty G_1 u_R' + k^2 \int_0^\infty G_2 v_I'$$
$$v_I' = v_I + k^2 \int_0^\infty G_3 u_R' + k^2 \int_0^\infty G_4 v_I' \tag{49}$$

where the Green's functions are

$$G_1(r, r') = u_I(r) u_R(r'), \quad r' < r$$
$$= u_R(r) u_I(r'), \quad r' > r$$
$$G_2(r, r') = -u_R(r) v_I(r') \tag{50}$$
$$G_3(r, r') = v_R(r) u_R(r')$$
$$G_4(r, r') = -v_I(r) v_R(r'), \quad r' < r,$$
$$= -v_R(r) v_I(r'), \quad r' > r.$$

The denominator of the Fredholm expansion is

$$D = 1 - k^2 \int_0^\infty [G_1(r, r) + G_4(r, r)] \, dr$$
$$+ \tfrac{1}{2} k^4 \left[\int_0^\infty [G_1(r, r) + G_4(r, r)] \, dr \right]^2$$
$$- \tfrac{1}{2} k^4 \int_0^\infty G_1(r, r') G_1(r', r) \, dr \, dr'$$
$$- k^4 \int_0^\infty G_2(r, r) \, G_3(r', r) \, dr \, dr'$$
$$- \tfrac{1}{2} k^4 \int_0^\infty G_4(r, r') \, G_4(r', r) \, dr \, dr' + \cdots \tag{51}$$

or by Eq. (50),

$$D = 1 + k^2 \int_0^\infty [v_{\mathrm{I}}(r)v_{\mathrm{R}}(r) - u_{\mathrm{R}}(r)u_{\mathrm{I}}(r)]dr$$

$$+ {}^1\!/_2\, k^4 \left[\int_0^\infty [v_{\mathrm{I}}(r)v_{\mathrm{R}}(r) - u_{\mathrm{R}}(r)u_{\mathrm{I}}(r)]\, dr \right]^2$$

$$- k^4 \int_0^\infty (v_{\mathrm{I}}^2 - u_{\mathrm{R}}^2)\, dr \int_0^r v_{\mathrm{R}}^2\, dr'$$

$$- k^4 \int_0^\infty u_{\mathrm{R}}^2\, dr \int_r^\infty (u_{\mathrm{I}}^2 - v_{\mathrm{R}}^2)\, dr' + \ldots \qquad (52)$$

The functions u_{R}, u_{I}, v_{R}, and v_{I} are all known for the model potential, and are

$$u_{\mathrm{R}} \begin{cases} 0, & r < r_c \\ 1, & r > r_c \end{cases} \qquad (53)$$

u_{I} is not needed for $r < r_c$

$$u_{\mathrm{I}} = -\mathrm{r}, \quad \mathrm{r} > r_c$$

$$v_{\mathrm{R}} = -\mathrm{r}$$

$$v_{\mathrm{I}} = 1$$

It is easy to check that Eq. (52) gives the denominator of Eq. (7). Thus the expansion shown in Eq. (7) results generally for any potential from the use of a Fredholm expansion of the solutions of Eq. (46). The rapid convergence of the series which appear in the numerator and denominator of a Fredholm expansion is well known in other problems in scattering theory.

References

(As48) J. Ashkin and Ta-You Wu, *Phys. Rev.* **73,** 986 (1948).
(Al53) Allred, Armstrong, and Rosen, *Phys. Rev.* **91,** 90 (1953).
(Ba49) H. Barschall and R. Taschek, *Phys. Rev.* **75,** 1819 (1949).
(Bl52) J. Blatt and L. Biedenharn, *Revs. Modern Phys.* **24,** 258 (1952).
(Br51) Brolley, Coon, and Fowler, *Phys. Rev.* **82,** 190 (1951).
(Br57) S. Brimberg, quoted in footnotes marked by an asterisk on pp. 46 and 51 of Hu57.
(Br58) K. Brueckner and J. Gammel, *Phys. Rev.* **109,** 1023 (1958).
(Bu51) Burgy, Ringo, and Hughes, *Phys. Rev.* **84,** 1160 (1951).
(Ch49a) G. Chew and M. Goldberger, *Phys. Rev.* **75,** 1637 (1949).
(Ch49b) R. Christian, *Phys. Rev.* **75,** 1675 (1949).
(Ch57) Christian, Gammel, and Thaler, unpublished results (1957); some results of this work are given in this article.
(Co52) Coon, Graves, and Barschall, *Phys. Rev.* **88,** 562 (1952).

(Da55)   Day, Mills, Perry, and Scherb, *Phys. Rev.* **98**, 279 (1955).
(Fe56)   H. Feshbach and E. Lomon, *Phys. Rev.* **102**, 891 (1956).
(Fi54)   Fields, Baker, and Adair, *Phys. Rev.* **94**, 389 (1954).
(Fo55)   L. Foldy and E. Eriksen, *Phys. Rev.* **98**, 775 (1955).
(Fo56)   J. Fowler and J. Brolley, *Revs. Modern Phys.* **28**, 103 (1956).
(Ga55a)   A. Galonsky and J. Judish, *Phys. Rev.* **100**, 121 (1955).
(Ga55b)   S. Gartenhaus, *Phys. Rev.* **100**, 900 (1955).
(Ga57a)   J. Gammel and R. Thaler, *Phys. Rev.* **107**, 291 (1957).
(Ga57b)   J. Gammel and R. Thaler, *Phys. Rev.* **107**, 1337 (1957).
(Ga57c)   Gammel, Christian, and Thaler, *Phys. Rev.* **105**, 311 (1957).
(Ha59)   Hadley, Kelley, Leith, Segré, Wiegand, and York, *Phys. Rev.* **75**, 351
          (1949).
(Ha53)   Hafner, Hornyak, Falk, Snow, and Coon, *Phys. Rev.* **89**, 204 (1953).
(He56)   W. Hess, *Univ. of Calif. Radiation Lab. Report* UCRL-4639 (1956).
(Hi50)   R. Hildebrand and C. Leith, *Phys. Rev.* **80**, 842 (1950).
(Hu57)   L. Hulthen and M. Sugawara, *Handbuch der Physik*, Springer-Verlag,
          Berlin, 1957, Vol. 39, p. 1.
(Ja50)   J. Jackson and J. Blatt, *Revs. Modern Phys.* **23**, 77 (1950).
(Ka56)   Kalos, Biedenharn, and Blatt, *Nuclear Phys.* **1**, 233 (1956).
(Me49)   Melkonian, Rainwater, and Havens, *Phys. Rev.* **75**, 1295 (1949).
(Pe57)   J. Perry and R. Smith, preliminary results, unpublished (1957).
(Po52)   Poss, Salant, and Yuan, *Phys. Rev.* **87**, 11 (1952).
(Ro56)   *Proceedings of the Sixth Annual Rochester Conference on High Energy
          Nuclear Physics*, Interscience, New York, 1956.
(Ro57)   *Proceedings of the Seventh Annual Rochester Conference on High Energy
          Nuclear Physics*, Interscience, New York, 1957.
(Se55)   J. Seagrave, *Phys. Rev.* **97**, 757 (1955).
(Sh45)   R. Sherr, *Phys. Rev.* **68**, 240 (1945).
(Si58)   P. Signell and R. Marshak, *Phys. Rev.* **109**, 1229 (1958).
(Sn52)   G. Snow, *Phys. Rev.* **87**, 21 (1952).
(St45a)   C. Storrs and D. Frisch, *Phys. Rev.* **95**, 1252 (1954).
(St54b)   R. Stahl and N. Ramsey, *Phys. Rev.* **96**, 1310 (1954).
(St57)   Stapp, Ypsilantis, and Metropolis, *Phys. Rev.* **105**, 302 (1957).
(Ta57)   A. Taylor, unpublished results (1957).
(Wi57)   R. Wilson, unpublished results (1957).

Nomenclature Scheme for Experimental Monoenergetic Nuclear Cross Sections

H. GOLDSTEIN

Division of Nuclear Science & Engineering, Columbia University, New York, N. Y.; formerly at Nuclear Development Corporation of America, White Plains, N. Y.

1. Introduction

The following scheme for cross section terminology and associated notation has been developed in the hope of lessening the present widespread diversity and ambiguity in the reporting of nuclear cross sections, especially in the neutron field. In the course of development, the scheme has had the benefit of many suggestions and much discussion by the members of the AEC Nuclear Cross Section Advisory Group. It has so far survived the test of consistent use in a number of reports and papers. The scheme is offered here in the wish that it may serve to facilitate communication among people interested in nuclear cross sections.

Several general restrictions should be noted. Only monoenergetic, microscopic cross sections are considered. The terminology is particularly adapted for reactions with bombarding energies below 20–30 Mev. Spallation reactions above these energies, and the various meson and strange particle reactions at still higher energies, could be fitted into the scheme only with difficulty. Next, the terminology is aimed particularly at the reporting of experimental results. The several theories of nuclear reactions have produced a number of *theoretical construct* cross sections, e.g., shape elastic, whose fortunes and meanings necessarily vary as the theories develop and are modified. No attempt has been made to fit these constructs into the general terminological framework. Finally, as presently constructed, the scheme ignores polarization. It is believed that suitable modifications can be invented to take polarization into account, but it is felt the field has not developed far enough to warrant any such attempt as yet.

The nomenclature is not intended to be a strait jacket. It is realized that for many specific investigations it may be more informative and less clumsy to use a special notation. It is suggested that in such cases the special nomenclature so introduced should be defined, at the beginning of the paper or article, in terms of the scheme proposed here.

2. General Principles of Notation

While it might be desirable to have only one scheme of notation, this becomes difficult in practice. A notation that is completely unambiguous is too clumsy to use at all times. In many instances the chances of confusion are small enough that an abbreviated notation may be used. Provision is therefore made for a number of simplified versions of the notation in addition to the general notation. An analogy may be drawn with the Ancient Egyptian way of writing which was based on a very elaborate *hieroglyphic* method used on monuments, but also had a simplified *hieratic* book script and a shorthand cursive *demotic* script for everyday use. The following description will first consider the general notation and then indicate the abbreviated forms which seem appropriate for the articles of this volume.

Certain general principles have been applied in almost all of the notation:

(1) The *type* of reaction is indicated by subscripts. The *variables* of the reaction (energy, angle, etc.) are indicated in parentheses following the cross section symbol, following the usual mathematical functional notation. Whether a cross section is total or differential for the reaction is indicated by the variables shown.

(2) Three classes of *type* subscripts are provided:

(a) Where both the bombarding and outgoing particles are specified for a reaction they are indicated in lower case with a comma following the bombarding particle, e.g., $\sigma_{n,p}$ for a reaction with neutrons in and protons out. For inelastic scattering the inelastically scattered particles are indicated by primes. So far, the following lower case symbols used have been: γ, β, n, p, d, t, α, f. The meanings of these subscripts are obvious with the possible exception of f which stands for all the outgoing particles in fission.

(b) Where the cross section represents a sum over a number of possible reactions the subscript consists of first a lower case letter designating the incident particle and secondly an upper case letter chosen more or less arbitrarily. An example is σ_{nT} for the total neutron cross section.

(c) The remaining class consists of a few symbols of such a time-honored usage that they cannot lightly be ejected, e.g., σ_{tr} for the transport cross section (suitably defined). The number of symbols in this class will be kept as small as possible.

(3) A variable present in all cross sections is the bombarding particle energy, indicated by E, without subscripts. In total cross sections this will be the only variable. With differential cross sections there will be more variables indicating the energies or angles of emerging particles. Variables for a given particle are separated by commas, groups of variables for the various particles are separated by semicolons. The particles are identified by lower case subscripts with two exceptions: there is no subscript for the bombarding particle, and where one or more of the emergent particles are of the same type as the incident they are marked by primes where needed for distinction. Examples are:

(a) $$\sigma_{n,n}\ (E)$$

total elastic neutron scattering cross section.

(b) $$\sigma_{n,n}\ (E,\ \theta)$$

differential elastic neutron scattering cross section.

(c) $$\sigma_{n,2n}\ (E;\ E',\ \theta)$$

cross section in the $(n,\ 2n)$ process for producing a secondary neutron of energy E' (in unit range dE') in direction θ per unit solid angle.

(d) $$\sigma_{p,n}\ (E;\ E_n,\ \theta_n)$$

cross section for the production of neutrons in the $(p,\ n)$ process with energy E_n in direction θ_n.

The use of biased or threshold detectors introduces the need for indicating a kind of differential cross section where all outgoing particles above or below a certain energy are included. This will be indicated by $>$ or $<$, respectively, after the semicolon, e.g.,

$$\sigma_{n,n'}\ (E;\ < E')$$

the cross section for inelastic scattering of neutrons to below energy E'. In inelastic scattering one often deals with cross sections for excitation of a given level. If, say, we are considering excitation of a level E_1 in neutron inelastic scattering this might be handled within the above framework as

$$\sigma_{n,\,n'}\,(E;\ E-E_1)$$

A simpler convention would seem to be to drop the E and write merely

$$\sigma_{n,\,n'}\,(E;\ E_1)$$

This procedure can cause no confusion if the subscript denoting the energy level in question is either a number or one of the customary summation indices i, j, or k.

(4) It is assumed that all energies are in the laboratory system, as this is customary for most cross section measurements. As to scattering angles it is suggested that θ be used for center-of-mass angles and ψ for the laboratory system.

(5) The main two quantities considered in the scheme are cross sections, σ, and spectra, N. Cross sections are always number of events or particles of a certain specified nature per incident flux. Spectra give the fraction of events or particles of the given nature per reaction event. Thus the integral of a spectrum over its differential variable gives the multiplicity, while the integral of the corresponding differential cross section is equal to the total cross section for that event times the multiplicity.

The above general scheme of notation has been used in two abbreviated forms. It is felt that the first of these is most appropriate for the subject matter of the present volume:

I. Where almost only one bombarding particle is considered, the subscript for the particle may be considered as understood where not indicated explicitly. Similarly the bombarding energy, as a ubiquitous variable need not be stated explicitly. Thus, in a discussion confined mainly to neutron cross sections, σ_T means the neutron total cross section, σ_n means the total elastic neutron scattering cross section, $\sigma_n\,(\theta)$ means the differential elastic neutron scattering cross section, but $\sigma_{\gamma,n}$ would be used if a photoneutron cross section was quoted. Occasional use may be found for the second scheme of abbreviation:

II. In addition to the abbreviations above, the variables may be displayed as righthand superscripts, e.g., σ_n^{θ} for the differential elastic neutron scattering cross section. This form is particularly useful for theoretical discussion where the parentheses might be reserved for dummy variables of integration.

3. Cross Section Terminology

The general outlines of the cross section nomenclature can be indicated by presenting in Fig. 1 the main scheme for neutron cross sections, using the first abbreviated notation. Most of the terms are familiar enough not to require detailed explanation. Note that elastic scattering includes all processes conserving neutron kinetic energy in the center-of-mass system, i.e., including spin flip without

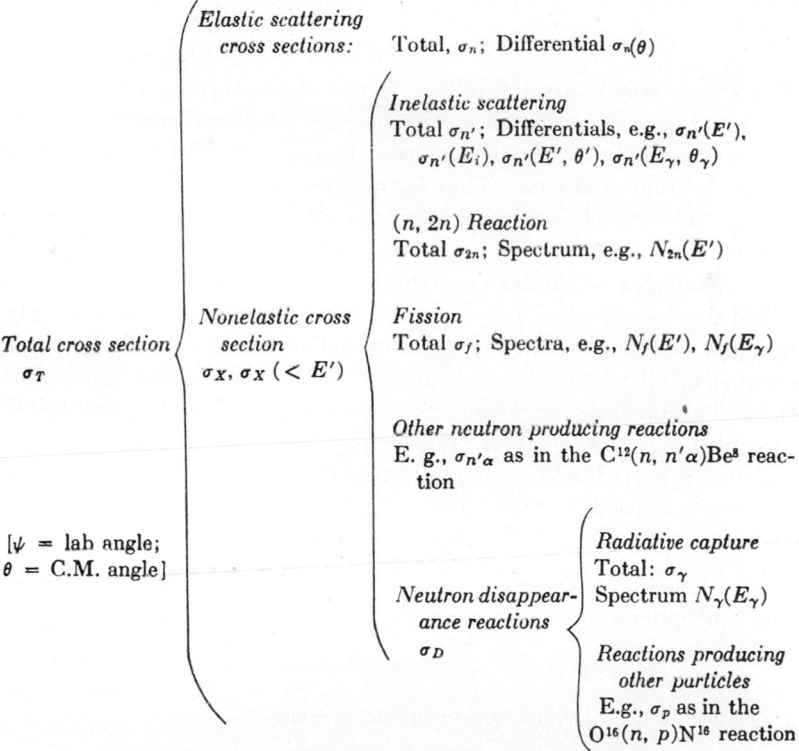

Figure 1. Scheme of neutron cross sections.

energy loss. For the sake of definiteness, it is proposed to reserve the term *inelastic scattering* to those situations in which the energy of nuclear excitation is lost solely by γ-ray emission. Otherwise inelastic scattering may overlap a number of other cross sections. It should be noted that for inelastic scattering there are both neutron and γ-ray cross sections and these are of course not simply related to each other. The integral of $\sigma_{n'}(E_\gamma)$ over all E_γ is not necessarily equal to the integral of $\sigma_{n'}(E')$ over all E', since cascade γ-ray emission can occur. For the same reason the cross section for inelastic neutron excitation of a level E_i, $\sigma_{n'}(E_i)$, will not necessarily be the same as the cross section $\sigma_{n'}(E_i)$ for emitting a γ ray of energy $E_\gamma = E_i$.

Two of the terms in Fig. 1 are relatively recent innovations. One is the *nonelastic cross section*, σ_X, which means just what the name implies, all excepting elastic:

$$\sigma_X = \sigma_T - \sigma_n$$

The other, still more unfamiliar, is the *disappearance cross section*, σ_D, which was invented to cover the sum of all processes in which the bombarding particle disappears with no particle of the same kind in the reaction products. Thus for neutrons, σ_γ, σ_p, σ_α, etc. are parts of σ_D. The name is admittedly infelicitous, but the term is often convenient.

A number of similar constructs (not indicated on Fig. 1) seem called for by certain current measuring techniques. For example, in some neutron experiments, the angle or energy distributions or number of all nonelastic neutrons are measured without unraveling the various processes occurring. The cross section involved here might be called σ_M, the *emission cross section*, i.e., the cross section for emitting a particle of the same kind as the bombarding particle. In the neutron case, for example,

$$\sigma_M = \sigma_{n'} + 2\sigma_{2n} + \nu_f \sigma_f + \ldots$$

The multiplicity associated with this cross section would be

$$\nu_M = \sigma_M / (\sigma_{n'} + \sigma_{2n} + \sigma_f + \ldots)$$

and there is the obvious conservation relation

$$\sigma_M / \nu_M = \sigma_X - \sigma_D$$

There are similar experiments which measure the γ rays emitted upon particle bombardment without deciding what reactions are involved. Here σ_G, the *γ-ray emission cross section*, may be used to describe the results.

There are also a number of cross sections chiefly associated with reactor technology which do not fit easily into the scheme of Fig. 1. One is the *scattering cross section*, σ_S, which seems currently to be used as the sum of elastic and inelastic cross sections:

$$\sigma_S = \sigma_n + \sigma_{n'}$$

The term may also prove useful for describing some neutron experiments. Thus angular distributions for scattered neutrons have been measured at the Argonne National Laboratory with energy insensitive detectors. Where fission or the $(n, 2n)$ process is known to be absent, the results of such an experiment should properly be called $\sigma_S(\theta)$.

The *absorption cross section*, σ_A, is often used in an offhand manner in the reactor field, but it seems most convenient (and closest to the majority usage) to treat it as everything *but* elastic and inelastic scattering:

$$\sigma_A = \sigma_T - \sigma_n - \sigma_{n'}$$

Thus σ_A bears the same relation to σ_S that σ_X does to σ_n.

$$\sigma_A = \sigma_T - \sigma_S$$

Another cross section involved almost uniquely with the motion of neutrons in matter is the *transport cross section*, σ_{tr}, which also has had its varying usage. It will be defined here as

$$\sigma_{tr} = \sigma_X + \int (1 - \cos \psi)\, \sigma_n (\psi)\, d\Omega$$

or

$$\sigma_{tr} = \sigma_T - \bar{\mu}\sigma_n$$

where $\bar{\mu}$, as defined in the laboratory system, is

$$\bar{\mu} = (1/\sigma_n) \int \sigma_n (\psi) \cos \psi d\Omega$$

A final cross section that may be mentioned is the activation cross section. Its use by now is becoming so rare that it seems best to retain the custom-hallowed designation as σ_{act}.

4. Examples of Suggested Usage

Perhaps the best way of indicating how the nomenclature works is to apply it to some previously reported data. Following are a few excerpts from papers published in the *Physical Review* which have been rewritten in the notation suggested above and in the style appropriate to this volume. Except for some simplification of the wording resulting from the use of a standardized terminology, the excerpts have otherwise been left unchanged. The reader may easily compare these revised excerpts with their originals.

(1) The $Be^9(n, 2n)$ reaction has a threshold of 1.85 Mev and therefore above 1.85 Mev this mode of decay competes with the (n, α) process. However, there is no published information on σ_{2n} for neutron energies below 4.0 Mev. At 4.0 Mev the cross section can be inferred from the measurements of Beyster *et al.* (Be55) of σ_X for Be, which is here the sum $\sigma_{n'} + \sigma_{2n} + \sigma_\alpha$. For Be, $\sigma_{n'}$ should be negligible because breakup into $Be^8 + n$ is energetically possible for excited states of Be^9 and this should overwhelm decay to the ground state by emission of γ rays. Beyster *et al.* found σ_X was 620 ± 30 mb. Since σ_α at E = 4.0 Mev is 85 mb, one sees that the $(n, 2n)$ reaction is 6 times more likely than the (n, α) reaction. The competition offered by the $(n, 2n)$ process probably accounts for the fall-off of σ_α at the higher neutron energies.

Penultimate paragraph of P. H. Stelson and E. C. Campbell, *Phys. Rev.* 106, 1252 (1957).

(2) The second example, Table I, is from V. V. Verbinski *et al.*, *Phys. Rev.* **108**, 779 (1957).

Table I. Observed Cross Sections for Emission of Protons of Energies Greater than E_p

Target	E_p(Mev)	$\sigma_p(>E_p)$(mb)
$_{12}$Mg	6.0	32 ± 4
$_{12}$Al	6.0	34 ± 6
..	..	..
..	..	..
..	..	..

(3) Table II is the third example and is the first table of R. C. Allen, *Phys. Rev.* **105,** 1796 (1957), as modified in *Nuclear Sci. and Eng.* **2,** 787 (1957).

Finally, the suggested use of some of the cross section notation is illustrated in the conceivable (but obviously purely imaginary) abstract given on page 2235.

Table II.   Experimental Values of U^{238} Nonelastic Cross Sections (barns)

E(kev)	σ_X	σ_γ	$\sigma_{n'}$	$\sigma_{n'}(E_i)$ $E_i = 50$ kev	$\sigma_{n'}(E_i)$ $E_i = 140$ kev
150	0.63 ± 0.2	0.19	0.44 ± 0.2	0.44 ± 0.2	—
250	0.63	0.15	0.48	0.19	0.29 ± 0.15
500	0.80	0.13	0.67	0.18	0.49 ± 0.25

ZZ27 The Interaction of 14.1-Mev Neutrons with Fg^{213}, H. Ibn Zahav, *Sigma National Laboratory.* Measurements have been made with a 5.2-kg sample of the separated isotope Fg^{213} (99.3 per cent purity) of the cross sections for 14.1-Mev neutrons produced by the D-T reaction. σ_T was found by transmission to be $6.83 \pm 0.02b$. A sphere transmission experiment gave σ_X as $3.76 \pm 0.07b$, indicating σ_n should be $3.07 \pm 0.08b$. Direct measurements have been made for $\sigma_n(\theta)$ for 14 angles from $20°$ to $175°$, and the integral of $\sigma_n(\theta)$ over all solid angle corresponds to $\sigma_n = 2.95 \pm 0.05b$, in good agreement with the sphere value. The energy and angular distributions of the nonelastic neutrons have been determined by the time-of-flight technique. Integration of the spectrum indicates $\sigma_M = 2.38b$. Combined with Katzenellenbogen's value of $\sigma_{2n} = 0.24b$, this leads to $\sigma_{n'} = 1.90b$. The small proportion of $(n, 2n)$ reaction is consistent with the high binding energy (13.2 Mev) of the last neutron in Fg^{213} and indicates most of the nonelastic neutrons arise from inelastic scattering, since fission has an even higher threshold. Comparison of $\sigma_{n'} + \sigma_{2n}$ with σ_X shows that σ_D is $1.62b$, most of it probably σ_p. Assuming that $N_{2n}(E')$ is a Maxwellian distribution with a temperature of 1.2 Mev and that $\sigma_{2n}(E', \theta')$ is isotropic, values of $\sigma_{n'}(E', \theta')$ have been derived from the observed distributions. In agreement with other measurements on neighboring elements, $\sigma_{n'}(<5$ Mev, $\theta')$ is isotropic, but $\sigma_{n'}(>5$ Mev, $\theta')$ is peaked in the forward direction nearly as strongly as $\sigma_n(\theta)$. However, $\sigma_{n'}(>5$ Mev) is only 12 per cent of $\sigma_{n'}$, indicating perhaps the small contribution from direct interaction. For $E' < 3$ Mev, $\sigma_{n'}(E')$ is fitted closely by a Maxwellian with a temperature of 1.4 Mev. Gamma rays from inelastic scattering have also been measured with a magnetic Compton spectrometer. No structure was observed except for a prominent peak in $N_{n'}(E_\gamma)$ at $E_\gamma = 3.2$ Mev, corresponding to the well-known first excited state in Fg^{213}. At this energy $\sigma_{n'}(E_\gamma)$ was measured to be $1.25b$ whereas $\sigma_{n'}(E_1)$ was observed from the neutron spectra to be $0.34b$. Clearly many of the more highly excited levels decay by cascade emission through the 3.2-Mev level. The high probability of cascade deexcitation is also indicated from the fact that σ_G, assuming isotropy of $\sigma_{n'}(E_\gamma, \theta_\gamma)$, is $4.27b$. The γ-ray multiplicity is thus 2.25. Similar measurements are in progress with separated samples of the other nine stable isotopes of the element Figmentium.

Recent Developments in Neutron Detection

F. W. K. FIRK*

Atomic Energy Research Establishment, Harwell, England

1. Introduction

Neutron detectors with increased efficiency, reduced background, and faster time resolution are constantly being sought. Two advances have been reported recently which provide neutron detectors with some of the characteristics mentioned above. First, the pulse-shape discrimination method, pioneered by Brooks (Br56,Br58, Br59,Br60), makes possible the efficient detection of fast neutrons when using certain organic scintillators in the presence of high γ-ray backgrounds. Second, the development by Ginther and Schulman (Gi58,Gi60) of glass scintillators, loaded with either boron or lithium, provides neutron detectors of reasonable efficiency and fast time resolution. The use of pulse-shape discrimination has rapidly become a standard technique in fast neutron spectroscopy. Experiments using Li⁶-loaded glass scintillators (Fi61,Sl61) have recently demonstrated the usefulness of these scintillators for detecting neutrons by the nanosecond time-of-flight technique in the difficult energy region from 10 to 100 kev.

2. The Pulse-Shape Discrimination Method

A. Decay Times and Light Intensities

In 1956 Wright (Wr56) reported that the scintillations produced by α particles and electrons in anthracene crystals had different decay times, 53 and 31 nanoseconds, respectively. Wright assumed in his analysis that the scintillation pulse could be described by an initial

---

* This work was done while the author was assigned as an exchange visitor with the Oak Ridge National Laboratory.

fast spike (duration $\gtrsim$ 10 nanoseconds), followed by a longer exponentially decaying component. The figures of 53 and 31 nanoseconds refer to the latter component. Shortly afterwards Brooks (Br56,Br56a) developed a scintillation counter and discrimination circuit capable of distinguishing fast neutrons from γ rays by means of the different "effective decay times" of the recoil proton and Compton electron scintillations. The first detector used by Brooks

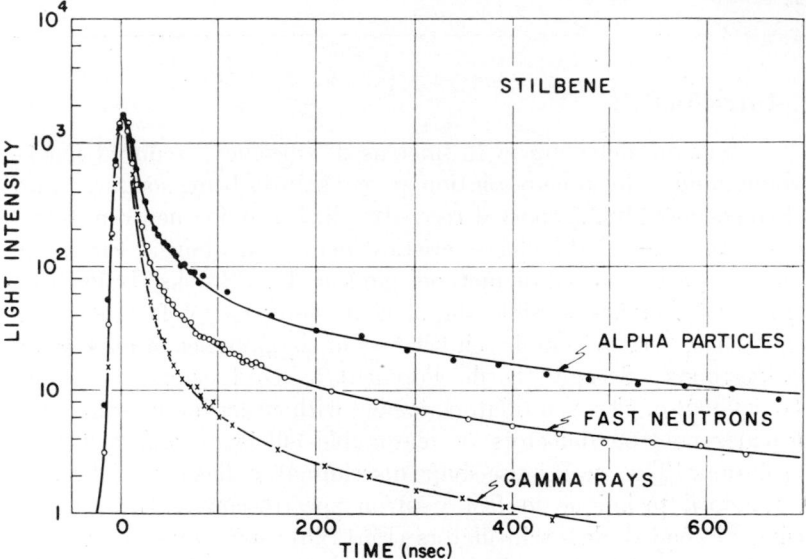

Figure 1. The scintillation response of stilbene to α particles, protons, and electrons normalized to the same peak height (Bo61).

(Br56a), incorporating a 1-in. thick stilbene crystal, detected 2-Mev neutrons with an efficiency of 10 per cent, whereas the detection efficiency for 2-Mev γ rays was less than 0.01 per cent.

The use of the term "effective decay time" is necessary to describe the pulse-shape discrimination system originally used by Brooks, since the work of Owen (Ow58) showed that the *decay times* of both the initial fast spike and the long-lived components, observed in organic scintillators, are in fact *independent* of the type of exciting particle. The differences occur in the *intensity* of the long-lived com-

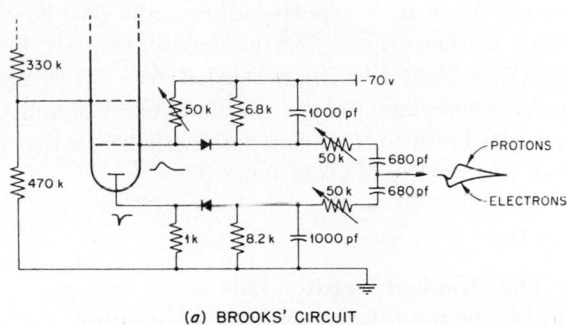

(a) BROOKS' CIRCUIT

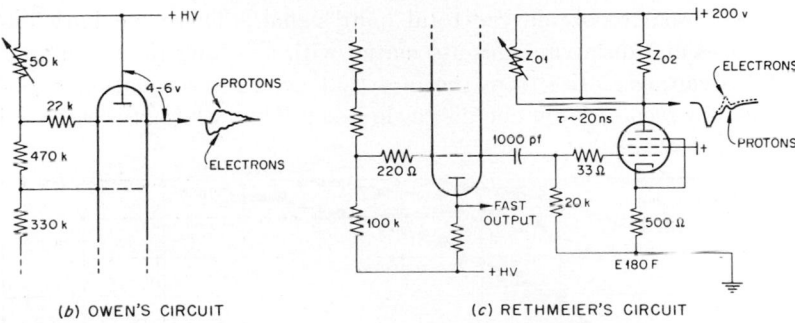

(b) OWEN'S CIRCUIT   (c) RETHMEIER'S CIRCUIT

Figure 2. The three categories of pulse-shape discrimination circuits currently in use.

ponents relative to the intensity of the initial fast spike.[1]   A typical example is shown in Fig. 1 taken from a recent paper by Bollinger and Thomas (Bo61). They have made precise measurements of the scintillation pulse shapes, as a function of the type of exciting particle, for a variety of organic and inorganic scintillators.   Referring to Fig. 1, the following inequalities hold:

$$R_{\text{alpha}} < R_{\text{proton}} < R_{\text{electron}}$$

where

$$R = \int_0^\tau I(t)\,dt \bigg/ \int_\tau^\infty I(t)\,dt, \quad \tau \approx 10 \text{ nanoseconds} \qquad (1)$$

[1] Neiler and Pethe (Ne61) have recently demonstrated that the frequency spectrum of light emitted in stilbene and anthracene crystals differs for α-particle or electron excitation.   The intensity of ultraviolet emission is enhanced in the α-particle case.

Many circuits have been reported during the past few years which are sensitive to the ratio of electric charge given by Eq. (1) (Br58, Fo58,Ow59,Br59,Ba60,Bl60,Br60,Da61,Re61). It is usual to use a simple voltage discriminator to simulate the inequality sign. The various circuits fall into three categories, shown in Fig. 2. Each has certain features worthy of attention.

B. Circuit Details

(1) **The Brooks Circuit.** This circuit compares the total light output during the scintillation with the light output during the initial fast spike. A relatively long integrating time constant is required (1 to 2 μsec) to obtain the total light signal. There are both advantages and disadvantages associated with this long time constant. The advantages arise from the fact that good discrimination is obtained for recoil proton energies as low as 200 kev where it is essential

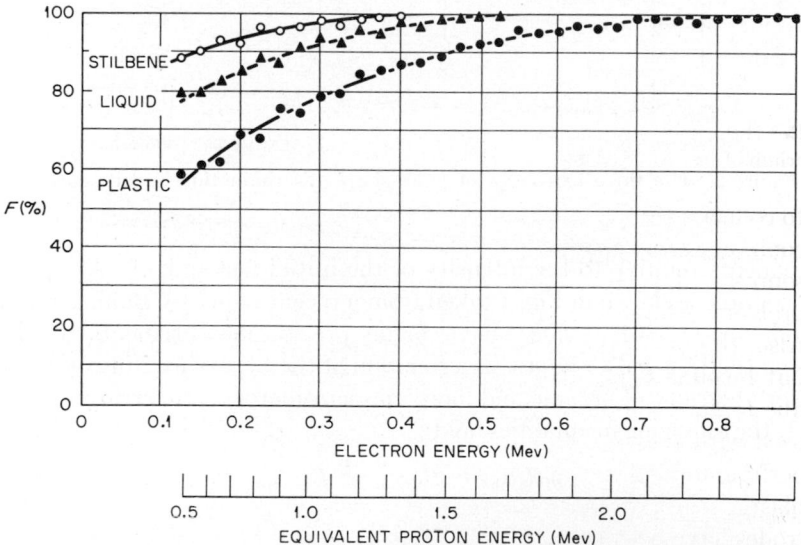

Figure 3. The quantitative performance of a typical Brooks' circuit using (a) a stilbene crystal; (b) a liquid scintillator (Nuclear Enterprises, Ltd., Type NE213); and (c) a plastic scintillator Type NE77. A bias δ is set to eliminate > 99 per cent of electron scintillations of any energy. The ordinate gives the percentage, F, of proton scintillations counted above δ, as a function of proton energy.

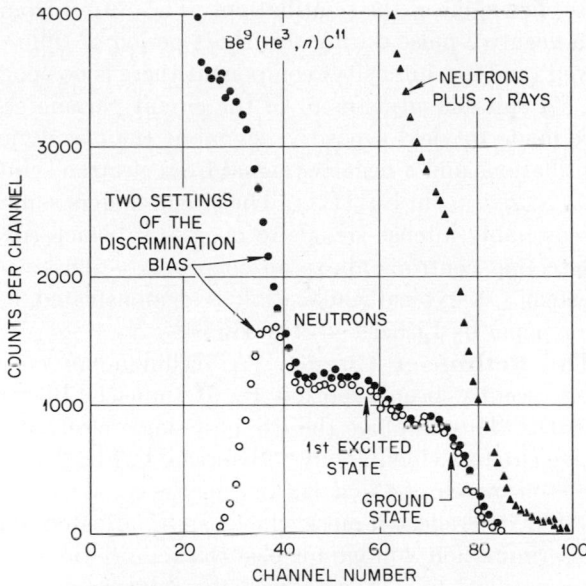

Figure 4. Pulse-height spectra from a liquid scintillator using the $Be^9(He^3,n)C^{11}$ reaction demonstrating the effect of an Owen pulse-shape discrimination circuit (Li59).

to collect as much information from the long-lived (but low intensity) components as possible. The disadvantages arise from a number of sources. The dead time of several microseconds can be a serious problem where high background counting rates are encountered. Also, the use of nonlinear circuit elements and two independent output terminals (the last dynode and collector) introduces difficulties due to gain shifts. In spite of these limitations the circuit has been used with success (Br59a). Figure 3 gives quantitative data on the performance of a typical Brooks circuit using stilbene, liquid, and plastic scintillators. (The problems associated with using two electrodes have been eliminated by Bloom *et al.* (Bl60), whose method requires a signal from a single electrode. The discrimination circuit is, however, still of the Brooks variety.)

(2) **The Owen Circuit.** Owen (Ow59) has approached the problem in a unique and simple way. By operating the last dynode and collector at a potential difference of only a few volts, it is possible to obtain space charge saturation of the last dynode during the initial

(and intense) fast spike of the scintillation. The output from the last dynode is a negative pulse during this short period of time. During the long-lived (and low intensity) component there is no space charge saturation. A suitable adjustment of the circuit parameters in Fig. 2(b) can be made to yield a positive signal at the last dynode from proton scintillations and a negative signal from electron scintillations [since $R_{proton} < R_{electron}$ in Eq. (1)]. The circuit suffers somewhat by requiring reasonably intense signals to operate satisfactorily. However, for detecting neutrons above an energy of $\sim$500 kev this is a popular system. A typical application is demonstrated in Fig. 4, taken from a paper by Litherland *et al.* (Li59).

(3) **The Rethmeier Circuit.** A technique of considerable interest has recently been reported by Rethmeier, Boersma, and Jonker (Re61). This employs the use of a single electrode and the use of passive circuit elements only. Referring to Fig. 2(c), it is seen that suitable mismatch of the delay line in the anode of the E180F amplifier results in a reflected pulse which can be adjusted to be above a certain discrimination voltage for electron scintillations and below for proton scintillations. Apart from the advantages of using a single electrode and passive circuit elements, the circuit is designed to provide a fast timing signal from the collector of the phototube. The delay time of the reflected signal is only 40 nanoseconds, so that high counting rates should be readily handled by the system. The major disadvantage would appear to be a lack of discrimination for proton energies less than 800 kev.

It is clear from the many experiments reported recently in the field of fast neutron physics that the identification of the type of particle by means of pulse-shape discrimination is one of the most powerful techniques to emerge in recent years.

3. Glass Scintillators

The difficulties associated with using organic scintillators for the prompt detection of neutrons below an energy of $\sim$100 kev have resulted in the widespread use of "nuclear reaction" detectors. The most suitable reactions are $B^{10}(n,\alpha)Li^7 + 480$ kev $\gamma + 2.3$ Mev and $Li^6(n,\alpha)T + 4.8$ Mev. The various detectors incorporating these reactions have been reviewed by Muehlhause in Chapter III.B.

Pulsed Van de Graaff machines have recently been developed to produce neutron bursts of a few nanoseconds duration (Go61).

The need to detect neutrons of less than 100 kev efficiently and with a time resolution of several nanoseconds is therefore apparent. The most successful prompt neutron detector in the neutron energy range under consideration has been the $NaI(Tl)$-B^{10} detector of Rae and Bowey (Ra53), subsequently developed by Good, Neiler, and Gibbons (Go58). This detector involves the observation of the 480-kev γ ray from the $B^{10}(n,\alpha\gamma)Li^7$ reaction. Good *et al.* (Go58) obtained a time resolution of $\sim$6 nanoseconds using a "fast-slow" coincidence system; the figure of 6 nanoseconds appears to be an electronic rather than an intrinsic limitation.

The work of Voitovetskii, Tolmacheva, and Arsaev (Vo59), and Bollinger, Thomas, and Ginther (Bo59) demonstrated that cerium-activated glass scintillators loaded with either lithium or boron are suitable for detecting slow ($<$10 ev) neutrons. Recently, Firk, Slaughter, and Ginther (Fi61) have reported the use of a Li^6-loaded glass scintillator for detecting neutrons up to $\sim$100 kev energy using nanosecond time-of-flight techniques. A detector time resolution of $<$2 nanoseconds was achieved.

A. *Preparation of Glass Scintillators*

(1) **Chemical Composition.** The compositions of a large number of boron- and lithium-loaded glass scintillators have been investigated by Ginther (Gi58, Gi60), with the objective of increasing the boron and lithium content, and simultaneously increasing the pulse height and a resolution of the (n,α) peaks.

A typical composition used successfully for detecting neutrons up to 100 kev energy is as follows:

$Li^6O_{1/2}$	0.355
$AlO_{3/2}$	0.075
$CeO_{3/2}$	0.02
$SiO_{3/2}$	0.55

where the numbers are molar ratios. This glass has the optical properties of those given by Ginther (Gi60).

(2) **Manufacture.** Details of the manufacture of glass scintillators have been given in a number of papers (Gi58,Gi60,Bi61,Fi61). The method used by Ginther consists of heating high purity ingredients to 1500 °C. in a platinum crucible. The process is carried out

in a reducing atmosphere to ensure that the cerium is in the cerous
ion form necessary for activating the scintillator.

B. *Neutron Detection Properties of Glass Scintillators*

(1) **Pulse-Height Spectra from the Reactions Li$^6(n,\alpha)$T +
4.8 Mev and B$^{10}(n,\alpha)$Li^7 + 480-kev γ + 2.3 Mev.**   Pulse-height
spectra from lithium- and boron-loaded glasses, when irradiated with
low energy neutrons (Fi61), are shown in Fig. 5.   For the lithium
glass, the well-defined peak with a full width at half maximum of 25
per cent is readily selected using a single-channel pulse-height analyzer.
The equivalent electron energy of the Li$^6(n,\alpha)$T peak is 1.6 Mev.

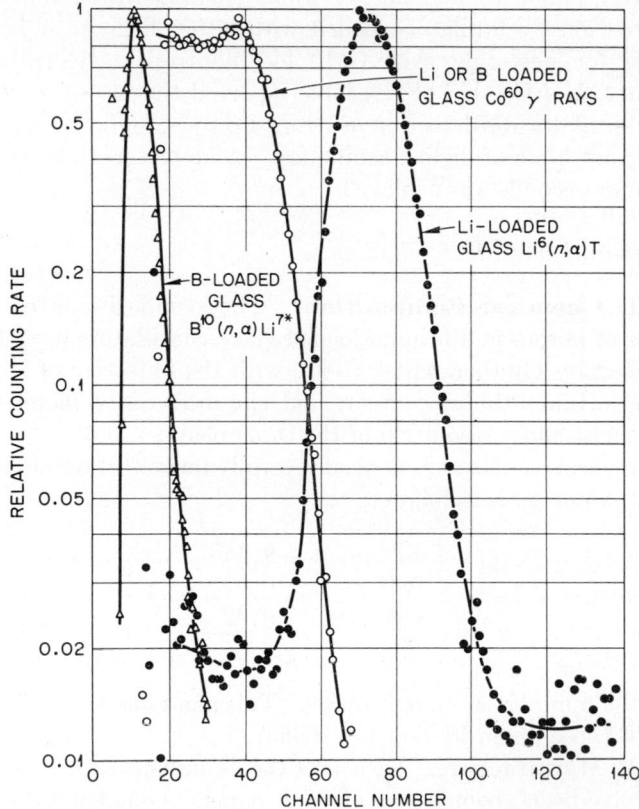

Figure 5. Typical pulse-height spectra in lithium- and boron-loaded glass
scintillators (Fi61).

Firk *et al.* (Fi61) concluded that the 2.1-Mev α particle contributes 400 kev and the 2.7-Mev triton contributes the remaining 1.2-Mev equivalent electron energy. This large difference in response to α particles and tritons is atypical of crystalline inorganic scintillators. The glass, however, does not have their regular structure and is therefore likely to exhibit unusual scintillation properties.

In the boron glass the $B^{10}(n,\alpha)Li^7$ peak occurs at an equivalent electron energy of 250 kev as shown in Fig. 5. The full width of the peak at half maximum is 50 per cent. It is not so surprising, in view of the above mentioned response to α particles and tritons, that the products of the $B^{10}(n,\alpha)Li^7$ reaction, with their high specific ionization, contribute a total equivalent electron energy of only 250 kev.

(2) **Gamma-Ray Sensitivity.** Ginther and Schulman (Gi58) have shown that cerium-activated glasses are useful detectors of γ rays. This is clearly a disadvantage when used for neutron detection. However, in the case of lithium glass, the pulse height of the (n,α) peak is such that γ rays of energy <1.3 Mev make a negligible contribution. This is demonstrated in Fig. 5 where the pulse-height spectrum from Co^{60} γ rays is compared with the (n,α) peak. The mass absorption coefficient for 1.3-Mev γ rays of a lithium glass having the composition given in Section 3.A(1) is ~ 0.055 cm^2/gm.

The low pulse height of the (n,α) peak in boron glass can be a serious drawback in many applications, since γ rays of only ~ 100 kev contribute to the (n,α) peak.

(3) **Time Characteristics of the Scintillation Pulse.** An important feature of a scintillator is the decay time of the light pulse. For cerium-activated glasses (both lithium- and boron-loaded) the main component has a decay time of ~ 100 nanoseconds (Bo59,Fi61).

(4) **Neutron Detection Efficiency.** The Li^6-loaded glass scintillator used by Firk *et al.* (Fi61) had an efficiency of 20 per cent for detecting 1-kev neutrons with a $1/v$ dependence up to ~ 50 kev. So far, boron-loaded glasses have been prepared containing only natural boron. The use of B^{10} in such glasses should enable efficiencies ~ 50 to 60 per cent to be attained for detecting 1-kev neutrons using a scintillator 1 cm thick.

C. *Applications to Nanosecond Time-of-Flight Measurements*

The first use of a Li^6-loaded glass scintillator for detecting 5- to 80-kev neutrons using nanosecond time-of-flight techniques has re-

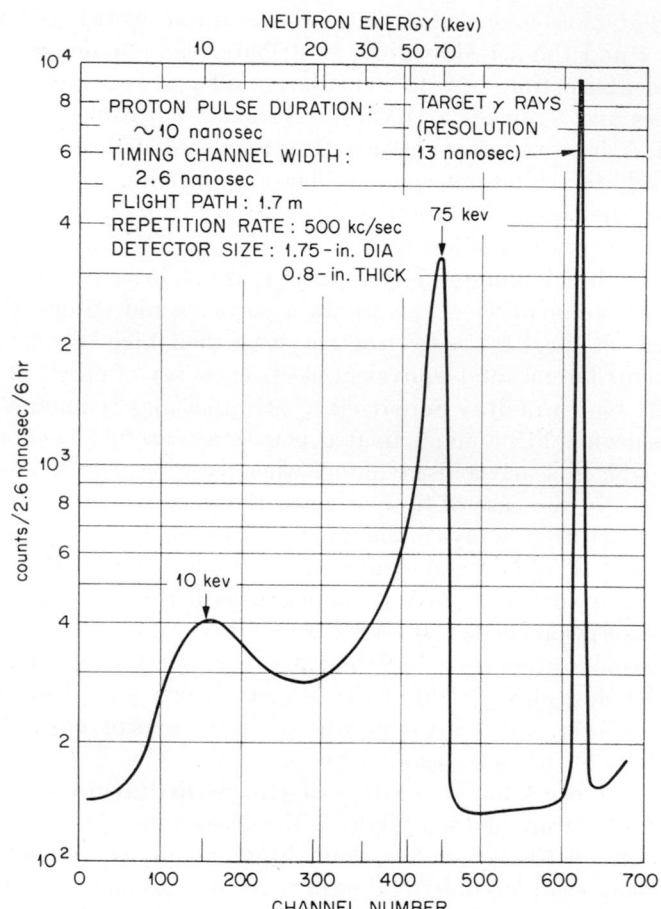

Figure 6. The observed neutron energy spectrum from the Li⁷(p,n)Be⁷ reaction using a Li⁶-loaded glass scintillator and nanosecond time-of-flight techniques. The time resolution of the glass scintillator was less than 2 nanoseconds (Fi61).

cently been reported (Fi61). These measurements were made using the Oak Ridge 3-Mv pulsed Van de Graaff machine and associated fast neutron time-of-flight spectrometer. A typical observed neutron energy spectrum from the Li⁷(p,n)Be⁷ reaction, for protons 15 kev above the reaction threshold, is shown in Fig. 6. A time resolution of <2 nanoseconds for the detector was determined by observing 1.4- to

1.8-Mev γ rays (equivalent to the $Li^6(n,\alpha)T$ peak) from the target of the Van de Graaff machine when using a beam-pulsing system which provided a burst duration of <2 nanoseconds (Go61). The efficiency of the Li^6-loaded glass scintillator was comparable with that of a 1-cm thick $B_4^{10}C$ slab and 4-in. diameter $\times$ 2-in. thick NaI(Tl) crystal previously used (Chapter IV.A). The lithium glass, however, has improved time resolution.

The low pulse height and relatively poor resolution of the $B^{10}(n,\alpha)$-Li^7 peak preclude the use of boron-loaded glasses from nanosecond time-of-flight measurements. The high neutron efficiencies obtainable with boron glasses would, however, make them suitable for many experiments not requiring excellent time resolution.

References

(Ba60)   Batchelor, Gilboy, Purnell, and Towle, *Nuclear Instr. and Methods* **8,** 146 (1960).
(Bi61)   A. M. Bishay, *J. Am. Ceramics Soc.* (in press).
(Bl60)   Bloom, Kaifer, and Schrader, *I.R.E. Trans. on Nuclear Sci.* NS-7, 170 (1960).
(Bo59)   Bollinger, Thomas, and Ginther, *Rev. Sci. Instr.* **30,** 1135 (1959).
(Bo61)   L. M. Bollinger and G. E. Thomas, *Rev. Sci. Instr.* (in press).
(Br56)   F. D. Brooks, "Organic Scintillators," in *Progress in Nuclear Physics*, Vol. 5, O. R. Frisch, ed., Pergamon Press, London, 1956, pp. 252–313.
(Br56a) F. D. Brooks, Harwell, private communication (1956).
(Br58)   F. D. Brooks, *Liquid Scintillation Counting*, C. B. Bell and F. N. Hayes, eds., Pergamon Press, London, 1958, p. 268.
(Br59)   F. D. Brooks, *Nuclear Instr. and Methods* **4,** 151 (1959).
(Br59a) F. D. Brooks and E. R. Rae, "Variation of $\eta/\bar{\nu}$ for U^{235}, *Atomic Energy Res. Establ. (Harwell) Report* NRDC 123 (1959).
(Br60)   Brooks, Pringle, and Funt, *I.R.E. Trans. on Nuclear Sci.* NS-7, 35 (1960).
(Da61)   W. Daehnick and R. Sherr, *Rev. Sci. Instr.* **32,** 666 (1961).
(Fi61)   Firk, Slaughter, and Ginther, *Nuclear Instr. and Methods* (in press)
(Fo58)   M. Forte, *Proc. Intern. Conf. Peaceful Uses Atomic Energy A/Conf.* 15/p/1514 (1958).
(Gi58)   F. J. Ginther and J. H. Schulman, *I.E.E. Trans. on Nuclear Sci.* NS-5, 92 (1958).
(Gi60)   R. J. Ginther, *I.R.E. Trans. on Nuclear Sci.* NS-7, 28 (1960).
(Go58)   Good, Neiler, and Gibbons, *Phys. Rev.* **109,** 926 (1958).
(Go61)   W. M. Good and R. F. King, private communication (1961).
(Li59)   Litherland, Almqvist, Batchelor, and Gove, *Phys. Rev. Letters* **2,** 104 (1959).
(Ne61)   J. H. Neiler and V. Pethe, ORNL, private communication (1961).
(Ow58)   R. B. Owen, *I.R.E. Trans. on Nuclear Sci.* NS-5, 198 (1958).
(Ow59)   R. B. Owen, *Nucleonics* **17,** 92 (1959).

(Ra53)   E. R. Rae and E. M. Bowey, *Proc. Phys. Soc.* **66A,** 1073 (1953).

(Re61)   Rethmeier, Boersma, and Jonker, *Nuclear Instr. and Methods* **10,** 240 (1961).

(Sl61)   Slaughter, Firk, and Ginther, *Bull. Am. Phys. Soc.* **6,** 275 (1961).

(Vo59)   Voitovetskii, Tolmacheva, and Arsaev, *Atomnaya En.* **6,** 321 and 472 (1959).

(Wr56)   G. T. Wright, *Proc. Phys. Soc.* **69B,** 358 (1956).

CUMULATIVE INDEX